# Concepts in

# Biology

**Fourteenth Edition**

Eldon D. Enger

Frederick C. Ross

David B. Bailey

*Delta College*

**McGraw Hill Education (India) Private Limited**
CHENNAI

*McGraw Hill Education Offices*
**Chennai** New York  St Louis  San Francisco  Auckland  Bogotá  Caracas
Kuala Lumpur  Lisbon  London  Madrid  Mexico City  Milan  Montreal
San Juan  Santiago  Singapore  Sydney  Tokyo  Toronto

**McGraw Hill Education (India) Private Limited**

CONCEPTS IN BIOLOGY, FOURTEENTH EDITION

**McGraw Hill Education (India) Edition 2015**

Fifth reprint 2017
**PRDDLCRRBMXZQ**

Reprinted in India by arrangement with McGraw-Hill Global Education Holdings, LLC, New York

Sales territories: India, Pakistan, Nepal, Bangladesh, Sri Lanka and Bhutan

**Library of Congress Cataloging-in-Publication Data**

Enger, Eldon D.
    Concepts in biology / Eldon D. Enger, Frederick C. Ross, David B. Bailey—14th ed.
        p.    cm
    Includes index.
    ISBN 978-0-07-340346-5— ISBN 0-07-340346-6 (hard copy: alk. Paper) 1. Biology.
I.  Ross, Frederick C. II. Bailey, David B. III. Title.
    QH308.2C66 2012
    570—dc22                                                      2010030158

**ISBN-13: 978-93-392-2484-4**
**ISBN-10: 93-392-2484-1**

**5 6 7 8 9 SAN 21 20 19 18 17**

Published by McGraw Hill Education (India) Private Limited, 444/1, Sri Ekambara Naicker Industrial Estate, Alapakkam, Porur, Chennai 600 116, Tamil Nadu, India, and printed at Sanat Printers, 312, EPIP, HSIIDC, Kundli, Sonepat, Haryana

Printed and bound in India

Visit us at: www.mheducation.co.in

# Meet the Authors

## Eldon D. Enger (Center)

Eldon D. Enger is a professor emeritus of biology at Delta College, a community college near Saginaw, Michigan. He received his B.A. and M.S. degrees from the University of Michigan. Professor Enger has over 30 years of teaching experience, during which he taught biology, zoology, environmental science, and several other courses, and he was very active in curriculum and course development. Professor Enger is an advocate for variety in teaching methodology. He feels that if students are provided with varied experiences, they are more likely to learn. In addition to the standard textbook assignments, lectures, and laboratory activities, his classes were likely to include writing assignments, student presentation of lecture material, debates by students on controversial issues, field experiences, individual student projects, and discussions of local examples and relevant current events.

Professor Enger has been a Fulbright Exchange Teacher to Australia and Scotland, and he received the Bergstein Award for Teaching Excellence and the Scholarly Achievement Award from Delta College.

Professor Enger is married, has two sons, and enjoys a variety of outdoor pursuits, such as cross-country skiing, hiking, hunting, fishing, camping, and gardening. Other interests include reading a wide variety of periodicals, beekeeping, singing in a church choir, and preserving garden produce.

## Frederick C. Ross (Right)

Fred Ross is a professor emeritus of biology at Delta College, a community college near Saginaw, Michigan. He received his B.S. and M.S. from Wayne State University, Detroit, Michigan, and has attended several other universities and institutions. Professor Ross has over 30 years of teaching experience, including junior and senior high school. He has been very active in curriculum development and has developed the courses "Infection Control and Microbiology" and "AIDS and Infectious Diseases," a PBS ScienceLine course. He has also been actively involved in the National Task Force of Two Year College Biologists (American Institute of Biological Sciences); N.S.F. College Science Improvement Program (COSIP); Evaluator for Science and Engineering Fairs; Michigan Community College Biologists (MCCB); Judge for the Michigan Science Olympiad and the Science Bowl; and a member of the Topic Outlines in Introductory Microbiology Study Group of the American Society for Microbiology.

Professor Ross involved his students in a variety of learning techniques and was a prime advocate of writing-to-learn. Besides writing, his students were typically engaged in active learning techniques, including use of inquiry based learning, the Internet, e-mail communications, field experiences, classroom presentation, and lab work. The goal of his classroom presentations was to actively engage the minds of his students in understanding the material, not just memorization of "scientific facts."

## David B. Bailey (Left)

David B. Bailey is an associate professor of biology at Delta College, a community college near Saginaw, Michigan. He received his B.A. from Hiram College, Hiram, Ohio, and his Ph.D. from Case Western Reserve University in Cleveland, Ohio. Dr. Bailey has been teaching in classrooms and labs for 10 years in both community colleges and 4-year institutions. He has taught general biology, introductory zoology, cell biology, molecular biology, biotechnology, genetics, and microbiology. Dr. Bailey is currently directing Delta's General Education Program.

Dr. Bailey strives to emphasize critical thinking skills so that students can learn from each other. Practicing the scientific method and participating in discussions of literature, religion, and movies, students are able to learn how to practice appropriate use of different critical thinking styles. Comparing different methods of critical thinking for each of these areas, students develop a much more rounded perspective on their world.

Dr. Bailey's community involvement includes participating with the Michigan Science Olympiad. In his spare time, he enjoys camping, swimming, beekeeping, and wine-making.

# Brief Contents

# Contents

# Table of Boxes

# Preface

The origin of this book remains deeply rooted in our concern for the education of college students in the field of biology. We believe that large, thick books intimidate introductory-level students who are already anxious about taking science courses. With each edition, we have worked hard to provide a book that is useful, interesting, and engaging to students while introducing them to the core concepts and current state of the science.

## The Fourteenth Edition

There are several things about the fourteenth edition of *Concepts in Biology* that we find exciting. This revision, as with previous editions, is very much a collaborative effort. When we approach a revision, we carefully consider comments and criticisms of reviewers and discuss how to address their suggestions and concerns. As we proceed through the revision process, we solicit input from one another and we critique each other's work. This edition has several significant changes.

### Opening Chapter Vignette
Nearly all of the chapter-opening vignettes are new. Each vignette is intended to draw the students into the chapter by showing how the material is relevant to their lives. To help meet this goal the vignettes have been redesigned to resemble a magazine layout to draw the attention of the reader.

### Concept Review
In this edition, each major numbered heading ends with a Concept Review feature, which consists of a series of questions that probe the reader's level of understanding of the material in the section. The purpose of this feature is to encourage the reader to review the material in the section if he or she cannot answer the questions.

### Enhanced Visuals and Page Layout
The visual elements of a text are extremely important to the learning process. Over 150 figures are new or have been modified. The purpose of these changes is to more clearly illustrate a concept or show examples of material discussed in the text.

## Major Content Changes
### Chapter 1 What Is Biology?

- Section 1.1, "Why the Study of Biology Is Important," and material in Section 1.2, "Cause-and-Effect Relationships," and "The Scientific Method" have been rewritten to better communicate these concepts.
- The material in Section 1.4 entitled "What Makes Something Alive?" has been reordered to present a more logical progression of ideas. Also in Section 1.4, "The Levels of Biological Organization and Emerging Properties" section has been rewritten and now includes the concept of emerging properties. In addition, "The Consequences of Not Understanding Biological Principles" has a new introduction designed to present the concept of selective acceptance of scientific evidence.

### Chapter 2 The Basics of Life: Chemistry

- Section 2.1 "Matter, Energy, and Life" was rewritten to consolidate the introductory material on basic chemistry.

### Chapter 3 Organic Molecules—The Molecules of Life

- New material in the section on proteins presents the concept of chaperone proteins.

### Chapter 4 Cell Structure and Function

- There is a new section, "Basic Cell Types," that introduces the characteristics that are unique to eukaryotic and noneukaryotic cells. It also presents the most current thoughts on the evolution and relationships among the Bacteria, Archaea, and Eucarya.
- There is a new section on the two groups of membrane proteins involved in facilitated diffusion: (a) carrier proteins and (b) ion channels.
- A new diagram illustrates how all living things are classified.

### Chapter 6 Biochemical Pathways—Cellular Respiration

- There are new summary presentations for each portion of cellular respiration, as suggested by reviewers' comments.

- There are several new figures and flow charts to enhance student understanding of these very complex pathways.

## Chapter 7 Biochemical Pathways—Photosynthesis

- There are new summary presentations for each portion of photosynthesis suggested by reviewers' comments.
- There are several new figures and flow charts to enhance student understanding of these very complex pathways.

## Chapter 8 DNA and RNA: The Molecular Basis of Heredity

- Sections 8.1, "DNA and the Importance of Proteins," and 8.2, "DNA Structure and Function," have been rewritten.
- There is a new section on epigenetics.
- Section 8.4, "Protein Synthesis," has been rewritten.
- There are new presentations on sickle cell anemia and other genetic abnormalities.

## Chapter 9 Cell Division—Proliferation and Reproduction

- A new section on epigenetics and cancer was added.

## Chapter 11 Applications of Biotechnology

- Information on genetically modified organisms has been extensively revised.

## Chapter 14 The Formation of Species and Evolutionary Change

- New information is presented on Ida, *Darwinius masillae,* and her probable place in human evolution.
- Information on the proposed new species (hobbit) from Indonesia has been made current.
- A new table on primate classification has been added.
- There is a new section that discusses the recently published information about *Ardipithecus.*

## Chapter 16 Community Interactions

- The material on the nature of biomes has been enhanced with additional photos and climographs to better illustrate the nature of each biome.
- A new section entitled "Modern Concepts of Succession and Climax" was added.

## Chapter 17 Population Ecology

- The section on gene flow and gene frequency was reorganized.
- New material on the random and clumped distribution in populations was added to the text.

## Chapter 19 The Origin of Life and the Evolution of Cells

- Section 19.3, "The 'Big Bang' and the Origin of the Earth," has new subheadings to help the reader follow the discussion.
- Section 19.4, "The Chemical Evolution of Life on Earth," was substantially reorganized and rewritten.
- Section 19.5, "Major Evolutionary Changes in Early Cellular Life," has had major sections rewritten.
- Table 19.1, "Summary of Characteristics of the Three Domains of Life," was rewritten and placed later in the chapter.
- Section 19.6, "The Geologic Timeline and the Evolution of Life," was rewritten to include new information, better sequencing of information, and more subheadings to aid the reader in following the discussion.

## Chapter 20 The Classification and Evolution of Organisms

- The section on Archaea was substantially rewritten to include the latest information on the variety of kinds of Archaea found in oceans and soil.

## Chapter 21 The Nature of Microorganisms

- Section 21.1, "What Are Microorganisms?" was substantially rewritten.
- The section on control of bacterial population now includes discussion of methicillin resistant *Staphylococcus.*
- The section on Archaea was substantially rewritten to include recent understanding of the nature of Archaea diversity.
- The section on Fungi has additional information on the classification of fungi and clarification on the meaning of yeast, mold, and mildew.

## Chapter 23 The Animal Kingdom

- The section on body cavities was substantially rewritten.
- Section 23.6, "Primitive Marine Animals," was substantially rewritten.
- Section 23.10, "Mollusca," was substantially rewritten.
- The section on terrestrial arthropods was substantially rewritten.

## Chapter 24 Materials Exchange in the Body

- The sections on white blood cells, platelets, and plasma were rewritten.

## Chapter 25 Nutrition: Food and Diet

- Throughout the chapter when food calories are being discussed the term *Calorie* is used rather than *kilocalorie.*

- There has been a major reorganization of the material.
- The old section 25.7, "Deficiency Diseases," has been eliminated and much of the material in the section has been moved to parts of the chapter dealing with protein metabolism, vitamins, and minerals.
- Section 25.2, "Kinds of Nutrients and Their Function," has been reorganized with subheadings that highlight the nature and function of nutrients, how the body manages the nutrients, and other factors that are important to nutrition. Much new material was added.
- Tables 25.1, "Sources of Essential Amino Acids," 25.2, "Sources and Functions of Vitamins," and 25.3, "Sources and Functions of Minerals," have been updated and reorganized to help the reader see the significance of the nutrients.
- Material on discretionary Calories was added to the exercise portion of the Food Guide Pyramid discussion.
- The sections on body mass index and weight control were integrated into the section on obesity.
- Section 25.6, "Eating Disorders," has been completely rewritten.
- Section 25.8, "Nutrition for Sports and Fitness," has been substantially rewritten.

## Chapter 26 The Body's Control Mechanisms and Immunity

- The section on negative and positive feedback was rewritten.
- Table 26.2 on inflammation was reorganized.
- Table 26.3 on classes of antibodies was reorganized.
- A new heading, "Immune System Diseases," now includes discussion of allergies, autoimmune diseases, and immunodeficiency diseases, which were previously discussed in different sections.

## Chapter 27 Human Reproduction, Sex, and Sexuality

- A new section 27.2, "The Sexuality Spectrum," includes a reorganized discussion of intersexual anatomy, transsexual behavior, and homosexuality.
- A new section 27.3, "Components of Sexual Behavior," now discusses sexual attraction, foreplay, and intercourse.
- The section on contraception was significantly reorganized and rewritten.

## Other Significant Changes

Thirty-seven new boxed readings have been added or substituted for boxed readings that had become dated:

HOW SCIENCE WORKS 2.2: Greenhouse Gases and Their Relationship to Global Warming

HOW SCIENCE WORKS 3.1: Organic Compounds: Poisons to Your Pets!

OUTLOOKS 3.2: So You Don't Eat Meat! How to Stay Healthy

OUTLOOKS 3.3: What Happens When You Deep-Fry Food?

HOW SCIENCE WORKS 4.2: Cell Membrane Structure and Tissue Transplants

HOW SCIENCE WORKS 5.1: Don't Be Inhibited—Keep Your Memory Alive

HOW SCIENCE WORKS 7.1: Solution to Global Energy Crisis Found in Photosynthesis?

HOW SCIENCE WORKS 8.1: Scientists Unraveling the Mystery of DNA

OUTLOOKS 8.1: Life in Reverse—Retroviruses

OUTLOOKS 8.3: One Small Change—One Big Difference!

HOW SCIENCE WORKS 9.1: The Concepts of Homeostasis and Mitosis Applied

OUTLOOKS 11.1: The First DNA Fingerprint in a Criminal Case

OUTLOOKS 12.1: Your Skin Color, Gene Frequency Changes, and Natural Selection

OUTLOOKS 13.2: Genetic Diversity and Health Care

OUTLOOKS 14.1: Evolution and Domesticated Cats

OUTLOOKS 15.1: Changes in the Food Chain of the Great Lakes

OUTLOOKS 15.2: Dead Zones

HOW SCIENCE WORKS 15.1: Scientists Accumulate Knowledge About Climate Change

HOW SCIENCE WORKS 16.1: Whole Ecosystem Experiments

OUTLOOKS 16.1: Varzea Forests—Seasonally Flooded Amazon Tropical Forests

OUTLOOKS 17.1: Marine Turtle Population Declines

HOW SCIENCE WORKS 18.1: Males Raised the Young in Some Species of Dinosaurs

HOW SCIENCE WORKS 19.1: The Oldest Rocks on Earth

HOW SCIENCE WORKS 20.1: New Information Causes Changes in Taxonomy and Phylogeny

OUTLOOKS 20.1: A Bacterium That Controls Animal Reproduction

HOW SCIENCE WORKS 21.1: How Many Microbes Are There?

OUTLOOKS 21.1: Food Poisoning/Foodborne Illness/Stomach Flu

OUTLOOKS 21.3: The Marine Microbial Food Web

HOW SCIENCE WORKS 22.1: Using Information from Tree Rings

OUTLOOKS 23.1: The Problem of Image

HOW SCIENCE WORKS 23.1: Genes, Development, and Evolution

OUTLOOKS 24.1: Blood Doping

OUTLOOKS 24.2: Newborn Jaundice

OUTLOOKS 25.3: Muscle Dysmorphia

OUTLOOKS 25.5: Nutritional Health Products and Health Claims

OUTLOOKS 26.1: The Immune System and Transplants

OUTLOOKS 27.2: Causes of Infertility

# Features

**—Opening Vignette** The vignette is designed to pique students' interest and help them recognize the application and relevance of the topics presented in each chapter. The fourteenth edition also introduces bulleted questions for further reflections.

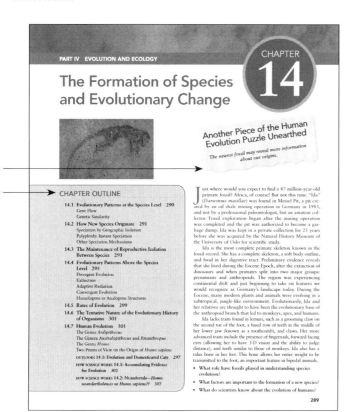

**—Chapter Outline** At the opening of each chapter, the outline lists the major headings in the chapter, as well as the boxed readings.

**—Background Check** The Background Check lists the key concepts students should already understand to get the most out of the chapter. Chapter references are included for review purposes.

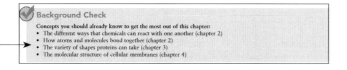

**—Quality Visuals** The line drawings and photographs illustrate concepts or associate new concepts with previously mastered information. Every illustration emphasizes a point or helps teach a concept.

**—Topical Headings** Throughout each chapter, headings subdivide the material into meaningful sections that help readers recognize and organize information.

## How Science Works and Outlooks

Each of these boxed readings was designed to catch readers' interest by providing alternative views, historical perspectives, or interesting snippets of information related to the content of the chapter.

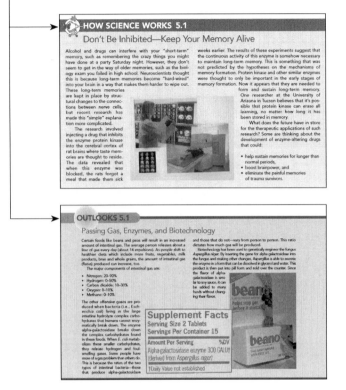

## Thinking Critically

This feature gives students an opportunity to think through problems logically and arrive at conclusions based on the concepts presented in the chapters.

## Page-Referenced Key Terms

A list of page-referenced key terms in each chapter helps students identify the vocabulary they need to understand the concepts and ideas presented in the chapter. Definitions are found in the glossary at the end of the text. Students can practice learning key terms with interactive flash cards at www.mhhe.com/enger14e.

## Chapter Summary

The summary at the end of each chapter clearly reviews the concepts presented.

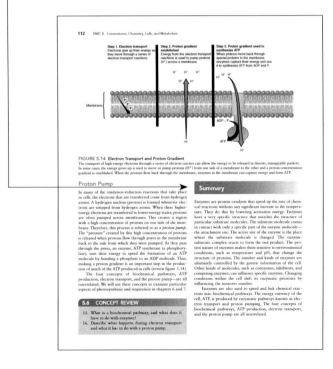

**Concept Review Questions** At the end of each numbered section of the text there are review questions that help students assess their understanding of the material. Concept review questions are answered at www.mhhe.com/enger14e.

**5.1  CONCEPT REVIEW**

1. What is the difference between a catalyst and an enzyme?
2. How do enzymes increase the rate of a chemical reaction?

**Basic Review Questions** Students can assess their knowledge by answering the basic review questions. The answers to the basic review questions are given at the end of the question set so students can get immediate feedback.

This partnership allows you and your students access to McGraw-Hill's Connect™ and Create™ right from within your Blackboard course–all with one single sign-on.

Not only do you get single sign-on with Connect and Create, you also get deep integration of McGraw-Hill content and content engines right in Blackboard. Whether you're choosing a book for your course or building Connect assignments, all the tools you need are right where you want them—inside of Blackboard.

Gradebooks are now seamless. When a student completes an integrated Connect assignment, the grade for that assignment automatically (and instantly) feeds your Blackboard grade center.

McGraw-Hill and Blackboard can now offer you easy access to industry leading technology and content, whether your campus hosts it, or we do. Be sure to ask your local McGraw-Hill representative for details.

### McGraw-Hill Connect™ Biology

www.mhhe.com/enger14e McGraw-Hill Connect Biology provides online presentation, assignment, and assessment solutions. It connects your students with the tools and resources they'll need to achieve success.

With Connect Biology you can deliver assignments, quizzes, and tests online. A robust set of questions and activities are aligned with learning outcomes. As an instructor, you can edit existing questions and author entirely new problems. You can also track individual student performance—by question, assignment, or in relation to the class overall—with detailed grade reports. Integrate grade reports easily with Learning Management Systems (LMS), such as WebCT and Blackboard.

ConnectPlus™ Biology provides students with all the advantages of Connect Biology, plus 24/7 online access to an eBook. This media-rich version of the book is available through the McGraw-Hill Connect platform and allows seamless integration of text, media, and assessments.

To learn more, visit

www.mcgrawhillconnect.com

## Teaching and Learning Tools

### McGraw-Hill Higher Education and Blackboard® have teamed up

Blackboard, the Web-based course-management system, has partnered with McGraw-Hill to better allow students and faculty to use online materials and activities to complement face-to-face teaching. Blackboard features exciting social learning and teaching tools that foster more logical, visually impactful and active learning opportunities for students. You'll transform your closed-door classrooms into communities where students remain connected to their educational experience 24 hours a day.

## Create

With McGraw-Hill Create™, www.mcgrawhillcreate.com, you can easily rearrange chapters, combine material from other content sources, and quickly upload content you have written like your course syllabus or teaching notes. Find the content you need in Create by searching through thousands of leading McGraw-Hill textbooks. Arrange your book to fit your teaching style. Create even allows you to personalize your book's appearance by selecting the cover and adding your name, school, and course information. Order a Create book and you'll receive a complimentary print review copy in 3–5 business days or a complimentary electronic review copy (eComp) via email in minutes. Go to www.mcgrawhillcreate.com today and register to experience how McGraw-Hill Create™ empowers you to teach *your* students *your* way.

## Animations for a New Generation

Dynamic, 3D animations of key biological processes bring an unprecedented level of control to the classroom. Innovative features keep the emphasis on teaching rather than entertaining.

- An options menu lets you control the animation's level of detail, speed, length, and appearance, so you can create the experience you want.
- Draw on the animation using the white board pen to highlight important areas.
- The scroll bar lets you fast forward and rewind while seeing what happens in the animation, so you can start at the exact moment you want.
- A scene menu lets you instantly jump to a specific point in the animation.
- Pop ups add detail at important points and help students relate the animation back to concepts from lecture and the textbook.
- A complete visual summary at the end of the animation reminds students of the big picture.
- Animation topics include: Cellular Respiration, Photosynthesis, Molecular Biology of the Gene, DNA Replication, Cell Cycle and Mitosis, Membrane Transport, and Plant Transport.

## Computerized Test Bank

A comprehensive computerized test bank powered by McGraw-Hill's flexible electronic testing program EZ Test Online. EZ Test Online allows you to create paper and online tests or quizzes in this easy to use program! A new tagging scheme allows you to sort questions by Bloom's difficulty level, topic, and section of the book. Imagine being able to create and access your test or quiz anywhere, at any time, without installing the testing software. Now, with EZ Test Online, instructors can select questions from multiple McGraw-Hill test banks or author their own, and then either print the test for paper distribution or give it online.

## Presentation Tools

**Everything you need for outstanding presentations in one place!**

### www.mhhe.com/enger14e

- *FlexArt Image PowerPoints®* files include every piece of art from the text. The art has been sized and cropped to provide superior presentations. Labels can be edited and repositioned on figures. Tables, photographs, and unlabeled art pieces are also included.
- *Lecture PowerPoint files with Animations*—include animations that illustrate important processes embedded in the lecture material.
- *Animation PowerPoint* files include animations only are provided in PowerPoint.
- *Labeled JPEG Image* files include full-color digital files of all illustrations that can be readily incorporated into presentations, exams, or custom-made classroom materials.
- *Base Art Image* files include unlabeled digital files of all illustrations.

## Presentation Center

In addition to the images from your book, this online digital library contains photos, artwork, animations, and other media from an array of McGraw-Hill textbooks that can be used to create customized lectures, visually enhanced tests and quizzes, compelling course websites, or attractive printed support materials.

## My Lectures—Tegrity

**Tegrity Campus™** records and distributes your class lecture, with just a click of a button. Students can view your lecture anytime/anywhere via computer, iPod, or mobile device. It indexes as it records your PowerPoint presentations and anything shown on your computer so students can use keywords to find exactly what they want to study. Tegrity is available as an integrated feature of McGraw-Hill Connect™ Biology or as a standalone.

## Instructor's Manual

The Instructor's manual contains an overview and a list of goals and objectives for each chapter.

## Laboratory Manual

The laboratory manual features 30 carefully designed, class-tested learning activities. Each exercise contains an introduction to the material, step-by-step procedures, ample space to record and graph data, and review questions. The activities give students an opportunity to go beyond reading and studying to actually participate in the process of science.

## Companion Website

**www.mhhe.com/enger14e**

The Enger: *Concepts in Biology* companion website allows students to access a variety of free digital learning tools that include:

- Chapter-level quizzing
- Animations
- Vocabulary flashcards
- Virtual Labs

Biology Prep, also available on the companion website, helps students to prepare for their upcoming coursework in biology. This website enables students to perform self assessments, conduct self-study sessions with tutorials, and perform a post-assessment of their knowledge in the following areas:

- Introductory Biology Skills
- Basic Math Review I and II
- Chemistry
- Metric System
- Lab Reports and Referencing

## McGraw-Hill: Biology Digitized Video Clips

ISBN (13) 978-0-312155-0
ISBN (10) 0-07-312155-X

McGraw-Hill is pleased to offer an outstanding presentation tool to text adopting instructors—digitized biology video clips on DVD! Licensed from some of the highest-quality science video producers in the world, these brief segments range from about five seconds to just under three minutes in length and cover all areas of general biology from cells to ecosystems. Engaging and informative, McGraw-Hill's digitized videos will help capture students' interest while illustrating key biological concepts and processes such as mitosis, how cilia and flagella work, and how some plants have evolved into carnivores.

## Acknowledgments

A large number of people have helped us write this text. Our families continued to give understanding and support as we worked on this revision. We acknowledge the thousands of students in our classes who have given us feedback over the years concerning the material and its relevancy. They were the best possible sources of criticism.

We gratefully acknowledge the invaluable assistance of the following reviewers throughout the development of the manuscript:

Reviewers for the Fourteenth Edition:

Stephen Ebbs, *Southern Illinois University–Carbondale*
Andrew Goliszek, *North Carolina A&T State University*
Voletta Williams, *Alcorn State University*
Don Ratcliffe, *Ivy Tech Community College*
Leba Sarkis, *Aims Community College*
Krishna Raychoudhury, *Benedict College*
John Murphy, *Southwest Baptist University*
Masood Mowlavi, *Delta College*
James Shepherd, *Zane State College*
Tracey Miller, *Edmonds Community College*
Frank Torrano, *American River College*
Charles Woods, *Miles College*

We also want to express our appreciation to the entire McGraw-Hill book team for their wonderful work in putting together this edition. Janice Roerig-Blong, publisher, has supported this project with enthusiasm and creative ideas. Michael Hackett, sponsoring editor, and Jolynn Kilburg, S4Carlisle Publishing Services, oversaw the many facets of the developmental stages. Sandy Wille kept everything running smoothly through the production process. Lori Hancock assisted with the photos. Tara McDermott provided us with a beautiful design. Tamara Maury promoted the text and educated the sales reps on its message.

CHAPTER

1

# What Is Biology?

## Foodborne Illness on the Rise

*As Population Increases So Does Concern for Food Safety.*

More than ever before, people around the world are worried about the safety of their food. Foodborne illnesses are diseases caused by infectious microbes (germs) or poisons that enter your body if you eat contaminated food. They result in sickness or death. The chemical contamination of baby formula made in China in 2008 was responsible for at least four infant deaths and over 53,000 illnesses. Everybody is at risk of foodborne illness. In fact, World Health Organization (WHO) scientists have stated that foodborne illnesses have become major problems in both developed and developing countries. Meats, vegetables, salads, snacks, fast food, vegetarian snacks, and even desserts have been found to be sources of foodborne illness. It is the variety of outbreaks that most troubles scientists and government health officials who are responsible for investigating and making recommendations for controlling outbreaks. WHO reported that the global incidence of death from diarrheal diseases caused by foodborne disease was 1.8 million. Diarrhea is a major cause of malnutrition in infants and young children. In the United States of America (USA), there are an estimated 76 million cases of foodborne diseases each year. These result in about 325,000 hospitalizations and 5,000 deaths. Food contamination has huge social and economic consequences on communities and their healthcare systems.

- How would a scientist approach the claim that the increase in foodborne illness is the result of a greater interest by consumers in eating fresh, uncooked foods?

- How would scientists go about identifying the cause of a foodborne illness?

- Should supersized food-processing companies be split into smaller, more easily regulated businesses?

## Background Check

**Concepts you should already know to get the most out of this chapter:**
At the beginning of each chapter, you will find a list of concepts or ideas that are helpful in understanding the content of the chapter. Since this is the first chapter, there is no special background required. However, you should:
- Have an open mind
- Be willing to learn

## 1.1 Why the Study of Biology Is Important

Many students question the need for science courses, such as biology, especially when their area of study is not science-related. However, it is becoming increasingly important for everyone to be able to recognize the power and limitations of science. In a democracy, it is assumed that the public has gathered enough information to make intelligent decisions. This is why an understanding of the nature of science and fundamental biological concepts is so important for any person, regardless of his or her occupation. *Concepts in Biology* was written with this philosophy in mind. This book presents core concepts selected to help you become more aware of how biology influences nearly every aspect of your life.

Most of the important questions of today can be considered from philosophical, scientific, and social points of view. However, none of these approaches individually answers those questions. For example, it is a fact that the human population of the world is growing rapidly. Philosophically, we may all agree that the rate of population growth should be slowed. Science can provide information about how populations grow and which actions will be the most effective in slowing population growth. Science can also develop effective methods of birth control. Social leaders can suggest strategies for population control that are acceptable within a society. It is important to recognize that science does not have the answers to all of our problems. In this situation, society must make the fundamental philosophical decisions about reproductive rights and the morality of various control methods if human population growth is to be controlled.

While science may raise many questions that are difficult for society to answer, science can challenge humanity to re-examine long-held beliefs. As science reports facts and trends, this new information can force us to rethink our view of the world. One example of this is the idea of human race. Only recently have we been able to look at all the genetic information that makes up a human. Now, it is possible to determine the genetic differences between different races of humans. Interestingly, the genetic differences between individual people of the same race can be greater than the differences among individuals who were thought to be of different races. The reason for this is that the number of genes that we typically associate with racial differences is very small when compared to the number of genes needed to make a person (figure 1.1).

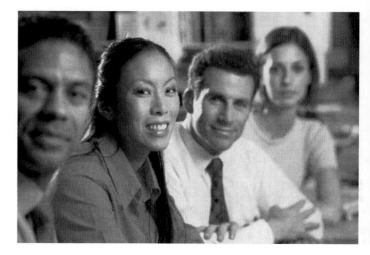

**FIGURE 1.1 What's the Difference?**
Despite superficial differences, different human races are overwhelmingly similar genetically.

Consider how this new information challenges the human perception of race. Humans define country borders and fight wars on the basis of race. This is true even though what makes up genetic differences between races is inconsequential to what makes us human.

## 1.1 CONCEPT REVIEW

1. Why is a basic understanding of science important for all citizens?
2. Describe two areas where scientific discoveries have caused us to rethink previously held beliefs.

## 1.2 Science and the Scientific Method

Most textbooks define **biology** as the science that deals with life. This definition seems clear until you begin to think about what the words *science* and *life* mean.

**Science** is actually a *process* used to solve problems or develop an understanding of repetitive natural events that involves the accumulation of knowledge and the testing of possible answers. The process has become known as the *scientific method*. The **scientific method** is a way of gaining information (facts) about the world by forming possible answers to questions, followed by rigorous testing to determine if the proposed explanations are supported by the facts.

## Basic Assumptions in Science

When using the scientific method, scientists make some basic assumptions:

- There are specific causes for naturally reoccurring events observed in the natural world.
- The causes for events in nature can be identified.
- There are general rules or principles that can be used to describe what happens in nature.
- An event that occurs repeatedly probably has the same cause each time it occurs.
- What one person observes can be observed by others.
- The same fundamental rules of nature apply, regardless of where and when they occur.

For example, we have all observed lightning with thunderstorms. According to the assumptions that have just been stated, we should expect that there is a cause of all cases of lightning, regardless of where or when they occur, and that all people could make the same observations. We know from scientific observations and experiments that

(1) lightning is caused by a difference in electrical charge,
(2) the behavior of lightning follows the same general rules as those for static electricity, and
(3) all lightning that has been measured has had the same cause wherever and whenever it has occurred regardless of who made the observation.

## Cause-and-Effect Relationships

Scientists distinguish between situations that are merely correlated (happen together) and those that are correlated and show *cause-and-effect relationships*. Many events are correlated, but not all correlations show cause-and-effect. When an event occurs as a direct result of a previous event, a cause-and-effect relationship exists. For example, lightning and thunder are correlated and have a cause-and-effect relationship. Lightning causes thunder.

The relationship between ingesting microorganisms and foodborne illness can be difficult to figure out. Because people have experienced bacterial, viral, or fungal infections, many assume that all microbes cause disease. In addition, the media portray all microbes as dangerous. Companies tell us that you should buy their antimicrobial product. They claim that their product will kill all the microbes, and therefore you will not come down with a foodborne illness. However, scores of different scientists have demonstrated through countless laboratory experiments that only a small number of microbes are *pathogenic*; that is, capable of causing harm. In fact, it turns out that most microbes are beneficial. These

experiments have led to the identification of specific mechanisms by which pathogens cause harm. For example, a specific toxin (poison) can be collected from a suspect bacterium, purified, and administered to a laboratory animal in its food. If the animal displays the predicted foodborne illness symptoms, the experiment lends credibility to the fact that the microbe is responsible for that illness. Knowing that a cause-and-effect relationship exists enables us to make a prediction. If the same set of circumstances occurs in the future, the same effect will result.

## The Scientific Method

The term *scientifically* is used in commercials, "science" programs on TV, public meetings, and in many other situations. Is this term being used correctly? In most cases the answer is "no!" In most of these situations, the term *scientifically* is used to mean "precisely," or with great accuracy. Science is a method that requires setting up a control group to which the experimental group is compared.

The scientific method involves an orderly, careful search for information. The method involves a continual checking and rechecking to see if previous conclusions are still supported by new evidence. If new evidence is not supportive, scientists discard or change their original ideas. Thus, scientific ideas undergo constant reevaluation, criticism, and modification as new discoveries are made. This can be very bewildering to the general public and can lead to people making comments such as, "Can't they make up their minds?" or "That's not what they said the last time." The scientific method has several important components:

- Careful observation
- The construction and testing of hypotheses
- An openness to new information and ideas
- A willingness to submit one's ideas to the scrutiny of others

The purpose of this method is to help scientists avoid making faulty assumptions and false claims. It is closely tied to the assumptions listed earlier and consists of several widely accepted steps (figure 1.2). However, scientists do not typically follow these steps from the first step (observation) to the last (communication). They take advantage of the work done by others and jump in and out of this series at various places.

### Observation

Scientific inquiry begins with an observation. We make an **observation** when we use our senses (i.e., smell, sight, hearing, taste, touch) or an extension of our senses (e.g., microscope, sound recorder, X-ray machine, thermometer) to record an event.

However, there is a difference between a scientific observation and simple awareness. For example, you might hear a sound or see something without really observing it. You have probably seen a magician, an illusionist, or a mystic perform tricks, but do you really know what's going on 'behind the

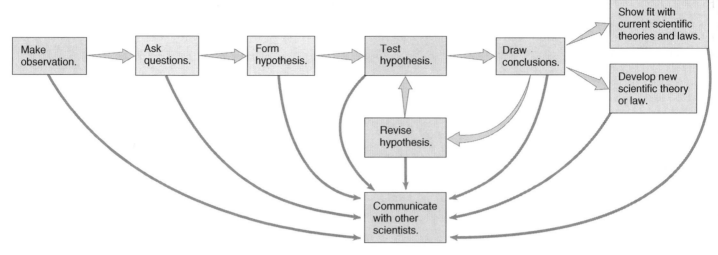

**FIGURE 1.2 The Scientific Method**
The scientific method is a way of thinking that involves making hypotheses about observations and testing the validity of the hypotheses. When hypotheses are disproved, they are revised and tested in their new form. Throughout the scientific process, people communicate their ideas. Scientific theories and laws develop as a result of people recognizing broad areas of agreement about how the world works. These laws and theories help people develop their approaches to scientific questions.

(a)

(b)

**FIGURE 1.3 Observation**
Careful observation is an important part of the scientific method. *(a)* This technician is making observations on the characteristics of soil and recording the results. *(b)* What is really going on here? What are you not observing?

scenes'? (figure 1.3) When scientists talk about their observations, they are referring to careful, thoughtful recognition of an event—not just casual notice. Scientists train themselves to improve their observational skills, because careful observation is important in all parts of the scientific method.

## Questioning and Exploration

As scientists make observations, they begin to develop *questions*. How does this happen? What causes it to occur? When will it take place again? Can I control the event to my benefit? Forming questions is not as simple as it might seem, because the way you ask questions determines how you answer them. A question that is too broad or too complex may be impossible to answer; therefore, a great deal of effort is put into asking the question in the right way. In some situations, this is the most time-consuming part of the scientific method; asking the right question is critical to how you look for answers.

Let's say that you have observed a cat catch, kill, and eat a mouse. You could ask several kinds of questions:

| 1a. What motivates a cat to hunt? | 1b. Do cats hunt more when they are hungry? |
|---|---|
| 2a. Why did the cat kill the mouse? | 2b. Is the killing behavior of the cat instinctive or learned? |
| 3a. Did the cat like the taste of the mouse? | 3b. If given a choice between mice and canned cat food, which would cats choose? |

Although questions 1a, 2a, and 3a are good questions, it would be very difficult to design an experiment to evaluate them. On the other hand questions 1b, 2b, and 3b lend themselves to experiment. The behavior of hungry and recently fed cats could be compared. The behavior of mature cats that have not had an opportunity to interact with live mice could be compared to that of mature cats who had accompanied their mothers as they hunted and killed mice. Cats could be offered a choice between a mouse and canned cat food and their choices could be recorded (figure 1.4).

Once a decision has been made about what question to ask, scientists *explore other sources of knowledge* to gain more information. Perhaps the question has already been answered by someone else. Perhaps several possible answers have already been rejected. Knowing what others have already done can save time and energy. This process usually involves reading appropriate science publications, exploring information on the Internet, and contacting fellow scientists interested in the same field of study. After exploring these sources of information, a decision is made about whether to continue to consider the question. If the scientist is still intrigued by the question, he or she constructs a formal hypothesis and continues the process of inquiry at a different level.

## Constructing Hypotheses

A **hypothesis** is a statement that provides a possible answer to a question or an explanation for an observation that can be tested. A good hypothesis must have the following characteristics:

(1) It must be logical.
(2) It must account for all the relevant information currently available.
(3) It must allow one to predict future events relating to the question being asked.
(4) It must be testable.

Do cats hunt more when they are hungry?

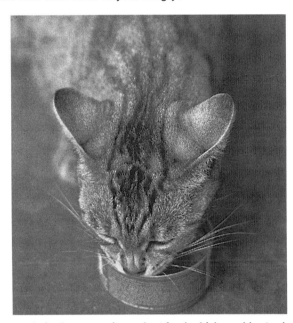

If given a choice between mice and cat food, which would cats choose?

**FIGURE 1.4  Questioning**
The scientific method involves forming questions about what you observe.

(5) Furthermore, if one has a choice of several hypotheses, one should use the simplest one with the fewest assumptions.

Just as deciding which questions to ask is often difficult, forming a hypothesis requires much critical thought and mental exploration.

## Testing Hypotheses

Scientists test a hypothesis to see if it is supported or disproved. If they disprove the hypothesis, they reject it and must construct a new hypothesis. However, if they cannot disprove a hypothesis, they are more confident in the *validity* (able to be justified; on target) of the hypothesis, even though they have not proven it true in all cases and for all time. Science always allows for the questioning of ideas and the substitution of new explanations as new information is obtained. As new information is obtained, an alternative hypothesis may become apparent and may explain the situation better than the original hypothesis. It is also possible, however, that the scientists have not made the appropriate observations to indicate that the hypothesis is wrong.

The test of a hypothesis can take several forms.

### (1) Collecting relevant information

In some cases collecting relevant information that already exists may be an adequate test of a hypothesis. For example, suppose you visited a cemetery and observed, from reading the tombstones, that an unusually large number of people of various ages died in the same year. You could hypothesize that an epidemic of disease or a natural disaster caused the deaths. To test this hypothesis, you could consult historical newspaper accounts for that year.

### (2) Making additional observations

Often making additional observations may be all that is necessary to test a hypothesis. For example, suppose you hypothesized that a certain species of bird uses holes in trees as places to build nests. You could observe several birds of the species and record the kinds of nests they build and where they build them.

### (3) Devising an experiment

A common method for testing a hypothesis involves devising an experiment. An **experiment** is a re-creation of an event or occurrence in a way that enables a scientist to support or disprove a hypothesis. In every experiment, the scientist tries to identify if there is a relationship between two events. This can be difficult, because a particular event may involve many separate factors, called **variables.** For example when a bird sings many activities of its nervous and muscular systems are involved. It is also stimulated by a wide variety of environmental factors. Understanding the variables involved in bird song production might seem an impossible task. To help unclutter such a situation, scientists break it up into a series of simple questions and use a *controlled experiment* to answer each question.

A **controlled experiment** allows scientists to construct a situation so that only one variable is present. A typical controlled experiment includes two groups: one group in which the variable is manipulated in a particular way and one group in which there is no manipulation. The group in which there is no manipulation of the variable is called the **control group;** the other group is called the **experimental group.**

The situation involving bird song production would have to be broken down into a large number of simple questions, such as the following:

Do both males and females sing?
Do they sing during all parts of the year?
Is the song the same in all cases?
Do some birds sing more than others?
What parts of their body are used to produce the song?
What situations cause birds to start or stop singing?

Each question would provide the basis for the construction of a hypothesis, which could be tested by an experiment. Each experiment would provide information about a small part of the total process of bird song production. For example, in order to test the hypothesis that male sex hormones produced by the testes are involved in stimulating male birds to sing, an experiment could be performed in which one group of male birds had their testes removed (the experimental group) but the control group was allowed to develop normally.

The presence or absence of testes would be manipulated by the scientist in the experiment and would be the **independent variable.** The singing behavior of the males would be the **dependent variable,** because, if sex hormones are important, the singing behavior observed will change, depending on whether the males have testes or not (the independent variable). In an experiment, there should be only one independent variable, and the dependent variable is expected to change as a direct result of the manipulation of the independent variable. After the experiment, the new data (facts) gathered would be analyzed. If there were no differences in singing between the two groups, scientists could conclude that the independent variable (presence or absence of testes) evidently did not have a cause-and-effect relationship with the dependent variable (singing). However, if there were a difference, it would be likely that the independent variable caused the difference between the control and experimental groups. In the case of songbirds, removal of the testes does change their singing behavior.

Scientists draw their most *reliable* (trustworthy) conclusions from multiple experiments. This is because random events having nothing to do with the experiment may have altered one set of results and suggest a cause-and-effect relationship when none actually exists. For example, if the experimental group of birds became ill with bird flu, they would not sing. Scientists use several strategies to avoid the effects of random events in their experiments; including using large numbers of animals in experiments and having other scientists repeat their experiments at other locations. With these strategies, it is less likely that random events will lead to false conclusions.

Scientists must try to make sure that an additional variable is not accidentally introduced into experiments. For example, the operation necessary to remove the testes of male birds might cause illness or discomfort in some birds, resulting in less singing. A way to overcome this difficulty would be to subject all the birds to the same surgery but to remove the testes of only half of them. (The control birds would still have their testes.) The results of an experiment are only scientifically convincing when there is just one variable, when the experiment has been repeated many times, and when the results for all experiments are the same.

During experimentation, scientists learn new information and formulate new questions, which can lead to even more experiments. One good experiment can result in many new questions and experiments. For example, the discovery of the structure of the DNA molecule by James D. Watson and Francis W. Crick (1953), resulted in thousands of experiments and stimulated the development of the entire field of molecular biology (figure 1.5).

As the processes of questioning and experimentation continue, it often happens that new evidence continually and consistently supports the original hypothesis and other closely related hypotheses. When the scientific community sees how these hypotheses and facts fit together into a broad pattern, they come together to write a scientific theory or law.

## The Development of Theories and Laws

As observations are made and hypotheses are tested, a pattern may emerge that leads to a general conclusion. This process of developing general principles from the examination of many sets of specific facts is called **inductive reasoning,** or **induction.** For example, when people examine hundreds of species of birds, they observe that all kinds lay eggs. From these observations, they may develop the principle that laying eggs is a fundamental characteristic of birds, without examining every species of bird.

Once such a principle is established, it can be used to predict additional observations in nature. The process of using general principles to predict the specific facts of a situation is called **deductive reasoning,** or **deduction.** For example, after the general principle that birds lay eggs is established, one might deduce that a newly discovered species of bird also lays eggs. In the process of science, both induction and deduction are important thinking processes used to increase our understanding of the nature of our world and to formulate scientific theories and laws.

You have probably heard people say "I have a theory" about such-and-such an event. However, scientists would say you have a *guess* or a *suspicion* about what is going on, not a theory. When scientists use the term *theory*, they mean something very different. A scientific **theory** is a widely accepted, plausible, general statement about fundamental concepts in science that explain *why* things happen. An example of a biological theory is the germ theory of disease. This theory states that certain diseases, called *infectious* diseases, are caused by living microorganisms that are capable of being transmitted from one person to another. When these microorganisms reproduce within a person and the populations of microorganisms increase, they cause disease. As you can see, this is a very broad statement, which is the result of years of observation, questioning, experimentation, and data analysis. The germ theory of disease provides a broad overview of the nature of infectious diseases and methods for their control. However, we also recognize that each kind of microorganism has particular characteristics, which determine the kind of disease condition it causes and the appropriate methods of treatment. Furthermore, we recognize that there are many diseases that are not caused by microorganisms, such as genetic diseases.

Theories are different from hypotheses. A hypothesis provides a possible explanation for a specific question; a theory is a broad concept that shapes how scientists look at the world and how they frame their hypotheses. For example, when a new disease is encountered, one of the first questions asked is "What causes this disease?" A hypothesis might be constructed, which states, "The disease is caused by a microorganism." This is a logical hypothesis, because it is consistent with the general theory that many kinds of diseases are caused by microorganisms (the germ theory of disease).

Because theories are broad, unifying statements, there are few of them. However, just because theories exist does not mean that testing stops. As scientists continue to gain new information, they may find exceptions to a theory or, rarely, disprove a theory.

A **scientific law** is a uniform or constant fact of nature that describes *what* happens in nature. An example of a biological law is the biogenetic law, which states that all living things come from preexisting living things. Although

**FIGURE 1.5 One Discovery Leads to Others**
The discovery of the structure of the DNA molecule was followed by much research into how the molecule codes information, how it makes copies of itself, and how the information is put into action.

laws describe what happens and theories describe why things happen, there is one way in which laws and theories are similar. Both laws and theories have been examined repeatedly and are regarded as excellent predictors of how nature behaves.

## Communication

One central characteristic of the scientific method is the importance of communication among colleagues. For the most part, science is conducted out in the open, under the critical eyes of others who are interested in the same kinds of questions. An important part of the communication process involves the publication of articles in scientific journals about one's research, thoughts, and opinions. This communication can occur at any point during the process of scientific discovery.

Scientists may ask questions about unusual observations. They may publish preliminary results of incomplete experiments. They may publish reports that summarize large bodies of material. And they may publish strongly held opinions that are not supportable with current data. This provides other scientists with an opportunity to criticize, make suggestions, or agree (figure 1.6). Scientists attend conferences, where they can engage in dialog with colleagues. They also interact in informal ways by phone and the Internet. The result is that most of science is subjected to examination by many minds as it is discovered, discussed, and refined.

Table 1.1 summarizes the processes involved in the scientific method and gives an example of how scientific investigation proceeds from an initial question to the development of theories and laws.

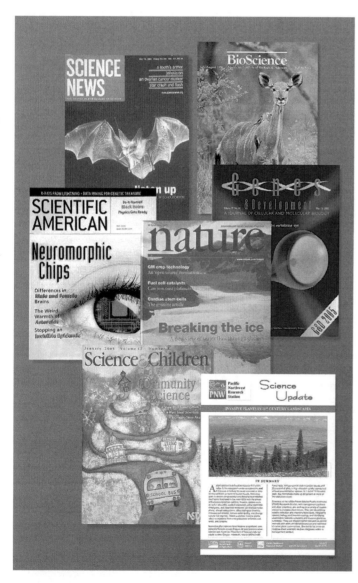

**FIGURE 1.6 Communication**
One important way that scientists communicate is through publications in scientific journals.

### 1.2　CONCEPT REVIEW

3. What is the difference between simple correlation and a cause-and-effect relationship?
4. How does a hypothesis differ from a scientific theory or a scientific law?
5. List three objects or processes you use daily that are the result of scientific investigation.
6. The scientific method cannot be used to deny or prove the existence of God. Why?
7. What are controlled experiments? Why are they necessary to support a hypothesis?
8. List the parts of the scientific method.

## 1.3　Science, Nonscience, and Pseudoscience
### Fundamental Attitudes in Science

As you can see from our discussion of the scientific method, a scientific approach to the world requires a certain way of thinking. A scientist is a healthy skeptic who separates facts from opinions (views based solely on personal judgment). Ideas are accepted because there is much supporting evidence from numerous studies, not because influential or famous people have strongly held opinions.

Careful attention to detail is also important. Because scientists publish their findings and their colleagues examine their work, they have a strong desire to produce careful work that can be easily defended. This does not mean that scientists do not speculate and state opinions. When they do, however, they take great care to clearly distinguish scientific facts from personal opinion.

There is also a strong ethic of honesty. Scientists are not saints, but the fact that science is conducted openly in front of one's peers tends to reduce the incidence of dishonesty. In addition, the scientific community strongly condemns and

**TABLE 1.1**   The Nature of the Scientific Method

| Component of Science Process | Description of Process | Example of the Process in Action |
|---|---|---|
| Make observations. | Recognize that something has happened and that it occurs repeatedly. (*Empirical evidence is gained from experience or observation.*) | Doctors observe that many of their patients who are suffering from tuberculosis fail to be cured by the use of the medicines (antibiotics) traditionally used to treat the disease. |
| Ask questions. | Ask questions about the observation, evaluate the questions, and keep the ones that will be answerable. | Have the drug companies modified the antibiotics? Are the patients failing to take the antibiotics as prescribed? Has the bacterium that causes tuberculosis changed? |
| Explore other sources of information. | Go to the library. Talk to others who are interested in the same problem. Communicate with other researchers to help determine if your question is a good one or if others have already answered it. | Read medical journals. Contact the Centers for Disease Control and Prevention. Consult experts in tuberculosis. Attend medical conventions. Contact drug companies and ask if their antibiotic formulation has been changed. |
| Form a hypothesis. | Pose a possible answer to your question. Be sure that it is testable and that it accounts for all the known information. Recognize that your hypothesis may be wrong. | Hypothesis: Tuberculosis patients who fail to be cured by standard antibiotics have tuberculosis caused by antibiotic-resistant populations of the bacterium *Mycobacterium tuberculosis*. |
| Test the hypothesis (experimentation). | Set up an experiment that will allow you to test your hypothesis using a control group and an experimental group. Be sure to collect and analyze the data carefully. | Set up an experiment in which samples of tuberculosis bacteria are collected from two groups of patients: those who are responding to antibiotic therapy and those who are not responding to antibiotic therapy. Grow the bacteria in the lab and subject them to the antibiotics normally used to see if the bacteria from these two groups of patients respond differently. Experiments consistently show that the patients who are not recovering have strains of bacteria that are resistant to the antibiotic being used. |
| Find agreement with existing scientific laws and theories or construct new laws or theories. | If your findings are seen to fit with current information, the scientific community will recognize them as being consistent with current scientific laws and theories. In rare instances, a new theory or law may develop as a result of research. | Your results are consistent with the following laws and theories: <br>• Mendel's laws of heredity state that characteristics are passed from parent to offspring. <br>• The theory of natural selection predicts that, when populations of *Mycobacterium tuberculosis* are subjected to antibiotics, the bacteria that survive will pass on their ability to survive exposure to antibiotics to the next generation and that the next generation will have a higher incidence of these characteristics. |
| Form a conclusion and communicate it. | You arrive at a conclusion. Throughout the process, communicate with other scientists by both informal conversation and formal publications. | You conclude that the antibiotics are ineffective because the bacteria are resistant to the antibiotics. You write a scientific article describing the experiment and your conclusions. |

severely penalizes those who steal the ideas of others, perform shoddy science, or falsify data. Any of these infractions can lead to the loss of one's job and reputation.

## Theoretical and Applied Science

The scientific method has helped us understand and control many aspects of our natural world. Some information is extremely important in understanding the structure and functioning of things in nature but at first glance appears to have little practical value. For example, the discovery of the structure of deoxyribonucleic acid (DNA) answered a fundamental question about the nature of genetic material. Many

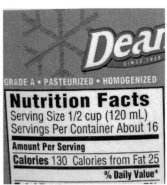

**FIGURE 1.8 Louis Pasteur and Pasteurized Milk**
Louis Pasteur (1822–1895) performed many experiments while he studied the question of the origin of life, one of which led directly to the food-preservation method now known as pasteurization.

people asked why such research would be done or funded by their taxes. However, as individuals began to use this new knowledge, they developed many practical applications for it. For example, scientists known as *genetic engineers* have altered the chemical code system of microorganisms, in order to produce many new drugs, such as antibiotics, hormones, and enzymes. To do this, genetic engineers needed information from the basic, theoretical sciences of microbiology, molecular biology, and genetics (figure 1.7).

Another example of how fundamental research can lead to practical application is the work of Louis Pasteur (1822–1895), a French chemist and microbiologist. Pasteur was interested in the highly theoretical question, "Could life be generated from nonliving material?" Much of his theoretical work led to practical applications in disease control. His theory that microorganisms cause diseases and decay led to the development of vaccinations against rabies and the development of pasteurization for the preservation of foods (figure 1.8).

## Science and Nonscience

Both scientists and nonscientists seek to gain information and improve understanding in their fields of study. The differences between science and nonscience are based on the assumptions and methods used to gather and organize information and, most important, the way the assumptions are tested. The difference between a scientist and a nonscientist is that a scientist continually challenges and tests principles and assumptions to determine cause-and-effect relationships. A nonscientist may not be able to do so or may not believe that this is important. For example, a historian may have the opinion that, if President Lincoln had not appointed Ulysses S. Grant to be a general in the Union Army, the Confederate States of America would have won the Civil War. Although there can be considerable argument about the topic, there is no way that it can be tested. Therefore, such speculation about historical events is not scientific. This does not mean that

(a)

(b)

**FIGURE 1.7 Genetic Engineering**
Genetic engineers have modified the genetic code of bacteria, such as *Escherichia coli*, commonly found in the colon *(a)* to produce useful products, such as vitamins, protein, and antibiotics. The bacteria can be cultured in vats, where the genetically modified bacteria manufacture their products *(b)*. The products can be extracted from the mixture in the vat.

history is not a respectable field of study, only that it is not science. Historians simply use the standards of critical thinking that are appropriate to their field of study and that can provide insights into the role military leadership plays in the outcome of conflicts.

Once you understand the scientific method, you won't have any trouble identifying astronomy, chemistry, physics, geology, and biology as sciences. But what about economics, sociology, anthropology, history, philosophy, and literature? All of these fields may make use of certain central ideas that are derived in a logical way, but they are also nonscientific in some ways. Some things are beyond science and cannot be approached using the scientific method. Art, literature, theology, and philosophy are rarely thought of as sciences. They are concerned with beauty, human emotion, and speculative thought, rather than with facts and verifiable laws.

Many fields of study have both scientific and nonscientific aspects. For example, the styles of clothing people wear are often shaped by the artistic creativity of designers and shrewd marketing by retailers. Originally, animal hides, wool, cotton, and flax were the only materials available, and the color choices were limited to the natural colors of the material or dyes extracted from nature. Scientific discoveries led to the development of synthetic fabrics and dyes, machines to construct clothing, and new kinds of fasteners that allowed for new styles and colors (figure 1.9).

Similarly, economists use mathematical models and established economic laws to make predictions about future economic conditions. However, the reliability of predictions is a central criterion of science, so the regular occurrence of unpredicted economic changes indicates that economics is far from scientific. Many aspects of anthropology and sociology are scientific, but

they cannot be considered true sciences, because many of the generalizations in these fields cannot be tested by repeated experimentation. They also do not show a significantly high degree of cause-and-effect, or they have poor predictive value.

## Pseudoscience

**Pseudoscience** (*pseudo* = false) is a deceptive practice that uses the appearance or language of science to convince, confuse, or mislead people into thinking that something has scientific validity. When pseudoscientific claims are closely examined, they are not found to be supported by unbiased tests.

For example, nutrition is a respectable scientific field; however, many individuals and organizations make unfounded claims about their products and diets (figure 1.10). Because of nutritional research, we all know that we must obtain certain nutrients, such as amino acids, vitamins, and minerals, from the food we eat or we may become ill. However, in most cases, it has not been demonstrated that the nutritional supplements so vigorously advertised are as useful or desirable as claimed. Rather, the advertisements select bits of scientific information about the fact that amino acids, vitamins, and minerals are essential to good health and then use this information to create the feeling that nutritional supplements are necessary or can improve health. In reality, the average person eating a varied diet can obtain all these nutrients in adequate amounts.

Another related example involves the labeling of products as organic or natural. Marketers imply that organic or natural

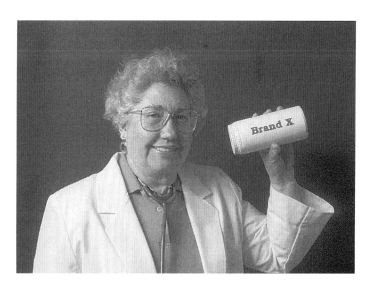

**FIGURE 1.10** Pseudoscience—"Nine out of 10 Doctors Surveyed Recommend Brand X"
Pseudoscience is designed to mislead. There are several ways in which this image and the statement can be misleading. You can ask yourself two questions. First, is the person in the white coat a physician? Second, how many doctors were asked for a recommendation and how were they selected? If only 10 doctors were asked, the sample size was too small. Perhaps the doctors who participated were selected to obtain the desired outcome. Finally, the doctors could have been surveyed in such a way as to obtain the desired answer, such as "Would you recommend Brand X over Dr. Pete's snake oil?"

**(a)**          **(b)**

**FIGURE 1.9** Science and Culture
Although the design of clothing is not a scientific enterprise, scientific discoveries have altered the choices available. *(a)* Originally, clothing could be made only from natural materials with simple construction methods. *(b)* The discovery of synthetic fabrics and dyes and the invention of specialized fasteners resulted in increased variety and specialization of clothing.

products have greater nutritive value because they are organically grown (grown without pesticides or synthetic fertilizers) or because they come from nature. Although there are questions about the health effects of trace amounts of pesticides in foods, no scientific study has shown that a diet of natural or organic products has any benefit over other diets. The poisons curare, strychnine, and nicotine are all organic molecules that are produced in nature by plants that can be grown organically, but we wouldn't want to include them in our diet.

## The Limitations of Science

Science is a way of thinking that involves testing possible answers to questions. Therefore, the scientific method can be applied only to questions that have factual bases. Ethical, moral, and religious concerns are not scientific endeavors. Questions about such topics cannot be answered using the scientific method. What makes a painting great? What is the best type of music? Which wine is best? Is there a God? These questions are related to values, beliefs, and tastes; therefore, the scientific method cannot be used to answer them.

(a) **Scientists thought that the Sun revolved around the Earth**.

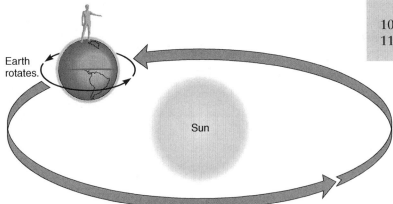

(b) **We now know that the Earth rotates on its axis and revolves around the Sun**

**FIGURE 1.11 Science Is Willing to Challenge Previous Beliefs**
Science must always be aware that new discoveries may force a reinterpretation of previously held beliefs. *(a)* Early scientists thought that the Sun revolved around the Earth. This was certainly a reasonable theory at the time. People saw the Sun rise in the east and set in the west, and it looked as if the Sun moved through the sky. *(b)* Today, we know that the Earth revolves around the Sun and that the apparent motion of the Sun in the sky is caused by the Earth rotating on its axis.

Science is also limited by the ability of people to figure out how the natural world works. People are fallible and do not always come to the right conclusions because they lack information or misinterpret it. However science is self-correcting and, as new information is gathered, old, incorrect ways of thinking are changed or discarded. For example, at one time scientists were sure that the Sun went around the Earth. They observed that the Sun rose in the east and traveled across the sky to set in the west. Because scientists could not feel the Earth moving, it seemed perfectly logical that the Sun traveled around the Earth. Once they understood that the Earth rotated on its axis, they began to realize that the rising and setting of the Sun could be explained in other ways. A completely new concept of the relationship between the Sun and the Earth developed (figure 1.11). Although this kind of study seems rather primitive to us today, this change in thinking about the relationship between the Sun and the Earth was a very important step forward in our understanding of the universe.

People need to understand that science cannot answer all the problems of our time. Although science is a powerful tool, there are many questions it cannot answer and many problems it cannot solve. Most of the problems societies face are generated by the behavior and desires of people. Famine, drug abuse, war, and pollution are human-caused and must be resolved by humans. Science provides some important tools for social planners, politicians, and ethical thinkers. However, science does not have, nor does it attempt to provide, all the answers to the problems of the human race. Science is merely one of the tools at our disposal.

### 1.3   CONCEPT REVIEW

9. What is the difference between science and nonscience?
10. How can you identify pseudoscience?
11. Why is political science not a science?

### 1.4   The Science of Biology

The science of biology is, broadly speaking, the study of living things. However, there are many specialty areas of biology, depending on the kind of organism studied or the goals a person has. Some biological studies are theoretical, such as establishing an evolutionary tree of life, understanding the significance of certain animal behaviors, or determining the biochemical steps involved in photosynthesis. Other fields of biology are practical—for example, medicine, crop science, plant breeding, and wildlife management. There is also just plain fun biology—fly-fishing for trout or scuba diving on a coral reef.

At the beginning of the chapter, we defined *biology* as the science that deals with life. But what distinguishes living things from those that are not alive? You would think that a biology textbook could answer this question easily. However, this is more than just a theoretical question. In recent years, it has become necessary to construct legal definitions of *life*, especially of when it begins and ends. The legal definition of *death* is important, too, because it may determine whether a person will receive life insurance benefits or if body parts may be used in transplants. In the case of a heart transplant, the person donating the heart may be legally "dead" but the heart certainly isn't. It is removed while it is still alive, even though the person is not. In other words, there are different kinds of death. There is death of the whole living unit and death of each cell within the living unit. A person actually "dies" before every cell has died. Death, then, is the absence of life, but that still doesn't tell us what life is.

Similarly, there has been much controversy over the question of when life begins. Certainly, the egg and the sperm that participate in fertilization are both alive, as is the embryo that results. However, from a legal and moral perspective, the question of when an embryo is considered a separate living thing is a very different proposition.

## What Makes Something Alive?

Living things have abilities and structures not found in things that were never living. The ability to interact with their surroundings to manipulate energy and matter is unique to living things. **Energy** is the ability to do work or cause things to move. **Matter** is anything that has mass and takes up space. Developing an understanding of how living things modify matter and use energy will help you appreciate how living things differ from nonliving objects. Living things show five characteristics that nonliving things do not: (1) unique structural organization, (2) metabolic processes, (3) generative processes, (4) responsive processes, and (5) control processes. It is important to recognize that, although these characteristics are typical of all living things, they may not all be present in each organism at every point in time. For example, some individuals may reproduce or grow only at certain times. This section briefly introduces these basic characteristics of living things, which will be expanded on in the rest of the text.

### Unique Structural Organization

The **unique structural organization** of living things can be seen at the molecular, cellular, and organism levels. Molecules such as DNA and proteins are produced by living things and are unique to each kind of living thing. **Cells** are the fundamental structural units of all living things. Cells have an outer limiting membrane and several kinds of internal structures. Each structure has specific functions. Some living things, such as people, consist of trillions of cells, whereas others, such as bacteria and yeasts, consist of only one cell. Nonliving materials, such as rocks, water, and gases, do not have a cellular structure.

An **organism** is any living thing that is capable of functioning independently, whether it consists of a single cell or a complex group of interacting cells (figure 1.12). Each kind of organism has specific structural characteristics, which it

*Euplotes*

**Yeast**

**Orchid**

**DNA helix**

**Humans**

**FIGURE 1.12 Structural Organization**
Each organism, whether it is simple or complex, independently carries on metabolic, generative, responsive, and control processes. It also contains special molecules, a cellular structure, and other structural components. DNA is a molecule unique to living things. Some organisms, such as yeast or the protozoan *Euplotes*, consist of single cells, whereas others, such as orchids and humans, consist of many cells organized into complex structures.

shares with all other organisms of the same kind. You recognize an African elephant, a redwood tree, or a sunflower as having certain characteristics, although other organisms may not be as easy to distinguish.

### Metabolic Processes

All the chemical reactions involving molecules required for a cell to grow, reproduce and make repairs are referred to as its **metabolism**. Metabolic properties keep a cell alive. The energy that organisms use is stored in the chemical bonds of complex molecules. Even though different kinds of organisms have different ways of metabolizing **nutrients** or food, we are usually talking about three main activities: taking in nutrients, processing them, and eliminating wastes.

Energy is expended when living things take in nutrients (raw materials) from their environment (figure 1.13). Many animals take in these materials by eating other organisms.

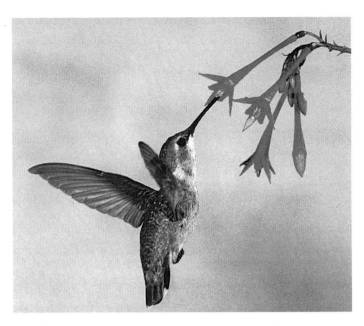

**FIGURE 1.13 Metabolism**
The metabolic processes of this hummingbird include the intake of nutrients in the form of nectar from flowers.

Microorganisms and plants absorb raw materials into their cells to maintain their lives. Nutrient processing takes place once the nutrients are inside the organism or its cells. Most animals have organs that assist in processing nutrients. In all organisms, once inside cells, nutrients enter a network of chemical reactions. These reactions process the nutrients to manufacture new parts, make repairs, reproduce, and provide energy for essential activities. Waste elimination occurs because not all materials entering a living thing are valuable to it. Some portions of nutrients are useless or even harmful, and organisms eliminate these portions as waste. Metabolic processes also produce unusable heat energy, which can be considered a waste product. Microorganisms, plants, and many tiny animals eliminate useless or harmful materials through their cell surfaces, but more complex animals have special structures for getting rid of these materials.

## Generative Processes

**Generative processes** are activities that result in an increase in the size of an organism—*growth*—or an increase in the number of individuals in a population—*reproduction* (figure 1.14). Growth and reproduction are directly related to metabolism, because neither can occur without gaining and processing nutrients.

During growth, living things add to their structure, repair parts, and store nutrients for later use. In large organisms, growth usually involves an increase in the number of cells present.

Reproduction is also an essential characteristic of living things. Because all organisms eventually die, life would cease to exist without reproduction. Organisms can reproduce in two basic ways. Some reproduce by *sexual reproduction*, in which two individuals each contribute sex cells, which leads to the creation of a new, unique organism. *Asexual reproduction* (without sex) occurs when an organism makes identical

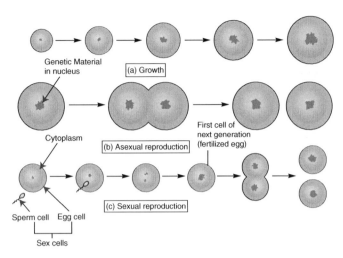

**FIGURE 1.14 Generative Processes**
Generative processes as they relate to cells.

copies of itself. Many kinds of plants and animals reproduce asexually when a part of the organism breaks off the parent organism and regenerates the missing parts.

## Responsive Processes

**Responsive processes** allow organisms to react to changes in their surroundings in a meaningful way. There are three categories of responsive processes: *irritability, individual adaptation*, and *evolution*, which is also known as *adaptation of populations*.

Irritability is an individual's ability to recognize that something in its surroundings has changed (a stimulus) and respond rapidly to it, such as your response to a loud noise, beautiful sunset, or bad smell. The response occurs only in the individual receiving the stimulus, and the reaction is rapid, because there are structures and processes already in place that receive the stimulus and cause the response. One-celled organisms, such as protozoa and bacteria, can sense and orient to light. Many plants orient their leaves to follow the sun. Animals use sense organs, nerves, and muscles to monitor and respond to changes in their environment.

Individual adaptation also results from an organism's reaction to a stimulus, but it is slower than an irritability response, because it requires growth or some other fundamental change in an organism. For example, during the summer the varying hare has brown fur. However, the shortening days of autumn cause the genes responsible for the production of brown pigment to be "turned off" and new, white hair grows (figure 1.15). Plants also show individual adaptation to changing day length. Lengthening days stimulate the production of flowers and shortening days result in falling leaves. Similarly, your body will adapt to lower oxygen levels by producing more oxygen-carrying red blood cells. Many athletes like to train at high elevations because the increased number of red blood cells resulting from exposure to low oxygen levels delivers more oxygen to their muscles.

Evolution involves genetic changes in the characteristics displayed within a population. It is a slow change in the genetic makeup of a *population* of organisms over many generations.

**Summer coat**　　　　　　　　**Winter coat**

## FIGURE 1.15 Individual Adaptation
The change in coat color of this varying hare is a response to changing environmental conditions.

Evolution enables a species (a population of a specific kind of organism) to adapt to long-term changes in its environment (figure 1.16). For example, between about 1.8 million and 11,000 years ago, the climate was cold and large continental glaciers covered northern Europe and North America. The plants and animals were adapted to these conditions. As the climate slowly warmed over the last 11,000 years, many of these species went extinct, whereas others adapted and continue in a modified form. For example, mammoths and mastodons were unable to adapt to the changing environment and became extinct, but some species, such as moose, elk, and wolves, were able to adapt to a warming environment and still exist today. Similarly, the development of the human brain and its ability to reason allowed our prehuman ancestors to craft and use tools. Their use of tools allowed them to survive and succeed in a great variety of environmental conditions.

## Control Processes
**Control processes** are mechanisms that ensure an organism will carry out all metabolic activities in the proper sequence (*coordination*) and at the proper rate (*regulation*).

Coordination occurs within an organism at several levels. At the metabolic level, all the chemical reactions of an organism are coordinated and linked together in specific pathways. The control of all the reactions ensures efficient, stepwise handling of the nutrients needed to maintain life. The molecules responsible for coordinating these metabolic reactions are known as *enzymes*. **Enzymes** are molecules, produced by organisms, that are able to control the rate at which life's chemical reactions occur. Enzymes also regulate the amount of nutrients processed into other forms. Enzymes will be discussed in detail in chapter 5.

Coordination also occurs at the organism level. When an insect walks, the muscles of its six legs are coordinated, so that orderly movement results. In plants, regulatory chemicals assure the proper sequence of events that result in growth in the spring and early summer, followed by flowering and the development of fruit later in the year.

*Regulation* involves altering the rate of processes. Many of the internal activities of an organism are interrelated and regulated, so that a constant internal environment is maintained. The process of maintaining a constant internal environment is called **homeostasis.** For example, when we begin to exercise we use up oxygen more rapidly, so the amount of oxygen in the blood falls. In order to maintain a constant internal environment, the body must obtain more oxygen. This requires more rapid contractions of the muscles that cause breathing and a more rapid and

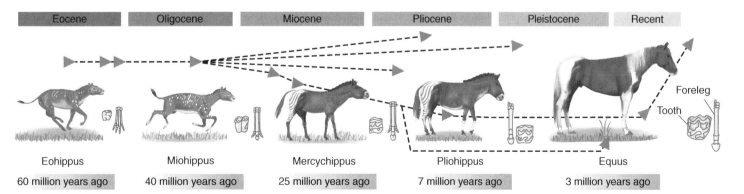

## FIGURE 1.16 Evolution
A principle that all scientists work with is the fact that things change over time. We know that chemicals react to become other kinds of substances, mountains crumble, rivers change course, and organisms reproduce and die. Evolution is also a change, but one that takes generations of time and results in descendents with a different genetic makeup than their ancestors. This sequence shows five species that illustrate that body size, leg structure, and food habits changed over time in horses.

forceful pumping of the heart to get blood to the lungs. These activities must occur together at the right time and at the correct rate; when they do, the level of oxygen in the blood will remain normal while supporting the additional muscular activity (figure 1.17).

## The Levels of Biological Organization and Emerging Properties

At this point you might be asking, "How can I possibly keep all this in my head?" Even biologists have difficulty keeping track of the vast amount of information being generated by researchers around the world. When you or biologists seek solutions to problems, it should be viewed at several levels at the same time. Doing this helps scientists create connections between different concepts. To be able to do this yourself, you must understand what these levels are. In order to help you, and biologists, conceptualize

the relationships that exist at these various levels, this information has been organized into table 1.2. Return to this table as you move through the text to jog your memory and regain your perspective should you get confused.

Scientists recognize these levels as a ladder of increasing complexity from atoms to biosphere, each displaying new properties not seen on the previous step. These never-before-seen features that result from

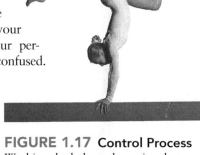

**FIGURE 1.17 Control Process** Working the balance beam involves coordination of heart rate, breathing rate, and muscular activity in a controlled manner.

**TABLE 1.2   Levels of Organization for Living Things**

| Level | Characteristics/Explanation | Example/Application |
|---|---|---|
| Biosphere | The worldwide ecosystem | Human activity affects the climate of the Earth. Global climate change and the hole in ozone layer are examples of human impacts on the biosphere. |
| Ecosystem | Communities (groups of populations) that interact with the physical world in a particular place | The Everglades ecosystem involves many kinds of organisms, the climate, and the flow of water to south Florida. |
| Community | Populations of different kinds of organisms that interact with one another in a particular place | The populations of trees, insects, birds, mammals, fungi, bacteria, and many other organisms interact in any location. |
| Population | A group of individual organisms of a particular kind | The human population currently consists of over 6 billion individuals. The current population of the California condor is about 220 individuals. |
| Organism | An independent living unit | Some organisms consist of many cells—you, a morel mushroom, a rose bush. Others are single cells—yeast, pneumonia bacterium, *Amoeba*. |
| Organ system | A group of organs that work together to perform a particular function | The circulatory system consists of a heart, arteries, veins, and capillaries, all of which are involved in moving blood from place to place. |
| Organ | A group of tissues that work together to perform a particular function | An eye contains nervous tissue, connective tissue, blood vessels, and pigmented tissues, all of which are involved in sight. |
| Tissue | Groups of cells that work together to perform particular functions | Blood, muscle cells, and the layers of the skin are all groups of cells and each performs a specific function. |
| Cell | The smallest unit that displays the characteristics of life | Some organisms are single cells. Within multicellular organisms are several kinds of cells—heart muscle cells, nerve cells, white blood cells. |
| Molecules | Specific arrangements of atoms | Living things consist of special kinds of molecules, such as proteins, carbohydrates, and DNA, as well as common molecules, such as water. |
| Atoms | The fundamental units of matter | There are about 100 different kinds of atoms such as hydrogen, oxygen, and nitrogen. |

**FIGURE 1.18** Emerging Properties
The properties you recognize as a car only become evident when the component parts are correctly assembled.

the interaction of simple components when they form much more complex substances are called **emergent properties** (figure 1.18). For example, when atoms on the first level interact to form molecules on the second level, new properties emerge that are displayed by the molecules (e.g., the ability to serve as genetic material). In turn, these molecules work together to form the parts of the next higher level, cells. Again, cells have a whole new set of emergent properties—all of life's characteristics. Continuing on, cells become organized into tissues; tissues into organs; organs into organ systems; and organ systems into organisms. All of these levels of organization exist within you as an individual.

These levels continue to provide you with a biological context for the world around you. Organisms are grouped into populations on the basis of where they live. Several populations are defined as a community. Now, the levels of organization start to include nonliving environmental characteristics, too. Communities and their environment form ecosystems. Several ecosystems form biomes and, finally, several biomes form the biosphere of our planet. As before, novel properties emerge as you rise through the chart. At the highest level, some scientists begin to view our planet as a type of living entity that has unique emergent properties not found at lower levels of organization.

## The Significance of Biology in Our Lives

To a great extent, we owe our high standard of living to biological advances in two areas: food production and disease control. Plant and animal breeders have modified organisms to yield greater amounts of food than did older varieties. A good example is the changes that have occurred in corn. Corn, a kind of grass, produces its seeds on a cob. The original corn plant had very small cobs, which were perhaps only 3 or 4 centimeters long. Selective breeding has produced varieties of corn with much

larger cobs and more seeds per cob, increasing the yield greatly. In addition, plant breeders have created varieties, such as sweet corn and popcorn, with special characteristics. Similar improvements have occurred in wheat, rice, oats, other cereal grains and fruits (figure 1.19). The improvements in the plants, along with better farming practices (also brought about through biological experimentation), have greatly increased food production.

Animal breeders also have had great successes. The pig, chicken, and cow of today are much different animals from those available even 100 years ago. Chickens lay more eggs, beef cattle grow faster, and dairy cows give more milk. All these improvements increase the amount of food available and raise our standard of living.

Biological research has also improved food production by developing controls for the disease organisms, pests, and weeds that reduce yields. Biologists must understand the nature of these harmful organisms to develop effective control methods.

There also has been fantastic progress in the area of human health. An understanding that diseases such as cholera, typhoid fever, and dysentery spread from one person to another through the water supply led to the development of treatment plants for sewage and drinking water. Recognizing that diseases such as botulism and salmonella spread through food led to guidelines for food preservation and preparation that greatly reduced the incidence of these diseases. Many other diseases, such as polio, whooping cough, measles, and mumps, can be prevented by vaccinations (How Science Works 1.1). Unfortunately, the vaccines have worked so well that some people no longer bother to get them. Furthermore, we have discovered that adults need to be revaccinated for some of these diseases. Therefore, we see that some diseases, such as diphtheria, whooping cough, and chicken pox are reappearing among both children and adults.

(a)                                             (b)

**FIGURE 1.19** Biological Research Improves Food Production
*(a)* One food that has seen a vast increase in production and variation is the tomato. Tomatoes (*Lycopersicon* sp.) originated on the western coast of South America in Peru. Wild tomato species have tiny fruits, and only the red ones are edible. *(b)* Over the centuries, selective breeding and biotechnology have resulted in the generation of hundreds of varieties of this vegetable.

# HOW SCIENCE WORKS 1.1

## Edward Jenner and the Control of Smallpox

Edward Jenner (1749–1823) was born in Berkeley, Gloucestershire, in western England. He wanted to become a doctor, so he became an apprentice to a local doctor. This was the typical training for physicians at that time. After his apprenticeship, he went to London and studied with an eminent surgeon. In 1773, he returned to Berkeley and practiced medicine there for the rest of his life.

At that time in Europe and Asia, smallpox was a common disease, which nearly everyone developed, usually early in life. Many children died of it, and many who survived were disfigured by scars. It was known that people who had had smallpox once were protected from future infection. If children were deliberately exposed to smallpox when they were otherwise healthy, a mild form of the disease often developed, and they were protected from future smallpox infections. Indeed, in the Middle East, people were deliberately infected by scratching material from the pocks of an infected person into their skin. This practice was introduced to England in 1717 by Lady Mary Wortley Montagu, the wife of the ambassador to Turkey. She had observed the practice of deliberate infection in Turkey and had had her own children inoculated. This practice had become common in England by the early 1700s, and Jenner carried out such deliberate inoculations as part of his practice. He also frequently came into contact with individuals who had smallpox, as well as people infected with cowpox— a mild disease similar to smallpox.

In 1796, Jenner introduced a safer way to protect against smallpox as a result of his 26-year study of cowpox and smallpox. Jenner had made two important *observations*. First, many milkmaids and other farmworkers developed a mild illness, with pocklike sores, after milking cows that had cowpox sores on their teats. Second, very few of those who had been infected with cowpox became sick with smallpox. He asked the *question* "Why don't people who have had cowpox get

smallpox?" He developed the *hypothesis* that the mild disease caused by cowpox somehow protected them from the often fatal smallpox. This led him to perform an *experiment*. In his first experiment, he took puslike material from a sore on the hand of a milkmaid named Sarah Nelmes and rubbed it into small cuts on the arm of an 8-year-old boy named James Phipps. James developed the normal mild infection typical of cowpox and completely recovered. Subsequently, Jenner inoculated James with material from a smallpox patient. (Recall that this was a normal practice at the time.) James did not develop any disease. Jenner's *conclusion* was that deliberate exposure to cowpox had protected James from smallpox. Eventually the word *vaccination* was used to describe the process. It was derived from the Latin words for *cow* (*vacca*) and *cowpox disease* (*vaccinae*) (box figure).

When these results became known, public reaction was mixed. Some people thought that vaccination was the work of the devil. However, many European rulers supported Jenner by encouraging their subjects to be vaccinated. Napoleon and the empress of Russia were very influential and, in the United States, Thomas Jefferson had some members of his family vaccinated. Many years later, following the development of the *germ theory of disease*, it was discovered that cowpox and smallpox are caused by viruses that are similar in structure. Exposure to the cowpox virus allows the body to develop immunity against both the cowpox virus and the smallpox virus. In the mid-1900s a slightly different virus was used to develop a vaccine against smallpox, which was used worldwide. In 1979, almost 200 years after Jenner developed his vaccination, the Centers for Disease Control and Prevention (CDC) in the United States and the World Health Organization (WHO) of the United Nations declared that smallpox had been eradicated.

The painting depicts Edward Jenner vaccinating James Phipps.

---

They have not been eliminated, and people who are not protected by vaccinations are still susceptible to them. By helping us understand how the human body works, biological research has led to the development of treatments that can control chronic diseases, such as diabetes, high blood pressure, and even some kinds of cancer. Unfortunately, all these advances in health contribute to another major biological problem: the increasing size of the human population.

## The Consequences of Not Understanding Biological Principles

A lack of understanding biological principles, and the inability to distinguish between valid scientifically obtained facts and personal opinions, can have significant consequences. Some people practice "selective acceptance of scientific evidence." They have "faith" in the health products and procedures that have

# HOW SCIENCE WORKS 1.1 (*continued*)

| Vaccine/ Age | Birth | 1 month | 2 months | 4 months | 6 months | 12 months | 15 months | 18 months | 24 months | 4–6 years | 11–12 years | 13–18 years | 19–49 years | 50–64 years | 65 or older |
|---|---|---|---|---|---|---|---|---|---|---|---|---|---|---|---|
| **Recommended Immunization Schedule United States, 2007** | | | | | | | | | | | | | | | |
| Hep B (hepatitis B) | First | Second | | | | Third | | | Hep B series if needed (3 doses) | | | | | | |
| DTP: diphtheria, tetanus, pertussis (whooping cough) | | | First | Second | Third | | Fourth | | | Fifth | Tetanus & diphtheria | | 1 dose tetanus every 10 years | | |
| HIB (*Haemophilus* influenzae type B - influenza ) | | | First | Second | Third | Fourth | | | | | | | | | |
| IPV (inactivated polio vaccine) | | | First | Second | Third | | | | | Fourth | | | | | |
| PCV (Pneumococcal conjugate - pneumonia) | | | First | Second | Third | Fourth | Additional vaccinations if high-risk | | | | | | | 1–2 doses | 1 dose |
| MMR: Measles, mumps, rubella (German measles) | | | | | | First | | | | Second | | | 1–2 doses | 1 dose | |
| Varicella (chicken pox) | | | | | First | | | Second | | | | | | 2 doses | |
| Influenza (flu) | | | | | 2 doses | | | | | | If high risk | | | | |
| MPSV4 (Meningococcal - viral meningitis) | | | | | | | | | | | 1 or more doses if high-risk | | | | |
| HPV (Human papilloma virus) | | | | | | | | | | | 3 doses (female) | | | | |
| Rotavirus | | | 1 dose | | | | | | | | | | | | |
| *Source:* Centers for Disease Control and Prevention | | | | | | | | | | | | | | | |

Today, vaccinations (immunizations) are used to control many diseases that used to be common. Many of them were known as childhood diseases, because essentially all children got them. Today, they are rare in populations that are vaccinated. The following chart shows the schedule of immunizations recommended by the Advisory Committee on Immunization Practices of the American Academy of Pediatrics and American Academy of Family Physicians.

resulted from "good science" (e.g., antibiotics, heart transplants) but don't "believe" or have "faith" in others (e.g., vaccinations, genetic engineering, stem cells).

## Inability to See a Bigger Picture

There are some people who believe that you can get the flu by getting the vaccine in spite of scientific evidence to the contrary. While the vaccine may cause certain side effects (problems that occur in addition to the desired healing effect), it does not contain any viruses capable of causing infection. These people (1) confuse the side effects with actual flu symptoms; (2) don't realize that the vaccine they received does not protect against other, related strains of influenza virus; or (3) may have already been infected before receiving the vaccine. In fact, by refusing to get vaccinated they jeopardize others in their community. By being vaccinated and becoming immune to the virus, they serve as a barrier to the spread of the virus, helping to prevent others from becoming infected. If enough people become immune as the result of immunization, there is less chance that others will get the illness.

## Lack of Understanding the Interconnectedness of Ecological Systems

At one time, it was thought that the protection of specific land areas would preserve endangered ecosystems. However, it is now recognized that many activities outside park and preserve boundaries are also important. For example, although Everglades National Park in Florida has been well managed by the National Park Service, this ecosystem is experiencing significant destruction. Commercial and agricultural development adjacent to the park has caused groundwater levels in the Everglades to drop so low that the park's very existence is threatened. Fertilizer has entered the park from surrounding farmland and has encouraged the growth of plants that change the nature of the ecosystem. In 2000, Congress authorized the expenditure of $1.4 billion to begin to implement a plan that will address the problems of water flow and pollution. The major goals are to reduce the amount of nutrients entering from farms and to increase the flow of water to the Everglades from Lake Okeechobee to the north.

## The Damage Caused by Exotic Species

In North America, the introduction of exotic (foreign) species of plants and animals has had disastrous consequences in a number of cases (figure 1.20). Both the American chestnut and the American elm have been nearly eliminated by diseases that were introduced by accident. Another accidental introduction, the zebra mussel, has greatly altered freshwater lakes and rivers in the central and eastern parts of the United States. They filter tiny organisms from the water and deprive native organisms of this food source. In addition, they attach themselves to native mussels, often causing their death.

Other organisms have been introduced on purpose because of shortsightedness or a lack of understanding about biology. The European starling and the English (house) sparrow were both introduced into this country by people who thought they were doing good. Both of these birds have multiplied greatly and have displaced some native birds. Many people want to have exotic animals as pets. When these animals escape or are intentionally released, they can become established in local ecosystems and endanger native organisms. For example, Burmese pythons are commonly kept as pets. Today, they are common in the Everglades and kill and eat native species. Large pythons have even been observed attacking alligators. The introduction of exotic plants has also caused problems. At one time, people were encouraged to plant a shrub known as autumn olive as a wildlife food. The plant produces many small fruits, which are readily eaten

**Starling**

**Zebra Mussels**

**FIGURE 1.20 Exotic Animals**
Exotic organisms such as starlings and zebra mussels have altered natural ecosystems by replacing native species.

by many kinds of birds and mammals. However, because the animals eat the fruits and defecate the seeds everywhere, autumn olive spreads rapidly. Today, it is recognized as an invasive plant needing to be controlled.

## Ethical Concerns

Advances in technology and our understanding of human biology have presented us with difficult ethical issues, which we have not been able to resolve satisfactorily. Major advances in health care have prolonged the lives of people who would have died if they had lived a generation earlier. Many of the techniques and machines that allow us to preserve and extend life are extremely expensive and are therefore unavailable to most citizens of the world. Many people lack even the most basic health care, while people in the rich nations of the world spend millions of dollars to have cosmetic surgery and to keep comatose patients alive with the assistance of machines.

## Future Directions in Biology

Where do we go from here? Although the science of biology has made major advances, many problems remain to be solved. For example, scientists are seeking major advances in the control of the human population, and there is a continued interest in the development of more efficient methods of producing food.

One area that will receive more attention in the next few years is ecology. Climate change, pollution, and the destruction of natural ecosystems to feed a rapidly increasing human population are severe problems. We face two tasks: The first is to improve technology and our understanding about how things work in our biological world; the second, and probably the more difficult, is to educate people that their actions determine the kind of world in which future generations will live.

Another area that will receive much attention in the next few years is the relationship between genetic information and such diseases as Alzheimer's disease, stroke, arthritis, and cancer. These and many other diseases are caused by abnormal body chemistry, which is the result of hereditary characteristics. Curing hereditary diseases is a big job. It requires a thorough understanding of genetics and the manipulation of hereditary information in all of the trillions of cells of the organism.

It is the intent of science to learn what is going on by gathering facts objectively and identifying the most logical courses of action. It is also the role of science to identify cause-and-effect relationships and note their predictive value in ways that will improve the environment for all forms of life—including us. Scientists should also make suggestions to politicians and other policy makers about which courses of action are the most logical from a scientific point of view.

### 1.4  CONCEPT REVIEW

12. Describe three advances that have occurred as a result of biology.
13. List three mistakes that could have been avoided had we known more about living things.
14. What is biology?
15. List five characteristics of living things.
16. What is the difference between regulation and coordination?

## Summary

The science of biology is the study of living things and how they interact with their surroundings. Science can be distinguished from nonscience by the kinds of laws and rules that are constructed to unify the body of knowledge. Science involves the continuous testing of rules and principles by the collection of new facts. In science, these rules are usually arrived at by using the scientific method—observation, questioning, the exploration of resources, hypothesis formation, and the testing of hypotheses. When general patterns are recognized, theories and laws are formulated. If a rule is not testable, or if no rule is used, it is not science. Pseudoscience uses scientific appearances to mislead.

Living things show the characteristics of (1) a unique structural organization, (2) metabolic processes, (3) generative processes, (4) responsive processes, and (5) control processes. Biology has been responsible for major advances in food production and health. The incorrect application of biological principles has sometimes led to the destruction of useful organisms and the introduction of harmful ones. Many biological advances have led to ethical dilemmas, which have not been resolved. In the future, biologists will study many things. Two areas that are certain to receive attention are ecology and the relationship between heredity and disease.

## Key Terms

*Use the interactive flash cards on the* **Concepts in Biology,** *14/e website to help you learn the meaning of these terms.*

atoms 16
biology 2
biosphere 16
cells 13
community 16
control group 6
control processes 15
controlled experiment 6
deductive reasoning
  (deduction) 7
dependent variable 6
ecosystem 16
emergent properties 17
energy 13
enzymes 15
experiment 6
experimental group 6
generative processes 14
homeostasis 15
hypothesis 5
independent variable 6

inductive reasoning
  (induction) 7
matter 13
metabolism 13
molecules 16
nutrients 13
observation 3
organ 16
organ system 16
organism 13
population 16
pseudoscience 11
responsive processes 14
science 2
scientific law 7
scientific method 3
theory 7
tissue 16
unique structural
  organization 13
variables 6

## Basic Review

1. Which one of the following distinguishes science from nonscience?

   a. the collection of information

   b. the testing of a hypothesis

   c. the acceptance of the advice of experts

   d. information that never changes

2. A hypothesis must account for all available information, be logical, and be _____.

3. A scientific theory is

   a. a guess as to why things occur.

   b. always correct.

   c. a broad statement that ties together many facts.

   d. easily changed.

4. Pseudoscience is the use of the appearance of science to _____.

5. Economics is not considered a science because

   a. it does not have theories.

   b. it does not use facts.

   c. many economic predictions do not come true.

   d. economists do not form hypotheses.

6. Reproduction is

   a. a generative process.

   b. a responsive process.

   c. a control process.

   d. a metabolic process.

7. The smallest independent living unit is the _____.

8. The smallest unit that displays characteristics of life is the _____.

9. An understanding of the principles of biology will prevent policy makers from making mistakes. (T/F)

10. Three important advances in the control of infectious diseases are safe drinking water, safe food, and _____.

11. If data are able to be justified and are on target with other evidence, scientists say that these data are

    a. valid.

    b. reliable.

    c. expected.

    d. appropriate.

12. Which is not a basic assumption in science?

    a. There are specific causes for events observed in the natural world.

    b. There are general rules or patterns that can be used to describe what happens in nature.

    c. Events that occur only once probably have a single cause.

    d. The same fundamental rules of nature apply, regardless of where and when they occur.

13. A variable that changes in direct response to how another variable is manipulated is known as

    a. the dependent variable.

    b. the independent variable.

    c. the reliable variable.

    d. a hypothesis.

14. Features that result from the interaction of simple components when they form much more complex substances are called

    a. organizational properties.

    b. emergent properties.

    c. adaptive traits.

    d. evolutionary traits.

**Answers**
1. b   2. testable   3. c   4. mislead   5. c   6. a   7. organism
8. cell   9. F   10. vaccination   11. a   12. c   13. a   14. b

## Thinking Critically

**The Scientific Method and Climate Change**
One important trait that all scientists should share is skepticism. They should consistently and constantly ask the question, "Are you sure that's right?" When considering the question of global warming, scientists might ask, "Is there a scientific basis that global warming is primarily due to greenhouse gases that are manmade?" The carbon dioxide content of the atmosphere is the highest it has been in millions of years and the rate of increase is unparalleled. What must scientists do to demonstrate a cause-and-effect relationship? As a scientist, how would you go about determining if this is simply a correlation and not a cause-and-effect relationship? How would you determine if there is a cause-and-effect relationship between the exponential increase in world human population in the last century and the increase in greenhouse gases? If the evidence ultimately points to a correlation, is it wise to ignore the potential risks associated with global warming?

CHAPTER

2

# The Basics of Life
## Chemistry

**CFLs, A Bright Idea With Potential Health Problems**

*Lightbulbs cause for concern?*

## CHAPTER OUTLINE

Fluorescent lightbulbs were invented in the 1890s. However, it wasn't until the 1970s that compact fluorescent lights (CFLs), were developed as a spinoff of a world-wide oil shortage. The shortage stimulated research into ways of getting people to use the more energy-efficient bulbs. CFLs use only about 25% of the energy needed to produce the same amount of light as an incandescent bulb and last about 10 times longer. Replacing incandescent bulbs with CFLs will reduce the amount of fossil fuels burned to generate electricity, thus reducing greenhouse gases such as carbon dioxide. Ultimately, this will help to control global warming.

All fluorescent bulbs contain the element mercury, essential for their operation. Electricity vaporizes the mercury, causing it to emit UV light, which, in turn, causes other chemicals to light up; that is, they fluoresce. At first glance CFLs might seem to be a win-win situation (i.e., longer-lasting, lower-energy bulbs and less greenhouse gases). However, there is another problem.

Once released, certain bacteria can change mercury into the molecule methylmercury, which is highly toxic to the brain, heart, kidneys, lungs, and immune system, and is especially harmful to fetuses and children. In fact, about one in six children in the United States is at risk for learning disabilities from exposure to methylmercury. According to the EPA, the amount of mercury released from CFL bulbs can exceed U.S. federal guidelines for chronic exposure. As more CFLs are used, it may become essential to regulate their use and disposal.

- **What are elements and molecules?**
- **What should you do if one of these CFL bulbs breaks or wears out?**
- **Will you stop using such potentially dangerous products in favor of safer ones?**

## Background Check

**Concepts you should already know to get the most out of this chapter:**
- The scientific method (chapter 1)
- Features that make something alive (chapter 1)
- The levels of biological organization (chapter 1)

## 2.1 Matter, Energy, and Life

All living things have the ability to use matter and energy to their advantage. Bees, bacteria, broccoli—in fact, all organisms—use energy to move about, respond to change, reproduce, make repairs and grow; in other words, to stay alive. **Energy** is the ability to do work or cause things to move. There are two general types of energy: *kinetic* and *potential*. A flying bird displays **kinetic energy,** or energy of motion. **Potential energy** is described as stored energy. When we talk about the energy in **chemicals,** substances used or produced in processes that involve changes in matter, we are talking about the potential energy in matter. **Matter** is anything that has mass[1] and takes up space. This energy has the potential to be converted to kinetic energy used to do life's work. Since energy has predictable properties, all organisms have similar ways of handling it.

There are five forms of energy, and each can be either kinetic or potential: (1) mechanical, (2) nuclear, (3) electrical, (4) radiant, and (5) chemical. All organisms interact in some way with these forms of energy. A race horse or a track athlete displays potential mechanical energy at the start line; the energy becomes kinetic mechanical energy when the athlete is running (figure 2.1). Nuclear energy is the form of energy from reactions involving the innermost part of matter, the atomic nucleus. In a nuclear power plant, nuclear energy is used to generate electrical energy. Electrical energy is associated with the movement of charged particles. All organisms use charged particles as a part of their metabolism. Radiant energy is most familiar as heat and visible light, but there are other forms as well, such as X-radiation and microwaves. Chemical energy is a kind of internal potential energy. It is stored in matter and can be released as kinetic energy when chemicals are changed from one form to another. For example, the burning of natural gas involves converting the chemical energy of gas into heat and light. A more controlled process releases the potential chemical energy from food in living systems, allowing them to carry out life's activities.

One of the predictable properties of energy is known as the **law of conservation of energy,** or the *first law of thermodynamics.* This law says that energy is not created or destroyed; but,

**FIGURE 2.1  Potential and Mechanical Energy**
This horse has converted the potential energy in its food to the kinetic energy of motion. This is why, for centuries, horses have been called "hay burners."

energy can be converted from one form to another. For example, potential energy can become kinetic energy, and electrical energy can become heat energy as in a glowing CFL. However, the total energy in a system remains the same. Because living systems use energy, these systems are also subject to this law. As a result, when biologists study energy use in living organisms and ecosystems, they must account for all the energy.

Scientists define all living things as being composed of matter. There is no scientific evidence of a living thing composed of pure energy (despite what you might see on television), or being spiritual. To understand how organisms use these elements, you need to understand some basic principles about matter. **Chemistry** is the science concerned with the study of the composition, structure, and properties of matter and the changes it undergoes (figure 2.2).

### 2.1  CONCEPT REVIEW

1. What is potential energy?
2. Why is the first law of thermodynamics important to biology?

---

[1]Don't confuse the concepts of mass and weight. *Mass* refers to an amount of matter, whereas *weight* refers to the amount of force with which an object is attracted by gravity. Because gravity determines weight, your weight would be different on the Moon than it is on Earth, but your mass would be the same.

**FIGURE 2.2 Biology and Chemistry Working Together**
In order to understand living things, researchers must investigate both their structure and their function. At the core of modern biology is an understanding of molecular structure, including such molecules as DNA, the molecule of which genes are composed.

## 2.2 The Nature of Matter

The idea that substances are composed of very small particles goes back to early Greek philosophers. During the fifth century B.C., Democritus wrote that matter was empty space filled with tremendous numbers of tiny, indivisible particles called *atoms*. (The word *atom* is from the Greek word meaning uncuttable.)

### Structure of the Atom

Recall from chapter 1 that atoms are the smallest units of matter that can exist alone. **Elements** are fundamental chemical substances made up of collections of only one kind of atom. For example, hydrogen (the most basic element), helium, lead, gold, potassium, and iron are all elements. There are over 100 elements. To understand how the atoms of various elements differ from each other, we need to look at the structure of atoms (How Science Works 2.1).

Atoms are constructed of three major subatomic particles: *neutrons*, *protons*, and *electrons*. A **neutron** is a heavy *subatomic* (units smaller than an atom) particle that does not have a charge; it is located in the central core of each atom. The central core is called the **atomic nucleus**. The mass of the atom is concentrated in the atomic nucleus. A **proton** is a heavy subatomic particle that has a positive charge; it is also located in the atomic nucleus. An **electron** is a light subatomic particle with a negative electrical charge that moves about outside the atomic nucleus in regions known as *energy levels* (figure 2.3). An **energy level** is a region of space surrounding the atomic nucleus that contains electrons with certain amounts of energy. The number of electrons an atom has determines the space, or volume, an atom takes up.

All the atoms of an element have the same number of protons. The number of protons determines the element's identity. For example, carbon always has 6 protons; no other element has that number. Oxygen always has 8 protons. The **atomic number** of an element is the number of protons in an atom of that element; therefore, each element has a unique atomic number. Because oxygen has 8 protons, its atomic number is 8. The mass of a proton is $1.67 \times 10^{-24}$ grams. Because this is an extremely small mass and is awkward to express, 1 proton is said to have a mass of 1 **atomic mass unit** (abbreviated as AMU) (table 2.1).

### Elements May Vary in Neutrons but Not Protons

Although all atoms of the same element have the same number of protons and electrons, they do not always have the same number of neutrons. In the case of oxygen, over 99% of the atoms have 8 neutrons, but others have more or fewer neutrons. Each atom of the same element with a different number of neutrons is called an **isotope** of that element. Since neutrons have a mass very similar to that of protons, isotopes that have more neutrons have a greater mass than those that have fewer neutrons.

Elements occur in nature as a mixture of isotopes. The **atomic weight** of an element is an average of all the isotopes present in a mixture in their normal proportions. For example, of all the hydrogen isotopes on Earth, 99.985% occur as an isotope without a neutron and 0.015% as an isotope with 1 neutron. There is a third isotope with 2 neutrons, and is even more rare. When the math is done to account for the relative amounts of these three isotopes of hydrogen, the atomic weight turns out to be 1.0079 AMU.

The sum of the number of protons and neutrons in the nucleus of an atom is called the **mass number**. Mass numbers are used to identify isotopes. The most common isotope of hydrogen has 1 proton and no neutrons. Thus, its mass number is 1 (1 proton + 0 neutrons = 1) also called protium. A hydrogen atom with 1 proton and 1 neutron has a mass number of 1 + 1, or 2, and is referred to as hydrogen-2, also called deuterium. A hydrogen atom with 1 proton and 2 neutrons has a mass number of 1 + 2, or 3, and is referred to as hydrogen-3, also called tritium (figure 2.4). All three isotopes of hydrogen are found on Earth, but the most frequently occurring has 1 AMU and is commonly called *hydrogen*. Most scientists use the term *hydrogen* in a generic sense (i.e., the term is not specific but might refer to any or all of these isotopes).

### Subatomic Particles and Electrical Charge

Subatomic particles were named to reflect their electrical charge. Protons have a positive (+) electrical charge. Neutrons are neutral because they lack an electrical charge (0). Electrons have a negative (−) electrical charge. Because positive and negative particles are attracted to one another, electrons are

# HOW SCIENCE WORKS 2.1

## The Periodic Table of the Elements

Traditionally, the elements have been represented in a shorthand form by letters called *chemical symbols*. The table that displays these symbols is called *periodic* because the properties of the elements recur periodically (at regular intervals) when the elements are listed in order of their size. The table has horizontal rows of elements called *periods*. The vertical columns are called *families*. The periods and families consist of squares, with each element having its own square in a specific location. This arrangement has a meaning, both about atomic structure and about chemical functions. The periods are numbered from 1 to 7 on the left side. Period 1, for example, has only two elements: H (hydrogen) and He (helium). Period 2 starts with Li (lithium) and ends with Ne (neon). The two rows at the bottom of the table are actually part of periods 6 and 7 (between

atomic numbers 57 and 72, 89 and 104). They are moved so that the table is not so wide.

Families are identified with Roman numerals and letters at the top of each column. Family IIA, for example, begins with Be (beryllium) at the top and has Ra (radium) at the bottom. The A families are in sequence from left to right. The B families are not in sequence, and one group contains more elements than the others. The elements in vertical columns have similar arrangements of electrons, and that structure is responsible for the chemical properties of an element. Don't worry—you will not have to memorize the entire table. The 11 main elements comprising living things have the chemical symbols C, H, O, P, K, I, N, S, Ca, Fe, and Mg. (A mnemonic trick to help you remember them is CHOPKINS CaFé, Mighty good!).

**Periodic Table of the Elements**

The table provides information about all the known elements. Notice that the atomic weights of the elements increase as you read left to right along the periods. Reading top to bottom in a family gives you a glimpse of a group of elements that have similar chemical properties.

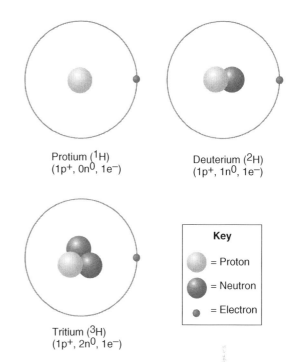

**FIGURE 2.4 Isotopes of Hydrogen**
Isotopes vary in the number of neutrons they contain in the atomic nucleus. Take a look at the three isotopes of hydrogen shown here and compare the nuclei. Since the mass of an atom is located in the nucleus, these three isotopes will differ in their weights.

**FIGURE 2.3 Atomic Structure**
All the atoms of an element have the same number of protons and determine the element's uniqueness. The fuzzy areas in the left column show how the electrons create the volume of the atoms. Those in the right column show individual electrons where they might be in their energy levels.

**TABLE 2.1 Comparison of Atomic Particles**

|  | Protons | Neutrons | Electrons |
|---|---|---|---|
| Location | Nucleus | Nucleus | Outside nucleus |
| Charge | Positive (+) | None (neutral) | Negative (−) |
| Number present | Identical to atomic number | Atomic weight minus atomic number | Equal to number of protons |
| Mass | 1 AMU | 1 AMU | 1/1,836 AMU |

held near the nucleus. However, their kinetic energy (motion) keeps them from combining with the nucleus. The overall electrical charge of an atom is neutral (0) because the number of protons (positively charged) equals the number of electrons (negatively charged). For instance, hydrogen, with 1 proton, has 1 electron; carbon, with 6 protons, has 6 electrons. You can determine the number of either of these two particles in an atom if you know the number of the other particle.

Scientists' understanding of the structure of an atom has changed since the concept was first introduced. At one time, people thought of atoms as miniature solar systems, with the nucleus in the center and electrons in orbits, like satellites, around the nucleus. However, as more experimental data were gathered and interpreted, a new model was formulated.

## The Position of Electrons

In contrast to the "solar system" model, electrons are now believed to occupy certain areas around the nucleus—the energy levels. Each energy level contains electrons moving at approximately the same speed; therefore, electrons of a given level have about the same amount of kinetic energy. Each energy level is numbered in increasing order, with energy level 1 containing electrons closest to the nucleus, with the lowest amount of energy. The electrons in energy level 2 have more energy and are farther from the nucleus than those found in energy level 1. Electrons in energy level 3 having electrons with even more energy are still farther from the nucleus than those in level 2 and so forth.

Electrons do not encircle the atomic nucleus in two-dimensional paths. Some move around the atomic nucleus in a three-dimensional region that is spherical, forming cloud-like or fuzzy layers about the nucleus. Others move in a manner that resembles the figure 8, forming fuzzy regions that look like dumbbells or hourglasses (figure 2.5).

The first energy level is full when it has 2 electrons. The second energy level is full when it has 8 electrons; the third energy level, 8; and so forth (table 2.2). Also note in table 2.2 that, for some of the atoms (He, Ne, Ar), the outermost energy level contains the maximum number of electrons it can hold. Elements such as He and Ne, with filled outer energy levels, are particularly stable.

All atoms have a tendency to seek such a stable, filled outer energy level arrangement, a tendency referred to as the *octet (8) rule*. (Hydrogen and helium are exceptions to this rule and have a filled outer energy level when they have 2 electrons.) The rule states that atoms attempt to acquire an outermost energy level with 8 electrons through processes called **chemical reactions**. Because elements such as He and Ne have full outermost energy levels under ordinary circumstances, they do not normally undergo chemical reactions. These elements are referred to as *inert* or *noble* (implying that they are too special to interact with other elements). Atoms of other elements have outer energy levels that are not full. For example, H, C, Mg, and Ca will undergo reactions to fill their outermost energy level in order to become stable. *It is important for chemists and biologists to focus on electrons in the outermost energy level, because it is these electrons that are involved in the chemical activities of all life.*

## 2.2  CONCEPT REVIEW

3. What is meant by an "energy level"?
4. Define *subatomic particle*.
5. Why do chemicals undergo reactions?

## 2.3  The Kinetic Molecular Theory and Molecules

Greek philosopher Aristotle (384–322 B.C.) rejected the idea of atoms. He believed that matter was continuous and made up of only four parts: earth, air, fire, and water. Aristotle's belief about matter predominated through the 1600s. Galileo and Newton, however, believed the ideas about matter being composed of tiny particles, or atoms, because this theory seemed to explain matter's behavior. Widespread acceptance of the atomic model did not occur, however, until strong evidence was developed through the science of chemistry in the late 1700s and early 1800s. The experiments finally led to a collection of assumptions about the small particles of matter and the space around them; these assumptions came to be known as the kinetic molecular theory.

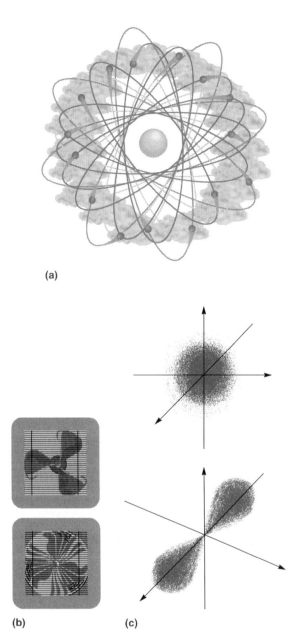

(a)

(b)    (c)

**FIGURE 2.5  The Electron Cloud**
Electrons are moving around the nucleus so fast that they can be thought of as forming a cloud around it, rather than an orbit or a single track. *(a)* You might think of the electron cloud as hundreds of photographs of an atom. Each photograph shows where an electron was at the time the picture was taken. However, when the next picture is taken, the electron has moved to a different place. In effect, an electron appears to be everyplace in its energy level at the same time, just as the fan blade of a window fan is everywhere at once when it is running. *(b)* No matter where you stick your finger in the fan, you will be touched by the moving blade. Although we are able to determine where an electron is at a given time, we do not know the exact path it uses to go from one place to another. *(c)* This is a better way to represent the positions of electrons in spherical and hourglass configurations.

**TABLE 2.2  Number of Electrons in Energy Level**

| Element | Symbol | Atomic Number | Energy Level 1 | Energy Level 2 | Energy Level 3 | Energy Level 4 |
|---|---|---|---|---|---|---|
| Hydrogen | H | 1 | 1 | | | |
| Helium | He | 2 | 2 | | | |
| Carbon | C | 6 | 2 | 4 | | |
| Nitrogen | N | 7 | 2 | 5 | | |
| Oxygen | O | 8 | 2 | 6 | | |
| Neon | Ne | 10 | 2 | 8 | | |
| Sodium | Na | 11 | 2 | 8 | 1 | |
| Magnesium | Mg | 12 | 2 | 8 | 2 | |
| Phosphorus | P | 15 | 2 | 8 | 5 | |
| Sulfur | S | 16 | 2 | 8 | 6 | |
| Chlorine | Cl | 17 | 2 | 8 | 7 | |
| Argon | Ar | 18 | 2 | 8 | 8 | |
| Potassium | K | 19 | 2 | 8 | 8 | 1 |
| Calcium | Ca | 20 | 2 | 8 | 8 | 2 |

The **kinetic molecular theory** states that all matter is made up of tiny particles, which are in constant motion.

## The Formation of Molecules

Because atoms tend to fill their outer energy levels, they often interact with other atoms. Recall from chapter 1 that a **molecule** is the smallest particle of a chemical compound and is a definite and distinct, electrically neutral group of bonded atoms. Some atoms, such as oxygen, hydrogen, and nitrogen, bond to form *diatomic* (*di* = two) molecules. In our atmosphere, these elements are found as the gases $H_2$, $O_2$, and $N_2$. The subscript indicates the number of atoms of an element in a single molecule of a substance. Other elements are not normally diatomic but exist as single, or *monatomic* (*mon* = one), units—for example, the gases helium (He) and neon (Ne). These chemical symbols, or initials, indicate a single atom of that element.

Two or more different kinds of atoms can combine, forming a compound. A **compound** is a chemical substance made up of atoms of two or more elements combined in a specific ratio and arrangement. The attractive forces that hold the atoms of a molecule together are called **chemical bonds.** Molecules can consist of two or more atoms of the same element (such as $O_2$ or $N_2$) or of specific numbers of atoms of different elements (figure 2.6).

The **formula** of a compound describes what elements it contains (as indicated by a chemical symbol) and in what proportions they occur (as indicated by the subscript number). For example, pure water is composed of two atoms of hydrogen and one atom of oxygen. It is represented by the chemical formula $H_2O$. The subscript "2" indicates two atoms of the element hydrogen, and the symbol for oxygen without a subscript indicates that there is only 1 atom of oxygen present in this molecule.

### 2.3  CONCEPT REVIEW

6. What is the difference between an atom and an element?
7. What is the difference between a molecule and a compound?

## 2.4  Molecules and Kinetic Energy

Common experience shows that all matter has a certain amount of kinetic energy. For instance, if you were to open a bottle of perfume in a closed room with no air movement, it wouldn't take long for the aroma to move throughout the room. The kinetic molecular theory explains this by saying that the molecules *diffuse*, or spread, throughout the room because they are in constant, random motion. This theory also predicts that the rate at which they diffuse depends on the temperature of the room—the higher the air temperature, the greater the kinetic energy of the molecules and the more rapid the diffusion of the perfume.

**Temperature** is a measure of the average kinetic energy of the molecules making up a substance. The two most common numerical scales used to measure temperature are the Fahrenheit scale and the Celsius scale. When people comment on the temperature of something, they usually are making a comparison. For example, they may say that the air temperature today is

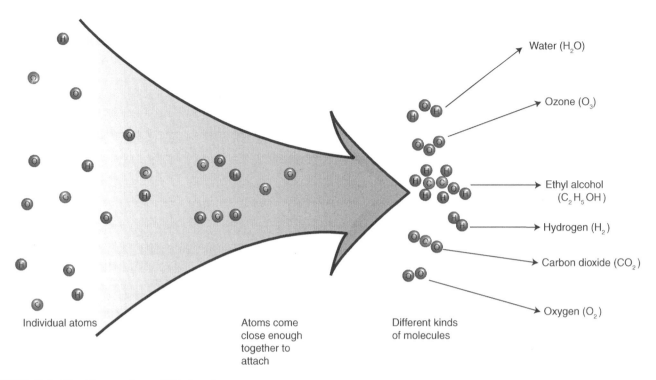

**FIGURE 2.6 The Formation of Molecules**
This figure shows how atoms of carbon, hydrogen and oxygen come together to form different kinds of molecules. If two atoms of hydrogen attach to one of oxygen, the result is a molecule of water ($H_2O$). Depending on the kinds of atoms involved and their numbers, other kinds of molecules, compounds, can be formed.

"colder" or "hotter" than it was yesterday. They may also refer to a scale for comparison, such as "the temperature is 20°C [68°F]."

**Heat** is the total internal kinetic energy of molecules. Heat is measured in units called *calories*. A **calorie** is the amount of heat necessary to raise the temperature of 1 gram of water 1 degree Celsius (°C). The concept of heat is not the same as the concept of temperature. Heat is a *quantity* of energy. Temperature deals with the comparative hotness or coldness of things. The heat, or internal kinetic energy, of molecules can change as a result of interactions with the environment. This is what happens when you rub your hands together. Friction results in increased temperatures because molecules on one moving surface catch on another surface, stretching the molecular forces that are holding them. They are pulled back to their original position with a "snap," resulting in an increase of vibrational kinetic energy. *Heat (measured in calories) and temperature (measured in Celsius or Fahrenheit) are not the same thing but are related to one another.* The heat that an object possesses cannot be measured with a thermometer. What a thermometer measures is the temperature of an object. The temperature is really a measure of how fast

Thermometer

the molecules of the substance are moving and how often they bump into other molecules, a measure of their kinetic energy. If heat energy is added to an object, the molecules vibrate faster. Consequently, the temperature rises, because the added heat energy results in a speeding up of the movement of the molecules. Although there is a relationship between heat and temperature, the amount of heat, in calories, that an object has depends on the size of the object and its particular properties, such as its density, volume, and pressure.

Why do we take a person's body temperature? The body's size and composition usually do not change in a short time, so any change in temperature means that the body has either gained or lost heat. If the temperature is high, the body has usually gained heat as a result of increased metabolism. This increase in temperature is a symptom of abnormality, as is a low body temperature.

## 2.4 CONCEPT REVIEW

8. On what basis are solids, liquids, and gases differentiated?
9. What relationship does kinetic energy have to the three phases of matter?
10. What is the difference between temperature and heat?
11. What is a calorie?

## 2.5 Physical Changes—Phases of Matter

There are implications to the kinetic molecular theory. First, the amount of kinetic energy that particles contain can change. Molecules can gain from or lose energy to their surroundings, resulting in changes in their behavior. Second, molecules have an attraction for one another. This force of attraction is important in determining the phase in which a particular kind of matter exists.

The amount of kinetic energy molecules have, the strength of the attractive forces between molecules, and the kind of arrangements they form result in three **phases of matter:** solid, liquid, and gas (figure 2.7). A **solid** (e.g., bone) consists of molecules with strong attractive forces and low kinetic energy. The molecules are packed tightly together. With the least amount of kinetic energy of all the phases of matter, these molecules vibrate in place and are at fixed distances from one another. Powerful forces bind them together. Solids have definite shapes and volumes under ordinary temperature and pressure conditions. The hardness of a solid is its resistance to forces that tend to push its molecules farther apart. There is less kinetic energy in a solid than in a liquid of the same material.

A **liquid** (e.g., the water component of blood and lymph) has molecules with enough kinetic energy to overcome the attractive forces that hold molecules together. Thus, although the molecules are still strongly attracted to each other, they are slightly farther apart than in a solid. Because they are moving more rapidly, and the attractive forces can be overcome, they sometimes slide past each other. Although liquids can change their shape under ordinary conditions, they maintain a fixed volume under ordinary temperature and pressure conditions—that is, a liquid of a certain volume will take the shape of the container into which it is poured, but it will take up the same amount of space regardless of the container's shape. This gives liquids the ability to *flow,* so they are called *fluids.*

A **gas** (e.g., air) is made of molecules that have a great deal of kinetic energy. The attraction the gas molecules have for each other is overcome by the speed with which the individual molecules move. Because gas molecules are moving faster than the molecules of solids or liquids, their collisions tend to push them farther apart, so a gas expands to fill its container. The shape of the container and the pressure determine the shape and volume of the gas. The term *vapor* is used to describe the gaseous form of a substance, that is normally in the liquid phase. For example, water vapor is the gaseous form of liquid water and mercury vapor in CFLs is the gaseous form of liquid mercury (How Science Works 2.2).

### 2.5 CONCEPT REVIEW

12. Which phase of matter is composed of molecules that vibrate around a fixed position and are held in place by strong molecular forces?
13. Which phase of matter is composed of molecules that can rotate and roll over each other because the kinetic energy of the molecules is able to overcome the molecular forces?
14. Which phase of matter is composed of atoms or molecules with the greatest amount of kinetic energy?

## 2.6 Chemical Changes—Forming New Kinds of Matter

Atoms interact with other atoms to fill their outermost energy level with electrons to become more stable. When these chemical reactions take place, the result is a change in matter in which different chemical substances are created by forming or breaking chemical bonds. When a chemical reaction occurs

(a)

(b)

(c)

**FIGURE 2.7 Phases of Matter**
*(a)* In a solid, such as this rock, molecules vibrate around a fixed position and are held in place by strong molecular forces. *(b)* In a liquid, molecules can rotate and roll over each other, because the kinetic energy of the molecules is able to overcome the molecular forces. *(c)* Inside the bubble, gas molecules move rapidly in random, free paths.

# HOW SCIENCE WORKS 2.2

## Greenhouse Gases and Their Relationship to Global Warming

What actually causes global warming? An explanation is relatively straightforward: several greenhouse gases. Carbon dioxide ($CO_2$), chlorofluorocarbons ($CCl_3F$), methane ($CH_4$), and nitrous oxide ($N_2O$) are called greenhouse gases because they let sunlight enter the atmosphere to warm the Earth's surface. When this energy is reradiated as infrared radiation (heat), it is absorbed by these gases in the atmosphere. Because the effect is similar to what happens in a greenhouse (the glass allows light to enter but retards the loss of heat), these gases are called *greenhouse gases*, and the warming thought to occur from their increase is called the *greenhouse effect*. What do we know about these gases?

### Carbon dioxide ($CO_2$)

- The most abundant of the greenhouse gases
- Sources include
  - Cellular respiration
  - Burning of fossil fuels (i.e., gasoline, coal)
  - Deforestation (i.e., the loss of plants using $CO_2$ in photosynthesis)

### Chlorofluorocarbons ($CCl_3F$)

- Sole source is from human activities
- Used as coolants in refrigerators and air conditioners, as cleaning solvents, propellants in aerosol containers, and as expanders in foam products

- 15,000 times more efficient than the greenhouse gas, $CO_2$
- Use of chlorofluorocarbons and similar compounds is being phased out worldwide.

### Methane ($CH_4$)

- Small amount found naturally in the atmosphere
- Sources include
  - Burning of fossil fuels
  - Most from biological sources (i.e., wetlands, rice fields, livestock, bacteria)

### Nitrous oxide ($N_2O$)

- Minor part of atmosphere
- Sources include
  - Burning of fossil fuels
  - Nitrogen-containing fertilizers
  - Deforestation

| Greenhouse Gas | Pre-1750 Concentration (ppm) | Concentration (ppm) (2007) | Contribution to Global Warming (percent) |
|---|---|---|---|
| Carbon dioxide ($CO_2$) | 280 | 382 | 60 |
| Methane ($CH_4$) | 0.608 | 1.78 | 20 |
| Chlorofluoro-carbons ($CCl_3F$) | 0 | 0.00088 | 14 |
| Nitrous oxide ($N_2O$) | 0.270 | 0.321 | 6 |

*Source:* Data from Intergovernmental Panel on Climate Change, with updates from Oak Ridge National Laboratory.

the interacting atoms may become attached, or bonded, to one another by a chemical bond. Two types of bonds are (1) ionic bonds and (2) covalent bonds.

## Ionic Bonds and Ions

Any positively or negatively charged atom or molecule is called an **ion. Ionic bonds** are formed after atoms *transfer* electrons to achieve a full outermost energy level. Electrons are donated or received in the transfer, forming a positive and a negative ion, a process called *ionization*. The force of attraction between oppositely charged ions forms ionic bonds, and *ionic compounds*

are the result. Ionic compounds are formed when an element from the left side of the periodic table (those eager to gain electrons) reacts with an element from the right side (those eager to donate electrons). This results in the formation of a stable group, which has an orderly arrangement and is a crystalline solid.

Ions and ionic compounds are very important in living systems. For example, sodium chloride is a crystal solid known as table salt. A positively charged sodium ion is formed when a sodium atom loses 1 electron. This results in a stable, outermost energy level with 8 electrons. When an atom of chlorine receives an electron to stabilize its outermost

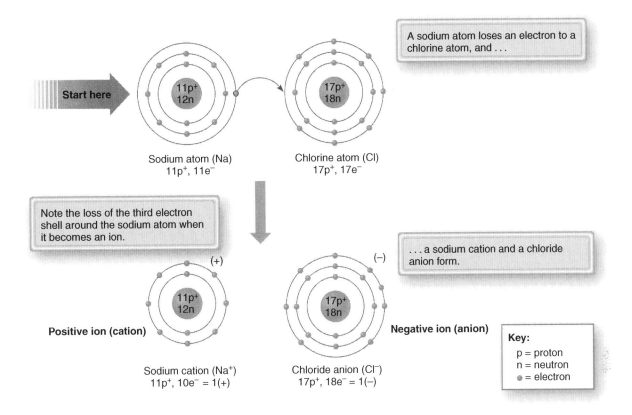

A sodium atom loses an electron to a chlorine atom, and . . .

Sodium atom (Na)
11p⁺, 11e⁻

Chlorine atom (Cl)
17p⁺, 17e⁻

Start here

Note the loss of the third electron shell around the sodium atom when it becomes an ion.

. . . a sodium cation and a chloride anion form.

(+)

11p⁺
12n

Positive ion (cation)

Sodium cation (Na⁺)
11p⁺, 10e⁻ = 1(+)

(−)

17p⁺
18n

Negative ion (anion)

Chloride anion (Cl⁻)
17p⁺, 18e⁻ = 1(−)

Key:
p = proton
n = neutron
● = electron

**FIGURE 2.8 Ion Formation**
A sodium atom has 2 electrons in the first energy level, 8 in the second energy level, and 1 in the third level. When it loses its 1 outer electron, it becomes a sodium cation.

energy level, it becomes a negative ion. All positively charged ions are called *cations* and all negative charged ions are called *anions* (figure 2.8). When these oppositely charged ions are close to one another, the attractive force between them forms an ionic bond. Ionic crystals form by the addition of ions to the outer surface of a small cluster of starter ions or seeds (figure 2.9). The dots in the following diagram represent the electrons in the outermost energy levels of each atom. This kind of diagram is called an electron dot formula.

$$Na \cdot + \cdot \overset{\cdot\cdot}{\underset{\cdot\cdot}{Cl}} : \longrightarrow Na^+ Cl^-$$

When many ionic compounds (crystals) are dissolved in water, the ionic bonds are broken and the ions separate, or *dissociate*, from one another. For example, solid sodium chloride dissociates in water to become ions in solution:

$$NaCl \rightarrow Na^+ + Cl^-$$

Any substance that dissociates into ions in water and allows the conduction of electric current is called an *electrolyte*.

## Covalent Bonds

Most substances do not have the properties of ionic compounds, because they are not composed of ions. Most substances are composed of electrically neutral groups of atoms that are tightly bound together. As noted earlier, many gases are diatomic, occurring naturally as two of the same kinds of atoms bound together as an electrically neutral molecule. Hydrogen, for example, occurs as molecules of $H_2$ and no ions are involved. The hydrogen atoms are held together by a **covalent bond,** a chemical bond formed by the sharing of a pair of electrons. In the diatomic hydrogen molecule, each hydrogen atom contributes a single electron to the shared pair. Hydrogen atoms both share one pair of electrons, but other elements might share more than one pair.

Consider how the covalent bond forms between two hydrogen atoms by imagining two hydrogen atoms moving toward one another. Each atom has a single electron. As the atoms move closer and closer together, their outer energy levels begin to overlap. Each electron is attracted to the oppositely charged nucleus of the other atom and the overlap tightens. Then, the repulsive forces from the like-charged nuclei stop the merger. A state of stability is reached between the 2 nuclei and 2 electrons, because the outermost energy level is full and an $H_2$ molecule has been formed. The electron pair is now shared by both atoms, and the attraction of each nucleus for the electron of the other holds the atoms together (figure 2.10).

Dots can be used to represent the electrons in the outer energy levels of atoms. If each atom shares one of its electrons with the other, the two dots represent the bonding pair of electrons shared by the two atoms. Bonding pairs of electrons

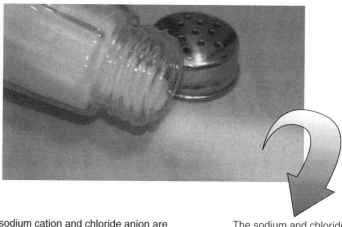

A sodium atom loses an electron to a chlorine atom.

The sodium cation and chloride anion are attracted to each other and form an ionic bond.

The sodium and chloride ions held together by ionic bonds form a salt crystal.

Sodium atom    Chlorine atom

Sodium cation ($Na^+$)  +  Chloride anion ($Cl^-$)

Na    +    Cl    ⟶    NaCl

Na⁺  Cl⁻

**FIGURE 2.9  Crystals**
A crystal is composed of ions that are bonded together and form a three-dimensional structure. Crystals grow with the addition of atoms to their outside surface.

are often represented by a simple line between two atoms, as in the following example:

H : H   is shown as   H – H

and

:O:   is shown as   O
H ·· H              H  H

A covalent bond in which a single pair of electrons is shared by two atoms is called a *single covalent bond* or, simply, a single bond. Some atoms can share more than one electron pair. A double bond is a covalent bond formed when *two pairs* of electrons are shared by two atoms. This happens mostly in compounds involving atoms of the elements C, N, O, and S. For example, ethylene, a gas given off by ripening fruit, has a double bond between the two carbons (figure 2.11). The electron dot formula for ethylene is

H       H        H        H
:C :: C:   or    C = C
H       H        H        H

A triple bond is a covalent bond formed when *three pairs* of electrons are shared by two atoms. Triple bonds occur mostly in compounds with atoms of the elements C and N. Atmospheric nitrogen gas, for example, forms a triple covalent bond:

N ⫶⫶ N   or   N ≡ N

**2.6   CONCEPT REVIEW**

15. Why are the outermost electrons of an atom important?
16. Name two kinds of chemical bonds that hold atoms together. How do these bonds differ from one another?

## 2.7  Water: The Essence of Life

Water seems to be a simple molecule, but it has several special properties that make it particularly important for living things. A water molecule is composed of two atoms of hydrogen and

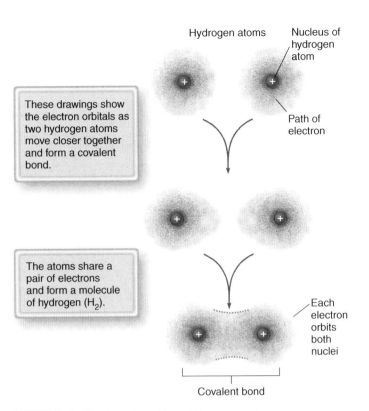

Hydrogen atoms

Nucleus of hydrogen atom

Path of electron

These drawings show the electron orbitals as two hydrogen atoms move closer together and form a covalent bond.

The atoms share a pair of electrons and form a molecule of hydrogen (H₂).

Each electron orbits both nuclei

Covalent bond

**FIGURE 2.10 Covalent Bond Between Atoms**
When two hydrogen atoms come so close to each other that the locations of the outermost electrons overlap, an electron from each one can be shared to "fill" the outermost energy levels. After the hydrogen atoms have bonded, a new electron distribution pattern forms around the entire molecule, and both electrons share the outermost molecular energy level.

one atom of oxygen joined by covalent bonds. However, the electrons in these covalent bonds are not shared equally. Oxygen, with 8 protons, has a greater attraction for the shared electrons than does hydrogen, with its single proton. Therefore, the shared electrons spend more time around the oxygen part of the molecule than they do around the hydrogen. As a result, the oxygen end of the molecule is more negative than the hydrogen end.

When the electrons in a covalent bond are not equally shared, the molecule is said to be *polar* and the covalent bonds are called *polar covalent bonds*.

When the negative end of a polar molecule is attracted to the positive end of another polar molecule, the hydrogen is located between the two molecules. Because in polar molecules the positive hydrogen end of one molecule is attracted to the negative end of another molecule, these attractive forces are often called *hydrogen bonds*. **Hydrogen bonds** can be intermolecular (between molecules) or intramolecular

**FIGURE 2.11 Ethylene and the Ripening Process**
The ancient Chinese knew from observation that fruit would ripen faster if placed in a container of burning incense, but they did not realize the incense released ethylene. We now know that ethylene stimulates the ripening process; it is used commercially to ripen fruits that are picked green.

(within molecules) forces of attraction. They occur only between hydrogen and oxygen or hydrogen and nitrogen. As intramolecular forces, *hydrogen bonds hold molecules together. Because they do not bond atoms together, they are not considered true chemical bonds.* This attraction is usually represented as three dots between the attracted regions. This weak force of attraction is not responsible for forming molecules, but it is important in determining the three-dimensional shape of a molecule. For example, when a very large molecule, such as a protein, has some regions that are slightly positive and others that are slightly negative, these areas attract each other and result in the coiling or folding of these threadlike molecules (figure 2.12). Because water is a polar covalent compound (it has slightly + and – ends), it has several significant physical and biological properties (Outlooks 2.1).

## Mixtures and Solutions

A **mixture** is matter that contains two or more substances that are not in set proportions (figure 2.13). A **solution** is a liquid mixture of ions or molecules of two or more substances. For example, salt water can be composed of varying amounts of NaCl and H₂O. If the components of the mixture are distributed equally throughout, the mixture is homogeneous. The process of making a solution is called *dissolving*. The amounts of the component parts of a solution are identified by the terms *solvent* and *solute*. The **solvent** is the component present in the larger amount. The **solute** is the component that dissolves in the solvent. Many combinations of solutes and solvents are

(a)

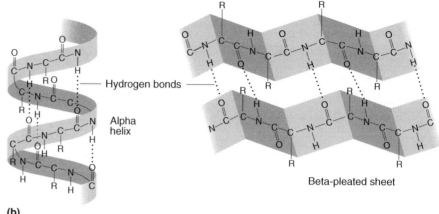

(b)

**FIGURE 2.12** **Hydrogen Bonds**

*(a)* Water molecules arrange themselves so that their positive portions are near the negative portions of other water molecules. When enough gather together, water droplets form. It is this kind of intermolecular bonding that accounts for water's unique chemical and physical properties. Without such bonds, life as we know it on Earth would be impossible. *(b)* The large protein molecules here also have polar areas. When the molecules are folded so that the partially positive areas are near the partially negative areas, a slight attraction forms and tends to keep them folded or twisted.

possible. If one of the components of a solution is a liquid, it is usually identified as the solvent. An *aqueous solution* is a solution of a solid, liquid, or gas in water. When sugar dissolves in water, sugar molecules separate from one another. The molecules become uniformly dispersed throughout the molecules of water. In an aqueous salt solution, however, the salt dissociates into sodium and chlorine ions.

The relative amounts of solute and solvent are described by the *concentration* of a solution. In general, a solution with a large amount of solute is "concentrated," and a solution with much less solute is "dilute," although these are somewhat arbitrary terms.

**2.7 CONCEPT REVIEW**

17. What is the difference between a polar molecule and a nonpolar molecule?
18. What is different about a hydrogen bond in comparison with covalent and ionic bonds?
19. What is the difference between a solute and a solvent?
20. What relationship does kinetic energy have to homogeneous solutions?

## 2.8 Chemical Reactions

When compounds are broken or formed, new materials with new properties are produced. This kind of a change in matter is called a *chemical change*, and the process is called a *chemical reaction*. In a chemical reaction, the elements stay the same but the compounds and their properties change when the atoms are bonded in new combinations. All living things use energy and matter. In other words, they are constantly performing chemical reactions.

Chemical reactions produce new chemical substances with greater or smaller amounts of potential energy. Energy is absorbed to produce new chemical substances with more potential energy. Energy is released when the new chemical substances produced have less potential energy. For example, new chemical substances are produced in green plants through the process of *photosynthesis*. A green plant uses radiant energy (sunlight), carbon dioxide, and water to produce new chemical materials and oxygen. These new chemical materials, the stuff that makes up leaves, roots, and wood, contain more chemical energy than the carbon dioxide and water from which they were formed.

A **chemical equation** is a way of describing what happens in a chemical reaction. For example, the chemical reaction of photosynthesis is described by the equation

$$\text{Light} + 6\,CO_2 + 6\,H_2O \rightarrow C_6H_{12}O_6 + 6\,O_2$$

| energy | carbon dioxide | water | plant material | oxygen |
|---|---|---|---|---|
| (sunlight) + | molecules + | molecules → | (ex., sugar) + | molecules |

In chemical reactions, **reactants** are the substances that are changed (in photosynthesis, the carbon dioxide molecules and water molecules); they appear on the left side of the equation. The equation also indicates that energy is absorbed; the term *energy* appears on the left side. The arrow indicates

# OUTLOOKS 2.1

## Water and Life—The Most Common Compound of Living Things

1. **Water has a high surface tension.** Because water molecules are polar, hydrogen bonds form between water molecules, and they stick more to one another than to air molecules. Thus, water tends to pull together to form a smooth surface where water meets air. This layer can be surprisingly strong. For instance, some insects can walk on the surface of a pond. The tendency of water molecules to stick to each other and to some other materials explains why water can make things wet. It also explains why water climbs through narrow tubes, called capillary tubes. This *capillary* action also helps water move through soil, up the vessels in plants' stems, and through the capillaries (tiny blood vessels) in animals.

2. **Water has unusually high heats of vaporization and fusion.** Because polar water molecules stick to one another, an unusually large amount of heat energy is required to separate them. Water resists changes in temperature. It takes 540 calories of heat energy to convert 1 gram of liquid water to its gaseous state, water vapor. This means that large bodies of water, such as lakes and rivers, must absorb enormous amounts of energy before they will evaporate and leave the life within them high and dry. This also means that humans can get rid of excess body heat by sweating because, when the water evaporates, it removes heat from the skin. On the other hand, a high heat of fusion means that this large amount of heat energy must be removed from liquid water before it changes from a liquid to its solid state, ice. Therefore, water can remain liquid and a suitable home for countless organisms long after the atmospheric temperature has reached the freezing point, 0°C (32°F).

3. **Water has unusual density characteristics.** Water is most dense at 4°C. As heat energy is lost from a body of water and its temperature falls below 4°C, its density decreases and this less dense, colder water is left on top. As the surface water reaches the freezing point and changes from its liquid to its solid phase, the molecules form new arrangements, which resemble a honeycomb. The spaces between the water molecules make the solid phase, ice, less dense than the water beneath and the ice floats. It is the surface water that freezes to a solid, covering the denser, liquid water and the living things in it.

4. **Water's specific gravity is also an important property.** Water has a density of 1 gram/cubic centimeter at 4°C. Anything with a higher density sinks in water, and anything with a lower density floats. *Specific gravity* is the ratio of the density of a substance to the density of water. Therefore, the specific gravity of water is 1.00. Any substance with a specific gravity less than 1.00 floats. If you mix water and gasoline, the gasoline (specific gravity of 0.75) floats to the top. People also vary in the specific gravity of their bodies. Some persons find it very easy to float in water, whereas others find it impossible. This is directly related to each person's specific gravity, which is a measure of the person's ratio of body fat to muscle and bone.

5. **Water is considered the universal solvent,** because most other chemicals can be dissolved in water. This means that wherever water goes—through the ground, in the air, or through an organism—it carries chemicals. Water in its purest form is even capable of acting as a solvent for oils.

6. **Water comprises 50–60% of the bodies of most living things.** This is important, because the chemical reactions of all living things occur in water.

7. **Water vapor in the atmosphere is known as humidity, which changes with environmental conditions.** The ratio of how much water vapor is in the air to how much water vapor could be in the air at a certain temperature is called *relative humidity*. Relative humidity is closely associated with your comfort. When the relative humidity and temperature are high, it is difficult to evaporate water from your skin, so it is more difficult to cool yourself and you are uncomfortably warm.

8. **Water's specific gravity changes with its physical phase. Ice is also more likely to change from a solid to a liquid (melt) as conditions warm.** If the specific gravity of water did not decrease when it freezes, then the ice would likely sink and never thaw. Our life-giving water would be trapped in ocean-sized icebergs. Ice also provides a protective layer for the life under the ice sheet.

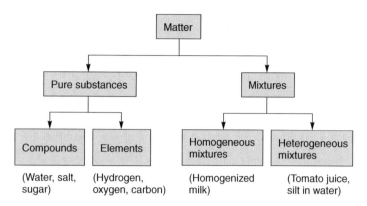

**FIGURE 2.13 How Do Mixtures Compare?**
Matter can be a pure substance or a mixture. The term *homogeneous* means "the same throughout." Homogenized milk has the same composition throughout the container. Before milk was homogenized (i.e., vigorously shaken to break fat into small globules), it was a heterogeneous mixture and it would "separate." The cream (which floats to the top) could be skimmed off the milk leaving skimmed milk. A heterogeneous mixture does not have the same composition throughout.

the direction in which the chemical reaction is occurring; it means "yields." The new chemical substances are on the right side and are called **products**. Reading the photosynthesis reaction as a sentence, you would say, "Carbon dioxide and water use energy to react, yielding plant materials and oxygen."

Notice in the photosynthesis reaction that there are numbers preceding some of the chemical formulas and subscripts within each chemical formula. The number preceding each of the chemical formulas indicates the number of each kind of molecule involved in the reaction. The subscripts indicate the number of each kind of element in a single molecule of that compound. Chemical reactions always take place in whole number ratios. That is, only whole molecules can be involved in a chemical reaction. It is not possible to have half a molecule of water serve as a reactant or become a product. Half a molecule of water is not water. Furthermore, the numbers of atoms of each element on the reactant side must equal the numbers on the product side. Because the preceding equation has equal numbers of each element (C, H, O) on both sides, the equation is said to be "balanced."

Five of the most important chemical reactions that occur in organisms are (1) oxidation-reduction, (2) dehydration synthesis, (3) hydrolysis, (4) phosphorylation, and (5) acid-base reactions.

## Oxidation-Reduction Reactions

An **oxidation-reduction reaction** is a chemical change in which electrons are transferred from one atom to another and, with it, the energy contained in its electrons. As implied by the name, such a reaction has two parts and each part tells what happens to the electrons. *Oxidation* describes what happens to the atom or molecule that loses an electron. *Reduction* describes what happens to the atom or molecule that gains an electron. When the term *oxidation* was first used, it specifically

meant reactions involving the combination of oxygen with other atoms. But fluorine, chlorine, and other elements were soon recognized to participate in similar reactions, so the definition was changed to describe the shifts of electrons in the reaction. The name also implies that, in any reaction in which oxidation occurs, reduction must also take place. One cannot take place without the other. Cellular respiration is an oxidation-reduction reaction that occurs in all cells:

$$C_6H_{12}O_6 + 6\ O_2 \rightarrow 6\ H_2O + 6\ CO_2 + energy$$

sugar + oxygen → water + carbon + energy
dioxide

In this cellular respiration reaction, sugar is being oxidized (losing its electrons) and oxygen is being reduced (gaining the electrons from sugar). The high chemical potential energy in the sugar molecule is released, and the organism uses some of this energy to perform work. In the previously mentioned photosynthesis reaction, water is oxidized (loses its electrons) and carbon dioxide is reduced (gains the electrons from water). The energy required to carry out this reaction comes from the sunlight and is stored in the product, sugar.

## Dehydration Synthesis Reactions

**Dehydration synthesis reactions** are chemical changes in which water is released and a larger, more complex molecule is made (synthesized) from smaller, less complex parts. The water is a product formed from its component parts (H and OH), which are removed from the reactants. Proteins, for example, consist of a large number of amino acid subunits joined together by dehydration synthesis:

$$NH_2CH_2CO\text{---}OH + H\text{---}NHCH_2CO\text{---}OH$$
amino acid 1 + amino acid 2

↓

$$NH_2CH_2CO\text{---}NHCH_2CO\text{---}OH + H\text{---}OH$$
Protein + water ($H_2O$)

The building blocks of protein (amino acids) are bonded to one another to synthesize larger, more complex product molecules (i.e., protein). In dehydration synthesis reactions, water is produced as smaller reactants become chemically bonded to one another, forming fewer but larger product molecules.

## Hydrolysis Reactions

**Hydrolysis reactions** are the opposite of dehydration synthesis reactions. In a hydrolysis reaction, water is used to break the reactants into smaller, less complex products:

$$NH_2CH_2CO\text{---}NH\ CH_2CO\text{---}OH + H\text{---}OH$$
Protein + water ($H_2O$)

↓

$$NH_2CH_2CO\text{---}OH + H\text{---}NH\ CH_2CO\text{---}OH$$
amino acid 1 + amino acid 2

A more familiar name for this chemical reaction is *digestion*. This is the kind of chemical reaction that occurs when a protein food, such as meat, is digested. Notice in the previous example that the H and OH component parts of the reactant water become parts of the building block products.

## Phosphorylation Reactions

A **phosphorylation reaction** takes place when a cluster of atoms known as a *phosphate group*

$$
-O-\overset{\displaystyle O^-}{\underset{\displaystyle O^-}{\overset{|}{\underset{|}{P}}}}=O \qquad = P
$$

is added to another molecule. This cluster is abbreviated in many chemical formulas in a shorthand form as P, and only the P is shown when a phosphate is transferred from one molecule to another. This is a very important reaction, because the bond between a phosphate group and another atom contains the potential energy that is used by all cells to power numerous activities. Phosphorylation reactions result in the transfer of their potential energy to other molecules to power the activities of all organisms (figure 2.14).

**FIGURE 2.14 Phosphorylation and Muscle Contractions**
When the phosphate group is transferred between molecules, energy is released which powers muscle contractions.

| high potential energy | low potential energy | | low potential energy | high potential energy |
|---|---|---|---|---|
| Q–P | + Z | → | Q | + Z–P |

This type of reaction is commonly involved in providing the kinetic energy needed by all organisms. It can also take place in reverse. When this occurs, energy must be added from the environment (sunlight or another phosphorylated molecule) and is stored in the newly phosphorylated molecule.

## Acid-Base Reactions

**Acid-base reactions** take place when the ions of an acid interact with the ions of a base, forming a salt and water (see section 2.9). An aqueous solution containing dissolved acid is a solution containing hydrogen ions. If a solution containing a second ionic basic compound is added, a mixture of ions results. While they are mixed together, a reaction can take place—for example,

$$
H^+ Cl^- + Na^+ OH^- \rightarrow Na^+ Cl^- + HOH
$$

| hydrochloric acid | + sodium hydroxide | → sodium chloride | + water $(H_2O)$ |
|---|---|---|---|

In an acid-base reaction, the H from the acid becomes chemically bonded to the OH of the base. This type of reaction frequently occurs in organisms and their environment. Because acids and bases can be very harmful, reactions in which they neutralize one another protect organisms from damage.

### 2.8 CONCEPT REVIEW

21. Give an example of an ion exchange reaction.
22. What happens during an oxidation-reduction reaction?
23. Explain the difference between a reactant and a product.

## 2.9 Acids, Bases, and Salts

Acids, bases, and salts are three classes of biologically important compounds (table 2.3). Their characteristics are determined by the nature of their chemical bonds. **Acids** are ionic compounds that release hydrogen ions in solution. A hydrogen atom without its electron is a proton. You can think of an acid, then, as a substance able to donate a proton to a solution. Acids have a sour taste, such as that of citrus fruits. However, tasting chemicals to see if they are acids can be very hazardous, because many are highly corrosive. An example of a common acid is the phosphoric acid—$H_3PO_4$—in cola soft drinks. It is a dilute solution of this acid that

| **TABLE 2.3**   Some Common Acids, Bases, and Salts | | |
|---|---|---|
| **Acids** | | |
| Acetic acid | $CH_3COOH$ | Weak acid found in vinegar |
| Carbonic acid | $H_2CO_3$ | Weak acid of carbonated beverages that provides bubbles or fizz |
| Lactic acid | $CH_3CHOHCOOH$ | Weak acid found in sour milk, sauerkraut, and pickles |
| Phosphoric acid | $H_3PO_4$ | Weak acid used in cleaning solutions, added to carbonated cola beverages for taste |
| Sulfuric acid | $H_2SO_4$ | Strong acid used in batteries |
| **Bases** | | |
| Sodium hydroxide | $NaOH$ | Strong base also called lye or caustic soda; used in oven cleaners |
| Potassium hydroxide | $KOH$ | Strong base also known as caustic potash; used in drain cleaners |
| Magnesium hydroxide | $Mg(OH)_2$ | Weak base also known as milk of magnesia; used in antacids and laxatives |
| **Salts** | | |
| Alum | $Al(SO_4)_2$ | Found in medicine, canning, and baking powder |
| Baking soda | $NaHCO_3$ | Used in fire extinguishers, antacids, baking powder, and sodium bicarbonate |
| Chalk | $CaCO_3$ | Used in antacid tablets |
| Epsom salts | $MgSO_4 \cdot H_2O$ | Used in laxatives and skin care |
| Trisodium phosphate (TSP) | $Na_3PO_4$ | Used in water softeners, fertilizers, and cleaning agents |

gives cola drinks their typical flavor. Hydrochloric acid is another example:

Acids are ionically bonded molecules, which when placed in water dissociate, releasing hydrogen ($H^+$) ions.

A **base** is the opposite of an acid, in that it is an ionic compound, which, when dissolved in water, removes hydrogen ions from solution. Bases, or *alkaline* substances, have a slippery feel on the skin. They have a caustic action on living tissue by converting the fats in living tissue into a water-soluble substance. A similar reaction is used to make soap by mixing a strong base with fat. This chemical reaction gives soap its slippery feeling. Bases are also used in alkaline batteries. Weak bases have a bitter taste—for example, the taste of broccoli, turnip, and cabbage. Many kinds of bases release a group of hydrogen ions known as a **hydroxide ions, or an $OH^-$ group**. This group is composed of an oxygen atom and a hydrogen atom bonded together, but with an additional electron. The hydroxide ion is negatively charged; therefore, it will remove positively charged hydrogen ions from solution. A very strong base used in oven cleaners is sodium hydroxide, $NaOH$. Notice that ions that are free in solution are always written with the type and number of their electrical charge as a superscript.

Basic (alkaline) substances are ionically bonded molecules, which when placed in water dissociate, releasing hydroxide ($OH^-$) ions.

Acids and bases are also spoken of as being strong or weak (Outlooks 2.2). Strong acids (e.g., hydrochloric acid) are those that dissociate nearly all of their hydrogens when in solution. Weak acids (e.g., phosphoric acid) dissociate only a small percentage of their hydrogens. Strong bases dissociate nearly all of their hydroxides ($NaOH$); weak bases, only a small percentage. The weak base sodium bicarbonate, $NaHCO_3$, will react with acids in the following manner:

$$NaHCO_3 + HCl \rightarrow NaCl + CO_2 + H_2O$$

Notice that sodium bicarbonate does not contain a hydroxide ion but it is still a base, because it removes hydrogen ions from solution.

The degree to which a solution is acidic or basic is represented by a quantity known as **pH**. The pH scale is a measure of hydrogen ion concentration (figure 2.15). A pH of 7 indicates that the solution is neutral and has an equal number of $H^+$ ions and $OH^-$ ions to balance each other. As the pH number gets smaller, the number of hydrogen ions in the solution increases. A number higher than 7 indicates that the solution has more $OH^-$ than $H^+$. Pure water has a pH of 7. As the pH number gets larger, the number of hydroxide ions increases.

## OUTLOOKS 2.2

# Maintaining Your pH—How Buffers Work

Acids, bases, and salts are called *electrolytes*, because, when these compounds are dissolved in water, the solution of ions allows an electrical current to pass through it. Salts provide a variety of ions essential to the human body. Small changes in the levels of some ions can have major effects on the functioning of the body. The respiratory system and kidneys regulate many of the body's ions. Because many kinds of chemical activities are sensitive to changes in the pH of the surroundings, it is important to regulate the pH of the blood and other body fluids within very narrow ranges. Normal blood pH is about 7.4. Although the respiratory system and kidneys are involved in regulating the pH of the blood, there are several systems in the blood that prevent wide fluctuations in pH.

*Buffers* are mixtures of *weak acids* and the *salts of weak acids* that tend to maintain constant pH, because the mixture can either accept or release hydrogen ions ($H^+$). The weak acid can release hydrogen ions ($H^+$) if a base is added to the solution, and the negatively charged ion of the salt can accept hydrogen ions ($H^+$) if an acid is added to the solution.

One example of a buffer system in the body is a phosphate buffer system, which consists of the weak acid dihydrogen phosphate ($H_2PO_4^-$) and the salt of the weak acid monohydrogen phosphate ($HPO_4^=$).

$$H_2PO_4^- \rightleftharpoons H^+ + HPO_4^=$$

weak acid          hydrogen   +   salt of
                   ion            weak acid

(The two arrows indicate that this is in balance, with equal reactions in both directions.) The addition of an acid to the mixture causes the equilibrium to shift to the left.

$$H_2PO_4^- \rightleftharpoons + HPO_4^= + \text{added } H^+$$

Notice that the arrow pointing to the right is shorter than the arrow pointing to the left. This indicates that $H^+$ is combining with $HPO_4^-$ and additional $H_2PO_4^-$ is being formed. This removes the additional hydrogen ions from solution and ties them up in the $H_2PO_4^-$, so that the amount of free hydrogen ions in the solution remains constant.

Similarly, if a base is added to the mixture, the equilibrium shifts to the right, additional hydrogen ions are released to tie up the hydroxyl ions, and the pH remains unchanged.

$$H_2PO_4^- + \text{added } OH^- \rightleftharpoons HPO_4^= + H^+OH^-$$

Seawater is a buffer solution that maintains a pH of about 8.2. Buffers are also added to medicines and to foods. Many lemon-lime carbonated beverages, for example, contain citric acid and sodium citrate (salt of the weak acid), which forms a buffer in the acid range. The beverage label may say that these chemicals are to impart and regulate "tartness." In this case, the tart taste comes from the citric acid, and the addition of sodium citrate makes it a buffered solution.

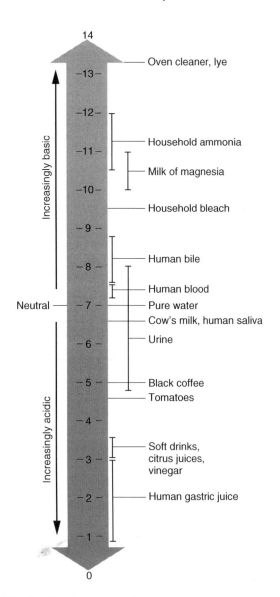

FIGURE 2.15 **The pH Scale**
The concentration of acid (proton donor or electron acceptor) is greatest when the pH number is lowest. As the pH number increases, the concentration of base (proton acceptor or electron donor) increases. At a pH of 7, the concentrations of $H^+$ and $OH^-$ are equal. As the pH number gets smaller, the solution becomes more acidic. As the pH number gets larger, the solution becomes more basic, or alkaline.

It is important to note that the pH scale is logarithmic—that is, a change in one pH number is actually a 10-fold change in real numbers of $OH^-$ or $H^+$. For example, there is 10 times more $H^+$

When water dissociates, it releases both hydrogen ($H^+$) and hydroxide ($OH^-$) ions. It is neither a base nor an acid. Its pH is 7, neutral.

in a solution of pH 5 than in a solution of pH 6 and 100 times more $H^+$ in a solution of pH 4 than in a solution of pH 6.

**Salts** are ionic compounds that do not release either $H^+$ or $OH^-$ when dissolved in water; thus, they are neither acids nor bases. However, they are generally the result of the reaction between an acid and a base in a solution. For example, when an acid, such as HCl, is mixed with NaOH in water, the $H^+$ and the $OH^-$ combine with each other to form pure water, $H_2O$. The remaining ions ($Na^+$ and $Cl^-$) join to form the salt NaCl:

$$HCl + NaOH \rightarrow Na^+ + Cl^- + H^+ + OH^- \rightarrow$$
$$NaCl + H_2O$$

The chemical reaction that occurs when acids and bases react with each other is called *neutralization*. The acid no longer acts as an acid (it has been neutralized) and the base no longer acts as a base.

As you can see from figure 2.15, not all acids or bases produce the same pH. Some compounds release hydrogen ions very easily, cause low pHs, and are called strong acids. Hydrochloric acid (HCl) and sulfuric acid ($H_2SO_4$) are strong acids (figure 2.16a). Many other compounds give up their hydrogen ions grudgingly and therefore do not change pH very much. They are known as weak acids. Carbonic acid ($H_2CO_3$) and many organic acids found in living things are weak acids. Similarly, there are strong bases, such as sodium hydroxide (NaOH) and weak bases, such as sodium bicarbonate—$Na^+(HCO_3)^-$.

(a)                          (b)

FIGURE 2.16 **Strong Acid and Strong Base**
*(a)* Hydrochloric acid (HCl) has the common name of muriatic acid. It is a strong acid used in low concentrations to clean swimming pools and brick surfaces. It is important that you wear protective equipment when working with a solution of muriatic acid. *(b)* Liquid-Plumr® is a good example of a drain cleaner with a strong base. The active ingredient is NaOH.

## 2.9 CONCEPT REVIEW

24. What does it mean if a solution has a pH of 3, 12, 2, 7, or 9?
25. If the pH of a solution changes from 8 to 9, what happens to the hydroxide ion concentration?

## Summary

The study of life involves learning about the structure and function of organisms. All organisms display the chemical and physical properties typical of all matter and energy. The two kinds of energy used by organisms are potential and kinetic. The kinetic molecular theory states that all matter is made up of tiny particles, which are in constant motion.

Energy can be neither created nor destroyed, but it can be converted from one form to another. Potential energy and kinetic energy can be interconverted. The amount of kinetic energy that the molecules of various substances contain determines whether they are solids, liquids, or gases. Temperature is a measure of the average kinetic energy of the molecules making up a substance. Heat is the total internal kinetic energy of molecules. The random motion of molecules, which is due to their kinetic energy, results in their being distributed throughout available space, forming mixtures.

There are many kinds of atoms, whose symbols and traits are described by the periodic table of the elements. These atoms differ from one another by the number of protons and electrons they contain. Each is given an atomic number, based on the number of protons in the nucleus, and an atomic weight, an average of all the isotopes of a particular element. The mass number is the sum of the number of protons and neutrons in the nucleus of an atom.

All matter is composed of atoms, which are composed of an atomic nucleus and electrons. The atomic nucleus can contain protons and neutrons, whereas the electrons encircle the nucleus at different energy levels. Atoms tend to seek their most stable configuration and follow the octet rule, which states that they all seek a filled outermost energy level.

Atoms may be combined by chemical reactions into larger units called molecules. There are many kinds of molecules. Two kinds of chemical bonds allow molecules to form—ionic bonds and covalent bonds. A third bond, the hydrogen bond, is a weaker bond that holds molecules together and may help large molecules maintain a specific shape. Molecules are described by their chemical formulas, which state the number and kinds of components of which they are composed.

An ion is an atom that is electrically unbalanced. Ions interact to form ionic compounds, such as acids, bases, and salts. Compounds that release hydrogen ions when mixed in water are called acids; those that remove hydrogen ions are called bases. A measure of the hydrogen ions present in a solution is the pH of the solution.

Water is one of the most important compounds required by all organisms. This polar molecule has many unique properties, which allow organisms to survive and reproduce. Without water, life as we know it on Earth would not be possible.

How atoms achieve stability is the nature of chemical reactions. Five of the most important chemical reactions that occur in organisms are (1) oxidation-reduction, (2) dehydration synthesis, (3) hydrolysis, (4) phosphorylation, and (5) acid-base reactions.

Acids, bases, and salts are three classes of biologically important molecules. The hydrogen ion releasing or acquiring properties of acids and bases make them valuable in all organisms.

Salts are a source of many essential ions. Although acids and bases may be potentially harmful, buffer systems help in maintain pH levels.

## Key Terms

*Use the interactive flash cards on the* **Concepts in Biology,** *14/e website to help you learn the meaning of these terms.*

acid-base reactions 39
acids 39
atomic mass unit 25
atomic nucleus 25
atomic number 25
atomic weight 25
bases 40
calorie 30
chemical bonds 29
chemical equation 36
chemical reaction 28
chemicals 24
chemistry 24
compound 29
covalent bond 33
dehydration synthesis reactions 38
electron 25
elements 25
energy 24
energy level 25
formula 29
gas 31
heat 30
hydrogen bonds 35
hydrolysis reactions 38
hydroxide ions 40
ion 32

ionic bonds 32
isotope 25
kinetic energy 24
kinetic molecular theory 29
law of conservation of energy 24
liquid 31
mass number 25
matter 24
mixture 35
molecule 29
neutron 25
oxidation-reduction reaction 38
pH 40
phases of matter 31
phosphorylation reaction 39
potential energy 24
products 38
proton 25
reactants 36
salts 42
solid 31
solute 35
solution 35
solvent 35
temperature 29

## Basic Review

1. _____ is the total internal kinetic energy of molecules.

2. The atomic weight of the element sodium is
   a. 22.989.
   b. 11.
   c. 10.252.
   d. 11 + 22.989.

3. Which is *not* a pure substance?
   a. the compound sugar
   b. the element oxygen
   c. a mixture of milk and honey
   d. the compound table salt

4. When a covalent bond forms between two kinds of atoms that are the same, the result is known as a
   a. mixture.
   b. crystal.
   c. dehydration chemical reaction.
   d. diatomic molecule.

5. In this kind of chemical reaction, two molecules interact, resulting in the formation of a molecule of water and a new, larger end product.
   a. hydrolysis
   b. dehydration synthesis
   c. phosphorylation
   d. acid-base reaction

6. Which of the following is an acid?
   a. HCl
   b. NaOH
   c. KOH
   d. $CaCO_3$

7. Salts are compounds that do not release either _____ or _____ ions when dissolved in water.

8. This intramolecular force under the right conditions can result in a molecule that is coiled or twisted into a complex, three-dimensional shape.
   a. covalent bond
   b. ionic bond
   c. hydrogen bond
   d. cement bond

9. A triple covalent bond is represented by which of the following?
   a. a single, fat, straight line
   b. a single, thin, straight line
   c. three separate, thin lines
   d. three thin, curved lines

10. Electron clouds, or routes, traveled by electrons are sometimes drawn as spherical or _____ shapes.

11. Atoms of the same element differ from ions of that element because
    a. they have different numbers of electrons.
    b. their proton numbers are not the same.
    c. their neutrons numbers are not the same.
    d. there is no difference between an atom and an ion of the same element.

12. When someone uses the expression "you're full of hot air," he is referring to which phase of matter?
    a. solid
    b. liquid
    c. gas
    d. hydrogen

13. When a person is "running a fever," she is experiencing an increase in her body's _____.

14. Ions that are bonded together and form a three-dimensional structure are called a _____.

15. A bottle of soda or pop is best described as
    a. a heterogeneous mixture.
    b. a compound.
    c. a homogeneous mixture.
    d. a pure substance.

**Answers**
1. Heat  2. a  3. c  4. d  5. b  6. a  7. $H^+$, $OH^-$  8. c
9. c  10. hourglass  11. a  12. c  13. temperature
14. crystal  15. c

## Thinking Critically

**Chemicals Around the House**
Sodium bicarbonate ($NaHCO_3$) is a common household chemical known as baking soda, bicarbonate of soda, or bicarb. It has many uses and is a component of many products, including toothpaste and antacids, swimming pool chemicals, and headache remedies. When baking soda comes in contact with hydrochloric acid, the following reaction occurs:

$$HCl + NaHCO_3 \rightarrow NaCl + CO_2 + H_2O$$

What happens to the atoms in this reaction? In your description, include changes in chemical bonds, pH, and kinetic energy. Why is baking soda such an effective chemical in the previously mentioned products? Try this at home: Place a pinch of sodium bicarbonate ($NaHCO_3$) on a plate. Add two drops of vinegar. Observe the reaction. Based on the previous reaction, can you explain chemically what has happened?

# Organic Molecules— The Molecules of Life

## Down the Toilet— But Then What?

*Scientists Increasingly Concerned About the Water We Drink.*

It has been reported that a vast array of pharmaceuticals have been found in the drinking water supplies of at least 41 million Americans. Many of these are organic compounds and include antibiotics, anti-convulsants, mood stabilizers, and sex hormones. Organic compounds can be very complex and long-lasting molecules. How do these drugs get into the water? One way is by unmetabolized drugs that are excreted in urine. Also, healthcare providers recommend that unused medications be flushed down the toilet. In addition, these compounds get into the water supply on occasion by accidental spills that can result in contamination of our water. One U.S. Environmental Protection Agency (EPA) administrator stated that this problem is a growing concern. The EPA is taking this issue seriously because neither sewage treatment nor water purification can remove all drugs.

As scientists learn from their research, more specific questions are formulated that relate to long-term health effects of pharmaceutical contamination of our water. For example, a popular osteoporosis drug, Fosamax, has been linked to severe musculoskeletal pain and a serious bone disease called osteonecrosis of the jaw (ONJ), also known as "dead jaw" and "fossy jaw." Microbial biofilms, a mix of bacteria and sticky organic compounds, appear to be the cause of this side effect. If the drugs reach high enough levels of contamination in our water supply, will we see an increase in ONJ in people who don't even take this medication?

Some dentists are observing the eruption of second molar teeth in children as young as 8 years old. Normally these do not appear until a person is about 12 or 13 years old. Might there be a cause-and-effect relationship with some pharmaceutical contaminant in our water supply?

- What makes organic molecules different from other molecules?

- What is the structure of various organic compounds?

- Is there a point at which the cure is worse than the disease?

## Background Check

**Concepts you should already know to get the most out of this chapter:**
- The nature of matter (chapter 2)
- Chemical changes that can occur in matter (chapter 2)
- The key characteristics of water (chapter 2)
- The different types of chemical reactions (chapter 2)

## 3.1 Molecules Containing Carbon

The principles and concepts discussed in chapter 2 apply to all types of matter—nonliving as well as living. Living systems are composed of various types of molecules. Most of the chemicals described in chapter 2 do not contain carbon atoms and, so, are classified as **inorganic molecules.** This chapter is mainly concerned with more complex structures, **organic molecules,** which contain carbon atoms arranged in rings or chains. The words *organic, organism, organ,* and *organize* are all related. Organized objects have parts that fit together in a meaningful way. Organisms are living things that are organized. Animals, for example, have organ systems within their bodies, and their organs are composed of unique kinds of molecules that are *organic.*

The original meanings of the terms *inorganic* and *organic* came from the fact that organic materials were thought either to be alive or to be produced only by living things. A very strong link exists between organic chemistry and the chemistry of living things, which is called **biochemistry** or biological chemistry. Modern chemistry has considerably altered the original meanings of the terms *organic* and *inorganic,* because it is now possible to manufacture unique organic molecules that cannot be produced by living things. Many of the materials we use daily are the result of the organic chemist's art. Nylon, aspirin, polyurethane varnish, silicones, Plexiglas, food wrap, Teflon, and insecticides are just a few of the unique synthetic molecules that have been invented by organic chemists (figure 3.1). Plastics such as low-density polyethylene (LDPE) used to make garbage bags are extremely stable molecules that require hundreds of years to break down.

Many organic chemists have taken their lead from living organisms and have been able to produce organic molecules more efficiently, or in forms that are slightly different from the original natural molecules. Some examples of these are rubber, penicillin, certain vitamins, insulin, and alcohol (figure 3.2).

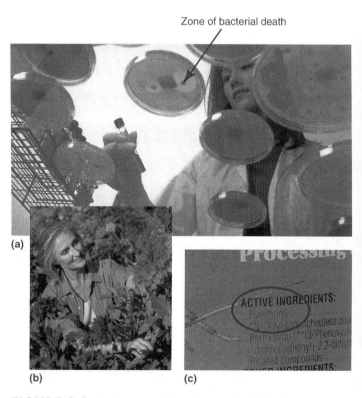

**FIGURE 3.2 Natural and Synthetic Organic Compounds**
*(a)* This researcher is testing antibiotics produced by microbes isolated from the environment. Each paper disk, containing a different antibiotic, is placed on the surface of a Petri dish with growing, disease-causing bacteria. The presence of a "dead zone" around a disk indicates that the antibiotic has spread through the gel and is able to inhibit or kill the bacteria. *(b)* Certain types of chrysanthemums produce the insecticide Pyrethrin. *(c)* It can be found as an "active ingredient" in many commercially available ant- and cockroach-killing products.

**FIGURE 3.1 Some Common Synthetic Organic Materials**
These are only a few examples of products containing useful organic compounds invented and manufactured by chemists.

Another example is the insecticide Pyrethrin. It is based on a natural insecticide and is widely used for agricultural and domestic purposes. It is derived from a certain type of chrysanthemum plant, *Pyrethrum cinerariaefolium.*

## Carbon: The Central Atom

All organic molecules, whether natural or synthetic, have certain common characteristics. The carbon atom, which is the central atom in all organic molecules, has some unusual properties that contribute to the nature of an organic compound. Carbon is unique in that it can combine with other carbon atoms to form long chains. In many cases, the ends of these chains may join together to form rings (figure 3.3).

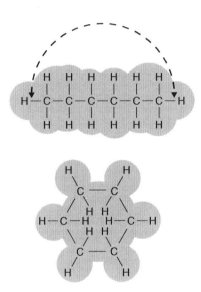

**FIGURE 3.3 Chain and Ring Structures**
The ring structure shown on the bottom is formed by joining the two ends of a chain of carbon atoms.

Also unusual is that these bonding sites are all located at equal distances from one another because the 4 outer-most electrons do not stay in the standard positions described in chapter 2. They distribute themselves differently, enabling them to be as far apart as possible (figure 3.4). Carbon atoms are usually involved in covalent bonds. Because carbon has four places it can bond, the carbon atom can combine with four other atoms by forming four separate, *single covalent bonds* with other atoms. This is the case with the methane molecule, which has four hydrogen atoms attached to a single carbon atom (review figure 3.4). Pure methane is a colorless, odorless gas that makes up 95% of natural gas. The aroma of natural gas is the result of mercaptan and trimethyl disulfide added for safety to let people know when a leak occurs.

Some atoms may be bonded to a single atom more than once. This results in a slightly different arrangement of bonds around the carbon atom. An example of this type of bonding occurs when oxygen is attracted to a carbon. An atom of oxygen has 2 electrons in its outermost energy level. If it shares 1 of these with a carbon and then shares the other with the same carbon, it forms a *double covalent bond.* A **double bond** is two covalent bonds formed between two atoms that share two pairs of electrons. Oxygen is not the only atom that can form double bonds, but double bonds are common between oxygen and carbon. The double bond is denoted by two lines between the two atoms:

$$-C=O$$
$$|$$

Since carbon has 4 electrons in its outer energy level, two carbon atoms might form double bonds between each other and then bond to other atoms at the remaining bonding sites. Figure 3.5 shows several compounds that contain double bonds.

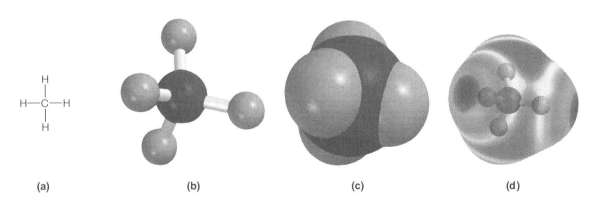

**FIGURE 3.4 Models of a Methane Molecule**
The structures of molecules can be modeled in many ways. For the sake of simplicity, diagrams of molecules such as the gas methane can be *(a)* two-dimensional drawings, although in reality they are three-dimensional molecules and take up space. The model shown in *(b)* is called a ball-and-stick model. Part *(c)* is a space-filling model, while *(d)* is a computer-generated model. Each time you see the various ways in which molecules are displayed, try to imagine how much space they actually occupy.

O $=$ C $=$ O

Carbon dioxide

Acetone

Vinyl chloride

**FIGURE 3.5 Double Bonds**
These diagrams show several molecules that contain double bonds in red. A double bond is formed when two atoms share two pairs of electrons with each other.

Some organic molecules contain *triple covalent bonds;* the flammable gas acetylene, HC≡CH, is one example. Others—such as hydrogen cyanide HC≡N—have biological significance. This molecule inhibits the production of energy and can cause death as can other organic molecules. (How Science Works 3.1).

## The Complexity of Organic Molecules

Although many kinds of atoms can be part of an organic molecule, only a few are commonly found. Hydrogen (H) and oxygen (O) are almost always present. Nitrogen (N), sulfur (S), and phosphorus (P) are also very important in specific types of organic molecules.

An enormous variety of organic molecules is possible, because carbon is able to (1) bond at four different places, (2) form long chains and rings, and (3) combine with many other kinds of atoms. The types of atoms in the molecule are important in determining the properties of the molecule. The

# HOW SCIENCE WORKS 3.1

# Organic Compounds: Poisons to Your Pets!

The opening vignette concerning the pharmaceutical contamination of our water supply has far-reaching health implications to humans. However, we should not forget our pets, whose metabolism is not necessarily the same as that of humans. Organic compounds can affect them differently—most people have organic compounds around the house or garage that are toxic to dogs.

**Ibuprofen**—This nonsteroidal, anti-inflammatory (NSAID) might help relieve the pain of a person's headache, but if ingested by a dog, it can cause stomach and kidney problems in the animal. It can also alter the dog's nervous system, resulting in depression and seizures.

**Acetaminophen**—While a common pain medication for people, this drug can cause liver failure, swelling of the face and paws, and a problem with oxygen transport in the blood in a dog. If a dog ingests acetaminophen, it will probably need to be hospitalized.

**Chocolate**—Two toxic compounds in chocolate are theobromine and caffeine. **Theobromine** is found in candy, tea, and cola beverages. Since dogs and kittens metabolize this compound very slowly, it can remain in their bodies long enough to cause nausea, vomiting, diarrhea, and increased urination. Depending on the amount of chocolate the pet has ingested, it can also cause seizures, internal bleeding, heart attacks, and eventually death. **Caffeine** in coffee, tea, and cola drinks can result in vomiting, diarrhea, tremors, heart arrhythmias, and seizures in pets. Notice how similar the molecular structure of theobromine is to caffeine.

**Ibuprofen**

**Acetaminophen**

**Theobromine**

**Caffeine**

Glucose
$C_6H_{12}O_6$

Galactose
$C_6H_{12}O_6$

Fructose
$C_6H_{12}O_6$

**FIGURE 3.6 Structural Formulas for Several Hexoses**
Three 6-carbon sugars—hexoses (*hex* = 6; *-ose* = sugar)—are represented here. All have the same empirical formula ($C_6H_{12}O_6$), but each has a different structural formula. These three are called *structural isomers*. Structural isomers have different chemical properties from one another.

three-dimensional arrangement of the atoms within the molecule is also important. Because most inorganic molecules are small and involve few atoms, a group of atoms can be usually arranged in only one way to form a molecule. There is only one arrangement for a single oxygen atom and two hydrogen atoms in a molecule of water. In a molecule of sulfuric acid, there is only one arrangement for the sulfur atom, the two hydrogen atoms, and the four oxygen atoms.

Sulfuric (battery) acid

However, consider these two organic molecules:

Dimethyl ether

Ethyl alcohol
(as found in alcohol beverages)

Both the dimethyl ether and the ethyl alcohol contain two carbon atoms, six hydrogen atoms, and one oxygen atom, but they are quite different in their arrangement of atoms and in the chemical properties of the molecules. The first is an ether; the second is an alcohol. Because the ether and the alcohol have the same number and kinds of atoms, they are said to have the same *empirical formula*, which in this case can be written $C_2H_6O$. An empirical formula simply indicates the number of each kind of atom within the molecule. The arrangement of the atoms and their bonding within the molecule are indicated in a *structural formula*. Figure 3.6 shows several structural formulas for

the empirical formula $C_6H_{12}O_6$. Molecules that have the same empirical formula but different structural formulas are called *isomers*.

## The Carbon Skeleton and Functional Groups

At the core of all organic molecules is a **carbon skeleton,** which is composed of rings or chains (sometimes branched) of carbon. It is this carbon skeleton that determines the overall shape of the molecule. The differences among various kinds of organic molecules are determined by three factors: (1) the length and arrangement of the carbon skeleton, (2) the kinds and location of the atoms attached to it, and (3) the way these attached atoms are combined. These specific combinations of atoms, called **functional groups,** are frequently found on organic molecules. The kind of functional groups attached to a carbon skeleton determine the specific chemical properties of that molecule. By learning to recognize some of the functional groups, you can identify an organic molecule and predict something about its activity. Figure 3.7 shows some of the functional groups that are important in biological activity. Remember that a functional group does not exist by itself; it is part of an organic molecule. Outlooks 3.1 explains how chemists and biologists diagram the kinds of bonds formed in organic molecules.

## Macromolecules of Life

**Macromolecules** (*macro* = large) are very large organic molecules. We will look at four important kinds of macromolecules: carbohydrates, proteins, nucleic acids, and lipids. Carbohydrates, proteins, and nucleic acids are all *polymers* (*poly* = many; *mer* = segments). **Polymers** are combinations

# OUTLOOKS 3.1

## Chemical Shorthand

You have probably noticed that sketching the entire structural formula of a large organic molecule takes a great deal of time. If you know the structure of the major functional groups, you can use several shortcuts to more quickly describe chemical structures. When multiple carbons with 2 hydrogens are bonded to each other in a chain, it is sometimes written as follows:

It can also be written:

$$-CH_2-CH_2-CH_2-CH_2-CH_2-CH_2-CH_2-CH_2-CH_2-CH_2-CH_2-CH_2-$$

More simply, it can be written $(-CH_2-)_{12}$. If the 12 carbons were in a pair of two rings, we probably would not label the carbons or hydrogens unless we wished to focus on a particular group or point. We would probably draw the two 6-carbon rings with only hydrogen attached as follows:

$$(-CH_2-)_{12}$$

Don't let these shortcuts throw you. You will soon find that you will be putting a —H group onto a carbon skeleton and neglecting to show the bond between the oxygen and hydrogen. Structural formulas are regularly included in the package insert information of most medications.

---

of many smaller, similar building blocks called *monomers* (*mono* = single) bonded together (figure 3.8).

Although lipids are macromolecules, they are not polymers. A polymer is similar to a pearl necklace or a boat's anchor chain. All polymers are constructed of similar segments (pearls or links) hooked together to form one large product (necklace or anchor chain).

The monomers in a polymer are usually combined by a dehydration synthesis reaction (*de* = remove; *hydro* = water; *synthesis* = combine). This reaction occurs when two smaller molecules come close enough to have an —OH removed from one and an —H removed from the other. These are combined to form a new water molecule ($H_2O$), and the remaining two segments are combined to form the macromolecule.

Figure 3.9a shows the removal of water from between two monomers. Notice that, in this case, the structural formulas are used to help identify where this is occurring. The chemical equation also indicates the removal of water. You can easily recognize a dehydration synthesis reaction, because the reactant side of the equation shows numerous, small molecules, whereas the product side lists fewer, larger products and water.

The reverse of a dehydration synthesis reaction is known as hydrolysis (*hydro* = water; *lyse* = to split or break). Hydrolysis is the process of splitting a larger organic molecule into two or more component parts by adding water (figure 3.9b). The digestion of food molecules in the stomach is an example of hydrolysis.

| Functional Group | Structural Formula | Organic Molecule with Functional Group | Example |
|---|---|---|---|
| Hydroxyl (alcohol) | —OH | Carbohydrates | Ethanol |
| Carbonyl | $\overset{O}{\underset{\parallel}{-C-}}$ | Carbohydrates | Acetaldehyde |
| Carboxyl | $-C\overset{O}{\underset{OH}{\diagdown}}$ | Fats | Acetic acid |
| Amino | $-N\overset{H}{\underset{H}{\diagdown}}$ | Proteins | Alanine |
| Sulfhydryl | —S—H | Proteins | β-mercaptoethanol |
| Phosphate | $-O-\overset{O^-}{\underset{O}{\overset{\mid}{\underset{\parallel}{P}}}}-O^-$ | Nucleic acids | Glycerol phosphate |
| Methyl | $-\overset{H}{\underset{H}{\overset{\mid}{\underset{\mid}{C}}}}-H$ | Fats | Pyruvate |

**FIGURE 3.7 Functional Groups**

These are some of the groups of atoms that frequently attach to a carbon skeleton. The nature of the organic compound changes as the nature of the functional group changes from one molecule to another.

## 3.1  CONCEPT REVIEW

1. What is the difference between inorganic and organic molecules?
2. What two characteristics of the carbon molecule make it unique?
3. Diagram an example of the following functional groups: amino, alcohol, carboxyl.
4. Describe five functional groups.
5. List three monomers and the polymers that can be constructed from them.

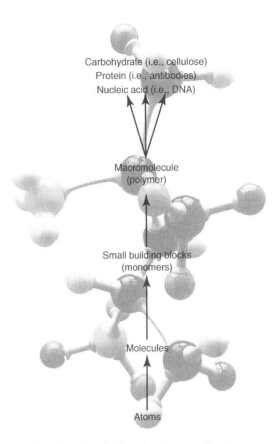

**FIGURE 3.8 Levels of Chemical Organization**

As a result of bonding specific units of matter in specific ways, molecules of enormous size and complexity are created.

## 3.2  Carbohydrates

**Carbohydrates** are composed of carbon, hydrogen, and oxygen atoms linked together to form monomers called *simple sugars* or *monosaccharides* (*mono* = single; *saccharine* = sweet, sugar). Carbohydrates play a number of roles in living things. They are an immediate source of energy (sugars), provide shape to certain cells (cellulose in plant cell walls), and are the components of many antibiotics and coenzymes. They are also an essential part of the nucleic acids, DNA and RNA. The ability to taste sweetness is a genetic trait. Geneticists have found two forms of a gene that are known to encode for the sweet taste receptors, and people whose ancestors are from Europe have the keenest sensitivity to sweets.

### Simple Sugars

The empirical formula for a simple sugar is easy to recognize, because there are equal numbers of carbons and oxygens and twice as many hydrogens—for example, $C_3H_6O_3$ or $C_5H_{10}O_5$. The ending *-ose* indicates that you are dealing with a carbohydrate. Simple sugars are usually described by the number of carbons in the molecule. A tri*ose* has 3 carbons, a pent*ose* has 5, and a hex*ose* has 6. If you remember that the number of carbons equals the number of oxygen atoms and that the number of hydrogens is double that number, these names tell you the empirical formula for the simple sugar.

Simple sugars, such as glucose, fructose, and galactose, provide the chemical energy necessary to keep organisms alive. *Glucose*, $C_6H_{12}O_6$, is the most abundant simple sugar; it serves as a food and a basic building block for other carbohydrates. Glucose (also called *dextrose*) is found in the sap of plants; in the human bloodstream, it is called *blood sugar*. Corn syrup, which is often used as a sweetener, is mostly glucose. Fructose, as its name implies, is the sugar that occurs in fruits *(fruit sugar)*, and you also see it on food labels as high fructose corn syrup. Glucose and fructose have the same empirical formula but have different structural formulas—that is, they are isomers (refer to figure 3.6). Honey is a mixture of glucose and fructose. This mixture of glucose and fructose is also formed when table sugar (sucrose) is reacted with water in the presence of an acid, a reaction that takes place in the preparation of canned fruit and candies. The mixture of glucose and fructose is called *invert sugar*. Thanks to fructose, invert sugar is about twice as sweet to the taste as the same amount of sucrose. Invert sugar also attracts water (is hygroscopic). Brown sugar feels moister than white, granulated sugar because it contains more invert sugar. Therefore, baked goods made with brown sugar are moist and chewy.

**Brown-sugar Cookies**

Cells can use simple sugars as building blocks of other more complex molecules such as the genetic material, DNA, and the important energy transfer molecule, ATP. DNA contains the simple sugar deoxyribose, and ATP contains the simple sugar ribose.

## Complex Carbohydrates

Simple sugars can be combined with each other to form **complex carbohydrates** (figure 3.10). When two simple sugars bond to each other, a *disaccharide* (*di* = two) is formed; when three bond together, a *trisaccharide* (*tri* = three) is formed. Generally, a complex carbohydrate that is larger than this is called a *polysaccharide* (*poly* = many). For example, when glucose and fructose are joined together, they form a disaccharide, with the loss of a water molecule (review figure 3.9).

Sucrose (table sugar) is the most common disaccharide. Sucrose occurs in high concentrations in sugarcane and sugar beets. It is extracted by crushing the plant materials, then dissolving the sucrose with water. The water is evaporated and the crystallized sugar is decolorized with charcoal to produce white sugar. Other common disaccharides are *lactose* (milk sugar) and *maltose* (malt sugar). All three of these disaccharides have similar properties, but maltose tastes only about one-third as sweet as sucrose. Lactose tastes only about one-sixth as sweet as sucrose (Table 3.1).

All the complex carbohydrates are polysaccharides and formed by dehydration synthesis reactions. Some common examples of polysaccharides are starch and glycogen. Cellulose is an important polysaccharide used in constructing the cell walls of plant cells. Humans cannot digest (hydrolyze) this complex carbohydrate, so we are not able to use it as an energy source. On the other hand, animals known as ruminants (e.g., cows and sheep) and termites have microorganisms within their digestive tracts that digest cellulose, making it an energy source for them. Plant cell walls add bulk or fiber to our diet, but no calories. Fiber is an important addition to the diet, because it helps control weight and reduces the risk of colon cancer. It also controls constipation and diarrhea, because these large, water-holding molecules make these conditions less of a problem.

| TABLE 3.1 Relative Sweetness of Various Sugars and Sugar Substitutes | |
|---|---|
| Type of Sugar or Artificial Sweetener | Relative Sweetness |
| Lactose (milk sugar) | 0.16 |
| Maltose (malt sugar) | 0.33 |
| Glucose | 0.75 |
| **Sucrose (table sugar)** | **1.00** |
| Fructose (fruit sugar) | 1.75 |
| Cyclamate | 30.00 |
| Aspartame | 150.00 |
| Stevia | 300.00 |
| Saccharin | 350.00 |
| Sucralose | 600.00 |

**Source of Milk Sugar**

Glucose    +    Fructose ⟶ Sucrose    +    Water

**(a) Dehydration synthesis**

Water    +    Sucrose ⟶ Glucose    +    Fructose

**(b) Hydrolysis**

**FIGURE 3.9  Polymer Formation and Breakdown**
*(a)* In the dehydration synthesis reaction illustrated here, the two —OH groups line up next to each other, so that an —OH group can be broken from one of the molecules and an —H can be removed from the other. The H— and the —OH are then combined to form water, and the oxygen that remains acts as a connection between the two sugar molecules. *(b)* A hydrolysis reaction is the opposite of a dehydration synthesis reaction. Carefully compare the two.

**(a) Cellulose**          **(b) Plant starches**          **(c) Glycogen**

Amylopectin     Amylose

**FIGURE 3.10  Complex Carbohydrates**
Three common complex carbohydrates are *(a)* cellulose (wood fibers), *(b)* amylose and amylopectin (plant starches), and *(c)* glycogen (sometimes called animal starch). Glycogen is found in muscle cells. Notice how all are similar in that they are all polymers of simple sugars, but they differ in how they are joined together. Although many organisms are capable of digesting (hydrolyzing) the bonds that are found in glycogen and plant starch molecules, few are able to break those that link the monosaccharides of cellulose.

**3.2   CONCEPT REVIEW**

6. Give two examples of simple sugars and two examples of complex sugars.
7. What are the primary characteristics used to identify a compound as a carbohydrate?

**3.3   Proteins**

**Proteins** are polymers made up of monomers known as *amino acids*. An **amino acid** is a short carbon skeleton that contains an amino functional group (nitrogen and two hydrogens) attached on one end of the skeleton and a carboxylic acid group at the other end. In addition, the carbon

**FIGURE 3.11 The Structure of an Amino Acid**
An amino acid is composed of a short carbon skeleton with three functional groups attached: an amino group, a carboxylic acid group (acid group), and an additional group, the side chain that is different for each kind of amino acid.

skeleton may have one of several different "side chains" on it (figure 3.11). There are about 20 naturally occurring amino acids (Outlooks 3.2).

## The Structure of Proteins

Amino acids can bond together by dehydration synthesis reactions. When two amino acids undergo dehydration synthesis, the nitrogen of the amino group of one is bonded to the carbon of the acid group of another. This covalent bond is termed a *peptide bond* (figure 3.12).

You can imagine that, by using 20 different amino acids as building blocks, you can construct millions of combinations. Each of these combinations is termed a **polypeptide** chain. A specific polypeptide is composed of a specific sequence of amino acids bonded end to end. Protein molecules are composed of individual polypeptide chains or groups of chains forming a particular configuration. There are four levels, or degrees, of protein structure: primary, secondary, tertiary, and quaternary structure.

### Primary Structure

A listing of the amino acids in their proper order within a particular polypeptide is its *primary structure* (figure 3.13a). The specific sequence of amino acids in a polypeptide is controlled by the genetic information of an organism. **Genes** *are specific portions of DNA that serve as messages that tell the cell to link particular amino acids in a specific order; that is, they determine a polypeptide's primary structure. The kinds of side chains on these amino acids influence the shape that the polypeptide forms, as well as its function.*

## OUTLOOKS 3.2

## So You Don't Eat Meat! How to Stay Healthy

Humans require nine amino acids in their diet: threonine, tryptophan, methionine, lysine, phenylalanine, isoleucine, valine, histidine, and leucine. They are called *essential amino acids* because the body is not able to manufacture them. The body uses these essential amino acids in the synthesis of the proteins required for good health. For example, the sulfur-containing amino acid methionine is essential for the absorption and transportation of the elements selenium and potassium. It also prevents excess fat buildup in the liver, and it traps heavy metals, such as lead, cadmium, and mercury, bonding with them so that they can be excreted from the body. Because essential amino acids are not readily available in most plant proteins, they are most easily acquired through meat, fish, and dairy products.

If this is the case, how do people avoid nutritional deficiency if for economic or personal reasons do not eat meat, poultry, fish, meat products, dairy products, and honey? People who exclude all animal products from their diet are called *vegans*. Those who include only milk are called *lacto-vegetarians*; those who include eggs are *ovo-vegetarians*, and those who include both eggs and milk are *lacto-ovo vegetarians*. For anyone but a true vegan, the essential amino acids can be provided in even a small amount of milk and eggs. True vegans can get all their essential amino acids by eating certain combinations of plants or plant products. Even though there are certain plants that contain all of these amino acids (*soy*, lupin, *hempseed*, *chia seed*, *amaranth*, *buckwheat*, and *quinoa*) most plants contain one or more of the essential amino acids. However, by eating the right combination of different plants, it is possible to get all the essential amino acids in one meal. These combinations are known as *complementary foods*.

**Vegetarian Meal**

**FIGURE 3.12  Peptide Covalent Bonds**

The bond that results from a dehydration synthesis reaction between amino acids is called a peptide bond. This bond forms as a result of the removal of the hydrogen and hydroxide groups. In the formation of this bond, the nitrogen is bonded directly to the carbon. This tripeptide is made up of the amino acids glycine, alanine, and leucine. The side chain unique to each amino acid is shown in color.

Many polypeptides fold into globular shapes after they have been made as the molecule bends. Some of the amino acids in the chain can form bonds with their neighbors.

## Secondary Structure

Some sequences of amino acids in a polypeptide are likely to twist, whereas other sequences remain straight. These twisted forms are referred to as the *secondary structure* of polypeptides (figure 3.13b). For example, at this secondary level some proteins (e.g., hair) take the form of an *alpha helix:* a shape like that of a coiled spring. Like most forms of secondary structure, the shape of the alpha helix is maintained by hydrogen bonds formed between different amino acid side chains at different locations within the polypeptide. Remember from chapter 2 that these forces of attraction do not form molecules but result in the orientation of one part of a molecule to another part within the same molecule. Other polypeptides form hydrogen bonds that cause them to make several flat folds that resemble a pleated skirt. This is called a *beta-pleated sheet.*

## Tertiary Structure

It is possible for a single polypeptide to contain one or more coils and pleated sheets along its length. As a result, these different portions of the molecule can interact to form an even more complex globular structure. This occurs when the coils and pleated sheets twist and combine with each other. The complex, three-dimensional structure formed in this manner is the polypeptide's *tertiary* (third-degree) *structure* (figure 3.13c). A good example of tertiary structure can be seen when a coiled electric cord becomes so twisted that it folds around and back on itself in several

places. The oxygen-holding protein found in muscle cells, myoglobin, displays tertiary structure. It is composed of a single (153 amino acids) helical molecule folded back and bonded to itself in several places.

## Quaternary Structure

Frequently, several different polypeptides, each with its own tertiary structure, twist around each other and chemically combine. The larger globular structure formed by these interacting polypeptides is referred to as the protein's *quaternary* (fourth-degree) *structure.* The individual polypeptide chains are bonded to each other by the interactions of certain side chains, which can form disulfide covalent bonds (figure 3.13d). One group of proteins that form quaternary structure are *immunoglobulins,* also known as *antibodies.* They are involved in fighting infectious diseases such as the flu, the mumps, and chicken pox.

## The Form and Function of Proteins

If a protein is to do its job effectively, it is vital that it has a particular three-dimensional shape. The protein's shape can be altered by changing the order of the amino acids, which causes different cross-linkages to form. Figure 3.14 shows the importance of the protein's three-dimensional shape, another emergent property.

For example, normal hemoglobin found in red blood cells consists of two kinds of polypeptide chains, called the alpha and beta chains. The beta chain is 146 amino acids long. If just one of these amino acids is replaced by a different one, the hemoglobin molecule may not function properly. A classic example of this results in a condition known as *sickle-cell anemia.* In this case, the sixth amino acid in the beta chain,

## FIGURE 3.13 Levels of Protein Structure

*(a)* The primary structure of a protein molecule is simply a list of its amino acids in the order in which they occur. *(b)* This shows the secondary structure of protein molecules or how one part of the molecule is attached to another part of the same molecule. *(c)* If already folded parts of a single molecule attach at other places, the molecule is said to display tertiary (third-degree) structure. *(d)* Quaternary (fourth-degree) structure is displayed by molecules that are the result of two separate molecules (each with its own tertiary structure) combining into one large macromolecule.

which is normally glutamic acid, is replaced by valine. What might seem like a minor change causes the hemoglobin to fold differently. The red blood cells that contain this altered hemoglobin assume a sickle shape when the body is deprived of an adequate supply of oxygen.

In other situations, two proteins may have the same amino acid sequence but they do not have the same three-dimensional form. The difference in shape affects how they function. Mad cow disease (bovine spongiform encephalopathy—BSE), chronic wasting disease in deer and Creutzfeldt-Jakob disease (CJD) in humans are caused by rogue proteins called *prions*. The prions that cause these diseases have an amino acid sequence identical to a normal brain protein but are folded differently. The normal brain protein contains helical segments, whereas the corresponding segments of the prion protein are pleated sheets.

When these malformed proteins enter the body, they cause normal proteins to fold differently. This causes the death of brain cells which causes loss of brain function and eventually death.

Changing environmental conditions also influence the shape of proteins. Energy in the form of heat or light may break the hydrogen bonds within protein molecules. When this occurs, the chemical and physical properties of the protein are changed and the protein is said to be **denatured.** (Keep in mind that a protein is a molecule, not a living thing, and therefore cannot be "killed.") A common

**Denatured Egg White**

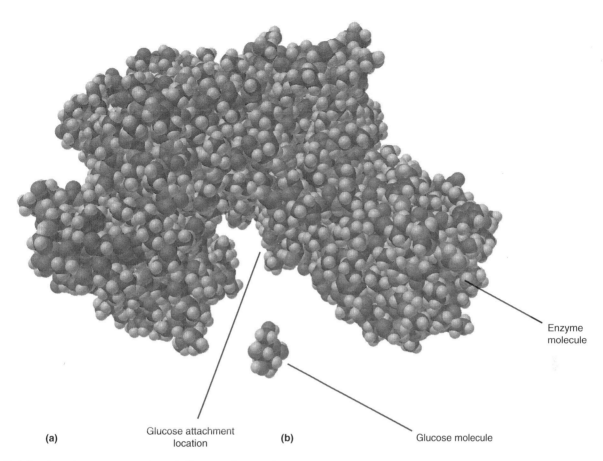

**(a)**                    Glucose attachment          **(b)**                Glucose molecule
                              location

## FIGURE 3.14   The Three-Dimensional Shape of Proteins

*(a)* The specific arrangement of amino acids in a polypeptide allows the amino acid side chains to bond with other amino acids. These stabilizing interactions result in a protein with a specific surface geometry. The large molecule pictured is an enzyme, a protein molecule that acts as a tool to speed the rate of a chemical reaction. Without having this specific shape, this protein would not be able to attach to the smaller *(b)* glucose molecule and chemically change the glucose molecule.

example of this occurs when the gelatinous, clear portion of an egg is cooked and the protein changes to a white solid. Some medications, such as insulin, are proteins and must be protected from denaturation so as not to lose their effectiveness. For protection, such medications may be stored in brown bottles to protect them from light or may be kept under refrigeration to protect them from heat.

## What Do Proteins Do?

There are thousands of kinds of proteins in living things, and they can be placed into three categories based on the functions they serve. **Structural proteins** are important for maintaining the shape of cells and organisms. The proteins that make up cell membranes, muscle cells, tendons, and blood cells are examples of structural proteins. The protein collagen, found throughout the human body, gives tissues shape, support, and strength.

**Regulator proteins,** the second category of proteins, help determine what activities will occur in the organism. Regulator proteins include *enzymes*, *chaperones*, and some *hormones*.

These molecules help control the chemical activities of cells and organisms. Enzymes speed the rate of chemical reactions and will be discussed in detail in chapter 5. Some examples of enzymes are the digestive enzymes in the intestinal tract. The job of a chaperone is to help other proteins fold into their proper shape. For example, some chaperones act as heat shock proteins—that is, they help repair heat-damaged proteins. Three hormones that are regulator proteins are insulin, glucagon, and oxytocin. Insulin and glucagon, produced by different cells of your pancreas, control the amount of glucose in the blood. If insulin production is too low, or if the molecules are improperly constructed, glucose molecules are not removed from the bloodstream at a fast enough rate. The excess sugar is then eliminated in the urine. Other symptoms of excess "sugar" in the blood include excessive thirst and even loss of consciousness. When blood sugar is low, glucagon is released from the pancreas to stimulate the breakdown of glycogen. The disease caused by improperly functioning insulin is known as *diabetes*. Oxytocin, a third protein hormone, stimulates the contraction of the uterus during childbirth. It is an organic molecule that has been produced artificially (e.g., Pitocin), and used by physicians to induce labor.

**Carrier proteins** are the third category. These pick up molecules at one place and transport them to another. For example, proteins from your food attach to cholesterol circulating in your blood to form *lipoproteins*, which are carried from the digestive system throughout the body.

---

## 3.4  Nucleic Acids

**Nucleic acids** are complex organic polymers that store and transfer genetic information within a cell. There are two types of nucleic acids: deoxyribonucleic acid (DNA) and ribonucleic acid (RNA). DNA serves as genetic material, whereas RNA plays a vital role in using genetic information to manufacture proteins. All nucleic acids are constructed of monomers known as **nucleotides.** Each nucleotide is composed of three parts: (1) a 5-carbon simple sugar molecule, which may be ribose or deoxyribose, (2) a phosphate group, and (3) a nitrogenous base. The nitrogenous base may be one of five types. Two of the types are the larger, double-ring molecules adenine and guanine. The smaller bases are the single-ring bases thymine, cytosine, and uracil (i.e., A, G, T, C, and U) (figure 3.15). Nucleotides (monomers) are linked together in long sequences (polymers), so that the sugar and phosphate sequence forms a "backbone" and the nitrogenous bases stick out to the side. DNA has deoxyribose sugar and the bases A, T, G, and C, whereas RNA has ribose sugar and the bases A, U, G, and C (figure 3.16).

**(a) Nucleotide**

(1) Ribose        (2) Deoxyribose

**(b) Sugars:**

(1) Adenine        (2) Guanine        (3) Cytosine        (4) Uracil        (5) Thymine

**(c) Nitrogenous bases:**

**(d) A phosphate group**

**FIGURE 3.15  The Building Blocks of Nucleic Acids**
*(a)* A complete DNA nucleotide composed of a sugar, phosphate, and a nitrogenous base. *(b)* The two possible sugars used in nucleic acids, ribose and deoxyribose. *(c)* The five possible nitrogenous bases: adenine (A), guanine (G), cytosine (C), uracil (U), and thymine (T). *(d)* A phosphate group.

**(a) DNA single strand**    **(b) RNA**

**Coding Strand**    **Non-coding Strand**

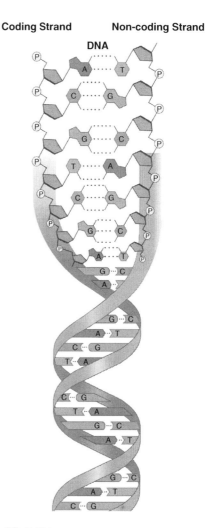

**FIGURE 3.16  DNA and RNA**
*(a)* A single strand of DNA is a polymer composed of nucleotides. Each nucleotide consists of deoxyribose sugar, phosphate, and one of four nitrogenous bases: A, T, G, or C. Notice the backbone of sugar and phosphate. *(b)* RNA is also a polymer, but each nucleotide is composed of ribose sugar, phosphate, and one of four nitrogenous bases: A, U, G, or C.

## DNA

**Deoxyribo*nucleic acid* (DNA)** is composed of two strands, which form a twisted, ladderlike structure thousands of nucleotides long (figure 3.17). The two strands are attached by hydrogen bonds between their bases according to the base-pair rule. *The base-pairing rule states that adenine always pairs with thymine, A with T (in the case of RNA, adenine always pairs with uracil—A with U) and guanine always pairs with cytosine—G with C.*

A T (or A U) and G C

A meaningful genetic message, a gene, is written using the nitrogenous bases as letters along a section of a strand of DNA, such as the base sequence CATTAGACT. The strand that contains this message is called the *coding strand*, from which comes the term *genetic code.* To make a protein, the cell reads the coding strand and uses sets of 3 bases. In the example sequence, sets of three bases are CAT, TAG, and ACT. This system is the basis of the genetic code for all organisms. Directly opposite the coding strand is a sequence

**FIGURE 3.17  DNA**
The genetic material is really double-stranded DNA molecules comprised of sequences of nucleotides that spell out an organism's genetic code. The coding strand of the double molecule is the side that can be translated by the cell into meaningful information. The genetic code has the information for telling the cell what proteins to make, which in turn become the major structural and functional components of the cell. The non-coding strand is unable to code for such proteins.

of nitrogenous bases that are called *non-coding*, because the sequence of letters make no "sense," but this strand protects the coding strand from chemical and physical damage. Both strands are twisted into a helix—that is, a molecule turned around a tubular space, like a twisted ladder.

The information carried by DNA can be compared to the information in a textbook. Books are composed of words (constructed from individual letters) in particular combinations, organized into chapters. In the same way, DNA is composed of tens of thousands of nucleotides (letters) in specific three letter sequences (words) organized into genes (chapters). Each chapter gene carries the information for producing a protein, just as the chapter of a book carries information relating to one idea. The

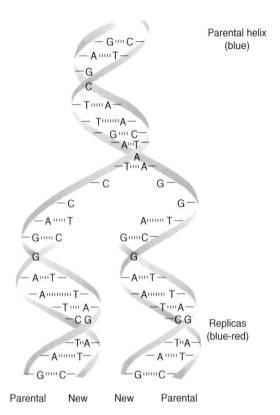

FIGURE 3.18 **Passing on Information to the Next Generation**
This is a generalized illustration of DNA replication. Each daughter cell receives a copy of the double helix. The helices are identical to each other and identical to the original double strands of the parent cell.

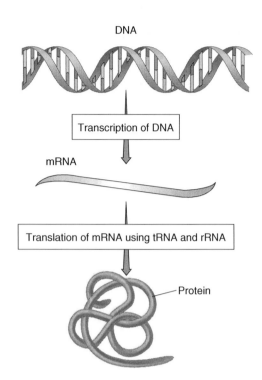

FIGURE 3.19 **The Role of RNA**
The entire process of protein synthesis begins with DNA. All forms of RNA (messenger, transfer, and ribosomal) are copies of different sequences of coding strand DNA and each plays a different role in protein synthesis. When the protein synthesis process is complete, the RNA can be reused to make more of the same protein coded for by the mRNA.

order of nucleotides in a gene is directly related to the order of amino acids in the protein for which it codes. Just as chapters in a book are identified by beginning and ending statements, different genes along a DNA strand have beginning and ending signals. They tell when to start and when to stop reading the gene. Human body cells contain 46 strands (books) of helical DNA, each containing many genes (chapters). These strands are called **chromosomes** when they become super-coiled in preparation for cellular reproduction. Before cellular reproduction, the DNA makes copies of the coding and non-coding strands, ensuring that the offspring, or *daughter* cells, will receive a full complement of the genes required for their survival (figure 3.18). A gene is a segment of DNA that is able to (1) replicate by directing the manufacture of copies of itself; (2) mutate, or chemically change, and transmit these changes to future generations; (3) store information that determines the characteristics of cells and organisms; and (4) use this information to direct the synthesis of structural, carrier, and regulator proteins.

## RNA

*Ribonucleic acid* (**RNA**) is found in three basic forms. **Messenger RNA (mRNA)** is a single-strand copy of a portion of the coding strand of DNA for a specific gene. When

mRNA is formed on the surface of the DNA, the base-pair rule applies. However, because RNA does not contain thymine, it pairs U with A instead of T with A. After mRNA is formed and peeled off, it links with a cellular structure called the *ribosome*, where the genetic message can be translated into a protein molecule. Ribosomes contain another type of RNA, **ribosomal RNA (rRNA)**. rRNA is also an RNA copy of DNA, but after being formed it becomes twisted and covered in protein to form a ribosome. The third form of RNA, **transfer RNA (tRNA)**, is also a copy of different segments of DNA, but when peeled off the surface each segment takes the form of a cloverleaf. tRNA molecules are responsible for transferring or carrying specific amino acids to the ribosome, where all three forms of RNA come together and cooperate in the manufacture of protein molecules (figure 3.19).

Whereas the specific sequence of nitrogenous bases correlates with the coding of genetic information, the energy transfer function of nucleic acids is correlated with the number of phosphates each contains. A nucleotide with 3 phosphates has more energy than a nucleotide with only 1 or 2 phosphates. All of the different nucleotides are involved in transferring energy in phosphorylation reactions. One of the most important, ATP (adenosine *tri*phosphate) and its role in metabolism will be discussed in chapter 6.

10. Describe how DNA differs from and is similar to RNA both structurally and functionally.
11. List the nitrogenous bases that base-pair in DNA and in RNA.

## 3.5 Lipids

There are three main types of **lipids**: *true fats* (e.g., olive oil), *phospholipids* (the primary component of cell membranes), and *steroids* (some hormones). In general, lipids are large, nonpolar (do not have a positive end and a negative end), organic molecules that do not dissolve easily in polar solvents, such as water. For example, nonpolar vegetable oil molecules do not dissolve in polar water molecules; they separate. Molecules in this group are generally called **fats.** They are not polymers, as are carbohydrates, proteins, and nucleic acids. Fats are soluble in nonpolar substances, such as ether or acetone. Just like carbohydrates, lipids are composed of carbon, hydrogen, and oxygen. They do not, however, have the same ratio of carbon, hydrogen, and oxygen in their empirical formulas. Lipids generally have very small amounts of oxygen, compared with the amounts of carbon and hydrogen. *Simple lipids* are not able to be broken down into smaller, similar subunits. *Complex lipids* can be hydrolyzed into smaller, similar units.

### True (Neutral) Fats

**True (neutral) fats** are important, complex organic molecules that are used to provide energy, among other things. The building blocks of a fat are a *glycerol* molecule and *fatty acids.* **Glycerol** is a carbon skeleton that has three alcohol groups attached to it. Its chemical formula is $C_3H_5(OH)_3$. At room temperature, glycerol looks like clear, lightweight oil. It is used under the name *glycerin* as an additive to many cosmetics to make them smooth and easy to spread.

$$H - \underset{\underset{H}{|}}{\overset{\overset{OH}{|}}{C}} - \underset{\underset{H}{|}}{\overset{\overset{OH}{|}}{C}} - \underset{\underset{H}{|}}{\overset{\overset{OH}{|}}{C}} - H$$
Glycerol

A **fatty acid** is a long-chain carbon skeleton that has a carboxyl functional group. True (neutral) fat molecules that form from a glycerol molecule and 3 attached fatty acids are called *triglycerides;* those with 2 fatty acids are *diglycerides;* those with 1 fatty acid are *monoglyceride* (figure 3.20). Triglycerides account for about 95% of the fat stored in human tissue.

If the carbon skeleton of a fatty acid molecule has as much hydrogen bonded to it as possible, it is called **saturated.** The saturated fatty acid shown in figure 3.21a is stearic acid, a component of solid meat fats, such as bacon fat. Notice

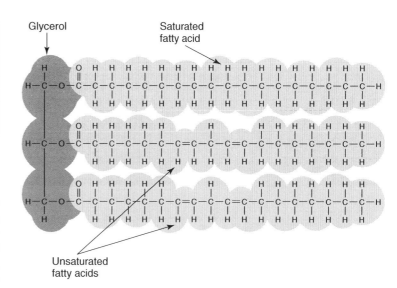

**FIGURE 3.20  A Triglyceride Molecule**
The arrangement of the 3 fatty acids (yellow) attached to a glycerol molecule (red) is typical of the formation of a fat. The structural formula of the fat appears to be very cluttered until you dissect the fatty acids from the glycerol; then, it becomes much more manageable. This example of a triglyceride contains a glycerol molecule, 2 unsaturated fatty acids (linoleic acid), and a third saturated fatty acid (stearic acid).

that, at every point in this structure, the carbon has as much hydrogen as it can hold. Saturated fats are generally found in animal tissues—they tend to be solids at room temperatures. Some other examples of saturated fats are butter, whale blubber, suet, lard, and fats associated with such meats as steak and pork chops.

A fatty acid is said to be **unsaturated** if the carbons are double-bonded to each other at one or more points. The occurrence of a double bond in a fatty acid is indicated by the Greek letter ω (omega), followed by a number indicating the location of the first double bond in the molecule. Counting begins from the omega end, that is the end farthest from the carboxylic acid functional group. Oleic acid, one of the fatty acids found in olive oil, is comprised of 18 carbons with a single double bond between carbons 9 and 10. Therefore, it is chemically designated C18:Iω9 and is a monounsaturated fatty acid. This fatty acid is commonly referred to as an omega-9 fatty acid. The unsaturated fatty acid in figure 3.21b is linoleic acid, a component of sunflower and safflower oils. Notice that there are two double bonds between the carbons and fewer hydrogens than in the saturated fatty acid. Linoleic acid is chemically a polyunsaturated fatty acid with two double bonds and is designated C18:2ω6, an omega-6 fatty acid. This indicates that the first double bond of this 18-carbon molecule is between carbons 6 and 7. Because the human body cannot make this fatty acid and must be taken in as a part of the diet, it is called an *essential fatty acid.* The other essential fatty acid, linolenic acid (figure 3.21c), is C18:3ω3; it has three double bonds. This fatty acid is commonly

**(a) Stearic acid**

**(b) Linoleic acid (omega-6)**

**(c) Alpha-linolenic acid (omega-3)**

**FIGURE 3.21 Structure of Saturated and Unsaturated Fatty Acids**
*(a)* Stearic acid is an example of a saturated fatty acid. *(b)* Linoleic acid is an example of an unsaturated fatty acid. It is technically an omega-6 fatty acid, because the first double bond occurs at carbon number 6. *(c)* An omega-3 fatty acid, linolenic acid. Both linoleic and linolenic acids are essential fatty acids for humans.

referred to as an omega-3 fatty acid. One key function of these essential fatty acids is the synthesis of the prostaglandin hormones that are necessary in controlling cell growth and specialization. Many food manufacturers are now adding omega-3 fatty acids to their products, based on evidence that these reduce the risk of cardiovascular disease.

| Sources of Omega-3 Fatty Acids | Sources of Omega-6 Fatty Acids |
|---|---|
| Certain fish oils (salmon, sardines, herring) | Corn oil |
| | Peanut oil |
| Flaxseed oil | Cottonseed oil |
| Soybeans | Soybean oil |
| Soybean oil | Sesame oil |
| Walnuts | Sunflower oil |
| Canola oil | Safflower oil |
| Green, leafy vegetables | |

Many unsaturated fat molecules are plant fats or oils—they are usually liquids at room temperatures. Peanut, corn, and olive oils are mixtures of true fats and are considered unsaturated because they have double bonds between the carbons of the carbon skeleton (Outlooks 3.3). A polyunsaturated fatty acid is one that has several double bonds in the carbon skeleton. When glycerol and 3 fatty acids are combined by three dehydration synthesis reactions, a fat is formed. That dehydration synthesis is almost exactly the same as the reaction that causes simple sugars to bond.

*cis* double bond: oleic acid

*trans* double bond: elaidic acid

In nature, most unsaturated fatty acids have hydrogen atoms that are on the same side of the double-bonded carbons. These are called *cis* fatty acids. If the hydrogens are on opposite sides of the double bonds, they are called *trans* fatty acids. *Trans* fatty acids are found naturally in grazing animals, such as cattle and sheep. Therefore, humans acquire them in their diets in the form of meat and dairy products. *Trans* fatty acids are also formed during the *hydrogenation* of either vegetable or fish oils. The hydrogenation process breaks the double bonds in the fatty acid chain and adds more hydrogen atoms. This can change the liquid to a solid. Many product labels list the term *hydrogenated*. This process extends shelf life and allows producers to convert oils to other solids, such as margarine.

Clinical studies have shown that *trans* fatty acids tend to raise total blood cholesterol levels, but less than the more

## OUTLOOKS 3.3

# What Happens When You Deep-Fry Food?

You have probably noticed that deep-fried foods are covered with some sort of breading or batter. The coating forms a barrier and protects the underlying food (e.g., chicken or cheese) from being burned when it is placed in the hot oil. This means that your food is being cooked indirectly, not directly, as you would cook a hot dog on a grill. Deep-fried foods cook quickly because fats and oils can be heated to higher temperatures before they boil. Cooking at these higher temperatures keeps the cooking fats and oils from getting inside the food. If the fat or oil is not hot enough, the food will be greasy. If the oil is too hot, the coating will burn before the food inside can be cooked the way you like it. Even though there is some variation in oil temperature due to the thickness and kind of food being deep-fried, the general rule is to have your oil at 375°F (190°C). The best oils to use for stir-frying are those that can be heated to a high temperature without smoking (e.g., canola, peanut, or grapeseed oil).

saturated fatty acids. Dietary *trans* fatty acids also tend to raise the so-called bad fats (low-density lipoproteins, LDLs) and lower the so-called good fats (high-density lipoproteins, HDLs) when consumed instead of *cis* fatty acids. Scientific evidence indicates that this increases the risk for heart disease (Outlooks 3.4). Because of the importance of *trans* fatty acids in cardiovascular health, the U.S. Department of Health and Human Services (HHS) requires that the amount of *trans* fatty acids in foods be stated under the listed amount of saturated fat. The HHS suggests that a person eat no more than 20 grams of saturated fat a day (about 10% of total calories), including *trans* fatty acids.

Fats are important molecules for storing energy. There is more than twice as much energy in a gram of fat as in a gram of sugar—9 Calories versus 4 Calories. This is important to an organism, because fats can be stored in a relatively small space yet yield a high amount of energy. Fats in animals also provide protection from heat loss; some animals have an insulating layer of fat under the skin. The thick layer of blubber in whales, walruses, and seals prevents the loss of internal body heat to the cold, watery environment in which they live. The same layer of fat and the fat deposits around some organs (such as the eyes, kidneys and heart) cushion the organs from physical damage.

## Phospholipids

**Phospholipids** are a class of complex, water-insoluble organic molecules that resemble neutral fats but have a phosphate-containing group ($PO_4$) in their structure (figure 3.22). Phospholipids are important because they are a major component of cell membranes. Without these lipids, the cell contents would not be separated from the exterior environment. Some

**Key:**
- Polar
- Nonpolar
- Phosphate group

**FIGURE 3.22  A Phospholipid Molecule**

This molecule is similar to a fat but has a phosphate group (yellow) in its structure. You can think of phospholipid molecules as having a "head" with two strings dangling down. The head portion is the glycerol and phosphate group, which is polar and soluble in water. The strings are the fatty acid segments of the molecule and are nonpolar and not water-soluble.

# OUTLOOKS 3.4

## Fat and Your Diet

When triglycerides are eaten in fat-containing foods, digestive enzymes hydrolyze them into glycerol and fatty acids. These molecules are absorbed by the intestinal tract and coated with protein to form lipoprotein, as shown in the accompanying diagram. The combination allows the fat to dissolve better in the blood, so that it can move throughout the body in the circulatory system.

Five types of lipoproteins found in the body are

1. Chylomicrons
2. Very-low-density lipoproteins (VLDLs)
3. Low-density lipoproteins (LDLs)
4. High-density lipoproteins (HDLs)
5. Lipoprotein a [Lp(a)]

Chylomicrons are very large particles formed in the intestine; they are 80–95% triglycerides. As the chylomicrons circulate through the body, cells remove the triglycerides in order to make sex hormones, store energy, and build new cell parts. When most of the triglycerides have been removed, the remaining portions of the chylomicrons are harmlessly destroyed.

The VLDLs and LDLs are formed in the liver. VLDLs contain all types of lipid, protein, and 10–15% cholesterol, whereas the LDLs are about 50% cholesterol. As with the chylomicrons, the body uses these molecules for the fats they contain. However, in some people, high levels of LDL and lipoprotein a [Lp(a)] in the blood are associated with atherosclerosis, stroke, and heart attack. It appears that saturated fat disrupts the clearance of LDLs from the bloodstream. Thus, while in the blood, LDLs may stick to the insides of the vessels, forming deposits, which restrict blood flow and contribute to high blood pressure, strokes, and heart attacks. Even though they are 30% cholesterol, a high level of HDLs (made in the intestine), compared with LDLs and [Lp(a)], is associated with a lower risk for atherosclerosis. One way to reduce the risk of this disease is to lower your intake of LDLs and [Lp(a)]. This can be done by reducing your consumption of saturated fats. An easy way to remember the association between LDLs and HDLs is "L = Lethal" and "H = Healthy" or "Low = Bad" and "High = Good." The federal government's cholesterol guidelines recommend that all adults get a full lipoprotein profile (total cholesterol, HDL, LDL, and triglycerides) once every five years.

They also recommend a sliding scale for desirable LDL levels; however, recent studies suggest that one's LDL level should be as low as possible.

Taking certain drugs is one way to control the level of lipoproteins in the body. Statins are a group of medicines (e.g., simvastatin, atorvastatin) that work by blocking the action of enzymes that control the rate of cholesterol production in the

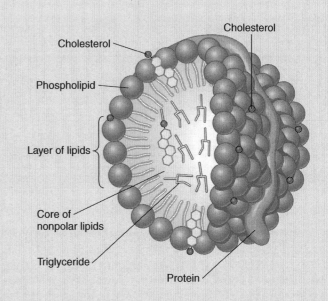

body. Their use can lower cholesterol 20–60%. They also increase the liver's ability to remove low-density lipoproteins. An additional benefit is a slight increase in high-density lipoproteins and a decrease in triglycerides.

**Total cholesterol goal values:**

- 75–169 mg/dL (milligram per deciliter) for those age 20 and younger
- 100–199 mg/dL for those over age 21

**Low-density lipoprotein (LDL) goal values:**

- Less than 70 mg/dL for those with heart or blood vessel disease and for other patients at very high risk of heart disease (those with metabolic syndrome)
- Less than 100 mg/dL for high-risk patients (for example, some patients who have diabetes or multiple heart disease risk factors)
- Less than 130 mg/dL otherwise

**Very-low-density lipoprotein (VLDL) goal values:**

- Less than 40 mg/dL

**High-density lipoprotein (HDL) goal value:**

- Greater than 45 mg/dL (the higher the better)

**Triglyceride goal value:**

- Less than 150 mg/dL

**FIGURE 3.23** **Steroids**
*(a)* Cholesterol is produced by the human body and is found in cell membranes. *(b)* Testosterone increases during puberty, causing the male sex organs to mature. *(c)* Progesterone is a female sex hormone produced by the ovaries and placenta. Notice the slight structural differences among these molecules.

of the phospholipids are better known as *lecithins*. Found in cell membranes, lecithins help in the emulsification of fats—that is, they help separate large portions of fat into smaller units. This allows the fat to mix with other materials. Lecithins are added to many types of food for this purpose (chocolate bars, for example). Some people take lecithin as nutritional supplements because they believe it leads to healthier hair and better reasoning ability. But once inside the intestines, lecithins are destroyed by enzymes, just as any other phospholipid is. Because phospholipids are essential components of the membranes of all cells, they will also be examined in chapter 4.

## Steroids

**Steroids,** another group of lipid molecules, are characterized by their arrangement of interlocking rings of carbon. Many steroid molecules are sex hormones. Some of them regulate reproductive processes, such as egg and sperm production (see chapter 27); others regulate such things as salt concentration in the blood. Figure 3.23 illustrates some of the steroid compounds, such as testosterone and progesterone, that are typically manufactured by organisms and also in the laboratory as pharmaceuticals. We have already mentioned one steroid molecule: cholesterol. Serum cholesterol (the kind found in your blood and associated with lipoproteins) has been implicated in many cases of atherosclerosis. However, your body makes this steroid for use as a component of cell membranes. Cholesterol is necessary for the manufacture of vitamin D, which assists in the proper development of bones and teeth. Cholesterol molecules in your skin react with ultraviolet light to produce vitamin D. The body also uses it to make bile acids. These products of the liver are channeled into your intestine to emulsify fats.

Regulating the amount of cholesterol in the body to prevent its negative effects can be difficult, because we consume it in our diet. Recall that diets high in saturated fats increase the risk for diseases such as atherosclerosis. By watching your diet, you can reduce the amount of cholesterol in your blood serum by about 20%, as much as taking a cholesterol-lowering drug. Therefore, it is best to eat foods that are low in cholesterol. Because many foods that claim to be low- or no-cholesterol have high levels of saturated fats, they should also be avoided in order to control serum cholesterol levels.

## 3.5 CONCEPT REVIEW

12. Describe three kinds of lipids.
13. What is meant by HDL, LDL, and VLDL? Where are they found? How do they relate to disease?

## Summary

The chemistry of living things involves a variety of large and complex molecules. This chemistry is based on the carbon atom and the fact that carbon atoms can connect to form long chains or rings. This results in a vast array of molecules. The structure of each molecule is related to its function. Changes in the structure may result in abnormal functions, called disease. Some of the most common types of organic molecules found in living things are carbohydrates, lipids, proteins, and nucleic acids. Table 3.2 summarizes the major types of biologically important organic molecules and how they function in living things.

**TABLE 3.2** Types of Organic Molecules Found in Living Things

| Type of Organic Molecule | Basic Subunit | Function | Examples |
|---|---|---|---|
| Carbohydrates | Simple sugar/monosaccharides | Provide energy | Glucose<br>Cellulose, starch, glycogen |
| Proteins | Amino acid | Maintain the shape of cells and parts of organisms | Cell membrane<br>Hair<br>Antibodies<br>Clotting factors<br>Enzymes<br>Muscle |
| | | As enzymes, regulate the rate of cell reactions | Ptyalin in the mouth |
| | | As hormones, affect physiological activity, such as growth or metabolism | Insulin |
| | | Serve as molecules that carry other molecules to distant places in the body | Lipoproteins, hemoglobin |
| Nucleic acids | Nucleotide | Store and transfer genetic information that controls the cell | DNA |
| | | Are involved in protein synthesis | RNA |
| Lipids<br>1. Fats | Glycerol and fatty acids | Provide energy<br>Provide insulation<br>Serve as shock absorbers | Lard<br>Olive oil<br>Linseed oil<br>Tallow |
| 2. Phospholipids | Glycerol, fatty acids, and phosphate group | Form a major component of the structure of the cell membrane | Cell membrane |
| 3. Steroids and prostaglandins | Structure of interlocking carbon rings | Often serve as hormones that control the body processes | Testosterone<br>Vitamin D<br>Cholesterol |

## Key Terms

*Use the interactive flash cards on the **Concepts in Biology, 14/e** website to help you learn the meaning of these terms.*

amino acid 53
biochemistry 46
carbohydrates 51
carbon skeleton 49
carrier proteins 58
chromosomes 60
complex carbohydrates 52

denatured 56
deoxyribonucleic acid (DNA) 58
double bond 47
fats 61
fatty acid 61
functional groups 49

genes 54
glycerol 61
inorganic molecules 46
lipids 61
macromolecules 49
messenger RNA (mRNA) 60
nucleic acids 58
nucleotides 58
organic molecules 46
phospholipids 63
polymers 49
polypeptide 54

proteins 53
regulator proteins 57
ribonucleic acid (RNA) 58
ribosomal RNA (rRNA) 60
saturated 61
steroids 65
structural proteins 57
transfer RNA (tRNA) 60
true (neutral) fats 61
unsaturated 61

## Basic Review

1. A(n) _____ formula indicates the number of each kind of atom within a molecule.
2. The name of this functional group, –NH$_2$, is
   a. amino.
   b. alcohol.
   c. carboxylic acid.
   d. aldehyde.
3. Molecules that have the same empirical formula but different structural formulas are called
   a. ions.
   b. isomers.
   c. icons.
   d. radicals.
4. Which is *not* a macromolecule?
   a. carbohydrate
   b. protein
   c. sulfuric acid
   d. steroid
5. Which is *not* a polymer?
   a. insulin
   b. DNA
   c. fatty acid
   d. RNA
6. The monomer of a complex carbohydrate is
   a. an amino acid.
   b. a monosaccharide.
   c. a nucleotide.
   d. a fatty acid.
7. When blood sugar is low, this protein hormone is released from the pancreas to stimulate the breakdown of glycogen.
   a. glucagon
   b. estrogen
   c. oxytocin
   d. glycine
8. Mad cow disease is caused by a
   a. virus.
   b. bacteria.
   c. prion.
   d. hormone.
9. _____ occurs when the shape of a macromolecule altered as a result of exposure to excess heat or light.
10. By watching your diet it is possible to reduce the amount of cholesterol in your blood serum by about _____%.
11. Organic compounds that do not have their proper _____ are not likely to function properly in a cell.
12. The genetic material of many organisms belongs to which major category of organic compounds?
    a. carbohydrate
    b. protein
    c. nucleic acid
    d. lipid
13. "Oh no! The doctor said my cholesterol was too high." I guess I'll have to keep an eye on the amount of _____ I eat.
14. Many types of birth control pills contain compounds called _____, one of which is estrogen.
15. Beta-pleated sheets found in protein molecules is an example of _____ structures.

**Answers**
1. empirical  2. a  3. b  4. c  5. c  6. b  7. a  8. c
9. Denaturation  10. 20%  11. 3-D shape  12. c  13. lipids
14. steroids  15. secondary

## Thinking Critically

Archaeologists, anthropologists, chemists, biologists, and healthcare professionals agree that the drinking of alcohol dates back thousands of years. Evidence also exists that this practice has occurred in most cultures around the world. Use the Internet to search out answers to the following questions:

1. What is the earliest date for which there is evidence for the production of ethyl alcohol?
2. In which culture did alcohol drinking first occur?
3. What is the molecular formula and structure of ethanol?
4. Do alcohol and water mix?
5. How much ethanol is consumed in the form of beverages in the United States each year?
6. What is the legal limit to be considered intoxicated in your state?
7. How is the legal limit in your state measured?
8. Why is there a tax on alcoholic beverages?
9. How do the negative effects of drinking alcohol compare for men and women?
10. Have researchers demonstrated any beneficial effects of drinking alcohol?

Compare what you thought you knew to what you can now support with scientific evidence.

# Cell Structure and Function

### Cadavers Source of Healing Power

*Is there a risk?*

Most people think that bones are lifeless; however, they are actually living, growing tissues. Bone is composed of many kinds of living cells surrounded by a bone matrix made of minerals and proteins. Certain bone cells are a source of *red* and *white blood cells* while others are engaged in a process known as *bone remodeling*—much like the process a sculptor uses when creating a piece of art from clay. Remodeling occurs throughout life and is the result of the absorption of bone followed by the formation of new bone. Cells known as *osteoblasts* are responsible for adding new bone matrix, whereas *osteoclasts* remove old matrix. Remodeling takes place as a result of bone loss due to stress, disease or breakage.

Following certain accidents or diseases, bone cells are unable to remodel the damage. However, researchers have discovered that healing can be promoted by using protein bone matrix from cadavers—dead bodies. This tissue is rich in growth factors that signal bone cells to multiply and promote repair. Are there drawbacks? There is only a limited supply of this matrix because it comes from human donors, and there is a risk of transmitting viruses to the recipient.

- **What is the basic makeup of a cell?**

- **How do growth factors signal cells?**

- **In order to become a bone matrix organ donor, should a person undergo screening to check for hidden viruses?**

## Background Check

**Concepts you should already know to get the most out of this chapter:**
- The atomic and molecular nature of matter (chapter 2)
- Some molecules can be very large (chapter 3)
- There are millions of different kinds of molecules and that each kind of molecule has specific physical properties (chapter 2)
- Kinetic molecular theory (chapter 2)

## 4.1 The Development of the Cell Theory

The **cell theory** states that all living things are made of cells. The **cell** is the basic structural and functional unit of living things and is the smallest unit that displays the characteristics of life. However, the concept of a cell did not emerge all at once but, rather, was developed and modified over several centuries. It is still being modified today. The ideas of hundreds of people were important in the development of the cell theory, but certain key people can be identified.

### Some History

The first person to use the term *cell* was Robert Hooke (1635–1703) of England. He used a simple kind of microscope to study thin slices of cork from the bark of a cork oak tree (figure 4.1). He saw many cubicles fitting neatly together, which reminded him of the barren rooms (cells) in a monastery. He used the term *cell* when he described his observations in 1665 in the publication *Micrographia*, the first picture book of science to come off the press, with 38 beautiful engravings. The book became a best-seller. The tiny cork boxes Hooke saw, and described in his book were, in fact, only the cell walls that surrounded the once living portions of these plant cells.

We now know that the **cell wall** of a plant cell is produced on the outside of the cell and is composed of the complex carbohydrate called cellulose. It provides strength and protection to the living contents of the cell. Although the cell wall appears to be a rigid, solid layer of material, it is actually composed of many interwoven strands of cellulose molecules. Thus, most kinds of molecules pass easily through it.

Anton van Leeuwenhoek (1632–1723), a Dutch merchant who sold cloth, was one of the first individuals to carefully study magnified cells. He apparently saw a copy of Hooke's *Micrographia* and began to make his own microscopes, so that he could study biological specimens. He was interested in magnifying glasses, because magnifiers were used to count the number of threads in cloth. He used a very simple kind of microscope that had only one lens. Basically, it was a very powerful magnifying glass (figure 4.2). What made his microscope better than others of the time was his ability to grind very high-quality lenses. He used his skill at lens grinding to make about 400 lenses during his lifetime. One of his lenses

**(a)** **(b)**

**FIGURE 4.1 Hooke's Observations**
*(a)* The concept of a cell has changed considerably over the past 300 years. Robert Hooke's idea of a cell was based on his observation of slices of cork (cell walls of the bark of the cork oak tree). *(b)* Hooke constructed his own simple microscope to be able to make these observations.

**FIGURE 4.2 Anton van Leeuwenhoek's Microscope**
Although van Leeuwenhoek's microscope had only one lens, the lens quality was so good that he was able to see cells clearly. This replica of his microscope shows that it is a small, simple apparatus.

was able to magnify 270 times. Van Leeuwenhoek made thousands of observations of many kinds of microscopic objects. He also made very detailed sketches of the things he viewed with his simple microscopes and communicated his findings to

Robert Hooke and the Royal Society of London. His work stimulated further investigation of magnification techniques and descriptions of cell structures.

When van Leeuwenhoek discovered that he could see things moving in pond water using his microscope, his curiosity stimulated him to look at a variety of other things. He studied many things such as blood, semen, feces, and pepper, for example. He was the first to see individual cells and recognize them as living units, but he did not call them cells. The name he gave to the "little animals" he saw moving around in the pond water was *animicules.*

Although Hooke, van Leeuwenhoek, and others continued to make observations, nearly 200 years passed before it was generally recognized that all living things are made of cells and that these cells can reproduce themselves. In 1838, Mathias Jakob Schleiden of Germany stated that all plants are made up of smaller cellular units. In 1839, Theodor Schwann, another German, published the idea that all animals are composed of cells.

Soon after the term *cell* caught on, it was recognized that the cell wall of plant cells was essentially lifeless and that it was really the contents of the cell that had "life." This living material was termed **protoplasm,** which means *first-formed substance.* Scientists used the term *protoplasm* to distinguish between the living portion of the cell and the nonliving cell wall. As better microscopes were developed, people began to distinguish two different regions of protoplasm. One region, called the *nucleus,* appeared as a central body within a more fluid material surrounding it. Today, we know the **nucleus** is the part of a cell that contains the genetic information. **Cytoplasm** was the name given to the fluid portion of the protoplasm surrounding the nucleus. Although the term *protoplasm* is seldom used today, the term *cytoplasm* is still common.

The development of special staining techniques, better light microscopes, and ultimately powerful electron microscopes revealed that the cytoplasm contains many structures, called **organelles** *(little organs).* Further research has shown that each kind of organelle has certain functions related to its structure.

## Basic Cell Types

All living things are cells or composed of cells, and all cells share three basic traits: They all have an *outer membrane, cytoplasm,* and *genetic material.* However, about 400 years of research has revealed a variety of differences among cells. For example, we know that while all the cells in your body have been derived from one, single, fertilized egg cell, bone cells show structural differences in comparison to brain cells. They not only look different under the microscope, but perform very different metabolically. As scientists studied the cells of even more diverse organisms such as bacteria, plants, animals, fungi, algae, and protozoans, it became clear that there were even greater differences. Some of these differences were structural; others only became evident by doing chemical analysis. As a result of these investigations,

biologists have categorized cells into two general types: **eukaryotic** and **prokaryotic (noneukaryotic) cells** (figure 4.3). The cells of plants, animals, fungi, protozoa, and algae are eukaryotic, and are placed in a category called **Eucarya.** All eukaryotic cells have their genetic material surrounded by a nuclear membrane forming the cellular nucleus. They also have a large number and variety of complex organelles, each specialized in the metabolic function it performs. In general, they are large in comparison to noneukaryotic cells. There are two categories of prokaryotic cells: **Bacteria** and **Archaea.** Neither of these cell types has a nuclear membrane; therefore they lack a cellular nucleus. In addition, they display unique chemical and metabolic characteristics but do not have the variety and number of organelles seen in eukaryotes. Bacteria and Archaea are classified into a group referred to as the **Prokaryotes.** From studying a vast amount of data, biologists have tried to understand the evolutionary relationship among these cell types. The previous hypothesized evolutionary relationship among these cell types was:

However, current data points to a different evolutionary pattern:

The fossil record shows evidence of prokaryotes 3.5 billion years ago. Eucarya show up in the fossil record about 1.8 billion years ago.

### 4.1   CONCEPT REVIEW

1. Describe how the concept of the cell has changed over the past 200 years.
2. What features do all cell types have in common?

## 4.2   Cell Size

Cells of different kinds vary greatly in size (figure 4.4). In general, the cells of Bacteria and Archaea are much smaller than those of eukaryotic organisms. Prokaryotic cells are typically 1–2 micrometers in diameter, whereas eukaryotic cells are typically 10–100 times larger.

Some basic physical principles determine how large a cell can be. A cell must transport all of its nutrients and all of its wastes through its outer membrane to stay alive. Cells are

(a)

(b)

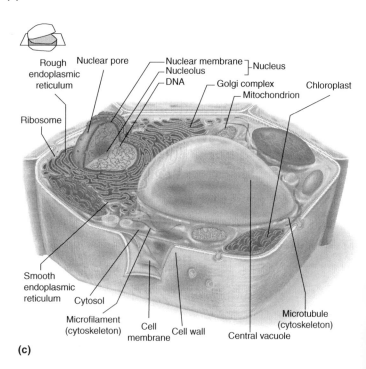

(c)

**FIGURE 4.3 Major Cell Types**
There are two major types of cells eukaryotic and noneukaryotic. Eukaryotic cells are 10 to 100 times larger than noneukaryotic cells such as this *(a)* bacterium. These drawings (not to scale) highlight the structural differences between them. The generalized eukaryotic cells are *(b)* an animal and *(c)* a plant cell.

limited in size because, as a cell becomes larger, adequate transport of materials through the membrane becomes more difficult. The difficulty arises because, as the size of a cell increases, the amount of living material (the cell's volume) increases more quickly than the size of the outer membrane (the cell's surface area). As cells grow, the amount of surface area increases by the square ($X^2$) but volume increases by the cube ($X^3$). This mathematical relationship between the surface area and volume is called the *surface area-to-volume*

*ratio* and is shown for a cube in figure 4.5. Notice that, as the cell becomes larger, both surface area and volume increase. Most important, volume increases *more* quickly than surface area, causing the surface area-to-volume ratio to decrease. As the cell's volume increases, the cell's metabolic requirements increase but its ability to satisfy those requirements is limited by the surface area through which the needed materials must pass. Consequently, most cells are very small.

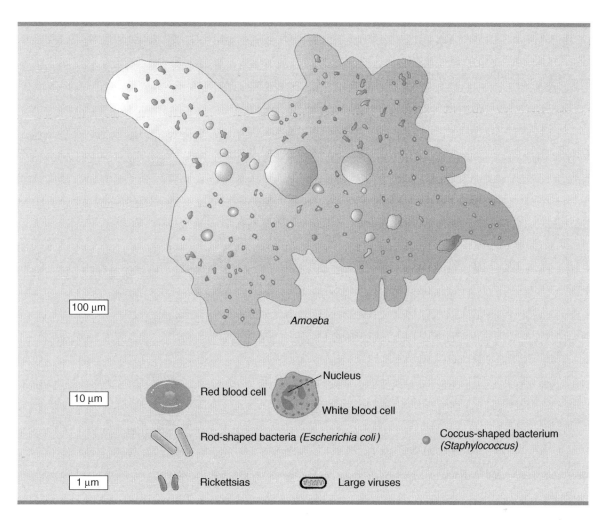

100 μm

*Amoeba*

Nucleus

10 μm — Red blood cell — White blood cell

Rod-shaped bacteria (*Escherichia coli*) — Coccus-shaped bacterium (*Staphylococcus*)

1 μm — Rickettsias — Large viruses

**FIGURE 4.4  Comparing Cell Sizes**
Most cells are too small to be seen with the naked eye. Bacteria and Archaea cells are generally about 1–2 micrometers in diameter. Eukaryotic cells are much larger and generally range between 10 and 100 micrometers. A micrometer is 1/1,000 of a millimeter. A sheet of paper is about 1/10 of a millimeter thick, which is about 100 micrometers. Therefore, some of the largest eukaryotic cells are just visible to the naked eye.

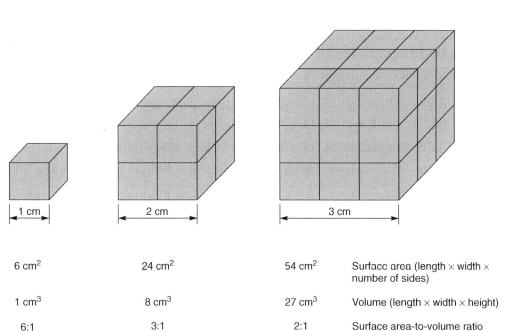

1 cm          2 cm          3 cm

| 6 cm² | 24 cm² | 54 cm² | Surface area (length × width × number of sides) |
| 1 cm³ | 8 cm³ | 27 cm³ | Volume (length × width × height) |
| 6:1 | 3:1 | 2:1 | Surface area-to-volume ratio |

**FIGURE 4.5  Surface Area-to-Volume Ratio**
As the size of an object increases, its volume increases faster than its surface area. Therefore, the surface area-to-volume ratio decreases.

There are a few exceptions to this general rule, but they are easily explained. For example, what we call the yolk of a chicken's egg cell is a single cell. However, the only part of an egg cell that is metabolically active is a small spot on its surface. The largest portion of the egg cell is simply inactive stored food called *yolk*. Similarly, some plant cells are very large but consist of a large, centrally located region filled with water. Again, the metabolically active portion of the cell is at the surface, where exchange of materials with the surroundings is possible.

---

## 4.2 CONCEPT REVIEW

3. On the basis of surface area-to-volume ratio, why do cells tend to remain small?
4. What happens to the surface-to-volume ratio when folds are made in a cell's outer membrane?

---

## 4.3 The Structure of Cellular Membranes

One feature common to all cells is the presence of **cellular membranes,** thin sheets composed primarily of phospholipids and proteins. The current model of how cellular membranes are constructed is known as the *fluid-mosaic model.* The **fluid-mosaic model,** considers cellular membranes to consist of two layers of phospholipid molecules and that the individual phospholipid molecules are able to move about within the structure of the membrane (How Science Works 4.1). Many kinds of proteins and some other molecules are found among the phospholipid molecules within the membrane and on the membrane surface. The individual molecules of the membrane remain associated with one another because of the physical interaction of its molecules with its surroundings. The phospholipid molecules of the membrane have two ends, which differ chemically. One end, which contains phosphate, is soluble in water and is therefore called **hydrophilic** (*hydro* = water; *phile* = loving). The other end of the phospholipid molecule consists of fatty acids, which are not soluble in water, and is called **hydrophobic** (*phobia* = fear).

In diagrams, phospholipid molecules are commonly represented as a balloon with two strings (figure 4.6). The balloon represents the water-soluble phosphate portion of the molecule and the two strings represent the 2 fatty acids. Consequently, when phospholipid molecules are placed in water, they form a double-layered sheet, with the water-soluble (hydrophilic) portions of the molecules facing away from each other. This is commonly referred to as a *phospholipid bilayer* (figure 4.7). If phospholipid molecules are shaken in a glass of water, the molecules automatically form

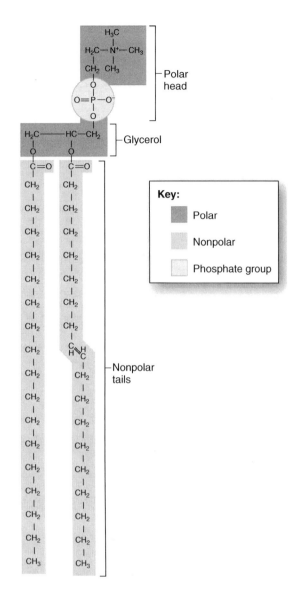

**FIGURE 4.6 A Phospholipid Molecule**
Phospholipids have a hydrophobic (water-insoluble) portion and a hydrophilic (water-soluble) portion. The hydrophilic portion contains phosphate and is represented as a balloon in many diagrams. The fatty acids are represented as two strings on the balloon.

double-layered membranes. It is important to understand that the membranes formed are not rigid but, rather, resemble a heavy olive oil in consistency. The component phospholipid molecules are in constant motion as they move with the surrounding water molecules and slide past one another. Other molecules found in cell membranes are cholesterol, proteins, and carbohydrates.

Because cholesterol is not water-soluble, it is found in the middle of the membrane, in the hydrophobic region. It appears to play a role in stabilizing the membrane and keeping it flexible. There are many different proteins associated with the membrane. Some are found on the surface, some are partially submerged in the membrane, and others traverse the

# HOW SCIENCE WORKS 4.1

## Developing the Fluid-Mosaic Model

The fluid-mosaic model describes the current understanding of how cellular membranes are organized and function. As is typical during the development of most scientific understandings, the fluid-mosaic model was formed as a result of the analysis of data from many experiments. We will look at three characteristics of cellular membranes and how certain experiments and observations about these characteristics led scientists to develop the fluid-mosaic model.

1. *What is the chemical nature of cellular membranes and how do they provide a barrier between the contents of the cell and the cell's environment?*

    In 1915, scientists isolated cellular membranes from other cellular materials and chemically determined that they consisted primarily of lipids and proteins. The scientists recognized that, because lipids do not mix with water, a layer of lipid could serve as a barrier between the watery contents of a cell and its watery surroundings.

2. *How are the molecules arranged within the membrane?*

    Nearly 10 years after it became known that cellular membranes consist of lipids and proteins, two scientists reasoned from the chemical properties of lipids and proteins that cellular membranes probably consist of two layers of lipid. This arrangement became known as a bilayer. They were able to make this deduction because they understood the chemical nature of lipids and how they behave in water. But this model did not account for the proteins, which were known to be an important part of cellular membranes because proteins were usually isolated from cellular membranes along with lipids. Also, artificial cellular membranes—made only of lipids—did not have the same chemical properties as living cellular membranes.

    The first model to incorporate proteins into the cellular membrane was incorrect. It was called the sandwich model, because it placed the lipid layers of the cellular membrane between two layers of protein, which were exposed to the cell's watery environment and cytoplasm. Although incorrect, the sandwich model was very popular into the 1960s, because it was supported by images from electron microscopes, which showed two dark lines, with a lighter area between them.

    One of the biggest problems with the sandwich model was that the kinds of proteins isolated from the cellular membrane were strongly hydrophobic. A sandwich model with the proteins on the outside required these

hydrophobic proteins to be exposed to water, which would have been an unstable arrangement.

In 1972, two scientists proposed that the hydrophobic proteins are actually made stable because they are submerged in the hydrophobic portion of the lipid bilayer. This hypothesis was supported by an experimental technique called freeze-fracture.

Freeze-fracture experiments split a frozen lipid bilayer, so that the surface between the two lipid layers could be examined by electron microscopy. These experiments showed large objects (proteins) sitting in a smooth background (phospholipids), similar to the way nuts are suspended in the chocolate of a flat chocolate bar. These experiments supported the hypothesis that the proteins are not on the surface but, rather, are incorporated into the lipid bilayer.

3. *How do these protein and lipid molecules interact with one another within the cellular membrane?*

    The answer to this question was provided by a series of hybrid-cell experiments. In these experiments, proteins in a mouse cell and proteins in a human cell were labeled differently. The two cells were fused, so that their cellular membranes were connected. At first, one-half of the new hybrid cell contained all mouse proteins. The other half of the new hybrid cell contained all human proteins. However, over several hours, the labeled proteins were seen to mix until the mouse and human proteins were evenly dispersed. Seeing this dispersion demonstrated that molecules in cellular membranes move. Cellular membranes consist of a mosaic of protein and lipid molecules, which move about in a fluid manner.

membrane and protrude from both surfaces. These proteins serve a variety of functions, including:

1. helping transport molecules across the membrane,
2. acting as attachment points for other molecules, and
3. functioning as identity tags for cells.

Carbohydrates are typically attached to the membranes on the outside of cells. They appear to play a role in cell-to-cell interactions and are involved in binding with regulatory molecules.

**Outside of cell**

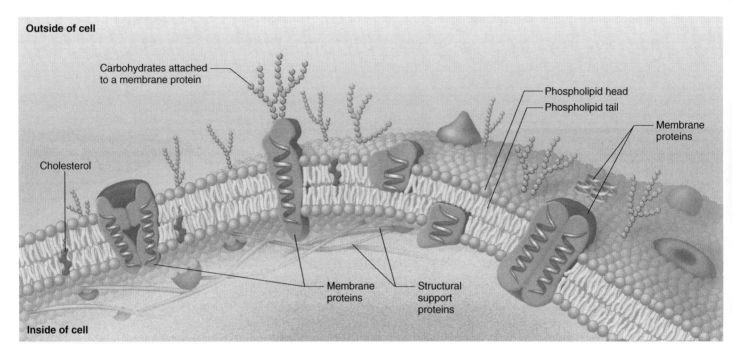

Carbohydrates attached to a membrane protein

Phospholipid head
Phospholipid tail

Membrane proteins

Cholesterol

Membrane proteins

Structural support proteins

**Inside of cell**

**FIGURE 4.7 The Nature of Cellular Membranes**
The membranes in all cells are composed primarily of protein and phospholipids. Two layers of phospholipid are oriented so that the hydrophobic fatty acid tails extend toward each other and the hydrophilic phosphate-containing heads are on the outside. Proteins are found buried within the phospholipid layer and are found on both surfaces of the membrane. Cholesterol molecules are also found among the phospholipid molecules. Carbohydrates are often attached to one surface of the membrane.

---

**4.3 CONCEPT REVIEW**

5. What are the prime molecules that make up cell membranes?
6. Describe the structure of cellular membranes based on the fluid-mosaic model.

## 4.4 Organelles Composed of Membranes

Although all cells have membranes, eukaryotic cells have many more organelles composed of membranes than do Bacteria and Archaea. Organelles are involved in specialized metabolic activities, the movement of molecules from one side of the membrane to the other, the identification of molecules, and many other activities. In the following section about the plasma membrane, many of these special properties will be discussed in detail.

### Plasma Membrane

The outer limiting boundary of all cells is known as the **plasma membrane,** or **cell membrane.** It is composed of a phospholipid bilayer and serves as a barrier between the cell contents and the external environment. However, it is not just a physical barrier. The plasma membrane has many different functions. In many ways, it acts in a manner analogous to a border between countries, separating but also allowing controlled movement from one side to the other. The plasma membrane performs several important activities.

### Metabolic Activities

Because the plasma membrane is part of a living unit, it is metabolically active. Many important chemical reactions take place within the membrane or on its inside or outside surface. Many of these chemical reactions involve transport of molecules.

### Movement of Molecules Across the Membrane

Cells must continuously receive nutrients and rid themselves of waste products—one of the characteristics of life. There is constant traffic of molecules from the external *matrix*, or environment, across the plasma membrane. The surrounding matrix is rich in many kinds of important compounds including nutrients, growth factors, and hormones. See section 4.7 for a detailed discussion of the many ways by which molecules enter and leave cells. Many of the proteins that are associated with the plasma membrane are involved in moving molecules across the membrane. Some proteins are capable of moving from one side of the plasma membrane to the other and shuttle certain molecules across the membrane. Others extend from one side of the membrane to the other and form channels through which substances can travel. Some of these channels operate like border checkpoints, which open and close when circumstances dictate. Some molecules pass through the membrane passively, whereas others are assisted by metabolic activities within the membrane.

## Inside and Outside
The inside of the plasma membrane is different from its outside. The carbohydrates that are associated with the plasma membrane are usually found on the outside of the membrane, where they are bound to proteins or lipids. Many important activities take place on only one of the surfaces of the plasma membrane because of the way the two sides differ.

## Identification
The outside surface of the plasma membrane has many proteins, which act as recognition molecules. Each organism has a unique combination of these molecules. Thus, the presence of these molecules enables one cell or one organism to recognize cells that are like it and those that are different. For example, if a disease organism enters your body, the cells of your immune system use the proteins on the invader's surface to identify it as being foreign. Immune system cells can then destroy the invader (How Science Works 4.2).

## Attachment Sites
Some molecules on the outside surface of the plasma membrane serve as attachment sites for specific chemicals, bacteria, protozoa, white blood cells, and viruses. Many dangerous agents cannot stick to the surface of cells and therefore do not cause harm. For this reason, cell biologists explore the exact structure and function of these cell surface molecules. They are also attempting to identify molecules that can interfere with the binding of viruses and bacteria to cells in the hope of controlling infections. For example, human immunodeficiency virus (HIV) attaches to specific molecules on the surface of certain immune system cells and nerve cells. If these attachment sites could be masked, the virus would not be able to attach to the cells and cause disease. Drugs that function this way are called "blockers."

## Signal Transduction
Another way in which attachment sites are important is in signal transduction. **Signal transduction** is the process by which cells detect specific signals from the surrounding intercellular matrix and transmit these signals to the cell's interior. These signals can be physical (electrical or heat) or chemical. Some chemicals are capable of passing directly through the membrane of specific target cells. Once inside, they can pass on their message to regulator proteins. These proteins then enter into chemical reactions, which result in a change in the cell's behavior. For example, estrogen produced in one part of the body travels through the bloodstream and passes through the tissue to make direct contact with specific target cells. Once the hormone passes through the plasma membrane of the target cells, the message is communicated to begin the process of female sex organ development. This is like a person smelling the cologne of his or her date through a curtain. The aroma molecules pass through the curtain to the person's nose and stimulate a response.

However, most signal molecules are not capable of entering cells in such a direct manner but remain in the external environment (i.e., outside their target cells). When they arrive at the cell, they attach to a receptor site molecule embedded in the membrane. The signal molecule is often

 ## HOW SCIENCE WORKS 4.2
## Cell Membrane Structure and Tissue Transplants

In humans, there is a group of protein molecules, collectively known as *histocompatibility antigens* (*histo* = tissue), that are located on the cell surface. Each person has a specific combination of these proteins. It is the presence of these antigens that is responsible for the rejection of transplanted tissues or organs from donors that are "incompatible." In large part, a person's pattern of histocompatibility antigens is hereditary; for instance, in identical twins, the cells of both individuals have a very high percentage of similar proteins. Therefore, in transplant situations, the cells of the immune system would see the cells of the donor twin to be the same as those on the cell surfaces of the recipient twin. When closely related donors are not available, physicians try to find donors whose histocompatibility antigens are as similar as possible to those of recipients.

called the *primary messenger.* The receptor–signal molecule combination initiates a sequence of events within the membrane that transmits information through the membrane to the interior, generating internal signal molecules, called *secondary messengers.*

The secondary messengers are molecules or ions that begin a cascade of chemical reactions causing the target cell to change how it functions (figure 4.8). This is like your mother sending your little brother to tell you it is time for dinner. Your mother provides the primary message, your little brother provides the secondary message, and you respond by going home. In a cell, such signal transduction results in a change in the cell's chemical activity. Often, this is accomplished by turning genes on or off. For example, when a signal molecule called *epidermal growth factor (EGF)* attaches to the receptor protein of skin cells, it triggers a chain of events inside the plasma membrane of the cells. These changes within the plasma membrane produce secondary messengers, ultimately leading to gene action, which in turn causes cell growth and division.

## Endoplasmic Reticulum

There are many other organelles in addition to the plasma membrane, that are composed of membranes. Each of these membranous organelles has a unique shape or structure associated with its particular functions. One of the most common organelles found in cells, the **endoplasmic reticulum (ER)**, consists of folded membranes and tubes throughout the cell (figure 4.9). This system of membranes provides a large surface on which chemical activities take place. Because the ER has an enormous surface area, many chemical reactions can be carried out in an extremely small space. Picture the vast surface area of a piece of newspaper crumpled into a tight little ball. The surface contains hundreds of thousands of tidbits of information in an orderly arrangement, yet it is packed into a very small volume.

Proteins on the surface of the ER are actively involved in controlling and encouraging chemical activities—whether they are reactions involving cell growth and development or reactions resulting in the accumulation of molecules from the environment. The arrangement of the proteins allows them to control the sequences of metabolic activities, so that chemical reactions can be carried out very rapidly and accurately.

On close examination with an electron microscope, it is apparent that there are two types of ER—rough and smooth. The rough ER appears rough because it has *ribosomes* attached to its surface. **Ribosomes** are nonmembranous organelles that are associated with the synthesis of proteins from amino acids. They are "protein-manufacturing machines." Therefore, cells with an extensive amount of rough ER—for example, human pancreas cells—are capable of synthesizing large quantities of proteins. Smooth ER lacks attached ribosomes but is the site of many other important cellular chemical activities. Fat metabolism and detoxification reactions involved in the destruction of toxic substances, such as alcohol and drugs occur on this surface. Human liver cells are responsible for detoxification reactions and contain extensive smooth ER.

In addition, the spaces between the folded membranes serve as canals for the movement of molecules within the cell. This system of membranes allows for the rapid distribution of molecules within a cell.

**(a)** Receptor and internal chemical not bound together

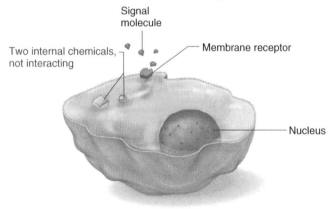

Signal molecule

Two internal chemicals, not interacting

Membrane receptor

Nucleus

**(b)** Binding of signal molecule and membrane receptor causes the two separate chemicals to bind and interact. This new internal chemical causes further internal chemical changes in the cell that then cause a change in cell shape.

Signal molecule binds to receptor; receptor changes shape

New molecule resulting from the combination of two separate chemicals

**FIGURE 4.8 Signal Transduction and Secondary Messengers**
Signal transduction results in chemical changes within the cell and is the result of cell membrane receptors binding with signal molecules from outside the cell. Secondary messengers inside the cell then communicate this information to appropriate molecules, sometimes to DNA.

Rough endoplasmic reticulum

Ribosomes

Smooth endoplasmic reticulum

**FIGURE 4.9 Endoplasmic Reticulum**
The endoplasmic reticulum consists of folded membranes located throughout the cytoplasm of the cell. Some endoplasmic reticulum has ribosomes attached and appears rough. Many kinds of molecules are manufactured on the surfaces of endoplasmic reticulum.

## Golgi Apparatus

Another organelle composed of membrane is the **Golgi apparatus.** Animal cells contain several such structures and plant cells contain hundreds. The typical Golgi apparatus consists of 5 to 20 flattened, smooth membranous sacs, which resemble a stack of flattened balloons (figure 4.10). The Golgi apparatus has several functions:

1. it modifies molecules shipped to it from elsewhere in the cell,
2. it manufactures some polysaccharides and lipids, and
3. it packages molecules within sacs.

There is a constant traffic of molecules through the Golgi apparatus. Tiny, membranous sacs called *vesicles* deliver molecules to one surface of the Golgi apparatus. Many of these vesicles are formed by the endoplasmic reticulum and contain proteins. These vesicles combine with the sacs of the Golgi apparatus and release their contents into it. Many kinds of chemical reactions take place within the Golgi apparatus. Ultimately, new sacs, containing "finished products," are produced from the surface of the Golgi apparatus.

The Golgi apparatus produces many kinds of vesicles. Each has a different function. Some are transported within the cell and combine with other membrane structures, such as the endoplasmic reticulum. Some migrate to the plasma membrane and combine with it. These vesicles release molecules such as mucus, cellulose, glycoproteins, insulin, and enzymes to the outside of the cell. In plant cells, cellulose-containing vesicles are involved in producing new cell wall material. Finally, some of the vesicles produced by the Golgi apparatus contain enzymes that can break down the various molecules of the cell, causing its destruction. These vesicles are known as *lysosomes.*

## Lysosomes

**Lysosomes** are tiny vesicles that contain enzymes capable of digesting carbohydrates, nucleic acids, proteins, and lipids. Because cells are composed of these molecules, these enzymes

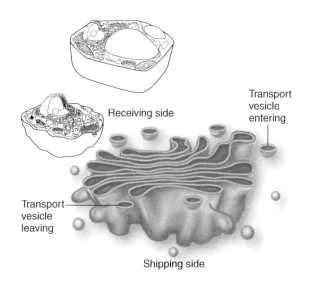

Receiving side

Transport vesicle entering

Transport vesicle leaving

Shipping side

**FIGURE 4.10 Golgi Apparatus**
The Golgi apparatus is a series of membranous sacs that accept packages of materials and produce vesicles containing specific molecules. Some packages of materials are transported to other parts of the cell. Others are transported to the plasma membrane and release their contents to the exterior of the cell.

must be controlled in order to prevent the destruction of the cell. This control is accomplished very simply. The enzymes of lysosomes function best at a pH of about 5. The membrane, which is the outer covering of the lysosome, transports hydrogen ions into the lysosome and creates the acidic conditions these enzymes need. Since the pH of a cell is generally about 7, these enzymes will not function if released into the cell cytoplasm.

The functions of lysosomes are basically digestion and destruction. For example, in many kinds of protozoa, such as *Paramecium* and *Amoeba,* food is taken into the cell in the form of a membrane-enclosed food vacuole. Lysosomes combine with food vacuoles and break down the food particles into smaller molecules, which the cell can use.

In a similar fashion, lysosomes destroy disease-causing microorganisms, such as bacteria, viruses, and fungi. The microorganisms become surrounded by membranes from the endoplasmic reticulum. Lysosomes combine with the membranes surrounding these invaders and destroy them. This kind of activity is common in white blood cells that engulf and destroy disease-causing organisms.

Lysosomes are also involved in the breakdown of worn-out cell organelles by fusing with them and destroying them (figure 4.11).

## Peroxisomes

Another organelle that consists of many kinds of enzymes surrounded by a membrane is the *peroxisome.* **Peroxisomes** were first identified by the presence of an enzyme, catalase, that breaks down hydrogen peroxide ($H_2O_2$). Peroxisomes

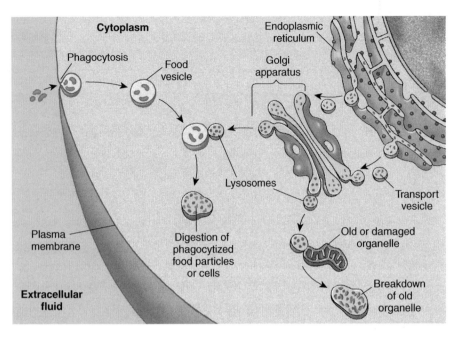

**FIGURE 4.11 Lysosome Function**
Lysosomes contain enzymes that are capable of digesting many kinds of materials. They are involved in the digestion of food vacuoles, harmful organisms, and damaged organelles.

differ from lysosomes in that peroxisomes are not formed by the Golgi apparatus and they contain different enzymes. It appears that the membrane surrounding peroxisomes is formed from the endoplasmic reticulum and the enzymes are imported into this saclike container. The enzymes of peroxisomes have been shown to be important in many kinds of chemical reactions. These include the breakdown of long-chain fatty acids, the synthesis of cholesterol, and the synthesis of plasma membrane lipids used in nerve cells.

## Vacuoles and Vesicles

There are many kinds of membrane-enclosed containers in cells known as *vacuoles* and *vesicles*. **Vacuoles** are the larger structures and **vesicles** are the smaller ones. They are frequently described by their function. In most plants, there is one huge, centrally located, water-filled vacuole. Many kinds of protozoa have specialized water vacuoles called *contractile vacuoles* which are able to forcefully expel excess water that has accumulated in the cytoplasm. The contractile vacuole is a necessary organelle in cells that live (figure 4.12) in freshwater because water constantly diffuses into the cell. Animal cells typically have many small vacuoles and vesicles throughout the cytoplasm.

## Nuclear Membrane

Just as a room is a place created by walls, a floor, and a ceiling, a cell's nucleus is a place created by the **nuclear membrane.** If the nuclear membrane were not formed around the cell's genetic material, the organelle called the cellular nucleus would not exist. This membrane separates the genetic material (DNA) from the cytoplasm. Because they are separated, the cytoplasm and the nuclear contents can maintain different chemical compositions. The nuclear membrane is composed

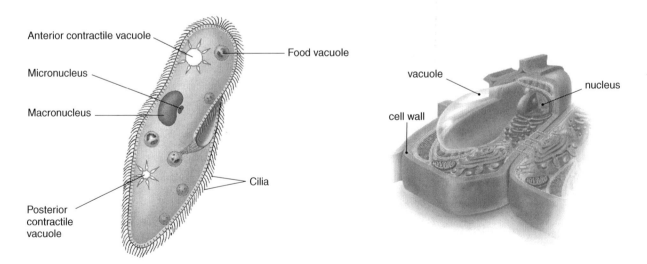

**FIGURE 4.12 Vacuoles**
Vacuoles are membrane-enclosed sacs that contain a variety of materials. Often, in many kinds of protozoa, food is found inside vacuoles. Plant cells have a large central vacuole filled with water. Some freshwater organisms have contractile vacuoles that expel water from the cell.

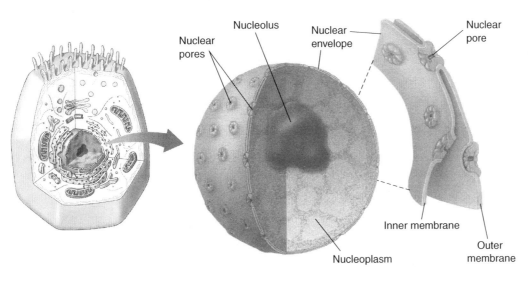

Nucleolus

Nuclear pores

Nuclear envelope

Nuclear pore

Nuclear pore

Inner membrane

Outer membrane

Nucleoplasm

**FIGURE 4.13 Nuclear Membrane**
The nuclear membrane is a double membrane separating the nuclear contents from the cytoplasm. Pores in the nuclear membrane allow molecules as large as proteins to pass through.

of two layers and has openings called *nuclear pore complexes* (figure 4.13). The nuclear pore complexes consist of proteins, which collectively form barrel-shaped pores. These pores allow relatively large molecules, such as RNA, to pass through the nuclear membrane. Thousands of molecules move in and out through these pores each second.

## The Endomembrane System—Interconversion of Membranes

It is important to remember that all membranous structures in cells are composed of two layers of phospholipid with associated proteins and other molecules. Furthermore, all of these membranous organelles can be converted from one form to another (figure 4.14). For example, the plasma membrane is continuous with the endoplasmic reticulum; as a cell becomes larger, some of the endoplasmic reticulum moves to the surface to become plasma membrane. Similarly, the nuclear membrane is connected to the endoplasmic reticulum. Remember also that the Golgi apparatus receives membrane-enclosed packages from the endoplasmic reticulum and produces lysosomes that combine with other membrane-enclosed structures and secretory vesicles that fuse with the plasma membrane. Thus, this entire set of membranes is constantly swapping pieces.

## Energy Converters—Mitochondria and Chloroplasts

Two other organelles composed of membranes are *mitochondria* and *chloroplasts*. Both types of organelles are associated with energy conversion reactions in the cell. Mitochondria and chloroplasts are different from other kinds of membranous structures in four ways. First, their membranes are chemically different from those of other membranous organelles; second, they are composed of two layers of

membrane—an inner and an outer membrane; third, both of these structures have ribosomes and DNA that are similar to those of bacteria; fourth, these two structures have a certain degree of independence from the rest of the cell—they have a limited ability to reproduce themselves but must rely on DNA from the cell nucleus for assistance. It is important to understand that cells cannot make mitochondria or chloroplasts by themselves. The DNA of the organelle is necessary for their reproduction.

### Mitochondrion

The **mitochondrion** is an organelle that contains the enzymes responsible for aerobic cellular respiration. It consists of an outer membrane and an inner folded membrane. The individual folds of the inner membrane are known as **cristae** (figure 4.15a). **Aerobic cellular respiration** is the series of enzyme-controlled reactions involved in the release of energy from food molecules and requires the participation of oxygen molecules.

$$\left(\begin{array}{l}\text{Food}\\\text{molecules}\end{array} + \text{Oxygen} \rightarrow \begin{array}{l}\text{Carbon}\\\text{dioxide}\end{array} + \text{Water} + \begin{array}{l}\text{Energy for}\\\text{cell activity}\end{array}\right)$$

Some of the enzymes responsible for these reactions are dissolved in the fluid inside the mitochondrion and are made using DNA in the mitochondria (mDNA). Others are incorporated into the structure of the membranes and are arranged in an orderly sequence.

The number of mitochondria per cell varies from less than 10 to over 1,000 depending on the kind of cell. Cells involved in activities that require large amounts of energy, such as muscle cells, contain the most mitochondria. When cells are functioning aerobically, the mitochondria swell with activity. When this activity diminishes, though, they shrink and appear as threadlike structures. The details of the reactions involved in aerobic cellular respiration and their relationship to the structure of mitochondria will be discussed in chapter 6.

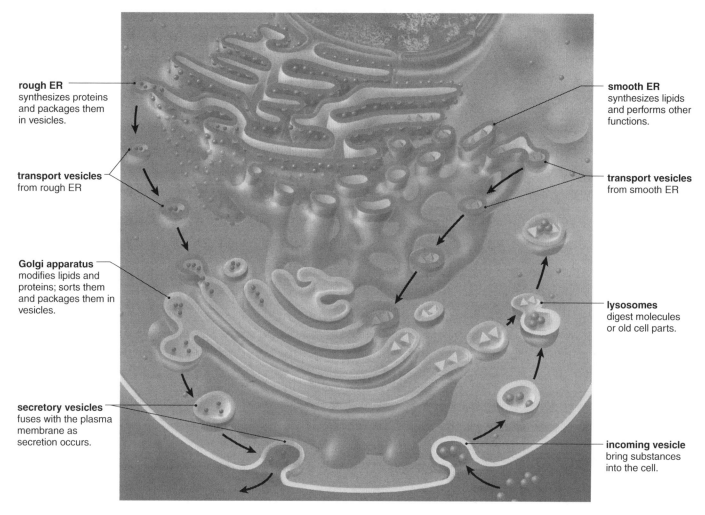

**rough ER**
synthesizes proteins
and packages them
in vesicles.

**transport vesicles**
from rough ER

**Golgi apparatus**
modifies lipids and
proteins; sorts them
and packages them in
vesicles.

**secretory vesicles**
fuses with the plasma
membrane as
secretion occurs.

**smooth ER**
synthesizes lipids
and performs other
functions.

**transport vesicles**
from smooth ER

**lysosomes**
digest molecules
or old cell parts.

**incoming vesicle**
bring substances
into the cell.

## FIGURE 4.14 The Endomembrane System

Eukaryotic cells contain a variety of organelles composed of membranes that consist of two layers of phospholipids and associated proteins. Each organelle has a unique shape and function. Many of these organelles are interconverted from one to another as they perform their essential functions.

## Chloroplast

The **chloroplast** is a membranous saclike organelle responsible for the process of photosynthesis. Chloroplasts contain the green pigment, **chlorophyll,** and are found in cells of plants and other eukaryotic organisms that carry out photosynthesis. The cells of some organisms contain one large chloroplast; others contain hundreds of smaller chloroplasts. **Photosynthesis** is a metabolic process in which light energy is converted to chemical bond energy. Chemical-bond energy is found in food molecules.

$$\left(\begin{array}{l}\text{Carbon}\\\text{dioxide}\end{array} + \text{Water} + \begin{array}{l}\text{Light}\\\text{energy}\end{array} \rightarrow \begin{array}{l}\text{Organic}\\\text{molecules}\end{array} + \text{Oxygen}\right)$$

A study of the ultrastructure—that is, the structures seen with an electron microscope—of a chloroplast shows that the entire organelle is enclosed by a membrane. Inside are other membranes throughout the chloroplast, forming networks and structures of folded membrane. As shown in figure 4.15b, in some areas, these membranes are stacked up or folded back on themselves. Chlorophyll molecules are attached to these membranes and are called **thylakoids.** Thylakoids that are stacked on top of one another form the **grana** of the chloroplast. The space between the grana, which has no chlorophyll, is known as the **stroma.** The details of how photosynthesis occurs and how this process is associated with the structure of the chloroplast will be discussed in chapter 7.

### 4.4 CONCEPT REVIEW

7. List the membranous organelles of a eukaryotic cell and describe the function of each.
8. Define the following terms: stroma, grana, cristae.
9. Describe the functions of the plasma membrane.

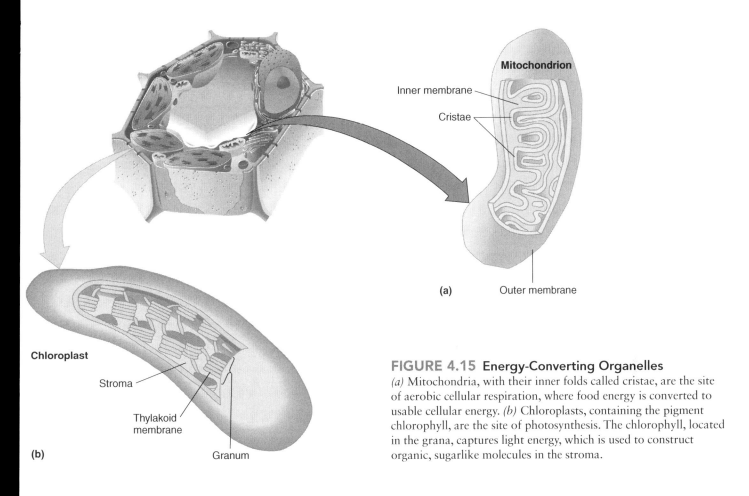

**Mitochondrion**

Inner membrane

Cristae

**(a)**  Outer membrane

**Chloroplast**

Stroma

Thylakoid membrane

**(b)**  Granum

## FIGURE 4.15 Energy-Converting Organelles

*(a)* Mitochondria, with their inner folds called cristae, are the site of aerobic cellular respiration, where food energy is converted to usable cellular energy. *(b)* Chloroplasts, containing the pigment chlorophyll, are the site of photosynthesis. The chlorophyll, located in the grana, captures light energy, which is used to construct organic, sugarlike molecules in the stroma.

## 4.5 Nonmembranous Organelles

Suspended in the cytoplasm and associated with the membranous organelles are various kinds of structures that are not composed of phospholipids and proteins arranged in sheets. These are referred to as *nonmembranous organelles*.

### Ribosomes

Ribosomes are nonmembranous organelles responsible for the synthesis of proteins from amino acids. They are composed of RNA and protein. Each ribosome is composed of two subunits—a large one and a small one (figure 4.16). Ribosomes assist in the process of joining amino acids together to form proteins. Many ribosomes are attached to the endoplasmic reticulum. Because ER that has attached ribosomes appears rough when viewed through an electron microscope it is called rough ER. Areas of rough ER are active sites of protein production. Many ribosomes are also found floating freely in the cytoplasm wherever proteins are being assembled. Cells that are actively producing protein (e.g., liver cells) have great

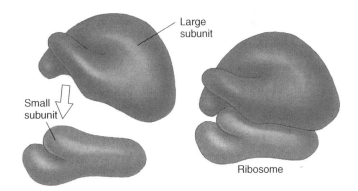

Large subunit

Small subunit

Ribosome

## FIGURE 4.16 Ribosomes

Each ribosome is constructed of two subunits. Each of the subunits is composed of protein and RNA. These globular organelles are associated with the construction of protein molecules from individual amino acids. The 2009 Nobel Prize in Chemistry was awarded to Drs. Venkatraman Ramakrishan, Thomas A. Steitz, and Ada E. Yonath for determining the structure and function of ribosomes.

numbers of free and attached ribosomes. The details of how ribosomes function in protein synthesis will be discussed in chapter 8.

## Microtubules, Microfilaments, and Intermediate Filaments

The interior of a cell is not simply filled with liquid cytoplasm. Among the many types of nonmembranous organelles found there are elongated protein structures known as **microtubules, microfilaments (actin filaments),** and **intermediate filaments.** All three types of organelles interconnect and some are attached to the inside of the plasma membrane, forming the **cytoskeleton** of the cell (figure 4.17). These cellular components provide the cell with shape, support, and the ability to move.

Think of the cytoskeleton components as the internal supports and cables required to construct a circus tent. The shape of the flexible canvas cover (i.e., the plasma membrane) is determined by the location of internal tent poles (i.e., microtubules) and the tension placed on them by attached wire or rope cables (i.e., intermediate filaments and microfilaments). Just as in the tent analogy, when one of the microfilaments or intermediate filaments is adjusted, the shape of the entire cell changes. For example, when a cell is placed on a surface to which it cannot stick, the internal tensions created by the cytoskeleton components can pull together and cause the cell to form a sphere.

During cell division, microtubules and microfilaments are involved in moving the chromosomes that contain the DNA and making other adjustments needed to make two

Intermediate filament

Microtubule

Actin filament (microfilament)

Plasma membrane

**(a)**

**(b)**

**FIGURE 4.17 The Cytoskeleton**
Microtubules, microfilaments (actin filaments), and intermediate filaments are all interconnected within the cytoplasm of the cell. *(a)* These structures, along with connections to other cellular organelles, form a cytoskeleton for the cell. The cellular skeleton is not a rigid, fixed-in-place structure but, rather, changes as the actin and intermediate filaments and microtubule component parts are assembled and disassembled. *(b)* The elements of the cytoskeleton have been labeled with a fluorescent dye to make them visible. The microtubules have fluorescent red dye, and actin filaments are green.

cells from one. Microfilaments and microtubules of the cytoskeleton also transport organelles from place to place within the cytoplasm. In addition, information can be transported through the cytoskeleton. Enzymes attached to the cytoskeleton are activated when the cell is touched. Some of these events even affect gene activity.

## Centrioles

An arrangement of two sets of microtubules at right angles to each other makes up a structure known as a **centriole**. Each set of microtubules is composed of nine groups of short microtubules arranged in a cylinder (figure 4.18). The centrioles of many cells are located in a region called the *centrosome*. The centrosome is often referred to as the microtubule organizing center and is usually located close to the nuclear membrane.

During cell division, centrioles are responsible for organizing microtubules into a complex of fibers known as the *spindle*. The individual microtubules of the spindle are called *spindle fibers*. The spindle is the structure to which chromosomes are attached, so that they can be separated properly during cell division. The functions of centrioles and spindle fibers in cell division will be referred to again in chapter 9. One curious fact about centrioles is that they are present in most animal cells but not in many types of plant cells, although plant cells do have a centrosome. Other structures, called *basal bodies*, resemble centrioles and are located at the base of cilia and flagella.

## Cilia and Flagella

Many cells have microscopic, hairlike structures known as cilia and flagella, projecting from their surfaces (figure 4.19). These structures are composed of microtubles and are

covered by plasma membrane. In general, **flagella** are long and few in number and move with an undulating whiplike motion; **cilia** are short and more numerous and move back and forth like oars on a boat. Both function to move the cell through its environment or to move the environment past the cell. Both cilia and flagella are constructed of a cylinder of nine sets of microtubules similar to those in the centriole, but they have an additional two microtubules in the center. This is often referred to as the *9 + 2 arrangement* of microtubules.

The cell can control the action of these microtubular structures, enabling them to be moved in a variety of ways. The protozoan *Paramecium* is covered with thousands of cilia, which move in a coordinated, rhythmic way to move the cell through the water. A *Paramecium* can stop when it encounters an obstacle, reverse its direction, and then move forward in a new direction. Similarly, the cilia on the cells that line the human trachea beat in such a way that they move mucus and particles trapped in the mucus from the lungs. Many single-celled algae have flagella that beat in such a way that the cells swim toward a source of light.

Some kinds of Bacteria and Archaea also have flagella. However, their structure and the way they function are quite different from those of eukaryotic cells.

## Inclusions

**Inclusions** are collections of materials that do not have as well defined a structure as the organelles we have discussed so far. They might be concentrations of stored materials, such as starch grains, sulfur, or oil droplets, or they might be a collection of miscellaneous materials known as **granules.** Unlike organelles, which are essential to the survival of a cell, inclusions are generally only temporary sites for the storage of nutrients and wastes.

Some inclusion materials are harmful to other cells. For example, cells of the rhubarb plant contain an inclusion composed of oxalic acid, an organic acid. If you eat rhubarb leaves, the oxalic acid dissolves and later recrystalizes in the kidneys, contributing to kidney stones. The crystals might also cause harm to the glomeruli in the kidneys. Eating the stalks is unlikely to cause these problems since the concentration of oxalic acid is less in the stalks than in the leaves. Similarly, certain bacteria store, in their inclusions, crystals of a substance known to be harmful to insects. Spraying plants with these bacteria is a biological method of controlling the insect pest population while not interfering with the plant or with humans.

In the past, cell structures such as ribosomes, mitochondria, and chloroplasts were also called *granules* because their structure and function were not clearly known. As scientists learn more about inclusions and other unidentified particles in the cells, they, too, will be named and more fully described.

Microtubule triplet

**FIGURE 4.18  The Centriole**
These two sets of short microtubules are located just outside the nuclear membrane in many types of cells.

**FIGURE 4.19 Cilia and Flagella**

Cilia and flagella have the same structure and function. They are composed of groups of microtubules in a 9 + 2 arrangement, are surrounded by plasma membrane, and function like oars or propellers that move the cell through its environment or move the environment past the cell. Flagella are less numerous and longer than cilia.

Outer microtubule pair

Plasma membrane

Central microtubule pair

Microtubules

Flagellum

Cilium

Cilia on surface

**4.5 CONCEPT REVIEW**

10. List the nonmembranous organelles of the cell and describe their functions.

## 4.6 Nuclear Components

As stated at the beginning of this chapter, one of the first structures to be identified in eukaryotic cells was the nucleus. If the nucleus is removed from a eukaryotic cell or the cell loses its nucleus, the cell can live only a short time. For example, human red blood cells begin life in bone marrow, where they have nuclei. Before they are released into the bloodstream to carry oxygen and carbon dioxide, they lose their nuclei. As a consequence, red blood cells are able to function only for about 120 days before they disintegrate.

When nuclei were first identified, it was noted that certain dyes stained some parts of the nuclear contents more than others. The parts that stained more heavily were called **chromatin,** which means colored material. Today, we know that chromatin is composed of long molecules of DNA, along with proteins. Most of the time, the chromatin is arranged as a long, tangled mass of threads in the nucleus. However, during cell division, the chromatin becomes tightly coiled into short, dense structures called **chromosomes** (*chromo* = color; *some* = body). Chromatin and

## FIGURE 4.20 **The Nucleus**

The nucleus is bounded by two layers of membrane which separate it from the cytoplasm. The nucleus contains DNA and associated proteins in the form of chromatin material or chromosomes, nucleoli, and the nucleoplasm. Chromosomes are tightly coiled chromatin.

chromosomes are really the same molecules, but they differ in structural arrangement.

In addition to chromosomes, the nucleus may also contain one, two, or several *nucleoli*. A **nucleolus** is the site of ribosome manufacture. Specific parts of the DNA become organized within the nucleus to produce ribosomes. A nucleolus is composed of this DNA, specific granules, and partially completed ribosomes.

The final component of the nucleus is its liquid matrix, called the **nucleoplasm.** It is a mixture composed of water, nucleic acids, the molecules used in the construction of ribosomes, and other nuclear material (figure 4.20).

### 4.6  CONCEPT REVIEW

11. Define the following terms: chromosome, chromatin.
12. What is a nucleolus?
13. What other type of molecules are attached to DNA in chromosomes?

### 4.7  Exchange Through Membranes

If a cell is to stay alive, it must be able to exchange materials with its surroundings. Because all cells are surrounded by a plasma membrane, the nature of the membrane influences what materials can pass through it. There are six ways in which materials enter and leave cells: diffusion, osmosis, facilitated diffusion, active transport, endocytosis, and exocytosis. The same mechanisms are involved in the movement of materials across the membranes of the various cellular organelles such as golgi, mitochondria, and chloroplasts.

### Diffusion

A basic principle of physics states that all molecules are in a constant state of motion. Although in solids molecules tend to vibrate in place, in liquids and gases they are able to move past one another. Because the motion of molecules is random, there is a natural tendency in gases and liquids for molecules of different types to mix completely with each other.

Consider a bottle of perfume or cologne. When you open the bottle, the perfume molecules and air molecules begin to mix and you smell the perfume. Perfume molecules leave the bottle and enter the bottle. Molecules from the air enter and leave the bottle. However, more perfume molecules leave the bottle than enter it. This overall movement is termed **net movement,** the movement in one direction minus the movement in the opposite direction. The direction in which the greatest number of molecules of a particular kind moves (net movement) is determined by the difference in concentration of the molecules in different places. **Diffusion** is the net movement of a kind of molecule from a place where that molecule is in higher concentration to a place where that molecule is less concentrated. The difference in concentration of the molecules over a distance is known as a **concentration gradient** or **diffusion gradient** (figure 4.21). When no concentration gradient exists, the movement of molecules is equal in all directions, and the system has reached a state of **dynamic equilibrium**. There is an equilibrium because there is no longer a net movement (diffusion), because the movement in one direction equals the movement in the other. It is dynamic, however, because the system still has energy, and the molecules are still moving.

The rate at which diffusion takes place is determined by several factors. Diffusion occurs faster if the molecules are small, if they are moving rapidly, and if there is a large concentration gradient.

### Diffusion in Cells

Diffusion is an important means by which materials are exchanged between a cell and its environment. For example, cells constantly use oxygen in various chemical reactions. Consequently, the oxygen concentration in cells always remains low. The cells, then, contain a lower concentration

Low concentration

High concentration

**FIGURE 4.21 Concentration Gradient**
The difference in concentrations of molecules over a distance is called a concentration gradient. When the top of this perfume bottle is removed, a concentration gradient is formed. The highest concentration is inside, decreasing as you measure farther away from the bottle.

of oxygen than does the environment outside the cells. This creates a concentration gradient, and the oxygen molecules always diffuse from the outside of the cell to the inside.

Diffusion can take place as long as there are no barriers to the free movement of molecules. In the case of a cell, the plasma membrane surrounds the cell and serves as a partial barrier to the movement of molecules through it. Because the plasma membrane allows only certain molecules to pass through it, it is **selectively permeable.** A molecule's ability to pass through the membrane depends on its size, electrical charge, and solubility in the phospholipid membrane. In general, the membrane allows small molecules, such as oxygen or water, to pass through but prevents the passage of larger molecules. The membrane also regulates the passage of ions. If a particular portion of the membrane has a large number of positive ions on its surface, positively charged ions in the environment will be repelled and prevented from crossing. Molecules that are able to dissolve in phospholipids, such as vitamins A and D, can pass through the membrane rather easily; however, many molecules cannot pass through at all.

The cell has no control over the rate or direction of diffusion. The direction of diffusion is determined by the relative concentration of specific molecules on the two sides of the membrane. Diffusion is a passive process that does not require any energy expenditure on the part of the cell. The energy that causes diffusion to occur is supplied by the kinetic energy of the molecules themselves.

### Diffusion in Large Organisms

In large animals, many cells are buried deep within the body. If it were not for the animals' circulatory systems, cells would have little opportunity to exchange gases or other molecules directly with their surroundings. Oxygen can diffuse into blood through the membranes of the lungs, gills, or other moist surfaces of an animal's body. The circulatory system then transports the oxygen-rich blood throughout the body, and the oxygen automatically diffuses into cells. This occurs because the concentration of oxygen inside cells is lower than that of the blood. The opposite is true of carbon dioxide. Animal cells constantly produce carbon dioxide as a waste product, so there is always a high concentration of it within the cells. These molecules diffuse from the cells into the blood, where the concentration of carbon dioxide is kept constantly low, because the blood is pumped to the moist surfaces (e.g., gills, lungs) and the carbon dioxide again diffuses into the surrounding environment. In a similar manner, many other types of molecules constantly enter and leave cells.

The health of persons who have difficulty getting enough oxygen to their cells can be improved by increasing the concentration gradient. Oxygen makes up about 20 percent of the air. If this concentration is artificially raised by supplying a special source of oxygen, diffusion from the lungs to the blood will take place more rapidly.

## Osmosis

Water molecules easily diffuse through cell membranes. **Osmosis** is the net movement (diffusion) of water molecules through a selectively permeable membrane. Although osmosis is important in living things, it will take place in any situation in which there is a selectively permeable membrane and a difference in water concentration in the solutions on opposite sides of the membrane. For example, consider a solution of 90% water and 10% sugar separated by a selectively permeable membrane from a sugar solution of 60% water and 40% sugar (figure 4.23). The membrane allows water molecules to pass freely but prevents the larger sugar molecules from crossing. There is a higher concentration of water molecules in one solution, compared with the concentration of water molecules in the other. Therefore, more of the water molecules move from the solution with 90% water to the other solution, with 60% water. Be sure that you recognize (1) that osmosis is really diffusion in which the diffusing substance is water and (2) that the regions of different concentrations are separated by a membrane that is more permeable to water than the substance dissolved in the water.

**FIGURE 4.22  Diffusion**
As a result of molecular motion, molecules move from areas where they are concentrated to areas where they are less concentrated. The machine in the photo is called a *hyperbaric* (*hyper* = above; *baric* = pressure) *chamber*. It is used to treat people who have certain kinds of infections (e.g., gangrene) or other conditions in which high concentrations of oxygen are beneficial. The concentration of the oxygen in the chamber is higher than in the atmospheric pressure, encouraging diffusion, and the gas pressure in the chamber is higher than atmospheric pressure. Both contribute to getting oxygen into the gangrenous tissue.

It is important to understand that, when one adds something to a water solution, the percentage of the water in the solution declines. For example, pure water is 100% water. If you add salt to the water, the solution contains both water and salt and the percentage of water is less than 100%. Thus, the more material you add to the solution, the lower the percentage of water.

### Osmosis in Cells

A proper amount of water is required if a cell is to function efficiently. Too much water in a cell may dilute the cell contents and interfere with the chemical reactions necessary to keep the cell alive. Too little water in the cell may result in a buildup of poisonous waste products. As with the diffusion of other molecules, osmosis is a passive process, because the cell has no control over the diffusion of water molecules. This means that the cell can remain in balance with an environment only if that environment does not cause the cell to lose or gain too much water.

If cells contain a concentration of water and dissolved materials equal to that of their surroundings, the cells are said to be **isotonic** to their surroundings. For example, the ocean contains many kinds of dissolved salts. Organisms such as sponges, jellyfishes, and protozoa are isotonic to the ocean, because the amount of material dissolved in their cellular water is equal to the amount of salt dissolved in the ocean's water.

If an organism is to survive in an environment that has a different concentration of water than does its cells, it must expend energy to maintain this difference. Organisms that live in freshwater have a lower concentration of water (a higher concentration of dissolved materials) than their surrounding and tend to gain water by osmosis very rapidly. They are said to be **hypertonic** to their surroundings, and the

| 60% water 40% sugar | Selectively permeable membrane | 90% water 10% sugar |

Direction of net movement of water molecules

**FIGURE 4.23  Osmosis**
When two solutions with different percentages of water are separated by a selectively permeable membrane, there will be a net movement of water from the solution with the highest percentage of water to the one with the lowest percentage of water.

surroundings are **hypotonic,** compared with the cells. These two terms are always used to compare two different solutions. The hypertonic solution is the one with more dissolved material and less water; the hypotonic solution has less dissolved material and more water.

The concept of osmosis is important in medical situations. Often, people are given materials by intravenous injections. However, the solutions added must have the right balance between water and dissolved substances, or red blood cells may be injured (figure 4.24). Similarly, during surgery organs are bathed in a solution that is isotonic to the cells of the body.

## Regulating Water Balance

If an organism is to survive in an environment that has a different concentration of water than does its cells, it must expend energy to maintain this difference.

Organisms whose cells gain water by osmosis must expend energy to eliminate any excess if they are to keep from swelling and bursting. Many kinds of freshwater protozoa have special organelles called contractile vacuoles that fill with water and periodically empty, forcing the water from the cell. The kidneys of freshwater fish are designed to get rid of the water they constantly receive as a result of osmosis from

their surroundings. Similarly, organisms that are hypotonic to their surroundings (have a higher concentration of water than their surroundings) must drink water or their cells will shrink. Most ocean fish are in this situation. They lose water by osmosis to their salty surroundings and must drink seawater to keep their cells from shrinking. Because they are taking in additional salt with the seawater they drink, they must expend energy to excrete this excess salt.

Since terrestrial animals like us are not bathed in a watery solution, we do not gain and lose water through our surfaces by osmosis. However, we do lose water due to evaporation. Thus, we must drink water to replace that lost. Our desire to drink is directly related to the osmotic condition of the cells in our body. If we are dehydrated, we develop a thirst and drink some water. This is controlled by cells in the brain. Under normal conditions, when we drink small amounts of water, the cells of the brain swell a little, and signals are sent to the kidneys to rid the body of excess water. By contrast, persons who are dehydrated, such as marathon runners, may drink large quantities of water in a very short time following a race. This rapid addition of water to the body may cause abnormal swelling of brain cells, because the excess water cannot be gotten rid of rapidly enough. If this happens, the person may lose consciousness or even die because the brain cells have swollen too much.

## Water Balance in Plant Cells

Plant cells also experience osmosis. If the water concentration outside the plant cell is higher than the water concentration inside, more water molecules enter the cell than leave. This creates internal pressure within the cell. But plant cells do not burst, because they are surrounded by a strong cell wall. Lettuce cells that are crisp are ones that have gained water so that there is high internal pressure. Wilted lettuce has lost some of its water to its surroundings, so that it has only slight internal pressure. Osmosis occurs when you put salad dressing on a salad. Because the dressing has a very low water concentration, water from the lettuce diffuses from the cells into the surroundings. Salad that has been "dressed" too long becomes limp and unappetizing (table 4.1).

## Controlled Methods of Transporting Molecules

So far, we have considered only situations in which cells have no control over the movement of molecules. Cells cannot rely solely on diffusion and osmosis, however, because many of the molecules they require either cannot pass through the plasma membrane or occur in relatively low concentrations in the cell's surroundings.

### Facilitated Diffusion

Some molecules move across the membrane by interacting with specific membrane proteins. When the rate of diffusion of a substance is increased in the presence of such a protein, it is called **facilitated diffusion.** Because this movement is still diffusion, the net direction of movement is

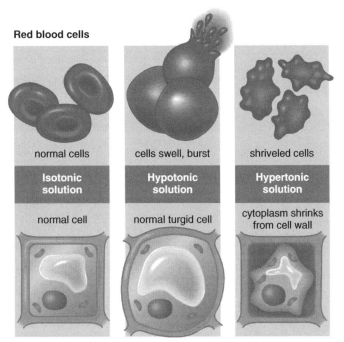

**Red blood cells**

normal cells | cells swell, burst | shriveled cells

**Isotonic solution** | **Hypotonic solution** | **Hypertonic solution**

normal cell | normal turgid cell | cytoplasm shrinks from cell wall

**Plant cells**

## FIGURE 4.24 Osmotic Influences on Cells

Cells are affected by the amount of dissolved materials in the water that surrounds them. When in an isotonic situation the cells neither gain nor lose water. In a hypotonic solution water diffuses from the surroundings into the cell. Animal cells will swell and burst but plant cells have a tough cell wall surrounding the cell contents and the pressure generated on the inside of the cell causes it to become rigid. Both plant and animal cells shrink when in a hypertonic solution because water moves from the cells which have the higher water concentration to the surroundings.

**TABLE 4.1**   Effects of Osmosis on Various Cell Types

| Cell Type | What Happens When Cell Is Placed in Hypotonic Solution | What Happens When Cell Is Placed in Hypertonic Solution |
|---|---|---|
| With cell wall (e.g., bacteria, fungi, plants) | Water enters the cell, causing it to swell and generate pressure. However, the cell does not burst because the presence of an inelastic cell wall on the outside of the plasma (cell) membrane prevents the membrane from stretching and rupturing. | Water leaves the cell and the cell shrinks. The plasma membrane pulls away from inside the cell wall; the cell contents form a small mass. |
| Without cell wall (e.g., human red blood cells) | Water enters the cell and it swells, causing the plasma membrane to stretch and rupture. | Water leaves the cell and it shrinks into a compact mass. |

from high to low concentration. The action of the carrier does not require an input of energy other than the molecules' kinetic energy. Therefore, this is considered a *passive transport* method, although it can occur only in living organisms with the necessary proteins. There are two groups of membrane proteins involved in facilitated diffusion: (1) *carrier proteins* and (2) *ion channels*. When a carrier protein attaches to the molecule to be moved across the membrane, the combination molecule changes shape. This shape change enables the molecule to be shifted from one side of the membrane to the other. The carrier then releases the molecule and returns to its original shape (figure 4.25a). Ion channels do not really attach to the molecule being transported through the membrane, but operate like gates. The opening and closing of a channel is controlled by changes in electrical charge at the pore, or "gate-keeping" signal molecules (figure 4.25b).

## Active Transport

When molecules are moved across the membrane from an area of *low* concentration to an area of *high* concentration, the cell must expend energy. This is the opposite direction molecules move in osmosis and diffusion. The process of using a carrier protein to move molecules up a concentration gradient is called **active transport** (figure 4.26). Active transport is very specific: Only certain molecules or ions can be moved in this way, and they must be carried by specific proteins in the membrane. The action of the carrier requires an input of energy other than the molecules' kinetic energy; therefore, this process is termed *active* transport. For example, some ions, such as sodium and potassium, are actively pumped across plasma membranes. Sodium ions are pumped *out* of cells up a concentration gradient. Potassium ions are pumped *into* cells up a concentration gradient.

## Endocytosis and Exocytosis

Larger particles or collections of materials can be transported across the plasma membrane by being wrapped in membrane, rather than passing through the membrane molecule by molecule. When materials enter a cell in this manner, it is called **endocytosis.** When materials are transported out of cells in membrane-wrapped packages, it is known as **exocytosis** (figure 4.27). Endocytosis can be divided into three sorts of

activities: phagocytosis, pinocytosis, and receptor mediated endocytosis.

**Phagocytosis** is the process of engulfing large particles, such as cells. For example, protozoa engulf food and white blood cells engulf bacteria by wrapping them with membrane and taking them into the cell. Because of this, white blood cells often are called *phagocytes.* When phagocytosis occurs, the material to be engulfed touches the surface of the cell and causes a portion of the outer plasma membrane to be indented. The indented plasma membrane is pinched off inside the cell to form a sac containing the engulfed material. Recall that this sac, composed of a single membrane, is called a vacuole. Once inside the cell, the membrane of the vacuole fuses with the membrane of lysosomes, and the enzymes of the lysosomes break down the contents of the vacuole.

**Pinocytosis** is the process of engulfing liquids and the materials dissolved in the liquids. In this form of endocytosis, the sacs that are formed are very small, compared with those formed during phagocytosis. Because of their small size they are called vesicles. In fact, an electron microscope is needed to see vesicles.

**Receptor mediated endocytosis** is the process in which molecules from the cell's surroundings bind to receptor molecules on the plasma membrane. The membrane then folds in and engulfs these molecules. Because receptor molecules are involved, the cell can gather specific necessary molecules from its surroundings and take the molecules into the cell.

Exocytosis occurs in the same manner as endocytosis. Membranous sacs containing materials from the cell migrate to the plasma membrane and fuse with it. This results in the sac contents' being released from the cell. Many materials, such as mucus, digestive enzymes, and molecules produced by nerve cells, are released in this manner.

## 4.7   CONCEPT REVIEW

14. Describe what happens during the process of endocytosis.
15. How do diffusion, facilitated diffusion, osmosis, and active transport differ?
16. What will happen if an animal is placed in a hypertonic solution?

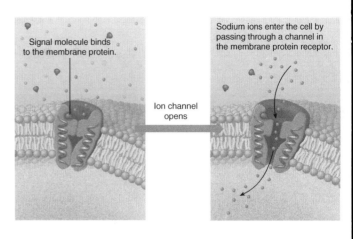

(b)

(a)

## FIGURE 4.25  Mechanisms for Facilitated Diffusion

*(a)* The molecules being moved through the membrane attach to a specific transport carrier protein in the membrane. This causes a change in the shape of the protein, which propels the molecule or ion from inside to outside or from outside to inside. *(b)* Ion channels can be opened or closed to allow these sodium ions to be transported to the other side of the membrane. When the signal molecule binds to the ion channel protein, the gate is opened.

**Outside of a cell**

Fluid has a high concentration of Na⁺

**Inside of a cell**

Cytoplasm has a high concentration of K⁺

**1** Three Na⁺ bind to the cytoplasmic side of the protein.

**2** Phosphate is transferred from ATP to the protein.

**3** Phosphorylation changes the shape of the protein, moving Na⁺ across the membrane.

**4** K⁺ binds to the protein, causing phosphate release.

**5** Release of phosphate changes the shape of the protein, moving K⁺ to the cytoplasm.

**Key:**

• Sodium ion

◆ Potassium ion

## FIGURE 4.26  Active Transport

The action of the carrier protein requires an input of energy (the compound ATP) other than the kinetic energy of the molecules; therefore, this process is termed *active* transport. Active transport mechanisms can transport molecules or ions up a concentration gradient from a low concentration to a higher concentration.

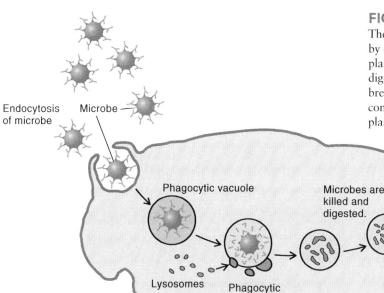

Endocytosis of microbe

Microbe

Phagocytic vacuole

Microbes are killed and digested.

Exocytosis of debris

Lysosomes

Phagocytic vacuole fuses with lysosomes.

**FIGURE 4.27 Endocytosis and Exocytosis**
The sequence illustrates a white blood cell engulfing a microbe by endocytosis. The bacterium is surrounded by a portion of the plasma membrane. Once inside the cell, lysosomes add their digestive enzymes to the phagocytic vacuole, which speeds the breakdown of the contents of the vacuole. Finally, the vacuole containing the digested material moves to the inner surface of the plasma membrane, where the contents are discharged by exocytosis.

## 4.8    Prokaryotic and Eukaryotic Cells Revisited

Now that you have an idea of how cells are constructed, we can look at the great diversity of the kinds of cells that exist. You already know that there are significant differences between prokaryotic and eukaryotic cells.

Because prokaryotic (noneukaryotic) and eukaryotic cells are so different and prokaryotic cells show up in the fossil records much earlier, the differences between the two kinds of cells are used to classify organisms. Thus, biologists have classified organisms into three large categories, called **domains**. The following diagram illustrates how living things are classified:

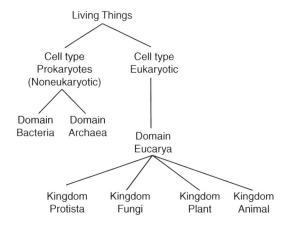

The Domain Bacteria contains most of the microorganisms and can be found in a wide variety of environments. The Domain Archaea contains many kinds of microorganisms that

have significant biochemical differences from the Bacteria. Many of the Archaea have special metabolic abilities and live in extreme environments of high temperature or extreme saltiness. Although only a few thousand Bacteria and only about 200 Archaea have been described, recent DNA studies of seawater and soil suggest that there are millions of undescribed species. In all likelihood, these noneukaryotic organisms far outnumber all the species of eukaryotic organisms combined. All other living things are comprised of eukaryotic cells.

### Prokaryotic Cell Structure

Prokaryotic cells, the Bacteria and Archaea, do not have a typical nucleus bound by a nuclear membrane, nor do they contain mitochondria, chloroplasts, Golgi, or extensive networks of endoplasmic reticula. However, prokaryotic cells contain DNA and enzymes and are able to reproduce and engage in metabolism. They perform all of the basic functions of living things with fewer and simpler organelles. Although some Eubacteria have a type of green photosynthetic pigment and carry on photosynthesis, they do so without chloroplasts and use somewhat different chemical reactions.

Most Bacteria are surrounded by a *capsule*, or slime layer, which is composed of a variety of compounds. In certain bacteria, this layer is responsible for their ability to stick to surfaces, forming *biofilms* (e.g., the film of bacteria on teeth), and to resist phagocytosis. Many bacteria also have fimbriae, hairlike protein structures, which help the cell stick to objects. Those with flagella are capable of propelling themselves through the environment. Below the capsule is the rigid cell wall, comprised of a unique protein/carbohydrate complex called peptidoglycan. This gives the cell the strength to resist osmotic pressure changes and gives it shape. Just beneath the wall is the plasma membrane. Thinner and with a slightly different chemical composition from that of eukaryotes, the plasma membrane carries out the same functions as the plasma membrane in eukaryotes. Most bacteria are either rod-shaped (bacilli), spherical (cocci), corkscrew-shaped (spirilla), or comma-shaped (vibrio). The genetic material within the cytoplasm is DNA in the form of a loop.

The Archaea share many characteristics with the Bacteria. Many have a rod or spherical shape, although some are square or triangular. Some have flagella and have cell walls, but the cell walls are made of a different material than that of bacteria.

One significant difference between the cells of Bacteria and Archaea is in the chemical makeup of their ribosomes. The ribosomes of Bacteria contain different proteins from those found in the cells of Eucarya or Archaea. Bacterial ribosomes are also smaller. This discovery was important to medicine, because many cellular forms of life that cause common diseases are bacterial. As soon as differences in the ribosomes were noted, researchers began to look for ways in which to interfere with the bacterial ribosome's function, but *not* interfere with the ribosomes of eukaryotic cells. **Antibiotics,** such as streptomycin, are the result of this research. This drug combines with bacterial ribosomes and causes bacteria to die because it prevents production of the proteins essential to survival of bacteria. Because eukaryotic ribosomes differ from bacterial ribosomes, streptomycin does not interfere with the normal function of the ribosomes in human cells.

## Eukaryotic Cell Structure

Eukaryotic cells contain a true nucleus and most of the membranous organelles described earlier. Eukaryotic organisms can be further divided into several categories, based on the specific combination of organelles they contain. The cells of plants, fungi, protozoa and algae, and animals are all eukaryotic. The most obvious characteristic that sets plants and algae apart from other organisms is their green color, which indicates that the cells contain chlorophyll in chloroplasts. Chlorophyll is necessary for photosynthesis—the conversion of light energy into chemical-bond energy in food molecules. Another distinguishing characteristic of plant and algal cells is that their cell walls are made of cellulose (table 4.2).

The fungi are a distinct group of organisms that lack chloroplasts but have a cell wall. However, the cell wall is made from a polysaccharide, called chitin, rather than cellulose. Organisms that belong in this category of eukaryotic cells include yeasts, molds, mushrooms, and the fungi that cause such human diseases as athlete's foot, jungle rot, and ringworm.

Eukaryotic organisms that lack cell walls and chloroplasts are placed in separate groups. Organisms that consist of only one cell are called protozoans—examples are *Amoeba* and *Paramecium*. They have all the cellular organelles described in this chapter except the chloroplast; therefore, protozoans must consume food as do fungi and multicellular animals.

## The Cell—The Basic Unit of Life

Although the differences in these groups of organisms may seem to set them worlds apart, their similarity in cellular structure is one of the central themes unifying the field of biology. One can obtain a better understanding of how cells operate in general by studying specific examples. Because the organelles have the same general structure and function, regardless of the kind of cell in which they are found, we can learn more about how mitochondria function in plants by studying how mitochondria function in animals. There is a commonality among all living things with regard to their cellular structure and function. The fact that all eukaryotic organisms have the same cellular structures is strong evidence that they all evolved from a common ancestor.

## 4.8 CONCEPT REVIEW

17. List five differences in structure between prokaryotic and eukaryotic cells.
18. What two types of organisms have prokaryotic cell structure?

## Summary

The concept of the cell has developed over a number of years. Initially, only two regions, the cytoplasm and the nucleus, could be identified. At present, numerous organelles are recognized as essential components of both noneukaryotic and eukaryotic cell types. The structure and function of some of these organelles are compared in table 4.3. This table also indicates whether the organelle is unique to noneukaryotic or eukaryotic cells or is found in both.

The cell is the common unit of life. Individual cells and their structures are studied to discover how they function as individual living organisms and as parts of many-celled beings. Knowing how prokaryotic and eukaryotic organisms resemble each other and differ from each other helps physicians control some organisms dangerous to humans.

There are several ways in which materials enter or leave cells. These include diffusion and osmosis, which involve the net movement of molecules from an area of high to low concentration. In addition, there are several processes that involve activities on the part of the cell to move things across the membrane. These include facilitated diffusion, which uses carrier molecules to diffuse across the membrane; active transport, which uses energy from the cell to move materials from low to high concentration; and endocytosis and exocytosis, in which membrane-enclosed packets are formed.

## TABLE 4.2 Comparison of Various Kinds of Cells

### Prokaryotic Cells

Cells are smaller than eukaryotic cells.

### Eukaryotic Cells

Cells are generally much larger than noneukaryotic cells.

DNA is found within a nucleus, which is separated from the cytoplasm by a membrane.

Cells contain many complex organelles.

DNA is not separated from the cytoplasm by a membrane.

Cells have few membranous organelles.

|  | Domain Archaea | Domain Eucarya | | | |
|---|---|---|---|---|---|
| **Domain Bacteria** | | | | | |
| Kingdoms not specified | Kingdoms Euryarchaeota, Korarchaeota, Krenarchaeota | Kingdom Protista | Kingdom Fungi | Kingdom Plantae | Kingdom Animalia |
| 1. Single-celled organisms | 1. Single-celled organisms | 1. Single-celled organisms commonly called algae and protozoa | 1. Multicellular organisms | 1. Multicellular organisms | 1. Multicellular organisms |
| 2. Some cause disease. | 2. They typically generate their own food. | 2. Some form colonies of cells. | 2. Cell wall contains chitin. | 2. Cell wall contains cellulose. | 2. They do not have a cell wall. |
| 3. Most are ecologically important. | 3. Most live in extreme environments. | 3. Some have cell walls and chloroplasts. | 3. None have chloroplasts. | 3. Chloroplasts are present. | 3. They lack chloroplasts. |
| 4. Cyanobacteria are able to perform a kind of photosynthesis. | | | 4. Many kinds of decay organisms and parasites are fungi. | | |
| | | | | | |
| Examples: *Streptococcus pneumoniae* and *Escherichia coli* | Examples: *Methanococcus* and *Thermococcus* | Examples: *Amoeba* and *Spirogyra* | Examples: yeast, molds, and mushrooms | Examples: moss, ferns, cone-bearing trees, and flowering plants | Examples: worms, insects, starfish, frogs, reptiles, birds, and mammals |

Note: Viruses are not included in this classification system, because viruses are not composed of the basic cellular structural components. They are composed of a core of nucleic acid (DNA or RNA, never both) and a surrounding coat, or capsid, composed of protein. For this reason, viruses are called acellular or noncellular.

**TABLE 4.3    Summary of the Structure and Function of the Cellular Organelles**

| Organelle | Type of Cell in Which Located | Structure | Function |
|---|---|---|---|
| Plasma membrane | Prokaryotic and eukaryotic | Membranous; typical membrane structure; phospholipid and protein present | Controls passage of some materials to and from the environment of the cell |
| Inclusions (granules) | Prokaryotic and eukaryotic | Nonmembranous; variable | May have a variety of functions |
| Chromatin material | Prokaryotic and eukaryotic | Nonmembranous; composed of DNA and proteins | Contains the hereditary information the cell uses in its day-to-day life and passes it on to the next generation of cells |
| Ribosomes | Prokaryotic and eukaryotic | Nonmembranous; protein and RNA structure | Are the site of protein synthesis |
| Microtubules, microfilaments, and intermediate filaments | Eukaryotic | Nonmembranous; strands composed of protein | Provide structural support and allow for movement |
| Nuclear membrane | Eukaryotic | Membranous; double membrane formed into a single container of nucleoplasm and nucleic acids | Separates the nucleus from the cytoplasm |
| Nucleolus | Eukaryotic | Nonmembranous; group of RNA molecules and DNA located in the nucleus | Is the site of ribosome manufacture and storage |
| Endoplasmic reticulum | Eukaryotic | Membranous; folds of membrane forming sheets and canals | Is a surface for chemical reactions and intracellular transport system |
| Golgi apparatus | Eukaryotic | Membranous; stack of single membrane sacs | Is associated with the production of secretions and enzyme activation |
| Vacuoles and vesicles | Eukaryotic | Membranous; microscopic single membranous sacs | Contain a variety of compounds |
| Peroxisomes | Eukaryotic | Membranous; submicroscopic membrane-enclosed vesicle | Contain enzymes to break down hydrogen peroxide and perform other functions |
| Lysosomes | Eukaryotic | Membranous; submicroscopic membrane-enclosed vesicle | Separate certain enzymes from cell contents |
| Mitochondria | Eukaryotic | Membranous; double membranous organelle: large membrane folded inside a smaller membrane | Are the site of aerobic cellular respiration associated with the release of energy from food |
| Chloroplasts | Eukaryotic | Membranous; double membranous organelle: inner membrane contains chlorophyll | Are the site of photosynthesis associated with the capture of light energy and the synthesis of carbohydrate molecules |
| Centriole | Eukaryotic | Two clusters of nine microtubules | Is associated with cell division |
| Contractile vacuole | Eukaryotic | Membranous; single-membrane container | Expels excess water |
| Cilia and flagella | Eukaryotic and prokaryotic | Nonmembranous; prokaryotes composed of a single type of protein arranged in a fiber that is anchored into the cell wall and membrane; eukaryotes consist of tubules in a 9 + 2 arrangement | Cause movement |

## Key Terms

*Use the interactive flash cards on the* **Concepts in Biology,** *14/e website to help you learn the meaning of these terms.*

actin filaments 84
active transport 91
aerobic cellular respiration 81
antibiotics 94
Archaea 71
Bacteria 71
cell 70
cell theory 70
cell wall 70
cellular membranes 74
centriole 85
chlorophyll 82
chloroplast 82
chromatin 86
chromosome 86
cilia 85
concentration gradient (diffusion gradient) 88
cristae 81
cytoplasm 71
cytoskeleton 84
diffusion 87
domain 93
dynamic equilibrium 88
endocytosis 91
endoplasmic reticulum (ER) 78
Eucarya 71
eukaryotic cells 71
exocytosis 91
facilitated diffusion 90
flagella 85
fluid-mosaic model 74
Golgi apparatus 79
grana 82
granules 85

hydrophilic 74
hydrophobic 74
hypertonic 89
hypotonic 90
inclusions 85
intermediate filaments 84
isotonic 89
lysosomes 79
microfilaments 84
microtubules 84
mitochondrion 81
net movement 87
noneukaryotic cells 71
nuclear membrane 80
nucleolus 87
nucleoplasm 87
nucleus 71
organelles 71
osmosis 89
peroxisomes 79
phagocytosis 91
photosynthesis 82
pinocytosis 91
plasma membrane (cell membrane) 76
prokaryotes 71
protoplasm 71
receptor mediated endocytosis 91
ribosomes 78
selectively permeable 88
signal transduction 77
stroma 82
thylakoid 82
vacuoles 80
vesicles 80

## Basic Review

1. The first structure to be distinguished within a cell was the _____.
2. Membranous structures in cells are composed of
   a. phosopholipid.
   b. cellulose.
   c. ribosomes.
   d. chromatin.
3. The Golgi apparatus produces
   a. ribosomes.
   b. DNA.
   c. lysosomes.
   d. endoplasmic reticulum.
4. If a cell has chloroplasts, it is able to carry on photosynthesis. (T/F)
5. The nucleolus is
   a. where the DNA of the cell is located.
   b. found only in prokaryotic cells.
   c. found in the cytoplasm.
   d. where ribosomes are made and stored.
6. Diffusion occurs
   a. if molecules are evenly distributed.
   b. because of molecular motion.
   c. only in cells.
   d. when cells need it.
7. Prokaryotic cells are larger than eukaryotic cells. (T/F)
8. Osmosis involves the diffusion of _____ through a selectively permeable membrane.
9. The structure of the plasma membrane contains proteins. (T/F)
10. Which one of the following have cell walls made of cellulose?
    a. animals
    b. protozoa
    c. fungi
    d. plants
11. The _____ _____ manufactures some polysaccharides and lipids and packages molecules within sacs.

12. Which is an example of a noneukaryotic cell?

    a. muscle cell

    b. bacterium

    c. fungal cell

    d. virus

13. The internal structural framework or cytoskeleton of a cell is composed of which combination of elements?

    a. microtubules, microfilaments, and intermediate filaments

    b. centrioles, actin, and intermediate filaments

    c. ER, nuclear membrane, and Golgi

    d. thylakoid, cristae, and centrioles

14. When a cell is placed in a _____ solution, it loses water and it shrivels.

15. These cell components are involved in the destruction of microbes.

    a. carrier proteins

    b. phagocytic vacuoles

    c. centrioles

    d. eucarya

**Answers**

1. nucleus   2. a   3. c   4. T   5. d   6. b   7. F
8. water   9. T   10. d   11. Golgi apparatus   12. b   13. a
14. hypertonic   15. b

## Thinking Critically

**Athletes and Osmosis**

We all know that as we exercise, we sweat and, as a result, lose water and salt. These materials must be replaced. Athletes who participate in extremely long events of several hours have a special concern. They need to replace the water on a regular basis during the event. If they drink large quantities of water at one time at the end of the event, they may dilute their blood to the point that they develop hyponatremia. This condition can result in swelling of the cells of the brain and lead to mental confusion and, in extreme cases, collapse and death.

1. What is hyponatremia?
2. What is a "sports drink"?
3. How is one of these drinks supposed to help an athlete?
4. What is the point of the drinks various colors and flavors?
5. How could the kinds of liquids you drink affect your cell's osmotic balance?
6. Why can drinking electrolyte-free water at the end of an endurance athletic event cause the brain to swell?
7. Should sports drinks be available to children in school cafeterias?

CHAPTER

5

# Enzymes, Coenzymes, and Energy

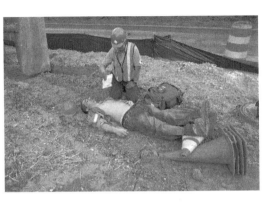

## Man Survives Body Temperature of 115.7!

*Alcohol, drugs, and high temperatures just don't mix.*

Fifty-two-year-old Willie Jones of Atlanta, Georgia, has been documented as having survived the highest body temperature ever recorded. Jones's core body temperature reached 115.7°F (46.5°C). He was admitted to the hospital with heatstroke (hyperthermia) on July 10, 1980, when the outside temperature reached 90°F (32.2°C). Hyperthermia may be caused by a combination of environmental exposure, physical exertion, infection, malfunction of temperature regulation mechanisms in the brain, and/or by various drugs.

The Centers for Disease Control and Prevention (CDC) reported that from 1999–2003 there were 1,203 deaths associated with hyperthermia; 345 (29%) were associated with "external causes (e.g., unintentional poisonings)." Willie suffered from environmental heatstroke, made worse by alcohol consumption. In fact, this patient's peak body temperature was probably higher, since an accurate measurement was not made until 25 minutes after body-cooling devices were used. Other drugs that can cause this condition include amphetamines, cocaine, atropine, diphenhydramine, antidepressants, and antipsychotics.

Heatstroke victims commonly develop multisystem organ failure, resulting from damage to the body's proteins, breakdown of muscle, and a bleeding disorder of the body's clotting and anti-clotting mechanisms. Willie never developed the clotting disorder or muscle breakdown despite extreme hyperthermia, thanks to the actions of emergency department personnel.

- How are the body's proteins affected by high temperatures?
- What happens to proteins when the environmental temperature drops?
- Will such information influence people to use alcohol and drugs more carefully?

## Background Check

**Concepts you should already know to get the most out of this chapter:**
- The different ways that chemicals can react with one another (chapter 2)
- How atoms and molecules bond together (chapter 2)
- The variety of shapes proteins can take (chapter 3)
- The molecular structure of cellular membranes (chapter 4)

## 5.1   How Cells Use Enzymes

All living things require energy and building materials in order to grow and reproduce. Energy may be in the form of visible light, or it may be in energy-containing covalent bonds found in nutrients. **Nutrients** are molecules required by organisms for growth, reproduction, and repair. The formation, breakdown, and rearrangement of molecules to provide organisms with essential energy and building blocks are known as *biochemical reactions*. Most reactions require an input of energy to get them started; this energy is referred to as **activation energy**. Activation energy is used to make reactants unstable and more likely to react (figure 5.1).

If organisms are to survive, they must obtain sizable amounts of energy and building materials in a very short time. Experience tells us that the sugar in candy bars contains the potential energy needed to keep us active, as well as building materials to help us grow (sometimes to excess!). Yet, random chemical processes alone could take millions of years to break down a candy bar. Of course, living things cannot wait that long. To sustain life, biochemical reactions must occur at extremely rapid rates. One way to increase the rate of any chemical reaction and make its energy and component parts available to a cell is to increase the temperature of the reactants. In general, the hotter the reactants, the faster they will react. However, this method of increasing reaction rates has a major

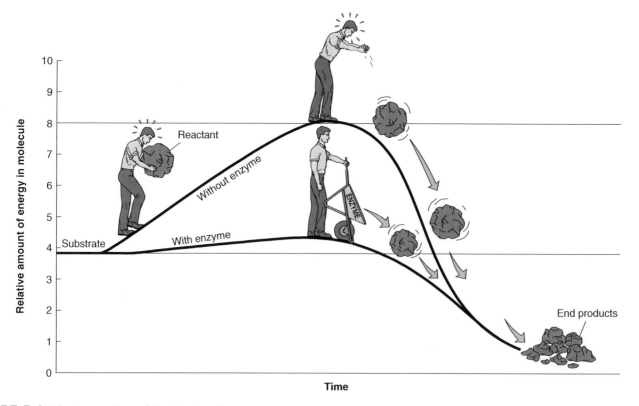

**FIGURE 5.1  The Lowering of Activation Energy**
Enzymes operate by lowering the amount of energy needed to get a reaction going—the activation energy. When this energy is lowered, the nature of the bonds is changed, so they are more easily broken. Although the figure shows the breakdown of a single reactant into many end products (as in a hydrolysis reaction), the lowering of activation energy can also result in bonds being broken so that new bonds may be formed in the construction of a single, larger end product from several reactants (as in a synthesis reaction).

drawback when it comes to living things: Organisms die because cellular proteins are *denatured* before the temperature reaches the point required to sustain the biochemical reactions necessary for life. This is of practical concern to people who are experiencing a fever. Should the fever stay too high for too long, major disruptions of cellular biochemical processes could be fatal.

Organisms have evolved a way of increasing the rate of chemical reactions without increasing the temperature. This involves using a **catalyst,** a chemical that speeds the reaction but is not used up in the reaction. It can be recovered unchanged when the reaction is complete. Catalysts lower the amount of activation energy needed to start the reaction (refer to figure 5.1). A cell manufactures specific proteins that act as catalysts. An **enzyme** is a protein molecule that acts as a catalyst to speed the rate of a reaction. Enzymes are found throughout the cell and can be used over and over again until they are worn out or broken. The production of these protein catalysts is under the direct control of an organism's genetic material (DNA). The instructions for the manufacture of all enzymes are found in the genes of the cell. How the genetic information is used to direct the synthesis of these specific protein molecules will be discussed in chapter 8.

### 5.1 CONCEPT REVIEW

1. What is the difference between a catalyst and an enzyme?
2. How do enzymes increase the rate of a chemical reaction?

## 5.2 How Enzymes Speed Chemical Reaction Rates

As the instructions for the production of an enzyme are read from the genetic material, a specific sequence of amino acids is linked together at the ribosomes. Once bonded, the chain of amino acids folds and twists to form a molecule with a particular three-dimensional shape.

### Enzymes Bind to Substrates

It is the nature of its three-dimensional shape, size, and electric charge that allows an enzyme to combine with a reactant and lower the activation energy. Each enzyme has a specific size and three-dimensional shape, which in turn is specific to the kind of reactant with which it can combine. The enzyme physically fits with the reactant. The molecule to which the enzyme attaches itself (the reactant) is known as the **substrate.** When the enzyme attaches itself to the substrate molecule, a new, temporary molecule—the **enzyme-substrate complex**—is formed (figure 5.2). When the substrate is combined with the enzyme, its chemical bonds are less stable and more likely to be altered and form new bonds. The enzyme is specific because it has a particular shape, which can combine only with specific parts of certain substrate molecules (Outlooks 5.1).

You can think of an enzyme as a tool that makes a job easier and faster. For example, the use of an open-end crescent wrench can make the job of removing or attaching a nut and bolt go much faster than doing the same job by hand. To do this job, the proper wrench must be used. Just any old tool (screwdriver or hammer) won't work! The enzyme must also physically attach itself to the substrate; therefore, there is a specific **binding site,** or **attachment site,** on the enzyme surface. Figure 5.3 illustrates the specificity of both wrench and enzyme. Note that the wrench and enzyme are recovered unchanged after they have been used. This means that the enzyme and wrench can be used again. Eventually, like wrenches, enzymes wear out and have to be replaced by synthesizing new ones using the instructions provided by the cell's genes. Generally, only very small quantities of enzymes are necessary, because they work so fast and can be reused.

Both enzymes and wrenches are specific in that they have a particular surface geometry, or shape, which matches the geometry of their respective substrates. Note that both the enzyme and the wrench are flexible. The enzyme can bend or

**FIGURE 5.2 Enzyme-Substrate Complex Formation**
During an enzyme-controlled reaction, the enzyme and substrate come together to form a new molecule—the enzyme-substrate complex molecule. This molecule exists for only a very short time. During that time, the activation energy is lowered and bonds are changed. The result is the formation of a new molecule or molecules, called the end products of the reaction. Notice that the enzyme comes out of the reaction intact and ready to be used again.

## Passing Gas, Enzymes, and Biotechnology

Certain foods like beans and peas will result in an increased amount of intestinal gas. The average person releases about a liter of gas every day (about 14 expulsions). As people shift to healthier diets which include more fruits, vegetables, milk products, bran and whole grains, the amount of intestinal gas (flatus) produced can increase, too.

The major components of intestinal gas are:

- Nitrogen: 20–90%
- Hydrogen: 0–50%
- Carbon dioxide: 10–30%
- Oxygen: 0–10%
- Methane: 0–10%

The other offensive gases are produced when bacteria (i.e., *Escherichia coli*) living in the large intestine hydrolyze complex carbohydrates that humans cannot enzymatically break down. The enzyme alpha-galactosidase breaks down the complex carbohydrates found in these foods. When *E. coli* metabolizes these smaller carbohydrates, they release hydrogen and foul-smelling gases. Some people have more of a gas problem than others do. This is because the ratios of the two types of intestinal bacteria—those that produce alpha-galactosidase and those that do not—vary from person to person. This ratio dictates how much gas will be produced.

Biotechnology has been used to genetically engineer the fungus *Aspergillus niger*. By inserting the gene for alpha galactosidase into the fungus and making other changes, Aspergillus is able to secrete the enzyme in a form that can be dissolved in glycerol and water. This product is then put into pill form and sold over the counter. Since the flavor of alpha-galactosidase is similar to soy sauce, it can be added to many foods without changing their flavor.

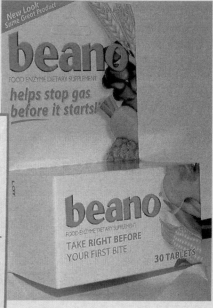

## Supplement Facts

**Serving Size 2 Tablets**
**Servings Per Container 15**

| Amount Per Serving | %DV |
|---|---|
| Alpha-galactosidase enzyme 300 GALU† (derived from *Aspergillus niger*) | |

†Daily Value not established

Substrate     **Leads to hydrolysis**     End product

Active site

Enzyme + Enzyme

Enzyme-substrate complex

Enzyme + Enzyme

End product     **Leads to synthesis**     Substrate

**(b)**

**FIGURE 5.3  It Fits, It's Fast, and It Works**

*(a)* Although removing the wheel from this bicycle could be done by hand, using an open-end crescent wrench is more efficient. The wrench is adjusted and attached, temporarily forming a nut-bolt-wrench complex. Turning the wrench loosens the bonds holding the nut to the bolt and the two are separated. Using the wrench makes the task much easier. *(b)* An enzyme will "adjust itself" as it attaches to its substrate, forming a temporary enzyme-substrate complex. The presence and position of the enzyme in relation to the substrate lowers the activation energy required to alter the bonds.

**(a)**

fold to fit the substrate, just as the wrench can be adjusted to fit the nut. This is called the *induced fit hypothesis*. The fit is induced because the presence of the substrate causes the enzyme to mold or adjust itself to the substrate as the two come together.

The **active site** is the place on the enzyme that causes a specific part of the substrate to change. It is the place where chemical bonds are formed or broken. (Note in the case illustrated in figure 5.3 that the active site is the same as the binding site. This is typical of many enzymes.) This site is where the activation energy is lowered and the electrons are shifted to change the bonds. The active site may enable a positively charged surface to combine with the negative portion of a reactant. Although the active site molds itself to a substrate, enzymes cannot fit all substrates. Enzymes are specific to certain substrates or a group of very similar substrate molecules. One enzyme cannot speed the rate of all types of biochemical reactions. Rather, a special enzyme is required to control the rate of each type of reaction occurring in an organism.

## Naming Enzymes

Because an enzyme is specific to both the substrate to which it can attach and the reaction it can encourage, a unique name can be given to each enzyme. The first part of an enzyme's name is usually the name of the molecule to which it can become attached. The second part of the name indicates the type of reaction it facilitates. The third part of the name is "-ase," the ending that indicates it is an enzyme. For example, *DNA polymerase* is the name of the enzyme that attaches to the molecule DNA and is responsible for increasing its length through a polymerization reaction. Some enzymes (e.g., pepsin and trypsin) were identified before a formal naming system was established and are still referred to by their original names. The enzyme responsible for the dehydration synthesis reactions among several glucose molecules to form glycogen is known as *glycogen synthetase*. The enzyme responsible for breaking the bond that attaches the amino group to the amino acid arginine is known as *arginine aminase*. When an enzyme is very common, its formal name is shortened: The salivary enzyme involved in the digestion of starch is *amylose* (starch) *hydrolase*; it is generally known as *amylase*. Other enzymes associated with the human digestive system are noted in table 24.2.

## 5.3   Cofactors, Coenzymes, and Vitamins

Certain enzymes need an additional molecule to help them function. **Cofactors** are inorganic ions or organic molecules that serve as enzyme helpers. Ions such as zinc, iron, and magnesium assist enzymes in their performance as catalysts. These ions chemically combine with the enzyme. A **coenzyme** is an organic molecule that functions as a cofactor. They are made from molecules such as certain amino acids, nitrogenous bases, and vitamins. **Vitamins** are a group of unrelated organic molecules used in the making of certain coenzymes; they also play a role in regulating gene action. Vitamins are either water-soluble (e.g., vitamin B complex) or fat-soluble (e.g., vitamin A). For example, the vitamin riboflavin ($B_2$) is metabolized by cells and becomes **flavin adenine dinucleotide (FAD)**. The vitamin niacin is metabolized by cells and becomes **nicotinamide adenine dinucleotide (NAD$^+$)**. Coenzymes such as NAD$^+$ and FAD are used to carry electrons to and from many kinds of oxidation-reduction reactions. NAD$^+$, FAD, and other coenzymes are bonded only temporarily to their enzymes and therefore can assist various enzymes in their reaction. Vitamins are required in your diet because cells are not able to manufacture these molecules (figure 5.4).

Another vitamin, pantothenic acid, becomes coenzyme A (CoA), a molecule used to carry a specific 2-carbon functional group, **acetyl** (-COCH$_3$), generated in one reaction to another reaction. Like enzymes, the cell uses inorganic cofactors, coenzymes, and vitamins repeatedly until these molecules are worn out and destroyed. Coenzymes play vital roles in metabolism. Without them, most cellular reactions would come to an end and the cell would die.

## 5.4   How the Environment Affects Enzyme Action

An enzyme forms a complex with one substrate molecule, encourages a reaction to occur, detaches itself, and then forms a complex with another molecule of the same substrate. The number of molecules of substrate with which a single enzyme molecule can react in a given time (e.g., reactions per minute) is called the **turnover number.**

Sometimes, the number of jobs an enzyme can perform during a particular time period is incredibly large—ranging

**FIGURE 5.4 The Role of Coenzymes**

$NAD^+$ is a coenzyme that works with the enzyme alcohol dehydrogenase (ADase) during the breakdown of alcohol in the liver. This coenzyme helps by carrying the hydrogen from the alcohol molecule after it is removed by the enzyme. Notice that the hydrogen on the alcohol is picked up by the $NAD^+$. The use of the coenzyme $NAD^+$ makes the enzyme function more efficiently, because one of the end products of this reaction (hydrogen) is removed from the reaction site. If anything interferes with the formation of $NAD^+$ (i.e., niacin deficiency or high temperatures), the breakdown of alcohol becomes less efficient, allowing the alcohol to cause cell damage.

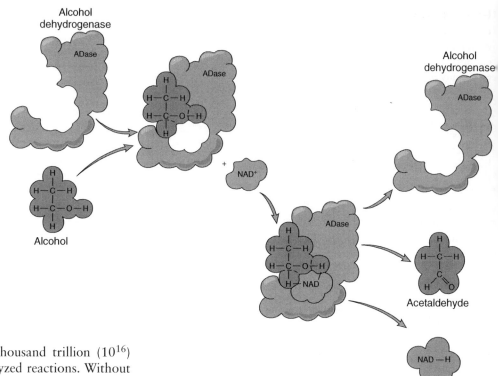

between a thousand ($10^3$) and 10 thousand trillion ($10^{16}$) times faster per minute than uncatalyzed reactions. Without the enzyme, perhaps only 50 or 100 substrate molecules might be altered in the same time. With this in mind, let's identify the ideal conditions for an enzyme and consider how these conditions influence the turnover number.

## Temperature

An important condition affecting enzyme-controlled reactions is the environmental temperature (figure 5.5), which has two effects on enzymes: (1) It can change the rate of molecular motion, and (2) it can cause changes in the shape of an enzyme. An increase in environmental temperature increases molecular motion. Therefore, as the temperature of an enzyme-substrate system increases, the amount of product molecules formed increases, up to a point. The temperature at which the rate of formation of enzyme-substrate complex is fastest is termed the *optimum temperature*. *Optimum* means the best or most productive quantity or condition. In this case, the optimum temperature is the temperature at which the product is formed most rapidly. As the temperature decreases below the optimum, molecular motion slows, and the rate at which the enzyme-substrate complexes form decreases. Even though the enzyme is still able to operate, it does so very slowly. Foods can be preserved by storing them in freezers or refrigerators because the enzyme-controlled reactions of the food and spoilage organisms are slowed at lower temperatures.

When the temperature is raised above the optimum, some of the enzyme molecules are changed in such a way that they can no longer form the enzyme-substrate complex; thus, the reaction slows. If the temperature continues to increase, more and more of the enzyme molecules become inactive. If the temperature is high enough, it causes permanent changes in the three-dimensional shape of the molecules. The surface

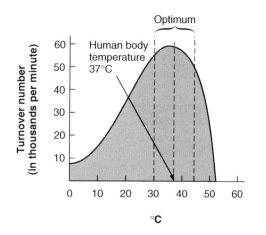

**FIGURE 5.5 The Effect of Temperature on Turnover Number**

As the temperature increases, the turnover number increases. The increasing temperature increases molecular motion and may increase the number of times an enzyme contacts and combines with a substrate molecule. Temperature may also influence the shape of the enzyme molecule, making it fit better with the substrate. At high temperatures, the enzyme molecule is irreversibly changed, so that it can no longer function as an enzyme. At that point, it has been denatured. Notice that the enzyme represented in this graph has an optimum (best) temperature range of between 30°C and 45°C.

geometry of the enzyme molecule is not recovered, even when the temperature is reduced. Recall the wrench analogy. When a wrench is heated above a certain temperature, the metal begins to change shape. The shape of the wrench is changed

**FIGURE 5.6** **The Effect of pH on the Turnover Number**
As the pH changes, the turnover number changes. The ions in solution alter the environment of the enzyme's active site and the overall shape of the enzyme. The enzymes illustrated here are human amylase, pepsin, and trypsin. Amylase is found in saliva and is responsible for hydrolyzing starch to glucose. Pepsin is found in the stomach and hydrolyzes protein. Trypsin is produced in the pancreas and enters the small intestine, where it also hydrolyzes protein. Notice that each enzyme has its own pH range of activity, the optimum (shown in the color bars) being different for each.

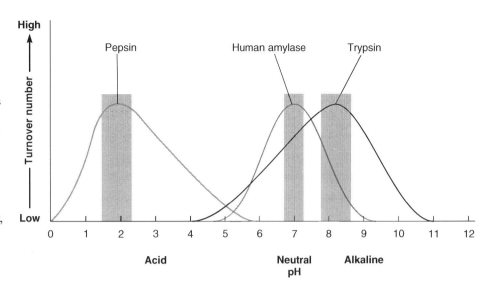

permanently, so that, even if the temperature is reduced, the surface geometry of the end of the wrench is permanently lost. When this happens to an enzyme, it has been *denatured*. A denatured enzyme is one whose protein structure has been permanently changed, so that it has lost its original biochemical properties. Because enzymes are molecules and are not alive, they are not killed but, rather, denatured. For example, although egg white is not an enzyme, it is a protein and provides a common example of what happens when denaturation occurs as a result of heating. As heat is applied to the egg white, it is permanently changed from a runny substance to a rubbery solid (denatured).

Many people have heard that fevers cause brain damage. Brain damage from a fever can result from the denaturation of proteins if the fever is over 42°C (107.6°F). However, denaturation and brain damage from fevers is rare, because untreated fevers seldom go over 40.5°C (105°F) unless the child is overdressed or trapped in a hot place. Generally, the brain's thermostat will stop the fever from going above (41.1°C) 106°F. Children with a rectal temperature of 106°F or higher also have a greater risk for serious bacterial infection and for viral illness, or both.

## pH

Another environmental condition that influences enzyme action is pH. The three-dimensional structure of a protein leaves certain side chains exposed. These side chains may attract ions from the environment. Under the right conditions, a group of positively charged hydrogen ions may accumulate on certain parts of an enzyme. In an environment that lacks these hydrogen ions, this would not happen. Thus, variation in the enzyme's shape could be caused by a change in the number of hydrogen ions present in the solution. Because the environmental pH is so important in determining the shapes of protein molecules, there is an optimum pH for each specific enzyme. The enzyme will fit with the substrate only when it has the proper shape, and it has the proper shape only when it is at the right pH. Many enzymes function best at a pH close to neutral (7). However, a number of enzymes perform best at pHs quite different from 7. Pepsin, an enzyme found in the stomach, works well at an acid pH of 1.5 to 2.2, whereas arginase, an enzyme in the liver, works well at a basic pH of 9.5 to 9.9 (figure 5.6).

## Enzyme-Substrate Concentration

In addition to temperature and pH, the concentration of enzymes, substrates, and products influences the rates of enzymatic reactions. Although the enzyme and the substrate are in contact with one another for only a short time, when there are huge numbers of substrate molecules it may happen that all the enzymes present are always occupied by substrate molecules. When this occurs, the rate of product formation cannot be increased unless the number of enzymes is increased. Cells can do this by synthesizing more enzymes. However, just because there are more enzyme molecules does not mean that any one enzyme molecule will work any faster. The turnover number for each enzyme stays the same. As the enzyme concentration increases, the amount of product formed increases in a specified time. A greater number of enzymes are turning over substrates; they are not turning over substrates faster. Similarly, if enzyme numbers are decreased, the amount of product formed declines.

We can also look at this from the point of view of the substrate. If substrate is in short supply, enzymes may have to wait for a substrate molecule to become available. Under these conditions, as the amount of substrate increases, the amount of product formed increases. The increase in product is the result of more substrate being available to be changed. When there is a very large amount of substrate, all the enzymes will be occupied all the time. However, if given enough time, even a small amount of enzyme can eventually change all the substrate to product; it just takes longer.

## 5.5 Cellular-Control Processes and Enzymes

In any cell, there are thousands of kinds of enzymes. Each controls specific chemical reactions and is sensitive to changing environmental conditions, such as pH and temperature. For a cell to stay alive in an ever-changing environment, its countless chemical reactions must be controlled. Recall from chapter 1 that control processes are mechanisms that ensure that an organism will carry out all metabolic activities in the proper sequence (coordination) and at the proper rate (regulation). The *coordination* of enzymatic activities in a cell results when specific reactions occur in a given sequence— for example, $A \rightarrow B \rightarrow C \rightarrow D \rightarrow E$. This ensures that a particular nutrient will be converted to a particular end product necessary to the survival of the cell. Should a cell be unable to coordinate its reactions, essential products might be produced at the wrong time or never be produced at all, and the cell would die. The *regulation* of biochemical reactions is the way a cell controls the amount of chemical product produced. The expression "having too much of a good thing" applies to this situation. For example, if a cell manufactures too much lipid, the presence of those molecules could interfere with other life-sustaining reactions, resulting in the cell's death. On the other hand, if a cell does not produce enough of an essential molecule, such as a hydrolytic (digestive) enzyme, it might also die. The cellular-control process involves both enzymes and genes.

### Enzymatic Competition for Substrates

**Enzymatic competition** results whenever there are several kinds of enzymes available to combine with the same kind of substrate molecule. Although all these different enzymes may combine with the same substrate, they do not have the same chemical effect on the substrate, because each converts the substrate to different end products. For example, acetyl-coenzyme A (**acetyl-CoA**) is a substrate that can be acted upon by three different enzymes: citrate synthetase, fatty acid synthetase, and malate synthetase (figure 5.7). Which enzyme has the greatest success depends on the number of each type of enzyme available and the suitability of the environment for the enzyme's operation. The enzyme that is present in the

greatest number or is best suited to the job in the environment of the cell wins, and the amount of its end product becomes the greatest.

### Gene Regulation

The number and kind of enzymes produced are regulated by the cell's genes. It is the job of chemical messengers to inform the genes as to whether specific enzyme-producing genes should be turned on or off, or whether they should have their protein-producing activities increased or decreased. **Gene-regulator proteins** are chemical messengers that inform the genes of the cell's need for enzymes. Gene-regulator proteins that decrease protein production are called *gene-repressor proteins*, whereas those that increase protein production are *gene-activator proteins*. Look again at figure 5.7. If the cell were in need of protein, gene-regulator proteins could increase the amount of malate synthetase. This would result in an increase in the amount of acetyl-CoA being converted to malate. The additional malate would then be modified into one of the amino acids needed to produce the needed protein. On the other hand, if the cell required energy, an increase in the amount of citrate synthetase would cause more acetyl-CoA to be metabolized to release this energy. When the enzyme fatty acid synthetase is produced in greater amounts, it outcompetes the other two; the acetyl-CoA is used in fat production and storage.

### Inhibition

An **inhibitor** is a molecule that attaches itself to an enzyme and interferes with that enzyme's ability to form an enzyme-substrate complex (How Science Works 5.1). For example, one of the early kinds of pesticides used to spray fruit trees contained arsenic. The arsenic attached itself to insect enzymes and inhibited the normal growth and reproduction of insects. Organophosphates are pesticides that, at the right concentration, inhibit several enzymes necessary for the operation of the nervous system. When they are incorporated into nerve cells, they disrupt normal nerve transmission and cause the death of the affected organisms (figure 5.8). In humans, death that is due to pesticides is usually caused by uncontrolled muscle contractions, resulting in breathing failure.

#### Competitive Inhibition

Some inhibitors have a shape that closely resembles the normal substrate of the enzyme. The enzyme is unable to distinguish the inhibitor from the normal substrate, so it combines with either or both. As long as the inhibitor is combined with an enzyme, the enzyme is ineffective in its normal role. Some of these enzyme-inhibitor complexes are permanent. An inhibitor removes a specific enzyme as a functioning part of the cell. The reaction that enzyme catalyzes no longer occurs, and none of the product is formed. This is termed

## FIGURE 5.7 Enzymatic Competition

Acetyl-CoA can serve as a substrate for a number of reactions. Three such reactions are shown here. Whether it becomes a fatty acid, malate, or citrate is determined by the enzymes present. Each of the three enzymes can be thought of as being in competition for the same substrate—the acetyl-CoA molecule. The cell can partially control which end product will be produced in the greatest quantity by producing greater numbers of one kind of enzyme and fewer of the other kinds. If citrate synthetase is present in the highest quantity, more of the acetyl-CoA substrate will be acted upon by that enzyme and converted to citrate, rather than to the other two end products, malate and fatty acids.

(a) No end product is released

(b)

## FIGURE 5.8 Inhibition of Enzyme at Active Site

*(a)* Organophosphate pesticides are capable of attaching to the enzyme acetylcholinesterase, preventing it from forming an enzyme-substrate complex with its regular substrate. Since acetylcholinesterase is necessary for normal nerve cell function, organophosphates pesticides are nerve poison and kills organisms. *(b)* Many farmers around the world use organophosphates to control crop-damaging insects.

**competitive inhibition** because the inhibitor molecule competes with the normal substrate for the active site of the enzyme (figure 5.9).

Scientists use their understanding of enzyme inhibition to control disease. For instance, an anti-herpes drug is used to control herpes viruses responsible for lesions such as genital herpes or cold sores. The drug Valtrex inhibits the viral form of the enzyme DNA polymerase that is responsible for the production of compounds required for viral replication. As a result, the viruses are unable to replicate and cause

# HOW SCIENCE WORKS 5.1

## Don't Be Inhibited—Keep Your Memory Alive

Alcohol and drugs can interfere with your "short-term" memory, such as remembering the crazy things you might have done at a party Saturday night. However, they don't seem to get in the way of older memories, such as the biology exam you failed in high school. Neuroscientists thought this is because long-term memories become "hard-wired" into your brain in a way that makes them harder to wipe out. These long-term memories are kept in place by structural changes to the connections between nerve cells, but recent research has made this "simple" explanation more complicated.

The research involved injecting a drug that inhibits the enzyme protein kinase into the cerebral cortex of rat brains where taste memories are thought to reside. The data revealed that when this enzyme was blocked, the rats forgot a meal that made them sick

weeks earlier. The results of these experiments suggest that the continuous activity of this enzyme is somehow necessary to maintain long-term memory. This is something that was not predicted by the hypotheses on the mechanisms of memory formation. Protein kinase and other similar enzymes were thought to only be important in the early stages of memory formation. Now it appears that they are needed to form and sustain long-term memory. One researcher at the University of Arizona in Tucson believes that it's possible that protein kinase can erase all learning, no matter how long it has been stored in memory.

What does the future have in store for the therapeutic applications of such research? Some are thinking about the development of enzyme-altering drugs that could:

- help sustain memories for longer than normal periods,
- boost brainpower, and
- eliminate the painful memories of trauma survivors.

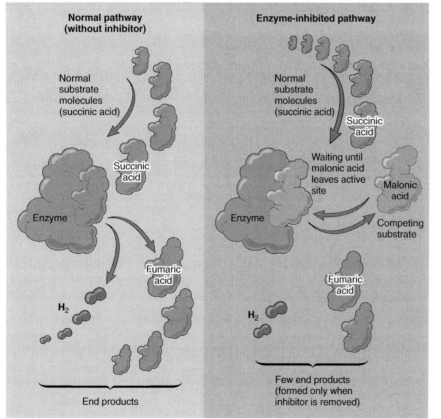

## FIGURE 5.9 Competitive Inhibition

The left-hand side of the illustration shows the normal functioning of the enzyme. On the right-hand side, the enzyme is unable to attach to succinic acid. This is because an inhibitor, malonic acid, is attached to the enzyme and prevents the enzyme from forming the normal complex with succinic acid. As long as malonic acid stays attached in the active site, the enzyme will be unable to produce fumaric acid. If the malonic acid is removed, the enzyme will begin to produce fumaric acid again. Its attachment to the enzyme in this case is not permanent but, rather, reduces the number of product molecules formed per unit of time, its turnover number.

harm to their host cells. Because people do not normally produce this enzyme, they are not harmed by this drug.

### Negative-Feedback Inhibition

**Negative-feedback inhibition** is another method of controlling the synthesis of many molecules within a cell. This control process occurs within an enzyme-controlled reaction sequence. As the number of end products increases, some product molecules *feed back* to one of the previous reactions and have a *negative effect* on the enzyme controlling that reaction; that is, they *inhibit*, or prevent, that enzyme from performing at its best.

If the enzyme is inhibited, the end product can no longer be produced at the same rapid rate, and its concentration falls. When there are too few end product molecules to have a negative effect on the enzyme, the enzyme is no longer inhibited. The enzyme resumes its previous optimum rate of operation, and the end product concentration begins to increase. With this kind of regulation, the amount of the product rises and falls within a certain range and never becomes too large or small.

---

### 5.5   CONCEPT REVIEW

13. What is enzyme competition, and why is it important to all cells?
14. Describe the nature and action of an enzyme inhibitor.

---

### 5.6   Enzymatic Reactions Used in Processing Energy and Matter

All living organisms require a constant supply of energy to sustain life. They obtain this energy through enzyme-controlled chemical reactions, which release the internal

potential energy stored in the chemical bonds of molecules (figure 5.10). Burning wood is a chemical reaction that results in the release of energy by breaking chemical bonds. The chemical bonds of cellulose are broken, and smaller end products of carbon dioxide ($CO_2$) and water ($H_2O$) are produced. There is less potential energy in the chemical bonds of carbon dioxide and water than in the complex organic cellulose molecules, and the excess energy is released as light and heat.

### Biochemical Pathways

In living things, energy is also released but it is released in a series of small steps and each is controlled by a specific enzyme. Each step begins with a substrate, which is converted to a product, which in turn becomes the substrate for a different enzyme. Such a series of enzyme-controlled reactions is called a **biochemical pathway,** or a **metabolic pathway.** The processes of photosynthesis, respiration, protein synthesis, and many other cellular activities consist of a series of biochemical pathways. Biochemical pathways that result in the breakdown of compounds are generally referred to as **catabolism.** Biochemical pathways that result in the synthesis of new, larger compounds are known as **anabolism.** Figure 5.11 illustrates the nature of biochemical pathways.

One of the amazing facts of nature is that most organisms use the same basic biochemical pathways. For example, the bacterium *E. coli* and human cells have an estimated 1,000 genes that are the same. These two drastically different cell types manufacture many of the same enzymes and, therefore, run many of the same pathways. However, because the kinds of enzymes an organism is able to produce depend on its genes,

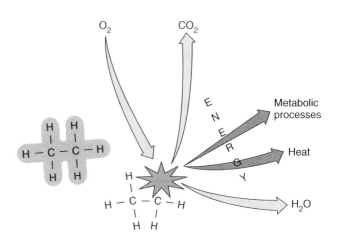

**FIGURE 5.10  Life's Energy: Chemical Bonds**
All living things use the energy contained in chemical bonds. As organisms break down molecules, they can use the energy released for metabolic processes, such as movement, growth, and reproduction. In all cases, there is a certain amount of heat released when chemical bonds are broken.

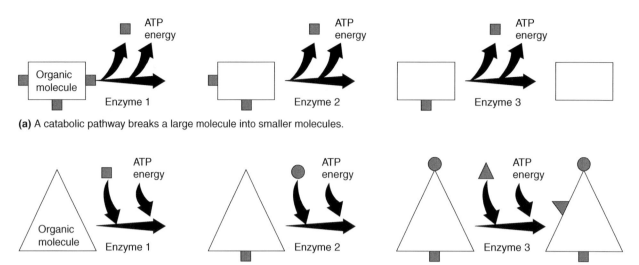

(a) A catabolic pathway breaks a large molecule into smaller molecules.

(b) An anabolic pathway combines smaller molecules to form a larger molecule.

**FIGURE 5.11 Biochemical Pathways**

Biochemical pathways are the result of a series of enzyme-controlled reactions. In each step, a substrate is acted upon by an enzyme to produce a product. The product then becomes the substrate for the next enzyme in the chain of reactions. Such pathways can be used to break down molecules, build up molecules, release energy, and perform many other actions.

some variation occurs in the details of the biochemical pathways. The fact that so many kinds of organisms use essentially the same biochemical processes is a strong argument for the idea of evolution from a common ancestor. Once a successful biochemical strategy evolved, the genes and the pathways were retained (conserved) through evolutionary descendents, with slight modifications of the scheme.

## Generating Energy in a Useful Form: ATP

The transfer of chemical energy within living things is handled by an RNA nucleotide known as **adenosine triphosphate (ATP)**. Chemical energy is stored when ATP is made and is released when it is broken apart. An ATP molecule is composed of a molecule of adenine (a nitrogenous base), ribose (a sugar), and 3 phosphate groups (figure 5.12). If only 1 phosphate is present, the molecule is known as adenosine monophosphate (AMP).

When a second phosphate group is added to the AMP, a molecule of **a**denosine **di**phosphate (ADP) is formed. The ADP, with the addition of even more energy, is able to bond to a third phosphate group and form ATP. (Recall from chapter 3 that the addition of phosphate to a molecule is called a *phosphorylation reaction.*) The bonds holding the last 2 phosphates to the molecule are easily broken to release energy for cellular processes that require energy. Because the bond between these phosphates is so easy for a cell to use, it is called a **high-energy phosphate bond**. These bonds are often shown as solid, curved lines (~) in diagrams. Both ADP and ATP, because they contain high-energy bonds, are very unstable molecules and readily lose their phosphates. When this occurs, the energy held in the phosphate's high-energy bonds can be transferred to a lower-energy molecule or

**FIGURE 5.12 Adenosine Triphosphate (ATP)**

An ATP molecule is an energy carrier. A molecule of ATP consists of several subunits: a molecule of adenine, a molecule of ribose, and 3 phosphate groups. The 2 end phosphate groups are bonded together by high-energy bonds. These bonds are broken easily, so they release a great amount of energy. Because they are high-energy bonds, they are represented by curved, solid lines.

released to the environment. Within a cell, specific enzymes (phosphorylases) speed this release of energy as ATP is broken down to ADP and P (phosphate). When the bond holding the third phosphate of an ATP molecule is broken, energy is released for use in other activities.

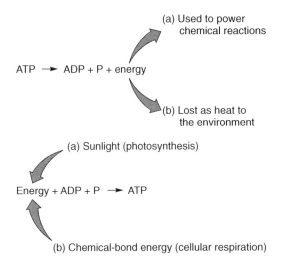

(a) Used to power chemical reactions

ATP → ADP + P + energy

(b) Lost as heat to the environment

(a) Sunlight (photosynthesis)

Energy + ADP + P → ATP

(b) Chemical-bond energy (cellular respiration)

When energy is being harvested from a chemical reaction or another energy source, such as sunlight, it is stored when a phosphate is attached to an ADP to form ATP.

An analogy that might be helpful is to think of each ATP molecule used in the cell as a rechargeable battery. When the power has been drained, it can be recharged numerous times before it must be recycled (figure 5.13).

## Electron Transport

Another important concept that can be applied to many different biochemical pathways is the mechanism of *electron transport*. Because the electrons of an atom are on its exterior, the electrons in the outer energy level can be lost more easily

to the surroundings, particularly if they receive additional energy and move to a higher energy level. When they fall back to their original position, they give up that energy. This activity takes place whenever electrons gain or lose energy. In living things, such energy changes are harnessed by special molecules that capture such "excited" electrons that can be transferred to other chemicals. These electron-transfer reactions are commonly called *oxidation-reduction reactions.* In oxidation-reduction (redox) reactions, the molecules losing electrons become oxidized and those gaining electrons become reduced. The molecule that loses the electron loses energy; the molecule that gains the electron gains energy.

There are many different electron acceptors or carriers in cells. However, the three most important are the coenzymes: *n*icotinamide *a*denine *d*inucleotide ($NAD^+$), *n*icotinamide *a*denine *d*inucleotide *p*hosphate ($NADP^+$), and *f*lavin *a*denine *d*inucleotide (FAD). Recall that niacin is needed to make $NAD^+$ and $NADP^+$ and the riboflavin is needed to make FAD. Because $NAD^+$, $NADP^+$, FAD, and similar molecules accept and release electrons, they are often involved in oxidation-reduction reactions. When $NAD^+$, $NADP^+$, and FAD accept electrons, they become negatively charged. Thus, they readily pick up hydrogen ions ($H^+$), so when they become reduced they are shown as NADH, NADPH, and $FADH_2$. Therefore, it is also possible to think of these molecules as *hydrogen carriers*. In many biochemical pathways, there is a series of enzyme controlled oxidation-reduction reactions (electron-transport reactions) in which each step results in the transfer of a small amount of energy from a higher-energy molecule to a lower-energy molecule (figure 5.14). Thus, electron transport is often tied to the formation of ATP.

**FIGURE 5.13  ATP: The Power Supply for Cells**
When rechargeable batteries in a flashlight have been drained of their power, they can be recharged by placing them in a specially designed battery charger. This enables the right amount of power from a power plant to be packed into the batteries for reuse. Cells operate in much the same manner. When the cell's "batteries," ATPs are drained while powering a job, such as muscle contraction, the discharged "batteries," ADPs can be recharged back to full ATP power.

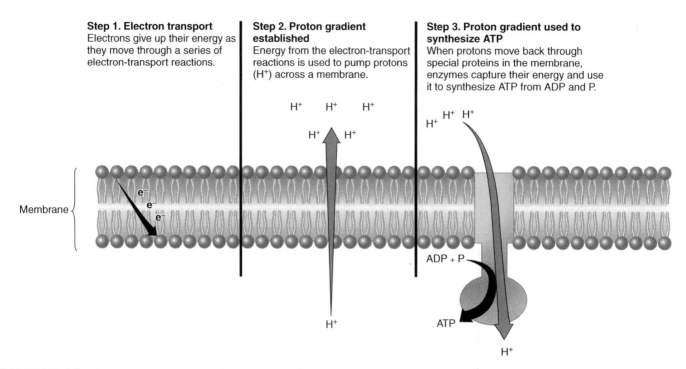

**Step 1. Electron transport**
Electrons give up their energy as they move through a series of electron-transport reactions.

**Step 2. Proton gradient established**
Energy from the electron-transport reactions is used to pump protons (H⁺) across a membrane.

**Step 3. Proton gradient used to synthesize ATP**
When protons move back through special proteins in the membrane, enzymes capture their energy and use it to synthesize ATP from ADP and P.

**FIGURE 5.14  Electron Transport and Proton Gradient**
The transport of high-energy electrons through a series of electron carriers can allow the energy to be released in discrete, manageable packets. In some cases, the energy given up is used to move or pump protons (H⁺) from one side of a membrane to the other and a proton concentration gradient is established. When the protons flow back through the membrane, enzymes in the membrane can capture energy and form ATP.

## Proton Pump

In many of the oxidation-reduction reactions that take place in cells, the electrons that are transferred come from hydrogen atoms. A hydrogen nucleus (proton) is formed whenever electrons are stripped from hydrogen atoms. When these higher-energy electrons are transferred to lower-energy states, protons are often pumped across membranes. This creates a region with a high concentration of protons on one side of the membrane. Therefore, this process is referred to as a *proton pump*. The "pressure" created by this high concentration of protons is released when protons flow through pores in the membrane back to the side from which they were pumped. As they pass through the pores, an enzyme, ATP synthetase (a phosphorylase), uses their energy to speed the formation of an ATP molecule by bonding a phosphate to an ADP molecule. Thus, making a proton gradient is an important step in the production of much of the ATP produced in cells (review figure 5.14).

The four concepts of biochemical pathways, ATP production, electron transport, and the proton pump—are all interrelated. We will use these concepts to examine particular aspects of photosynthesis and respiration in chapters 6 and 7.

## Summary

Enzymes are protein catalysts that speed up the rate of chemical reactions without any significant increase in the temperature. They do this by lowering activation energy. Enzymes have a very specific structure that matches the structure of particular substrate molecules. The substrate molecule comes in contact with only a specific part of the enzyme molecule—the attachment site. The active site of the enzyme is the place where the substrate molecule is changed. The enzyme-substrate complex reacts to form the end product. The protein nature of enzymes makes them sensitive to environmental conditions, such as temperature and pH, that change the structure of proteins. The number and kinds of enzymes are ultimately controlled by the genetic information of the cell. Other kinds of molecules, such as coenzymes, inhibitors, and competing enzymes, can influence specific enzymes. Changing conditions within the cell shift its enzymatic priorities by influencing the turnover number.

Enzymes are also used to speed and link chemical reactions into biochemical pathways. The energy currency of the cell, ATP, is produced by enzymatic pathways known as electron transport and proton pumping. The four concepts of biochemical pathways, ATP production, electron transport, and the proton pump are all interrelated.

### 5.6   CONCEPT REVIEW

15. What is a biochemical pathway, and what does it have to do with enzymes?
16. Describe what happens during electron transport and what it has to do with a proton pump.

# Key Terms

*Use the interactive flash cards on the **Concepts in Biology**, 14/e website to help you learn the meaning of these terms.*

acetyl 103
acetyl-CoA 106
activation energy 100
active site 103
adenosine triphosphate
 (ATP) 110
anabolism 109
binding site
 (attachment site) 101
biochemical pathway
 (metabolic pathway) 109
catabolism 109
catalyst 101
coenzyme 103
cofactors 103
competitive inhibition 107
enzymatic competition 106

enzyme 101
enzyme-substrate
 complex 101
flavin adenine
 dinucleotide (FAD) 103
gene-regulator proteins 106
high-energy phosphate
 bond 110
inhibitor 106
negative-feedback
 inhibition 109
nicotinamide adenine
 dinucleotide (NAD$^+$) 103
nutrients 100
substrate 101
turnover number 103
vitamins 103

# Basic Review

1. Something that speeds the rate of a chemical reaction but is not used up in that reaction is called a
   a. catalyst.
   b. catabolic molecule.
   c. coenzyme.
   d. ATP.
2. The amount of energy it takes to get a chemical reaction going is known as
   a. starting energy.
   b. ATP.
   c. activation energy.
   d. denaturation.
   e. Q.
3. A molecule that is acted upon by an enzyme is a
   a. cofactor.
   b. binding site.
   c. vitamin.
   d. substrate.

4. Your cells require _____ to manufacture certain coenzymes.
5. When a protein's three-dimensional structure has been altered to the extent that it no longer functions, it has been
   a. denatured.
   b. killed.
   c. anabolized.
   d. competitively inhibited.
6. Whenever there are several different enzymes available to combine with a given substrate, _____ results.
7. In _____, a form of enzyme control, the end product inhibits one step of its formation when its concentration becomes high enough.
8. Which of the following contains the greatest amount of potential chemical-bond energy?
   a. AMP
   b. ADP
   c. ATP
   d. ARP
9. Electron-transfer reactions are commonly called _____ reactions.
10. As electrons pass through the pores of cell membranes, an enzyme, _____ (a phosphorylase), uses electron energy to speed the formation of an ATP molecule by bonding a phosphate to an ADP molecule.
11. If a cleaning agent contains an enzyme that will get out stains that are protein in nature, it can also be used to take out stains caused by oil. (T/F)
12. Keeping foods in the refrigerator helps make them last longer because the lower temperature _____ enzyme activity.
13. ATP is generated when hydrogen ions flow from a _____ to a _____ concentration after they have been pumped from one side of the membrane to the other.
14. What are teams competing for in a football game? _____
15. A person who is vitamin deficient will most likely experience a _____ in their metabolism.

**Answers**
1. a  2. c  3. d  4. vitamins  5. a  6. enzymatic competition
7. negative feedback  8. c  9. oxidation-reduction  10. ATP synthetase  11. F  12. slows/inhibits  13. higher, lower  14. the ball  15. disruption

## Thinking Critically

**Nobel Prize Work**

The following data were obtained by a number of Nobel Prize–winning scientists from Lower Slobovia. As a member of the group, interpret the data with respect to the following:

1. Enzyme activities
2. Movement of substrates into and out of the cell
3. Competition among various enzymes for the same substrate
4. Cell structure

**Data**

a. A lowering of the atmospheric temperature from 22°C to 18°C causes organisms to form a thick, protective coat.

b. Below 18°C, no additional coat material is produced.

c. If the cell is heated to 35°C and then cooled to 18°C, no coat is produced.

d. The coat consists of a complex carbohydrate.

e. The coat will form even if there is a low concentration of simple sugars in the surroundings.

f. If the cell needs energy for growth, no cell coats are produced at any temperature.

CHAPTER

6

# Biochemical Pathways— Cellular Respiration

## Mutation Leads to Personal Energy Crisis

*Genes You Inherit from Mom Can Be Harmful.*

Ten-year-old Latisha Franklin has suffered from her own personal energy crisis since she was four. Latisha has been diagnosed with an uncommon illness, an abnormality called mitochondrial encephalopathy, or MELAS. MELAS is the acronym for *m*itochondrial *e*ncephalopathy, *l*actic *a*cidosis, and *s*troke-like episodes. It is caused by mutations in the DNA found in her mitochondria, mDNA. Mitochondria manufacture proteins using their own DNA. Enzymes help to produce useful chemical bond energy for cells, ATP. mDNA differs from the chromosomes found in the nucleus. They are much smaller and circular. Any changes (mutations) in mDNA can have far-reaching effects on the body's ability to control energy production.

Latisha has suffered encephalopathy in the form of epilepsy-like seizures and migraine-like headaches. She has also had severe muscle pain caused by excess lactic acid in her muscles, and stroke-like symptoms leading to paralysis and confusion.

The mutations that cause MELAS and the chemical changes that occur in mitochondria have been identified; however, there is no cure. Medical professionals can only manage symptoms.

- **In what molecular form do cells use chemical-bond energy?**

- How are these energy-containing molecules generated by cells?

- Why would a strict vitamin regimen be helpful in managing Latisha's symptoms?

## Background Check

**Concepts you should already know to get the most out of this chapter:**
- Features of oxidation-reduction chemical reactions (chapter 2)
- The structure of carbohydrates (chapter 3)
- The structure and function of mitochondria and the types of cells in which they are located (chapter 4)
- How enzymes work in conjunction with ATP, electron transport, and a proton pump (chapter 5)

## 6.1  Energy and Organisms

There are hundreds of different chemical reactions taking place within the cells of organisms. Many of these reactions are involved in providing energy for the cells. Organisms are classified into groups based on the kind of energy they use. Organisms that are able to use basic energy sources, such as sunlight, to make energy-containing organic molecules from inorganic raw materials are called **autotrophs** (*auto* = self; *troph* = feeding). There are also prokaryotic organisms that use inorganic chemical reactions as a source of energy to make larger organic molecules. This process is known as **chemosynthesis**. Therefore, there are at least two kinds of autotrophs: Those that use light are called *photosynthetic* autotrophs and those that use inorganic chemical reactions are called *chemosynthetic* autotrophs. All other organisms

require organic molecules as food and are called **heterotrophs** (*hetero* = other; *troph* = feeding). Heterotrophs get their energy from the chemical bonds of food molecules, such as carbohydrates, fats, and proteins, which they must obtain from their surroundings.

Within eukaryotic cells, certain biochemical processes are carried out in specific organelles. Chloroplasts are the sites of photosynthesis, and mitochondria are the sites of most of the reactions of cellular respiration (figure 6.1). Because prokaryotic cells lack mitochondria and chloroplasts, they carry out photosynthesis and cellular respiration within the cytoplasm or on the inner surfaces of the cell membrane or on other special membranes. Table 6.1 provides a summary of the concepts just discussed and how they are related to one another.

This chapter will focus on the reactions involved in the processes of cellular respiration. In **cellular respiration,**

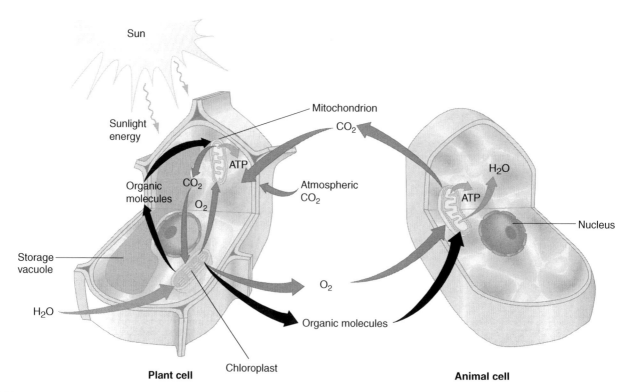

**FIGURE 6.1  Biochemical Pathways That Involve Energy Transformation**
Photosynthesis and cellular respiration both involve a series of chemical reactions that control the flow of energy. Organisms that contain photosynthetic machinery are capable of using light, water, and carbon dioxide to produce organic molecules, such as sugars, proteins, lipids, and nucleic acids. Oxygen is also released as a result of photosynthesis. In aerobic cellular respiration, organic molecules and oxygen are used to provide the energy to sustain life. Carbon dioxide and water are also released during aerobic respiration.

**TABLE 6.1   Summary of Biochemical Pathways, Energy Sources, and Kinds of Organisms**

| Autotroph or Heterotroph | Biochemical Pathways | Energy Source | Kinds of Organisms | Notes |
|---|---|---|---|---|
| Autotroph | Chemosynthesis | Inorganic chemical reactions | Certain Bacteria and Archaea | There are many types of chemosynthesis. |
| Autotroph | Photosynthesis | Light | Certain Bacteria and Archaea | Photosynthesis in Bacteria and Archaea differs from photosynthesis that takes place in the chloroplasts of eukaryotic organisms. |
| | | | Eucarya—plants and algae | Photosynthesis takes place in chloroplasts. |
| Autotroph and heterotroph | Cellular respiration | Oxidation of large, organic molecules | Bacteria and Archaea | There are many forms of cellular respiration. Some organisms use aerobic cellular respiration; others use anaerobic cellular respiration. Cellular respiration in Bacteria and Archaea does not take place in mitochondria. |
| | | | Eucarya—plants, animals, fungi, algae, protozoa | Most Eucarya use aerobic cellular respiration and it takes place in mitochondria. |

organisms control the release of chemical-bond energy from large, organic molecules and use the energy for the many activities necessary to sustain life. All organisms, whether autotrophic or heterotrophic, must carry out cellular respiration if they are to survive. Because nearly all organisms use organic molecules as a source of energy, they must obtain these molecules from their environment or manufacture these organic molecules, which they will later break down. Thus, photosynthetic organisms produce food molecules, such as carbohydrates, for themselves as well as for all the other organisms that feed on them. There are many variations of cellular respiration. Some organisms require the presence of oxygen for these processes, called *aerobic* processes. Other organisms carry out a form of respiration that does not require oxygen; these processes are called *anaerobic*.

### 6.1   CONCEPT REVIEW

1. How do autotrophs and heterotrophs differ?
2. What is chemosynthesis?
3. How are respiration and photosynthesis related to autotrophs and heterotrophs?

## 6.2   An Overview of Aerobic Cellular Respiration

**Aerobic cellular respiration** is a specific series of enzyme-controlled chemical reactions in which oxygen is involved in the breakdown of glucose into carbon dioxide and water; the chemical-bond energy from glucose is released to the cell in the form of ATP. The following equation summarizes this process as it occurs in your cells and those of many other organisms:

$$\text{glucose} + \text{oxygen} \rightarrow \begin{array}{c}\text{carbon}\\\text{dioxide}\end{array} + \text{water} + \text{energy}$$
$$C_6H_{12}O_6 + 6\,O_2 \rightarrow 6\,CO_2 + 6\,H_2O + \text{energy}$$
$$(\text{ATP} + \text{heat})$$

Covalent bonds are formed by atoms sharing pairs of fast-moving, energetic electrons. Therefore, the covalent bonds in the sugar glucose contain chemical potential energy. The removal of the electrons from glucose results in glucose being *oxidized*. Of all the covalent bonds in glucose (O—H, C—H, C—C), those easiest to get at are the C—H and O—H bonds on the outside of the molecule. When these bonds are broken, two things happen:

1. The energy of the electrons can ultimately be used to phosphorylate ADP molecules to produce higher-energy ATP molecules.
2. Hydrogen ions (protons) are released and pumped across membranes, creating a gradient. When they flow back to the side from which they were pumped, their energy is used to generate even more ATP (refer to chapter 5, Proton Pump).

These high-energy electrons cannot be allowed to fly about at random because they would quickly combine with other molecules, causing cell death. Electron-transfer molecules, such as $NAD^+$ and FAD, hold electrons temporarily before passing them on to other molecules. ATP is formed when these transfers take place (see chapter 5). Once energy

## FIGURE 6.2 Aerobic Cellular Respiration and Oxidation-Reduction Reaction

During aerobic cellular respiration, a series of oxidation-reduction reactions takes place. When the electrons are removed (oxidation) from sugar, it is unable to stay together and breaks into smaller units. The reduction part of the reaction occurs when these electrons are attached to another molecule. In aerobic cellular respiration, the electrons are eventually picked up by oxygen and the negatively charged oxygen attracts two positively charged hydrogen ions ($H^+$) to form water.

has been removed from electrons for ATP production, the electrons must be placed in a safe location. In *aerobic* cellular respiration, these electrons are ultimately attached to oxygen. Oxygen serves as the final resting place of the less energetic electrons. When the electrons are added to oxygen, it becomes a negatively charged ion, $O^=$.

Because the oxygen has gained electrons, it has been *reduced. Thus, in the aerobic cellular respiration of glucose, glucose is oxidized and oxygen is reduced.* A molecule cannot simply lose its electrons—they have to go someplace! If something is oxidized (loses electrons), something else must be reduced (gains electrons). Eventually, the positively charged hydrogen ions ($H^+$) that were released from the glucose molecule combine with the negatively charged oxygen ion ($O^=$) to form water ($H_2O$).

As all the hydrogens are stripped off the glucose molecule, the remaining carbon and oxygen atoms are rearranged to form individual molecules of $CO_2$. All the hydrogen originally a part of the glucose has been moved to the oxygen to form water. All the remaining carbon and oxygen atoms of the original glucose are now in the form of $CO_2$. The energy released from this process is used to generate ATP (figure 6.2).

In cells, these reactions take place in a particular order and in particular places within the cell. In eukaryotic cells, the process of releasing energy from food molecules begins in the cytoplasm and is completed in the mitochondria. There are three distinct enzymatic pathways involved (figure 6.3): glycolysis, the Krebs cycle, and the electron-transport system.

## Glycolysis

**Glycolysis** (*glyco* = sugar; *lysis* = to split) is a series of enzyme-controlled, anaerobic reactions that takes place in the cytoplasm of cells, which results in the breakdown of glucose with

the release of electrons and the formation of ATP. During glycolysis, the 6-carbon sugar glucose is split into two smaller, 3-carbon molecules, which undergo further modification to form pyruvic acid or pyruvate.[1] Enough energy is released to produce two ATP molecules. Some of the bonds holding hydrogen atoms to the glucose molecule are broken, and the electrons are picked up by electron carrier molecules ($NAD^+$) and transferred to a series of electron-transfer reactions known as the electron-transport system (ETS).

## The Krebs Cycle

The **Krebs cycle** is a series of enzyme-controlled reactions that takes place inside the mitochondrion, which completes the breakdown of pyruvic acid with the release of carbon dioxide, electrons, and ATP. During the Krebs cycle, the pyruvic acid molecules produced from glycolysis are further broken down. During these reactions, the remaining hydrogens are removed from the pyruvic acid, and their electrons are picked up by the electron carriers $NAD^+$ and FAD. These electrons are sent to the electron-transport system. A small amount of ATP is also formed during the Krebs cycle. The carbon and oxygen atoms that are the remains of the pyruvic acid molecules are released as carbon dioxide ($CO_2$).

## The Electron-Transport System (ETS)

The **electron-transport system (ETS)** is a series of enzyme-controlled reactions that converts the kinetic energy of hydrogen electrons to ATP. The electrons are carried to the electron-transport system from glycolysis and the Krebs cycle as NADH and $FADH_2$. The electrons are transferred through a series of oxidation-reduction reactions involving enzymes until eventually the electrons are accepted by oxygen atoms

---

[1] Several different ways of naming organic compounds have been used over the years. For our purposes, pyruvic acid and pyruvate are really the same basic molecule although technically, pyruvate is what is left when pyruvic acid has lost its hydrogen ion: pyruvic acid → $H^+$ + pyruvate. You also will see terms such as lactic acid and lactate and citric acid and citrate and many others used in a similar way.

**FIGURE 6.3 Aerobic Cellular Respiration: Overview**
*(a)* This sequence of reactions in the aerobic oxidation of glucose is an overview of the energy-yielding reactions of a cell. *(b)* Glycolysis, the Krebs cycle, and the electron-transport system (ETS) are each a series of enzyme-controlled reactions that extract energy from the chemical bonds in a glucose molecule. During glycolysis, glucose is split into pyruvic acid and ATP and electrons are released. During the Krebs cycle, pyruvic acid is further broken down to carbon dioxide with the release of ATP and the release of electrons. During the electron-transport system, oxygen is used to accept electrons, and water and ATP are produced. *(c)* Glycolysis takes place in the cytoplasm of the cell. Pyruvic acid enters mitochondria, where the Krebs cycle and electron-transport system (ETS) take place.

to form oxygen ions ($O^=$). During this process, a great deal of ATP is produced. The ATP is formed as a result of a proton gradient established when the energy of electrons is used to pump protons across a membrane (refer to chapter 5). The subsequent movement of protons back across the membrane results in ATP formation. The negatively charged oxygen atoms attract two positively charged hydrogen ions to form water ($H_2O$).

Aerobic respiration can be summarized as follows. *Glucose* enters glycolysis and is broken down to pyruvic acid, which enters the Krebs cycle, where the pyruvic acid molecules are further dismantled. The remains of the pyruvic acid molecules are released as *carbon dioxide*. The electrons and hydrogen ions released from glycolysis and the Krebs cycle are transferred as NADH and $FADH_2$ to the electron-transport system, where the electrons are transferred to *oxygen* available from the atmosphere. When hydrogen ions attach to oxygen ions, *water* is formed. *ATP* is formed during all three stages of aerobic cellular respiration, but most comes from the electron-transfer system.

## 6.2  CONCEPT REVIEW

4. Aerobic cellular respiration occurs in three stages. Name these and briefly describe what happens in each stage.
5. Which cellular organelle is involved in the process of aerobic cellular respiration?

## 6.3  The Metabolic Pathways of Aerobic Cellular Respiration

It is a good idea to begin with the simplest description and add layers of understanding as you go to additional levels. Therefore, this discussion of aerobic cellular respiration is divided into two levels:

1. a fundamental description and
2. a detailed description.

Ask your instructor which level is required for your course of study.

### Fundamental Description

#### Glycolysis
Glycolysis is a series of enzyme-controlled reactions that takes place in the cytoplasm. During glycolysis, a 6-carbon sugar molecule (glucose) has energy added to it from two ATP molecules. Adding this energy makes some of the bonds of the glucose molecule unstable, and the glucose molecule is more easily broken down. After passing through several more enzyme-controlled reactions, the 6-carbon glucose is broken down to two 3-carbon molecules known as glyceraldehyde-3-phosphate (also known as PGA, or phosphoglyceraldehyde), which undergo additional reactions to form pyruvic acid ($CH_3COCOOH$).

Enough energy is released by this series of reactions to produce four ATP molecules. Because two ATP molecules were used to start the reaction and four were produced, there is a *net gain* of two ATPs from the glycolytic pathway (figure 6.4). During the process of glycolysis, some hydrogens and their electrons are removed from the organic molecules being processed and picked up by the electron-transfer molecule $NAD^+$ to form NADH. Enough hydrogens are released during glycolysis to form 2 NADHs. The NADH with its extra electrons contains a large amount of potential energy, which can be used to make ATP in the electron-transport system. The job of the coenzyme $NAD^+$ is to transport these energy-containing electrons and protons safely to the electron-transport system. Once they have dropped off their electrons, the oxidized $NAD^+$s are available to pick up more electrons and repeat the job.

## Fundamental Summary of One Turn of Glycolysis

## The Krebs Cycle

The series of reactions known as the Krebs cycle takes place within the mitochondria of cells. It gets its name from its discoverer, Hans Krebs, and the fact that the series of reactions begins and ends with the same molecule; it cycles. The Krebs cycle is also known as the citric acid cycle and the TriCarboxylic Acid cycle (TCA). The 3-carbon pyruvic acid molecules released from glycolysis enter the mitochondria. These are acted upon by specific enzymes made using genetic information found on DNA located within the mitochondria (mDNA). One of these carbons is stripped off and the remaining 2-carbon fragment is attached to a molecule of *coenzyme A (CoA)*, becoming a compound called **acetyl-CoA.** Coenzyme A is made from pantethine (pantothenic acid), a form of vitamin $B_5$. Acetyl-CoA is the molecule that proceeds through the Krebs cycle. At the time the acetyl-CoA is produced, 2 hydrogens are attached to $NAD^+$ to form NADH. The carbon atom that was removed is released as carbon dioxide.

## Summary of Changes as Pyruvic Acid is Converted to Acetyl-CoA

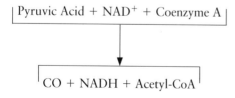

During the Krebs cycle (figure 6.5), the acetyl-CoA is completely oxidized (i.e., the remaining hydrogens and their

**FIGURE 6.4 Glycolysis: Fundamental Description**
Glycolysis is the biochemical pathway many organisms use to oxidize glucose. During this sequence of chemical reactions, the 6-carbon molecule of glucose is oxidized. As a result, pyruvic acid is produced, electrons are picked up by $NAD^+$, and ATP is produced.

electrons are removed). Most of the electrons are picked up by $NAD^+$ to form NADH, but at one point in the process FAD picks up electrons to form $FADH_2$. Regardless of which electron carrier is being used, the electrons are sent to the electron-transport system. The remaining carbon and oxygen atoms are combined to form $CO_2$. As in glycolysis, enough energy is released to generate 2 ATP molecules. At the end of the Krebs cycle, the acetyl portion of the acetyl-CoA has been completely broken down (oxidized) to $CO_2$. The CoA is released and available to be used again. The energy in the molecule has been transferred to ATP, NADH, or $FADH_2$. Also, some of the energy has been released as heat. For each of the acetyl-CoA molecules that enters the Krebs cycle, 1 ATP, 3 NADHs, and 1 $FADH_2$ are produced. If we count the NADH produced during glycolysis, when acetyl-CoA was formed, there are a total of 4 NADHs for each pyruvic acid that enters a mitochondrion.

## Fundamental Summary of One Turn of the Krebs Cycle

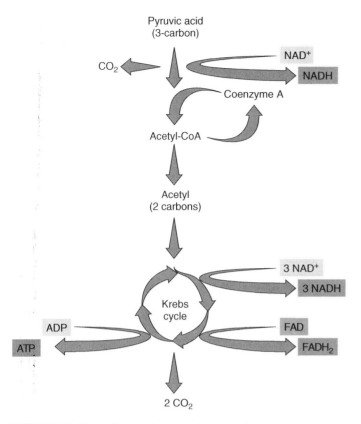

## FIGURE 6.5  Krebs Cycle: Fundamental Description

The Krebs cycle takes place in the mitochondria of cells to complete the oxidation of glucose. During this sequence of chemical reactions, a pyruvic acid molecule produced from glycolysis is stripped of its hydrogens. The hydrogens are picked up by NAD$^+$ and FAD for transport to the ETS. The remaining atoms are reorganized into molecules of carbon dioxide. Enough energy is released during the Krebs cycle to form 2 ATPs. Because 2 pyruvic acid molecules were produced from glycolysis, the Krebs cycle must be run twice in order to complete their oxidation (once for each pyruvic acid).

## The Electron-Transport System

Of the three steps of aerobic cellular respiration, (glycolysis, Krebs cycle, and electron-transport system) cells generate the greatest amount of ATP from the electron-transport system (figure 6.6). During this stepwise sequence of oxidation-reduction reactions, the energy from the NADH and FADH$_2$ molecules generated in glycolysis and the Krebs cycle is used to produce ATP. Iron-containing *cytochrome* (*cyto* = cell; *chrom* = color) enzyme molecules are located on the membranes of the mitochondrion. The energy-rich electrons are passed *(transported)* from one cytochrome to another, and the energy is used to pump protons (hydrogen ions) from one side of the membrane to the other. The result of this is a higher concentration of hydrogen ions on one side of the membrane. As the concentration of hydrogen ions increases on one side, a proton gradient builds up. Because of this concentration gradient, when a membrane channel is opened, the protons flow back to the side from which they were pumped. As they

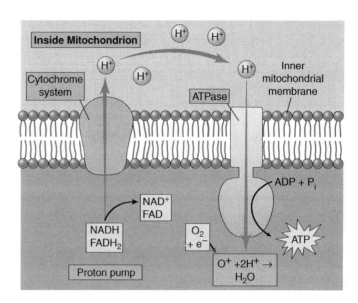

## FIGURE 6.6  The Electron-Transport System: Fundamental Description

The electron-transport system (ETS) is also known as the cytochrome system. With the help of enzymes, the electrons are passed through a series of oxidation-reduction reactions. The energy the electrons give up is used to pump protons (H$^+$) across a membrane in the mitochondrion. When protons flow back through the membrane, enzymes in the membrane cause the formation of ATP. The protons eventually combine with the oxygen that has gained electrons, and water is produced.

pass through the channels, a phosphorylase enzyme (ATP synthetase, also referred to as ATPase) speeds the formation of an ATP molecule by bonding a phosphate to an ADP molecule (phosphorylation). When all the electrons and hydrogen ions are accounted for, a total of 32 ATPs are formed from the electrons and hydrogens removed from the original glucose molecule. The hydrogens are then bonded to oxygen to form water.

## Fundamental Summary of the Electron-Transport System

$$32\ ADP + 10\ NADH + 2\ FADH_2 + 6\ O_2$$
(free)
$$32\ ATP + 10\ NAD^+ + 2\ FAD + 12\ H_2O$$

## Detailed Description

### Glycolysis

The first stage of the cellular respiration process takes place in the cytoplasm. This first step, known as glycolysis, consists of the enzymatic breakdown of a glucose molecule without the use of molecular oxygen. Because no oxygen is required, glycolysis is called an anaerobic process. The glycolysis pathway can be divided into two general sets of reactions. The first reactions make the glucose molecule unstable, and later oxidation-reduction reactions are used to synthesize ATP and capture hydrogens.

Because glucose is a very stable molecule and will not automatically break down to release energy, some energy must be added to the glucose molecule in order to start glycolysis. In glycolysis, the initial glucose molecule gains a phosphate to become glucose-6-phosphate, which is converted to fructose-6-phosphate. When a second phosphate is added, fructose-1,6-bisphosphate ($P—C_6—P$) is formed. This 6-carbon molecule is unstable and breaks apart to form two 3-carbon, glyceraldehyde-3-phosphate molecules.

Each of the two glyceraldehyde-3-phosphate molecules acquires a second phosphate from a phosphate supply normally found in the cytoplasm. Each molecule now has 2 phosphates attached to form 1,3-bisphosphoglycerate ($P—C_3—P$). A series of reactions follows, in which energy is released by breaking chemical bonds that hold the phosphates to 1,3-bisphosphoglycerate. The energy and the phosphates are used to produce ATP. Since there are two 1,3-bisphosphoglycerate molecules each with 2 phosphates, a total of 4 ATPs are produced. Because 2 ATPs were used to start the process, a net yield of 2 ATPs results. In addition, 4 hydrogen atoms detach from the carbon skeleton and their electrons are transferred to $NAD^+$ to form NADH, which transfers the electrons to the electron-transport system. The 3-carbon pyruvic acid molecules that remain are the raw material for the Krebs cycle. Because glycolysis occurs in the cytoplasm and the Krebs cycle takes place inside mitochondria, the pyruvic acid must enter the mitochondrion before it can be broken down further (figure 6.7).

## Summary of Detailed Description of Glycolysis
The process of glycolysis takes place in the cytoplasm of a cell, where glucose ($C_6H_{12}O_6$) enters a series of reactions that:

1. requires the use of 2 ATPs,
2. ultimately results in the formation of 4 ATPs,
3. results in the formation of 2 NADHs, and
4. results in the formation of 2 molecules of pyruvic acid ($CH_3COCOOH$).

**FIGURE 6.7 Glycolysis: Detailed Description**
Glycolysis is a process that takes place in the cytoplasm of cells. It does not require the use of oxygen, so it is an anaerobic process. During the first few steps, phosphates are added from ATP and ultimately the 6-carbon sugar is split into two 3-carbon compounds. During the final steps in the process, $NAD^+$ accepts electrons and hydrogen to form NADH. In addition, ATP is produced. Two ATPs form for each of the 3-carbon molecules that are processed in glycolysis. Because there are two 3-carbon compounds, a total of 4 ATPs are formed. However, because 2 ATPs were used to start the process, there is a net gain of 2 ATPs. Pyruvic acid (pyruvate) is left at the end of glycolysis.

Because 2 molecules of ATP are used to start the process and a total of 4 ATPs are generated, each glucose molecule that undergoes glycolysis produces a net yield of 2 ATPs.

## OUTLOOKS 6.1

# What Happens When You Drink Alcohol

Ethyl alcohol ($CH_3CH_2OH$) is a 2-carbon organic compound with a single alcoholic functional group. Because it is soluble in water, it is easily absorbed into the bloodstream. After an alcoholic beverage enters the body, it is spread by the circulatory system rapidly throughout the body and enters the brain. The majority of the alcohol is absorbed from the stomach (20%) and small intestine (80%). The more a person drinks, the higher the blood alcohol level. How fast alcohol is absorbed depends on several factors.

1. Food in the stomach slows absorption.
2. Strenuous physical exercise decreases absorption.
3. Drugs (e.g., nicotine, marijuana, and ginseng) increase absorption.

Ninety percent of ethyl alcohol is oxidized in mitochondria to acetate ($CH_3CH_2OH + NAD^+ \rightarrow CH_3CHO + NADH$). The acetate is then converted to acetyl-CoA that enters the Krebs cycle where ATP is produced. Alcohol is high in calories (1g = 7,000 calories, or 7 *food* calories). A standard glass of wine has about 15 g of alcohol and about 100 kilocalories. The 10% not metabolized is eliminated in sweat or urine, or given off in breath. It takes the liver one hour to deal with one unit of alcohol. A unit of alcohol is:

- 250 ml (1/2 pint) of ordinary strength beer/lager.
- One glass (125 ml/4 fl oz) of wine.
- 47 ml/1.5 oz of sherry/vermouth.
- 47 ml/1.5 oz of liquor.

If alcohol is consumed at a rate faster than the liver can break it down, the blood alcohol level rises. This causes an initial feeling of warmth and light-headedness. However, alcohol is a depressant, that is, it decreases the activity of the nervous system. At first, it may inhibit circuits in the brain that normally inhibit a person's actions. This usually results in a person becoming more talkative and active—uninhibited. However, as the alcohol's effect continues, other changes can take place. These include increased aggression, loss of memory, and loss of motor control.

Long-term, excessive use of alcohol can cause damage to the liver, resulting in the development of a fatty liver, alcoholic hepatitis, and alcoholic cirrhosis. It can also interfere with the kidneys' regulation of water, sodium, potassium, calcium, and phosphate and with the kidney's ability to maintain a proper acid-base balance, and produce hormones. It also causes low blood sugar levels, dehydration, high blood pressure, strokes, heart disease, birth defects, osteoporosis, and certain cancers.

Drinking alcohol in moderation does have some health benefits if the beverage contains antioxidants (for example, red wines and dark beers). The antioxidants in red wine (polyphenols) appear to counteract the negative effect of chemicals called free radicals released during metabolism. Free radicals are known to destroy cell components and cause mutations, damage which can lead to heart disease and cancers. Antioxidants protect against this kind of harm by capturing free radicals.

## The Krebs Cycle

After pyruvate (pyruvic acid) enters the mitochondrion, it is first acted upon by an enzyme, along with a molecule known as *coenzyme A (CoA)* (figure 6.8). This results in three significant products. Hydrogen atoms are removed and NADH is formed, a carbon is removed and carbon dioxide is formed, and a 2-carbon fragment is formed, which temporarily attaches to coenzyme A to produce acetyl-coenzyme A. (These and subsequent reactions of the Krebs cycle take place in the fluid between the membranes of the mitochondrion.) The acetyl coenzyme A enters the series of reactions known as the Krebs cycle. During the Krebs cycle, the acetyl-CoA is systematically dismantled. Its hydrogen atoms are removed and the remaining carbons are released as carbon dioxide (Outlooks 6.1).

The first step in this process involves the acetyl-CoA. The acetyl portion of the complex is transferred to a 4-carbon compound called *oxaloacetate (oxaloacetic acid)* and a new 6-carbon citrate molecule (citric acid) is formed. The coenzyme A is released to participate in another reaction with pyruvic acid. This newly formed citrate is broken down in a series of reactions, which ultimately produces oxaloacetate, which was used in the first step of the cycle (hence, the names Krebs cycle, citric acid cycle, and tricarboxylic acid cycle). The compounds formed during this cycle are called *keto acids*.

In the process, electrons are removed and, along with protons, become attached to the coenzymes $NAD^+$ and FAD. Most become attached to $NAD^+$ but some become attached to FAD. As the molecules move through the Krebs cycle, enough energy is released to allow the synthesis of 1 ATP molecule for each acetyl-CoA that enters the cycle. The ATP is formed from ADP and a phosphate already present in the mitochondria. For each pyruvate molecule that enters a mitochondrion and is processed through the Krebs cycle, 3 carbons are released as 3 carbon dioxide molecules, 5 pairs of hydrogen atoms are removed and become attached to NAD⁺ or FAD, and 1 ATP molecule is generated. When both pyruvate molecules have been processed through the Krebs cycle, (1) all the original carbons from the glucose have been released into the atmosphere as 6 carbon dioxide molecules; (2) all the hydrogen originally found on the glucose has been transferred to either NAD⁺ or FAD to form NADH or FADH₂; and (3) 2 ATPs have been formed from the addition of phosphates to ADPs (review figure 6.8).

## Summary of Detailed Description of the Eukaryotic Krebs Cycle

The Krebs cycle takes place within the mitochondria. For each acetyl-CoA molecule that enters the Krebs cycle:

1. The three carbons from a pyruvate are converted to acetyl-CoA and released as carbon dioxide ($CO_2$). One $CO_2$ is actually released before acetyl-CoA is formed.
2. Five pairs of hydrogens become attached to hydrogen carriers to become 4 NADHs and 1 FADH₂. One of the NADHs is released before acetyl-CoA enters the Krebs cycle.
3. One ATP is generated.

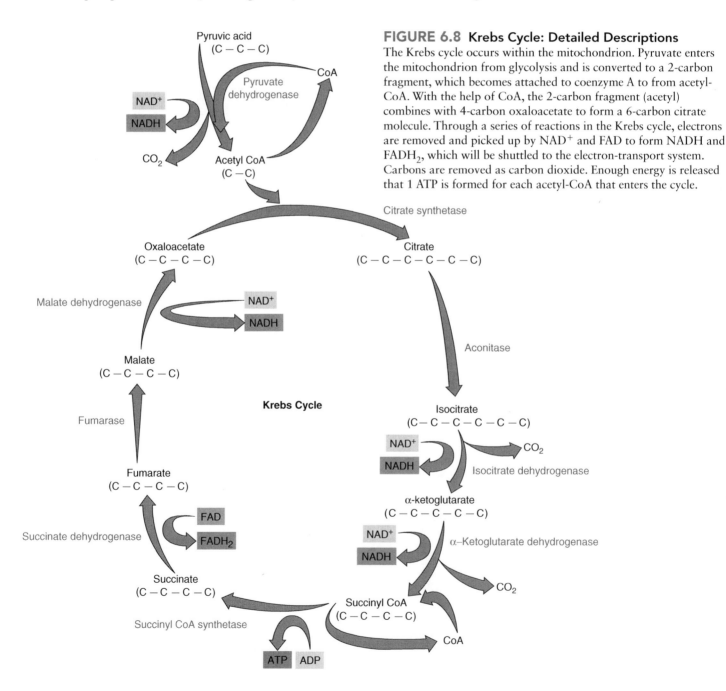

**FIGURE 6.8 Krebs Cycle: Detailed Descriptions**
The Krebs cycle occurs within the mitochondrion. Pyruvate enters the mitochondrion from glycolysis and is converted to a 2-carbon fragment, which becomes attached to coenzyme A to from acetyl-CoA. With the help of CoA, the 2-carbon fragment (acetyl) combines with 4-carbon oxaloacetate to form a 6-carbon citrate molecule. Through a series of reactions in the Krebs cycle, electrons are removed and picked up by NAD⁺ and FAD to form NADH and FADH₂, which will be shuttled to the electron-transport system. Carbons are removed as carbon dioxide. Enough energy is released that 1 ATP is formed for each acetyl-CoA that enters the cycle.

## The Electron-Transport System

The series of reactions in which energy is transferred from the electrons and protons carried by NADH and FADH$_2$ is known as the electron-transport system (ETS) (figure 6.9). This is the final stage of aerobic cellular respiration and is dedicated to generating ATP. The reactions that make up the electron-transport system are a series of oxidation-reduction reactions in which the electrons are passed from one electron carrier molecule to another until, ultimately, they are accepted by oxygen atoms. The negatively charged oxygen combines with the hydrogen ions to form water. It is this step that makes the process aerobic. Keep in mind that potential energy increases whenever things experiencing a repelling force are pushed together, such as adding the third phosphate to an ADP molecule. Potential energy also increases whenever things that attract each other are pulled apart, as in the separation of the protons from the electrons.

Let's now look in just a bit more detail at what happens to the electrons and protons that are carried to the electron-transport systems by NADH and FADH$_2$ and how these activities are used to produce ATP. The mitochondrion consists of two membranes—an outer, enclosing membrane and an inner, folded membrane. The reactions of the ETS are associated with this inner membrane. Within the structure of the membrane are several *enzyme complexes*, which perform particular parts of the ETS reactions (review figure 6.9). The production of ATPs involves two separate but connected processes. Electrons carried by NADH enter reactions in enzyme complex I, where they lose some energy and are eventually picked up by a coenzyme (coenzyme Q). Electrons from FADH$_2$ enter enzyme complex II and also are eventually transferred to coenzyme Q. Coenzyme Q transfers the electrons to enzyme complex III. In complex III, the electrons lose additional energy and are transferred to cytochrome c, which transfers electrons to enzyme complex IV. In complex IV, the electrons are eventually transferred to oxygen. As the electrons lose energy in complex I, complex III, and complex IV, additional protons are pumped into the intermembrane space. When these protons flow down the concentration gradient through channels in the membrane, phosphorylase enzymes (ATPase) in the membrane are able to use the energy to generate ATP.

A total of 12 pairs of electrons and hydrogens are transported to the ETS from glycolysis and the Krebs cycle for each glucose that enters the process. In eukaryotic organisms, the pairs of electrons can be accounted for as follows: 2 pairs are carried by NADH and were generated during glycolysis outside the mitochondrion, 8 pairs are carried as NADH and were generated within the mitochondrion, and 2 pairs are carried by FADH$_2$ and were generated within the mitochondrion.

- For each of the 8 NADHs generated within the mitochondrion, enough energy is released to produce 3 ATP molecules. Therefore, 24 ATPs are released from these electrons carried by NADH.

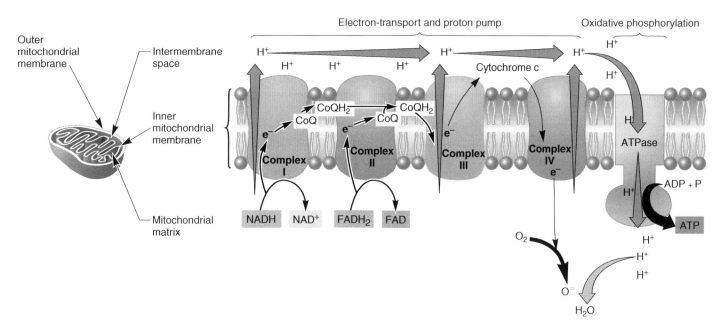

## FIGURE 6.9  The Electron-Transport System: Detailed Description

Most of the ATP produced by aerobic cellular respiration comes from the ETS. NADH and FADH$_2$ deliver electrons to the enzymes responsible for the ETS. There are several protein complexes in the inner membrane of the mitochondrion, each of which is responsible for a portion of the reactions that yield ATP. The energy of electrons is given up in small amounts and used to pump protons into the intermembrane space. When these protons flow back through pores in the membrane, ATPase produces ATP. The electrons eventually are transferred to oxygen and the negatively charged oxygen ions accept protons to form water.

- In eukaryotic cells, the electrons released during glycolysis are carried by NADH and converted to 2 $FADH_2$ in order to shuttle them into the mitochondria. Once they are inside the mitochondria, they follow the same pathway as the other 2 $FADH_2$s from the Krebs cycle.

The electrons carried by $FADH_2$ are lower in energy. When these electrons go through the series of oxidation-reduction reactions, they release enough energy to produce a total of 8 ATPs. Therefore, a total of 32 ATPs are produced from the hydrogen electrons that enter the ETS.

Finally, a complete accounting of all the ATPs produced during all three parts of aerobic cellular respiration results in a total of 36 ATPs: 32 from the ETS, 2 from glycolysis, and 2 from the Krebs cycle.

### Summary of Detailed Description of the Eukaryotic Electron-Transport System

The electron-transport system takes place within the mitochondrion, where:

1. Oxygen is used up as the oxygen atoms accept hydrogens from NADH and $FADH_2$ forming water ($H_2O$).
2. $NAD^+$ and FAD are released, to be used over again.
3. Thirty-two ATPs are produced.

### 6.3   CONCEPT REVIEW

6. For glycolysis, the Krebs cycle, and the electron-transport system, list two molecules that enter and two that leave each pathway.
7. How is each of the following involved in aerobic cellular respiration: $NAD^+$, pyruvic acid, oxygen, and ATP?

### 6.4   Aerobic Cellular Respiration in Prokaryotes

The discussion so far in this chapter has dealt with the process of aerobic cellular respiration in eukaryotic organisms. However, some prokaryotic cells also use aerobic cellular respiration. Because prokaryotes do not have mitochondria, there are some differences between what they do and what eukaryotes do. The primary difference involves the electrons carried from glycolysis to the electron-transport system. In eukaryotes, the electrons released during glycolysis are carried by NADH and transferred to FAD to form $FADH_2$ in order to get the electrons across the outer membrane of the mitochondrion. Because $FADH_2$ results in the production of fewer ATPs than NADH, there is a cost to the eukaryotic cell of getting the electrons into the mitochondrion. This transfer is not necessary in prokaryotes, so they are able to produce a theoretical 38 ATPs for each glucose metabolized, rather than the 36 ATPs produced by eukaryotes (table 6.2).

**TABLE 6.2** Aerobic ATP Production: Prokaryotes vs. Eukaryotic Cells

| Stage of Aerobic Cellular Respiration | Prokaryotes | Eukaryotes |
|---|---|---|
| Glycolysis | Net gain 2 ATP | Net gain 2 ATP |
| Krebs cycle | 2 ATP | 2 ATP |
| ETS | 34 ATP | 32 ATP |
| Total | 38 ATP | 36 ATP |

### 6.4   CONCEPT REVIEW

8. How is aerobic cellular respiration different in prokaryotic and eukaryotic organisms?

### 6.5   Anaerobic Cellular Respiration

Although aerobic cellular respiration is the fundamental process by which most organisms generate ATP, some organisms do not have the necessary enzymes to carry out the Krebs cycle and ETS. Most of these are Bacteria or Archaea, but there are certain eukaryotic organisms, such as yeasts, that can live in the absence of oxygen and do not use their Krebs cycle and ETS. Even within multicellular organisms, there are differences in the metabolic activities of cells. For example some of your cells are able to survive for periods of time without oxygen. However, all cells still need a constant supply of ATP. An organism that does not require $O_2$ as its final electron acceptor is called *anaerobic* (*an* = without; *aerob* = air) and performs **anaerobic cellular respiration**. Although some anaerobic organisms do not use oxygen, they are capable of using other inorganic or organic molecules as their final electron acceptors. The acceptor molecule might be sulfur, nitrogen, or other inorganic atoms or ions. It might also be an organic molecule, such as pyruvic acid ($CH_3COCOOH$). Anaerobic respiration is an incomplete oxidation and results in the production of smaller electron-containing molecules and energy in the form of ATP and heat (figure 6.10).

Many organisms that perform anaerobic cellular respiration use the glycolytic pathway to obtain energy. **Fermentation** is the word used to describe anaerobic pathways that oxidize glucose to generate ATP by using an organic molecule as the ultimate hydrogen electron acceptor. Electrons removed from sugar in the earlier stages of glycolysis are added to the pyruvic acid formed at the end of glycolysis. Depending on the kind of organism and the specific enzymes it possesses, the pyruvic acid can be converted into lactic acid, ethyl alcohol, acetone, or other organic molecules (figure 6.11).

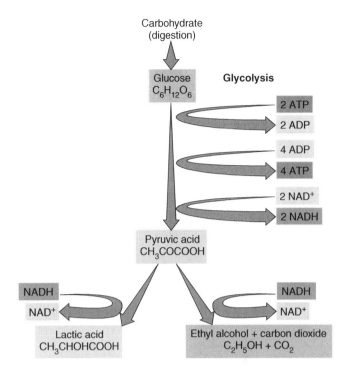

**FIGURE 6.10  Anaerobic Cellular Respiration in Perspective**
This flowchart shows the relationships among the various types of cellular respiration and the descriptive terminology used. Notice that all begin with a molecular source of energy and end with the generation of ATP.

Organisms that produce ethyl alcohol have genes for the production of enzymes that guide electrons onto pyruvic acid. This reaction results in the conversion of pyruvic acid to ethyl alcohol (ethanol) and carbon dioxide. Other organisms have different genes, produce different enzymes, carry out different reactions, and, therefore, lead to the formation of different end products of fermentation. The formation of molecules such as alcohol and lactic acid is necessary to regenerate the $NAD^+$ needed for continued use in glycolysis. It must be done here, because it is not being regenerated by an ETS, as happens in aerobic respiration. Although many products can be formed from pyruvic acid, we will look at only two fermentation pathways in more detail.

## Alcoholic Fermentation

**Alcoholic fermentation** is the anaerobic respiration pathway that yeast cells follow when oxygen is lacking in their environment. In this pathway, the pyruvic acid ($CH_3COCOOH$) is converted to ethanol (a 2-carbon alcohol, $CH_3CH_2OH$) and carbon dioxide. Yeast cells then are able to generate only 4 ATPs from glycolysis. The cost for glycolysis is still 2 ATPs; thus, for each glucose a yeast cell oxidizes, it profits by 2 ATPs.

Although during alcoholic fermentation yeasts get ATP and discard the waste products ethanol and carbon dioxide, these waste products are useful to humans. In making bread, the carbon dioxide is the important end product; it

| Fermentation Product | Possible Source | Importance |
|---|---|---|
| Lactic acid | Bacteria: *Lactobacillus bulgaricus* | Aids in changing milk to yogurt |
| | *Homo sapiens* Muscle cells | Produced when $O_2$ is limited; results in pain and muscle inaction |
| Ethyl alcohol +$CO_2$ | Yeast: *Saccharomyces cerevisiae* | Brewing and baking |

**FIGURE 6.11  Fermentations**
The upper portion of this figure is a simplified version of glycolysis. Many organisms can carry out the process of glycolysis and derive energy from it. The ultimate end product is determined by the kinds of enzymes the specific organism can produce. The synthesis of these various molecules is the organism's way of oxidizing NADH to regenerate $NAD^+$ and reducing pyruvic acid to a new end product.

becomes trapped in the bread dough and makes it rise—the bread is *leavened*. Dough that has not undergone this process is called *unleavened*. The alcohol produced by the yeast evaporates during the baking process. In the brewing industry, ethanol is the desirable product produced by yeast cells. Champagne, other sparkling wines, and beer are products that contain both carbon dioxide and alcohol. The alcohol accumulates, and the carbon dioxide in the bottle makes them sparkling (bubbly) beverages. In the manufacture of many wines, the carbon dioxide is allowed to escape, so these wines are not sparkling; they are called "still" wines.

**Summary of Alcohol Fermentation**

1. Starts with glycolysis
   a. Glucose is metabolized to pyruvic acid.
   b. A net of 2 ATP is made.
2. During alcoholic fermentation
   a. pyruvic acid is reduced to form ethanol.
   b. carbon dioxide is released.
3. Yeasts do this in
   a. leavened bread.
   b. sparkling wine.

## Lactic Acid Fermentation

In **lactic acid fermentation,** the pyruvic acid ($CH_3COCOOH$) that results from glycolysis is converted to lactic acid ($CH_3CHOHCOOH$) by the transfer of electrons that had been removed from the original glucose. In this case, the net profit is again only 2 ATPs per glucose. The buildup of the waste product, lactic acid, eventually interferes with normal metabolic functions and the bacteria die. The lactic acid waste product from these types of anaerobic bacteria are used to make yogurt, cultured sour cream, cheeses, and other fermented dairy products. The lactic acid makes the milk protein coagulate and become pudding-like or solid. It also gives the products their tart flavor, texture, and aroma (Outlooks 6.2).

In the human body, different cells have different metabolic capabilities. Nerve cells must have a constant supply of oxygen to conduct aerobic cellular respiration. Red blood cells lack mitochondria and must rely on the anaerobic process of lactic acid fermentation to provide themselves with energy. Muscle cells can do either. As long as oxygen is available to skeletal muscle cells, they function aerobically. However, when oxygen is unavailable—because of long periods of exercise or

heart or lung problems that prevent oxygen from getting to the skeletal muscle cells—the cells make a valiant effort to meet energy demands by functioning anaerobically.

When skeletal muscle cells function anaerobically, they accumulate lactic acid. This lactic acid must ultimately be metabolized, which requires oxygen. Therefore, the accumulation of lactic acid represents an *oxygen debt*, which must be repaid in the future. It is the lactic acid buildup that makes muscles tired when we exercise. When the lactic acid concentration becomes great enough, lactic acid fatigue results. As a person cools down after a period of exercise, breathing and heart rate stay high until the oxygen debt is repaid and the level of oxygen in the muscle cells returns to normal. During this period, the lactic acid that has accumulated is converted back into pyruvic acid. The pyruvic acid can then continue through the Krebs cycle and the ETS as oxygen becomes available. In addition to what is happening in the muscles,

---

## OUTLOOKS 6.2

# Souring vs. Spoilage

The fermentation of carbohydrates to organic acid products, such as lactic acid, is commonly called *souring*. Cultured sour cream, cheese, and yogurt are produced by the action of fermenting bacteria. Lactic-acid bacteria of the genus *Lactobacillus* are used in the fermentation process. While growing in the milk, the bacteria convert lactose to lactic acid, which causes the proteins in the milk to coagulate and come out of solution to form a solid curd. The higher acid level also inhibits the growth of spoilage microorganisms.

Spoilage, or putrefaction, is the anaerobic respiration of proteins with the release of nitrogen and sulfur-containing organic compounds as products. Protein fermentation by the bacterium *Clostridium* produces foul-smelling chemicals such as putrescine, cadaverine, hydrogen sulfide, and methyl mercaptan. *Clostridium perfringens* and *C. sporogenes* are the two anaerobic bacteria associated with the disease gas gangrene. A gangrenous wound is a foul-smelling infection resulting from the fermentation activities of those two bacteria.

much of the lactic acid is transported by the bloodstream to the liver, where about 20% is metabolized through the Krebs cycle and 80% is resynthesized into glucose.

## Summary of Lactic Acid Fermentation

1. Starts with glycolysis
   a. Glucose is metabolized to pyruvic acid.
   b. A net of 2 ATP is made.
2. During lactic acid fermentation
   a. pyruvic acid is reduced to form lactic acid.
   b. no carbon dioxide is released.
3. Muscle cells have the enzymes to do this, but brain cells do not.
   a. Muscle cells can survive brief periods of oxygen deprivation, but brain cells cannot.
   b. Lactic acid "burns" in muscles.

## 6.6  Metabolic Processing of Molecules Other Than Carbohydrates

Up to this point, we have discussed only the methods and pathways that allow organisms to release the energy tied up in carbohydrates (sugars). Frequently, cells lack sufficient carbohydrates for their energetic needs but have other materials from which energy can be removed. Fats and proteins, in addition to carbohydrates, make up the diet of many organisms. These three foods provide the building blocks for the cells, and all can provide energy. Carbohydrates can be digested to simple sugars, proteins can be digested to amino acids, and fats can be digested to glycerol and fatty acids. The basic pathways organisms use to extract energy from fat and protein are the same as for carbohydrates: glycolysis, the Krebs cycle, and the electron-transport system. However, there are some additional steps necessary to get fats and proteins ready to enter these pathways at several points in glycolysis and the Krebs cycle where fats and proteins enter to be respired.

### Fat Respiration

A triglyceride (also known as a neutral fat) is a large molecule that consists of a molecule of glycerol with 3 fatty acids attached to it. Before these fats can be broken down to release energy, they must be converted to smaller units by digestive processes. Several enzymes are involved in these steps. The first step is to break the

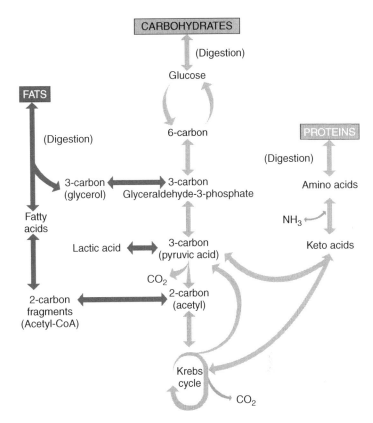

**FIGURE 6.12  The Interconversion of Fats, Carbohydrates, and Proteins**
Cells do not necessarily use all food as energy. One type of food can be changed into another type to be used as raw materials for the construction of needed molecules or for storage. Notice that many of the reaction arrows have two heads (i.e., these reactions can go in either direction). For example, glycerol can be converted into glyceraldehyde-3-phosphate and glyceraldehyde-3-phosphate can become glycerol.

bonds between the glycerol and the fatty acids. Glycerol is a 3-carbon molecule that is converted into glyceraldehyde-3-phosphate. Because glyceraldehyde-3-phosphate is involved in one of the steps in glycolysis, it can enter the glycolysis pathway (figure 6.12 ). The remaining fatty acids are often long molecules (typically 14 to 20 carbons long), which also must be processed before they can be further metabolized. First, they need to enter the mitochondrion, where subsequent reactions take place. Once inside the mitochondrion, each long chain of carbons that makes up the carbon skeleton is hydrolyzed (split by the addition of a water molecule) into 2-carbon fragments. Next, each of the 2-carbon fragments is carried into the Krebs cycle by coenzyme A molecules. Once in the Krebs cycle, they proceed through the Krebs cycle just like the acetyl-CoAs from glucose (Outlooks 6.3).

By following the glycerol and each 2-carbon fragment through the cycle, you can see that each molecule of fat has the potential to release several times as much ATP as does a molecule of glucose. Each glucose molecule has 6 pairs of hydrogen, whereas a typical molecule of fat has up to 10 times that number. This is why fat makes such a good long-term energy

# Body Odor and Bacterial Metabolism

In our culture, natural body odor is considered by most to be undesirable. Body odor is the result of bacteria metabolizing chemicals released by glands called aprocrine glands. These glands are associated with hair follicles and are especially numerous within the scalp, underarms, and genitals. They produce fatty acids and other compounds that are secreted onto the skin when people sweat as a result of becoming overheated, exercising, or being stressed. Bacteria metabolize these compounds in perspiration, releasing other compounds responsible for body odor.

A number of factors affect how bacteria metabolize fatty acids and, therefore, the strength and nature of a person's body odor. Hereditary factors can play an important role, as evidenced by the genetic abnormality, hyperhidrosis. People with this condition experience excessive perspiration. Diabetes, low blood sugar, menopause,

kidney disease, or liver disease can lead to profuse sweating in some cases. Foods, such as garlic and onions, and spices, such as curry, can lead to stronger body aroma. Caffeine, in coffee, tea, sodas, and chocolate, also affects body odor. People with an imbalance of magnesium and zinc are also more likely to generate more pungent body odors.

These bacteria are usually controlled with commercially available products. Deodorants mask the odors, antiperspirants reduce the flow of perspiration, antiseptics destroy the microorganisms, and soaps remove them. Most antiperspirants work by using aluminum compounds (aluminum chlorhydrate) that reduce the flow of sweat and are moderately antibacterial. If a person is allergic to such compounds, it may be necessary to use deodorant soaps with more powerful antimicrobials, such as chlorhexidine.

storage material. It is also why it takes so long for people on a weight-reducing diet to remove fat. It takes time to use all the energy contained in the fatty acids. On a weight basis, there are twice as many calories in a gram of fat as there are in a gram of carbohydrate.

Fats are an excellent source of energy and the storage of fat is an important process. Furthermore, other kinds of molecules can be converted to fat. You already know that people can get fat from eating sugar. Notice in figure 6.12 that both carbohydrates and fats can enter the Krebs cycle and release energy. Although people require both fats and carbohydrates in their diets, they need not be in precise ratios; the body can make some interconversions. This means that people who eat excessive amounts of carbohydrates will deposit body fat. It also means that people who starve can generate glucose by breaking down fats and using the glycerol to synthesize glucose.

## Summary of Fat Respiration
1. Fats are broken down into
   a. glycerol.
   b. fatty acids.
2. Glycerol
   a. is converted to glyceraldehyde-3-phosphate.
   b. enters glycolysis.
3. Fatty acids
   a. are converted to acetyl-CoA.
   b. enter the Kreb's cycle.
4. Each molecule of fat fuels the formation of many more ATP than glucose.
   a. This makes it a good energy-storage molecule.

## Protein Respiration

Proteins can be catabolized and interconverted just as fats and carbohydrates are (review figure 6.12). The first step in using protein for energy is to digest the protein into individual amino acids. Each amino acid then needs to have the amino group (—NH$_2$) removed, a process (deamination) that takes place in the liver. The remaining non-nitrogenous part of the protein is converted to keto acid and enters the respiratory cycle as acetyl-CoA, pyruvic acid, or one of the other types of molecules found in the Krebs cycle. As the acids progress through the Krebs cycle, the electrons are removed and sent to the ETS, where their energy is converted into the chemical-bond energy of ATP. The amino group that was removed from the amino acid is converted into ammonia. Some organisms excrete ammonia directly; others convert ammonia into other nitrogen-containing compounds, such as urea (humans) or uric acid (birds). All of these molecules are toxic, increase the workload of the liver, can damage the kidneys and other organs, and must be eliminated. They are transported in the blood to the kidneys, where they are eliminated. In the case of a high-protein diet, increasing fluid intake will allow the kidneys to remove the urea or uric acid efficiently.

When proteins are eaten, they are digested into their component amino acids. These amino acids are then available to be used to construct other proteins. Proteins cannot be stored; if they or their component amino acids are not needed immediately, they will be converted into fat or carbohydrates or will be metabolized to provide energy. This presents a problem for individuals who do not have ready access to a continuous source of amino acids in their diet (e.g., individuals on a low-protein diet).

# HOW SCIENCE WORKS 6.1

## Applying Knowledge of Biochemical Pathways

As scientists have developed a better understanding of the processes of aerobic cellular respiration and anaerobic cellular respiration, several practical applications of this knowledge have developed:

1. Newborn human infants have a modified respiratory plan that allows them to shut down the ATP production of their mitochondria in certain fatty tissue. Even though ATP production is reduced, it allows them to convert fat directly to heat to keep them warm.
2. Studies have shown that horses metabolize their nutrients 20 times faster during the winter than the summer.
3. Although for centuries people have fermented beverages such as beer and wine, they were often plagued by sour products that were undrinkable. Once people understood that there were yeasts that produced alcohol under anaerobic conditions and bacteria that converted alcohol to acetic acid under aerobic conditions, it was a simple task to prevent acetic acid production by preventing oxygen from getting to the fermenting mixture.
4. When it was discovered that the bacterium that causes gas gangrene is anaerobic and is, in fact, poisoned by the presence of oxygen, various oxygen therapies were developed to help cure patients with gangrene. Some persons with gangrene are placed in hyperbaric chambers, with high oxygen levels under pressure. In other patients, only the affected part of the body is enclosed. Under such conditions, the gangrene-causing bacteria die or are inhibited (see figure 4.22).
5. When physicians recognized that the breakdown of fats releases ketone bodies, they were able to diagnose diseases such as diabetes and anorexia more easily, because people typically have low amounts of carbohydrates and therefore metabolize fats. The ketones produced by excess breakdown of fats results in foul-smelling breath.

**Winter Baby and Blanket**

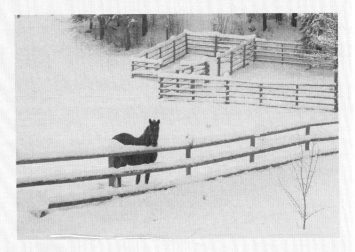

**No Blanket Needed**

If they do not have a source of dietary protein, they must break down proteins from important cellular components to supply the amino acids they need. This is why proteins and amino acids are considered an important daily food requirement.

## Summary of Protein Respiration

1. Proteins are digested into amino acids.
2. Then amino acids have the amino group removed,
   a. generating a keto acid (acetic acid, pyruvic acid, etc.), and
   b. entering the Kreb's cycle at the appropriate place.

One of the most important concepts is that carbohydrates, fats, and proteins can all be used to provide energy. The fate of any type of nutrient in a cell depends on the cell's momentary needs. An organism whose daily food-energy intake exceeds its daily energy expenditure will convert only the necessary amount of food into energy. The excess food will be interconverted according to the enzymes present and the organism's needs at that time. In fact, glycolysis and the Krebs cycle allow molecules of the three major food types (carbohydrates, fats, and proteins) to be interchanged.

As long as a person's diet has a certain minimum of each of the three major types of molecules, a cell's metabolic machinery can manipulate molecules to satisfy its needs. If a person is on a starvation diet, the cells will use stored carbohydrates first. When the carbohydrates are gone (after about 2 days), the cells begin to metabolize stored fat. When the fat is gone (after a few days to weeks), proteins will be used. A person in this condition is likely to die (How Science Works 6.1).

## 6.6   CONCEPT REVIEW

10. What are the differences between fat and protein metabolism biochemical pathways?
11. Describe how carbohydrates, fats, and proteins can be interconverted from one to another.

## Summary

In aerobic cellular respiration, organisms convert foods into energy (ATP) and waste materials (carbon dioxide and water). Three distinct metabolic pathways are involved in aerobic cellular respiration: glycolysis, the Krebs cycle, and the electron-transport system. Glycolysis takes place in the cytoplasm of the cell, and the Krebs cycle and electron-transport system take place in mitochondria. Organisms that have oxygen can perform aerobic cellular respiration. Organisms and cells that do not use oxygen perform anaerobic cellular respiration (fermentation) and can use only the glycolysis pathway. Aerobic cellular respiration yields much more ATP than anaerobic cellular respiration. Glycolysis and the Krebs cycle serve as a molecular interconversion system: Fats, proteins, and carbohydrates are interconverted according to the cell's needs.

## Key Terms

*Use the interactive flash cards on the **Concepts in Biology**, 14/e website to help you learn the meaning of these terms.*

acetyl-CoA 120
aerobic cellular
  respiration 117
alcoholic fermentation 127
anaerobic cellular
  respiration 126
autotrophs 116
cellular respiration 116

chemosynthesis 116
electron-transport system
  (ETS) 118
fermentation 126
glycolysis 118
heterotrophs 116
Krebs cycle 118
lactic acid fermentation 128

## Basic Review

1. Organisms that are able to use basic energy sources, such as sunlight, to make energy-containing organic molecules from inorganic raw materials are called
   a. autotrophs.
   b. heterotrophs.
   c. aerobic.
   d. anaerobic.

2. Cellular respiration processes that do not use molecular oxygen are called
   a. heterotrophic.
   b. anaerobic.
   c. aerobic.
   d. anabolic.

3. The chemical activities that remove electrons from glucose result in the glucose being
   a. reduced.
   b. oxidized.
   c. phosphorylated.
   d. hydrolysed.

4. The positively charged hydrogen ions that are released from the glucose during cellular respiration eventually combine with _____ ion to form _____.
   a. another hydrogen, a gas
   b. a carbon, carbon dioxide
   c. an oxygen, water
   d. a pyruvic acid, lactic acid

5. The Krebs cycle and ETS are biochemical pathways performed in which eukaryotic organelle?
   a. nucleus
   b. ribosome
   c. chloroplast
   d. mitochondria

6. In a complete accounting of all the ATPs produced in aerobic cellular respiration in eukaryotic cells, there are a total of _____ ATPs: _____ from the ETS, _____ from glycolysis, and _____ from the Krebs cycle.
   a. 36, 32, 2, 2
   b. 38, 34, 2, 2
   c. 36, 30, 2, 4
   d. 38, 30, 4, 4

7. Anaerobic pathways that oxidize glucose to generate ATP energy by using an organic molecule as the ultimate hydrogen acceptor are called
   a. fermentation.
   b. reduction.
   c. Krebs.
   d. electron pumps.

8. When skeletal muscle cells function anaerobically, they accumulate the compound _____, which causes muscle soreness.
   a. pyruvic acid
   b. malic acid
   c. carbon dioxide
   d. lactic acid

9. Each molecule of fat can release _____ of ATP, compared with a molecule of glucose.
   a. smaller amounts
   b. the same amount
   c. larger amounts
   d. only twice the amount

10. Some organisms excrete ammonia directly; others convert ammonia into other nitrogen-containing compounds, such as
    a. urea or uric acid.
    b. carbon dioxide.
    c. sweat.
    d. fat.

11. The ATP generating process in mitochondria works by using which of the following?
    a. proton pump
    b. DNA
    c. oxygen pump
    d. chlorophyll

12. Which best explains the need to reduce pyruvic acid in fermentation?
    a. Fermenting cells cannot produce water.
    b. Not enough energy would be produced to keep them alive.
    c. There is no oxygen available to accept the electrons.
    d. $NAD^+$ needs to be regenerated for continued use in glycolysis.

13. Why don't human muscle cells produce alcohol and $CO_2$ during anaerobic respiration?
    a. They only carry out aerobic respiration.
    b. We do not have the genes to produce the enzymes needed to generate alcohol and $CO_2$.
    c. The cells would blow up with the gas produced.
    d. There is no way to destroy the alcohol.

14. What is the ultimate destination of hydrogen electrons in aerobic cellular respiration?
    a. pyruvic acid
    b. lactic acid
    c. oxygen
    d. water

15. Which electron carrier releases the most potential during the ETS?
    a. NADH
    b. FAD
    c. oxygen
    d. $NAD^+$

**Answers**
1. a   2. b   3. b   4. c   5. d   6. a   7. a   8. d   9. c   10. a
11. a   12. d   13. b   14. c   15. a

## Thinking Critically

**Personalizing Your Pathway**
Picture yourself as an atom of hydrogen tied up in a molecule of fat. You are present in the stored fat of a person who is starving. Trace the biochemical pathways you would be part of as you moved through the process of aerobic cellular respiration. Be as specific as you can in describing your location and how you got there, as well as the molecules of which you are a part. Of what molecule would you be a part at the end of this process?

CHAPTER

7

# Biochemical Pathways— Photosynthesis

## Designer Bacteria— Future Source of Biofuels?

*Genetically Modified to Generate Fuel.*

A team of scientists has transferred cellulose-making genes from one kind of bacterium to another. The photosynthetic bacteria receiving the genes, cyanobacteria, are able to capture and use sunlight energy to grow and reproduce. The added genes give them a new trait (i.e., the ability to manufacture large amounts of cellulose, sucrose and glucose). Because cyanobacteria (formerly known as blue-green algae) can also capture atmospheric nitrogen ($N_2$), they can be grown without costly, petroleum-based fertilizer.

The cellulose that is secreted is in a relatively pure, gel-like form that is easily broken down to glucose that can be fermented to produce ethanol and other biofuels. The biggest expense in making biofuels from cellulose is in using enzymes and mechanical methods to break cellulose down to fermentable sugars.

Genetically modified cyanobacteria could have several advantages in the production of biofuels. They can be grown in sunlit industrial facilities on nonagricultural lands and can grow in salty water that is unsuitable for other uses. This could reduce the amount of agricultural land needed to grow corn that is being fermented to biofuels. There are social and financial pressures to use more corn, sugar cane, and other food crops for nonfood uses throughout the world, thus reducing the amount of food crops. For example, Brazil is being pressured to cut more of the Amazon rainforest in order to grow more sugarcane to meet growing world energy needs.

- How does photosynthesis trap light energy?

- What happens in photosynthetic organisms that results in the production of organic compounds?

- Should our government provide the same agricultural support payments to those who grow cyanobacteria as it pays to corn farmers?

**Background Check**

Concepts you should already know to get the most out of this chapter:
- The energy levels and position of electrons encircling an atom (chapter 2)
- The basic structure and function of chloroplasts and the types of cell in which they are located (chapter 4)
- How enzymes work in conjunction with ATP, electron transport, and a proton pump (chapter 5)
- The differences between autotrophs and heterotrophs (chapter 6)

## 7.1 Photosynthesis and Life

Although there are hundreds of different chemical reactions taking place within organisms, this chapter will focus on the reactions involved in the processes of photosynthesis. Recall from chapter 4 that, in photosynthesis, organisms such as green plants, algae, and certain bacteria trap radiant energy from sunlight. They are then able to convert it into the energy of chemical bonds in large molecules, such as carbohydrates. Organisms that are able to make energy-containing organic molecules from inorganic raw materials are called autotrophs. Those that use light as their energy source are more specifically called *photosynthetic* autotrophs or photoautotrophs.

Among prokaryotes, there are many bacteria capable of carrying out photosynthesis. For example, the cyanobacteria described in the opening article are all capable of manufacturing organic compounds using light energy.

Among the eukaryotes, a few protozoa and all algae and green plants are capable of photosynthesis. Photosynthesis captures energy for use by the organisms that carry out photosynthesis and provides energy to organisms that eat photosynthetic organisms. An estimated 99.9% of life on Earth relies on photosynthesis for its energy needs (figure 7.1). Photosynthesis is also the major supplier of organic compounds used in the synthesis of other compounds, such as carbohydrates and proteins. It has been estimated that over 100 billion metric tons of sugar are produced annually by photosynthesis. Photosynthesis also converts about 1,000 billion metric tons of carbon dioxide into organic matter each year, yielding about 700 billion metric tons of oxygen. It is for these reasons that a basic understanding of this biochemical pathway is important (How Science Works 7.1).

### 7.1 CONCEPT REVIEW

1. What are photosynthetic autotrophs?
2. How do photosynthetic organisms benefit heterotrophs?

## 7.2 An Overview of Photosynthesis

Ultimately, the energy to power all organisms comes from the sun. An important molecule in the process of harvesting sunlight is **chlorophyll**, a green pigment that absorbs light energy. Through photosynthesis, light energy is transformed to chemical-bond energy in the form of ATP. ATP is then used to produce complex organic molecules, such as glucose. It is from these organic molecules that organisms obtain energy through the process of cellular respiration. Recall from chapter 4 that, in algae and the leaves of green plants, photosynthesis occurs in cells that contain organelles called chloroplasts. Chloroplasts have two distinct regions within them: the grana and the stroma. **Grana** consist of stacks of individual membranous sacs, called **thylakoids,** that contain chlorophyll. The **stroma** are the spaces between membranes (figure 7.2).

The following equation summarizes the chemical reactions photosynthetic organisms use to make ATP and organic molecules:

light energy + carbon dioxide + water $\rightarrow$ glucose + oxygen
light energy + $6 CO_2$ + $6 H_2O$ $\rightarrow$ $C_6H_{12}O_6$ + $6 O_2$

There are three distinct events in the photosynthetic pathway:

1. **Light-capturing events.** In eukaryotic cells, photosynthesis takes place within chloroplasts. Each chloroplast is surrounded by membranes and contains chlorophyll, along with other photosynthetic pigments. Chlorophyll and the other pigments absorb specific wavelengths of light. When specific amounts of light are absorbed by the photosynthetic pigments, electrons become "excited." With this added energy, these excited electrons can enter into the chemical reactions responsible for the production of ATP. These reactions take place within the grana of the chloroplast.

2. **Light-dependent reactions.** Light-dependent reactions use the excited electrons produced by the light-capturing

(a)

(b)

(c)

**FIGURE 7.1 Our Green Planet**

From space you can see that Earth is a green-blue planet. The green results from photosynthetic pigments found in countless organisms on land and in the blue waters. It is the pigments used in the process of photosynthesis that generate the organic molecules needed to sustain life. Should this biochemical process be disrupted for any reason (e.g., climate change), there would be a great reduction in the food supply to all living things.

## HOW SCIENCE WORKS 7.1

## Solution to Global Energy Crisis Found in Photosynthesis?

The most important chemical reaction on Earth, photosynthesis, is thought to have been around about 3 billion years. There has been plenty of time for this metabolic process to evolve into a highly efficient method of capturing light energy. Terrestrial and aquatic plants and algae are little solar cells that convert light into usable energy. They use this energy to manufacture organic molecules from carbon dioxide and water.

Photosynthetic organisms capture an estimated 10 times the global energy used by humans annually. Scientists and inventors have long recognized the value in being able to develop materials that mimic the light-capturing events of photosynthesis. The overall efficiency of photosynthesis is between 3–6% of total solar radiation that reaches the earth. Recently the National Energy Renewable Laboratory (NREL) verified that new organic-based photovoltaic solar cells have demonstrated 6% efficiency. They are constructed of a new family of photo-active polymers—polycarbazoles. Developers see their achievement as a major breakthrough and are hoping to develop solar cells with efficiencies in excess of 10%.

These cells have the ability to capture light energy and, at the same time, be used in many a variety of situations. Flexible plastic, leaf-like sheets can be attached to cell phones, clothing, awnings, roofs, toys, and windows to provide power to many kinds of electronic devices.

**Solar-powered fan helmet being tried by a traffic policeman**

events. Light-dependent reactions are also known as *light reactions*. During these reactions, excited electrons from the light-capturing events are used to produce ATP. As a by-product, hydrogen and oxygen are also produced. The oxygen from the water is released to the environment as $O_2$ molecules. The hydrogens are transferred to the electron carrier coenzyme $NADP^+$ to produce NADPH. ($NADP^+$ is similar to $NAD^+$, which was discussed in chapter 5.) These reactions also take place in the grana of the chloroplast. However, the NADPH and ATP leave the grana and enter the stroma, where the light-independent reactions take place.

3. **Light-independent reactions.** These reactions are also known as *dark reactions*, because light is not needed for them to occur. During these reactions, ATP and NADPH from the light-dependent reactions are used to attach $CO_2$ to a 5-carbon molecule, already present in the cell, to manufacture new, larger organic molecules. Ultimately, glucose ($C_6H_{12}O_6$) is produced. These light-independent reactions take place in the stroma in either the light or dark, as long as ATP and NADPH are available from the light-dependent stage. When the ATP and NADPH give up their energy and hydrogens, they turn back into ADP and $NADP^+$. The ADP and the $NADP^+$ are recycled back to the light-dependent reactions to be used over again.

The process of photosynthesis can be summarized as follows. During the light-capturing events, *light energy* is captured by chlorophyll and other pigments, resulting in excited electrons. The energy of these excited electrons is used during the light-dependent reactions to disassociate *water* molecules into hydrogen and oxygen, and the *oxygen* is released. Also during the light-dependent reactions, ATP is produced and $NADP^+$ picks up hydrogen released from water to form NADPH. During the light-independent reactions, ATP and NADPH are used to help combine *carbon dioxide* with a 5-carbon molecule, so that ultimately organic molecules, such as *glucose*, are produced (figure 7.3).

**FIGURE 7.2 The Structure of a Chloroplast, the Site of Photosynthesis**
Plant cells contain chloroplasts that enable them to store light energy as chemical energy. It is the chloroplasts that contain chlorophyll and that are the site of photosynthesis. The chlorophyll molecules are actually located within membranous sacs called thylakoids. A stack of *thylakoids* is known as a *granum*.

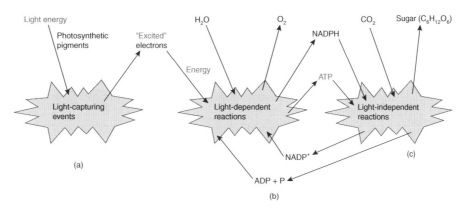

**FIGURE 7.3  Photosynthesis: Overview**
Photosynthesis is a complex biochemical pathway in plants, algae, and certain bacteria. This illustrates the three parts of the process: *(a)* the light-capturing events, *(b)* the light-dependent reactions, and *(c)* the light-independent reactions. The end products of the light-dependent reactions, NADPH and ATP, are necessary to run the light-independent reactions and are regenerated as NADP$^+$, ADP, and P. Water and carbon dioxide are supplied from the environment. Oxygen is released to the environment and sugar is manufactured for use by the plant.

## 7.2   CONCEPT REVIEW

3. Photosynthesis is a biochemical pathway that involves three kinds of activities. Name these and explain how they are related to each other.
4. Which cellular organelle is involved in the process of photosynthesis?

## 7.3   The Metabolic Pathways of Photosynthesis

It is a good idea to begin with the simplest description and add layers of understanding as you go to additional levels. Therefore, this discussion of photosynthesis is divided into two levels:

1. a fundamental description, and
2. a detailed description.

Ask your instructor which level is required for your course of study.

## Fundamental Description

### Light-Capturing Events

Light energy is used to drive photosynthesis during the light-capturing events. Visible light is a combination of many different wavelengths of light, seen as different colors. Some of these colors appear when white light is separated into its colors to form a rainbow. The colors of the electromagnetic spectrum that provide the energy for photosynthesis are correlated with different kinds of light-energy-absorbing pigments. The green chlorophylls are the most familiar and abundant. There are several types of this pigment. The two most common types are chlorophyll *a* and chlorophyll *b*. Both absorb strongly in the red and

**Carotenoids in tomato**

blue portions of the electromagnetic spectrum, although in slightly different portions of the spectrum (figure 7.4).

Chlorophylls reflect green light. That is why we see chlorophyll-containing plants as predominantly green. Other pigments common in plants are called **accessory pigments**. These include the *carotenoids* (yellow, red, and orange). They absorb mostly blue and blue-green light while reflecting the oranges and yellows. The presence of these pigments is generally masked by the presence of chlorophyll, but in the fall, when chlorophyll disintegrates, the reds, oranges, and yellows show through. Accessory pigments are also responsible for the brilliant colors of vegetables, such as carrots, tomatoes, eggplant, and peppers. Photosynthetic bacteria and various species of algae have other kinds of accessory pigments not found in plants. Having a combination of different pigments, each of which absorbs a portion of the light spectrum hitting it, allows the organism to capture much of the visible light that falls on it.

Any cell with chloroplasts can carry on photosynthesis. However, in most plants, leaves are specialized for photosynthesis and contain cells that have high numbers of chloroplasts (figure 7.5).

Chloroplasts are membrane-enclosed organelles that contain many thin, flattened sacs that contain chlorophyll. These chlorophyll-containing sacs are called *thylakoids* and a number of these thylakoids stacked together is known as a *granum*. In addition to chlorophyll, the thylakoids contain accessory pigments, electron-transport molecules, and enzymes. Recall that the fluid-filled spaces between the grana are called the stroma of

**(a)** Visible light varies from violet to red. It is a small part of the electromagnetic energy from the Sun that strikes Earth.

**Short wavelength**
**High energy**

Gamma rays

X rays

Ultraviolet radiation

Violet light has the shortest wavelength and the highest frequency of visible light.

400
450 — 475 nm
500
550
600
650
700 — 750 nm
750

Visible light

Wavelength in nanometers

Red light has the longest wavelength and the lowest frequency of visible light.

Near-infrared radiation

Infrared radiation

Microwaves

Radio waves

**Long wavelength**
**Low energy**

**(b)** Objects like this leaf get their colors from the visible light they reflect.

Sunlight            Reflected light

**FIGURE 7.4 The Electromagnetic Spectrum, Visible Light, and Chlorophyll**
Light is a form of electromagnetic energy that can be thought of as occurring in waves. Chlorophyll absorbs light most strongly in the blue and red portion of the electromagnetic spectrum but poorly in the green portions. The shorter the wavelength, the more energy it contains. Humans are capable of seeing only waves that are between about 400 and 740 nanometers (nm) long.

Cuticle
Epidermis
Mesophyll
Vascular bundle
Bundle sheath
Stroma
Chloroplasts

**FIGURE 7.5 Photosynthesis and the Structure of a Plant Leaf**
Plant leaves are composed of layers of cells that contain chloroplasts, which contain chlorophyll.

the chloroplast. The structure of the chloroplast is directly related to both the light-capturing and the energy-conversion steps of photosynthesis. In the light-capturing events, the pigments (e.g., chlorophyll), which are embedded in the membranes of the thylakoids, capture light energy and some of the electrons of pigments become excited. The chlorophylls and other pigments involved in trapping sunlight energy and storing it are arranged into clusters called **photosystems.** By clustering the pigments, photosystems serve as energy-gathering, or energy-concentrating, mechanisms that allow light to be collected more efficiently and excite electrons to higher energy levels.

## A Fundamental Summary of Light-Capturing Events

photons of light energy → excited electrons from chlorophyll

## Light-Dependent Reactions

The light-dependent reactions of photosynthesis also take place in the thylakoid membranes inside the chloroplast. The excited electrons from the light-capturing events are passed to protein molecules in the thylakoid membrane. The electrons are passed through a series of electron-transport steps, which result in protons being pumped into the cavity of the thylakoid. When the protons pass back out through the membrane to the outside of the thylakoid, ATP is produced. This is very similar to the reactions that happen in the electron-transport system (ETS) of aerobic cellular respiration. In addition, the chlorophyll that just lost its electrons to the chloroplast's electron-transport system regains electrons from water molecules. This results in the production of hydrogen ions, electrons, and oxygen gas. The next light-capturing event will excite this new electron and send it along the electron-transport system. As electrons finish moving through the electron-transport system, the coenzyme $NADP^+$ picks up the electrons and is reduced to NADPH. The hydrogen ions attach because, when $NADP^+$ accepts electrons, it becomes negatively charged ($NADP^-$). The positively charged $H^+$ are attracted to the negatively charged $NADP^-$. The oxygen remaining from the splitting of water molecules is released into the atmosphere, or it can be used by the cell in aerobic cellular respiration, which takes place in the mitochondria of plant cells. The ATP and NADPH molecules move from the grana, where the light-dependent reactions take place, to the stroma, where the light-independent reactions take place.

## A Fundamental Summary of the Light-Dependent Reactions

$$\text{excited electrons} + H_2O + ADP + NADP^+ \rightarrow$$
$$ATP + NADPH + O_2$$

## Light-Independent Reactions

The ATP and NADPH provide energy, electrons and hydrogens needed to build large, organic molecules. The light-independent reactions are a series of oxidation-reduction reactions, which combine hydrogen from water (carried by NADPH) with carbon dioxide from the atmosphere to form simple organic molecules, such as sugar. As $CO_2$ diffuses into the chloroplasts, the enzyme **Ribulose-1,5-bisphosphate carboxylase oxygenase (RuBisCO)** speeds the combining of the $CO_2$ with an already present 5-carbon sugar, **ribulose**. NADPH then donates its hydrogens and electrons to complete the reduction of the molecule. The resulting 6-carbon molecule is immediately split into two 3-carbon molecules of **glyceraldehyde-3-phosphate**. Some of the glyceraldehyde-3-phosphate molecules are converted through another series of reactions into ribulose. Thus, these reactions constitute a cycle, in which carbon dioxide and hydrogens are added and glyceraldehyde-3-phosphate and the original 5-carbon ribulose are produced. The plant can use surplus glyceraldehyde-3-phosphate for the synthesis of glucose. The plant can also use glyceraldehyde-3-phosphate to construct a wide variety of other organic molecules (e.g., proteins, nucleic acids), provided there are a few additional raw materials, such as minerals and nitrogen-containing molecules (figure 7.6).

## A Fundamental Summary of the Light-Independent Reactions

$$ATP + NADPH + \text{ribulose} + CO_2$$
$$\downarrow$$
$$ADP + NADP^+ + \text{complex organic molecule} + \text{ribulose}$$

## Detailed Description

### Light-Capturing Events

The energy of light comes in discrete packages, called *photons*. Photons of light having different wavelengths have different amounts of energy. A photon of red light has a different amount of energy than a photon of blue light. Pigments of different kinds are able to absorb photons of certain wavelengths of light. Chlorophyll absorbs red and blue light best and reflects green light. When a chlorophyll molecule is struck by and absorbs a photon of the correct wavelength, its electrons become excited to a higher energy level. This electron is replaced when chlorophyll takes an electron from a water molecule. The excited electron goes on to form ATP. The reactions that result in the production of ATP and the splitting of water take place in the thylakoids of chloroplasts. There are many different molecules involved, and most are embedded in the membrane of the thylakoid. The various molecules involved in these reactions are referred to as *photosystems*. A photosystem is composed of (1) an *antenna complex*, (2) a *reaction center*, and (3) other enzymes necessary to store the light energy as ATP and NADPH.

The antenna complex is a network of hundreds of chlorophyll and accessory pigment molecules, whose role is to capture photons of light energy and transfer the energy to a specialized portion of the photosystem known as the reaction center. When light shines on the antenna complex and strikes a chlorophyll molecule, an electron becomes excited. The energy of the excited electron is passed from one pigment to another through the antenna complex network. This series of excitations continues until the combined energies from several excitations are transferred to the reaction center, which consists of a complex of chlorophyll *a* and protein molecules. An electron is excited and passed to a primary electron acceptor molecule, oxidizing the chlorophyll and reducing the acceptor. Ultimately, the oxidized chlorophyll then has its electron replaced with another electron from a different electron donor. Exactly where this replacement electron comes from is the basis on which two different photosystems have been identified—photosystem I and photosystem II, which will be discussed in the next section.

## Summary of Detailed Description of the Light-Capturing Reactions

1. They take place in the thylakoids of the chloroplast.
2. Chlorophyll and other pigments of the antenna complex capture light energy and produce excited electrons.
3. The energy is transferred to the reaction center.
4. Excited electrons from the reaction center are transferred to a primary electron acceptor molecule.

## Light-Dependent Reactions

Both photosystems I and II have antenna complexes and reaction centers and provide excited electrons to primary electron acceptors. However, each has slightly different enzymes and

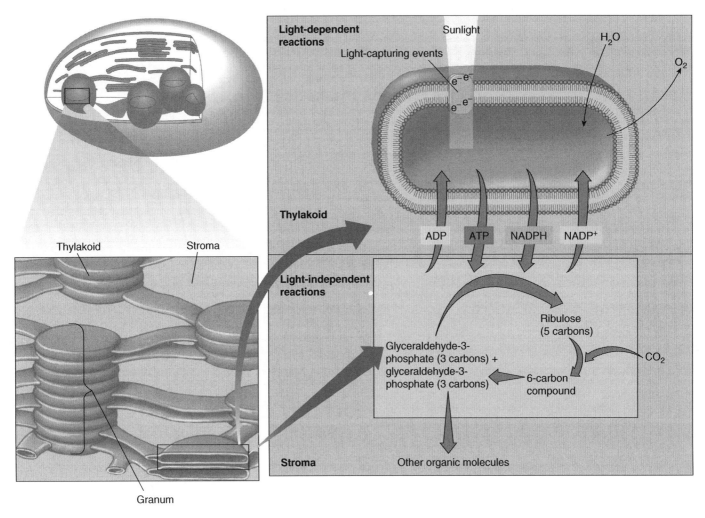

**FIGURE 7.6  Photosynthesis: Fundamental Description**

The process of photosynthesis involves light-capturing events by chlorophyll and other pigments. The excited electrons are used in the light-dependent reactions to split water, releasing hydrogens and oxygen. The hydrogens are picked up by NADP$^+$ to form NADPH and the oxygen is released. Excited electrons are also used to produce ATP. The ATP and NADPH leave the thylakoid and enter the stroma of the chloroplast, where they are used in the light-independent reactions to incorporate carbon dioxide into organic molecules. During the light-independent reactions, carbon dioxide is added to a 5-carbon ribulose molecule to form a 6-carbon compound, which splits into glyceraldehyde-3-phosphate. Some of the glyceraldehyde-3-phosphate is used to regenerate ribulose and some is used to make other organic molecules. The ADP and NADP$^+$ released from the light-independent reactions stage return to the thylakoid to be used in the synthesis of ATP and NADPH again. Therefore, each stage is dependent on the other.

other proteins associated with it, so each does a slightly different job. In actuality, photosystem II occurs first and feeds its excited electrons to photosystem I (figure 7.7). One special feature of photosystem II is that there is an enzyme in the thylakoid membrane responsible for splitting water molecules ($H_2O \rightarrow$ 2 H + O). The oxygen is released as $O_2$ and the electrons of the hydrogens are used to replace the electrons that had been lost by the chlorophyll. The remaining hydrogen ions (protons) are released to participate in other reactions. Thus, in a sense, the light energy trapped by the antenna complex is used to split water into H and O. The excited electrons from photosystem II are sent through a series of electron-transport reactions, in which they give up some of their energy. This is similar to the electron-transport system of aerobic cellular respiration. After passing through the electron-transport system, the electrons are accepted by chlorophyll molecules in photosystem I. While the

electron-transport activity is happening, protons are pumped from the stroma into the space inside the thylakoid. Eventually, these protons move back across the membrane. When they do, ATPase is used to produce ATP (ADP is phosphorylated to produce ATP). Thus, a second result of this process is that the energy of sunlight has been used to produce ATP.

The connection between photosystem II and photosystem I involves the transfer of electrons from photosystem II to photosystem I. These electrons are important because photons (from sunlight) are exciting electrons in the reaction center of photosystem I and the electrons from photosystem II replace those lost from photosystem I.

In photosystem I, light is trapped and the energy is absorbed in the same manner as in photosystem II. However, this system does not have the enzyme involved in splitting water; therefore, no $O_2$ is released from photosystem I. The high-energy electrons

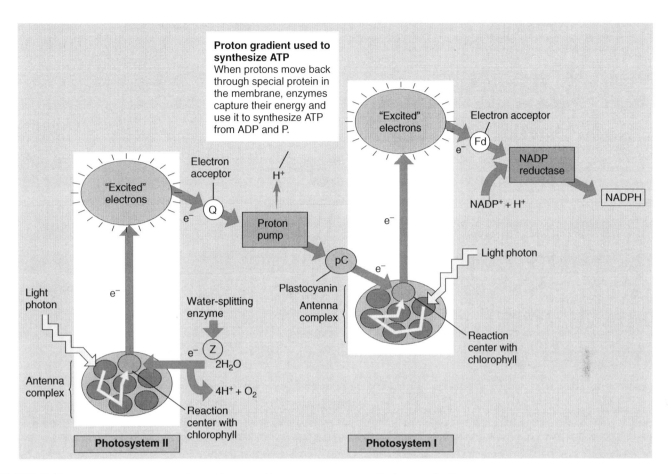

**FIGURE 7.7** **Photosystems II and I and How They Interact: Detailed Description**
Although light energy strikes and is absorbed by both photosystem II and I, what happens and how they interconnect are not the same. Notice that the electrons released from photosystem II end up in the chlorophyll molecules of photosystem I. The electrons that replace those "excited" out of the reaction center in photosystem II come from water.

leaving the reaction center of photosystem I make their way through a different series of oxidation-reduction reactions. During these reactions, the electrons are picked up by $NADP^+$, which is reduced to NADPH (review figure 7.7). Thus, the primary result of photosystem I is the production of NADPH.

## Summary of Detailed Description of the Light-Dependent Reactions of Photosynthesis

1. They take place in the thylakoids of the chloroplast.
2. Excited electrons from photosystem II are passed through an electron-transport chain and ultimately enter photosystem I.
3. The electron-transport system is used to establish a proton gradient, which produces ATP.
4. Excited electrons from photosystem I are transferred to $NADP^+$ to form NADPH.
5. In photosystem II, an enzyme splits water into hydrogen and oxygen. The oxygen is released as $O_2$.
6. Electrons from the hydrogen of water replace the electrons lost by chlorophyll in photosystem II.

## Light-Independent Reactions

The light-independent reactions take place within the stroma of the chloroplast. The materials needed for the light-independent reactions are ATP, NADPH, $CO_2$, and a 5-carbon starter molecule called *ribulose*. The first two ingredients (ATP and NADPH) are made available from the light-dependent reactions, photosystems II and I. The carbon dioxide molecules come from the atmosphere, and the ribulose starter molecule is already present in the stroma of the chloroplast from previous reactions.

Carbon dioxide is said to undergo *carbon fixation* through the **Calvin cycle** (named after its discoverer, Melvin Calvin). In the Calvin cycle, ATP and NADPH from the light-dependent reactions are used, along with carbon dioxide, to synthesize larger, organic molecules. As with most metabolic pathways, the synthesis of organic molecules during the light-independent reactions requires the activity of several enzymes to facilitate the many steps in the process. The fixation of carbon begins with carbon dioxide combining with the 5-carbon molecule ribulose to form an unstable 6-carbon molecule. This reaction is carried out by the enzyme Ribulose-1,5-bisphosphate carboxylase oxygenase (RuBisCO), reportedly the most abundant enzyme on the planet. The

## FIGURE 7.8  The Calvin Cycle: Detailed Description

During the Calvin cycle, ATP and NADPH from the light-dependent reactions are used to attach $CO_2$ to the 5-carbon ribulose molecule. The 6-carbon molecule formed immediately breaks down into two 3-carbon molecules. Some of the glyceraldehyde-3-phosphate formed is used to produce glucose and other, more complex organic molecules. In order to accumulate enough carbon to make a new glucose molecule, the cycle must turn six times. The remaining glyceraldehyde-3-phosphate is used to regenerate the 5-carbon ribulose to start the process again.

newly formed 6-carbon molecule immediately breaks down into two 3-carbon molecules, each of which then undergoes a series of reactions involving a transfer of energy from ATP and a transfer of hydrogen from NADPH. The result of this series of reactions is two glyceraldehyde-3-phosphate molecules. Because glyceraldehyde-3-phosphate contains 3 carbons and is formed as the first stable compound in this type of photosynthesis, this is sometimes referred to as the C3 photosynthetic pathway. Some of the glyceraldehyde-3-phosphate is used to synthesize glucose and other organic molecules, and some is used to regenerate the 5-carbon ribulose molecule, so this pathway is a cycle (figure 7.8). Outlooks 7.1 describes some other forms of photosynthesis that do not use the C3 pathway.

### Summary of Detailed Description of the Reactions of the Light-Independent Events

1. They take place in the stroma of chloroplasts:

$$CO_2 + ATP + NADPH + \text{5-carbon starter (ribulose)}$$
$$\downarrow$$
$$\text{glyceraldehyde-3-phosphate} + NADP^+ + ADP + P$$

2. ATP and NADPH from the light-dependent reactions leave the grana and enter the stroma.
3. The energy of ATP is used in the Calvin cycle to combine carbon dioxide to a 5-carbon starter molecule (ribulose) to form a 6-carbon molecule.
4. The 6-carbon molecule immediately divides into two 3-carbon molecules of glyceraldehyde-3-phosphate.
5. Hydrogens from NADPH are transferred to molecules in the Calvin cycle.
6. The 5-carbon ribulose is regenerated.
7. ADP and $NADP^+$ are returned to the light-dependent reactions.

## OUTLOOKS 7.1

# The Evolution of Photosynthesis

It is amazing that the processes of photosynthesis in prokaryotes and eukaryotes are so similar. The evolution of photosynthesis goes back over 3 billion years, when all life on Earth was prokaryotic and occurred in organisms that were aquatic. (There were no terrestrial organisms at the time.) Today, some bacteria perform a kind of photosynthesis that does not result in the release of oxygen. In general, these bacteria produce ATP but do not break down water to produce oxygen. Perhaps these are the descendents of the first organisms to carry out a photosynthetic process, and oxygen-releasing photosynthesis developed from these earlier forms of photosynthesis.

Evidence from the fossil record shows that, beginning approximately 2.4 billion years ago, oxygen was present in the atmosphere. Eukaryotic organisms had not yet developed, so the organisms responsible for producing this oxygen would have been prokaryotic. Today, many kinds of cyanobacteria perform photosynthesis in essentially the same way as plants, although they use a somewhat different kind of chlorophyll. As a matter of fact, it is assumed that the chloroplasts of eukaryotes are evolved from photosynthetic bacteria. Initially, the first eukaryotes to perform photosynthesis would have been various kinds of algae. Today, certain kinds of algae (red algae, brown algae, green algae) have specific kinds of chlorophylls and other accessory pigments different from the others. Because the group known as the green algae has the same chlorophylls as plants, it is assumed that plants are derived from this aquatic group.

The evolution of photosynthesis did not stop once plants came on the scene, however. Most plants perform photosynthesis in the manner described in this chapter. Light energy is used to generate ATP and NADPH, which are used in the Calvin cycle to incorporate carbon dioxide into glyceraldehyde-3-phosphate. Because the primary product of this form of photosynthesis is a 3-carbon molecule of glyceraldehyde-3-phosphate, it is often

Ripe barley crop–C3

Corn–C4

Jade plant–CAM

called C3 photosynthesis. Among plants, there are two interesting variations of photosynthesis, which use the same basic process but add interesting twists.

C4 photosynthesis is common in plants like grasses, such as corn (maize), crabgrass, and sugarcane that are typically subjected to high light levels. In these plants, carbon dioxide does not directly enter the Calvin cycle. Instead, the fixation of carbon is carried out in two steps, and two kinds of cells participate. It appears that this adaptation allows plants to trap carbon dioxide more efficiently from the atmosphere under high light conditions. Specialized cells in the leaf capture carbon dioxide and convert a 3-carbon compound to a 4-carbon compound. This 4-carbon compound then releases the carbon dioxide to other cells, which use it in the normal Calvin cycle typical of the light-independent reactions. Because a 4-carbon molecule is formed to "store" carbon, this process is known as C4 photosynthesis.

Another variation of photosynthesis is known as Crassulacean acid metabolism (CAM), because this mechanism was first discovered in members of the plant family, Crassulaceae. (A common example, *Crassula*, is known as the jade plant.) CAM photosynthesis is a modification of the basic process of photosynthesis that allows photosynthesis to occur in arid environments while reducing the potential for water loss. In order for plants to take up carbon dioxide, small holes in the leaves (stomata) must be open to allow carbon dioxide to enter. However, relative humidity is low during the day and plants would tend to lose water if their stomates were open. CAM photosynthesis works as follows: During the night, the stomates open and carbon dioxide can enter the leaf. The chloroplasts trap the carbon dioxide by binding it to an organic molecule, similar to what happens in C4 plants. The next morning, when it is light (and drier), the stomates close. During the day, the chloroplasts can capture light and run the light-dependent reactions. They then use the carbon stored the previous night to do the light-independent reactions.

## Glyceraldehyde-3-Phosphate: The Product of Photosynthesis

The 3-carbon glyceraldehyde-3-phosphate is the actual product of the process of photosynthesis. However, many textbooks show the generalized equation for photosynthesis as

$$6 CO_2 + 6 H_2O + light \rightarrow C_6H_{12}O_6 + 6 O_2$$

making it appear as if a 6-carbon sugar (hexose) were the end product. The reason a hexose ($C_6H_{12}O_6$) is usually listed as the end product is simply because, in the past, the simple sugars were easier to detect than was glyceraldehyde-3-phosphate.

Several things can happen to glyceraldehyde-3-phosphate. If a plant goes through photosynthesis and produces 12 glyceraldehyde-3-phosphates, 10 of the 12 are rearranged by a series of complex chemical reactions to regenerate the 5-carbon ribulose needed to operate the light-independent reactions stage. The other two glyceraldehyde-3-phosphates can be considered profit from the process. The excess glyceraldehyde-3-phosphate molecules are frequently changed into a hexose. So, the scientists who first examined photosynthesis chemically thought that sugar was the end product. It was only later that they realized that glyceraldehyde-3-phosphate is the true end product of photosynthesis.

Cells can do a number of things with glyceraldehyde-3-phosphate, in addition to manufacturing hexose (figure 7.9). Many other organic molecules can be constructed using glyceraldehyde-3-phosphate. Glyceraldehyde-3-phosphate can be converted to glucose molecules, which can be combined to form complex carbohydrates, such as starch for energy storage or cellulose for cell wall construction. In addition, other simple sugars can be used as building blocks for ATP, RNA, DNA, and other carbohydrate-containing materials.

The cell can also convert the glyceraldehyde-3-phosphate into lipids, such as oils for storage, phospholipids for cell membranes, or steroids for cell membranes. The glyceraldehyde-3-phosphate can serve as the carbon skeleton for the construction of the amino acids needed to form proteins. Almost any molecule that a green plant can manufacture begins with this glyceraldehyde-3-phosphate molecule. Finally, glyceraldehyde-3-phosphate can be broken down during cellular respiration. Cellular respiration releases the chemical-bond energy from glyceraldehyde-3-phosphate and other organic molecules and converts it into the energy of ATP. This conversion of chemical-bond energy enables the plant cell and the cells of all organisms to do things that require energy, such as grow and move materials (Outlooks 7.2).

### 7.3 CONCEPT REVIEW

5. How do photosystem I and photosystem II differ in the kinds of reactions that take place?
6. What does an antenna complex do? How is it related to the reaction center?
7. What role is played by the compound Ribulose-1,5-bisphosphate carboxylase oxygenase (RuBisCo)?
8. What role is played by the compound glyceraldehyde-3-phosphate?
9. Describe how photosystem II interacts with photosystem I.
10. What is the value of a plant to have more than one kind of photosynthetic pigment?

### 7.4 Other Aspects of Plant Metabolism

Photosynthetic organisms are able to manufacture organic molecules from inorganic molecules. Once they have the basic carbon skeleton, they can manufacture a variety of other complex molecules for their own needs—fats, proteins, and complex carbohydrates are some of the more common. However, plants produce a wide variety of other molecules for specific purposes. Among the molecules they produce are compounds that are toxic to animals that use plants as food. Many of these compounds have been discovered to be useful as medicines. Digitalis from the foxglove plant causes the hearts of animals that eat the plant to malfunction (figure 7.10). However, it can be used as a medicine in humans who have certain heart ailments. Molecules that paralyze animals have been used in medicine to treat specific ailments and relax muscles, so that surgery is easier to perform. Still others have been used as natural insecticides.

**FIGURE 7.9 Uses for Glyceraldehyde-3-Phosphate** The glyceraldehyde-3-phosphate that is produced as the end product of photosynthesis has a variety of uses. The plant cell can make simple sugars, complex carbohydrates, or even the original 5-carbon starter from it. The glyceraldehyde-3-phosphate can also serve as an ingredient of lipids and amino acids (proteins). In addition, it is a major source of metabolic energy provided from aerobic respiration in the mitochondria of plant cells.

## OUTLOOKS 7.2

# Even More Ways to Photosynthesize

Having gone through the information on photosynthesis, you might have thought that this was the only way for this biochemical pathway to take place. However, there are many prokaryotes capable of carrying out photosynthesis using alternative pathways. These Bacteria and Archaea have light-capturing pigments, but they are not the same as plant chlorophylls or the accessory pigments. The range of light absorption differs, allowing many of these Bacteria and Archaea to live in places unfriendly to plants. Some forms of photosynthetic bacteria do not release oxygen, but rather release other by-products such as $H_2$, $H_2S$, S, or organic compounds. Table 7.1 compares some of the most important differences between eukaryotic and prokaryotic photosynthesis.

**TABLE 7.1** Different Types of Photosynthesis

| Property | Eukaryotic | Prokaryotic—Cyanobacteria | Prokaryotic—Green and Purple Bacteria |
|---|---|---|---|
| Photosystem pigments | Chlorophyll *a*, *b*, and accessory pigments | Chlorophyll *a* and phycocyanin (blue-green pigment) | Combinations of bacteriochlorophylls *a*, *b*, *c*, *d*, or *e* absorb different wavelengths of light and some absorb infrared light. |
| Thylakoid system | Present | Present | Absent—pigments are found in vesicles called chlorosomes, or they are simply attached to plasma membrane. |
| Photosystem II | Present | Present | Absent |
| Source of electrons | $H_2O$ | $H_2O$ | $H_2$, $H_2S$, S, or a variety of organic molecules |
| $O_2$ production pattern | Oxygenic—release $O_2$ | Oxygenic | Anoxygenic—do not release $O_2$ May release S, other organic compounds other than that used as the source of electrons |
| Primary products of energy conversion | ATP + NADPH | ATP + NADPH | ATP |
| Carbon source | $CO_2$ | $CO_2$ | Organic and/or $CO_2$ |
| Example | Maple tree—*Acer* | *Anabaena* *Ocillatoria* *Nostoc* | Green sulfur bacterium—*Chlorobium* Green nonsulfur bacterium—*Chloroflexus* Purple sulfur bacterium—*Chromatium* Purple nonsulfur bacterium—*Rhodospirillum* |

Vitamins are another important group of organic molecules derived from plants. Vitamins are organic molecules that we cannot manufacture but must have in small amounts to maintain good health. The vitamins we get from plants are manufactured by them for their own purposes. By definition, they are not vitamins to the plant, because the plant makes them for its own use. However, because we cannot make them, we rely on plants to synthesize these important molecules for us, and we consume them when we eat foods containing them.

## 7.4 CONCEPT REVIEW

11. Is vitamin C a vitamin for an orange tree?

## 7.5 Interrelationships Between Autotrophs and Heterotrophs

The differences between autotrophs and heterotrophs were described in chapter 6. Autotrophs are able to capture energy to manufacture new organic molecules from inorganic molecules. Heterotrophs must have organic molecules as starting points. *However, it is important for you to recognize that all organisms must do some form of respiration.* Plants and other autotrophs obtain energy from food molecules, in the same manner as animals and other heterotrophs—by processing organic molecules through the respiratory pathways. This means that plants, like animals, require oxygen for the ETS portion of aerobic cellular respiration.

(a)

(b)

(c)

**FIGURE 7.10 Foxglove, *Cannabis*, and Coffee Plants**
*(a)* Foxglove, *Digitalis purpurea*, produces the compound cardenolide digitoxin, a valuable medicine in the treatment of heart disease. The drug containing this compound is known as digitalis. *(b) Cannabis sativais*, the source of marijuana, has been show to be effective in the treatment of pain, nausea, and vomiting, and acts as an antispasmodic and anticonvulsant. *(c)* The plant *Coffea arabica* is one source of the compound caffeine and has been shown to reduce the risk of diabetes and Parkinson's disease.

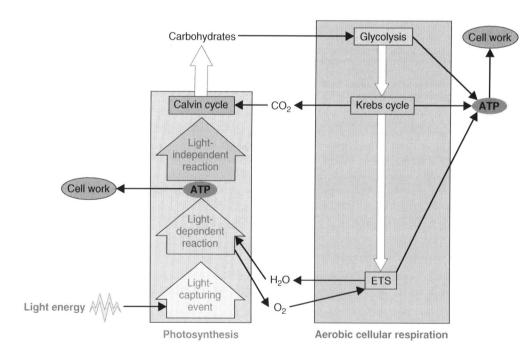

**FIGURE 7.11 The Interdependence of Photosynthesis and Aerobic Cellular Respiration**
Although both autotrophs and heterotrophs carry out cellular respiration, the photosynthetic process that is unique to photosynthetic autotrophs provides essential nutrients for both processes. Photosynthesis captures light energy, which is ultimately transferred to heterotrophs in the form of carbohydrates and other organic compounds. Photosynthesis also generates $O_2$, which is used in aerobic cellular respiration. The ATP generated by cellular respiration in both heterotrophs (e.g., animals) and autotrophs (e.g., plants) is used to power their many metabolic processes. In return, cellular respiration supplies two of the most important basic ingredients of photosynthesis, $CO_2$ and $H_2O$.

Many people believe that plants only give off oxygen and never require it. Actually, plants do give off oxygen in the light-dependent reactions of photosynthesis, but in aerobic cellular respiration they use oxygen, as does any other organism that uses aerobic respiration. During their life spans, green plants give off more oxygen to the atmosphere than they take in for use in respiration. The surplus oxygen given off is the source of oxygen for aerobic cellular respiration in both plants and animals. Animals are dependent on plants not only for oxygen but ultimately for the organic molecules necessary to construct their bodies and maintain their metabolism (figure 7.11).

Thus, animals supply the raw materials—$CO_2$, $H_2O$, and nitrogen—needed by plants, and plants supply the raw materials—sugar, oxygen, amino acids, fats, and vitamins—needed by animals. This constant cycling is essential to life on Earth. As long as the Sun shines and plants and animals remain in balance, the food cycles of all living organisms will continue to work properly.

## 7.5 CONCEPT REVIEW

12. Even though animals do not photosynthesize, they rely on the Sun for their energy. Why is this so?
13. What is an autotroph? Give an example.
14. Photosynthetic organisms are responsible for producing what kinds of materials?
15. Draw your own simple diagram that illustrates how photosynthesis and respiration are interrelated.

## Summary

Sunlight supplies the essential initial energy for making the large organic molecules necessary to maintain the forms of life we know. Photosynthesis is the process by which plants, algae, and some bacteria use the energy from sunlight to produce organic compounds. In the light-capturing events of photosynthesis, plants use chemicals, such as chlorophyll, to trap the energy of sunlight using photosystems. During the light-dependent reactions, they manufacture a source of chemical energy, ATP, and a source of hydrogen, NADPH. Atmospheric oxygen is released in this stage. In the light-independent reactions of photosynthesis, the ATP energy is used in a series of reactions (the Calvin cycle) to join the hydrogen from the NADPH to a molecule of carbon dioxide and form a simple carbohydrate, glyceraldehyde-3-phosphate. In subsequent reactions, plants use the glyceraldehyde-3-phosphate as a source of energy and raw materials to make complex carbohydrates, fats, and other organic molecules. Table 7.2 summarizes the process of photosynthesis.

## Key Terms

Use the interactive flash cards on the **Concepts in Biology, 14/e** website to help you learn the meaning of these terms.

accessory pigments 139
Calvin cycle 143
chlorophyll 136
glyceraldehyde-
    3-phosphate 141
grana 136
light-capturing events 136
light-dependent
    reactions 136
light-independent
    reactions 138
photosystems 140
ribulose 141
Ribulose-1,5-bisphosphate
    carboxylase oxygenase
    (RuBisCO) 141
stroma 136
thylakoids 136

## Basic Review

1. Which of the following is *not* able to carry out photosynthesis?
   a. algae
   b. cyanobacteria
   c. frogs
   d. broccoli

2. A _____ consists of stacks of membranous sacs containing chlorophyll.
   a. granum
   b. stroma
   c. mitochondrion
   d. cell wall

3. During the _____ reactions, ATP and NADPH are used to help combine carbon dioxide with a 5-carbon molecule, so that ultimately organic molecules, such as glucose, are produced.
   a. light-independent
   b. light-dependent
   c. Watson cycle
   d. Krebs cycle

## TABLE 7.2    Summary of Photosynthesis

| Process | Where in the Chloroplast It Occurs | Reactants | Products |
|---|---|---|---|
| Light-energy trapping events | In the chlorophyll molecules and accessory pigments of the thylakoids | Chlorophylls | Excited electrons |
| Light-dependent reactions | In the thylakoids of the grana | Water, ADP, $NADP^+$ | Oxygen, ATP, NADPH |
| Light-independent reactions | Stroma | Carbon dioxide, ribulose, ATP, NADPH | Glyceraldehyde-3-phosphate, ribulose, ADP, $NADP^+$ |

4. Pigments other than the green chlorophylls that are commonly found in plants are collectively known as _____. These include the carotenoids.

   a. chlorophylls

   b. hemoglobins

   c. accessory pigments

   d. thylakoids

5. This enzyme speeds the combining of $CO_2$ with an already present 5-carbon ribulose.

   a. DNAase

   b. ribose

   c. Ribulose-1,5-bisphosphate carboxylase oxygenase (RuBisCO)

   d. phosphorylase

6. Carbon dioxide undergoes carbon fixation, which occurs in the

   a. Calvin cycle.

   b. Krebs cycle.

   c. light-dependent reactions.

   d. photosystem I.

7. The chlorophylls and other pigments involved in trapping sunlight energy and storing it are arranged into clusters called

   a. chloroplasts.

   b. photosystems.

   c. cristae.

   d. thylakoids.

8. Light energy comes in discrete packages called

   a. $NADP^+$.

   b. lumina.

   c. photons.

   d. brilliance units.

9. The electrons released from photosystem _____ end up in the chlorophyll molecules of photosystem _____.

   a. I, II

   b. A, B

   c. B, A

   d. II, I

10. _____ are sacs containing chlorophylls, accessory pigments, electron-transport molecules, and enzymes.

    a. Thylakoids

    b. Mitochondria

    c. Photosystems

    d. Ribosomes

11. Which kind of organisms use respiration to generate ATP?

    a. plants

    b. animals

    c. algae

    d. all of the above

12. Plants, like animals, require _____ for the ETS portion of aerobic cellular respiration.

    a. silicone

    b. hydrogen

    c. nitrogen

    d. oxygen

13. _____ are an important group of organic molecules derived from plants. These are organic molecules that we cannot manufacture but must have in small amounts.

    a. Accessory pigments

    b. Vitamins

    c. Nitrogenous compounds

    d. Minerals

14. These prokaryotic organisms are capable of manufacturing organic compounds using light energy.

    a. algae

    b. protozoa

    c. cyanobacteria

    d. tomatoes

15. Chlorophyll-containing organisms look green because they reflect _____-colored light.

    a. green

    b. red

    c. yellow

    d. white

**Answers**

1. c  2. a  3. a  4. c  5. c  6. a  7. b  8. c  9. d  10. a
11. d  12. d  13. b  14. c  15. a

## Thinking Critically

**From a Metabolic Point of View**
Both plants and animals carry on metabolism. From a metabolic point of view, which of the two is the more complex organism? Include in your answer the following topics:

1. Cell structure
2. Biochemical pathways
3. Enzymes
4. Organic molecules
5. Photosynthetic autotrophy and heterotrophy

CHAPTER

8

# DNA and RNA

## The Molecular Basis of Heredity

### DNA Repair Shops Inside Living Cells?

Discovery could help NASA cope with the health threat posed to astronauts by radiation.

Astronauts are regularly exposed to cosmic radiation and, on occasion, their DNA is damaged. Because DNA carries a cell's genetic information, damage may result in cell death, cancers, or other abnormalities. Research has shown that cells have the ability to repair damaged DNA. However, while cells can often fix minor damage successfully, they sometimes botch major repairs that can make a cell even more prone to becoming cancerous. So rather than attempt to fix itself, the repair mechanisms can be blocked by enzymes, forcing a severely damaged cell to self-destruct. This actually keeps the astronaut healthier overall.

One hypothesis on how damaged DNA is repaired suggests that the repair happens right where the damage occurs. New research shows that some strands of DNA with minor damage are repaired on the spot. A second hypothesis proposes that cells move the most damaged DNA to special "repair shops" inside the cell. Scientists at NASA's Space Radiation Program suggest that rather than trying to gather the repair enzymes at the damage site, it might be more efficient to keep all these enzymes in "shops" near the chromosomes and take damaged DNA to them.

Should exposure to radiation increase for Earth-bound organisms, it will be important for scientist to understand the molecular biology of DNA repair. This better understanding could enable medical professionals to limit or control radiation-induced illness.

- Why would self-destruction of a mutated cell be beneficial to the overall health of a multicellular organism?

- How can a single change in DNA result in a fatal abnormality?

- Would you support federal funding of research into DNA repair mechanisms if there was no increase in radiation reaching the Earth?

## Background Check

**Concepts you should already know to get the most out of this chapter:**
- The structure and chemical properties of proteins and nucleic acids (chapter 3)
- The organization of cells and their genetic information (chapter 4)
- The role of proteins in carrying out the cell's chemical reactions (chapter 5)

### 8.1    DNA and the Importance of Proteins

This chapter focuses on what is notably life's most important class of organic compounds, nucleic acids. Scientists around the world have performed countless experiments that revealed the significant roles played by these compounds. **Deoxyribonucleic acid (DNA)** has been called the "blueprint for life," "master molecule," and "transforming principle."

Nucleic acids were discovered in 1869, when Swiss-born Johann Friedrich Meischer first isolated phosphate-containing acids from cells found in the bandages of wounded soldiers. In 1889 Richard Altman coined the term *nucleic acid*. However, it wasn't until 1950 that DNA became the front-running candidate for the genetic material. It was the work of Americans Alfred Hershey and Martha Chase (1952) that directly linked DNA to genetically controlled characteristics of the bacterium *Escherichia coli* (How Science Works 8.1).

## HOW SCIENCE WORKS 8.1

## Scientists Unraveling the Mystery of DNA

As recently as the 1940s, scientists did not understand the molecular basis of heredity. They understood genetics in terms of the odds that a given trait would be passed on to an individual in the next generation. This "probability" model of genetics left some questions unanswered:

- What is the nature of genetic information?
- How does the cell use genetic information?

### Genetic Material Is Molecular

As is often the case in science, accidental discovery played a large role in answering questions about the nature and use of genetic information. In 1928, a medical doctor, Frederick Griffith, was studying two bacterial strains that caused pneumonia. One of the strains was extremely virulent (highly dangerous) and therefore killed mice very quickly. The other strain was not virulent. Griffith observed something unexpected when *dead* cells of the virulent strain were mixed with *living* cells of the nonvirulent strain: The nonvirulent strain took on the virulent characteristics of the dead strain. Genetic information had been transferred from the dead, virulent cells to the living, nonvirulent cells. This observation was the first significant step in understanding the molecular basis of genetics because it provided scientists with a situation wherein the scientific method could be applied to ask questions and take measurements about the molecular basis of genetics. Until this point, scientists had lacked a method to provide supporting data.

This spurred the scientific community for the next 14 years to search for the identity of the "genetic molecule." A common hypothesis was that the genetic molecule would be one of the macromolecules—carbohydrates, lipids, proteins, or nucleic acids. During that period, many advances were made in how researchers studied cells. Many of the top minds in the field had

**DNA Double Helix**

formulated the hypothesis that the genetic molecule was protein. They had very good support for this hypothesis, too. Their argument boiled down to two ideas. The first idea is that proteins are found everywhere in the cell. It follows that, if proteins were the genetic information, they would be found wherever that information was used. The second idea is that proteins are structurally and chemically complex. They are made up of 20 different amino acids that come in a wide variety of sizes and shapes to make proteins with different properties. This complexity might account for all the genetic variety observed in nature.

On the other hand, very few scientists seriously considered the notion that DNA was the heritable material. After all, it was found only in the nucleus and consisted of only four monomers

Today we know that all organisms use nucleic acids as their genetic material to:

1. *store information* that determines the characteristics of cells and organisms;
2. *direct the synthesis* of proteins essential to the operation of the cell or organism;
3. *chemically change (mutate)* genetic characteristics that are transmitted to future generations; and
4. *replicate* prior to reproduction by directing the manufacture of copies of itself.

The cell's ability to make a particular protein comes from the genetic information stored in the cell's DNA. DNA contains *genes*, which are specific messages about how to construct a protein. Most of an organism's characteristics are the direct result of proteins. Proteins play a critical role in how cells successfully meet the challenges of being alive. For example, functional proteins like enzymes carry out important chemical reactions. Enzymes are so important to a cell that the cell will not live long if it cannot reliably create the proteins it needs for survival. Structural proteins like microtubules, intermediate filaments, and microfilaments are made with the help of enzymes. These proteins maintain cell shape and aid in movement.

Genetic information controls many cellular processes including:

1. the digestion and metabolism of nutrients, and the elimination of harmful wastes;
2. the repair and assembly of cell parts;
3. the reproduction of healthy offspring;
4. the ability to control when and how to react to changes in the environment; and
5. the coordination and regulation of all life's essential functions.

## HOW SCIENCE WORKS 8.1 *(continued)*

(nucleotides). How could this molecule account for the genetic complexity of life?

### Genetic Material Is DNA
In 1944, Oswald Avery and his colleagues provided the first evidence that DNA is the genetic molecule. They performed an experiment similar to Griffith's. Avery's innovation was to use purified samples of protein, DNA, lipids, and carbohydrates from the virulent bacterial strain to transfer the virulent characteristics to the nonvirulent bacterial strain. His data indicated that DNA contains genetic information. The scientific community was highly skeptical of these results for two reasons: (1) Scientists had expected the genetic molecule to be protein, so they hadn't expected this result. More importantly, (2) Avery didn't know how to explain how DNA functions as the genetic molecule. Because of the scientific community's mind-set, Avery's data were largely disregarded on the rationale that his samples were impure. Avery had already designed and carried out an experiment with appropriate controls to address this objection. He reported over 99% purity in the tested DNA samples. It took 8 additional years and a different type of experiment to establish DNA as the genetic molecule.

In 1952, Alfred Hershey and Martha Chase carried out the experiment that settled the question that DNA is the genetic material. Their experiment used a relatively simple genetic system—a bacteriophage. A bacteriophage is a type of virus that uses a bacterial cell as its host. The phage used in this experiment contained only DNA and protein. Hershey and Chase hypothesized that it was necessary for the phage's genetic information to enter the bacterial cell to create new phage. By radioactively labeling the DNA and the protein of the phage in different ways, Hershey and Chase were able to show that the DNA entered the bacterial cell, although very little protein did. They reasoned that since only DNA entered the cell, DNA must be the genetic information.

### The Structure and Function of DNA
Researchers then turned toward the issue of determining how DNA works as the heritable material. Scientists expected that the genetic molecule would have to do a number of things, such as store information, use the genetic information throughout the cell, be able to mutate, and be able to replicate itself. Their hypothesis was that the answer was hidden in the structure of the DNA molecule itself.

The investigation of how DNA functioned as the cell's genetic information took a wide variety of strategies. Some scientists looked at DNA from different organisms. They found that, in nearly every organism, the guanine (G) and cytosine (C) nucleotides were present in equal amounts. The same held true for adenine (A) and thymine (T). Later, this provided the basis for establishing the nucleic acid base-pairing rules.

Rosalind Franklin used X-ray crystallography to determine DNA's width, its helical shape, and the repeating patterns that occur along the length of the DNA molecule. Finally, two young scientists, James Watson and Francis Crick, put it all together. They simply listened to and read the information that was being discussed in the scientific community. Their key role was in the assimilation of all the data. They recognized the importance of the X-ray crystallography data in conjunction with the organic structures of the nucleotides and the data that established the base-pairing rules. Together, they created a model for the structure of DNA that accounts for all the things that a genetic molecule must do. They published an article describing this model in 1952. Ten years later, they were awarded the Nobel Prize for their work.

## 8.2 DNA Structure and Function

The way DNA accomplishes these cellular processes is related to its structure.

## DNA Structure

**Nucleic acids** are large polymers made of many repeating units called nucleotides. Each **nucleotide** is composed of a sugar molecule, a phosphate group, and a molecule called a *nitrogenous base*. DNA nucleotides contain one specific sugar, deoxyribose, and one of four different nitrogenous bases: **adenine** (A), **guanine** (G), **cytosine** (C), and **thymine** (T) (figure 8.1).

The DNA nucleotides can combine into a long linear DNA molecule that can pair with another linear DNA molecule. The two paired strands of DNA form a double helix, with the sugars and phosphates on the outside and the nitrogenous bases in the inside of the helix. The double helix is stabilized because nitrogenous bases are only able to match up (pair) with certain other nucleotides on the opposing strand. Pairing is determined by the molecular shape of the bases and their ability to form hydrogen bonds. Just which pairs come together is referred to as the *base-pair rule*. The rule states that adenine (A) pairs with thymine (T) and guanine (G) pairs with cytosine (C). Also notice in figure 8.2 that one strand ends with the number 3′, the three-prime strand, while the other is called the 5′, or five-prime strand. This is because the two strands run in opposite directions (i.e., one points in one direction while the other points in the opposite direction).

## Base Pairing in DNA Replication

When a cell grows and divides, two new daughter cells result (refer to chapter 1). Both daughter cells need DNA to survive, so the DNA of the parent cell is copied. One copy is provided to each new cell. **DNA replication** is the process by which a cell makes copies of its DNA. The process of DNA replication relies on DNA base-pairing rules and many enzymes. The general process of DNA replication involves several steps.

1. DNA replication begins as enzymes, called *helicases*, attach to the DNA and separate the two strands. This forms a replication bubble (figure 8.3a and b).
2. As helicases separate the two DNA strands, another enzyme, *DNA polymerase* helps attach new, incoming DNA nucleotides one at a time onto the surface of the exposed strands. Nucleotides enter each position according

**(a)** DNA nucleotide

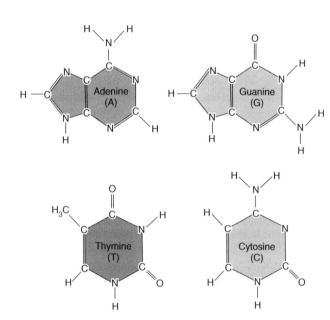

**(b)** The four nitrogenous bases that occur in DNA

**FIGURE 8.1 DNA Nucleotide Structure**
The nucleotide is the basic structural unit of all nucleic acids. All DNA nucleotides consist of three parts—a sugar, a nitrogenous base, and a phosphate group. *(a)* A thymine DNA nucleotide. *(b)* In DNA, the nitrogenous bases can be adenine, guanine, cytosine, and thymine.

to base-pairing rules—adenine (A) pairs with thymine (T), guanine (G) pairs with cytosine (C) (figure 8.3c and d).

3. In prokaryotic cells, this process starts at only one place along the cell's DNA molecule. This place is called the *origin of replication*. In eukaryotic cells, the replication process starts at the same time in several different places along the DNA molecule. As the points of DNA replication meet each other, they combine and a new strand of DNA is formed (figure 8.3e). The result is two identical, double-stranded DNA molecules.

DNA replication yields two double helices, which have identical nucleotide sequences. It has been estimated that there is only one error made for every $2 \times 10^9$ nucleotides. Because this error rate is so small, DNA replication is considered to be essentially error-free. A portion of the DNA polymerase that carries out DNA replication also edits or repairs the newly created DNA molecule for the correct base pairing. When an incorrect match is detected, DNA polymerase removes the incorrect nucleotide and replaces it. Newly made DNA molecules are eventually passed on to the daughter cells.

## The Repair of Genetic Information

Although DNA replication is highly accurate, errors and damage do occasionally occur to the DNA helix. However, the pairing arrangement of the nitrogenous bases allows damage on one strand to be corrected by reading the remaining undamaged strand. For example, if damage occurred to a strand that originally read *AGC* (perhaps it changed to *AAC*), the correct information is still found in the other strand that reads *TCG*. By using enzymes to read the undamaged strand, the cell can rebuild the *AGC* strand with the pairing rule that A pairs with T and G pairs with C. Another example of genetic repair is shown in figure 8.4.

## The DNA Code

DNA is important because it serves as a reliable way of storing information. The *order* of the nitrogenous bases in DNA is the genetic information that codes for proteins. This is similar to how a sequence of letters presents information in a sentence. For the cell, the letters of its alphabet consist only of the nitrogenous bases A, G, C, and T. The information needed to code for one protein can be thousands of nucleotides long. The nitrogenous bases are read in sets of three. Each sequence of three nitrogenous bases is a code word for a single amino acid. Proteins are made of a string that ranges from a few to thousands of amino acids. The order of the amino acids corresponds to the order of the code words in DNA (i.e., *ACC* is the code word for the amino acid tryptophan).

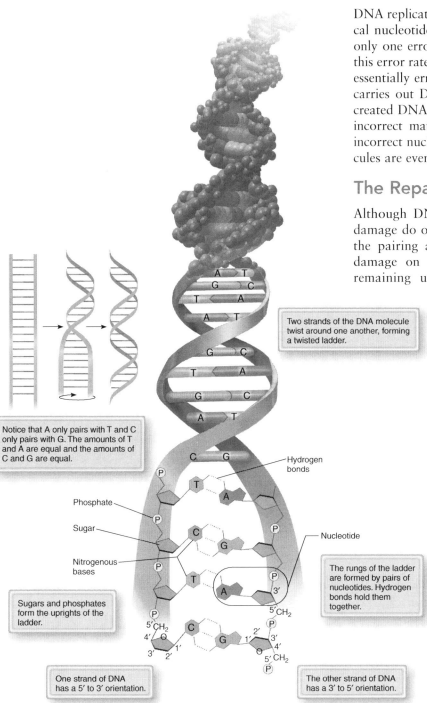

Two strands of the DNA molecule twist around one another, forming a twisted ladder.

Notice that A only pairs with T and C only pairs with G. The amounts of T and A are equal and the amounts of C and G are equal.

Phosphate

Sugar

Nitrogenous bases

Sugars and phosphates form the uprights of the ladder.

Hydrogen bonds

Nucleotide

The rungs of the ladder are formed by pairs of nucleotides. Hydrogen bonds hold them together.

One strand of DNA has a 5′ to 3′ orientation.

The other strand of DNA has a 3′ to 5′ orientation.

## FIGURE 8.2 Double-Stranded DNA

Polymerized deoxyribonucleic acid (DNA) is a helical molecule. The nucleotides within each strand are held together by covalent bonds. The two parallel strands are linked by hydrogen bonds between the base-paired nitrogenous bases.

The new strands of DNA form on each of the old DNA strands (figure 8.3e). In this way, the exposed nitrogenous bases of the original DNA serve as the pattern (template) on which the new DNA strand is formed. The completion of

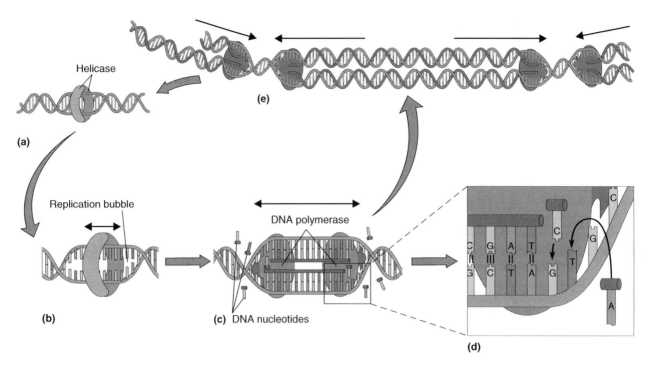

## FIGURE 8.3  DNA Replication

*(a)* Helicase enzymes bind to the DNA molecule. *(b)* The enzymes separate the two strands of DNA. *(c, d)* As the DNA strands are separated, new DNA nucleotides are added to the new strands by DNA polymerase. The new DNA strands are synthesized according to base-pairing rules for nucleic acids. *(e)* By working in two directions at once along the DNA strand, the cell is able to replicate the DNA more quickly. Each new daughter cell receives one of these copies.

## FIGURE 8.4  DNA Repair

*(a)* Undamaged DNA consists of two continuous strands held together at the nitrogenous bases (A, T, G, and C). *(b)* Damaged DNA has part of one strand missing. The thymine bases have been damaged and removed. *(c)* When one strand is damaged, it is possible to rebuild this strand by using the nucleotide sequence on the other side. In DNA, adenine (A) always pairs with thymine (T), and guanine (G) always pairs with cytosine (C).

## 8.3  RNA Structure and Function

Recall from chapter 3 that ribonucleic acid (RNA) is another type of nucleic acid and is important in protein production. RNA's nucleotides are different from DNA's nucleotides. RNA's nucleotides contain a *ribose* sugar whereas the nucleotides of DNA contain a *deoxyribose* sugar. Ribose and deoxyribose sugars differ by one chemical functional group (figure 8.5).

Ribose has an —OH group and deoxyribose has an —H group on the second carbon.

RNA differs from DNA in other important ways. RNA contains the nitrogenous bases **uracil** (U), guanine (G), cytosine (C), and adenine (A). Note that the sets of nitrogenous bases in DNA and RNA are also slightly different. RNA has uracil, whereas DNA has thymine. In addition, when RNA is synthesized from DNA, it exists only as a single strand. This is different from DNA because DNA is typically double-stranded.

Cells also use DNA and RNA differently. DNA is found in the cell's nucleus and is the original source for information to make proteins. RNA is made in the nucleus and then moves into the cytoplasm of the cell where it becomes directly involved in the process of protein assembly.

The protein-coding information in RNA comes directly from DNA. RNA is made by enzymes that read the protein-coding information in DNA. Like DNA replication, RNA synthesis also follows base-pairing rules where the RNA nitrogenous bases pair with the DNA nitrogenous bases: Guanine and cytosine still pair during RNA synthesis but RNA contains uracil, not thymine, so adenine in DNA pairs with uracil in RNA. The thymine in DNA still pairs with adenine in RNA (table 8.1).

## 8.3    CONCEPT REVIEW

6. What role does RNA play in the cell?
7. Describe three differences in the structure of DNA and RNA.

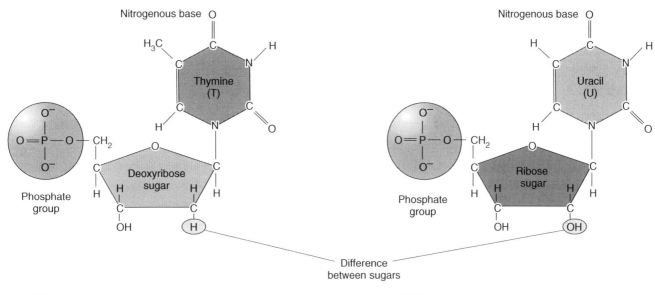

**(a)** DNA nucleotide                                  **(b)** RNA nucleotide

**FIGURE 8.5  A Comparison of DNA and RNA Nucleotides**
DNA and RNA differ from each other chemically and in the nitrogenous bases that are present in each molecule. *(a)* The deoxyribose sugar of DNA has a circled -H. DNA also contains the nitrogenous base thymine (T). *(b)* The ribose sugar of RNA has a circled -OH. RNA contains the nitrogenous base uracil (U) instead of thymine (T). Both DNA and RNA have the nitrogenous bases; adenine, guanine, and cytosine.

**TABLE 8.1  Nucleic Acid Base-Pairing Rules**

| DNA paired with DNA | | DNA paired with RNA | | RNA paired with RNA | |
|---|---|---|---|---|---|
| DNA | DNA | DNA | RNA | RNA | RNA |
| A pairs with T | | A pairs with U | | A pairs with U | |
| T pairs with A | | T pairs with A | | U pairs with A | |
| G pairs with C | | G pairs with C | | G pairs with C | |
| C pairs with G | | C pairs with G | | C pairs with G | |

## 8.4  Protein Synthesis

DNA and RNA are both important in the protein-making process. In the cell, the DNA nucleotides are used as a genetic alphabet, arranged in sets of three (e.g., *ATC, GGA, TCA, CCC*) to form code words in the DNA language. It is the sequence of these code words in DNA that dictates which amino acids are used, and the order in which they appear in a protein. DNA molecules are very long and code for many proteins along their length. Proteins are synthesized in two steps; *transcription* and *translation*.

### Step One: Transcription—Making RNA

**Transcription** is the process of using DNA as a template (stencil) to synthesize RNA. The enzyme **RNA polymerase** "reads" the sequence of DNA nitrogenous bases and follows the base-pairing rules between DNA and RNA to build the new RNA molecule (figure 8.6a–c). RNA polymerase attaches to the DNA and moves along the grooves scanning for base

sequences that act as markers, or signs, that a gene is nearby. The enzyme looks for a **promoter sequence** (figure 8.6d). This is a specific sequence of DNA nucleotides that indicates the location of a protein-coding region and identifies which of the two DNA strands should be used. The **coding strand** of DNA is the side that serves as a template for the synthesis of RNA. The strand of DNA that is not read directly by the enzymes is the **non-coding strand**. Without promoter sequences, RNA polymerase will not transcribe the gene.

Transcription begins when the enzyme separates the two strands of the double-stranded DNA. Separating the two strands exposes their nitrogenous bases, so that the coding strand can be "read." Reading is accomplished by bringing in new RNA nucleotides and base-pairing them with hydrogen bonds one at a time with the exposed DNA nucleotides. Once a match is made, the newly arrived RNA nucleotide is bonded in place by forming a covalent bond between the sugar of one RNA nucleotide and the phosphate of the next.

RNA polymerase stops transcribing the DNA when it reaches a termination sequence. **Termination sequences** are DNA nucleotide sequences that indicate when RNA polymerase should finish making an RNA molecule. Only one of the two strands of DNA is read to create a single strand of RNA for each gene.

There are several types of RNA: however, the three types we will focus on are *messenger RNA (mRNA), transfer RNA (tRNA),* and *ribosomal RNA (rRNA).* Each type of RNA is assembled in the nucleus from combinations of the same 4 nucleotides. However, each type of RNA has a distinct function in the process of protein synthesis that takes place in the cytoplasm. **Messenger RNA (mRNA)** carries the blueprint for making the necessary protein. **Transfer RNA (tRNA)** and **ribosomal RNA (rRNA)** are used in different ways to read the mRNA and bring the necessary amino acids together for assembly into a protein.

**(a)** RNA Polymerase separates DNA and starts RNA synthesis.

**(b)** RNA synthesis continues.
Newly forming RNA

**(c)** RNA synthesis is complete.
Newly forming RNA

**(d)**     Promoter sequence          Protein code     Termination sequence

## FIGURE 8.6 Transcription of DNA to RNA

This figure illustrates the basic events that occur during transcription. *(a)* An enzyme, RNA polymerase, attaches to the DNA at the promoter sequence *(see d)* and then separates the complementary strands. The enzyme then proceeds along the DNA strand in the correct direction to find the protein coding region *(see d)* of the gene. *(b)* As RNA polymerase moves down the coding strand, new complementary RNA nucleotides are base-paired to one of the exposed DNA strands. The base-paired RNA nucleotides are linked together by RNA polymerase to form a new RNA molecule that is complementary to the nucleotide sequence of the DNA. The termination sequence *(see d)* signals the RNA polymerase to end mRNA transcription, so that the RNA can leave the nucleus to aid in translation. *(c)* The newly formed (transcribed) RNA is then separated from the DNA molecule and used by the cell.

## Step Two: Translation—Making Protein

**Translation** is the process of using the information in RNA to direct protein synthesis by attaching amino acids to one another. The mRNA is read linearly in sets of three nucleotides called *codons*. A **codon** is a set of three nucleotides that codes for the placement of a specific amino acid. In the context of an mRNA molecule, the codon determines which amino acid should be added next to the protein during translation. Table 8.2 shows the mRNA nucleotide combinations of each codon and the

## TABLE 8.2   Amino Acid–mRNA Dictionary and the 20 Common Amino Acids and Their Abbreviations

These are the 20 common amino acids used in the protein synthesis operation of a cell. Each has a known chemical structure and is coded for by specific mRNA codons.

**Second letter**

| | | U | C | A | G | |
|---|---|---|---|---|---|---|
| **First letter** | **U** | UUU UUC } Phe – Phenylalanine<br>UUA UUG } Leu – Leucine | UCU UCC UCA UCG } Ser – Serine | UAU UAC } Tyr – Tyrosine<br>UAA UAG } Stop | UGU UGC } Cys – Cysteine<br>UGA Stop<br>UGG Trp – Tryptophan | U C A G |
| | **C** | CUU CUC CUA CUG } Leu – Leucine | CCU CCC CCA CCG } Pro- Proline | CAU CAC } His – Histidine<br>CAA CAG } Gln – Glutamine | CGU CGC CGA CGG } Arg – Arginine | U C A G |
| | **A** | AUU AUC AUA } Ile – Isoleucine<br>AUG Start / Met – Methionine | ACU ACC ACA ACG } Thr – Threonine | AAU AAC } Asn – Asparagine<br>AAA AAG } Lys – Lysine | AGU AGC } Ser – Serine<br>AGA AGG } Arg – Arginine | U C A G |
| | **G** | GUU GUC GUA GUG } Val – Valine | GCU GCC GCA GCG } Ala – Alanine | GAU GAC } Asp – Aspartic Acid<br>GAA GAG } Glu – Glutamic Acid | GGU GGC GGA GGG } Gly – Glycine | U C A G |

**Third letter**

corresponding amino acid. For example, the codon *UUU* corresponds to only the amino acid phenylalanine (Phe). There are 64 possible codons and only 20 commonly used amino acids, so there are multiple ways to code for many amino acids. For example, the codons *UCU, UCC, UCA,* and *UCG* all code for serine.

Recall from chapter 4 that a ribosome is a nonmembranous organelle that synthesizes proteins. A ribosome is made of proteins and a type of RNA called *ribosomal RNA (rRNA)*. Ribosomes usually exist in the cell as two pieces or subunits. There is a large subunit and a small subunit. During translation, the two subunits combine and hold the mRNA between them. With the mRNA firmly sandwiched into the ribosome, the mRNA's codons are read and protein synthesis begins.

The cell has many ribosomes available for protein synthesis. Any of the ribosomes can read any of the mRNAs that come from the cell's nucleus after transcription. Some ribosomes are free in the cytoplasm, whereas others are attached to the cell's rough endoplasmic reticulum (ER). Proteins destined to be part of the cell membrane or packaged for release from the cell are synthesized on ribosomes attached to the endoplasmic reticulum. Proteins that are to perform their function in the cytoplasm are synthesized on ribosomes that are not attached to the endoplasmic reticulum. The process of translation can be broken down into three basic steps: (1) initiation, (2) elongation, and (3) termination.

### Initiation

Protein synthesis begins with the small ribosomal subunit binding to a specific signal sequence of codons on the mRNA. The small ribosomal subunit moves along the mRNA and stops at the first *AUG* codon on the length of the RNA. This *AUG* codon is where translation begins. If an *AUG* is not found, translation does not occur. At the first *AUG* codon, the first amino acid (methionine, or MET) is positioned on the mRNA.

Amino acids are taken to the mRNA-ribosome complex by *transfer RNA*. Transfer RNA (tRNA) is responsible for matching the correct amino acid to the codons found in the mRNA nucleotide sequence (figure 8.7a). The cell's tRNAs are able to match amino acids to the mRNA codons because of base pairing. The portion of the tRNA that interacts with mRNA is called the **anticodon.** The anticodon of tRNA is a short sequence of nucleotides that base-pairs with the nucleotides in the mRNA molecule. The other end of the tRNA carries an amino acid. The correct match between tRNAs and amino acids is made by an enzyme in the cell.

The start codon, *AUG,* is the first codon that is read in the mRNA to make any protein. Since the tRNA that binds to the *AUG* codon carries the amino acid methionine, the first amino acid of every protein is methionine (figure 8.7). If this first methionine is not needed for proper function of the protein, it

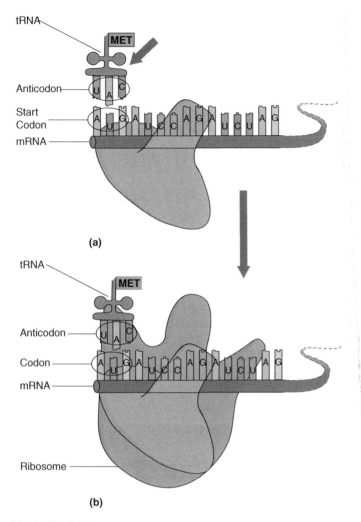

**FIGURE 8.7 Initiation**

*(a)* An mRNA molecule is positioned in the ribosome so that two codons are in position for transcription. The first of these two codons *(AUG)* is the initiation codon and is responsible for hydrogen bonding with the tRNA carrying the amino acid methionine (MET). The start tRNA aligns with the start codon. *(b)* The large subunit of the ribosome joins the small subunit. The ribosome is now assembled and able to translate the mRNA.

can be later clipped off of the protein. After the methionine-tRNA molecule is lined up over the start codon, the large subunit of the ribosome joins the small subunit to bind the mRNA. When the two subunits are together, with the mRNA in the middle, the ribosome is fully formed. The process of forming the rest of the protein is ready to begin (figure 8.7).

## Elongation

Once protein synthesis is started, the ribosome coordinates a recurring series of events. Each time the ribosome works through this series of events, a new amino acid is added to the growing protein. In this way, a ribosome is like an assembly line that organizes the steps of a complicated assembly process. For each new amino acid, a new tRNA arrives at the ribosome with its particular amino acid. The ribosome adds the new amino acid to the growing protein (figure 8.8).

## Termination

The ribosome will continue to add one amino acid after another to the growing protein unless it encounters a stop signal (figure 8.9). The stop signal, in the mRNA, is also a codon. The stop codon can be either *UAA, UAG,* or *UGA.* When any of these three codons appears during the elongation process, a chemical *release factor* enters the ribosome. The release factor causes the ribosome to detach from the protein. When the protein releases, the ribosomal subunits separate and release the mRNA. The mRNA can be used to make another copy of the protein or can be broken down by the cell to prevent any more of the protein from being made. The two pieces of the ribosome can also be reused.

## The Nearly Universal Genetic Code

The code for making protein from DNA is the same for nearly all cells. Bacteria, Archaea, algae, protozoa, plants, fungi and animals all use DNA to store their genetic information. They all transcribe the information in DNA to RNA. They all translate the RNA to synthesize protein using a ribosome. With very few exceptions, they all use the same three nucleotide codons to code for the same amino acid. In eukaryotic cells, transcription always occurs in the nucleus, and translation always occurs in the cytoplasm (figure 8.10).

The similarity of protein synthesis in all cells strongly argues for a common origin of all life forms. It also creates very exciting opportunities for biotechnology. It is now possible to synthesize human proteins, such as insulin, in bacteria, because bacteria and humans use the same code to make proteins. The production of insulin in this way can help create a cheap and plentiful source of medication for many of those who suffer from diabetes.

However, not all genetic information flows from DNA to RNA to proteins. Some viruses use RNA to store their genetic information. These viruses are called retroviruses. An example of a retrovirus is the *human immunodeficiency virus, HIV.* Retroviruses use their RNA to make DNA. This DNA is then used to transcribe more RNA. This RNA is then used to make proteins (Outlooks 8.1).

| 8.4 | CONCEPT REVIEW |
| --- | --- |

8. How does the manufacture of an RNA molecule differ from DNA replication?
9. If a DNA nucleotide sequence is TACAAAGCA, what is the mRNA nucleotide sequence that would base-pair with it?
10. What amino acids would occur in the protein chemically coded by the sequence of nucleotides in question 9?
11. How do tRNA, rRNA, and mRNA differ in function?
12. What are the differences among a promoter sequence, a termination sequence, and a release factor?
13. List the sequence of events that takes place when a DNA message is translated into protein.

**(a)**

**(b)**

**(c)**

**(d)** The cycle starts over with another tRNA bringing in a new amino acid to be added to the growing protein.

**FIGURE 8.8 Elongation**
*(a)* The two tRNAs align the amino acids isoleucine (ILE) and glutamine (GLN) so that they can be chemically attached to one another by forming a peptide bond. *(b)* Once the bond is formed, the first tRNA detaches from its position on the mRNA. *(c)* The ribosome moves down one codon on the mRNA. Another tRNA now aligns so that the next amino acid (ILE) can be added to the growing protein. *(d)* The process continues with a new tRNA, a new amino acid, and the formation of a new peptide bond.

## 8.5 The Control of Protein Synthesis

Cells have many protein-coding sequences. **Gene expression** occurs when a cell transcribes and translates a gene. Cells do not make all their proteins at once. It would be a great waste of resources. Cells can control which genes are used to make proteins. In fact, the differences between the types of cells in the human body are due to the differences in the proteins produced. Cells use many ways to control gene expression in response to environmental conditions. Some methods help increase or decrease the amount of enzyme that is made by the cell. Other methods help change amino acid sequences to form a new version of the enzyme.

## Controlling Protein Quantity

A cell process can be regulated by controlling how much of a specific enzyme is made. The cell regulates the amount of protein (enzymes are proteins) that is made by changing how much mRNA is available for translation into protein. The cell can use several strategies to control how much mRNA is transcribed.

### DNA Packaging

The genetic material of humans and other eukaryotic organisms consists of strands of coiled, double-stranded DNA, which have *histone* proteins attached along its length. The histone proteins and DNA are not arranged randomly but, rather, come together

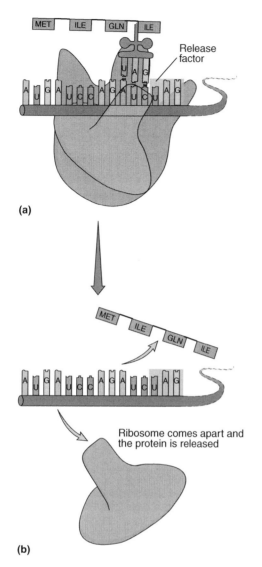

**(a)**

**(b)**

**FIGURE 8.9 Termination**

*(a)* A release factor will move into position over a termination codon—here, *UAG*. *(b)* The ribosome releases the completed amino acid chain. The ribosome disassembles and the mRNA can be used by another ribosome to synthesize another protein.

in a highly organized pattern (figure 8.11). When packaged, the double-stranded DNA spirals around repeating clusters of eight histone spheres. Histone clusters with their encircling DNA are called **nucleosomes.** These coiled DNA strands with attached proteins become visible during cell division and are called **nucleoproteins** or **chromatin fibers.** Condensed like this, a chromatin fiber is referred to as a **chromosome** (Outlooks 8.2). The degree to which the chromatin is coiled provides a method for long-term control of protein expression. In tightly coiled chromatin, the promoter sequence of the gene is tightly bound so that RNA polymerase cannot attach and initiate transcription. Loosely packaged chromatin exposes the promoter sequence so that transcription can occur.

## Enhancers and Silencers

**Enhancer** and **silencer sequences** are DNA sequences that act as binding sites for proteins. When proteins are bound to these sites, they affect the ability of RNA polymerase to transcribe a specific protein. Enhancer sequences increase protein synthesis by helping increase transcription. Silencer sequences decrease transcription. These DNA sequences are unique because they do not need to be close to the promoter to function and they are not transcribed.

## Transcription Factors

**Transcription factors** are proteins that control how available a promoter sequence is for transcription. The protein molecules bind to DNA around a gene's promoter sequence and influence RNA polymerase's ability to start transcription. There are many transcription factors in the cell. Eukaryotic transcription is so tightly regulated that transcription factors always guide RNA polymerase to the promoter sequence. A particular gene will not be expressed if its specific set of transcription factors is not available. Prokaryotic cells also use proteins to block or encourage transcription, but not to the extent that this strategy is used in eukaryotic cells.

## RNA Degradation

Cells also regulate gene expression by limiting the length of time that mRNA is available for translation. Enzymes in the cell break down the mRNA, so that it can no longer be used to synthesize protein. The time that a given mRNA molecule lasts in a cell is dependant on the nucleotide sequences in the mRNA itself. These sequences are in areas of the mRNA that do not code for protein.

## Controlling Protein Quality

Another way that cells can control gene expression is to change the amino acid sequences to form different versions of an enzyme. One of the most significant differences between prokaryotic and eukaryotic cells is that eukaryotic cells can make more than one type of protein from a single protein-coding region of the DNA. Eukaryotic cells are able to do this because the protein-coding regions of eukaryotic genes are organized differently than the genes found in prokaryotic (bacterial) cells. The fundamental difference is that the protein-coding regions in prokaryotes are continuous, whereas eukaryotic protein-coding regions are not. Many intervening sequences are scattered throughout the protein-coding sequence of genes in eukaryotic cells. These sequences, called **introns,** do not code for proteins. The remaining sequences, which are used to code for protein, are called **exons.** After the protein-coding region of a eukaryotic gene is transcribed into mRNA, the introns in the mRNA are cut out and the remaining exons are spliced together, end to end, to create a shorter version of the mRNA. It is this shorter version that is used during translation to produce a protein (figure 8.12).

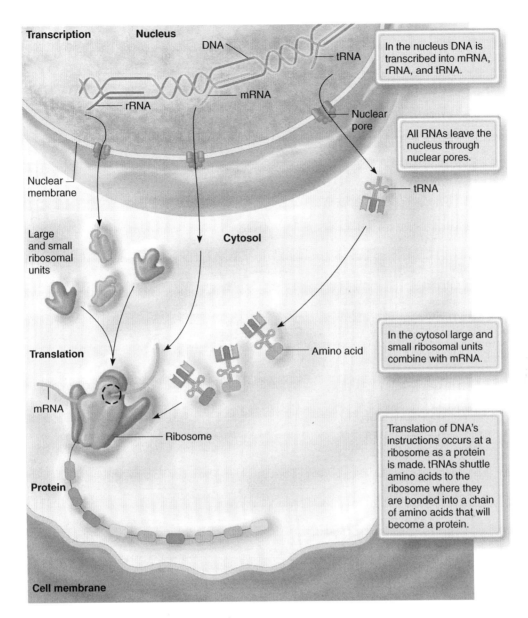

**FIGURE 8.10  Summary of Eukaryotic Protein Synthesis**
The genetic information in DNA is rewritten in the nucleus as RNA in the nucleus during transcription. The mRNA, tRNA, and rRNA move from the nucleus to the cytoplasm (cytosol), where the genetic information is read during translation by the ribosome.

One advantage of having introns is that a single protein-coding region can make more than one protein. Scientists originally estimated that humans had 80,000 to 100,000 genes. This was based on techniques that allowed them to estimate the number of *different proteins* found in humans. When the human genome was mapped, scientists were surprised to find that humans have only about 25,000 genes. This suggests that many of our genes are capable of making several different proteins.

It is possible to make several different proteins from the same protein-coding region by using different combinations of exons. **Alternative splicing** is the process of selecting which exons will be retained during the normal process of splicing. Alternative splicing can be a very important part of gene regulation. One protein-coding region in fruit flies, *sex-lethal*, can be spliced into two different forms. One form creates a full-sized, functional protein. The other form creates a very small protein with no function. For the fruit fly, the difference between the two alternatively spliced forms of *sex-lethal* is the difference between becoming a male or becoming a female fruit fly (Outlooks 8.3).

## Epigenetics

**Epigenetics** is the study of changes in gene expression caused by factors other than alterations in a cell's DNA. The term *epigenetics* actually means "in addition to genetics," (i.e., nongenetic factors that cause a cell's genes to express

## OUTLOOKS 8.1

## Life in Reverse—Retroviruses

Acquired immunodeficiency syndrome (AIDS) is caused by a retrovirus called human immunodeficiency virus (HIV). HIV is a spherical virus that has RNA as its genetic material surrounded by a protein coat. In addition, the virus is surrounded by a phospholipid layer taken on from the cell's plasma membrane when the virus exits the host cell. When persons become infected with HIV, the outer phospholipid membrane of the virus fuses with the plasma membrane of the host cell and releases the virus with its RNA into the cell. In addition to its RNA genetic material, HIV carries a few enzymes; one is reverse transcriptase. When HIV enters a suitable host cell, the virus first uses reverse transcriptase to produce a DNA copy of its RNA. (This is the reverse of the normal process in cells that involves the enzyme transcriptase using DNA to make RNA.) Because this is the reverse (*retro-*) of what normally happens in a cell, RNA viruses are called *retroviruses*. The DNA produced by reverse transcriptase is spliced into the host cell's DNA. Only then does HIV become an active, disease-causing parasite. Once a DNA copy of the virus RNA is inserted into the host cell's DNA, the virally derived DNA is used to make copies of the viral RNA and its protein coat.

Understanding how HIV differs from DNA-based organisms has two important implications. First, the presence of reverse transcriptase in a human can be looked upon as an indication of retroviral infection because reverse transcriptase is not manufactured by human cells. However, because HIV is only one of several types of retroviruses, the presence of the enzyme in an individual does not necessarily indicate an HIV infection. It only indicates a type of retroviral infection. Second, antiviral drug treatments for HIV take advantage of

Budding HIV virus

**Budding HIV Virus**
This electron micrograph shows HIV viruses leaving the cell. These viral particles can now infect another cell and continue the viral replication cycle unless medications prevent this from happening.

vulnerable points in the retrovirus's life cycle. For example, interference with reverse transcriptase blocks the virus's ability to make DNA and lessens its chances of integrating into the host's DNA. This gives an infected person's body the opportunity to destroy the viruses and reduces the chance that the person will develop symptoms of the disease. Once cleared of viruses, the likelihood that the individual will transmit the virus to others is decreased.

---

themselves differently). When an epigenetic change occurs, it might last for the life of the cell and can even be passed on to the next generation. This is what happens when a cell (e.g., stem cell) undergoes the process of differentiation. Stem cells are called *pluripotent* because they have the potential to be any kind of cell found in the body (i.e., muscle, bone, or skin cell). However, once they become differentiated they lose the ability to become other kinds of cells, and so do the cells they produce by cell division. For example, if a pluripotent cell were to express muscle protein genes and not insulin protein genes, it would differentiate into a muscle cell, not an insulin-producing cell.

Four examples of events that can cause an epigenetic effect are:

1. adding a methyl group to a cytosine in the gene changes it to methylcytosine. Since methylcytosine cannot be read during translation, the gene is turned off.
2. altering the shape of the histones around the gene. Modifying histones ensures that a differentiated cell would

stay differentiated, and not convert back into being a pluripotent cell.
3. having the protein that has already been transcribed return to the gene and keep it turned on.
4. splicing RNA into sequences not originally determined by the gene.

Some compounds are considered epigenetic carcinogens (i.e., they are able to cause cells to form tumors), but they do not change the nucleotide sequence of a gene. Examples include certain chlorinated hydrocarbons used as fungicides and some nickel-containing compounds.

## 8.5 CONCEPT REVIEW

14. Provide two examples of how a cell uses transcription to control gene expression.
15. Provide an example of why it is advantageous for a cell to control gene expression.

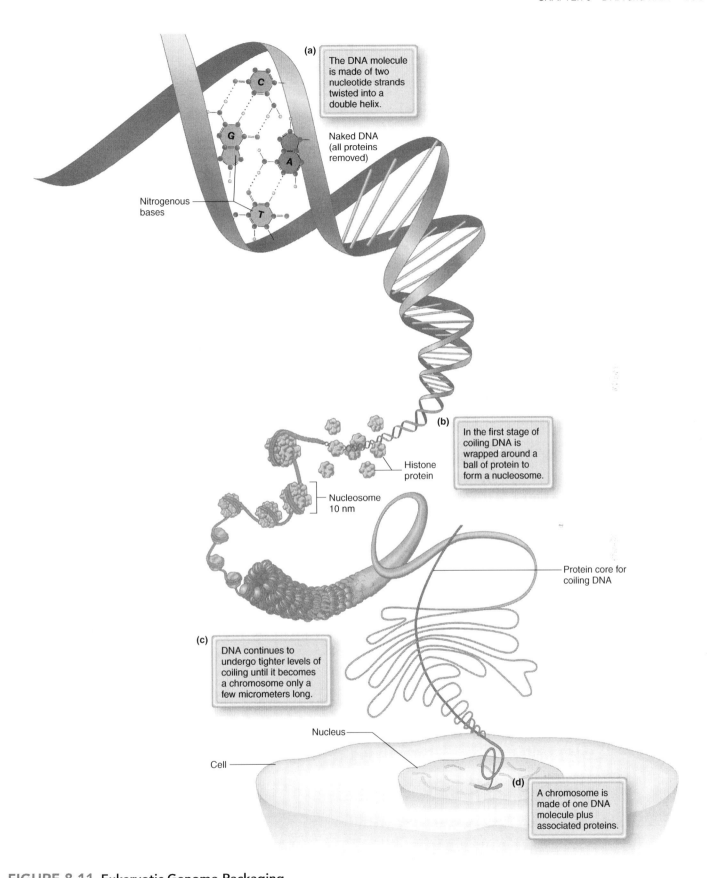

**(a)** The DNA molecule is made of two nucleotide strands twisted into a double helix.

Naked DNA (all proteins removed)

Nitrogenous bases

C

G

A

T

**(b)** In the first stage of coiling DNA is wrapped around a ball of protein to form a nucleosome.

Histone protein

Nucleosome 10 nm

Protein core for coiling DNA

**(c)** DNA continues to undergo tighter levels of coiling until it becomes a chromosome only a few micrometers long.

Nucleus

Cell

**(d)** A chromosome is made of one DNA molecule plus associated proteins.

**FIGURE 8.11  Eukaryotic Genome Packaging**

During certain stages in the life cycle of a eukaryotic cell, the DNA is tightly coiled to form a chromosome. To form a chromosome, the DNA molecule is wrapped around a group of several histone proteins. Together, the histones and the DNA form a structure called the nucleosome. The nucleosomes are stacked together in coils to form a chromosome.

# OUTLOOKS 8.2

## Telomeres

Each end of a chromosome contains a sequence of nucleotides called a **telomere**. In humans, these chromosome "caps" contain many copies of the following nucleotide base-pair sequence:

**TTAGGG**
**AATCCC**

Telomeres are very important segments of the chromosome. They are:

1. required for chromosome replication;
2. protect the chromosome from being destroyed by dangerous DNAase enzymes (enzymes that destroy DNA); and
3. keep chromosomes from bonding to one another end to end.

Evidence shows that the loss of telomeres is associated with cell "aging," whereas not removing them has been linked to cancer. Every time a cell reproduces itself, it loses some of its telomeres. However, in cells that have the enzyme telomerase, new telomeres are added to the ends of the chromosome each time the cells divide. Therefore, cells that have telomerase do

not age as other cells do, and cancer cells are immortal because of this enzyme. Telomerase enables chromosomes to maintain, if not increase, the length of telomeres from one cell generation to the next.

The yellow regions on this drawing of a chromosome indicate where the telomeres are.

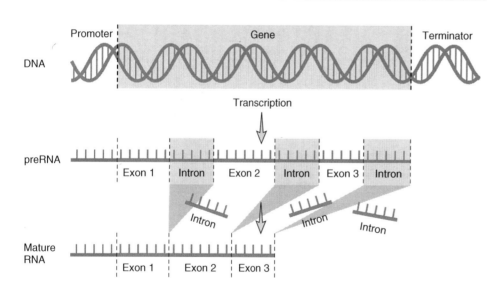

**FIGURE 8.12 Transcription of mRNA in Eukaryotic Cells**

This is a summary of the events that occur in the nucleus during the manufacture of mRNA in a eukaryotic cell. Notice that the original nucleotide sequence is first transcribed into an RNA molecule, which is later "clipped" and then rebonded to form a shorter version of the original. It is during this time that the introns are removed.

## 8.6 Mutations and Protein Synthesis

A **mutation** is any change in the DNA sequence of an organism. They can occur for many reasons, including errors during DNA replication. Mutations can also be caused by external factors, such as radiation, carcinogens, drugs, or even some viruses. It is important to understand that not all mutations cause a change in an organism. If a mutation occurs away from the protein-coding sequence and the DNA sequences that regulate its expression, it is unlikely that the change will be harmful to the organism. On occasion, the changes that

occur because of mutations can be helpful and will provide an advantage to the offspring that inherit that change.

Scientists are not yet able to consistently predict the effects that a mutation will have on the entire organism. Changes in a protein's amino acid sequence may increase or decrease the protein's level of activity. The mutations may also completely stop the protein's function. Less frequently, a change in the amino acid sequence may create a wholly novel function. In any case, to predict the effect that a mutation will have would require knowing how the proteins work in a variety of different cells, tissues, organs, and organ systems. With our current understanding, this is not always possible.

# One Small Change—One Big Difference!

Male and female fruit flies produce the same unspliced mRNA from the *sex-lethal* gene. A cellular signal determines if the fruit fly will develop as a female or a male. The manner in which the sex-lethal mRNA is spliced depends on the signal that is received. Females remove the third exon from the sex-lethal mRNA, whereas males leave the third exon in the mRNA. This is one example of alternative splicing. The female-specific mRNA can be translated by ribosomes to make a fully functional sex-lethal protein. This protein promotes female body development. The male-specific mRNA contains a stop codon in the third exon. This causes the ribosome to stop synthesis of the male's sex-lethal protein earlier than in the female version of the sex-lethal protein. The resulting protein is small and has no function. With no sex-lethal protein activity, the fruit fly develops as a male.

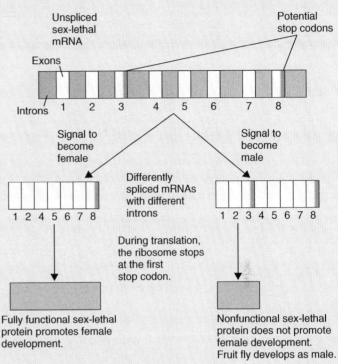

Our best method of understanding a mutation is to observe its effects directly in an organism that carries the mutation.

## Point Mutations

A **point mutation** is a change in a single nucleotide of the DNA sequence. Point mutations can potentially have a variety of effects even though they change only one nucleotide. Three different kinds of point mutations are recognized, (a) missense, (b) silent, and (c) nonsense.

### Missense Mutation

A **missense mutation** is a point mutation that causes the wrong amino acid to be used in making a protein. A sequence change that resulted in the codon change from *UUU* to *GUU* would use valine instead of phenylalanine. The shapes and chemical properties of enzymes are determined by the correct sequence of various types of amino acids. Substituting one amino acid for another can create an abnormally functioning protein.

The condition known as sickle-cell anemia provides a good example of the effect caused by a simple missense mutation. Hemoglobin is a protein in red blood cells that is responsible for carrying oxygen to the body's cells. Normal hemoglobin molecules are composed of four separate, different proteins. The proteins are arranged with respect to each

other so that they are able to hold an iron atom. The iron atom is the portion of hemoglobin that binds the oxygen.

In normal individuals, the amino acid sequence of the hemoglobin protein begins like this:

Val-His-Leu-Thr-Pro-*Glu-Glu-Lys* . . .

In some individuals, a single nucleotide of the hemoglobin gene has been changed. The result of this change is a hemoglobin protein with an amino acid sequence of:

Val-His-Leu-Thr-Pro-*Val*-Glu-Lys . . .

Glutamic acid (Glu) is coded by two codons: *GAA* and *GAG*. Valine is also coded by two codons: *GUA* and *GUG*. The change that causes the switch from glutamic acid to valine is a missense mutation. With this small change, the parts of the hemoglobin protein do not assemble correctly under low oxygen levels.

When the oxygen levels in the blood are low, many hemoglobin molecules stick together and cause the red blood cells to have a sickle shape, rather than their normal round, donut shape (figure 8.13). The results can be devastating:

- The red blood cells do not flow smoothly through the capillaries, causing the red blood cells to tear and be destroyed. This results in anemia.

(a)                           (b)

**FIGURE 8.13 Normal and Sickled Red Blood Cells**
*(a)* A normal red blood cell and *(b)* a cell having the sickle shape. This sickling is the result of a single amino acid change in the hemoglobin molecule.

- Their irregular shapes cause them to clump, clogging the blood vessels. This prevents oxygen from reaching the oxygen-demanding tissues. As a result, tissues are damaged.
- A number of physical disabilities may result, including weakness, brain damage, pain and stiffness of the joints, kidney damage, rheumatism, and, in severe cases, death.

## Silent Mutation

A **silent mutation** is a nucleotide change that results in either the placement of the same amino acid or a different amino acid but does not cause a change in the function of the completed protein. An example of a silent mutation is the change from *UUU* to *UUC* in the mRNA. The mutation from U to C does not change the amino acid present in the protein. It still results in the amino acid phenylalanine being used to construct the protein. Another example is shown in figure 8.14.

## Nonsense Mutation

Another type of point mutation, a **nonsense mutation,** causes a ribosome to stop protein synthesis by introducing a stop codon too early. For example, a nonsense mutation would be caused if a codon were changed from *CAA* (glutamine) to *UAA* (stop). This type of mutation results in a protein that is too short. It prevents a functional protein from being made because it is terminated too soon. Human genetic diseases that result from nonsense mutations include (a) cystic fibrosis (caused by certain mutations in the cystic fibrosis transmembrane conductance regulator gene), (b) Duchenne muscular dystrophy (caused by mutations in the dystrophin gene), and (c) beta thalassaemia (caused by mutations in the β-globin gene).

## Insertions and Deletions

Several other kinds of mutations involve larger spans of DNA than a change in a single nucleotide. Insertions and deletions are different from point mutations because they change the DNA sequence by adding and removing

nucleotides. An **insertion mutation** adds one or more nucleotides to the normal DNA sequence. This type of mutation can potentially add amino acids to the protein and change its function. A **deletion mutation** removes one or more nucleotides and can potentially remove amino acids from the protein and change its function.

### Frameshift Mutations

Insertions and deletions can also affect amino acids that are coded *after* the mutation by causing a *frameshift*. Ribosomes read the mRNA three nucleotides at a time. This set of three nucleotides is called a reading frame. A **frameshift mutation** occurs when insertions or deletions cause the ribosome to read the wrong sets of three nucleotides. Consider the example shown in figure 8.15. Frameshift mutations can result in severe genetic diseases such as Tay-Sachs and some types of familial hypercholesterolemia. Tay-Sachs disease (caused by mutations in the beta-hexosaminidase gene) affects the breakdown of lipids in lysosomes. It results in

**FIGURE 8.14 Kinds of Point Mutations**
A nucleotide substitution changes the protein only if the changed codon results in a different amino acid being substituted into a protein chain. *(a)* In the example, the original codon, *CAA*, calls for the amino acid glutamine. *(b)* A *silent* mutation is shown where the third position of the codon is changed. The codon *CAG* calls for the same amino acid as the original version (*CAA*). Because the proteins produced in example *(a)* and example *(b)* will be identical in amino acid sequence, they will function the same also. *(c)* A *nonsense* mutation is shown where the codon *UAA* stops the synthesis of the protein. *(d)* A *missense* mutation occurs when the nucleotide in the second position of the codon is changed. It now reads *AAA*. The codon *AAA* calls for the amino acid lysine. This mutation may alter protein function.

**Original mRNA sequence**

<u>AAA</u> <u>*UUU*</u> <u>GGG</u> <u>CCC</u>
Lys  Phe  Gly  Pro

Reading frame

**Effect of frameshift** ⌐————— Deleted nucleotides

<u>AAA</u> <u>U</u> <u>GG</u> <u>G</u> <u>CC</u> C
Lys  Trp  Ala

**FIGURE 8.15  Frameshift**
A frameshift causes the ribosome to read the wrong set of three nucleotides on the mRNA. Proteins produced by this type of mutation usually bear little resemblance to the normal protein that is usually produced. In this example, the normal sequence is shown for comparison with the mutated sequence. The mutated sequence is missing two uracil nucleotides. The underlining identifies sets of nucleotides that are read by the ribosome as a codon. A normal protein is made until after the deletion is encountered.

damage to the nervous system, including blindness, paralysis, psychosis, and early death of children.

### Mutations Caused by Viruses

Some viruses can insert their genetic code into the DNA of their host organism. When this happens, the presence of the new viral sequence may interfere with the cells' ability to use genetic information in that immediate area of the insertion. In such cases, the virus's genetic information becomes an insertion mutation. In the case of some retroviruses, such as the human papillomavirus (HPV), the insertion mutations increase the likelihood of cancer of the penis, anus, and cervical cancer. These cancers are caused when mutations occur in genes that help regulate when a cell divides (figure 8.16).

## Chromosomal Aberrations

A **chromosomal aberration** is a major change in DNA that can be observed at the level of the chromosome. Chromosomal aberrations involve many genes and tend to affect many different parts of the organism if it lives through development. There are four types of aberrations: *inversions, translocations, duplications,* and *deletions.* An **inversion** occurs when a chromosome is broken and a piece becomes reattached to its original chromosome, but in a flipped orientation. A **translocation** occurs when one broken segment of DNA becomes integrated into a different chromosome. **Duplications** occur when a portion of a chromosome is replicated and attached to the original section in sequence. **Deletion aberrations** result when a broken piece becomes lost or is destroyed before it can be reattached. All of these aberrations are considered mutations. Because of the large segments of DNA that are involved with these types of mutations, many genes can be affected.

In humans, chromosomal aberrations frequently prevent fetal development. In some cases, however, the pregnancy can be carried full term. In these situations, the effects of the mutations vary greatly. In some cases, there are no noticeable differences. In other cases, the effects are severe. Cri-du-chat (cry of the cat) is a disorder that is caused by a deletion of part of chromosome number 5. It occurs with between 1 in 25,000

**FIGURE 8.16  HPV**
Genital warts and some genital cancers (particularly cervical cancer) are caused by the human papillomavirus (HPV). Over 70 papillomaviruses are shown in this photo, taken through an electron microscope. Several HPV strains have been associated with a higher than normal incidence of cancer. This is because HPV creates insertion mutations in the cells it infects.

to 50,000 births. The key symptom is a high-pitched, cat-like cry of the infants. This is thought to be due to a variety of things that include poor muscle tone. Facial characteristics such as a small head, widely set eyes, and low-set ears are also typical. Mild to severe mental disabilities are also symptoms. There appears to be a correlation between the deletion size and the symptoms; larger regions of deleted DNA tends to correlate to more severe symptoms.

Many other forms of mutations affect DNA. Some damage to DNA is so extensive that the entire strand is broken, resulting in the synthesis of abnormal proteins or a total lack of protein synthesis. A number of experiments indicate that many street drugs, such as lysergic acid diethylamide (LSD), are mutagenic agents that cause DNA to break.

## Mutations and Inheritance

Mutations can be harmful to the individual who first gains the mutation, but changes in the structure of DNA may also have harmful effects on the next generation if they occur in the sex cells. Sex cells transmit genetic information from one generation to the next. Mutations that occur to DNA molecules can be passed on to the next generation only when the mutation is present in cells such as sperm and egg. In the next several chapters, we will look at how DNA is inherited. As you read the next chapters remember that DNA codes for proteins. Genetic differences between individuals are the result of slightly different enzymes.

### 8.6   CONCEPT REVIEW

16. Both chromosomal and point mutations occur in DNA. In what ways do they differ?
17. What is a silent mutation? Provide an example.

## Summary

The successful operation of a living cell depends on its ability to accurately use the genetic information found in its DNA. DNA replication results in an exact doubling of the genetic material. The process virtually guarantees that identical strands of DNA will be passed on to the next generation of cells. The production of protein molecules is under the control of the nucleic acids, the primary control molecules of the cell. The sequence of the bases in the nucleic acids, DNA and RNA, determines the sequence of amino acids in the protein, which in turn determine the protein's function. Protein synthesis involves the decoding of the DNA into specific protein molecules and the use of the intermediate molecules, mRNA and tRNA, at the ribosome. The process of protein synthesis is controlled by regulatory sequences in the nucleic acids. Errors in any of the protein coding sequences in DNA may produce observable changes in the cell's functioning and can lead to cell death.

## Key Terms

*Use the interactive flash cards on the **Concepts in Biology**, 14/e website to help you learn the meanings of these terms.*

| | |
|---|---|
| adenine 154 | missense mutation 167 |
| alternative splicing 163 | mutation 166 |
| anticodon 159 | non-coding strand 157 |
| chromosomal aberration 169 | nonsense mutation 168 |
| | nucleic acids 154 |
| chromosome 162 | nucleoproteins (chromatin fibers) 162 |
| coding strand 157 | |
| codon 158 | nucleosomes 162 |
| cytosine 154 | nucleotide 154 |
| deletion aberration 169 | point mutation 167 |
| deletion mutation 168 | promoter sequence 157 |
| deoxyribonucleic acid (DNA) 152 | ribosomal RNA (rRNA) 157 |
| DNA replication 154 | RNA polymerase 157 |
| duplications 169 | silencer sequences 162 |
| enhancer sequences 162 | silent mutation 168 |
| epigenetics 163 | telomere 166 |
| exons 162 | termination sequences 157 |
| frameshift mutation 168 | thymine 154 |
| gene expression 161 | transcription 157 |
| guanine 154 | transcription factors 162 |
| insertion mutation 168 | transfer RNA (tRNA) 157 |
| introns 162 | translation 158 |
| inversion 169 | translocation 169 |
| messenger RNA (mRNA) 157 | uracil 156 |

## Basic Review

1. Genetic information is stored in what type of chemical?
   a. proteins
   b. lipids
   c. nucleic acids
   d. sugars

2. The difference between ribose and deoxyribose is
   a. the number of carbon atoms.
   b. an oxygen atom.
   c. one is a sugar and one is not.
   d. No difference—they are the same molecule.

3. The nitrogenous bases in DNA
   a. hold the two DNA strands together.
   b. link the nucleotides together.
   c. are part of the genetic blueprint.
   d. Both a and c are correct.

4. Transcription copies genetic information
   a. from DNA to RNA.
   b. from proteins to DNA.
   c. from DNA to proteins.
   d. from RNA to proteins.

5. RNA polymerase starts synthesizing mRNA in eukaryotic cells because
   a. it finds a promoter sequence.
   b. transcription factors interact with RNA polymerase.
   c. the gene is in a region of loosely packed chromatin.
   d. All of the above are true.

6. Under normal conditions, translation
   a. forms RNA.
   b. reads in sets of three nucleotides called codons.
   c. occurs in the nucleus.
   d. All of the above statements are true.

7. The function of tRNA is to
   a. be part of the ribosome's subunits.
   b. carry the genetic blueprint.
   c. carry an amino acid to a working ribosome.
   d. Both a and c are correct.

8. Enhancers
   a. make ribosomes more efficient at translation.
   b. prevent mutations from occurring.
   c. increase the transcription of specific genes.
   d. slow aging.

9. The process that removes introns and joins exons from mRNA is called
   a. silencing.
   b. splicing.
   c. transcription.
   d. translation.

10. A deletion of a single base in the protein-coding sequence of a gene will likely create
    a. no problems.
    b. a faulty RNA polymerase.
    c. a tRNA.
    d. a frameshift.

11. Which is an example of a missense mutation?
    a. Tay-Sachs disease
    b. sickle-cell anemia
    c. HIV/AIDS
    d. virulent disease

12. Which best describes the sequence of events followed by the human immunodeficiency virus in its replication?
    a. DNA → RNA → protein
    b. RNA → RNA → protein
    c. RNA → DNA → RNA
    d. DNA → RNA → protein
    e. DNA → RNA → RNA

13. If the two subunits of a ribosome do not come together with an mRNA molecule, which will not occur?
    a. transcription
    b. translation
    c. replication
    d. All the above are correct.

14. Which of the following pairs would be incorrect according to the base-pairing rule?
    a. in DNA: AT
    b. in DNA: GC
    c. in RNA: UT
    d. in RNA: GC

15. Using the amino acid–nucleic acid dictionary, which amino acid would be coded for by the mRNA codon GAC?
    a. asparagine
    b. aspartic acid
    c. isoleucine
    d. valine

**Answers**
1. c   2. b   3. d   4. a   5. d   6. b   7. c   8. c   9. b   10. d
11. b   12. c   13. b   14. c   15. b

## Thinking Critically

**Gardening in Depth**
A friend of yours gardens for a hobby. She has noticed that she has a plant that no longer produces the same color of flower it did a few years ago. It used to produce red flowers; now, the flowers are white. Consider that petal color in plants is due to at least one enzyme that produces the color pigment. No color suggests no enzyme activity. Using what you know about genes, protein synthesis, and mutations, hypothesize what may have happened to cause the change in flower color. Identify several possibilities; then, identify what you would need to know to test your hypothesis.

CHAPTER

9

# Cell Division— Proliferation and Reproduction

## Unregulated Cell Division Can Result in Cancer

*New findings reveal how cells can become tumors.*

Cancer occurs when there is a problem with controlling how cells divide and replace themselves. A tumor forms when cells divide in an unregulated manner. As a tumor grows, some of its cells may change and move out of the tumor, enter the circulatory system, and establish new tumors in other places.

Scientists are starting to understand how cell growth is regulated. The picture that is emerging from this research is that many proteins are involved in cell growth regulation. When certain changes occur in the proteins (i.e., histones) that regulate the cell's growth, the cell might divide when it should not. Sometimes these mutations are inherited. Individuals with these mutations are more likely than others to develop cancer. Sometimes these mutations occur because of exposure to something in the environment.

- **How does a mutagen cause cancer?**
- **How do chemotherapy and radiation treatments stop cancer?**
- **If components of smoke from coal-fired power plants cause cancer, should laws be passed to regulate such emssions?**

# Background Check

**Concepts you should already know to get the most out of this chapter:**
- The organization of the cell and its nucleus (chapter 4)
- The function of enzymes in the cell (chapter 5)
- The genetic information of eukaryotic cells is found in DNA that is packaged into chromosomes (chapter 8)

## 9.1   Cell Division: An Overview

Two fundamental characteristics of life are the ability to grow and the ability to reproduce. Both of these characteristics depend on the process of *cell division*. **Cell division** is the process by which a single cell generates new daughter cells. Cell division serves many purposes. For single-celled organisms, it is a method of increasing their numbers. For multicellular organisms, it is a process that leads to growth, the replacement of lost cells, the healing of injuries, and the formation of reproductive cells.

There are three general types of cell division, each involving a parent cell. The first type of cell division is *binary fission* (figure 9.1). **Binary fission** is a method of cell division used by prokaryotic cells. During binary fission, the prokaryotic cell's single loop of DNA replicates, and becomes attached to the plasma membrane inside the cell. As a membrane forms inside the cell, the two DNA loops become separated into two daughter cells. This process ensures that each of the daughter cells receives the same information that was possessed by the parent cell. Some bacteria, such as *E. coli*, are able to undergo cell division as frequently as every 20 minutes. The second type of cell division, **mitosis,** is a method of eukaryotic cell division; like binary fission, it also results in daughter cells that are *genetically identical to the parent cell*. Eukaryotic cells have several chromosomes that are replicated and divided by complex processes between two daughter cells. The third type of cell division is **meiosis,** a method of eukaryotic cell division that results in daughter cells that have half the genetic information of the parent cell. These daughter cells contain half the genetic information of the parent cell, are not genetically identical to the parent cell from which they were produced, and can be used in sexual reproduction.

## Asexual Reproduction

For single-celled organisms, binary fission and mitosis are methods of *asexual reproduction*. **Asexual reproduction** binary fission and mitosis requires only one parent that divides and results in two organisms that are genetically identical to the parent. Prokaryotes typically undergo binary fission whereas single-celled and multicellular eukaryotes undergo mitosis.

In multicellular organisms, mitosis produces new cells that

- cause growth by increasing the number of cells,
- replace lost cells, and
- repair injuries.

In each case, the daughter cells require the same genetic information that was present in the parent cell. Because they have the

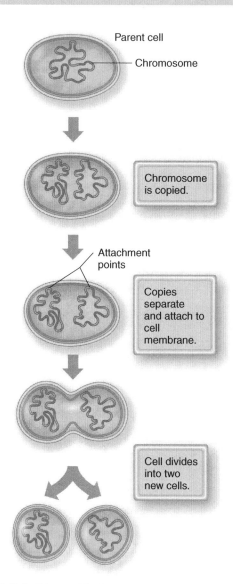

**FIGURE 9.1  Binary Fission**
This asexual form of reproduction occurs in bacteria. Each daughter cell that results has a copy of the loop of DNA found in the parent cell.

same DNA as the parent cell, the daughter cells are able to participate in the same metabolic activities as the parent cell.

## Sexual Reproduction

**Sexual reproduction** requires two parents to donate genetic information when creating offspring. *The result of sexual reproduction is a genetically unique individual.*

Meiosis is the process that produces the cells needed for sexual reproduction. Meiosis is different from mitosis; in meiosis, reproductive cells receive half of the parent cell's genetic information. The full complement of genetic information is restored after the reproductive cells (sperm and egg) join.

Understanding the purposes of cell division is an important part of understanding how cell division ensures that the daughter cells inherit the correct genetic information.

## 9.1   CONCEPT REVIEW

1. What are the three general types of cellular reproduction?
2. What is the purpose of binary fission and mitosis in comparison to meiosis?

## 9.2   The Cell Cycle and Mitosis

The **cell cycle** consists of all the stages of growth and division for a eukaryotic cell (figure 9.2). All eukaryotic cells go through the same basic life cycle, but different cells vary in the amount of time they spend in the various stages. The cell's life cycle is a continuous process without a beginning or an end. As cells complete one cycle, they begin the next.

**Interphase** is a stage of the cell cycle during which the cell engages in normal metabolic activities and prepares for the next cell division. Most cells spend the greater part of their life in the interphase stage. After the required preparatory steps the cell proceeds into the stages of mitosis. Mitosis is the portion of the cell cycle in which the cell divides its genetic information. Scientists split interphase and mitosis into smaller steps in order to describe how the cell divides in more detail. Interphase contains three distinct phases of cell activity—$G_1$, S, and $G_2$. During each of these parts of interphase, the cell is engaged in specific activities needed to prepare for cell division.

### The $G_1$ Stage of Interphase

During the $G_1$ stage of interphase, the cell gathers nutrients and other resources from its environment. These activities allow the cell to perform its normal functions. Gathering nutrients allows the cell both to grow in volume and to carry out its usual metabolic roles, such as producing tRNA, mRNA, ribosomes, enzymes, and other cell components.

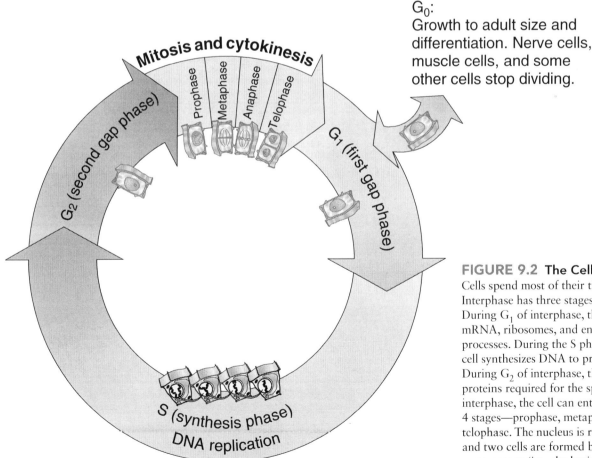

$G_0$:
Growth to adult size and differentiation. Nerve cells, muscle cells, and some other cells stop dividing.

**FIGURE 9.2   The Cell Cycle**
Cells spend most of their time in interphase. Interphase has three stages—$G_1$, S and $G_2$, During $G_1$ of interphase, the cell produces tRNA, mRNA, ribosomes, and enzymes for everyday processes. During the S phase of interphase, the cell synthesizes DNA to prepare for division. During $G_2$ of interphase, the cell produces the proteins required for the spindles. After interphase, the cell can enter mitosis. Mitosis has 4 stages—prophase, metaphase, anaphase, and telophase. The nucleus is replicated in mitosis and two cells are formed by cytokinesis. Once some organs (i.e., the brain) have completed development, some cells (i.e., nerve cells) enter the $G_0$ stage and stop dividing.

In multicellular organisms, the normal metabolic functions may be producing proteins for muscle contraction, photosynthesis, or glandular-cell secretion.

Often, a cell stays in $G_1$ for an extended period. This is a normal process. For cells that remain in the $G_1$ stage for a long time, the stage is often renamed the $G_0$ stage, because the cell is not moving forward through the cell cycle. In the $G_0$ stage, cells may become differentiated, or specialized in their function, such as becoming nerve cells or muscle cells. The length of time cells stay in $G_0$ varies. Some cells entering the $G_0$ stage remain there more or less permanently (e.g., nerve cells), while others can move back into the cell cycle and continue toward mitosis (e.g., cells for bone repair, wound repair). Still others divide more or less continuously (e.g., skin-, blood-forming cells).

If a cell is going to divide, it commits to undergoing cell division during $G_1$ and moves to the S stage.

## The S Stage of Interphase

A eukaryotic cell's genetic information, DNA, is found as a component of chromosomes. During the S stage of interphase, DNA synthesis (replication) occurs. With two copies of the genetic information, the cell can distribute copies to the daughter cells in the chromosomes. By following the cell's chromosomes, you can follow the cell's genetic information while mitosis creates two genetically identical cells.

The structure of a chromosome consists of DNA wrapped around histone proteins to form **chromatin.** The individual chromatin strands are too thin and tangled to be seen with a compound microscope. As a cell gets ready to divide, the chromatin coils and becomes visible as a chromosome. As chromosomes become more visible at the beginning of mitosis, you can see two threadlike parts lying side by side. Each parallel thread is called a *chromatid* (figure 9.3). A **chromatid** is one of two

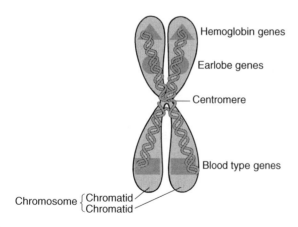

**FIGURE 9.3 Chromosomes**
During interphase, when chromosome replication occurs, the two strands of the DNA molecule unzip and two identical double-stranded DNA molecules are formed, which remain attached at the centromere. Each chromatid contains one of these DNA molecules. The two identical chromatids of the chromosome are sometimes termed a dyad, to reflect that there are two double-stranded DNA molecules, one in each chromatid. The DNA contains the genetic data. Different genes are shown here as different shapes along the DNA molecule.

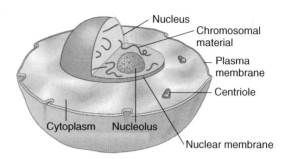

**FIGURE 9.4 Interphase**
Growth and the production of necessary organic compounds occur during this phase. If the cell is going to divide, DNA replication also occurs during interphase. The individual chromosomes are not visible, but a distinct nuclear membrane and nucleolus are present. (Some cells have more than one nucleolus.)

parallel parts of a chromosome. Each chromatid contains one DNA molecule. After DNA synthesis, the chromosome contains two DNA molecules, one in each chromatid. **Sister chromatids** are the 2 chromatids of a chromosome that were produced by replication and that contain the identical DNA. The **centromere** is the sequence of bases at the site where the sister chromatids are attached.

## The $G_2$ Stage of Interphase

The final stage of interphase is $G_2$. During the $G_2$ stage, final preparations are made for mitosis. The cell makes the cellular components it will need to divide successfully, such as the proteins it will use to move the chromosomes. At this point in the cell cycle, the nuclear membrane is intact. The chromatin has replicated, but it has not coiled and so the individual chromosomes are not yet visible (figure 9.4). The nucleolus, the site of ribosome manufacture, is also still visible during the $G_2$ stage.

| 9.2 | CONCEPT REVIEW |
| --- | --- |

3. What is the cell cycle?
4. What happens to chromosomes during interphase?

## 9.3 Mitosis—Cell Replication

When eukaryotic cells divide, two events occur. (1) The replicated genetic information of a cell is equally distributed in mitosis. (2) After mitosis, the cytoplasm of the cell also divides into two new cells. This division of the cell's cytoplasm is called **cytokinesis**—cell splitting.

The individual stages of mitosis transition seamlessly from one to the next. Because there are no clear-cut beginning or ending points for each stage, scientists use key events to identify the different stages of mitosis. The four phases are *prophase*, *metaphase*, *anaphase*, and *telophase*.

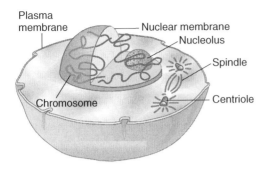

**FIGURE 9.5  Early Prophase**
Chromosomes begin to appear as thin, tangled threads and the nucleolus and nuclear membrane are present. The two sets of microtubules, known as the centrioles, begin to separate and move to opposite poles of the cell. A series of fibers, known as the spindle, will shortly begin to form.

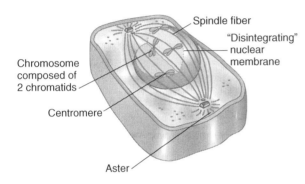

**FIGURE 9.6  Late Prophase**
In late prophase, the chromosomes appear as 2 chromatids connected at a centromere. The nucleolus and the nuclear membrane have disassembled. The centrioles have moved farther apart, the spindle is produced, and the chromosomes are attached to the spindle fibers.

## Prophase

**Key events:**

- Chromosomes condense.
- Spindle and spindle fibers form.
- Nuclear membrane disassembles.
- Nucleolus disappears.

As the $G_2$ phase of interphase ends, mitosis begins. **Prophase** is the first stage of mitosis. One of the first visible changes that identifies when the cell enters prophase is that the thin, tangled chromatin present during interphase gradually coils and thickens, becoming visible as separate chromosomes consisting of 2 chromatids (figure 9.5). As the nucleus disassembles during prophase, the nucleolus is no longer visible.

As the cell moves toward the end of prophase, a number of other events also occur in the cell (figure 9.6). One of these events is the formation of the *spindle* and its *spindle fibers*. The **spindle** is a structure, made of microtubules, that spans the cell from one side to the other. The **spindle fibers** consist of microtubules and are the individual strands of the spindle. As prophase

proceeds and the nuclear membrane gradually disassembles, the spindle fibers attach to the chromosomes. Spindle fibers must attach to the chromosomes so that the spindle fibers can move chromosomes during later stages of mitosis.

One difference between plant and animal cell division can be observed in prophase. In animal cells, the spindle forms between *centrioles*. In plants, the spindle forms without centrioles. **Centrioles** are cellular organelles comprised of microtubules. Centrioles replicate during the $G_2$ stage of interphase and begin to move to opposite sides of the cell during prophase. As the centrioles migrate, the spindle is formed between them and eventually stretches across the cell, so that spindle fibers encounter chromosomes when the nuclear membrane disassembles. Plant cells do not form their spindle between centrioles, but the spindle still forms during prophase.

Another significant difference between plant and animal cells is the formation of *asters* during mitosis. **Asters** are microtubules that extend outward from the centrioles to the plasma membrane of an animal cell. Whereas animal cells form asters, plant cells do not. Some scientists hypothesize that asters help brace the centriole against the animal plasma membrane by making the membrane stiffer. This might help in later stages of mitosis, when the spindle fibers and centrioles may need firm support to help with chromosome movement. It is believed that plant cells do not need to form asters because this firm support is provided by their cell walls.

## Metaphase

**Key event:**

- Chromosomes align at the equatorial plane of the cell.

During **metaphase,** the second stage of mitosis, the chromosomes align at the equatorial plane. There is no nucleus present during metaphase because the nuclear membrane has disassembled, and the spindle, which started to form during prophase, is completed. The chromosomes are at their most tightly coiled, are attached to spindle fibers and move along the spindle fibers until all their centromeres align along the equatorial plane of the cell (figure 9.7). At this stage in mitosis, each chromosome still consists of 2 chromatids attached at the centromere.

To understand the arrangement of the chromosomes during metaphase, keep in mind that the cell is a three-dimensional object. A view of a cell in metaphase from the side is an equatorial view. From this perspective, the chromosomes appear as if they were in a line. If we viewed the cell from a pole, looking down on the equatorial plane, the chromosomes would appear scattered about within the cell, even though they were all in a single plane.

## Anaphase

**Key event:**

- Sister chromatids move toward opposite ends of the cell.

**Anaphase** is the third stage of mitosis. The nuclear membrane is still absent and the spindle extends from pole to pole. The sister chromatids of each chromosome separate as they move along

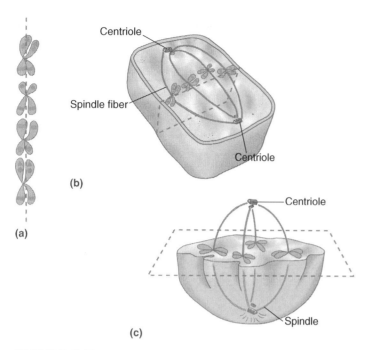

(b)

(a)

(c)

## FIGURE 9.7 Metaphase

*(a)* During metaphase, the chromosomes are moved by the spindle fibers and align at the equatorial plane. The equatorial plane is the region in the middle of the cell. Notice that each chromosome still consists of 2 chromatids. *(b)* When viewed from the edge of the plane, the chromosomes appear to be lined up. *(c)* When viewed from another angle, the chromosomes appear to be spread apart, as if on a tabletop.

the spindle fibers toward opposite poles (figure 9.8). When this separation of chromatids occurs, the chromatids become known as separate daughter chromosomes.

The sister chromatids separate because two important events occur. The first is that enzymes in the cell digest the portions of the centromere that holds the 2 chromatids together. The second event is that the chromatids begin to move. The **kinetochore** is a multi-protein complex attached to each chromatid at the centromere (figure 9.9). The kinetochore causes the shortening of the spindle fibers that are attached to it. By shortening the spindle fibers, the kinetochore pulls its chromatid toward the pole.

The two sets of daughter chromosomes migrating to opposite poles during anaphase have equivalent genetic information. This is true because the two chromatids of each chromosome, now called daughter chromosomes, were produced by DNA replication during the S stage of Interphase. Thus there are two equivalent sets of genetic information. Each set moves toward opposite poles.

## Telophase

**Key events:**

- Spindle fibers dissasemble.
- Nuclear membrane re-forms.
- Chromosomes uncoil.
- Nucleolus re-forms.

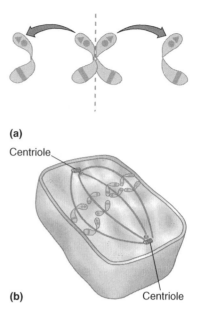

(a)

(b)

## FIGURE 9.8 Anaphase

*(a)* The pairs of chromatids separate after the centromeres replicate. *(b)* The chromatids, now called daughter chromosomes, are separating and moving toward the poles.

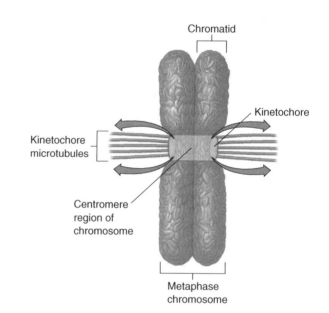

## FIGURE 9.9 Kinetochore

The kinetochore on the chromosome is where the spindle fibers bind to the chromosome. During anaphase, the two chromatids separate from each other as (each) kinetochore shortens the spindle fiber (to which it is attached), pulling the chromosome toward the centrioles.

During **telophase,** the cell finishes mitosis. The spindle fibers disassemble. The nuclear membrane forms around the two new sets of chromosomes, and the chromosomes begin to uncoil back into chromatin, so that the genetic information found on their DNA can be read by transcriptional enzymes. The nucleolus re-forms as the cell begins to make new ribosomes for

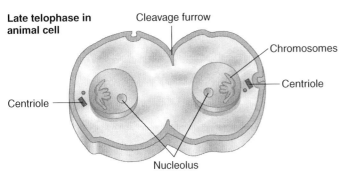

**FIGURE 9.10  Telophase**
During telophase, the spindle disassembles and the nucleolus and nuclear membrane reforms.

**FIGURE 9.11  Cytokinesis: Animal and Plant**
In animal cells, there is a pinching in of the cytoplasm, which eventually forms two daughter cells. Daughter cells in plants are formed when a cell plate separates the cell into two cells.

protein synthesis. The cell is preparing to reenter interphase. With the separation of genetic material into two new nuclei, mitosis is complete (figure 9.10).

## Cytokinesis

At the end of telophase a cell has two nuclei. The process of mitosis has prepared the two nuclei to be passed on to the daughter cells. Next, the process of cytokinesis creates the daughter cells. Cytokinesis is the process during which the cell contents are split between the two new daughter cells.

Different cell types use different strategies for achieving cytokinesis (figure 9.11). In animal cells, cytokinesis results from the formation of a *cleavage furrow*. The **cleavage furrow** is an indentation of the plasma membrane that pinches in toward the center of the cell, thus splitting the cytoplasm in two. In an animal cell, cytokinesis begins at the plasma membrane and proceeds to the center. In plant cells, a **cell plate** begins to form at the center of the cell and grows out to the plasma membrane. The cell plate is made of normal plasma membrane components. It is formed by both daughter cells, so that, when complete, the two cells have separate membranes. The cell wall is then formed between the newly formed cells.

The completion of mitosis and cytokinesis marks the end of one round of cell division. Each of the newly formed daughter

cells then starts the cell's cycle over by entering interphase at $G_1$. These cells can grow, replicate their DNA, and enter another round of mitosis and cytokinesis to continue the cell cycle or can stay metabolically active without dividing by staying in $G_0$.

## Summary

Mitosis is much more than splitting the cytoplasm of a cell into two parts (table 9.1). Much of the process is devoted to ensuring that the genetic material is split appropriately between the daughter cells. The sister chromatids formed during DNA replication, contain identical genetic information. The sister chromatids are separated to each of the resulting daughter cells. By dividing the genetic information as sister chromatids, the daughter cells inherit the same genetic information that was present in the parent cell. Because the daughter cells have the same genetic information as the parent, they can replace lost cells and have access to all the same genetic information as the parent cell. With the same genetic information, the daughter cells can have the same function.

### 9.3  CONCEPT REVIEW

5. Name the four stages of mitosis and describe what occurs in each stage.
6. During which stage of a cell's cycle does DNA replication occur?
7. At what phase of mitosis does a chromosome become visible?
8. List five differences between an interphase cell and a cell in mitosis.
9. Define the term *cytokinesis*.
10. What are the differences between plant and animal mitosis?
11. What is the difference between cytokinesis in plants and animals?

## 9.4  Controlling Mitosis

The cell-division process is regulated so that it does not interfere with the activities of other cells or of the whole organism. To determine if cell division is appropriate, many cells gather information about themselves and their environment. *Checkpoints* are times during the cell cycle when cells determine if they are prepared to move forward with cell division.

At these checkpoints, cells use proteins to evaluate their genetic health, their location in the body, and a need for more cells. Poor genetic health, the wrong location, and crowded conditions are typically interpreted as signals to wait. Good genetic health, the correct location, and uncrowded conditions are interpreted as signals to proceed with cell division.

The cell produces many proteins to gather this information and assess if cell division is appropriate. These proteins are made by one of two classes of genes. **Proto-oncogenes** code for proteins that encourage cell division. **Tumor-suppressor genes**

**TABLE 9.1   Summary of the Cell Cycle**

The stages of the cell cycle are shown in photographs and drawings for both animal and plant cells. The photographed animal cells are from whitefish blastulas. The photographed plant cells are from onion root tips.

| Stage | Animal Cells | | Plant Cells | | Summary |
|---|---|---|---|---|---|
| Interphase | | | | | As the cell prepares for mitosis, the chromosomes replicate during the S phase of interphase. |
| Early Prophase | | | | | The replicated chromatids begin to coil into recognizable chromosomes; the nuclear membrane fragments; spindle fibers form; nucleolus and nuclear membrane disintegrate. |
| Late Prophase | | | | | |
| Metaphase | | | | | Chromosomes attach to spindle fibers at their centromeres and then move to the equator. |
| Anaphase | | | | | Chromatids, now called daughter chromosomes, separate toward the poles. |
| Telophase | | | | | The nuclear membranes and nucleoli re-form; spindle fibers fragment; the chromosomes unwind and change from chromosomes to chromatin. |
| Late Telophase | | | | | |
| Daughter Cells | | | | | Cytokinesis occurs and two daughter cells are formed from the dividing cells. |

code for proteins that discourage cell division. A healthy cell receives signals from both groups of proteins about how appropriate it is to divide. The balance of information provided by these two groups of proteins allows for controlled cell division.

One tumor-suppressor gene is *p53*. Near the end of G$_1$, the protein produced by the *p53* gene identifies if the cell's DNA is damaged. If the DNA is healthy, *p53* allows the cell to divide (figure 9.12a). If the *p53* protein detects damaged DNA, it triggers other proteins to become active and repair the DNA. If the damage is too extensive for repair, the *p53* protein triggers an entirely different response from the cell. The *p53* protein causes the cell to self-destruct. **Apoptosis** is the process whereby a cell

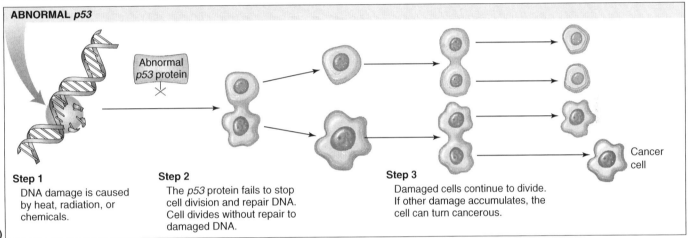

**FIGURE 9.12  The Function of *p53* Protein**
*(a)* Normal *p53* protein stops cell division until damaged DNA is repaired. If the DNA is unrepairable, the *p53* protein causes cell death.
*(b)* Mutated *p53* protein allows cells with damaged DNA to divide.

digests itself from the inside out. You might think of it as cellular suicide. In this scenario, apoptosis prevents mutated cells from continuing to grow. Other healthy cells will undergo cell division to replace the lost cell.

Consider the implications of a mutation within the *p53* gene. If the *p53* protein does not work correctly, then cells with damaged DNA may move through cell division. As these cells move through many divisions, their inability to detect damaged DNA disposes them to accumulate more mutations than do other cells. These mutations may occur in their proto-oncogenes and other tumor-suppressor genes. As multiple mutations occur in the genes responsible for regulating cell division, the cell is less likely to control cell division appropriately. When a cell is unable to control cell division, cancer can develop.

**9.4    CONCEPT REVIEW**

12. What are checkpoints?
13. What role does *p53* have in controlling cell division?

## 9.5  Cancer

Cancer is a disease caused by the failure to control cell division. This results in cells that divide too often and eventually interfere with normal body function. Scientists view cancer as a disease caused by mutations in the genes that regulate cell division. The mutations can be inherited or caused by agents in the environment. For example, the tar from cigarette smoke has been directly linked to mutations in the *p53* gene. The tar in cigarette smoke is categorized as both a *mutagen* and a *carcinogen*. **Mutagens** are agents that mutate, or chemically damage, DNA. **Carcinogens** are mutagens that cause cancer.

### Mutagenic and Carcinogenic Agents

Many agents have been associated with higher rates of cancer. The one thing they all have in common is their ability to alter the sequence of nucleotides in the DNA molecule. When damage occurs to DNA, the replication and transcriptional machinery may no longer be able to read the DNA's genetic information (figure 9.13).

**FIGURE 9.13 Carcinogens**
Carcinogenic agents come in many forms.

This is a partial list of mutagens that are found in our environment.

*Radiation*
X rays and gamma rays
Ultraviolet light
UV-A, from tanning lamps
UV-B, the cause of sunburn

*Chemicals*
Arsenic      Asbestos
Benzene      Alcohol
Dioxin      Cigarette tar
Polyvinyl chloride (PVC)      Food containing nitrates
Chemicals found in      (e.g., bacon)
    smoked meats and fish

Some viruses insert a copy of their genetic material into a cell's DNA. When this insertion occurs in a gene involved with regulating the cell cycle, it creates an insertion mutation, which may disrupt the cell's ability to control mitosis. Many of the viruses that are associated with higher rates of cancer are associated with a particular type of cancer (figure 9.14):

| *Viruses* | *Cancer* |
|---|---|
| Hepatitis B virus (HBV) | Liver cancer |
| Herpes simplex virus (HSV) type II | Uterine cancer |
| Epstein-Barr virus | Burkitt's lymphoma |
| Human T-cell lymphotropic virus (HTLV-1) | Lymphomas and leukemias |
| Papillomavirus | Several cancers |

Because cancer is caused by *changes* in DNA, scientists have found that a person's genetic makeup may be linked to developing certain cancers. A predisposition to develop cancer

**FIGURE 9.14 Cancer Caused by Viruses**
Cancer is both environmental and genetic. The hepatitis B virus is among the many agents that can increase the likelihood of developing cancer.

can be inherited from one's parents. The following cancers have been shown to be inherited:

Leukemias     Lung cancer
Certain skin cancers     Endometrial cancer
Colorectal cancer     Stomach cancer
Retinoblastomas     Prostate cancer
Breast cancer

When uncontrolled mitotic division occurs, a group of cells forms a *tumor* (How Science Works 9.1). A **tumor** is a mass of cells not normally found in a certain portion of the body. A **benign tumor** is a cell mass that does not fragment

**FIGURE 9.15 Skin Cancer**
Malignant melanoma is a type of skin cancer. It forms as a result of a mutation in pigmented skin cells. These cells divide repeatedly, giving rise to an abnormal mass of pigmented skin cells. The two large dark areas in the photograph, are the cancer on a person's back; the surrounding cells have the genetic information to develop into normal, healthy skin. This kind of cancer is particularly dangerous, because the cells break off and spread to other parts of the body (metastasize).

and spread beyond its original area of growth. A benign tumor can become harmful, however, by growing large enough to interfere with normal body functions. Some tumors are *malignant*. **Malignant tumors** are harmful because they may spread or invade other parts of the body (figure 9.15). Cells of these tumors **metastasize,** or move from the original site and begin to grow new tumors in other regions of the body (figure 9.16).

---

 **HOW SCIENCE WORKS 9.1**

## The Concepts of Homeostasis and Mitosis Applied

The total number of cells stays about the same during the adult life of an organism. It is kept at a constant number because the number of cells generated by mitosis equals the number that die. This homeostatic condition is achieved when the rate of mitosis equals the rate of cell death:

$$R_{(reproduction)} = D_{(death)}$$

Cancer may result if homeostasis is not maintained because cells are reproducing faster than they die:

$$R > D$$

For example, pancreatic cancer can result from the malfunctioning of apoptosis-signaling pathways. *Signaling pathways*

are biochemical reactions that trigger events in the cell. In this situation, a form of cancer, pancreatic cells are not signaled to die by apoptosis and they continue to divide unchecked.

On the other hand, if lost cells are not replaced by mitosis, the organism will no longer be able to maintain a stable, constant condition and die:

$$R < D$$

Biomedical researchers have applied this knowledge to control cells that have abnormally constant rates of mitosis. For example, certain cancer therapies affect signaling pathways by increasing apoptosis. The drug Taxol causes a significant increase in apoptosis in cancer cells.

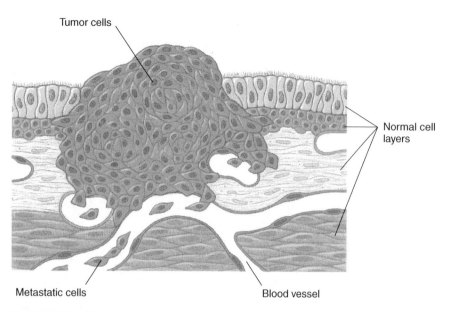

**FIGURE 9.16 Metastasizing Cells**
A tumor consists of cells that have lost their ability to control cell division. As these cells divide rapidly, they form a tumor and invade surrounding tissues. Cells metastasize when they reach blood vessels and are carried to other parts of the body. Once in their new locations, the cells continue to divide and form new tumors.

## Epigenetics and Cancer

Although many cancers are caused by mutations, it is thought that epigenetic effects cause more cancers than mutations. Epigenetics causes changes in the expression of genetic material but does not alter (mutate) the DNA. Cells are constantly manipulating their DNA and histone proteins to regulate gene expression including those controlling cell division. For a variety of reasons, cells may perform these functions improperly. Epigenetic changes important to carcinogenesis are the result of certain chemical reactions that affect the nitrogenous base cytosine and histone proteins. Such chemical changes can lead to malfunctions of oncogenes or tumor-suppressor genes. This allows cells whose division rate had previously been regulated, to begin nonstop division; a critical step in cancer development. These modifications to both DNA and histones are able to be passed on through mitosis and in some cases meiosis.

## Treatment Strategies

### The Surgical Removal of Cancer

Once cancer has been detected, it is often possible to eliminate the tumor. If the cancer is confined to a few specific locations, it may be possible to remove it surgically. Many cancers of the skin or breast are dealt with in this manner. The early detection of such cancers is important because early detection increases the likelihood that the cancer can be removed before it has metastasized (figure 9.17a). However, in some cases, surgery is impractical. Leukemia is a kind of cancer caused by the uncontrolled growth of white blood cells being formed in the bone marrow. In this situation, the cancerous cells spread throughout the body and cannot be removed surgically. Surgery is also

not useful when the tumor is located where it can't be removed without destroying necessary healthy tissue. For example, removing certain brain cancers can severely damage the brain. In such cases, other treatments may be used, such as chemotherapy and radiation therapy.

### Chemotherapy and Radiation Therapy

Scientists believe that chemotherapy and radiation therapy for cancer take advantage of the cell's ability to monitor cell division at the cell cycle checkpoints. By damaging DNA or preventing its replication, chemotherapy and radiation cause the targeted cancer cells to stop dividing and die. Other chemotherapeutic agents disrupt parts of the cell, such as the spindle, that are critical for cell division. Most common cancers cannot be controlled with chemotherapy alone. Chemotherapy is often used in combination with radiation therapy.

Radiation therapy uses powerful X rays or gamma rays to damage the DNA of the cancer cells (figure 9.17b). At times, radiation

**FIGURE 9.17 Surgical and Radiation Treatments of Cancer**
(a) Surgery is one option for treating cancer. Sometimes, if the cancer is too advanced or has already spread, other therapies (b) such as radiation are necessary.

can be used when surgery is impractical. This therapy can be applied from outside the body or by implanting radioactive "seeds" into the tumor. In both cases, a primary concern is to protect healthy tissue from the radiation's harmful effects. When radiation is applied from outside the body, a beam of radiation is focused on the cancerous cells and shields protect as much healthy tissue as possible.

Unfortunately, chemotherapy and radiation therapy can also have negative effects on normal cells. Chemotherapy may expose all the body's cells to the toxic ingredients and then weaken the body's normal defense mechanisms, because it decreases the body's ability to reproduce new white blood cells by mitosis. As a precaution against infection, cancer patients undergoing chemotherapy must be given antibiotics. The antibiotics help them defend against dangerous bacteria that might invade their bodies. Other side effects of chemotherapy include intestinal disorders and hair loss, which are caused by damage to the healthy cells in the intestinal tract and the skin that normally divide by mitosis.

### Whole-Body Radiation

Whole-body radiation is used to treat some leukemia patients, who have cancer of the blood-forming cells located in their bone marrow; however, not all of these cells are cancerous. A radiation therapy method prescribed for some patients involves the removal of some of their bone marrow and isolation of the noncancerous cells. The normal cells can then be grown in a laboratory. After these healthy cells have been cultured and increased in number, the patient's whole body is exposed to high doses of radiation sufficient to kill all the cancerous cells remaining in the bone marrow. Because this treatment can cause significant damage to the immune system, it is potentially deadly. As a precaution the patient is isolated from all harmful substances and infectious microbes. They are fed sterile food, drink sterile water, and breathe sterile air while being closely monitored and treated with antibiotics. The cultured noncancerous cells are injected back into the patient. As if the cells had a memory, they migrate back to their origins in the bone marrow, establish residence, and begin regulated cell division all over again.

Because radiation damages healthy cells, it is used very cautiously. In cases of extreme exposure to radiation, people develop *radiation sickness*. The symptoms of this disease include hair loss, bloody vomiting and diarrhea, and a reduced white blood cell count. Vomiting, nausea, and diarrhea occur because the radiation kills many of the cells lining the gut and interferes with the replacement of the intestine's lining, which is constantly being lost as food travels through. Hair loss occurs because radiation prevents cell division at the hair root; these cells must divide for the hair to grow. Radiation reduces white blood cells because it prevents their continuous replacement from cells in the bone marrow and lymph nodes. When radiation strikes these rapidly dividing cells and kills them, the lining of the intestine wears away and bleeds, hair falls out, and there are very few new white blood cells to defend the body against infection.

### Nanoparticle Therapy

The use of nanoparticle cancer therapy is being explored in many research labs. Nanoparticles cover a range between 1 and 100 nanometers in diameter and can be synthesized so that they attach only to specific cancer cells taken from a patient. They can be combined with cancer-specific, anticancer proteins. When injected into an organism, these combination particles travel throughout the body without causing harm or being rejected until they attach to their targeted cancer cells. When they combine with cell surface molecules, the anticancer drug is delivered and the cancer cell destroyed. While still in the research phase, nanoparticle cancer therapy has been shown to stop the growth of prostate, breast, and lung tumors in rodents.

### 9.5 CONCEPT REVIEW

14. Why is radiation used to control cancer?
15. List three factors associated with the development of cancer.
16. What role does epigenetics play in cancer development?

## 9.6 Determination and Differentiation

The process of mitosis enables a single cell to develop into an entire body, with trillions of cells. A **zygote** is the original single cell that results from the union of an egg and sperm. The zygote divides by mitosis to form genetically identical daughter cells. Mitotic cell division is repeated over and over until an entire body is formed.

Although the cells in the mature body are the same genetically, they do not all have the same function. There are nerve cells, muscle cells, bone cells, skin cells, and many other types. The difference among cell types is not in the genes they *possess,* but in the genes they *express* (i.e., through epigenetics).

**Determination** is the cellular process of deciding which genes a cell will express when mature. Determination marks the point where a cell commits to becoming a certain kind of cell and starts down the path of becoming that cell type. When a cell reaches the end of that path, it is said to be *differentiated.* A **differentiated** cell has become a particular cell type.

Skin cells provide a good example of determination and differentiation. Some skin cells produce hair; others do not. All the body's cells have the gene to produce hair, but not all cells do. When a cell starts to undergo the process of becoming a hair-producing cell, it is undergoing determination. Once the cell has become a hair-producing cell, it is differentiated. This differentiated cell is called a hair follicle cell (figure 9.18).

### 9.6 CONCEPT REVIEW

17. What is the difference between determination and differentiation?

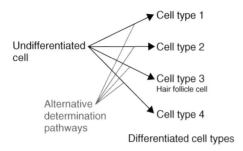

**FIGURE 9.18 Determination and Differentiation**
A cell starts as undetermined and undifferentiated. Specific genes are expressed to provide a cell its unique identity. Here, an undetermined cell goes through the process of determination to express the genes needed to be a hair follicle. When the process is complete and the hair follicle genes are expressed, the cell is differentiated.

## 9.7 Cell Division and Sexual Reproduction

Meiosis is a form of cell division involved in sexual reproduction. Meiosis has a different function than mitosis, the cell division that we have just been discussing. Mitosis is responsible for growth and repair of tissues. Meiosis is responsible for the production of eggs and sperm. The cells of sexually reproducing organisms have two sets of chromosomes and thus have two sets of genetic information. One set was received from the mother's egg, the other from the father's sperm. It is necessary for organisms that reproduce sexually to form sex cells having only one set of chromosomes.

If sex cells contained two sets of chromosomes, the zygote resulting from their union would have four sets of chromosomes with twice the total genetic information of the parents. With each new generation, the number of chromosomes would continue to increase. Thus, eggs and sperm must be formed by a method that reduces the amount of genetic information by half.

Scientists have terms to distinguish when a cell has either one or two copies of genetic information. **Haploid** cells carry only one complete set of their genetic information. **Diploid** cells carry two complete sets of their genetic information. Meiosis is the cell division process that generates haploid reproductive cells from diploid cells. In many sexually reproducing organisms, such as humans, meiosis takes place in the cells of organs that are devoted to reproduction—the **gonads.** The gonads in females are known as **ovaries;** in males, **testes.** Ovarian and testicular cells that divide by meiosis produce reproductive cells called *gametes.* **Gamete** is a general term for reproductive cells like eggs and sperm. These gametes are also referred to as *germ cells.* Algae and plants also possess organs for sexual reproduction. Some of these are very simple. In algae such as *Spirogyra,* individual cells become specialized for gamete production. In plants, the structures are very complex. In flowering plants, the **pistil** produces eggs, or ova, and the **anther** produces pollen, which contains sperm (figure 9.19).

In sexually reproducing organisms, the life cycle involves both mitosis and meiosis. In figure 9.20, the haploid number of chromosomes is noted as *n.* The zygote and all the resulting cells that give

**FIGURE 9.19 Haploid and Diploid Cells**
Both plants and animals produce cells with a haploid number of chromosomes. The male anther in plants and the testes in animals produce haploid male cells, sperm. In both plants and animals, the ovaries produce haploid female cells, eggs.

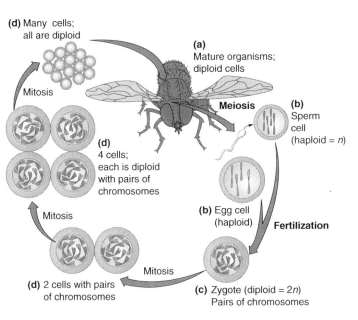

**FIGURE 9.20 The Life Cycle of a Fruit Fly**
*(a)* The diploid cells of this adult fruit fly have 8 chromosomes in their nuclei. *(b)* In preparation for sexual reproduction, the number of chromosomes must be reduced by half, so that the gametes will be haploid and have 4 chromosomes, *(c)* When the egg and sperm unite during fertilization, the original diploid number of 8 chromosomes will be restored. *(d)* The offspring will grow and produce new cells by mitosis.

rise to the adult fruit fly are diploid. The diploid number of chromosomes is noted as *2n*—mathematically, *n + n = 2n*. The gametes are produced by meiosis in female and male adult fruit flies. Notice that the male and female gamete each contain 4 chromosomes. Collectively, these 4 chromosomes represent one complete set of all the genetic information that is necessary for a fruit fly.

**Fertilization** is the joining of the genetic material from two haploid cells. During fertilization, each gamete contributes one set of genetic information (one set of chromosomes) toward forming a new organism. Recall that the zygote is the diploid cell that results from the egg and sperm combining their genetic information. The zygote contains two sets of genetic information on 8 chromosomes (4 from the egg and 4 from the sperm—two sets of chromosomes). The zygote divides by *mitosis* and the cells grow to become an adult fruit fly, which will then produce either eggs or sperm by meiosis in its gonads. The characteristics of the fruit fly will depend on the combination of genetic information it inherits from both parents on its 8 chromosomes.

Diploid cells have two sets of chromosomes—one set from each parent. Because chromosomes contain DNA, each chromosome has many genes along its length. Each chromosome in a diploid cell can be paired to another chromosome on the basis of the genes on those chromosomes. **Homologous chromosomes** have the same order of genes along their DNA (figure 9.21). Because of the similarity of genetic information in homologous chromosomes are the same size and their centromeres are found in the same locations. Each parent contributes one member of each of the pairs of the homologous chromosomes. **Non-homologous**

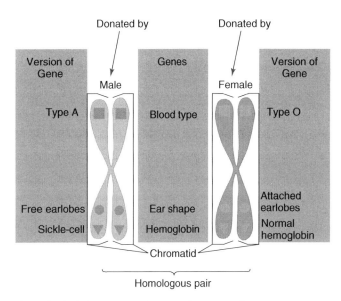

**FIGURE 9.21 A Pair of Homologous Chromosomes**
A pair of chromosomes are said to be homologous if they have genes for the same traits. Notice that the genes may not be identical, but the genes code for the same type of information. Homologous chromosomes are of the same length, have the same types of genes in the same sequence, and have their centromeres in the same location—one chromosome came from the male parent and the other from the female parent.

**chromosomes** have different genes on their DNA. The fruit fly has four pairs of homologous chromosomes—or 8 total chromosomes. Different species of organisms vary in the number of chromosomes they contain (table 9.2).

**TABLE 9.2 Chromosome Numbers**

| Organism | Diploid Number | Haploid Number |
|---|---|---|
| Jumper ant | 2 | 1 |
| Tapeworm | 4 | 2 |
| Mosquito | 6 | 3 |
| Housefly | 12 | 6 |
| Onion | 16 | 8 |
| Rice | 24 | 12 |
| Tomato | 24 | 12 |
| Cat | 38 | 19 |
| Gecko | 46 | 23 |
| **Human** | **46** | **23** |
| Rat | 46 | 23 |
| Chimpanzee | 48 | 24 |
| Potato | 48 | 24 |
| Horse | 64 | 32 |
| Dog | 78 | 39 |
| Stalked adder's tongue fern | 1,260 | 630 |

Before we move on and describe meiosis in detail, consider the different purposes of mitosis and meiosis: Mitosis results in cells that have the same number of chromosomes as the parent cell, whereas meiosis results in cells that have half the chromosomes as the parent cell. An important question to ask is, "how are the processes of mitosis and meiosis different, so that gametes receive only half of the parent cell's chromosomes?"

---

### 9.7    CONCEPT REVIEW

18. How do haploid cells differ from diploid cells?
19. Why is meiosis necessary in organisms that reproduce sexually?
20. Define the terms *zygote, fertilization,* and, *homologous chromosomes.*
21. Diagram fertilization as it would occur between a sperm and an egg with the haploid number of 3.

---

### 9.8    Meiosis—Gamete Production

Consider a cell that has only 4 chromosomes (figure 9.22). The two from the father are shown in blue and the two from the mother are in green. Notice in figure 9.22 that there are two pairs of homologous chromosomes. Each pair consists of a green chromosome and a blue chromosome. One pair is long. The other pair is short.

Meiosis involves two cell divisions and produces four cells. **Meiosis I** consists of the processes that occur during the first division, and **meiosis II** consists of the processes that occur during the second division. Before meiosis occurs, the cell is in interphase of the cell cycle. As with mitosis, the interphase that precedes meiosis includes DNA replication. Before DNA replication, chromosomes have only one chromatid. After DNA replication, chromosomes consist of two chromatids.

### Meiosis I

Meiosis I is a **reduction division,** in which the chromosome number in the two cells produced is reduced from diploid to haploid. The sequence of events in meiosis I is divided into four phases: prophase I, metaphase I, anaphase I, and telophase I.

### Prophase I
**Key events:**

- Chromosomes condense.
- Spindle and spindle fibers form.
- Nuclear membrane disassembles.
- Synapsis and crossing-over occur.

A number of important events occur during Prophase I. Several of these events also occur during prophase of mitosis: the nuclear membrane disassembles; the spindle fibers form; and the chromosomes condense. However, in meiosis, once the chromosomes are fully condensed, **synapsis** causes homologous chromosomes to move toward one another, so that the chromosomes lie next to each other. While the chromosomes are synapsed, *crossing-over* occurs. **Crossing-over** is the exchange of equivalent sections of DNA on homologous chromosomes. Crossing-over is shown in figure 9.23 as bits of blue on the green chromosome and bits of green on the blue chromosome. The crossing-over process is carefully regulated to make sure that the DNA sections that are exchanged contain equivalent information. This means that usually no information is lost or gained by either chromosome; genetic information is simply exchanged. Because the two members of each homologous pair of chromosomes came from different parents (one from the mother and one from father), there are minor differences in the DNA present on the two chromosomes. Crossing-over happens many times along the length of the homologous chromosomes.

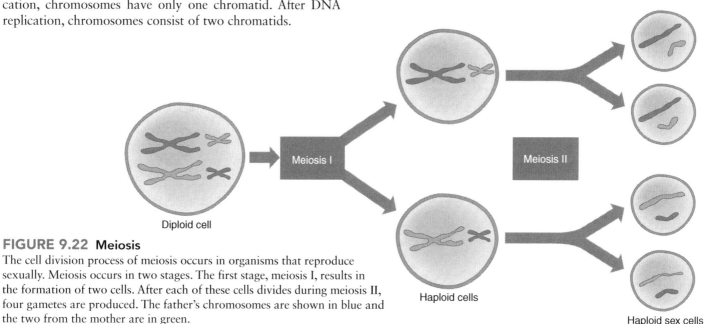

Diploid cell

Meiosis I

Meiosis II

Haploid cells

Haploid sex cells

**FIGURE 9.22    Meiosis**
The cell division process of meiosis occurs in organisms that reproduce sexually. Meiosis occurs in two stages. The first stage, meiosis I, results in the formation of two cells. After each of these cells divides during meiosis II, four gametes are produced. The father's chromosomes are shown in blue and the two from the mother are in green.

equator in homologous pairs and the homologous chromosomes (each consisting of two chromatids) separate.

## Anaphase I
**Key events:**

- Homologous chromosomes separate from each other.
- Chromosomes move toward cell's poles.
- Reduction occurs (diploid-2*n* to haploid-*n*).

Anaphase I is the stage during which homologous chromosomes separate (figure 9.25). During this stage, the chromosome number is *reduced from diploid to haploid.* The two members of each pair of homologous chromosomes move away from each other toward opposite poles. The direction each takes is determined by how each pair was originally oriented on the spindle.

This arrangement of chromosomes in anaphase I, causes the key difference between mitosis and meiosis. In anaphase of mitosis, chromatids separate from each other. In anaphase I of meiosis, homologous chromosomes separate from each other. Each chromosome is independently attached to a spindle fiber at its centromere. Unlike the anaphase stage of mitosis, in

**FIGURE 9.25  Anaphase I**
During this phase, one member of each homologous pair is segregated from the other member of the pair. Notice that the chromatids of the chromosomes do not separate.

anaphase I of meiosis the centromeres that hold the chromatids together do not divide. The chromosomes are still in their replicated form, consisting of 2 chromatids in anaphase I.

Because the homologous chromosomes and the genes they carry are being separated from one another, this process is called **segregation.** The way in which a single pair of homologous chromosomes segregates does not influence how other pairs of homologous chromosomes segregate. That is, each pair segregates independently of other pairs. This is known as **independent assortment** of chromosomes. Both segregation and independent assortment are key components in understanding how to solve genetics problems.

## Telophase I
**Key events:**

- Spindle fibers disassemble.
- Chromosomes uncoil.
- Nuclear membrane re-forms.
- Nucleoli reappear.

Nucleus

**FIGURE 9.23  Prophase I**
During prophase I, several visible changes occur as the cell prepares for division. The nuclear membrane is being broken down and the spindle begins to form. As the nuclear membrane disintegrates, the chromosomes can be moved throughout the cell. As the cell advances through prophase, the chromosomes also become more condensed and are paired as homologous pairs.

Crossing-over is very important, because it allows a more thorough mixing of genes from one generation to the next. Without crossing-over, each of the chromosomes an organism inherits in the mother's egg would be passed on exactly as it was to the organism's offspring.

## Metaphase I
**Key event:**

- Chromosomes align on equatorial plane as synapsed pairs.

In metaphase I, the centromere of each chromosome attaches to the spindle. The synapsed pair of homologous chromosomes moves into position on the cell's equatorial plane as a single unit. The orientation of the members of each pair of chromosomes is random with regard to the cell's poles. Figure 9.24 shows only one possible arrangement. An equally likely arrangement of chromosomes during this stage would be to flip the positions of two identically sized chromosomes. In the figure, this flipped arrangement would place all of the green chromosomes on one side of the cell. The number of possible arrangements increases with the number of chromosomes present in the cell. The arrangement is determined by chance.

Compare metaphase I of meiosis with metaphase of mitosis (figure 9.24 and figure 9.7). Note the different ways the chromosomes are arranged. In mitosis, each chromosome is arranged at the equator independently of the others and the chromatids will separate. In meiosis I the chromosomes are arranged at the

Spindle fibers

**FIGURE 9.24  Metaphase I**
Notice that the homologous chromosome pairs are arranged on the equatorial plane in the synapsed condition. The dotted line represents the equatorial plane. This cell shows one way the chromosomes could be lined up; however, a second arrangement is possible.

Telophase I consists of changes that return the cell to an interphase-like condition (figure 9.26). The chromosomes uncoil and become long, thin threads; the nuclear membrane reforms around them; and nucleoli reappear. Following this activity, cytokinesis divides the cytoplasm into two separate cells.

Because of meiosis I, the total number of chromosomes is divided equally, so that each daughter cell has one member of each homologous chromosome pair. This means that each cell receives one-half the genetic information of the parent cell, but it has 1 chromosome of each kind and thus has one full set of chromosomes. Each chromosome is still composed of 2 chromatids joined at the centromere. The chromosome number for the cells is reduced from diploid ($2n$) to haploid ($n$). In the cell we have been using as our example, the number of chromosomes is reduced from 4 to 2. The four pairs of chromosomes have been distributed to the two daughter cells.

Depending on the type of cell, there may be a time following telophase I when the cell engages in normal metabolic

activity corresponding to an interphase stage. Figure 9.27 summarizes the events in meiosis I.

## Meiosis II

Meiosis II includes four phases: prophase II, metaphase II, anaphase II, and telophase II. The two daughter cells formed during meiosis I both continue through meiosis II, so that four cells result from the two divisions. During the time between telophase I and the beginning of meiosis II, no DNA replication occurs. The genetic information in cells starting meiosis II is the same as that in cells ending meiosis I. *The events in the division sequence of meiosis II are the same as those that occur in mitosis.*

### Prophase II
**Key events:**

- Chromosomes condense.
- Spindle and spindle fibers form.
- Nuclear membrane disassembles.
- Nucleoli disassemble.

Prophase II is similar to prophase in mitosis; the nuclear membrane is disassembled and the spindle apparatus begins to form. However, it differs from prophase I in that the cells are haploid, not diploid (figure 9.28).

### Metaphase II
**Key event:**

- Chromosomes align at the equator in unpaired manner.

Metaphase II is typical of any metaphase stage, because the chromosomes attach by their centromeres to the spindle at

**FIGURE 9.26   Telophase I**
Cytokinesis occurs during telophase I. During cytokinesis, two cells are formed. Each cell is haploid, containing one set of chromosomes.

Nuclear envelope

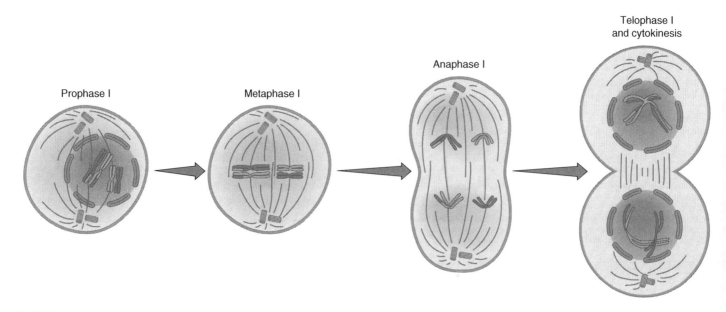

**FIGURE 9.27   Meiosis I**
The stages in meiosis I result in reduction division. This reduces the number of chromosomes in the parental cell from the diploid number to the haploid number in each of the two daughter cells.

**FIGURE 9.28 Prophase II**
The two daughter cells are preparing for the second division of meiosis.

Nuclear membrane

Spindle fibers

**FIGURE 9.29 Metaphase II**
During metaphase II, each chromosome lines up on the equatorial plane. Each chromosome is composed of 2 chromatids (a replicated chromosome) joined at a centromere.

**FIGURE 9.30 Anaphase II**
Anaphase II is very similar to anaphase of mitosis. The centromere of each chromosome divides and 1 chromatid separates from the other. As soon as this happens, they are no longer referred to as chromatids; each strand of nucleoprotein is now called a daughter chromosome.

**FIGURE 9.31 Telophase II**
During the telophase II stage, the nuclear membranes form, chromosomes uncoil. Cytokinesis occurs.

the equatorial plane of the cell. Because pairs of homologous chromosomes are no longer together in the same cell, each chromosome moves as a separate unit (figure 9.29).

## Anaphase II
**Key event:**

- Chromatids separate and begin to move to cell's poles.

Anaphase II of meiosis differs from anaphase I of meiosis in that, during anaphase II, the centromere of each chromosome divides, and the chromatids, now called *daughter chromosomes*, move to opposite poles. This is similar to mitosis (figure 9.30). There are no paired homologous chromosomes in this stage; therefore, segregation and independent assortment cannot occur as in meiosis I.

## Telophase II
**Key events:**

- Nuclear membrane re-forms.
- Chromosomes uncoil.
- Nucleoli reappear.
- Spindle fibers disassemble.

During telophase II, the cell returns to a nondividing condition. New nuclear membranes form, nucleoli reappear, chromosomes uncoil, the spindles disappear and cytokinesis occurs (figure 9.31).

Telophase II is followed by the maturation of the four cells into gametes—either sperm or eggs. In many organisms, including humans, egg cells are produced in such a manner that three of the four cells resulting from meiosis in a female disintegrate. However, because the one that survives is randomly chosen, the likelihood of obtaining any particular combination of genes is not affected. The events of meiosis II are shown in figure 9.32.

The stages of meiosis I and meiosis II are summarized in table 9.3. The differences between mitosis and meiosis have been identified throughout this chapter. A comparison of these two processes appears in table 9.4.

**TABLE 9.3**  Stages of Meiosis

| Interphase | | Diploid | As the diploid (2n) cell moves from $G_0$ into meiosis, the chromosomes replicate during the S phase of interphase. |
|---|---|---|---|
| Prophase I | | Diploid | The replicated chromatin begins to coil into recognizable chromosomes and the homologous chromosomes synapse; chromatids may cross-over; the nuclear membrane and nucleoli fragment; centrioles move to form the cell's poles; spindle fibers are formed. |
| Metaphase I | | Diploid | Synapsed homologous chromosomes attach to the spindle fibers at their centromeres. Pairs of homologous chromosomes align at the equator. |
| Anaphase I | | Transition | The two members of homologous pairs of chromosomes separate from each other as they move toward the poles of the cell. |
| Telophase I | | Haploid | The two newly forming daughter cells are now haploid (n) because each contains only one of each pair of homologous chromosomes; the nuclear membranes and nucleoli re-form; spindle fibers fragment; the chromosomes unwind and change from chromosomes (composed of 2 chromatids) to chromatin. |
| Prophase II | | Haploid | Each of the two haploid (n) daughter cells from meiosis I undergoes chromatin coiling to form chromosomes, each of which is composed of 2 chromatids; the nuclear membrane fragments; centrioles move to form the cell's poles; spindle fibers form. |
| Metaphase II | | Haploid | Chromosomes attach to the spindle fibers at the centromeres and move to the equator of the cell. |
| Anaphase II | | Haploid | Centromeres separate, allowing the 2 chromatids of a chromosome to separate toward the poles. |
| Telophase II | | Haploid | Four haploid (n) cells are formed from the division of the two meiosis I cells; the nuclear membranes and nucleoli re-form; spindle fibers fragment; the chromosomes unwind and change from chromosomes to chromatin; these cells become the sex cells (egg or sperm). |

## FIGURE 9.32  Meiosis II

During meiosis II, the centromere of each chromosome splits and each chromosome divides into separate chromatids. Four haploid cells are produced, each with 1 chromatid of each kind. These four haploid cells are gametes.

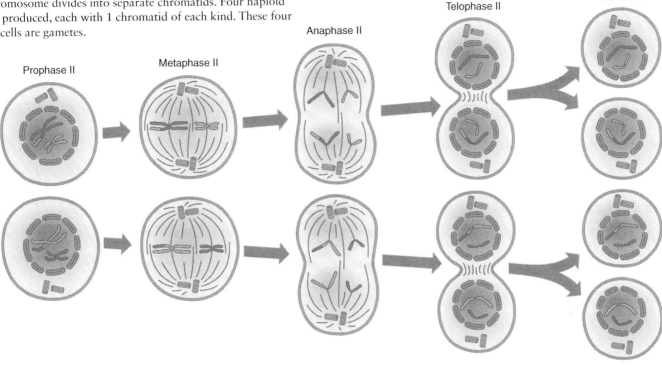

Prophase II   Metaphase II   Anaphase II   Telophase II   Gametes

## TABLE 9.4   Comparison of Mitosis and Meiosis

| Mitosis | Meiosis |
|---|---|
| 1. One division completes the process. | 1. Two divisions are required to complete the process. |
| 2. Chromosomes do not synapse. | 2. Homologous chromosomes synapse in prophase I. |
| 3. Homologous chromosomes do not cross-over. | 3. Homologous chromosomes cross-over in prophase I. |
| 4. Centromeres divide in anaphase. | 4. Centromeres divide in anaphase II but not in anaphase I. |
| 5. Daughter cells have the same number of chromosomes as the parent cell ($2n \rightarrow 2n$ or $n \rightarrow n$). | 5. Daughter cells have half the number of chromosomes as the parent cell ($2n \rightarrow n$). |
| 6. Daughter cells have the same genetic information as the parent cell. | 6. Daughter cells are genetically different from the parent cell. |
| 7. Mitosis generates body cells. | 7. Meiosis generates sex cells. |
| 8. Mitosis results in growth, the replacement of worn-out cells, and the repair of damage. | 8. Meiosis is necessary for sexual reproduction. |

### 9.8   CONCEPT REVIEW

22. Diagram the metaphase I stage of a cell with the diploid number of 8.
23. What is unique about prophase I?
24. In which phase of meiosis do daughter chromosomes form?
25. Why is it impossible for synapsis to occur during meiosis II?
26. Can a haploid cell undergo meiosis? Why or why not?
27. List three differences between mitosis and meiosis.

### 9.9   Genetic Diversity— The Biological Advantage of Sexual Reproduction

Cell division allows organisms to reproduce either asexually or sexually. There are advantages and disadvantages to both. Asexual reproduction always produces organisms that are genetically identical to the parent. A single organism, separated from others of its kind, can still reproduce if it can reproduce asexually. Organisms that can reproduce only sexually are at a disadvantage, because they require two different organisms to reproduce. Also, sexually reproducing populations tend to grow at a much slower rate than do asexually reproducing populations. However, asexually reproducing populations could be wiped out by a single disease or a change in living conditions, because the members of the population are genetically similar.

Sexual reproduction offers an advantage over asexual reproduction. Populations that have a large genetic diversity are more likely to survive. When living conditions change or a disease occurs, some members of the population are more likely to survive if the population consists of many, genetically different individuals.

One reason for learning meiosis is to see how the events of meiosis and fertilization create genetic variation within a population. Haploid cells from two different individuals combine to form new, unique combinations of genetic information. Each new organism, with its unique combination of genetic information, may be important to the survival of the species.

Genetic diversity in a population is due to differences in the types of genes present in individual organisms. Although all the members of the population have the genes for the same basic traits, the exact information coded in the genes may vary from individual to individual. An **allele** is a specific version of a gene. Examples of alleles are: blood type A versus blood type O, dark versus light skin, normal versus sickle-cell hemoglobin, and attached versus free earlobes.

Five factors create genetic diversity in offspring by creating either new alleles or new combinations of alleles: mutation, crossing-over, segregation, independent assortment, and fertilization.

## Mutation

Several types of mutations were discussed in chapter 8: point mutations and chromosomal aberrations. In point mutations, a change in a DNA nucleotide results in the production of a different protein. In chromosomal aberrations, genes are rearranged. Both types of mutations can create new proteins. Both types of mutations increase genetic diversity by creating new alleles.

Recall that epigenetic modifications to both DNA and histones are also able to be passed on through mitosis and, in some cases, meiosis. These result in different forms of gene expression displayed through determination.

## Crossing-Over

The second source of variation is crossing-over. **Crossing-over** is the exchange of equivalent portions of DNA between homologous chromosomes, which occurs during prophase I while homologous chromosomes are synapsed. Remember that a chromosome is a double strand of DNA. To break chromosomes and exchange pieces of them, bonds between sugars and phosphates are broken. This is done at comparable locations on both chromatids, and the two pieces switch places. After switching places, the two pieces of DNA are bonded together by re-forming the bonds between the sugar and the phosphate molecules.

Crossing-over allows new combinations of genetic information to occur. While mutations introduce new genetic information to the population, crossing-over introduces new combinations of previously existing information. An organism receives one set of genetic information from each of its parents. Each gamete contains chromosomes that have crossed-over and therefore contains some of the father's and some of the mother's genes. As a result, traits from the mother *and* from the father can be inherited on a single piece of DNA.

Examine figure 9.33 carefully to note precisely what occurs during crossing-over. This figure shows a pair of homologous chromosomes close to each other. Each gene occupies a specific place on the chromosome, its **locus**. Homologous chromosomes contain an identical order of genes, and chromosomes may contain thousands of genes.

Notice in figure 9.34 that, without crossing-over, only two kinds of genetically different gametes result. Two of the four gametes have one type of chromosome, whereas the other two have the other type of chromosome. With crossing-over, four genetically different gametes are formed. With just one cross-over, the number of genetically different gametes is doubled.

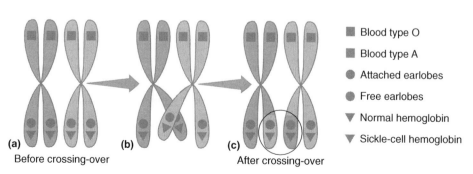

(a) Before crossing-over    (b)    (c) After crossing-over

■ Blood type O
■ Blood type A
● Attached earlobes
● Free earlobes
▼ Normal hemoglobin
▼ Sickle-cell hemoglobin

**FIGURE 9.33 Synapsis and Crossing-Over**
*(a)* While pairs of homologous chromosomes are in synapsis, *(b)* one part of 1 chromatid can break off and be exchanged for an equivalent part of its homologous chromatid. *(c)* As a result, new combinations of genetic information are created.

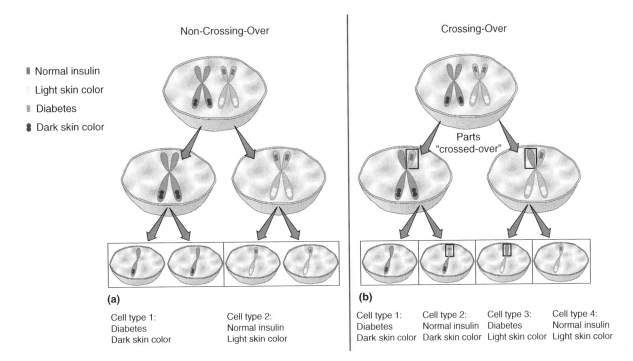

**FIGURE 9.34** **Variations Resulting from Crossing-Over**
Cells with identical genetic information are boxed together. *(a)* These cells resulted from meiosis without crossing-over. Only two unique cell types of cells were produced. Cell type 1—Diabetes, dark skin color. Cell type 2—Normal insulin, light skin color. *(b)* These cells had one cross-over. From one cross-over, the number of genetically unique gametes doubled from two to four. Type 1—Diabetes, dark skin color. Type 2—Normal insulin, dark skin color. Type 3—Diabetes, light skin color. Type 4—Normal insulin, light skin.

In fact, crossing-over can occur at a number of points on a chromosome; that is, there can be more than one cross-over per chromosome pair. Because crossing-over can occur at almost any point along the length of the chromosome, great variation is possible (figure 9.35).

The closer two genes are to each other on a chromosome (i.e., the more closely they are *linked*), the more likely they will stay together, because the chance of crossing-over occurring between them is lower than if they were far apart. Thus, there is a high probability that they will be inherited together. The farther apart two genes are, the more likely it is that they will be separated during crossing-over. This fact enables biologists to map the order of gene loci on chromosomes.

## Segregation

Recall that segregation is the process during which the alleles on homologous chromosomes separate during meiosis I. Review figure 9.34; the normal insulin allele and the diabetes allele are both present in the diploid cell. However, following meiosis the normal insulin allele and the diabetes allele are segregated into separate haploid cells away from the other allele. Half of this individual's gametes would carry genetic information for normal functional insulin. The other half of the individual's gametes would carry genetic information for non-functional insulin (diabetes). Consider if this individual's mate had the same genetic makeup. If the mate also had one normal gene for insulin production and one abnormal gene for diabetes, that person also would produce two kinds of gametes. Because of segregation, this couple could produce children that were genetically different from themselves. If both parents contributed a gamete that carried diabetes, their child would be diabetic. Other combinations of gametes would result in children without diabetes. Segregation increases genetic diversity by allowing parents to produce children that are genetically different from their parents and from their siblings.

## Independent Assortment

So far in discussing genetic diversity, we have dealt with only one pair of chromosomes. Now let's consider how genetic variation increases when we add a second pair of chromosomes.

**FIGURE 9.35** **Multiple Cross-Overs**
Crossing-over can occur several times between the chromatids of one pair of homologous chromosomes.

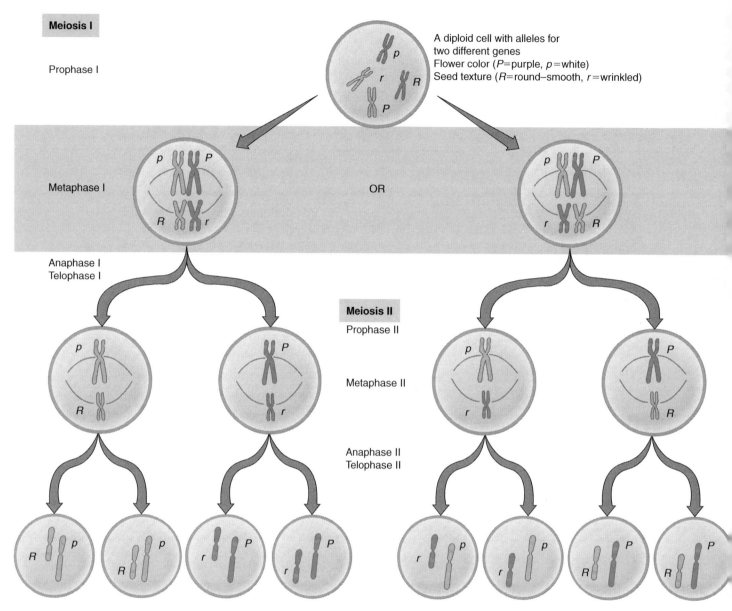

**FIGURE 9.36 The Independent Assortment of Homologous Chromosome Pairs**
The orientation of one pair of chromosomes on the equatorial plane does not affect the orientation of another pair of chromosomes. Note that different possible arrangements of chromosomes can be compared on the left and right side of this figure. Comparing the sets of cells that result from each initial arrangement will show the new genetic combinations that result from independent assortment.

Independent assortment is the segregation of homologous chromosomes independent of how other homologous pairs segregate.

Figure 9.36 shows chromosomes with traits for the garden pea plant. The chromosomes carrying alleles for flower color ($P$ = purple; $p$ = white) always separate from each other. The second pair of chromosomes with the information for seed texture also separates. Because the pole to which an individual chromosome moves is determined randomly, half the time the chromosomes divide so that the trait for purple flowers and the trait for round-smooth seeds move in one direction, whereas the trait for white flowers and the trait for wrinkled seeds move in the opposite direction. An equally

likely alternative is that, the trait for purple flowers and the trait for wrinkled seeds go together toward one pole of the cell, whereas the trait for white flowers and the trait for round-smooth seeds go to the other pole. With two pairs of homologous chromosomes there are four possible kinds of cells produced by independent assortment during meiosis.

With three pairs of homologous chromosomes, there are eight possible kinds of cells produced as a result of independent assortment. The number of possible chromosomal combinations of gametes is calculated by using the expression $2^n$, where $n$ equals the number of pairs of chromosomes. With three pairs of chromosomes, $n$ equals 3, so $2^n = 2^3 = 2 \times 2 \times 2 = 8$. With 23 pairs of chromosomes, as in human cells,

$2^n = 2^{23} = 8,388,608$. More than 8 million genetically different kinds of sperm cells or egg cells are possible from a single human parent. This number doesn't consider the additional possible sources of variation, such as mutation and crossing-over. Thus, when genetic variation due to mutation and crossing-over is added, the number of different gametes become incredibly large.

## Fertilization

Because of the large number of genetically different gametes resulting from independent assortment, segregation, mutation, and crossing-over, an incredibly large number of types of offspring can result. Because humans can produce millions of genetically different gametes, the number of kinds of offspring possible is infinite for all practical purposes, and each offspring is unique, with the exception of identical twins.

---

### 9.9   CONCEPT REVIEW

28. How much variation as a result of independent assortment can occur in cells with the following diploid numbers: 2, 4, 6, 8, and 22?
29. What are the major sources of variation in the process of meiosis?

---

### 9.10   Nondisjunction and Chromosomal Abnormalities

In the normal process of meiosis, the number of chromosomes in diploid cells is reduced to haploid. This involves segregating homologous chromosomes into separate cells during the first meiotic division. Occasionally, a pair of homologous chromosomes does not segregate properly and both chromosomes of a pair end up in the same gamete. **Nondisjunction** occurs when homologous chromosomes do not separate during meiosis. In figure 9.37, two cells are missing a chromosome and the genes that were carried on it. This condition usually results in the death of the cells. The other cells have an extra copy of a chromosome. This extra genetic information may also lead to the death of the cell. Some of these abnormal cells, however, do live and develop into sperm or eggs.

If one of these abnormal sperm or eggs unites with a normal gamete, the offspring will have an abnormal number of chromosomes. In **monosomy,** instead of the normal two chromosomes, a cell has just one of the pair of homologous chromosomes. In **trisomy,** a chromosome is present in three copies. All the cells that develop by mitosis from such zygotes will also have an abnormal number of chromosomes.

It is possible to examine cells and count chromosomes. Among the easiest cells to view are white blood cells. They are

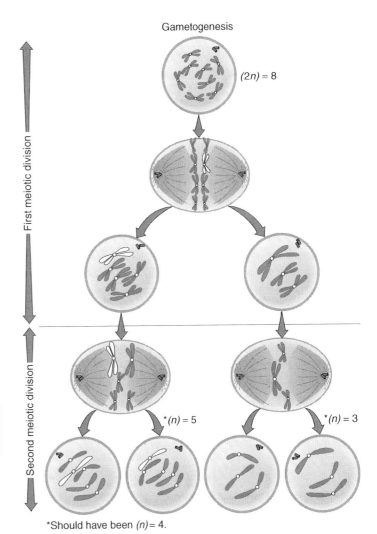

Gametogenesis

First meiotic division

Second meiotic division

$(2n) = 8$

*$(n) = 5$    *$(n) = 3$

*Should have been $(n) = 4$.

**FIGURE 9.37 Nondisjunction During Gametogenesis**
When a pair of homologous chromosomes fails to separate properly during meiosis I, gametogenesis results in gametes that have an abnormal number of chromosomes. Notice that two of the cells have an additional chromosome, whereas the other two are deficient by the same chromosome.

dropped onto a microscope slide, so that the cells are broken open and the chromosomes are separated. Photographs are taken of chromosomes from cells in the metaphase stage of mitosis. The chromosomes in the pictures can then be cut and arranged for comparison with known samples (figure 9.38). This picture of an individual's chromosomal makeup is referred to as a *karyotype.*

One example of the effects of nondisjunction is the condition known as **Down syndrome.** If a gamete with 2 number 21 chromosomes has been fertilized by a gamete containing the typical one copy of chromosome number 21, the resulting zygote has 47 chromosomes—one more than the expected count of 46 chromosomes (figure 9.38d). The child who developed from this fertilization has 47 chromosomes in every cell of his or her body as a result of mitosis and thus can have the symptoms characteristic of Down syndrome. These include

(a)

(b)

(c)

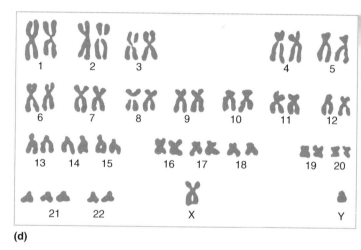

(d)

**FIGURE 9.38 Human Male and Female Chromosomes**
The randomly arranged chromosomes shown in the circle simulate metaphase cells spattered onto a microscope slide *(a)*. Those in parts *(b)* and *(c)* have been arranged into homologous pairs. Part *(b)* shows a male karyotype, with an X and a Y chromosome, and *(c)* shows a female karyotype, with two X chromosomes. *(d)* Notice that each pair of chromosomes is numbered and that the person from whom these chromosomes were taken has an extra chromosome number 21. The person with this trisomic condition might display a variety of physical characteristics, including slightly thickened eyelids, flattened facial features, a large tongue, and short stature and fingers. Most individuals also display some mental retardation. This condition is known as Down syndrome.

thickened eyelids, a large tongue, flattened facial features, short stature and fingers, some mental impairment, and faulty speech (figure 9.39).

In the past, it was thought that the mother's age at childbirth played an important role in the occurrence of trisomies, such as Down syndrome. In women, gametogenesis begins early in life, but cells destined to become eggs are put on hold during meiosis I. Beginning at puberty and ending at menopause, one of these cells completes meiosis I monthly. This means that cells released for fertilization later in life are older than those released earlier in life. Therefore, it was believed that the chances for abnormalities, such as nondisjunction, increase as the mother ages. However, the evidence no longer supports this age-egg link. Currently, the increase in the frequency of trisomies with age has been correlated with a decrease in the activity of a woman's immune system. As she ages, her immune system is less likely to recognize the difference between an abnormal and a normal embryo. This

means that miscarriage is less common and she is more likely to carry an abnormal fetus to full term.

Figure 9.40 illustrates the frequency of the occurrence of Down syndrome births at various ages in women. Notice that the frequency increases very rapidly after age 37. Physicians normally encourage older women who are pregnant to have the cells of their fetus checked to see if they have the normal chromosome number. Nondisjunction can occur in either the production of eggs or sperm, so either parent can be the cause of an abnormal chromosome number.

## 9.10   CONCEPT REVIEW

30. Define the term *nondisjunction*.
31. What is the difference between monosomy and trisomy?

**FIGURE 9.39  Down Syndrome**
Every cell in the body of a person with Down Syndrome has 1 extra chromosome. With special care, planning, and training, people with this syndrome can lead happy, productive lives.

**FIGURE 9.40  Down Syndrome as a Function of a Mother's Age**
Notice that, as the age of the woman increases, the frequency of births of children with Down Syndrome increases only slightly until the age of approximately 37. From that point on, the rate increases drastically. This increase is thought to occur because older women experience fewer miscarriages of abnormal embryos.

## Summary

Cell division is necessary for growth, repair, and reproduction. Mitosis and meiosis are two important forms of cell division. Cells go through a cell cycle, a nondividing period when normal cell activities take place followed by DNA replication, and cell division (mitosis and cytokinesis). Interphase is the period of growth and preparation for division. Mitosis is divided into four stages: prophase, metaphase, anaphase, and telophase. During mitosis, two daughter nuclei are formed from one parent nucleus. These nuclei have identical sets of chromosomes and genes that are exact copies of those of the parent. The regulation of mitosis is important if organisms are to remain healthy.

Regular divisions are necessary to replace lost cells and to allow for growth. However, uncontrolled cell division may result in cancer and disruption of the total organism's well-being.

Meiosis is a specialized process of cell division, resulting in the production of four cells, each of which has the haploid number of chromosomes. The total process involves two sequential divisions, during which one diploid cell reduces to four haploid cells. Mutations and various processes of meiosis, such as crossing-over, segregation, and independent assortment, ensure that all sex cells are unique. The various mechanisms that generate genetic diversity in sexually reproducing organisms assure that when two gametes unite, the individual offspring is genetically unique.

## Key Terms

*Use interactive flash cards on the* **Concepts in Biology,** *14/e website to help you learn the meaning of these terms.*

| | |
|---|---|
| allele 194 | kinetochore 178 |
| anaphase 177 | locus 194 |
| anther 186 | malignant tumors 183 |
| apoptosis 181 | meiosis 174 |
| asexual reproduction 174 | meiosis I 188 |
| asters 177 | meiosis II 188 |
| benign tumor 183 | metaphase 177 |
| binary fission 174 | metastasize 183 |
| carcinogens 181 | mitosis 174 |
| cell cycle 175 | monosomy 197 |
| cell division 174 | mutagens 181 |
| cell plate 179 | nondisjunction 197 |
| centrioles 177 | non-homologous |
| centromere 176 | chromosomes 187 |
| chromatid 176 | ovaries 186 |
| chromatin 176 | pistil 186 |
| cleavage furrow 179 | prophase 177 |
| crossing-over 188 | proto-oncogenes 179 |
| cytokinesis 176 | reduction division 188 |
| determination 185 | segregation 189 |
| differentiated 185 | sexual reproduction 174 |
| diploid 186 | sister chromatids 176 |
| Down syndrome 197 | spindle 177 |
| fertilization 187 | spindle fibers 177 |
| gamete 186 | synapsis 188 |
| gonads 186 | telophase 178 |
| haploid 186 | testes 186 |
| homologous | trisomy 197 |
| chromosomes 187 | tumor 183 |
| independent assortment 189 | tumor-suppressor genes 179 |
| interphase 175 | zygote 185 |

## Basic Review

1. What is the key difference between mitosis and meiosis?

   a. Mitosis involves two rounds of cell division, whereas meiosis involves one round of cell division.

   b. DNA is not split between cells in meiosis, but this does occur during mitosis.

   c. Mitosis produces cells genetically identical to the parent, whereas meiosis produces cells with half the genetic information as the parent.

   d. None of the above is correct.

2. Which of the following is true of interphase?

   a. The chromosomes line up on the equatorial plane.

   b. DNA replication occurs in this phase.

   c. The DNA in the cell halves.

   d. All of the above are true.

3. Chromosomes are most likely to appear to be lining up near the middle of the cell during which phase of mitosis?

   a. interphase

   b. prophase

   c. metaphase

   d. telophase

4. Which of the following types of information do cells use to determine if they will divide?

   a. genetic health

   b. their current location

   c. the need for more cells

   d. All of the above are correct.

5. *p53* mutations lead to cancer because

   a. DNA damage is not repaired.

   b. mutated cells are allowed to grow.

   c. multiple mutations in the cell's regulatory proteins occur.

   d. All of the above are correct.

6. Haploid cells

   a. carry two copies of the genetic information.

   b. carry one copy of the genetic information.

   c. carry partial copies of the genetic information.

   d. are mutant.

7. Reduction division occurs

   a. in meiosis II.

   b. in meiosis I.

   c. in mitosis.

   d. after fertilization.

8. Genetic diversity in the gametes of an individual i generated through:

   a. mitosis.

   b. independent assortment.

   c. crossing-over.

   d. both b and c.

9. Trisomy means

   a. that three copies of a chromosome are present.

   b. Down syndrome.

   c. that only three cells are present.

   d. none of the above.

10. A nondisjunction event occurs when

    a. homologous chromosomes did not separate correctly.

    b. non-homologous chromosomes did not separate correctly.

    c. daughter cells did not undergo cytokinesis correctly.

    d. None of the above is correct.

11. Chemical changes of chromatin (DNA and histones) that do not alter the nucleotide sequence are called _____ changes.

12. Mutagens can be carcinogens. (T/F)

13. _____ is the cellular process of deciding which genes a cell will express when mature.

14. The gonads in females are known as _____.

15. These features characterize which kind of cell division? (a) Homologous chromosomes do not cross-over. (b) Centromeres divide in anaphase.

**Answers**

1. c  2. b  3. c  4. d  5. d  6. b  7. b  8. d  9. a
10. a  11. epigenetic  12. T  13. Determination  14. ovaries
15. mitosis.

## Thinking Critically

**Cancer, *p53*, Antibodies and Nanoparticles**

A molecular oncologist and her colleagues at Georgetown University have developed a nanoparticle that is coated with a tumor-targeting antibody. The nanoparticle is able to locate primary and hidden metastatic tumor cells and deliver a fully functioning copy of the *p53* tumor-suppressor gene. The presence of the *p53* gene improves the efficacy of conventional cancer therapies such as chemo- and radiation therapy and reduces their side effects. Review the material on cell membranes, antibodies, cancer, and the role of *p53* and explain the details of this treatment to a friend. (You might explore the Internet for further information.)

# CHAPTER 10

# Patterns of Inheritance

## Geneticists Hard at Work

*Mendel would be pleased to know what his discovery is revealing.*

## CHAPTER OUTLINE

Since Gregor Mendel's work was accepted as "law" in the early 1900s, geneticists have made many important discoveries. This field has really exploded with new, life-changing or just plain interesting information since the era of molecular genetics came about during the 1950s and 1960s. Some of these discoveries revealed the existence of actual genes responsible for specific characteristics or conditions. Others help to explain the factors that control whether a gene is expressed or how its expression is modified.

Here just a few recent revelations from scientists working in the field of genetics:

✓ Certain soil bacteria have been discovered that have genes that allow them to feed exclusively on antibiotics. This is of concern because these bacteria live in close association with human and livestock pathogens.

✓ Charles Darwin proposed that human facial expressions are universal. Recent and continuing research is lending support to this hypothesis. Researchers found that, in fact, facial expressions are genetically determined.

✓ While the genetic abnormality causing Huntington's disease causes neurons in the brain to be destroyed, it also plays a role in destroying cancer cells. People with Huntington's are less likely than others to suffer from cancer. It appears that the *huntingtin* gene has more than one effect.

✓ The inheritance of "dominant black" coat color in domestic dogs involves a gene that is distinct from, but interacts with, the genes responsible for conventional coat pigmentation. Variations in this gene are responsible for the color differences in yellow, black, and brindle-colored dog breeds. This same gene is responsible for the production of a protein (β-defensin) that in other species is able to aid in the destruction of microbes. The presence of black coat color in wolves is the result of occasional interbreeding of dogs with black coat color and grey wolves.

✓ The gene *DISC1* (Disrupted-in-Schizophrenia 1) has been strongly implicated in cases of schizophrenia, major depression, bipolar disorder, and autism.

- Who was Mendel? What role did he play in the field of genetics?

- In order to make the discoveries noted in the article, what basic ideas do you need to understand?

- How might these discoveries influence your understanding of life?

## Background Check

**Concepts you should already know to get the most out of this chapter:**
- The connection between genes, DNA, and chromosomes (chapter 8)
- The patterns of chromosome movement during meiosis (chapter 9)
- The concepts of segregation and independent assortment (chapter 9)

## 10.1 Meiosis, Genes, and Alleles

**Genetics** is the branch of science that studies how the characteristics of living organisms are inherited. Classical genetics uses an understanding of meiosis to make predictions about the kinds of genes that will be inherited by the *offspring* of a sexually reproducing pair of organisms. **Offspring** are the descendants of a set of parents.

### Various Ways to Study Genes

The previous chapters of this text used the term *gene*. In chapter 8, a gene was described as a piece of DNA with the necessary information to code for a protein and regulate its expression. In chapter 9, on cell division, genes were described as locations on chromosomes. Both of these views are correct, because the DNA with the necessary information to make a protein is packaged into a chromosome. When a cell divides, the DNA is passed on to the daughter cells in chromosomes.

This chapter introduces another way to think about a gene. A gene is related to a characteristic of an organism, such as a color, a shape, or even the ability to break down a chemical. The characteristics usually result from the actions of proteins in the cell.

### What Is an Allele?

Recall from chapter 9 that an allele is a specific version of a gene. Consider a characteristic such as earlobe shape. Some earlobes are free and some are attached (figure 10.1). These types of earlobes are two versions, or alleles, of the "earlobe-shape" gene. The two different alleles of this gene produce different versions of the same type of protein. The effect of these different proteins results in different earlobe shapes. Thus, there is an allele for free earlobes and a different allele for attached earlobes.

### Genomes and Meiosis

A **genome** is a set of all the genes necessary to code for all of an organism's characteristics. In sexually reproducing organisms, a genome is diploid (*2n*) when it has two copies of each gene. When two copies of a gene are present, the two copies

(a)                    (b)

**FIGURE 10.1 Genes Control Structural Features**
Whether your earlobe is *(a)* free or *(b)* attached depends on the alleles you have inherited. As genes express themselves, their actions affect the development of various tissues and organs. In some people the expression results in the earlobe being separated from the side of the face during fetal development, forming a "free" lobe. In others, the lobe remains "attached."

need not be identical. The copies may be the same alleles, or they may be different alleles of the same gene.

The genome of a haploid (*n*) cell has only one copy of each gene. Sex cells, such as eggs and sperm, are haploid. Because sperm and eggs are haploid, they have only one allele of a gene (review meiosis in chapter 9). If the parent has two different alleles of a gene, the parent's sperm or eggs can have either version of the alleles, but not both at the same time. When a haploid sperm (*n*) from a male and a haploid egg (*n*) from a female combine, they form a diploid (*2n*) cell, called a *zygote*. The alleles in the sperm and the alleles in the egg combine to form a new genome that is different from either of the parents. This means that each new zygote is a unique combination of genetic information.

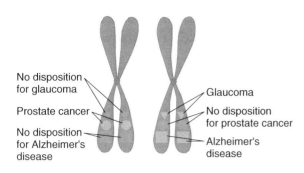

**FIGURE 10.2 Homologous Chromosomes—Human Chromosome 1**
Homologous chromosomes contain genes for the same characteristics at the same place. Different versions, or alleles, of the genes may be present on different chromosomes. This set of homologous chromosomes represents chromosome 1 in humans. Chromosome 1 is known to contain genes that play a role in glaucoma, prostate cancer, and Alzheimer's disease. The three genes shown here may be present in their normal form or in their altered, mutant form. Here, different genes are shown as specific shapes. The alleles for each gene are shown as different colors.

Meiosis is a cell's process of making haploid cells, such as eggs or sperm. Understanding the process of meiosis is extremely important to making genetic predictions. If you don't understand the cellular process of meiosis, your predictions will be less accurate. Figure 10.2 shows a pair of *homologous chromosomes* that have undergone DNA replication. After DNA replication, each homologous chromosome has two, exact copies of each allele, one on each chromatid.

When the cell undergoes meiosis I, the two homologous chromosomes go to different cells. This reduces the cell's genome from diploid to haploid. In meiosis II, the chromatids of each chromosome are separated into different daughter cells. The cells resulting from meiosis II mature to become sperm or eggs. The probability that an allele will be passed to a sperm or an egg is related to the number of times that allele is present in the cell before meiosis begins. These probabilities are used in making predictions in genetic crosses.

## 10.1   CONCEPT REVIEW

1. How does the term *gene* relate to the term *allele*?
2. Define the term *genome*.
3. What is meant by the symbols *n* and *2n*?

## 10.2   The Fundamentals of Genetics

Three questions represent the biological principles behind understanding the genetics problems presented in this chapter:

1. What alleles do the parents have?
2. What alleles are present in the gametes that the parents produce?
3. What is the likelihood that gametes with specific combinations of alleles will be fertilized?

To solve genetics problems and understand biological inheritance, it is necessary to understand how to answer each of these questions and to understand how the answer to one of these questions can affect the others.

## Phenotype and Genotype

The interaction of alleles determines the appearance of the organism. The **genotype** of an organism is the combination of alleles that are present in the organism's cells. The **phenotype** of an organism is how it appears outwardly and is a result of the organism's genotype.

Reconsider the example of earlobe type to explore the ideas of phenotype and genotype. Earlobes can be attached or free. If a person's earlobes are attached, the person's *phenotype* is "attached earlobes." Likewise, if a person's earlobes are free, his or her *phenotype* is "free earlobes." Each person has 2 alleles for earlobe type. However, the 2 alleles do not need to be identical.

To make understanding *genotype* easier, we can use a shorthand notation that is commonly used in genetics. The capital letter *E* can be used to represent the allele that codes for free earlobe development. A lowercase *e* can be used to refer to the allele that codes for attached earlobe development. Because each person has 2 alleles, a person can have one of these combinations of alleles:

- (*EE*)—2 alleles for free earlobes
- (*ee*)—2 alleles for attached earlobes
- (*Ee*)—1 allele for free earlobes and 1 allele for attached earlobes

The 2 alleles will interact with each other when they are in the same cell and their proteins are synthesized as described in chapter 9. Consider what happens in a cell when the allele combination is *EE*, *ee*, or even *Ee*. When the cell has *EE*, it is only capable of producing proteins associated with free earlobes. The organism will have free earlobes. When both alleles code for attached earlobe development (*ee*) then the person will develop attached earlobes. Continue reading to understand what happens when the cells are *Ee*.

## Dominant and Recessive Alleles

What does the organism look like if it has 1 allele that codes for free earlobes and 1 allele that codes for attached earlobes—(*Ee*)? In this particular situation, the organism develops free earlobes. The *E* allele produces proteins for free earlobes that "outperforms" the *e* allele. Therefore, *E* is able to dominate the appearance of the organism. A **dominant allele** is one that masks another allele (called the recessive allele) in the phenotype of an organism. A **recessive allele** is one that is masked by another, the dominant allele. In the previous example, the free earlobes allele (*E*) is dominant and the attached earlobes allele (*e*) is recessive, because in an (*Ee*) individual the phenotype that develops is free earlobes. Geneticists use the capital letter to denote that an allele is dominant. The lowercase letter denotes the recessive allele.

Take a closer look at the genotypes for free and attached earlobes. Notice that organisms with attached earlobes always have 2 *e* alleles (*ee*), whereas organisms with free earlobes might have 2 *E* alleles—(*EE*)—or both an *E* and an *e* allele—(*Ee*). A dominant allele may hide a recessive allele.

The term *recessive* has nothing to do with the significance or value of the allele—it simply describes how it is expressed when inherited with a dominant allele. The term *recessive* also has nothing to do with how frequently the allele is passed on to offspring.

In individuals with 2 different alleles, each allele has an equal chance of being passed on. The Gene Key that immediately follows this text organizes the information about how earlobe shape is inherited. This format will also be used later in this chapter to summarize information about other genes.

**Gene Key**
**Gene or Condition: earlobe shape**

| Allele Symbols | Possible Genotypes | Phenotype |
|---|---|---|
| *E* = free | *EE* | Free earlobes |
|  | *Ee* | Free earlobes |
| *e* = attached | *ee* | Attached earlobes |

*Summary:* Geneticists describe an organism by its genotype and its phenotype. One rule that describes how the genotype of an organism influences its phenotype involves the principle of dominant and recessive interaction.

*Application:* Use the dominant and recessive principle to infer information that is not provided. Example: If a person has attached earlobes, you can infer that his or her genotype is *ee*. If a person has free earlobes, you can infer that he or she has at least 1 *E* allele. The second allele is uncertain without additional information.

## Predicting Gametes from Meiosis

To predict the types of offspring that parents may produce, it is important to predict the kinds of alleles that may be in the sex cells produced by each parent. Remember that during meiosis the 2 alleles will end up in different sex cells. If an organism contains two copies of the same allele, such as in *EE* or *ee*, it can produce sex cells with only one type of allele. *EE* individuals can produce sex cells with only the *E* allele, likewise *ee* individuals can produce sex cells with only the *e* allele. The *Ee* individual can produce two different types of sex cells. Half of the sex cells carry the *E* allele. The other half carry the *e* allele. If an organism has 2 identical alleles for a characteristic and can produce sex cells with only one type of allele, the genotype of the organism is **homozygous** (*homo* = same or

like). If an organism has 2 different alleles for a characteristic and can produce two kinds of sex cells with different alleles, the organism is **heterozygous** (*hetero* = different). This is summarized in the Gene Key at the bottom of this page.

Notice that the 2 alleles separate into different sex cells. This is true whether the cell is homozygous or heterozygous. The **Law of Segregation** states that in a diploid organism the alleles exist as two separate pieces of genetic information, and that these two different pieces of genetic information are on different chromosomes and are separated into different cells during meiosis.

*Summary:* When sex cells form, they receive only 1 allele for each characteristic. Homozygous organisms can produce only one kind of sex cell. In heterozygous organisms, meiosis produces two genetically different sex cells. The 2 different alleles are represented equally in the sex cells that are produced. Half the cells contain 1 of the alleles and half the cells contain the other.

*Application:* Make two predictions using the Law of Segregation. The first prediction describes the genetic information a sex cell can carry. The second prediction describes the expected ratios of these sex cells. If the organism is homozygous, then all sex cells will be the same. If the organism is heterozygous, half of the sex cells will carry one allele (one out of two). The other allele will be in the other half of the sex cells.

## Fertilization

Recall from chapter 9 that **fertilization** is the process of two haploid (*n*) sex cells joining to form a zygote (2*n*). The zygote divides by mitosis to produce additional diploid cells as the new organism grows. The diploid genotype of all the cells of that organism is determined by the alleles carried by the two sex cells that joined to form the zygote.

A **genetic cross** is a planned breeding or mating between two organisms. Although the cross is planned, the exact sperm and egg that join when fertilization occurs are not entirely predictable, because the process of fertilization is random. Any one of the many different sperm produced by meiosis may fertilize a given egg. Despite this element of randomness, generalizations can be made about possible results from two parents. These generalizations can be seen by drawing a diagram called a *Punnett square*. A **Punnett square** shows the possible offspring of a particular genetic cross.

Genetic crosses can be designed to investigate one or more characteristics. A **single-factor cross** is designed to look at how one genetically determined characteristic is inherited. A unique single factor cross is a *monohybrid cross*. A **monohybrid cross** is a cross between two organisms that are both heterozygous for the one observed gene. A **double-factor cross** is a genetic

**Gene Key**
**Gene or Condition: earlobe type**

| Allele Symbols | Possible Genotype | Phenotype | Possible Sex Cells |
|---|---|---|---|
| *E* = free | *EE*-homozygous | Free earlobes | All sex cells have *E*. |
|  | *Ee*-heterozygous | Free earlobes | Half of sex cells have *E* and half have *e*. |
| *e* = attached | *ee*-homozygous | Attached earlobes | All sex cells have *e*. |

study in which two different genetically determined characteristics are followed from the parental generation to the offspring at the same time. Because double-factor crosses involve two genes, their outcomes are more complex than single-factor crosses. Let's look at the following single-factor cross where we observe earlobe attachment.

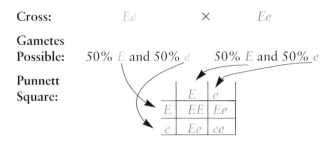

**Cross:**     *Ee*    ×    *Ee*

**Gametes Possible:**   50% *E* and 50% *e*    50% *E* and 50% *e*

**Punnett Square:**

|   | *E* | *e* |
|---|-----|-----|
| *E* | *EE* | *Ee* |
| *e* | *Ee* | *ee* |

The cross shown is between two heterozygous (*Ee*) individuals. The individuals in this cross can each produce two types of sex cells, *E* and *e*. The colors (red and blue) used in this monohybrid cross and Punnett square allow us to trace what happens to the sex cells from each parent. The top row lists the sex cells that can be produced by one parent, and the left-most column of the Punnett square lists the sex cells that can be produced by the other parent. The letter combinations within the four boxes represent the possible genotypes of the offspring. Each combination of letters is simply the combination of the alleles listed at the top of each column and the left of each row.

Let's look at the type of offspring that can be produced by this cross. The Punnett square contains three genotypes: *EE*, *Ee*, and *ee*. Additionally, by counting how many times each genotype is shown in the Punnett square, we can predict how frequently we expect to observe each genotype in the offspring of these parents. Here, we expect to see *Ee* twice for every time we see *EE* or *ee*. Remember that a Punnet square only generalizes. If many (*at least 30 or more*) offspring are produced from the cross, we might expect to see nearly 1/4 *EE*, 2/4 *Ee*, and 1/4 *ee*. Geneticists may abbreviate this ratio as 1:2:1. These ratios can be written in a different manner but still mean the same thing:

1/4 EE, 1/2 Ee, 1/4 ee

*Summary:* The outcome of a genetic cross cannot be exactly determined. The outcome can only be described by general trends.

*Application:* The Punnett square can be used to predict the types and ratios of offspring.

## 10.2 CONCEPT REVIEW

4. Distinguish between phenotype and genotype.
5. What types of symbols are typically used to express genotypes?
6. How many kinds of games are possible with the genotype *Aa*?
7. What is the difference between a single-factor cross and double-factor cross?

## 10.3 Probability vs. Possibility

Your ability to understand genetics depends on your ability to work with probabilities. This section will help you understand what probability is.

**Probability** is the mathematical chance that an event will happen, and it is expressed as a percentage or a fraction, like the values that we identified using the Punnett square in the previous example. Probability is not the same as *possibility*. Consider the common phrase "almost anything is possible" when reading the following question: "It is possible for me to win the lottery, but how probable is it?" Although it is possible to win the lottery, it is extremely unlikely. When we talk about something being probable, we actually talk mathematically—in ratios and percentages—such as, "The probability of my winning the lottery is 1 in 250,000."

It is possible to toss a coin and have it come up heads, but the probability of getting a head is a more precise statement than just saying it is possible to do so. The probability of getting a head is 1 out of 2 (1/2, or 0.5, or 50%), because there are two sides to the coin, only one of which is a head. Probability can be expressed as a fraction:

$$\text{probability} = \frac{\text{the number of events that can produce a given outcome}}{\text{the total number of possible outcomes}}$$

What is the probability of cutting a standard deck of cards and getting the ace of hearts? The number of times the ace of hearts can occur in a standard deck is 1. The total number of different cards in the deck is 52. Therefore, the probability of cutting to an ace of hearts is 1/52. What is the probability of cutting to any ace? The total number of aces in the deck is 4, and the total number of cards is 52. Therefore, the probability of cutting an ace is 4/52, or 1/13.

It is also possible to determine the probability of two independent events occurring together. *The probability of two or more events occurring simultaneously is the product of their individual probabilities.* When two six-sided dice are thrown, it is possible that both will be 4s. What is the probability that both will be 4s? The probability of one die being a 4 is one out of the six sides of the die, or 1/6. The probability of the other die being a 4 is also 1/6. Therefore, the probability of throwing two 4s is

$$1/6 \times 1/6 = 1/36$$

The concepts of probability and possibility are frequently used in solving genetics problems (How Science Works 10.1). Consider describing the genetic contents of the sex cells an individual will produce. Assume that the individual's genotype is *AA*. It is only *possible* for this individual to produce sex cells that carry the *A* allele. The *probability* of this occurring is 100%. Now consider an individual with the *Aa* genotype.

# HOW SCIENCE WORKS 10.1

## Cystic Fibrosis—What Is the Probability?

*Cystic fibrosis* is among the most common lethal genetic disorders that affect Caucasians. An estimated 30,000 people are affected by cystic fibrosis in North America. One in every 20 persons has a defective recessive allele that causes cystic fibrosis, but most of these individuals display no cystic fibrosis symptoms, because they are heterozygous and the recessive allele is masked by a normal dominant allele. Only those with two copies of the defective recessive gene develop symptoms. About 1,000 new cystic fibrosis cases are identified in the United States each year. The gene for cystic fibrosis occurs on chromosome 7; it is responsible for the manufacture of **c**ystic **f**ibrosis **t**ransmembrane **r**egulator (CFTR) protein. The CFTR protein controls the movement of chloride ions across the cell membrane.

There are many possible types of mutations in the CFTR gene. The most common mutation results in a CFTR protein with a deletion of a single amino acid. As a result, CFTR protein is unable to control the movement of chloride ions across the cell membrane. The major result is mucus filling the bronchioles, resulting in blocked breathing and frequent respiratory infections. It is also responsible for other symptoms:

1. A malfunction of sweat glands in the skin and the secretion of excess chloride ions
2. Clogging of the bile duct, which interferes with digestion and liver function
3. Mucus clogging the pancreas ducts, preventing the flow of digestive enzymes into the intestinal tract
4. Bowel obstructions caused by thickened stools
5. Sterility in males that is due to the absence of vas deferens and, on occasion, female sterility due to the presence of dense mucus-blocking sperm from reaching eggs.

One in 20 people have a recessive allele for cystic fibrosis. In this group, two or three individuals, on average, have the allele.

Consider the facts about the frequency of the cystic fibrosis gene in the population. What is the probability that any set of parents will have a child with cystic fibrosis? What is the probability that a person who carries the cystic fibrosis allele will marry someone who also has the allele?

---

It is *possible* for the *Aa* individual to produce *A* or *a* sex cells. The *probability* of a sex cell having *A* is 50%; only one of the two possibilities is *A*. Likewise, the probability of a sex cell having *a* is 50%; only one of the two possibilities is *a*.

In a genetics problem, the frequency with which alleles are present in gametes determines the likelihood that a couple will have children with a particular characteristic. Consider the possible fertilization events that *could* occur between an individual with the genotype *AA* and an individual with the genotype *aa* (the genetic cross *AA* × *aa*). To do this, use a Punnett square. First, predict the possible sex cells produced by each individual.

| Genotype | Possible Sex Cells |
|----------|--------------------|
| *AA*     | *A*                |
| *aa*     | *a*                |

Then, set up a Punnett square that shows the possible fertilization events between the sex cells shown.

|     | *a*  |
|-----|------|
| *A* | *Aa* |

The only possible offspring is *Aa*. The probability of obtaining an offspring with this genotype is 100%.

## 10.3   CONCEPT REVIEW

8. What is the difference between probability and possibility?
9. In what mathematical forms might probability be expressed?

## 10.4   The First Geneticist: Gregor Mendel

The inheritance patterns discussed in the section "Probability vs. Possibility" were initially described by Gregor Mendel—a member of the religious order of Augustinian monks. Mendel's (1822–1884) work was not generally accepted until the 1900s, when three men, working independently, rediscovered some of

**(a)** **(b)**

**FIGURE 10.3 Gregor Mendel and His Pea Plant Garden**
*(a)* Gregor Mendel was an Augustinian monk who used statistics to describe the inheritance patterns he observed in pea plants. *(b)* He carried out his investigations in this small garden of his monastery in Brno, Czech Republic where Mendel did his experiments.

the ideas that Mendel had formulated more than 30 years earlier. Because of his early work, the study of the pattern of inheritance that follows the laws formulated by Gregor Mendel is often called **Mendelian genetics** (figure 10.3).

Mendel's work established basic principles that allowed him and others to solve heredity problems. Heredity problems are concerned with determining which alleles are passed from parents to offspring and how likely it is that various types of offspring will be produced. Mendel performed experiments concerning the inheritance of certain characteristics in garden pea plants (*Pisum sativum*). From his work, Mendel developed the ideas of a genetic characteristic being dominant or recessive and categorized the inheritance patterns for a number of garden pea alleles by using rules of probability. Some of the phenotypes he used in his experiments are shown in table 10.1.

What made Mendel's work unique was that he initially studied only one trait at a time. In addition, he grouped the offspring by phenotype and counted them. Previous investigators tried to follow numerous traits at the same time. This made it very difficult to follow characteristics, and they did not determine the frequency of phenotypic groups. Therefore, they were unable to see any patterns in their data.

Mendel was very lucky to have chosen pea plants in his study because they naturally *self-pollinate*. This means that pea plants produce both pollen and eggs and that the eggs can be fertilized by haploid nuclei from their own pollen. When self-pollination occurs in pea plants over many generations, it is easier to develop a population of plants that is homozygous for a number of characteristics. Such a population is known as a *pure line*.

The following gene key organizes some of Mendel's findings. Remember that Mendel didn't know about DNA or even chromosomes! Mendel developed this way of thinking about genetics to explain the data he collected. He did this from the perspective of a mathematician—not a biologist.

| TABLE 10.1 Dominant and Recessive Traits in Pea Plants | | |
|---|---|---|
| Gene | Dominant Allele Phenotype | Recessive Allele Phenotype |
| Plant height | Tall | Dwarf |
| Pod shape | Full | Constricted |
| Pod color | Green | Yellow |
| Seed surface texture | Round | Wrinkled |
| Seed color | Yellow | Green |
| Flower color | Purple | White |

**Gene Key**
Gene or Condition: flower color

| Allele Symbols | Possible Genotypes | Phenotype | Possible Sex Cells |
|---|---|---|---|
| C = Purple | CC = homozygous | Purple | All sex cells have C (*pure line*) |
| | Cc = heterozygous | Purple | Half of sex cells have C and half have c |
| c = white | cc = homozygous | White | All sex cells have c (*pure line*) |

In one experiment, Mendel took a pure line of pea plants having purple flower color, removed the male parts (anthers), and discarded them, so that the plants could not self-pollinate. He then took anthers from a pure-breeding white-flowered plant and pollinated the antherless purple flower. These plants are called the parent generation, or $P_0$. When the pollinated flowers produced seeds, Mendel collected, labeled, and planted them. When these seeds germinated and grew, they eventually produced flowers. The offspring of the $P_0$ generation are called the $F_1$ generation. The *F* stands for *filial*, which is Latin for relating to a son or daughter. $F_1$ is read as the "F-one" generation or the "first filial" generation.

### Mendel's First Cross

| Observed | | Genetic Notation |
|---|---|---|
| $P_0$ *pure breeding purple* × *pure breeding white* | | $CC$ × $cc$ |
| | | |
| $F_1$ *100% produced purple flowers* | | $100\%$ $Cc$ |

All the $F_1$ plants resulting from this cross had purple flowers. One of the popular ideas of Mendel's day would have predicted that the purple and white colors would have blended, resulting in flowers that were lighter than the purple parent flowers. Another hypothesis would have predicted that the offspring would have had a mixture of white and purple flowers. Neither of these two hypotheses was supported by Mendel's results. He observed only purple flowers from this cross.

Mendel then crossed the $F_1$ pea plants (all of which had purple flowers) with each other to see what the next generation would be like. Had the white-flowered characteristic been lost completely? The seeds from this mating were collected and grown. When these plants flowered, three-fourths of them produced purple flowers and one-fourth produced white flowers. This generation is called the $F_2$ generation.

### Mendel's Second Cross

| Observed | | Genetic Notation |
|---|---|---|
| $F_1$ *Offspring from $P_0$ (purple)* × *offspring from $P_0$ (purple)* | | $Cc$ × $Cc$ |
| | | |
| $F_2$ *75% produced purple flowers* | | $25\%$ $CC$ + $50\%$ $Cc$ |
| | | $75\%$ *produced purple flowers* |
| *25% produced white flowers* | | $25\%$ $cc$ *produced white flowers* |

His experiments used similar strategies to investigate other traits. Pure-breeding tall pea plants were crossed with

pure-breeding dwarf plants. Pure-breeding plants with yellow pods were crossed with pure-breeding plants with green pods. Mendel recognized the same pattern for each characteristic in the $F_1$ generation: All the offspring showed the characteristics of one parent and not the other with no blending.

After analyzing these data, Mendel identified several genetic principles:

1. Organisms have two pieces of genetic information for each trait. It is now recognized that these are different alleles for each characteristic.
2. Because organisms have two pieces of genetic information for each characteristic, the alleles can be different. Mendel's **Law of Dominance** states that some alleles interact with each other in a dominant and recessive manner whereby the dominant allele masks the recessive allele.
3. Gametes fertilize randomly.
4. Mendel's Law of Segregation states that, when a diploid organism forms gametes, the two alleles for a characteristic separate from one another. In doing this, they move to different gametes and retain their individuality.

The application of Mendel's Law of Segregation may not be as apparent as the application of the Law of Dominance. The movements of chromosomes during meiosis separate the four copies (one on each chromatid) of each allele into four different sex cells. This causes only 1 allele of each gene to be present in each sex cell. We first observed this law in this chapter when we discussed sex cells and how alleles separate in both homozygous and heterozygous organisms. Finally, this law is the basis for the Punnett square, in which the possible alleles from each parent are placed in a separate row or column.

## 10.4   CONCEPT REVIEW

10. In your own words, describe Mendel's Law of Segregation.
11. Define *self-pollination*.
12. What is the "$F_1$ generation"?

## 10.5   Solving Genetics Problems

Many students become confused when they try to solve genetics problems because they are not sure where to begin or when it is appropriate to apply a principle. As a result, they move directly to drawing a Punnett square and begin to incorrectly fill it with letters. Developing an organized and consistent strategy will help solve such problems.

### Single-Factor Crosses

#### Problem Type: Single-Factor Cross

INTRODUCTORY PRINCIPLES:   Genetics problems can vary greatly in complexity and in the type of information that is provided. Let's start with a genetics problem that considers a single trait for which there are two alleles.

**CROSS 1:** The pod color of some pea plants is inherited so that green pods are dominant to yellow pods. A pea plant that is heterozygous for green pods is crossed to a pea plant that produces yellow pods. What proportion of the offspring will have green pods?

## Gene Key
Gene or Condition: pod color

| Allele Symbols | Possible Genotypes | Phenotype |
|---|---|---|
| G = green | GG | Green |
| | Gg | Green |
| g = yellow | gg | Yellow |

The question describes a gene affecting pea pod color. The two different phenotypes are green and yellow. The question also states that "green pods are dominant to yellow pods." Because of this statement, use a capital letter to represent the *green* allele and a lowercase letter to represent the *yellow* allele. We are using the letter G, but any other letter would work. The only requirement is to use the same letter for both alleles. The gene key table shows the type of information needed to describe how the alleles for a characteristic work together. A gene key is a reference that will help solve the problem.

Now, organize the actual genetic cross. Table 10.2 shows each step in a simple genetics problem and skills that may be necessary to move from one step to the next. This problem starts at the top row and works toward the bottom of the table. There are several steps in this process. The steps are represented by each row in the table. The rows are titled. "Parental phenotypes," "Parental genotypes," "Possible sex cells," "Offspring genotype," and "Offspring phenotype."

First, determine what information is provided in the question about the organisms that are involved in this cross. Identify the following pieces of information in the question.

- A pea plant with green pods is crossed to a pea plant with yellow pods.
- The green pea plant is heterozygous.
- The yellow pea plant is homozygous.

The question we are trying to answer is, "What proportion of the offspring will have green pods?" Solve the problem by using the table as a guide. These steps describe the process:

1. The first statement about the organisms being crossed is shown in the "Parental phenotypes" row as Green × Yellow. Using this information, the gene key, and the remaining two statements, we determine the parental genotypes. The reasoning described in this process is in the "Parental genotypes" row of table 10.2.

## TABLE 10.2  Steps in Solving a Genetics Problem

**Solution Pathway**

| Steps in Information Flow | The Problem |
|---|---|
| Parental phenotypes | By reading the problem, determine that one parent has green pods and the other yellow.<br><br>Green × Yellow |
| Parental genotypes | Organisms are diploid, so 2 alleles are needed for each parent. The green parent can be either GG or Gg (gene key). However, the problem states that this parent is heterozygous. The allele combination of Gg is the only green heterozygous combination. The gene key shows that the only genotype that produces yellow is gg.<br><br>Gg × gg |
| Possible sex cells | Because of the Law of Segregation, the alleles separate from each other when sex cells are formed in the parents. The Gg parent can produce two types of sex cells, G and g. The gg parent can produce only g sex cells.<br><br>G  g<br>g |
| Offspring genotype | Set up a Punnett square to show the possible fertilization events. This square will have one column and two rows, because one parent produces only one type of gamete and the other parent produces two types.<br><br>$\begin{array}{c\|c} & g \\ \hline G & Gg \\ \hline g & gg \end{array}$<br><br>50% Gg<br>50% gg |
| Offspring phenotype | Now, use the information in the gene key to determine the phenotypes of the offspring genotypes. Gg will appear as green. Yellow can be produced only by gg.<br><br>50% produce green pea pods (Gg).<br>50% produce yellow pea pods (gg). |

2. The next step is to use the parental genotypes to determine the parents' possible sex cells. It is necessary to apply Mendel's Law of Segregation to do this correctly. This process is described in the "Possible sex cells" row.

3. Now that the parents' gametes are identified, use a Punnett Square to predict the genotypes of the offspring. Create a Punnett square so that there is one row or column for each gamete. This process is shown in the "Offspring genotype" row.

4. Return to the gene key to determine the offspring phenotypes from the genotypes just produced with the Punnett square.

5. Finally, remember to look at the question that was asked. In this example, the question is what proportion of the offspring will produce green pea pods. The answer is 50%.

In this example, all the information from the problem fits into the gene key and the first rows of table 10.2. Not all problems are like this. Sometimes, a problem provides information about the offspring and requests information about the parents. Table 10.2 will help you do this as well. The principles that applied as you worked down the table still apply as you go the other direction.

## Problem Type: Single-Factor Cross

**INTRODUCTORY PRINCIPLES:** When both parents are heterozygous and the alleles are completely dominant and recessive to each other, the predicted offspring ratio is always 3:1 (75% of the dominant phenotype to 25% of the recessive phenotype.) If the genotypes of parents are not known and the offspring have a 3:1 ratio, then geneticists frequently infer that the parents are both heterozygous for the trait being considered.

To illustrate this 3:1 pattern of inheritance, consider the disorder phenylketonuria (PKU). People with phenylketonuria are unable to convert the amino acid phenylalanine into the amino acid tyrosine. The buildup of phenylalanine in the body prevents the normal development of the nervous system. Such individuals may become mentally retarded if their disease is not controlled.

Figure 10.4 shows the metabolic pathway in which the amino acid phenylalanine is converted to the amino acid tyrosine by the enzyme phenylalanine hydroxylase. Tyrosine is then used as a substrate by other enzymes. In the abnormal pathway, the substrate phenylalanine builds up, because the enzyme phenylalanine hydroxylase does not function correctly in people with PKU. As phenylalanine levels rise, it is converted to phenylpyruvic acid, which kills nerve cells.

**CROSS 2:** The normal condition is to convert phenylalanine to tyrosine. It is dominant over the condition for PKU. If both parents are heterozygous for PKU, what is the probability that they will have a child who is normal? A child with PKU?

As in the previous example, use the gene key to summarize this problem:

- There are 2 alleles. One is responsible for the normal condition and the other is for PKU.
- The normal condition is dominant over PKU. From this statement, infer that individuals with a normal phenotype can be either *PP* or *Pp*.

### Gene Key
Gene or Condition: Phenylketonuria

| Allele Symbols | Possible Genotypes | Phenotype |
|---|---|---|
| *P* = normal | *PP* | Normal |
| | *Pp* | Normal |
| *p* = phenylketonuria | *pp* | Phenylketonuria |

**FIGURE 10.4 Phenylketonuria (PKU)**
PKU is a recessive disorder located on chromosome 12. The diagram on the left shows how the normal pathway works. The diagram on the right shows an abnormal pathway. If the enzyme phenylalanine hydroxylase is not produced because of a mutated gene, the amino acid phenylalanine cannot be converted to tyrosine and is converted into phenylpyruvic acid, which accumulates in body fluids. The buildup of phenylpyruvic acid causes the death of nerve cells and ultimately results in mental retardation. Because phenylalanine is not converted to tyrosine, subsequent reactions in the pathway are also affected.

1. The problem states that "both parents are heterozygous for PKU." This describes the parental genotypes and determines the genotypes for both parents to be *Pp*. Enter this information on the "Parental Genotypes" row. Although it is not necessary to solve the problem, you can use the gene key to determine the parental phenotypes. *Pp* individuals are normal. *Note: This genetic problem does not start with the first row of table 10.3. A genetics problem can start at any point in the table and require that you determine things about either the parents or the offspring.*

2. Determine the possible sex cells. *Pp* individuals will have gametes that are *P* and *p*.

3. Determine the offspring genotypes using a Punnett square. Create your Punnett square so that there is one row or column for each gamete. Note that, in this situation, three different genotypes are produced—*PP*, *Pp*, and *pp*.

4. Determine the offspring phenotypes by using the gene key and combining genotypes with similar phenotypes.

5. Finally, answer the question that was asked from the problem. In this case, two questions were asked. The probability of having a normal child is 75%. The probability of having a child with PKU is 25%.

## TABLE 10.3 Solution Pathway

| Steps in Information Flow | The Problem |
|---|---|
| Parental phenotypes | Father × Mother<br>Normal × Normal |
| Parental genotypes | *Pp* × *Pp* |
| Possible sex cells | *P*  *P*<br>*p*  *p* |
| Offspring genotype | |  *P* | *p* |<br>| *P* | *PP* | *Pp* |<br>| *p* | *Pp* | *pp* | |
| Offspring phenotype | Normal — 25% *PP*, 50% *Pp*, 75% Total     Phenylketonuria — 25% Total |

## Double-Factor Crosses

Up to this point, we have worked only with single-factor crosses. Now we will consider how to handle genetics problems that involve following two distinct characteristics—double-factor crosses. In solving double-factor crosses, it is important to consider the principle Mendel identified as the *Law of Independent Assortment*. The **Law of Independent Assortment** states that alleles of one characteristic separate independently of the alleles of another. *This law is applied only when working with two genes for different characteristics that are on different chromosomes.* This is an important distinction, because genes that are positioned near each other on a chromosome tend to stay together during meiosis and therefore tend to be inherited together. If genes are inherited together, they are not assorting in a random manner. Their assortment is not independent of each other.

In genetics problems, the process of predicting the sex cells that can be produced in double-factor crosses is affected by independent assortment. The following example illustrates how independent assortment works. Recall that if an individual has the genotype *Aa*, we predict that 50% of his or her reproductive cells have the *A* allele and 50% have the *a* allele. This is an application of the Law of Segregation. If an individual has the genotype *Bb*, we can make a similar prediction with regard to the *B* and *b* alleles. What happens when we want to look simultaneously at both sets of alleles when the "A" characteristic is on a different chromosome from the "B" characteristic? What are the possible sex cells that could be produced for an individual that is *AaBb*?

In order to answer this question, we have to apply both the Law of Segregation *and* the Law of Independent Assortment. For now, we will assume that the two genes are on different chromosomes. As mentioned earlier, the law of segregation predicts that 50% of the gametes will have *A* and 50% will have *a*. Likewise 50% of the gametes will have *B* and 50% *b*. The Law of Independent Assortment says that, if a gamete receives an *A* allele, it has an equal chance of also receiving a *B* allele or a *b* allele. Thus, the sex cells that are predicted are *AB*, *Ab*, *aB*, and *ab*. Notice that

- every sex cell has either an *A* or an *a* but not both. Every sex cell has either a *B* or a *b* but not both. This means that all the sex cells have 1 and only 1 of the 2 alleles for each characteristic.
- each allele is found in 50% of the sex cells.
- the alleles for one characteristic are inherited independently from the other.

You can check to see if you have made correct choices by making sure that only one allele for each characteristic is present in a sex cell. Note that sex cells with allele combinations such as *AA* or *AaB* are incorrect. Both of these incorrect examples have more than 1 allele for a gene. The first example (*AA*) should have only a single *A* and is missing a copy of the *B* gene altogether. The second example (*AaB*) should have either the *A* or the *a* allele, but not both.

## Problem Type: Double-Factor Cross

**CROSS 3:** In humans, the allele for free earlobes is dominant over the allele for attached earlobes. The allele for dark hair dominates the allele for light hair. If both parents are heterozygous for earlobe shape and hair color, what types of offspring can they produce, and what is the probability for each type?

Just as in a single-factor cross, start by creating a gene key. You are working with two characteristics this time, so create a key for both. Remember that not all the information in the gene key is stated directly in the problem. From the problem, you should be able to identify that

- There are two genes—earlobe type and hair color.
- The free earlobe allele is dominant to the attached earlobe allele.
- The dark hair allele is dominant to the light hair allele.

From this information, you should be able to infer that

- Because the free earlobe allele is dominant, it can have two genotypes—*EE* and *Ee*.
- Because dark hair is dominant, it can have two genotypes—*HH* and *Hh*.

### Gene Key
Gene or Condition: earlobe type

| Allele Symbols | Possible Genotypes | Phenotype |
|---|---|---|
| *E* = free | *EE* | Free earlobes |
| | *Ee* | Free earlobes |
| *e* = attached | *ee* | Attached earlobes |

Gene or Condition: hair color

| Allele Symbols | Possible Genotypes | Phenotype |
|---|---|---|
| *H* = dark hair | *HH* | Dark hair |
| | *Hh* | Dark hair |
| *h* = light hair | *hh* | Light hair |

1. After you have the gene key complete, move on to the cross setup in table 10.4. The problem states that "both parents are heterozygous for earlobe shape and hair color." This is a description of the parents' genotypes. It means that both parents are *EeHh*. Place this information on the "Parental Genotypes" row. Although it is not necessary, you can use the gene key to determine what the parent's phenotypes are for earlobe type and hair color.

2. Determine the possible sex cells. *EeHh* individuals will have gametes that are *EH*, *Eh*, *eH*, and *eh*. This answer uses the Law of Segregation and the Law of Independent Assortment.

3. Determine the offspring genotypes using a Punnett square. Create your Punnett square so that there is one row or column for each gamete. Your Punnett square will create a 4 × 4 grid. Fill in the genotypes as shown.

4. Determine the offspring phenotypes by using the gene key and combining genotypes with similar phenotypes. In this problem, there will be four different groupings: (a) free earlobes and dark hair, (b) free earlobes and light hair, (c) attached earlobes and dark hair, and (d) attached earlobes and light hair.

5. Answer the question that was asked from the problem. The ratios are 9:3:3:1.

In cases where the alleles for each gene are completely dominant and recessive to each other and both parents are heterozygous for both characteristics, the predicted offspring ratio is 9:3:3:1. When scientists observe a 9:3:3:1 ratio, they suspect that both parents are heterozygous for both characteristics being considered.

## 10.5  CONCEPT REVIEW

13. What does it mean when geneticists use the term *independent assortment*?
14. What is a Punnett square?
15. What is the probability of each of the following sets of parents producing the given genotypes in offspring?

| Parents | Offspring |
|---|---|
| a. *AA* × *aa* | *Aa* |
| b. *Aa* × *Aa* | *Aa* |
| c. *Aa* × *Aa* | *aa* |
| d. *AaBb* × *AaBB* | *AABB* |
| e. *AaBb* × *AaBB* | *AaBb* |
| f. *AaBb* × *AaBb* | *AABB* |

16. What possible combinations of parental genotypes could produce an offspring with the genotype *Aa*?
17. In certain pea plants, the allele *T* for tallness is dominant over *t* for shortness.
    a. If a homozygous tall and homozygous short plant are crossed, what will be the phenotype and genotype of the offspring?
    b. If both individuals are heterozygous, what will be the phenotypic and genotypic ratios of the offspring?
18. Certain kinds of cattle have two alleles for coat color: R = red, and *r* = white. when an cow is heterozygous, it is spotted with red and white (roan). When two red alleles are present, it is red. When two white alleles are present it is white. The allele L, for lack of horns, is dominant over *l*, for presence of horns. If a bull and a cow both have the genotype *RrLl*, how many possible phenotypes of offspring can they have?

**TABLE 10.4  Solution Pathway**

| Steps in Information Flow | The Problem |
|---|---|
| Parental phenotypes | **Father × Mother**<br>Free earlobes  Free earlobes<br>Dark hair  Dark hair |
| Parental genotypes | The problem states that both parents are heterozygous for both characteristics.<br><br>$EeHh \times EeHh$ |
| Possible sex cells | Notice that the Law of Independent Assortment has been added as a skill that should be used for a double-factor cross. Both parents have the same genotypes, so they each produce the same types of gametes.<br><br>EH  EH<br>Eh  Eh<br>eH  eH<br>eh  eh |
| Offspring genotype | Set up a Punnett square to show the possible fertilization events.<br><br><table><tr><td></td><td>EH</td><td>Eh</td><td>eH</td><td>eh</td></tr><tr><td>EH</td><td>EEHH</td><td>EEHh</td><td>EeHH</td><td>EeHh</td></tr><tr><td>Eh</td><td>EEHh</td><td>EEhh</td><td>EeHh</td><td>Eehh</td></tr><tr><td>eH</td><td>EeHH</td><td>EeHh</td><td>eeHH</td><td>eeHh</td></tr><tr><td>eh</td><td>EeHh</td><td>Eehh</td><td>eeHh</td><td>eehh</td></tr></table> |
| Offspring phenotype | Count up the different genotypes and then combine them by similar phenotype using the information in the Gene Key. The Punnett square is 4 × 4, so each box counts for 1/16 of the possible offspring.<br><br>**Free Earlobes and Dark Hair**<br>1/16—EEHH<br>2/16—EEHh<br>2/16—EeHH<br>4/16—EeHh<br>9/16<br><br>**Free Earlobes and Light Hair**<br>1/16—EEhh<br>2/16—Eehh<br>3/16<br><br>**Attached Earlobes and Dark Hair**<br>1/16—eeHH<br>2/16—eeHh<br>3/16<br><br>**Attached Earlobes and Light Hair**<br>1/16—eehh<br>1/16 |

## 10.6 Modified Mendelian Patterns

Mendel's principles are most clearly observed under very select conditions in which alleles have consistent dominant/recessive interactions. So far, we have considered only a few straightforward cases. Most, however, may not fit these fundamental patterns. This section discusses several common inheritance patterns that do not fit the patterns that are generally associated with Mendelian genetics.

### Codominance

In some inheritance situations, alleles lack total dominant and recessive relationships and are both observed phenotypically to some degree. This behavior is not consistent with

Mendel's law of dominance. This inheritance pattern is called *codominance*. In **codominance**, the phenotype of both alleles is expressed in the heterozygous condition. Consequently, a person with the heterozygous genotype can have a phenotype very different from either of his or her homozygous parents. In problems involving codominant alleles, all capital symbols are used, and superscripts are added to represent the different alleles. The capital letters call attention to the fact that each allele can be detected phenotypically to some degree, even when in the presence of an alternative allele. For example, the coat colors (C) of shorthorn cattle are phenotypically red ($C^R C^R$), roan ($C^R C^W$), and white ($C^W C^W$). The roan coat is composed of individual hairs, which are either red or white. Together, they create the intermediate effect of roan.

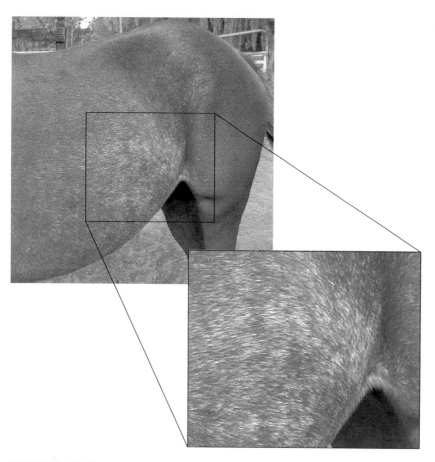

**FIGURE 10.5 Codominance**
The color of this breed of horse, an Arab, also displays the color called roan. Notice that there are places on the body where both white and red hairs are displayed.

Roan coat color can be seen in several other species, including horses (figure 10.5).

Another example of codominance occurs in certain horses. A pair of codominant alleles ($D^R$ and $D^W$) is known to be involved in the inheritance of these coat colors. Genotypes homozygous ($D^R D^R$) for the $D^R$ allele are chestnut-colored (reddish); heterozygous genotypes ($D^R D^W$) are palomino-colored (golden color with lighter mane and tail). Genotypes homozygous ($D^W D^W$) for the $D^W$ allele are almost white and called cremello.

## Incomplete Dominance

In **incomplete dominance,** the phenotype of a heterozygote is intermediate between the two homozygotes on a phenotypic gradient; that is, the phenotypes appear to be "blended" in heterozygotes. A classic example of incomplete dominance in plants is the color of the petals of snapdragons. There are 2 alleles for the color of these flowers. Because neither allele is recessive, we cannot use the traditional capital and lowercase letters as symbols for these alleles. Instead, the allele for white petals is the symbol $F^W$, and the one for red petals is $F^R$ (figure 10.6).

There are three possible combinations of these 2 alleles:

| Genotype | Phenotype |
|----------|-----------|
| $F^W F^W$ | White flower |
| $F^R F^R$ | Red flower |
| $F^R F^W$ | Pink flower |

(a) $F^R F^R$    (b) $F^W F^W$    (c) $F^W F^R$

**FIGURE 10.6 Incomplete Dominance**
The colors of these snapdragons are determined by two alleles for petal color, $F^W$ and $F^R$. There are three phenotypes because of the way in which the alleles interact with one another: *(a)* red, *(b)* white, and *(c)* pink. In the heterozygous condition, neither of the alleles dominates the other.

## TABLE 10.5 Solution Pathway

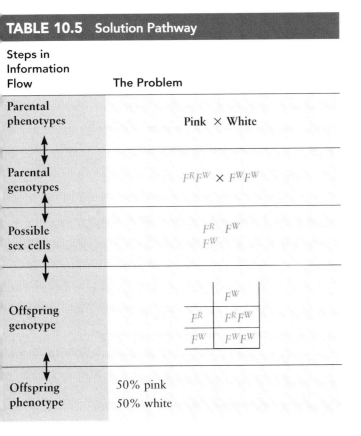

| Steps in Information Flow | The Problem |
|---|---|
| Parental phenotypes | Pink × White |
| Parental genotypes | $F^R F^W \times F^W F^W$ |
| Possible sex cells | $F^R$  $F^W$<br>$F^W$ |
| Offspring genotype | (Punnett square: top $F^W$; left $F^R$ → $F^R F^W$; left $F^W$ → $F^W F^W$) |
| Offspring phenotype | 50% pink<br>50% white |

Notice that there are only 2 different alleles, red and white, but there are three phenotypes—red, white, and pink. Both the red-flower allele and the white-flower allele partially express themselves when both are present, and this results in pink. The gene products of the 2 alleles interact to produce a blended result.

## Problem Type: Incomplete Dominance

CROSS 4: *If a pink snapdragon is crossed with a white snapdragon, what phenotypes can result, and what is the probability of each phenotype? Notice that the same principles used in earlier genetics problems still apply. Only the interpretation process between genotypes and phenotypes in the gene key is altered. (Table 10.5)*

### Gene Key
Gene: flower color

| Allele Symbols | Possible Genotypes | Phenotype |
|---|---|---|
| $F^W$ = White flowers | $F^W F^W$ | White |
| $F^R$ = Red flowers | $F^R F^R$ | Red |
| | $F^W F^R$ | Pink |

This cross results in two different phenotypes—pink and white. No red flowers can result, because this would require

that both parents be able to contribute at least 1 red allele. The white flowers are homozygous for white, and the pink flowers are heterozygous.

## Multiple Alleles

So far, we have discussed only traits that are determined by only 2 alleles: for example, *A, a.* However, there can be more than 2 different alleles for a single trait. The term **multiple alleles** refers to situations in which there are more than 2 possible alleles that control a particular trait. However, an organism still can have only a maximum of 2 of the alleles for the characteristic because diploid organisms have only 2 copies of each gene. A good example of a characteristic that is determined by multiple alleles is the ABO blood type. There are 3 alleles for blood type:

*Alleles**

$I^A$ = blood has type A antigens on red blood cell surface
$I^B$ = blood has type B antigens on red blood cell surface
$i$ = blood type O has neither type A nor type B antigens on red blood cell surface

In the ABO system, A and B show *codominance* when they are together in an individual, but both alleles are dominant over the O allele. These 3 alleles can be combined as pairs in six ways, resulting in four phenotypes. Review the gene key and the following problem to further explore the genetics of blood type.

## Problem Type: Multiple Alleles

CROSS 5: One aspect of blood type is determined by 3 alleles—A, B, and O. Allele A and allele B are codominant. Allele A and allele B are both dominant to allele O. A male heterozygous with blood type A and a female heterozygous with blood type B have a child. What are the possible phenotypes of their offspring?

### Gene Key
Gene: blood type

| Allele Symbols | Possible Genotypes | Phenotype |
|---|---|---|
| $i$ = Type O | $ii$ | Type O |
| $I^A$ = Type A | $I^A I^A$ | Type A |
| | $I^A i$ | Type A |
| $I^B$ = Type B | $I^B I^B$ | Type B |
| | $I^B i$ | Type B |
| | $I^A I^B$ | Type AB |

The solution for this problem is shown in Table 10.6.

*The symbols, *I* and *i* stand for the technical term referring to the antigenic carbohydrates attached to red blood cells, the immunogens. These alleles are located on human chromosome 9. The ABO blood system is not the only system used to type blood. Others include the Rh, MNS, and Xg systems.

## TABLE 10.6  Solution Pathway

| Steps in Information Flow | The Problem |
|---|---|
| Parental phenotypes ↕ | Type A × Type B |
| Parental genotypes ↕ | $I^A i \times I^B i$ |
| Possible sex cells ↕ | $I^A$  $I^B$<br>$i$  $i$ |
| Offspring genotype ↕ | <table><tr><td></td><td>$I^B$</td><td>$i$</td></tr><tr><td>$I^A$</td><td>$I^A I^B$</td><td>$I^A i$</td></tr><tr><td>$i$</td><td>$I^B i$</td><td>$i i$</td></tr></table> |
| Offspring phenotype | 25% Type AB ($I^A I^B$)<br>25% Type A ($I^A i$)<br>25% Type B ($I^B i$)<br>25% Type O ($ii$) |

## Polygenic Inheritance

Thus far, we have considered phenotypic characteristics that are determined by single genes. However, some characteristics are determined by the interaction of several genes. This is called *polygenic inheritance*. In **polygenic inheritance**, a number of different pairs of alleles combine their efforts to determine a characteristic. Skin color in humans is a good example of this inheritance pattern. According to some experts, genes for skin color are located at a minimum of three chromosomal locations or loci. At each of these loci, the allele for dark skin is dominant over the allele for light skin. Therefore, a wide variety of skin colors is possible, depending on how many dark-skin alleles are present (figure 10.7). The number of total dark-skin alleles (capital *D* in figure 10.7) from all three genes determines skin color.

Polygenic inheritance is common with characteristics that show great variety within the population. Some obvious polygenic traits in humans are height, skin color, eye color, and intelligence. The many levels of height, skin color, eye color, and intelligence makes it difficult to separate individuals into meaningful categories. There is an entire range of expression for polygenic characteristics. For example, height in humans ranges from tall to short, with many intermediate heights. Eye color varies in some populations from deep brown to the lightest blue. Although it is still unclear how many genes are involved in determining these characteristics, at least two or three different genes have been identified. (Outlooks 10.1).

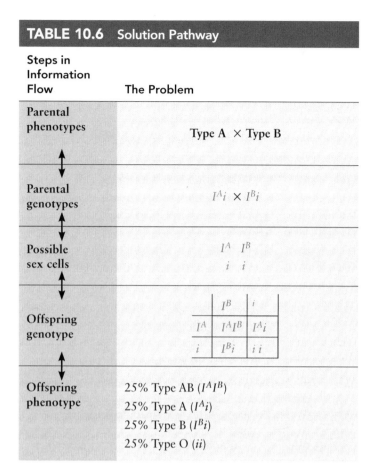

| | | | | | | | |
|---|---|---|---|---|---|---|---|
| Gene 1 | $d^1 d^1$ | $d^1 D^1$ | $d^1 D^1$ | $D^1 D^1$ | $D^1 d^1$ | $D^1 d^1$ | $D^1 D^1$ |
| Gene 2 | $d^2 d^2$ | $d^2 d^2$ | $d^2 D^2$ | $D^2 d^2$ | $D^2 d^2$ | $D^2 D^2$ | $D^2 D^2$ |
| Gene 3 | $d^3 d^3$ | $d^3 d^3$ | $d^3 d^3$ | $d^3 d^3$ | $D^3 D^3$ | $D^3 D^3$ | $D^3 D^3$ |
| Total number of dark-skin genes | 0<br>Very light | 1 | 2 | 3<br>Medium | 4 | 5 | 6<br>Very dark |
| # of light "d" alleles | 6 | 5 | 4 | 3 | 2 | 1 | 0 |
| # of dark "D" alleles | 0 | 1 | 2 | 3 | 4 | 5 | 6 |

**FIGURE 10.7 Polygenic Inheritance**

Skin color in humans is an example of polygenic inheritance. There are several different genes for skin color located on different chromosomes, each with dark and light alleles. The total number of dark *D* alleles present have an additive effect on skin color. The top portion of the figure shows examples of genotypes that can produce the different skin colors. The number of dark *D* alleles is more important than how the *D* alleles are distributed in the different genes.

# OUTLOOKS 10.1

## The Inheritance of Eye Color

It is commonly thought that eye color is inherited in a simple dominant/recessive manner, in which brown eyes are considered dominant over blue eyes. However, the real pattern of inheritance is more complicated than this. Eye color is determined by the amount of a brown pigment, melanin, present in the iris of the eye. If there is a large quantity of melanin on the anterior surface of the iris, the eyes are dark. Black eyes have a greater quantity of melanin than do brown eyes.

If melanin is absent from the front surface of the iris, the eyes appear blue, not because of a blue pigment but because blue wavelengths of light are reflected from the iris. The iris appears blue for the same reason that deep bodies of water tend to appear blue. There is no blue pigment in the water, but blue wavelengths of light are returned to the eye from the water. Just as black and brown eyes are determined

by the amount of pigment present, colors such as green, gray, and hazel are produced by the various amounts of melanin in the iris. If a very small amount of brown melanin is present in the iris, the eye tends to appear green, whereas relatively large amounts of melanin produce hazel eyes. If you examine the irises of people with green or hazel eyes, you will notice that specific parts of the iris have the brown pigment.

Several genes are probably involved in determining the quantity and placement of melanin. These genes interact in such a way that a wide range of eye color is possible. Eye color is probably determined by polygenic inheritance, just as skin color and height are. Some newborn babies have blue eyes that later become brown. This is because their irises have not yet begun to produce melanin.

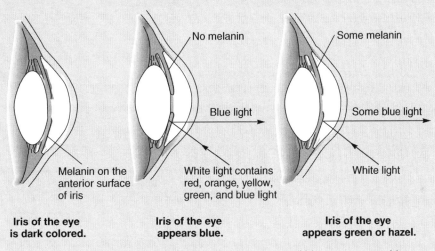

Blue eyes are due to a lack of pigment, not the presence of blue pigment. In blue eyes, blue light is reflected while other colors are absorbed. Green eyes absorb some blue light.

Polygenic traits are different from a characteristic such as blood type because blood type is determined by one gene locus; thus, there are a limited number of well-defined phenotypes (A, B, O, AB).

## Pleiotropy

Even though a single gene may produce only one type of protein, it often has a variety of effects on the phenotype of a person. The term **pleiotropy** (*pleio* = changeable) describes the multiple effects a single gene has on a phenotype. A good example of pleiotropy—PKU—has already been discussed. In addition to the mental retardation phenotype, several other phenotypes are associated with PKU. Whereas mental

retardation is caused by the buildup of phenylpyruvic acid, other phenotypes are caused by a lack of tyrosine, the next product in the pathway. Tyrosine is used by the human body to create two other important molecules—growth hormone and melanin. Growth hormone is needed for normal growth, and melanin is a skin pigment. Individuals with PKU have low levels of tyrosine because of the faulty enzyme; this results in abnormal growth and unusually pale skin, in addition to the presence of phenylpyruvic acid that can cause mental retardation.

Another example of pleiotropy is *Marfan syndrome*. This syndrome is a disorder of the body's connective tissue, but it can also have effects in many other organs. (Consider the phenotypic characteristics of the individual shown in figure 10.8.

(a)

(b)

(c)

(d)

### FIGURE 10.8 Marfan Syndrome

It is estimated that about 40,000 (1 out of 10,000) people in the United States have this autosomal dominant abnormality. Notice the common lanky appearance to the body and face of *(a)* this person with Marfan syndrome and *(b)* former U.S. president Abraham Lincoln. Photos *(c)* and *(d)* illustrate their unusually long fingers.

Some feel that the former U.S. president Abraham Lincoln also had Marfan syndrome. Do you see similarities?) The symptoms of Marfan syndrome generally include the following:

**Skeletal**
- Long arms and legs, disproportionate in length to the body
- Abnormally long fingers
- Skinniness
- Curvature of the spine
- Abnormally shaped chest, chest caves in or protrudes outward

**Eye Problems**
- Nearsightedness

**Heart and Aortic Problems**
- Weak or defective heart valves
- Weak blood vessels that rupture
- Inflammation of the heart

**Lung and Breathing Problems**
- Collapsed lungs
- Long pauses in breathing during sleep (sleep apnea)

Both PKU and Marfan syndrome are examples of alleles that have many different effects in an organism. Cystic fibrosis also shows pleiotropy. Review How Science Works 10.1—what information there supports this statement?

### 10.6 CONCEPT REVIEW

19. What is the difference between the terms *dominant* and *codominant*?
20. What is the probability of a child having type AB blood if one of the parents is heterozygous for type A blood and the other is heterozygous for type B blood? What other genotypes are possible in this child?

### 10.7 Linkage

Although Mendel's insight into the nature of inheritance was extremely important, there were many aspects of inheritance that Mendel did not explain. **Linkage** is a situation in which the genes for different characteristics are inherited together more frequently than would be predicted by probability. Linkage can be explained by examining chromosomes.

### Linkage Groups

Each chromosome has many genes located along its length. Mendel's inheritance patterns don't really describe the inheritance patterns of individual genes; they describe the inheritance patterns of chromosomes. Homologous chromosomes separate from each other (segregation). Non-homologous chromosomes separate from each other independently (independent assortment.) Because each chromosome has many genes on it, these genes tend to be inherited as a group. A **linkage group** is a set of genes located on the same chromosome. This means that they tend to be inherited together. The process of crossing-over, which occurs during prophase I of meiosis I, may split up these linkage groups. Crossing-over happens between homologous chromosomes donated by the mother and the father and results in a mixing of the allele combinations in gametes. This means that the child can have gene combinations not found in either parent alone. The closer two genes are to each other on a chromosome, the less likely crossing-over will occur between them and separate them.

## Autosomal Linkage

People and many other organisms have two types of chromosomes—sex chromosomes and autosomes. **Sex chromosomes** control the sex of an organism. **Autosomes** are chromosomes that are not directly involved in sex determination; they have the same kinds of genes on both members of the homologous pair of chromosomes. Of the 23 pairs of human chromosomes, 22 are autosomes. An example of autosomal linkage is found in figure 10.9. The three genes listed in this figure are on the same chromosome. If the genes sit closely enough to each other, they are likely to be inherited together.

## Sex Determination

Genes determine sexual characteristics in the same manner as other types of characteristics. In many organisms, special sex chromosomes carry sex-determining genes. Sex chromosomes are different between males and females of the same species. Autosomes carry the same genes in both sexes of a species. In humans, all other mammals, and some other organisms (e.g., fruit flies), the sex of an individual is determined by the presence of a certain chromosome combination. In mammals, the genes that determine maleness are located on a small chromosome known as the Y *chromosome*. The Y chromosome behaves as if it and another larger chromosome, known as the X *chromosome*, were homologous chromosomes. Males have one X and one Y chromosome. Females have two X chromosomes.

The sex of some animals is determined in a completely different way. In bees, for example, the females are diploid and the males are haploid. Other plants and animals have still other chromosomal mechanisms for determining their sex (Outlooks 10.2).

## Sex Linkage

**Sex linkage** occurs when genes are located on the chromosomes that determine the sex of an individual. The Y chromosome is much shorter than the X chromosome and has fewer genes for traits than found on the X chromosome (figure 10.10). Therefore, the X chromosome has many genes for which there is no matching gene on the Y chromosome. Some genes appear on both the X chromosome and Y chromosome. Other genes, however, are found only on the X chromosome or only on the Y chromosome. Females have two copies of the genes that are found only on the X chromosomes. Because males have both a Y chromosome with few genes on it and the X chromosome, many of the recessive characteristics present on the X chromosome appear more frequently in males than in females, who have two X chromosomes. Unusual sex-linked inheritance patterns occur because certain genes are found on only one of the two sex chromosomes. Genes found only on the X chromosome are said to be **X-linked genes.** Genes found only on the Y chromosome are said to be **Y-linked genes.**

Female phenotypes can be affected by the dominant and recessive allele interactions that Mendel identified. Males present a different case. Males only have one copy of the genes that are found on the X chromosome, because they have only one X chromosome. This one allele determines the male's phenotype. Some X-linked genes can result in abnormal traits, such as *color deficiency, hemophilia, brown teeth,* and at least two forms of *muscular dystrophy* (Becker's and Duchenne's).

Use the following problem as an example of how to work with X-linked genes. Notice that the same basic format is followed as in previous genetics problems. The major difference is that chromosomes are represented in this problem. Here, an X represents the X chromosome and a Y represents the Y chromosome. Genes that are linked to the X chromosome are shown as superscripts. The X and its superscript should be treated as a single allele. You have used superscripts before in a genetics problem to look at incomplete dominance and codominance.

### Problem Type: X-Linked

CROSS 6: In humans, the allele for normal color vision is dominant and the allele for color deficiency is recessive. Both alleles are X-linked. People who cannot detect the difference between certain colors, such as between red and green, are described as having "color-defective vision." A male who has normal vision mates with a female who is heterozygous for normal color vision. What type of children can they have in terms of these traits, and what is the probability for each type?

Huntington's disease

Narcolepsy

Parkinson's disease

**FIGURE 10.9 Chromosome** These are just three genes that are found on human chromosome number 4. Because all these genes are found on one chromosome or strand of DNA, they are considered to be members of one linkage group. Each chromosome represents a group of linked genes.

**Gene Key**
Gene or Condition: color vision

| Allele Symbols | Possible Genotypes | Phenotype |
|---|---|---|
| $X^B$ = normal color vision | Females ($X^B X^B$ or $X^B X^b$) | Female with normal color vision |
| $X^b$ = color-deficient vision | Males ($X^B Y$) | Male with normal color vision |
| | | |
| Y = no gene for color vision | Females ($X^b X^b$) | Female with color-defective vision |
| | Males ($X^b Y$) | Male with color-defective vision |

Note that, in solving sex-linked problems, the general process is the same as that for other genetics problems (table 10.7). The only significant difference is that the alleles are listed as superscripts to the chromosomes, so that the gender and phenotypes can be determined in the last few steps of the problem.

---

### 10.7 CONCEPT REVIEW

21. What is a linkage group?
22. Provide examples of genes that are linked.

---

### 10.8 Other Influences on Phenotype

You might assume that the dominant allele is always expressed in a heterozygous individual; however, it is not that simple. As in other areas of biology, there are exceptions. For example, the allele for six fingers (*polydactylism*) is dominant over the allele for five fingers in humans. Some people who have received the allele for six fingers have a fairly complete sixth finger; in others, it may appear as a little stub. In some cases, this dominant characteristic is not expressed or perhaps shows on only one hand. Thus, there may be variation in the degree to which an allele expresses

---

## OUTLOOKS 10.2

## The Birds and the Bees . . . and the Alligators

The determination of sex depends on the kind of organism it is. For example, in humans, the physical features that result in maleness are triggered by a gene on the Y chromosome. The lack of a Y chromosome results in a female individual. In other organisms, sex is determined by other combinations of chromosomes or environmental factors.

| Organism | Sex Determination |
|---|---|
| Mammals | Sex is chromosomally determined: XY individuals are male. |
| Birds | Sex is chromosomally determined: XY individuals are female. Rather than XY the letters WZ are used in birds. |
| Bees | Males (drones) are haploid and females (workers or queens) are diploid. |
| Certain species of alligators, turtles, and lizards | Egg incubation temperatures cause hormonal changes in the developing embryo; higher incubation temperatures cause the developing brain to shift sex in favor of the individual becoming a female. |
| Boat shell snails | Males can become females but will remain male if they mate and remain in one spot. |
| Shrimp, orchids, and some tropical fish | Males convert to females; on occasion, females convert to males, probably to maximize breeding. |
| African reed frog | Females convert to males, probably to maximize breeding. |

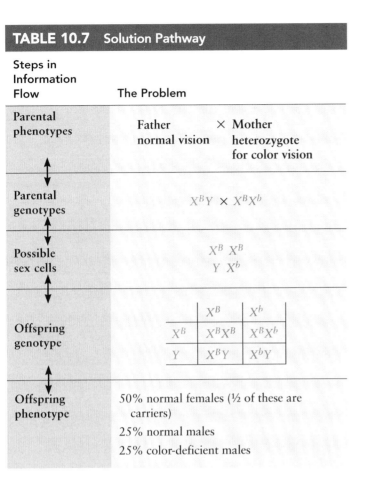

**TABLE 10.7 Solution Pathway**

| Steps in Information Flow | The Problem |
|---|---|
| Parental phenotypes | Father × Mother<br>normal vision heterozygote<br>for color vision |
| Parental genotypes | $X^B Y \times X^B X^b$ |
| Possible sex cells | $X^B\ X^B$<br>$Y\ X^b$ |
| Offspring genotype | |  | $X^B$ | $X^b$ |<br>|---|---|---|<br>| $X^B$ | $X^B X^B$ | $X^B X^b$ |<br>| $Y$ | $X^B Y$ | $X^b Y$ | |
| Offspring phenotype | 50% normal females (½ of these are carriers)<br>25% normal males<br>25% color-deficient males |

itself *in an individual*. Geneticists refer to this as *variable expressivity*.

Both internal and external environmental factors can influence the expression of genes. A characteristic whose expression is influenced by internal gene-regulating mechanisms is that of male-pattern baldness (figure 10.11). In males with a genetic disposition to balding, the enzyme 5-alpha-reductase is produced in high levels. 5-alpha-reductase uses testosterone in males to produce dihydrotestosterone (DHT). DHT slows down blood supply to the hair follicle and causes baldness. In nonbalding males, 5-alpha-reductase is produced at lower levels, DHT is not produced, and baldness does not occur. The internal environment in females has lower levels of testosterone, so DHT is not produced at high levels even if the 5-alpha-reductase is expressed. Differences in the internal environment of males and females alter the phenotype. An example of external environmental factors that affect gene expression is sunlight. Genes for freckles do not show themselves fully unless a person's skin is exposed to sunlight (figure 10.12).

Diet is an external environmental factor that can influence the phenotype of an individual. *Diabetes mellitus,* a metabolic disorder in which glucose in the blood is not properly metabolized and is passed out of the body in the urine, has a genetic basis. Some people who have a family history of diabetes are thought to have inherited the trait for this disease. Evidence indicates that they can delay the onset of the disease by reducing the amount of sugar in their diet. This change in the external environment influences gene expression

**FIGURE 10.10 Sex Chromosomes**
The human X chromosome contains over 1,400 genes and over 150 million base pairs, of which approximately 95% have been determined. The human Y chromosome contains about 200 genes and about 50 million base pairs, of which approximately 50% have been determined. A number of the genes linked on these chromosomes are listed.

**FIGURE 10.11  Baldness and the Expression of Genes**
It is a common misconception that males have genes for baldness
and females do not. Male-pattern baldness is a sex-influenced trait,
in which both males and females possess alleles coding for baldness.
These genes are turned on by high levels of the hormone
testosterone. This is an example of an internal gene-regulating
mechanism.

**FIGURE 10.12  The Environment and Gene Expression**
The expression of many genes is influenced by the environment.
The allele for dark hair in the cat is sensitive to temperature and
expresses itself only in the parts of the body that stay cool. The
allele for freckles expresses itself more fully when a person is
exposed to sunlight.

in much the same way that sunlight affects the expression of
freckles in humans. Similarly, diet is known to affect how the
genes for intelligence, pigment production, and body height
are expressed. Children who are deprived of protein during
their growing years are likely to have reduced intelligence,
lighter skin, and shorter overall height than children with
adequate protein in their diet.

Whether a honeybee larva will become a worker or a
queen is largely determined by its diet. Only larvae that are
fed "royal jelly" mature into queen bees. Recent evidence
indicates that royal jelly has the epigenetic effect of decreasing the expression of the gene that controls the transformation of larvae into workers.

## 10.8  CONCEPT REVIEW

23. What type of factor can cause a dominant allele to
    not be expressed?
24. Give two examples of environmentally influenced
    genetic traits.

## Summary

Genes are units of heredity composed of specific lengths of
DNA that determine the characteristics an organism displays.
Specific genes are at specific loci on specific chromosomes.
Mendel described the general patterns of inheritance in his
Law of Dominance, his Law of Segregation, and his Law of
Independent Assortment. Punnett squares help us predict
graphically the results of a genetic cross. The phenotype displayed by an organism is determined by the alleles present
and the ways the environment influences their expression. The
alternative forms of genes for a characteristic are called
alleles. There can be many different alleles for a particular
characteristic. Diploid organisms have two alleles for each
characteristic. Organisms with two identical alleles for a characteristic are homozygous; those with different alleles are
heterozygous. Some alleles are dominant over other alleles,
which are recessive. Sometimes, two alleles do not show
dominance and recessiveness but, rather, both express themselves. Codominance and lack of dominance are examples.
Often, a gene has more than one recognizable effect on the
phenotype of the organism. This situation is called pleiotropy.
Some characteristics are polygenic and are determined by
several pairs of alleles acting together to determine one

recognizable characteristic. In humans and some other animals, males have an X chromosome with a normal number of genes and a Y chromosome with fewer genes. Although the X and Y chromosomes are not identical, they behave as a pair of homologous chromosomes. Because the Y chromosome is shorter than the X chromosome and has fewer genes, many of the recessive characteristics present on the X chromosome appear more frequently in males than in females, who have two X chromosomes. The degree of expression of many genetically determined characteristics is modified by the internal or external environment of the organism.

## Key Terms

*Use interactive flash cards, on the **Concepts in Biology**, 14/e website to help you learn the meaning of these terms.*

autosomes 219
codominance 213
dominant allele 203
double-factor cross 204
fertilization 204
genetic cross 204
genetics 202
genome 202
genotype 203
heterozygous 204
homozygous 204
incomplete dominance 214
Law of Dominance 208
Law of Independent
 Assortment 211
Law of Segregation 204
linkage 218

linkage group 219
Mendelian genetics 207
monohybrid cross 204
multiple alleles 215
offspring 202
phenotype 203
pleiotropy 217
polygenic inheritance 216
probability 205
Punnett square 204
recessive allele 203
sex chromosomes 219
sex linkage 219
single-factor cross 204
X-linked genes 219
Y-linked genes 219

## Basic Review

1. Homologous chromosomes
    a. have the same genes in the same places.
    b. are identical.
    c. have the same alleles.
    d. All of the above are correct.

2. Phenotype is the combination of alleles that an organism has, whereas genotype is its appearance. (T/F)

3. A homozygous organism
    a. has the same alleles at a locus.
    b. has the same alleles at a gene.
    c. produces gametes that all carry the same allele.
    d. All of the above are correct.

4. Segregation happens during meiosis. (T/F)

5. The sex of an organism is determined by the number of chromosomes it possesses. (T/F)

6. Genes that are found only on the X chromosome in humans most consistently illustrate
    a. pleiotropy.
    b. the concept of diploid organisms.
    c. sex-linkage.
    d. All of the above are correct.

7. Double-factor crosses
    a. follow 2 alleles for 1 gene.
    b. follow the alleles for 2 genes.
    c. look at up to 4 alleles for 1 gene.
    d. None of the above are correct.

8. Mendelian principles apply when genes are found close to each other on the same chromosome. (T/F)

9. _____ occur when there are more than 2 alleles for a given gene.

10. Dominant alleles mask _____ alleles in heterozygous organisms.

11. The place where a gene is located on a chromosome is known as its _____.

12. The term _____ describes the multiple effects a gene has on a phenotype.

13. When a heterozygote appears to be a "blend" of the two parental phenotypes, the trait is considered to be exhibiting _____.

14. In the ABO system, A and B show _____ when they are together in an individual, but both alleles are dominant over the O allele.

15. What is the probability that parents heterozygous for a trait will have a homozygous offspring?

**Answers**
1. a  2. F  3. d  4. T  5. F  6. c  7. b  8. F  9. Multiple alleles  10. recessive  11. locus  12. pleiotropy  13. incomplete dominance  14. codominance  15. 50%

## Thinking Critically

**Nature vs. Nurture**

The breeding of dogs, horses, cats, and many other domesticated animals is done with purposes in mind—that is, producing offspring that have specific body types, colors, behaviors, and athletic abilities. Cows are bred to produce more meat or milk. Many grain crops are bred to produce more grain per plant. Similarly, some people have the muscle development to be great baseball players, whereas others cannot hit the ball. Some have great mathematical skills, whereas others have a tough time adding 2 + 2. How do you think you have been genetically programmed? What are your strengths? As a parent or child, what frustrations have you experienced in teaching or learning? What are the difficulties in determining which of your traits are genetic and which are not?

# CHAPTER
# 11

# Applications of Biotechnology

## CHAPTER OUTLINE

## Thinking of Preserving Baby's Cells?

*Banking on future medical treatments—skepticism required.*

How young can you be to donate blood? Normally, a baby's umbilical cord is discarded after birth. However, blood that remains in the cord contains stem cells that can be collected and preserved in hopes that it may be useful in the future. Stem cells have the ability to develop into any of your cells. Would you like to have some of your child's embryonic stem cells preserved so that they might be used to cure illness or repair injury? If the child experiences tissue or organ problems due to damage, disease, age, or genetic defects, these preserved cells might be used to generate tissues to repair or replace the damage. It is thought that these stem cells have the potential to be cloned and used to treat such conditions as: cancer, brain injury, juvenile diabetes, renal failure and spinal cord injuries. The cost of private cord blood banking is about $2,000 for collection and $125 per year for storage.

While at first glance this sounds to be "the way to go" in assuring that your child's future health problems may be dealt with efficiently, the procedure is controversial. Even though public cord blood banking is supported by the medical community, the American Academy of Pediatrics 2007 Policy Statement on Cord Blood Banking noted that physicians should be aware of unsubstantiated claims of private cord blood banks. Other aspects of this controversy center on issues and such facts as:

✓ The likelihood of using your own stem cells is 1 in 435.
✓ The European Union Group on Ethics states the legitimacy of commercial cord blood banks for such use should be questioned because they sell a service that presently has no real therapeutic value.
✓ Cord blood cells have the same genes as the donor and cannot be used to treat genetic diseases of the donor.

• **What are stem cells?**
• **What does it mean to clone cells?**
• **Would you buy into a cord blood donation program?**

## Background Check

**Concepts you should already know to get the most out of this chapter:**
- All organisms use the same genetic code to make proteins (chapter 8)
- DNA codes for genetic information that codes for the cell's proteins (chapter 8)
- Proteins influence how the organism or the cell looks, behaves, and functions (chapter 10)

## 11.1  Why Biotechnology Works

The discovery of DNA's structure in 1953 opened the door to a new era of scientific investigation. **Biotechnology** is a collection of techniques that provide the ability to manipulate the genetic information of an organism *directly*. As a result, scientists can accomplish tasks that were not feasible just 60 years ago. The field of biotechnology has enabled scientists to produce drugs more cheaply than before; to correct genetic mutations; to create cells that are able to break down toxins and pollutants in the environment; and to develop more productive livestock and crops. Biotechnology promises more advances in the near future.

The key to understanding biotechnology is understanding the significant role that DNA plays in determining the genetic characteristics of an organism. In the cell's nucleus, chromosomes are made of DNA and histone proteins. The genetic information for the cell is the sequence of nucleotides that make up the DNA molecule. Genes are regions of the DNA's nucleotide sequence that contain the information to direct the synthesis of specific proteins. In turn, these proteins produce the characteristics of the cell and organism when the gene is expressed by transcription and translation.

$$\text{DNA in nucleus} \rightarrow \text{proteins in cells} \rightarrow \text{phenotype of organism}$$

The nearly universal connection among DNA, protein expression, and the organism's phenotype is central to biotechnology. If an organism has a unique set of phenotypes, it has a unique set of DNA sequences. The more closely related organisms are, the more similar are their DNA sequences.

### 11.1  CONCEPT REVIEW

1. Why is the word *directly* so important to the understanding of the definition of biotechnology?
2. Why can DNA in one organism be used to make the same protein in another organism?

## 11.2  Comparing DNA

It is useful to distinguish between individual organisms on the basis of their DNA. Comparisons of DNA can be accomplished in two general ways. Both rely on the fact that genetically different organisms will have different nucleotide sequences in

their DNA. The two methods are DNA fingerprinting and DNA sequencing. DNA fingerprinting looks at patterns in specific portions of the DNA of an organism. DNA sequencing looks directly at the nucleotide sequence.

Because both of these approaches have advantages and disadvantages, scientists choose between them depending on their needs. DNA fingerprinting allows for a relatively quick look at larger areas of the organism's genetic information. It is useful to distinguish between organisms—such as possible suspects in a court trial. DNA sequencing creates a very detailed look at a relatively small region of the organism's genetic information. DNA sequencing is the most detailed look that we are able to have of the organism's genetic information.

### DNA Fingerprinting

**DNA fingerprinting** is a technique that uniquely identifies individuals on the basis of short pieces of DNA. Because no two people have the same nucleotide sequences, they do not generate the same lengths of DNA fragments when their DNA is cut with enzymes. Even looking at the many pieces of DNA that are produced in this manner is too complex. Therefore, scientists don't look at all the possible fragments but, rather, focus on differences found in pieces of DNA that form repeating patterns in the DNA. By focusing on these regions with repeating nucleotide sequences, it is possible to determine whether samples from two individuals have the same number of repeating segments (Outlooks 11.1).

#### DNA Fingerprinting Techniques

In the scenario presented in Outlooks 11.1, a crime was committed and the scientists had evidence in the form of body fluids from the criminal. These body fluids contained cells with the criminal's DNA. The DNA in these cells was used as a template to produce enough DNA for analysis. The **polymerase chain reaction** (**PCR**) is a technique used to generate large quantities of DNA from small amounts (How Science Works 11.1).

Using PCR and the suspect's DNA, scientists were able to replicate regions of human DNA that are known to vary from individual to individual. This created large quantities of DNA so that DNA fingerprinting could be performed. Scientists target areas of the suspect's DNA that contains *variable number tandem repeats*. **Variable number tandem repeats** (**VNTRs**) are sequences of DNA that are repeated a variable number of times from one individual to another. For example, in a given region of DNA, one person may have a DNA sequence

# The First Use of a DNA Fingerprint in a Criminal Case

In 1988, a baker in England was the first person in the world to be convicted of a crime on the basis of DNA evidence. Colin Pitchfork's crime was the rape and murder of two girls. The first murder occurred in 1983. The initial evidence in this case consisted of the culprit's body fluids, which contained his proteins and DNA. On the basis of the proteins, the police were able to create a molecular description of the culprit. The problem was that this description matched 10% of the males in the local population, and the police were unable to identify just one person. In 1986, there was another murder that closely matched the details of the 1983 killing. Another male, Richard Buckland, was the prime suspect for the second murder. In fact, while being questioned, Buckland admitted to the most recent killing but had no knowledge of the first killing. The clues still did not point consistently to a single person.

Meanwhile, the scientists at a nearby university had been working on a new forensic technique—DNA fingerprinting.

To track down the killer, police asked local men to donate blood or saliva samples. Between 4,000 and 5,000 local men participated in the dragnet. None of the volunteers matched the culprit's DNA. Interestingly, Buckland's DNA did not match the culprit's DNA, either. He was later released because his confession was false. It wasn't until after someone reported that Colin Pitchfork had asked a friend to donate a sample for him and offered to pay several others to do the same that police arrested Pitchfork. Pitchfork's DNA matched that of the killer's.

This is a good example of how biotechnology helps the search for truth within the justice system. The additional evidence from DNA was able to provide key information to identify the culprit.

---

repeated 4 times, whereas another may have the same sequence repeated 20 times (figure 11.1).

Once enough DNA was generated through PCR, the DNA needed to be treated so that the VNTRs would be detectable. To detect the varying number of VNTRs, the replicated DNA sample is cut into smaller pieces with **restriction enzymes**. **Restriction sites** are DNA nucleotide sequences that attract restriction enzymes. When the restriction enzymes bind to a restriction site, the enzyme cuts the DNA molecule into two molecules. **Restriction fragments** are the smaller DNA fragments that are generated after the restriction

**FIGURE 11.1 Variable Number Tandem Repeats**
Variable number tandem repeats (VNTRs) are short sequences of DNA that are repeated often. The repeated sequences are attached end-to-end. This illustration shows the VNTRs for three individuals. The individual in I has 8 repeats on 1 chromosome and 12 on the homologous chromosome. They are heterozygous. The individual in II is homozygous for 12 repeats. The individual in III is heterozygous for a different number of repeats—18 and 20.

enzyme has cut the selected DNA into smaller pieces. Some of the fragments of DNA that are generated by restriction enzymes will contain the regions with VNTRs. The fragments with VNTRs will vary in size from person to person because some individuals have more repeats than others. Restriction enzymes are used to create fragments of DNA that might be different from one individual to the next.

In DNA fingerprinting, scientists look for different lengths of restriction fragments as an indicator of differences in VNTRs.

**Electrophoresis** is a technique that separates DNA fragments on the basis of size (How Science Works 11.2). The shorter DNA molecules migrate more quickly than the long molecules. As differently sized molecules are separated, a banding pattern is generated. Each band is a differently sized restriction fragment. Each person's unique DNA banding pattern is called a DNA fingerprint (figure 11.2). The process of DNA fingerprinting includes the following basic stages:

1. DNA is obtained from a source, which may be as small as one cell.
2. PCR is used to make many copies of portions of the DNA that contain VNTRs.
3. Restriction enzymes are used to cut the VNTR DNA into pieces so that the VNTRs can be detected.
4. To detect the differences in the VNTRs, the pieces are separated by electrophoresis.
5. Comparisons between patterns can be made.

## DNA Fingerprinting Applications

With DNA fingerprinting, the more similar the banding patterns are from two different samples, the more likely the two samples are from the same person. The less similar the patterns, the less likely the two samples are from the

# HOW SCIENCE WORKS 11.1

## Polymerase Chain Reaction

Polymerase chain reaction (PCR) is a laboratory procedure for copying selected segments of DNA from larger DNA molecules. With PCR, a single cell can provide enough DNA for analysis and identification. Scientists start with a sample of DNA that contains the desired DNA region. The types of samples that can be used include semen, hair, blood, bacteria, protozoa, viruses, mummified tissues, and frozen cells. Targeting specific portions of DNA for replication enables biochemists to manipulate DNA more easily. When many copies of this DNA have been produced it is easy to find, recognize, and manipulate.

PCR is a test-tube version of the cellular DNA replication process and requires similar components. The DNA from the sample specimen serves as the template for replication. Free DNA nucleotides are used to assemble new strands of DNA. DNA polymerase, which has been purified from bacteria cells, is used to catalyze the PCR reaction.

DNA primers are short stretches of single-stranded DNA, which are used to direct the DNA polymerase to replicate only certain regions of the template DNA. These primer molecules are specifically designed to flank the ends of the target region's DNA sequence and point the DNA polymerase to the region between the primers. The PCR reaction is carried out by heating the target DNA, so that the two strands of DNA fall away from each other. This process is called *denaturation*. Once the nitrogenous bases on the target sequence are exposed and the reaction cools, the primers are able to attach to the template molecule. The primers *anneal* to the template. The primers *anneal* (that is, stick or attach) to the template. The primers are able to target a particular area of DNA because the primer nucleotide sequence pairs with the template DNA sequence using the base-pairing rules.

Purified DNA polymerase is the enzyme that drives the DNA replication process. The presence of the primer, attached to the DNA template and added nucleotides, serves as the substrate for the DNA polymerase. Once added, the polymerase extends the DNA molecule from the primer down the length of the DNA. Extension continues until the polymerase falls off of the template DNA. The enzyme incorporates the new DNA nucleotides in the growing DNA strand. It stops when it reaches the other end, having produced a new copy of the target sequence.

The elegance of PCR is that it allows the exponential replication of DNA. Exponential, or logarithmic, growth is a doubling in number with each round of PCR. With just one copy of template DNA, there will be a total of two copies at the end of one replication cycle. During the second round, both copies are used as a template. At the end of the second round, there is a total of 4 copies. The number of copies of the target DNA increases very quickly. With each round of replication, the number doubles—8, 16, 32, 64. Each round of replication takes only minutes. Thirty rounds of replication in PCR can be performed within 2.5 hours. Starting with just one copy of DNA and 30 rounds of replication, it is possible to produce over half a billion copies of the desired DNA segment.

Because this technique can create useful amounts of DNA from very limited amounts, it is a very sensitive test for the presence of specific DNA sequences. Frequently, the presence of a DNA sequence indicates the presence of an infectious agent or a disease-causing condition.

**PCR Replication**

During cycle one of PCR, the template DNA is denatured, so that the two strands of DNA separate. This allows the primers to attach (anneal) to the template DNA. DNA polymerase and DNA nucleotides, which are present for the reaction, create DNA by extending from the primers. During cycle 2, the same process occurs again, but the previous round of replication has made more template available for further replication. Each subsequent cycle essentially doubles the amount of DNA.

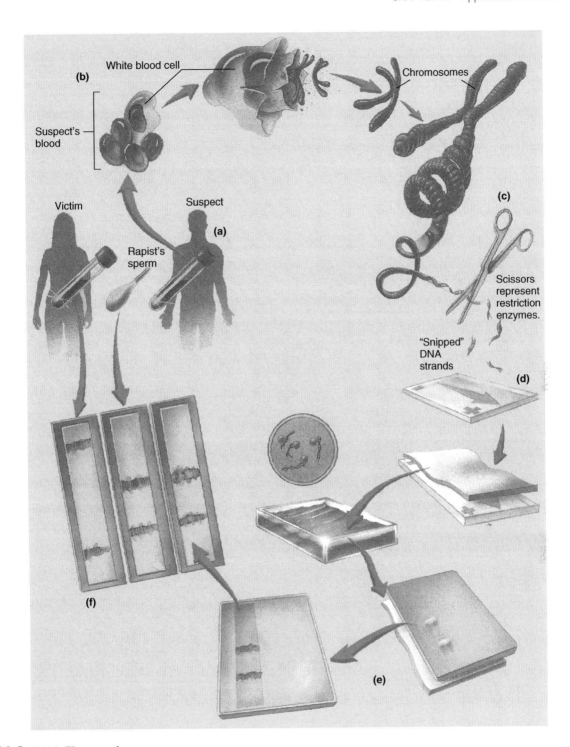

## FIGURE 11.2  DNA Fingerprints

*(a)* Because every person's DNA is unique, *(b)* when samples of an individual's DNA are collected and subjected to restriction enzymes, the cuts occur in different places and DNA fragments of different sizes result. *(c)* Restriction enzymes can cut DNA at places where specific sequences of nucleotides occur. *(d)* When the cut DNA fragments are separated by electrophoresis, *(e)* the smaller fragments migrate more quickly than the larger fragments. This produces a pattern, called a DNA fingerprint, that is unique and identifies the person who provided the DNA. *(f)* The victim's DNA is on the left. The rapist's DNA is in the middle. The suspect's DNA is on the right. The match in banding patterns between the suspect and the rapist indicates that they are the same.

# HOW SCIENCE WORKS 11.2

## Electrophoresis

Electrophoresis is a technique used to separate molecules, such as nucleic acids, proteins, or carbohydrates. Electrophoresis separates nucleic acids on the basis of size. DNA is too long for scientists to work with when taken directly from the cell. To make the DNA more manageable, scientists cut the DNA into smaller pieces. Restriction enzymes are frequently used to cut large DNA molecules into smaller pieces. After the DNA is broken into smaller pieces, electrophoresis is used to separate differently sized DNA fragments.

Electrophoresis uses an electric current to move DNA through a gel matrix. DNA has a negative charge because of the phosphates that link the nucleotides. In an electrical field, DNA migrates toward the positive pole. The speed at which DNA moves through the gel depends on the length of the DNA molecule. Longer DNA molecules move more slowly through the gel matrix than do shorter DNA molecules.

When scientists work with small areas of DNA, electrophoresis allows them to isolate specific stretches of DNA for other applications.

Mixture of DNA fragments of different sizes in solution placed at the top of "lanes" in the gel

Electric current applied; fragments migrate down the gel by size—smaller ones move faster (and therefore go farther) than larger ones

Completed gel

same person. In criminal cases, DNA samples from the crime site can be compared with those taken from suspects. If 100% of the banding pattern matches, it is highly probable that the suspect was at the scene of the crime and is the guilty party. The same procedure can be used to confirm a person's identity, as in cases of amnesia, murder, or accidental death.

DNA fingerprinting can be used in paternity cases that determine the biological father of a child. A child's DNA is a unique combination of both the mother's DNA and the father's DNA. The child's DNA fingerprint is unique, but all the bands in the child's DNA fingerprint should be found in either the mother's or the father's fingerprint. To

determine paternity, the child's DNA, the mother's DNA, and DNA from the man who is alleged to be the father are collected.

The DNA from all three is subjected to PCR, restriction enzymes, and electrophoresis. During analysis of the banding patterns, scientists account for the child's banding pattern by linking each DNA band to a DNA band of the mother and the presumed father. Bands that are common to both the biological mother and the child are identified and eliminated from further consideration. If all the remaining bands can be matched to the presumed father, it is extremely likely that he is the father (figure 11.3). If there are bands that do not match the presumed father's, then there are one

I **Child**

12 repeats

8 repeats

II **Mother**

12 repeats

12 repeats

III **1st possible father**

20 repeats

18 repeats

IV **2nd possible father**

18 repeats

8 repeats

(a)

I - Child
II - Mother
III - 1st possible father
IV - 2nd possible father

I  II  III  IV

20

18

12

8

(b)

**FIGURE 11.3 Paternity Determination**
*(a)* This illustration shows the VNTRs for four different individuals—a child, the mother, one possible father, and a second possible father. *(b)* Using PCR, electrophoresis, and DNA fingerprinting analysis, it is possible to identify the child's father. The mother possesses the "12" band and has passed that to her child. The mother did not give the child the child's "8" band because the mother does not have an "8" band herself. The child's "8" band must have come from the father. Of the two men under consideration, only man IV has the "8" band, so man IV is the father. Now stop for a moment and think about the principles of genetics. If man IV is the father, why doesn't the child have an "18" band?

of two conclusions: (1) The presumed father is not the child's biological father, or (2) the child has a new mutation that accounts for the unique band. This last possibility can usually be ruled out by considering multiple regions of DNA, because it is extremely unlikely that the child will have multiple new mutations.

## Gene Sequencing and the Human Genome Project

The Human Genome Project (HGP) was a 13-year effort to determine the human DNA sequence. Work began in 1990. It was first proposed in 1986 by the U.S. Department of Energy (DOE) and was cosponsored soon after by the National Institutes of Health (NIH). These agencies were the main research agencies within the U.S. government responsible for developing and planning the project. Estimates are that the United States spent over $3 billion on the Human Genome Project.

Many countries contributed both funds and labor resources to the Human Genome Project. At least 17 countries

other than the United States participated, including Australia, Brazil, Canada, China, Denmark, France, Germany, Israel, Italy, Japan, Korea, Mexico, the Netherlands, Russia, Sweden, and the United Kingdom. The Human Genome Project was one of the most ambitious projects ever undertaken in the biological sciences.

The data that these countries produced are stored in powerful computers, so that the information can be shared. To get an idea of the size of this project, consider that a human Y chromosome (one of the smallest of the human chromosomes) is composed of nearly 60 million paired nucleotides. The larger X chromosome may be composed of 150 million paired nucleotides. The entire human genome consists of 3.12 billion paired nucleotides. That is roughly the same number as all the letter characters found in about 2,000 copies of this textbook.

### Human Genome Project Techniques
Two kinds of work progressed simultaneously to determine the sequence of the human genome. First, *physical maps* were constructed by determining the location of specific "markers" and the proximity of these markers to genes. The markers were known sequences of DNA that could be located on the chromosome. This physical map was used to organize the vast amount of data produced by the second technique, which was for the labs to determine the exact order of nitrogenous bases of the DNA for each chromosome. Techniques exist for determining base sequences (How Science Works 11.3). The challenge is storing and organizing the information from these experiments, so that the data can be used.

A slightly different approach was adopted by Celera Genomics, a private U.S. corporation. Although Celera Genomics started later than the labs funded by the Department of Energy and National Institute of Health it was able to catch up and completed its sequencing at almost the same time as the government-sponsored programs by developing new techniques. Celera jumped directly to determining the DNA sequence of small pieces of DNA without the physical map. It then used computers to compare and contrast the short sequences, so that it could put them together and assemble the longer sequence. The benefit of having these two organizations as competitors was that, when they finished their research, they could compare and contrast results. Amazingly, the discrepancies between their findings were declared insignificant.

### Human Genome Project Applications
The first draft of the human genome was completed early in 2003, when the complete nucleotide sequence of all 23 pairs of human chromosomes was determined. By sequencing the human genome, it is as if we have now identified all the words in the human gene "dictionary." Continued analysis will provide the definitions for these words—what these words tell the cell to do.

The information provided by the human genome project is extremely useful in diagnosing diseases and providing genetic counseling to those considering having children. This

# HOW SCIENCE WORKS 11.3

## DNA Sequencing

DNA sequencing uses electrophoresis to separate DNA fragments of different lengths. A DNA synthesis reaction is set up that includes DNA from the region being investigated. The reaction also includes (1) DNA polymerase, (2) a specific DNA primer, (3) all DNA nucleotides (G, A, T, and C), and (4) a small amount of 4 kinds of chemically altered DNA nucleotides. DNA polymerase is the enzyme that synthesizes DNA in cells by using DNA nucleotides as a substrate. The DNA primer gives the DNA polymerase a single place to start the DNA synthesis reaction. All of these components work together to allow DNA synthesis in a manner very similar to cellular DNA replication.

The DNA sequencing process also adds nucleotides that have been chemically altered in two ways: (1) The altered nucleotides are called dideoxyribonucleosides because they contain a dideoxyribose sugar rather than the normal deoxyribose. Dideoxyribose has one less oxygen in its structure than deoxyribose. (2) The four kinds of dideoxyribonucleotides (A, T, G, C) are each labeled with a different flourescent dye so that each of the four nucleotides is colored differently. During DNA sequencing, the DNA polymerase randomly incorporates either a normal DNA nucleotide or a dideoxyribonucleotide. When the dideoxyribonucleoside is used, two things happen: (1) No more nucleotides can be added to the DNA strand, and

(2) the DNA strand is now tagged with the fluorescent label of the dideoxynucleotide that was just incorporated.

As a group, the DNA molecules that are created by this technique have the following properties:

1. They all start at the same point, because they all started with the same primer.
2. There are copies of DNA molecules that had their replication halted at each nucleotide in the sequence of the sample DNA when a dideoxyribose nucleotide was incorporated.
3. DNA molecules of the same length (number of nucleotides) are labeled with the same color of fluorescent dye.

Electrophoresis separates this collection of molecules by size, because the shortest DNA molecules move fastest. The DNA sequence is determined by reading the color sequence from the shortest DNA molecules to the longest DNA molecules. The pattern of colors matches the order of the nucleotides in the DNA. The color pattern that is generated by the sequencing gel is the order of the nucleotides. Automated sequencing is done by using a laser beam to read the colored bands. A printout is provided as peaks of color to show the order of the nucleotides.

information can identify human genes and proteins that can be targets for drugs and new gene therapies. Once it is known where an abnormal gene is located and how it differs in base sequence from the normal DNA sequence, steps could be taken to correct the abnormality. Further defining the human genome will also result in the discovery of new families of proteins and will help explain basic physiological and cell biological processes common to many organisms. All this information will increase the breadth and depth of the understanding of basic biology.

It was originally estimated that there were between 100,000 and 140,000 genes in the human genome, because scientists were able to detect so many different proteins. DNA sequencing data indicate that there are only about 20,000 protein-coding genes—only about twice as many as in a worm or a fly. Our genes are able to generate several different proteins per gene because of alternative splicing (figure 11.4). Alternative splicing occurs much more frequently than previously expected. Knowing this information provides insights into the evolution of humans and will make future efforts to work with the genome through bioengineering much easier.

There is a concern that, as our genetic makeup becomes easier to determine, some people may attempt to use this information for profit or political power. Consider that some health insurance companies refuse to insure people with "preexisting conditions" or those at "genetic risk" for certain abnormalities. Refusing to provide coverage would save these companies the expense of future medical bills incurred by "less than perfect" people. While this might be good for insurance companies, it raises major social questions about fair and equal treatment and discrimination.

Another fear is that attempts may be made to "breed out" certain genes and people from the human population to create a "perfect race." Intentions such as these superficially appear to have good intentions, but historically they have been used by many groups to justify discrimination against groups of individuals or even to commit genocide.

## Other Genomes

While some scientists refine our understanding of the human genome, others are sequencing the genomes of other organisms. Representatives of each major grouping of organisms have been investigated, and the DNA sequence data have been made available to the general public through a centralized government website. This centralized database has made the exchange and analysis of scientific information easier than ever (table 11.1). The information gained from these studies

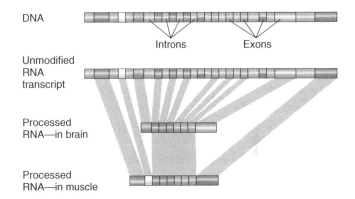

**FIGURE 11.4 Different Proteins—One Gene**
This illustration shows a stretch of DNA that contains a gene. Protein-coding regions (exons) of this gene are shown in different colors. Introns that do not code for protein and are not transcribed into RNA are shown in a single color—rust. Alternative splicing allows different tissue to use the same gene but make slightly different proteins. The gray bands show how some exons are used to form both proteins, whereas other exons are used on only one protein.

## TABLE 11.1 Completed and Current Genome Projects

The Human Genome Project has sparked major interest in nonhuman genomes. The investigation of some genomes has been very organized. Other investigations have been less directed, whereby only sequences of certain regions of interest have been reported. Regardless, information on many genomes is available at the National Center for Biotechnology Information website.

| Taxonomic Group | Genome Examples | Number of Different Genomes Represented |
|---|---|---|
| Viruses and retroviruses and bacteriphages | Herpes virus, human papillomavirus, HIV | Over 1,560 |
| Bacteria | Anthrax species, *Chlamydia* species, *Escherichia coli*, *Pseudomonas* species, *Salmonella* species | Over 200 |
| Archaea | *Halobacterium* species, *Methanococcus* species, *Pyrococcus* species, *Thermococcus* species | Over 21 |
| Protists | *Cryptosporidium* species, *Entamoeba histolytica*, *Plasmodium* species | Over 45 |
| Fungi | Yeast, *Aspergillus*, *Candida* | Over 70 |
| Plants | Thale cress (*Arabidopsis thaliana*), tomato, lotus, rice | Over 20 |
| Animals | Bee, cat, chicken, chimp, cow, dog, frog, fruit fly, mosquito, nematode, pig, rat, sea urchin, sheep, zebra fish | Over 100 |
| Cellular organelles | Mitochondria, chloroplasts | |

**FIGURE 11.5 Patterns in Protein Coding Sequences**
*(a)* Tandem clusters are identical or nearly identical repeats of one gene. *(b)* Segmental duplications are duplications of sets of genes. These may occur on the same chromosome or different chromosomes. *(c)* Multigene families are repeats of similar genes. The genes are similar because regions are conserved from gene to gene, but many regions have changed significantly.

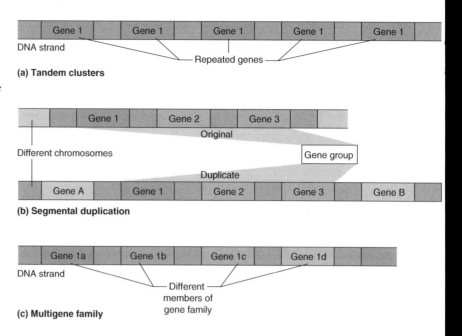

(a) **Tandem clusters**

(b) **Segmental duplication**

(c) **Multigene family**

might lead to new treatments for disease and a better understanding of evolutionary relationships.

## Patterns in Protein-Coding Sequences

As scientists sequenced the human genome and compared it with other genomes, certain patterns became apparent.

**Tandem clusters** are grouped copies of the same gene that are found on the same chromosome (figure 11.5). For example, the DNA that codes for ribosomal RNA is present in many copies in the human genome. From an evolutionary perspective, the advantage to the cell is the ability to create large amounts of gene product quickly from the genes found in tandem clusters.

**Segmental duplications** are groups of genes that are copied from 1 chromosome and moved as a set to another chromosome. These types of gene duplications allow for genetic backups of information. If either copy is mutated, the remaining copy can still provide the necessary gene product sufficient for the organism to live. Because the function of the mutated copy of the gene is being carried out by the normal gene, the mutated copy may take on new function if it accumulates additional mutations. This can allow evolution to occur more quickly (figure 11.5b).

**Multigene families** are groups of different genes that are closely related. When members of multigene families are closely inspected, it is clear that certain regions of the genes carry similar nucleotide sequences. Hemoglobin is a member of the globin gene family. There are several different hemoglobin genes in the human genome. Evolutionary patterns can be tracked at the molecular level by examining gene families across species. The portions of genes that show very little change across many species represent portions of the protein that are important for function. Scientists reason that regions that are important for function will be intolerant of change and stay unaltered over time. Again, using hemoglobin as an example, it is possible to compare the hemoglobin genes of different organisms to identify specific changes in the gene. Such

comparisons can lead to a better understanding of how organisms are related to each other evolutionarily (figure 11.5c).

The following are a few more interesting facts obtained by comparing genomes:

- Eukaryotic genomes are more complex than prokaryotic genomes. Eukaryotic genomes are, on average, nearly twice the size of prokaryotic genomes. Eukaryotic genomes devote more DNA to regulating gene expression. Only 1% of human DNA actually codes for protein.
- The number of genes in a genome is not a reflection of the size or complexity of an organism. Humans possess roughly 21,000 genes. Roundworms have about 26,000 genes, and rice plants possess 32,000 to 55,000 genes.
- Eukaryotes create multiple proteins from their genes because of alternative splicing. Prokaryotes do not. Nearly 25% of human DNA consists of intron sequences, which are removed during splicing. On average, each human gene makes between 4.5 and 5 different proteins because of alternative splicing.
- There are numerous, virtually identical genes found in very distantly related organisms—for example, mice, humans, and yeasts.
- Hundreds of genes found in humans and other eukaryotic organisms appear to have resulted from the transfer of genes from bacteria to eukaryotes at some point in eukaryotic evolution.
- Chimpanzees have 98–99% of the same DNA sequence as humans. All the human "races" are about 99.9% identical at the DNA level. In fact, there is virtually no scientific reason for the concept of "race," because the amount of variation *within* a race is as great as the amount of variation *between* races.
- Genes are unequally distributed between chromosomes and unequally distributed along the length of a chromosome.

## Patterns in Non-Coding Sequence

Protein-coding DNA is not the only reason for examining DNA sequences. The regions of DNA that do not code for protein are more important than once thought. Many non-coding sequences are involved with the regulation of gene expression.

A recent and more accurate map of the human genome from Britain focuses on *copy number variations*, or CNVs. These are segments in the genetic code that can be deleted or copied; most are deletions and a small number are duplications. The new map has also revealed that humans have:

1. 75 "jumping genes," or *transposable elements* (regions of the genetic code that can move from one place to another in the genome of an individual).
2. more than 250 genes that can lose one of the two copies in chromosomes and not causing any obvious consequences, and
3. 56 genes that can join together, potentially forming new genes.

## New Fields of Knowledge

The ability to make comparisons of the DNA of organisms has led to the development of three new fields in biology—*genomics*, *transcriptomics*, and *proteomics*. **Genomics** is the comparison of the genomes of different organisms to identify similarities and differences. Species relatedness and gene similarities can be determined from these studies. When the DNA sequence of a gene is known, **transcriptomics** looks at when, where, and how much mRNA is expressed from a gene. Finally, **proteomics** examines the proteins that are predicted from the DNA sequence. From these types of studies, scientists are able to identify gene families that can be used to determine how humans have evolved at a molecular level. They can also examine how genes are used in an organism throughout its body and over its life span. They can also better understand how a protein works by identifying common themes from one protein to the next.

## 11.3 The Genetic Modification of Organisms

For thousands of years, civilizations have attempted to improve the quality of their livestock and crops. Cows that produce more milk or more tender meat were valued over those that produced little milk or had tough meat. Initial attempts to develop improved agricultural stocks were limited to selective breeding programs, in which only the organisms with the desired characteristics were allowed to breed. As scientists asked more sophisticated questions about genetic systems, they developed ways to create and study mutations.

Although this approach was a very informative way to learn about the genetics of an organism, it lacked the ability to create a specific desired change. Creating mutations is a very haphazard process. However, today the results are achieved in a much more directed manner using biotechnology's ability to transfer DNA from one organism to another. **Transformation** takes place when a cell gains new genetic information from its environment. Once new DNA sequences are transferred into a host cell, the cell is genetically altered and begins to read the new DNA and produce new cell products, such as enzymes. The resulting new form of DNA is called **recombinant DNA.**

A **clone** is an exact copy of biological entities, such as genes, organisms, or cells. The term refers to the outcome, not the way the results are achieved. Many whole organisms "clone" themselves simply by how they reproduce; bacteria divide by cell division and produce two genetically identical cells. Strawberry plants clone themselves by sending out runners and establishing new plants. Many varieties of fruit trees and other plants are cloned by making cuttings of the plant and rooting the cuttings. With the development of advanced biotechnology techniques, it is now possible to clone specific genes from an organism. It is possible to put that cloned gene into the cell of an entirely different species.

## Genetically Modified Organisms

**Genetically modified (GM)** organisms contain recombinant DNA. Viruses, bacteria, fungi, plants, and animals are examples of organisms that have been engineered so that they contain genes from at least one unrelated organism.

As this highly sophisticated procedure has been refined, it has become possible to splice genes quickly and accurately from a variety of species into host bacteria or other host cells by a process called *gene cloning* (How Science Works 11.4). Genetically modified organisms are capable of expressing the protein-coding regions found on recombinant DNA. Thus, the organisms with the recombinant DNA can make products they were previously unable to make. Since they can rapidly reproduce to large numbers, industrial-sized cultures

# HOW SCIENCE WORKS 11.4

## Cloning Genes

Cloning a specific gene begins with cutting the source DNA into smaller, manageable pieces with restriction enzymes. Next, there are several basic steps that occur in the transfer of DNA from one organism to another:

1. The source DNA is cut into a usable size by using restriction enzymes.

   The source DNA is usually isolated from a large number of cells. Therefore, It consists of many copies of an organism's genome. The source DNA is cut into many small fragments with restriction enzymes. Isolating the small portion of DNA that contains the gene of interest can be difficult because the gene of interest is found on only a few of these fragments. To identify the desired fragments, scientists must search the entire collection. The search involves several steps.

2. The DNA fragments are attached to a carrier DNA molecule.

   The first step is to attach every fragment of source DNA to a carrier DNA molecule. A **vector** is the term scientists use to describe a carrier DNA molecule. Vectors usually contain special DNA sequences that facilitate attachment to the fragments of source DNA. Vectors also contain sequences that promote DNA replication and gene expression.

   A plasmid is one example of a vector that is used to carry DNA into bacterial cells. A **plasmid** is a circular piece of DNA that is found free in the cytoplasm of some bacteria. Therefore, the plasmid must be cut with a restriction enzyme, so that the plasmid DNA will have sticky ends, which can attach to the source DNA. The enzyme ligase creates the covalent bonds between the plasmid DNA and the source DNA, so that a new plasmid ring is formed with the source DNA inserted into the ring. The plasmid and its inserted source DNA is recombinant DNA. Because there are many different source DNA fragments, this process results in many different plasmids, each with a different piece of source DNA. All of these recombinant DNA plasmids constitute a **DNA library** for the entire source genome.

3. The carrier DNA molecule, with its attached source DNA, is moved into an appropriate cell for the carrier DNA. In the cell, the new DNA is replicated or expressed.

### Cutting Genomic DNA

The first step in cloning a specific gene is to cut the source DNA into smaller, manageable pieces with restriction enzymes.

### Creating Recombinant DNA

The source DNA is cut with restriction enzymes to create sticky ends. The vector DNA (orange) has compatible sticky ends, because it was cut with the same restriction enzyme. The enzyme ligase is used to bond the source DNA to the vector DNA.

## HOW SCIENCE WORKS 11.4 (*Continued*)

The second step in the cloning process is to mix the DNA library with bacterial cells that will take up the DNA molecules. Transformation occurs when a cell gains genetic information from its environment. Each transformed bacterial cell carries a different portion of the source DNA from the DNA library. These cells can be grown and isolated from one another.

The third step is to screen the DNA library contained within the many different transformed bacterial cells to find those that contain the DNA fragment of interest. Once the bacterial cells with the desired recombinant DNA are identified, the selected cells can be reproduced and, in the process, the desired DNA is cloned.

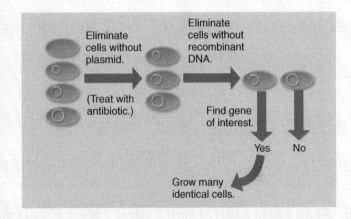

### Transformation
Bacterial cells pick up the plasmids with recombinant DNA and are transformed. Different cells pick up plasmids with different genomic DNA inserts.

### Screening the DNA Library
A number of techniques are used to eliminate cells that do not carry plasmids with attached source DNA. Once these cells are eliminated from consideration, the remaining cells are screened to find those that contain the genes of interest.

---

of bacteria can synthesize large quantities of proteins. For example, recombinant DNA procedures are responsible for the production of:

- Human insulin, used in the control of diabetes (figure 11.6)
- Nutritionally enriched "golden rice," capable of supplying poor people in less developed nations with beta-carotene, which is missing from normal rice
- Interferon, used as an antiviral agent
- Human growth hormone, used to stimulate growth in children lacking this hormone
- Somatostatin, a brain hormone implicated in growth.

The primary application of GM technology is to put herbicide-resistance or pest-resistance genes into crop plants. Edible GM crops are used mainly for animal feed. In agricultural practice, two kinds of genetically modified organisms have received particular attention. One involves the insertion of genes from a specific kind of bacterium called *Bacillus thuringiensis israeliensis* (Bti). Bti produces a protein that causes the destruction

**FIGURE 11.6 Human Insulin from Bacteria**
The gene-cloning process is used to place a copy of the human insulin gene into a bacterial cell. As the bacterial cell reproduces, the human DNA it contains is replicated along with the bacterial DNA. The insulin gene is expressed along with the bacterial genes and the colony of bacteria produces insulin. This bacteria-produced human insulin is both more effective and cheaper than previous therapies, which involved obtaining insulin from the pancreas of slaughtered animals.

(a)

(b)                                (c)

**FIGURE 11.7 Application of Genetically Modified Organisms**
Soybeans, corn, cotton, Hawaiian papaya, tomatoes, rapeseed, sugarcane, sugar beets, sweet corn, and rice are a short list of GM crops being grown and sold. *(a)* One of the most important applications of this technology involves the insertion of genes that make a crop plant resistant to herbicides. Therefore, the field can be sprayed with an herbicide and kill the weeds without harming the crop plant. *(b)* Normal rice does not produce significant amounts of beta-carotene. Beta-carotene is a yellow-orange compound needed in the diet to produce vitamin A. *(c)* Genetically modified "golden rice" can provide beta-carotene to populations that have no other sources of this nutrient.

of the lining of the gut of insects that eat it. It is a natural insecticide. To date, the gene has been inserted into the genetic makeup of several crop plants, including corn. In field tests, the genetically engineered corn was protected against some of its insect pests, but there was some concern that pollen grains from the corn might be blown to neighboring areas and affect nontarget insect populations. In particular, a study of monarch butterflies indicated that populations of butterflies adjacent to fields of this genetically engineered corn were negatively affected. One could argue that since the use of Bti corn results in less spraying of insecticides in cornfields, this is just a trade-off.

A second kind of genetically engineered plant involves inserting a gene for herbicide resistance into the genome of certain crop plants (figure 11.7a). The value of this to farmers is significant. For example, a farmer could plant cotton with very little preparation of the field to rid it of weeds. When both the cotton and the weeds begin to grow, the field could be sprayed with a specific herbicide that would kill the weeds but not harm the herbicide-resistant cotton. This has been field-tested and it works. Critics have warned that the genes possibly could escape from the crop plants and become part of the genome of the weeds that we are trying to control, thus creating "super-weeds."

Many more products have been manufactured using these methods. Genetically modified cells are not only used as factories to produce chemicals but also for their ability to break down many toxic chemicals. **Bioremediation** is the use of living organisms to remove toxic agents from the environment. There has been great success in using genetically modified bacteria to clean up oil spills and toxic waste dumps.

## Genetically Modified Foods

Although some chemicals have been produced in small amounts from genetically engineered microorganisms, crops such as turnips, rice, soybeans, potatoes, cotton, corn, and tobacco can generate tens or hundreds of kilograms of specialty chemicals per year. Such crops have the potential of supplying the essential amino acids, fatty acids, and other nutrients now lacking in the diets of people in underdeveloped and developing nations. Researchers have also shown, for example, that turnips can produce interferon (an antiviral agent), tobacco can create antibodies to fight human disease, oilseed rape plants can serve as a source of human brain hormones, and potatoes can synthesize human serum albumin that is indistinguishable from the genuine human blood protein (figure 11.7b and c).

Many GM crops also have increased nutritional value yet can be cultivated using traditional methods. There are many concerns regarding the development, growth, and use of GM foods. Although genetically modified foods are made of the same building blocks as any other type of food, the public is generally wary. Countries have refused entire shipments of GM foods that were targeted for hunger relief. However, we may eventually come to a point where we can no longer choose to avoid GM foods. As the world human population continues to grow, GM foods may be an important part of meeting the human population's need for food. The following are some of the questions being raised about genetically modified food:

- Is tampering with the genetic information of an organism ethical?
- Is someone or an agency monitoring these crops to determine if they are moving beyond their controlled ranges?
- What safety precautions should be exercised to avoid damaging the ecosystems in which GM crops are grown?
- What type of approval should these products require before they are sold to the public?
- Is it necessary to label these foods as genetically modified?

## Gene Therapy

The field of biotechnology allows scientists and medical doctors to work together and potentially cure genetic disorders. Unlike contagious diseases, genetic diseases cannot be transmitted, because they are caused by a genetic predisposition for a particular disorder—not separate, disease-causing organisms, such as bacteria and viruses. **Gene therapy** involves inserting genes, deleting genes, and manipulating the action of genes in order to cure or lessen the effect of genetic diseases. These therapies are very new and experimental. While these lines of investigation create hope, many problems must be addressed before gene therapy becomes a reliable treatment for many disorders.

The strategy for treating someone with gene therapy varies, depending on the disorder. When designing a gene therapy treatment, scientists have to ask exactly what the problem is. Is the mutant gene not working at all? Is it working normally but there is too little activity? Is there too much protein being made? Or is the gene acting in a unique, new manner? If there is no gene activity or too little gene activity, the scientists need to introduce a more active version of the gene. If there is too much activity or if the gene is engaging in a new activity, this excess activity must first be stopped and then the normal activity restored.

To stop a mutant gene from working, scientists must change it. This typically involves inserting a mutation into the protein-coding region of the gene or the region that is necessary to activate the gene. Scientists have used some types of viruses to do this in organisms other than humans. The difficulty in this technique is to mutate only that one gene without disturbing the other genes and creating more mutations in other genes. Developing reliable methods to accomplish this is a major focus of gene therapy. Once the mutant gene is silenced, the scientists begin the work of introducing a "good" copy of the gene. Again, there are many difficulties in this process:

- Scientists must find a way of returning the corrected DNA to the cell.
- The corrected DNA must be made a part of the cell's DNA, so that it is passed on with each cell division, it doesn't interfere with other genes, and it can be transcribed by the cell as needed (figure 11.8).
- Cells containing the corrected DNA must be reintroduced to the patient.

## The Cloning of Organisms

*Cloning* does not always refer to exchanging just a gene. Another type of cloning is the cloning of an entire organism. In this case, the goal is to create a new organism that is genetically identical to the previous organism. Cloning of multicellular organisms, such as Protists, plants, fungi and many kinds of invertebrate animals, often occur naturally during asexual reproduction and is duplicated easily in laboratories. The technique used to accomplish cloning in vertebrates is called *somatic cell nuclear transfer*. **Somatic cell nuclear transfer** removes a nucleus from a cell of the organism that will be cloned. After chemical treatment, that nucleus is placed into an egg cell that has had it original nucleus removed. The egg cell will use the new nucleus as genetic information. In successful cloning experiments with mammals, an electrical shock is used to stimulate the egg to begin to divide as if it were a normal embryo. After transferring the egg with its new nucleus into a uterus, the embryo grows normally. The resulting organism is genetically identical to the organism that donated the nucleus.

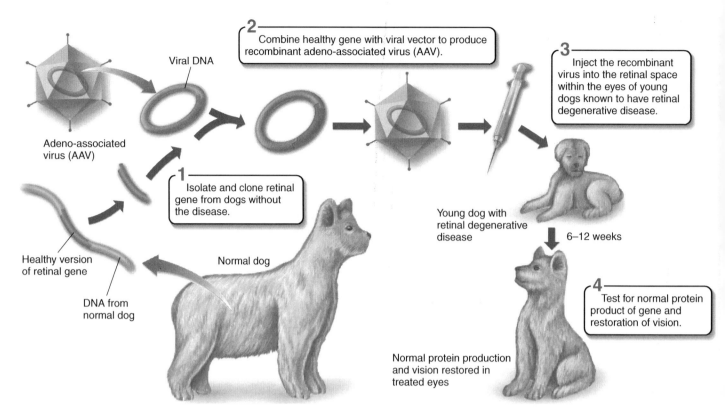

**FIGURE 11.8 Gene Therapy**
One method of introducing the correct genetic information to a cell is to use a virus as a vector. Here, a dog is treated for a degenerative disorder of the retina. The normal gene is spliced into the viral genome. The virus is then used to infect the defective retinal cells. When the virus infects the retinal cells, it carries the functional gene into the cell.

In 1996, a team of scientists from Scotland successfully carried out somatic cell nuclear transfer for the first time in sheep. The nucleus was taken from the mammary cell of an adult sheep. The embryo was transplanted into a female sheep's uterus, where it developed normally and was born (figure 11.9). This cloned offspring was named Dolly. This technique has been applied to many other animals, such as monkeys, goats, pigs, cows, mice, mules, and horses, and has been used successfully on humans. However, for ethical reasons, the human embryo was purposely created with a mutation that prevented the embryo from developing fully. The success rate of cloning animals is still very low for any animal, however; only 3–5% of the transplanted eggs develop into adults (figure 11.10).

A cloning experiment has great scientific importance, because it represents an advance in scientists' understanding of the processes of *determination* and *differentiation*. Recall that determination is the process a cell goes through to select which genes it will express. A differentiated cell has become a particular cell type because of the proteins that it expresses. Differentiation is more or less a permanent condition. The techniques that produced Dolly and other cloned animals use a differentiated cell and reverse the determination process, so that this cell is able to express all the genes necessary to create an entirely new organism. Until this point, scientists were not sure that this was possible.

## 11.3 CONCEPT REVIEW

9. A scientist can clone a gene. An organism can be a clone. How is the use of the word *clone* different in these instances? How is the use of the word *clone* the same in both uses?
10. What are some of the advantages of creating genetically modified (GM) foods? What are some of the concerns?
11. Describe how viruses are used in gene therapy.

## 11.4 Stem Cells

**Stem cells** are cells that are self-renewing and have not yet completed determination or differentiation, so they have the potential to develop into many different cell types. Scientists can generate stem cells by nuclear transfer techniques; they also occur naturally throughout the body. They are involved in many activities including tissue regeneration, wound healing, and cancer treatment.

If scientists had the ability to control differentiation it may allow the manipulation of an organism's cells or the insertion of cells into an organism to allow the regrowth of

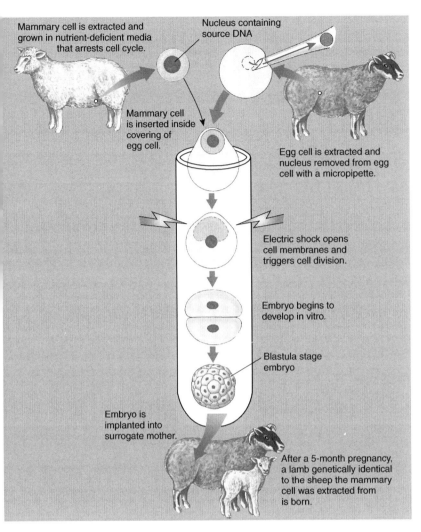

Mammary cell is extracted and grown in nutrient-deficient media that arrests cell cycle.

Nucleus containing source DNA

Mammary cell is inserted inside covering of egg cell.

Egg cell is extracted and nucleus removed from egg cell with a micropipette.

Electric shock opens cell membranes and triggers cell division.

Embryo begins to develop in vitro.

Blastula stage embryo

Embryo is implanted into surrogate mother.

After a 5-month pregnancy, a lamb genetically identical to the sheep the mammary cell was extracted from is born.

## FIGURE 11.9 Cloning an Organism

The nucleus from the donor sheep is combined with an egg from another sheep. The egg's nucleus had previously been removed. The egg, with its new nucleus, is stimulated to grow by an electrical shock. After several cell divisions, the embryo is artificially implanted in the uterus of a sheep, which will carry the developing embryo to term.

**(a) Copy Cat and her surrogate mother**

**(b) Rainbow the cat from which the nucleus to produce Copy Cat came.**

## FIGURE 11.10 Success Rate in Cloning Cats

Out of 87 implanted cloned embryos, CC (Copy Cat) is the only one to survive. This is comparable to the success rate in sheep, mice, cows, goats, and pigs. *(a)* Notice that CC is completely unlike her tabby surrogate mother. *(b)* "Rainbow" is her genetic donor, and both are female calico domestic shorthair cats.

**FIGURE 11.11 The Culturing of Embryonic Stem Cells**
After fertilization of an egg with sperm, the cell begins to divide and form a mass of cells. Each of these cells has the potential to become any cell in the embryo. Embryonic stem cells may be harvested at this point or at other points in the determination process.

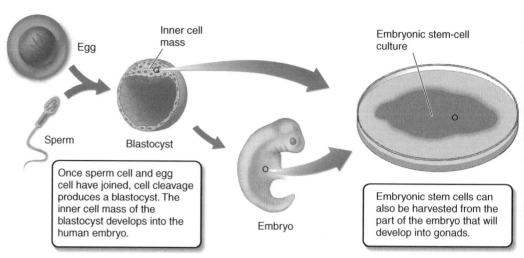

Egg

Sperm

Inner cell mass

Blastocyst

Once sperm cell and egg cell have joined, cell cleavage produces a blastocyst. The inner cell mass of the blastocyst develops into the human embryo.

Embryo

Embryonic stem-cell culture

Embryonic stem cells can also be harvested from the part of the embryo that will develop into gonads.

damaged tissues and organs in humans. This could aid in the cure or treatment of many medical problems, such as the repair of damaged knee cartilage, heart tissue from a heart attack, or damaged nerve tissue from spinal or head injuries. Some kinds of degenerative diseases occur because specific kinds of cells die or cease to function properly. Parkinson's disease results from malfunctioning brain cells, and many forms of diabetes are caused by malfunctioning cells in the pancreas. If stem cells could be used to replace these malfunctioning cells, normal function could be restored and the diseases cured.

## Embryonic and Adult Stem Cells

Because embryonic stem cells have not undergone determination and differentiation and have the ability to become *any* tissue in the body, they are of great interest to scientists. As an embryo develops, its stem cells go through the process of determination and differentiation to create all the necessary tissues. To study embryonic stem cells, scientists must remove them from embryos, destroying the embryos (figure 11.11).

Scientists have also explored other methods of obtaining stem cells. Embryonic stem cells reach an intermediary level of determination at which they are committed to becoming a particular *tissue* type, but not necessarily a particular *cell* type. An example of this intermediate determination occurs when stems cells become determined to be any one of several types of nerve cells but have not yet committed to becoming any one nerve cell. Scientists call these partially determined stem cells "tissue-specific." These types of stem cells can be found in adults. One example is hematopoietic stem cells. These cells are able to become the many different types of cells found in blood—red blood cells, white blood cells, and platelets (figure 11.12). The disadvantage of using these types of stem cells is that they have already become partially determined and do not have the potential to become every cell type.

## Personalized Stem Cell Lines

Scientists hope that eventually it will be possible to produce embryonic stem cells from somatic cells by using somatic cell nuclear transfer techniques similar to that used for cloning a sheep. This technique would involve transferring a nucleus from the patient's cell to a human egg that has had its original nucleus removed. The human egg would be allowed to grow and develop to produce embryonic stem cells. If the process of determination and differentiation can be controlled, new tissues, or even new organs, could be developed through what is termed *regenerative medicine*.

Under normal circumstances, organ transplant patients must always worry about rejecting their transplant and take strong immunosuppressant drugs to avoid organ rejection. Tissue and organs grown from customized stem cells would have the benefit of being immunologically compatible with the patient; thus, organ rejection would not be a concern (figure 11.13).

The potential therapeutic value of stem cells has resulted in the founding of many clinics around the world. These clinics offer stem cell-based therapies to patients with a variety of medical conditions. However the benefits of these therapies are as yet unproven and, it fact, have the potential for serious harm. "Stem cell tourism" is a phrase being used to describe this industry. Desperate patients travel to these clinics in hopes that such therapies will save their lives. This new industry is teeming with "medical tourist traps" offering unproven medical treatments to unsuspecting consumers. Unfortunately, the days of customized stem cells, stem cell therapies, and organ culture are still in the future.

## 11.4 CONCEPT REVIEW

12. Embryonic stem cells are found in embryos, and adult stem cells are found in adults. In what other ways are they different?
13. What benefits does stem cell research offer?
14. What are some of the concerns with research on stem cells?

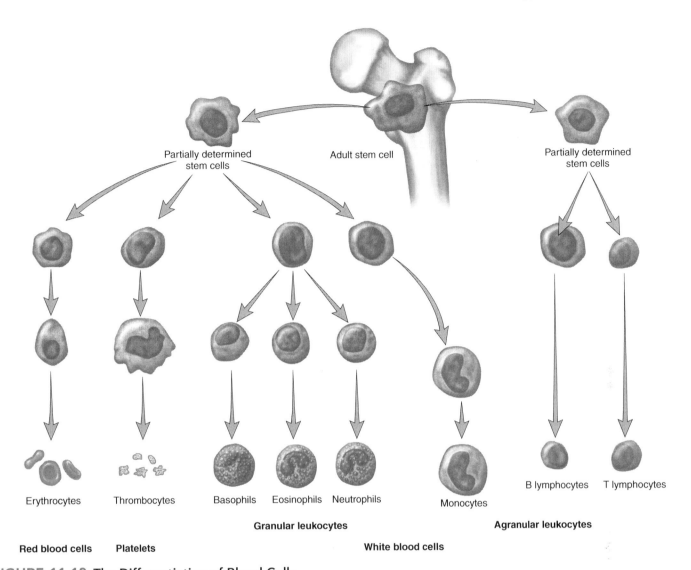

**FIGURE 11.12 The Differentiation of Blood Cells**
One type of adult stem cell gives rise to various forms of blood cells. These stem cells are found in the red bone marrow, where they divide. Some of the stem cells differentiate and change their gene expression to become a specific cell type. The differentiated blood cells are shown across the bottom of the image.

## 11.5 Biotechnology Ethics

Scientific advances frequently present society with ethical questions that must be resolved. For example, when first introduced, immunization and in vitro fertilization were highly controversial procedures. How will new technology be used safely? Who will benefit? Should the technology be used to make a profit? Biotechnology is no different.

Many feel that biotechnology is dangerous. There are concerns about contaminating the environment with organisms that are modified genetically in the lab. What would be the impact of such contamination? Biotechnology also allows scientists to examine molecularly the genetic characteristics of an individual. How will this ability to characterize individuals be used? How will it be misused? Others feel that biotechnology is akin to playing God.

## What Are the Consequences?

One way to explore the ethics of biotechnology is to weigh its pros against its cons. This method of thinking considers all the consequences and implications of biotechnology. Which outweighs the other? The benefits of nearly everything discussed in this chapter include a greater potential for better medical treatment, cures for disease, and a better understanding of the world around us. What price must we pay for these advances?

- The development of these technologies may mean that our personal genetic information becomes public record. How might this information be misused? Insurance companies might deny coverage or charge exorbitant premiums for individuals with genetic diseases.

**FIGURE 11.13 Customized Stem Cell Lines**

One potential use of biotechnology is the production of customized stem cell lines. In this application a somatic cell from a patient would be inserted into a human egg from which the nucleus has been removed. The egg would divide and generate stem cells. These cells could then be cultured and used for therapy. In this example the stem cells could be used to create pancreatic cells to treat a diabetic patient.

- Cloning technology allows the creation of genetically modified foods that increase production and are more nutritious. Is this ethical if the genetically modified organism suffers because of disorders and pain caused by the change? Are you willing to risk the potential problems of a genetically modified organism becoming part of the ecosystem? How might the introduction of genetically modified species alter ecosystems and their delicate balance?

## Is Biotechnology Inherently Wrong?

Another way to explore the ethics of biotechnology is to ask if it violates principles that are valued by society. What aspects of biotechnology threaten the principles of the Bill of Rights? Basic human rights? Religious beliefs? Quality of life issues? Animal rights issues? Which of these sets of principles should be used to help us decide if biotechnology is ethical?

- Is it inherently wrong to produce genetically modified foods? Should companies be allowed to grow genetically modified crops? Should the foods be labeled as genetically modified when sold? How does this impact you as a consumer or simply as a person?
- Is it inherently wrong to manipulate genes? Are humans wise enough to use biotechnology safely? Is this something that only God should control? Would you have your child genetically altered as a fetus to prevent a genetic disease? Would you have your child genetically altered as a fetus to enhance desirable characteristics, such as intelligence, or even to control gender? Do you feel that one situation is morally justified but the other is not?
- Is it inherently wrong to harvest embryonic stem cells? Stem cells may provide new avenues of treatment for many disorders. Although there are several sources of stem cells, the cells of most interest are embryonic stem cells. Harvesting

these cells destroys the embryo. Even if the embryo is not yet aware of its environment and does not sense pain, is it ethical to use human embryos to advance the treatment of disease?

• Are we morally obligated to search for cures and treatments? Can we stop research if people still need treatment and cures?

Clearly, these are issues that our society will debate for some time. Many of these issues have been debated for decades and bring forward very strong feelings and very different world views. As you continue to hear more about biotechnology in your day-to-day life, consider how that form of biotechnology may affect you.

## 11.5 CONCEPT REVIEW

15. Match each of the following questions to the appropriate statements.

| Ethical Principle | Statements |
| --- | --- |
| What are the consequences? | The benefits of biotechnology more than compensate for its problems. |
| Is biotechnology inherently wrong? | Regardless of the benefits of biotechnology, we should not tamper with organisms in this way. |
| Is the manipulation of an organism's genes playing God? | Religion and science do not conflict with one another. |

16. List three of the benefits of biotechnology in your life today.

## Summary

Advances in biotechnology are possible because organisms use a common genetic language to make proteins. New techniques, such as DNA fingerprinting and DNA sequencing, allow scientists to compare DNA directly. These techniques involve multiple steps, including the polymerase chain reaction, the use of restriction enzymes, and electrophoresis. One large-scale analysis was the Human Genome Project. Scientists are hopeful that the information gained from the Human Genome Project will allow the better diagnosis and treatment of many medical conditions. The genomes of many other organisms have also been characterized, resulting in the new fields of biology called genomics, transcriptomics, and proteomics. The commonality of the genetic code allows DNA from one organism to be used by a different species. The techniques used to clone a gene and to clone an entire organism differ. Cloning a gene involves a number of techniques, including screening a DNA library.

Cloning an organism involves somatic cell nuclear transfer. Stem cells have the potential to become multiple cell types. Many feel that the controlled growth of stem cells can be a medical treatment for many incurable medical conditions. The social concern surrounding biotechnology has created an ethical debate, which asks two fundamental questions:

• Do the benefits of biotechnology outweigh the problems?
• Are some aspects of biotechnology inherently wrong?

## Key Terms

*Use the interactive flash cards on the* **Concepts in Biology,** *14/e website to help you learn the meaning of these terms.*

bioremediation 239
biotechnology 226
clone 235
DNA fingerprinting 226
DNA library 236
electrophoresis 227
gene therapy 239
genetically modified (GM) 235
genomics 235
multigene families 234
plasmid 236
polymerase chain reaction (PCR) 226
proteomics 235

recombinant DNA 235
restriction enzymes 227
restriction fragments 227
restriction sites 227
segmental duplications 234
somatic cell nuclear transfer 239
stem cells 240
tandem clusters 234
transcriptomics 235
transformation 235
variable number tandem repeats (VNTRs) 226
vector 236

## Basic Review

1. Information in DNA can code for the same protein in any organism. (T/F)

2. DNA fingerprinting
   a. directly examines nucleotide sequence.
   b. examines segments of DNA, which vary in length between individuals.
   c. transfers DNA from one person to another.
   d. uses stem cells.

3. Restriction fragments
   a. are used in a technique that sequences DNA.
   b. create many copies of DNA from a small amount.
   c. are pieces of DNA cut by enzymes at specific sites.
   d. are pieces of protein cut by enzymes at specific sites.

4. A technique that separates DNA fragments of different lengths is
   a. electrophoresis.
   b. DNA sequencing.
   c. polymerase chain reaction.
   d. DNA fingerprinting.
5. The Human Genome Project
   a. was an international effort.
   b. determined the sequence of a healthy human genome.
   c. allows comparisons of the human genome with that of other organisms.
   d. All of the above are correct.
6. The term *cloning* can be applied to which of the following situations?
   a. creating an exact copy of a fragment of DNA
   b. creating a second organism that is genetically identical to the first
   c. using a restriction enzyme
   d. Both a and b are correct.
7. Which of the following terms best describes an organism that possesses a cloned fragment of DNA from another species?
   a. uncloned
   b. genetically modified (GM)
   c. differentiated
   d. genomic
8. Stem cell research is controversial because
   a. of the source of stem cells.
   b. stem cells may cure certain diseases.
   c. stem cells are not yet differentiated.
   d. stem cells are not yet determined.
9. DNA libraries are
   a. stored in computers, so that they can be easily searched.
   b. are an index of various organisms.
   c. collections of DNA fragments that represent the genome of an organism.
   d. a person's unique electrophoresis banding pattern.
10. Restriction enzymes
    a. cut DNA randomly.
    b. cut DNA at specific sequences.
    c. can create sticky ends.
    d. Both b and c are correct.
11. _____ is the process a cell goes through to select which genes it will express.

12. This procedure removes a nucleus from a cell of the organism that will be cloned.
    a. somatic cell nuclear transfer
    b. transposition
    c. cloning
    d. electrophoresis
13. Scientists have used some types of _____ to transfer genes from one cell type to another.
14. _____ DNA is DNA that has been constructed by inserting new pieces of DNA into it from another organism.
15. This field of study examines the proteins that are predicted from the DNA sequence.
    a. genomics
    b. proteomics
    c. transcriptomics
    d. restriction enzyme technology

**Answers**
1. T  2. b  3. c  4. a  5. d  6. d  7. b  8. a  9. c
10. d  11. Determination  12. a  13. viruses or plasmids
14. Recombinant  15. b

## Thinking Critically

**Crime Scene Work with DNA**
An 18-year-old college student reported that she had been raped by someone she identified as a "large, tanned white man." A student in her biology class fitting that description was said by eyewitnesses to have been, without a doubt, in the area at approximately the time of the crime. The suspect was apprehended and, on investigation, was found to look very much like someone who lived in the area and who had a previous record of criminal sexual assaults.

Samples of semen from the woman's vagina were taken during a physical exam after the rape. Cells were also taken from the suspect.

He was brought to trial but was found to be innocent of the crime based on evidence from the criminal investigations laboratory. His alibi—that he had been working alone on a research project in the biology lab—held up. Without PCR genetic fingerprinting, the suspect would surely have been wrongly convicted, based solely on circumstantial evidence provided by the victim and the eyewitnesses.

Place yourself in the position of the expert witness from the criminal laboratory who performed the PCR genetic fingerprinting tests on the two specimens. The prosecuting attorney has just asked you to explain to the jury what led you to the conclusion that the suspect could not have been responsible for this crime. Remember, you must explain this to a jury of 12 men and women who, in all likelihood, have little or no background in the biological sciences.

# CHAPTER 12

# Diversity Within Species and Population Genetics

## Conservation—Right Down To Your Genes

*Nature saves the best and to be shared by many.*

It has been estimated that there are 10,000,000,000 different kinds of genes distributed among Earth's living organisms. However, some of these genes are responsible for controlling similar biochemical pathways among many types of organisms. Biologists say these genes are "conserved." That is, they are similar and generally show little variation. For example, genes that control fundamental biochemical processes such as cellular respiration are strongly conserved across different kinds of organisms. The aerobic cellular respiration process carried out by the bacterium *Escherichia coli* is almost the same as that performed by human beings, *Homo sapiens*, and the maple tree, *Acer saccharum*. Other genes are more specialized and unique to certain species. For example, a certain strain of cholera bacteria (*Vibrio cholerae*) contains a unique gene allowing these bacteria to better survive as human pathogens. These genes have not been conserved across species.

Species that are very common, for example, *E. coli*, usually have great genetic diversity. Genetic diversity within the species makes it highly likely that the species will be able to adapt and survive in ever-changing environments. Species with a great deal of genetic diversity are also more likely to continue to exist for longer periods. On the other hand, species with limited diversity do not have the same genetic resources to cope with a changing environment, and are threatened with extinction. Many organisms on the verge of extinction, for example, cheetahs (*Acinonyx jubatus*), are in this position. In the past, cheetahs were known to be in Asia, Europe, and Africa. However, they now exist only in a small population in sub-Saharan Africa and in an even smaller group in northern Iran.

- What is the value of genetic diversity?
- Why do some species have little genetic diversity?
- Are extinctions that humans cause a problem?

## Background Check

**Concepts you should already know to get the most out of this chapter:**
• The molecular basis of heredity (chapter 8)
• The source of genetic diversity (chapter 9)
• How meiosis, genes, and alleles are related to one another (chapter 10)
• Mendel's laws of inheritance (chapter 10)

## 12.1 Genetics in Species and Populations

Plants, animals, and other kinds of organisms exist not only as genetic individuals but also as part of a larger, interbreeding group. An understanding of two terms—*species* and *population*—is necessary, because these are interconnected. A **species** consists of all the organisms potentially capable of breeding naturally among themselves and having offspring that also interbreed successfully. As of 2009, the results of a world-wide effort (Catalogue of Life) to record all species has identified over 1,160,000 species. A **population** is a group of organisms that are potentially capable of breeding naturally and are found in a specified area at the same time.

The concept of a species accounts for individuals from *different* populations that interbreed successfully. Since biologists designate populations as the organisms found in a particular place at a particular time, most populations consist of only a portion of all the members of the species. For example, the dandelion population in a city park on the third Sunday in July is only a small portion of all dandelions on the planet. However, a population can also be all the members of a species—for example, the human population of the world in 2008 or all the current members of the endangered whooping cranes.

**Population genetics** is the study of the kinds of genes within a population, their relative numbers, and how these numbers change over time. This information is used as the basis for classifying organisms and studying evolutionary change. From the standpoint of genetics, a population consists of a large number of individuals, each with its own set of alleles. However, the populations may contain many more different alleles than any one member of the species. Any one organism has a specific genotype consisting of all the genetic information that organism has in its DNA. A diploid organism has a maximum of 2 different alleles for a gene, because it has inherited an allele from each parent. In a population, however, there may be many more than 2 alleles for a specific characteristic. In humans, there are 3 alleles for blood type (A, B, and O) within the population, but an individual can have only up to 2 of the alleles (figure 12.1).

Theoretically, all members of a population are able to exchange genetic material. Therefore, we can think of all the genetic information of all the individuals of the same group as a *gene pool*. A **gene pool** consists of all the alleles of all the individuals in a population. Because each organism is like a container of a particular set of these alleles, the gene pool contains much more genetic variation than does any one of the

**FIGURE 12.1 Genetic Diversity in Individuals and Populations**
Any individual can have only 2 alleles for a particular gene, but the population can have several alleles of that gene.

individuals. A gene pool is like a gumball machine containing red, blue, yellow, and green balls (alleles). For 25 cents and a turn of the knob, two gumballs are dispensed from the machine. Two red gumballs, a red and a blue, a yellow and a green, or any of the other possible color combination may result from any one gumball purchase.

A person buying gumballs will receive no more than 2 of the 4 possible gumball colors and only 1 of 10 possible color combinations. Similarly, individuals can have no more than 2 of the many alleles for a given gene contained within the gene pool and only 1 of several possible combinations of alleles.

**Gene Pools**

1. How do the concepts of *species* and *genetically distinct populations* differ?
2. Why is it that a population can be more genetically diverse that an individual?
3. Give an example of a gene pool containing a number of separate populations.

## 12.2   The Biological Species Concept

A species is a population of organisms that share a gene pool and are reproductively isolated from other populations. This definition of a species is often called the **biological species concept**; it involves the understanding that organisms of different species do not interchange genetic information—that is, they don't reproduce with one another. *An individual organism is not a species but, rather, is a member of a species*; some people refer to the "male" or "female" species. This is an incorrect understanding of the species concept. A correct statement would be, "the male of the species." A clear understanding of the concept of species is important as we begin to consider how genetic material is passed around within populations as sexual reproduction takes place. It will also help in considering how evolution takes place.

If we examine the chromosomes of reproducing organisms, we find that they are equivalent in number and size and usually carry very similar groups of genes. In the final analysis, the biological species concept assumes that the genetic similarity of organisms is the best way to identify a species, regardless of where or when they exist. Individuals of a species usually are not evenly distributed within a geographic region but, rather, occur in clusters as a result of barriers that restrict movement or the local availability of resources. Local populations with distinct genetic combinations may differ quite a bit from one place to another. There may be differences in the kinds of alleles and the numbers of each kind of allele in different populations of the same species. Note in figure 12.2

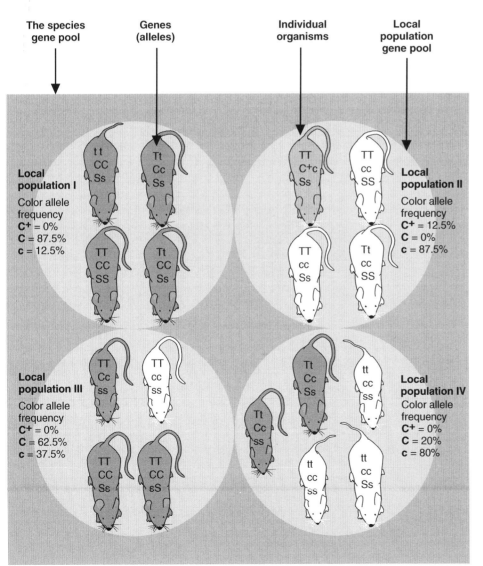

**The species gene pool**   **Genes (alleles)**   **Individual organisms**   **Local population gene pool**

**Local population I**

Color allele frequency
**C⁺** = 0%
**C** = 87.5%
**c** = 12.5%

**Local population II**

Color allele frequency
**C⁺** = 12.5%
**C** = 0%
**c** = 87.5%

**Local population III**

Color allele frequency
**C⁺** = 0%
**C** = 62.5%
**c** = 37.5%

**Local population IV**

Color allele frequency
**C⁺** = 0%
**C** = 20%
**c** = 80%

**FIGURE 12.2 Genes, Populations, and Gene Pools**
Each individual shown here has a specific combination of alleles that constitutes its genotype. The frequency of a specific allele varies from one local population to another. Each local population has a gene pool that is somewhat different from the others. Notice how differences in the frequencies of particular alleles in local populations affect the appearance of the individuals. *Assume that* $T$ = long tail; $t$ = short tail; $C^+$ = gray color; $C$ = brown color; $c$ = white color; $S$ = large size; and $s$ = small size.

that, within the gene pool of the species, there are 3 possible alleles for color ($C^+$, $C$, and $c$). However, how often these alleles appear in the population—the frequencies of these alleles—is different in the four local populations, and the difference in how often an allele occurs is reflected in the colors seen in the individuals of the population.

## Gene and Allele Frequencies

**Gene frequency** and **allele frequency** are defined as how often an allele is found in a population. In general, the term *gene frequency* is used when describing the idea that there are genetic differences between populations. The term *allele frequency* is used when specifically discussing how common a particular form of a gene (allele) is compared, with other forms. For example, the frequency of the blond hair allele is high in northern Europe but low in Africa.

Allele frequency is commonly stated in terms of a percentage or a decimal fraction (e.g., 10%, or 0.1; 50%, or 0.5). It is a mathematical statement of how frequently an allele is found in a population. It is possible for two populations of the same species to have all the same alleles, but with very different frequencies.

As an example, all humans are of the same species and, therefore, constitute one, large gene pool found on Earth. There are, however, many distinct, local populations scattered around the world. These, more localized populations show many distinguishing characteristics, which have been perpetuated from generation to generation. In Africa, alleles for dark skin, tightly curled hair, and a flat nose have very high frequencies. In Europe, the allele frequencies for light skin, straight hair, and a narrow nose are the highest (Outlooks 12.1). People in Asia tend to have moderately colored skin, straight hair, and broad noses (figure 12.3). All three of these populations have alleles for dark skin and light skin, straight hair and curly hair, narrow noses and broad noses. The three differ, however, in the frequencies of these alleles. Once a mixture of alleles is present in a population, that mixture tends to maintain itself, unless something changes the frequencies. In other words, allele frequencies do not change without reason. With the development of transportation, more people have moved from one geographic area to another, and human allele frequencies have begun to change. Ultimately, as barriers to interracial marriage (both geographic and sociological) are leveled, the human gene pool will show fewer and fewer geographically distinct populations.

People think that allele frequency has something to do with dominance and recessiveness, but this is not true. Often in a population, recessive alleles are more frequent than their dominant

counterparts. Straight hair, blue eyes, and light skin are all recessive characteristics, yet they are quite common in the populations of certain European countries. See table 12.1 for other examples. What really determines the frequency of an

### TABLE 12.1 Recessive Traits with a High Frequency of Expression

Many recessive characteristics are extremely common in some human populations. The corresponding dominant characteristic is also shown here.

| Recessive | Dominant |
|---|---|
| Light skin color | Dark skin color |
| Straight hair | Curly hair |
| Five fingers | Six fingers |
| Type O blood | Type A or B blood |
| Normal hip joints | Dislocated hip birth defect |
| Blue eyes | Brown eyes |
| Normal eyelids | Drooping eyelids |
| No tumor of the retina | Tumor of the retina |
| Normal fingers | Short fingers |
| Normal thumb | Extra joint in the thumb |
| Normal fingers | Webbed fingers |
| Ability to smell | Inability to smell |
| Normal tooth number | Extra teeth |
| Presence of molars | Absence of molars |

**FIGURE 12.3 Allele Frequency Differences Among Humans**
Different physical characteristics displayed by people from different parts of the world are an indication that allele frequencies differ as well.

# OUTLOOKS 12.1

## Your Skin Color, Gene Frequency Changes, and Natural Selection

For centuries we have classified humans into "races" based on superficial traits. One of the most obvious is skin color. Fill out any survey and you will probably find a category asking you to identify yourself according to race. Skin color is almost always what comes to mind when you decide if you are Caucasian, African-American, Hispanic, or mixed. But are there genes involved in this trait? When did humans develop different skin colors? What factors may have led to and stabilized the existence of different-colored groups of people?

Yes, skin color is regulated by your genes. In fact, several genes are involved in the polygenic inheritance of pigment production. Scientists had thought that beginning about 40,000 years ago, modern humans in Europe began to grow paler as they migrated farther north. They hypothesized that pale skin allows more sunlight to penetrate the skin. This allowed more UV light to stimulate the production of vitamin D, used in bone growth and many other essential pathways. One of the genes that apparently causes pale skin, known as SLC24A5, has been identified in many Europeans (but not in Asians). There are two forms of this gene that control the

production of proteins used for skin pigmentation. The proteins produced by these two alleles differ by only one amino acid. Almost all Africans and East Asians carry the "dark" form of the gene, whereas 98% of Europeans have the other—the "pale" gene. Careful analysis of DNA now suggests that the source of the pale gene was a mutation and that it increased in frequency in European populations more recently than previously thought, most likely between 6,000 and 12,000 years ago.

---

allele in a population is the allele's value to the organisms possessing it. Dark-skin alleles are valuable to people living under the bright sun in tropical regions. These alleles are less valuable to those living in the less intense sunlight of the cooler European countries. This idea of the value of alleles and how it affects allele frequency will be dealt with more fully when the process of natural selection is discussed in chapter 13.

## Subspecies, Breeds, Varieties, Strains, and Races

Within a population, genetic material is repackaged into new individuals from one generation to the next. Often, there is very little adding or subtracting of genetic material from a local population of organisms, and a widely distributed species consists of a number of more or less separate groups, known as **subspecies** (or **breeds, varieties, strains,** or **races**). All of these terms are used to describe distinct populations within a species. However, certain terms are used more frequently than others, depending on one's field of interest. For example, dog breeders use the term *breed*, horticulturalists use the term *variety*, microbiologists use the term *strain*, and anthropologists use the term *race* (Outlooks 12.2). The most general and most widely accepted term is *subspecies*. Look again at figure 12.2. The gene pool of the species consists of all the alleles of all individuals of the 4 separate populations. A local that shows differences from other local populations is considered a subspecies. For example, the American robin is found throughout North America from southern Canada to central Mexico (figure 12.4). Of the seven subspecies of this common thrush (*Turdus* = *thrush*),

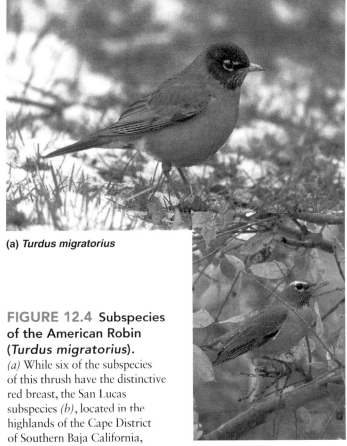

(a) *Turdus migratorius*

**FIGURE 12.4 Subspecies of the American Robin (*Turdus migratorius*).** *(a)* While six of the subspecies of this thrush have the distinctive red breast, the San Lucas subspecies *(b),* located in the highlands of the Cape District of Southern Baja California, Mexico, has an under belly that is a pale gray-brown.

(b) *Turdus migratorius confirmis*

# OUTLOOKS 12.2

## Biology, Race, and Racism

The concept of racial difference among groups of people must be approached carefully. Three distortions can occur when people use the term *race*. First, the designation of race focuses on differences, most of which are superficial. Skin color, facial features, and hair texture are examples. Although these characteristics are easy to see, they are arbitrary, and an emphasis on them tends to obscure the fact that humans are all fundamentally the same, with minor variations in the frequency of certain alleles. A second problem with the concept of race is that it is very difficult to separate genetic from cultural differences among people. People tend to equate cultural characteristics with genetic differences. Culture is learned and, therefore, is an acquired characteristic not based on the genes a person inherits. Cultures do differ, but these differences cannot be inherited and therefore used as a basis for claiming genetic distinctions. Third, a study of the human genome has revealed that there are usually more genetic differences within so-called racial groups than between them. Because of such distortions, the concept that humans can be divided into racial groups is no longer popular among scientists.

**Changing attitudes**

---

the San Lucas robin, *Turdus migratorius confinis* is found in the highlands of Baja California. It is distinct from the others in having a pale gray-brown under belly instead of the 'robin red breast.'

Most robins have alleles for red breast coloration; very few individuals have alleles for gray-brown. Since the San Lucas robins are geographically isolated from the main gene pool, they only mate with one another. Thus, the different color patterns result from a higher incidence of gray-brown color alleles in the Baja California populations and a high frequency of the red breast alleles in the other populations.

### 12.2   CONCEPT REVIEW

4. Describe the biological species concept.
5. What is meant by the terms *gene frequency* and *allele frequency*?
6. How are the terms *gene* and *allele frequency* used differently?
7. Give an example of a human characteristic that has a high frequency in Europe and a low frequency in Africa.

## 12.3   How Genetic Diversity Comes About

**Genetic diversity** is a term used to describe genetic differences among members of a population. *High genetic diversity* indicates many different kinds of alleles for each characteristic,

and *low genetic diversity* indicates that nearly all the individuals in the population have the same alleles. A large gene pool with high genetic diversity is more likely to contain some genetic combinations that will allow the organisms to adapt to a new environment; whereas low genetic diversity can have devastating consequences. A number of mechanisms introduce genetic diversity into a population.

### Mutations

*Mutations* introduce new genetic information into a population by modifying alleles that are already present. Sometimes, a mutation introduces a new allele into the gene pool of a species. At other times, a mutation may introduce an allele that was absent in a local population, although it is present in other populations of the species. All the different alleles for a trait originated as a result of mutations some time in the past and have been maintained within the gene pool of the species as they have been passed from generation to generation during reproduction. Many mutations are harmful, but very rarely one will occur that is valuable to the organism. If a mutation produces a harmful allele, the allele remains uncommon in the population. For example, the *Anopheles* mosquito is responsible for transmitting malaria in many African countries. At some point in the past, mutations occurred in the DNA of these mosquitoes that

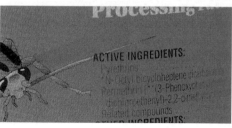

made some individuals tolerant to the insecticide Pyrethrin, even before the chemical had been used. These alleles remained very rare in these insect populations until Pyrethrin was used. Then, these alleles became very valuable to the mosquitoes that carried them. Because the mosquitoes that lacked the alleles for tolerance died when they came into contact with Pyrethrin, more of the Pyrethrin-tolerant individuals were left to reproduce the species; therefore, the Pyrethrin-tolerant alleles became much more common in these populations. Scientists have recently found up to 90% Pyrethrin resistance in *Anopheles* mosquitoes that live in several African countries.

## Sexual Reproduction

Although the process of *sexual reproduction* does not create new alleles, it tends to generate new *genetic combinations* when the genetic information from two individuals mixes

**Corn**

during fertilization, generating a unique individual. This doesn't directly change the frequency of alleles within the gene pool. However, the new member may have a unique combination of characteristics. This combination may be so superior to those of other members of the population that the new member will be much more successful in producing offspring. In a corn population, for example, there may be alleles for resistance to corn blight (a fungal disease) and to attack by insects. Corn plants that possess both of these characteristics will be more successful than corn plants that have only one of these qualities. They will probably produce more offspring (corn seeds) than the others, because they will survive both fungal and insect attacks. Thus, there will be a change in the allele frequency for these characteristics in future generations.

## Migration

The *migration* of individuals from one genetically distinct population to another is also an important way for alleles to be added to or subtracted from a local population. Whenever an organism leaves one population and enters another, it subtracts its genetic information from the population it left and adds it to the population it joins. If it contains rare alleles, it may significantly affect the allele frequency of both populations. The extent of migration need not be great; however, as long as alleles are entering or leaving a population, the gene pool will change.

Many animal populations in zoos are in danger of dying out because of severe inbreeding or line breeding (breeding with near relatives), resulting in reduced genetic diversity (figure 12.5). Often, when genetic diversity is reduced, deleterious recessive alleles in closely related mates are passed to offspring in a homozygous state, resulting in offspring that have reduced chances of survival. Most zoo managers have recognized the importance of increasing genetic diversity in their small populations of animals and have instituted programs of loaning breeding animals to distant zoos in an effort to increase genetic diversity. In effect, they are attempting to simulate the natural migration that frequently introduces new alleles from distant populations. Captive breeding program have been critical in saving many species, including Guam rails, California condors, Przewalski's horses, scimitar-horned oryx, *Partula* snails, and Spix's macaws.

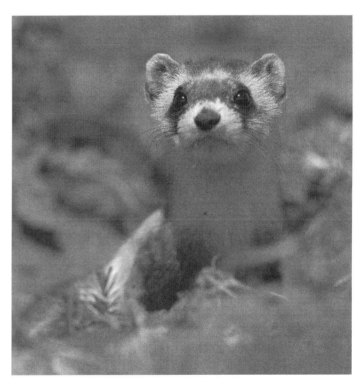

**FIGURE 12.5 Captive Breeding of the Black-Footed Ferret**
In October 1985, the Wyoming Game and Fish Department, in cooperation with the U.S. Fish & Wildlife Service, started the captive breeding program for North America's most endangered mammal, the black-footed ferret. Attention was paid to making sure that as much genetic variation was retained as possible—for example, they maintained a sperm bank of particularly valuable males. As a result, the successful return of black-footed ferrets to the plains of the American West began in 1991. The total wild population of black-footed ferrets in 2007 was over 750 individuals in the United States. Biologists hope that a new population census will show a further increase in wild black-footed ferrets. However, biologists still fear that a lack of genetic diversity may jeopardize the populations.

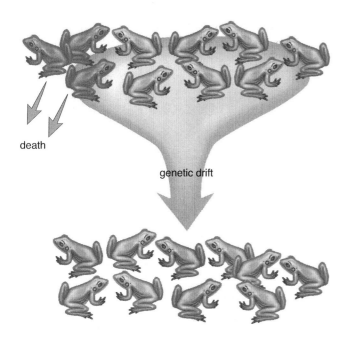

**FIGURE 12.6 Genetic Drift**
The gene pool of a small population may not have the same proportion of alleles as the previous generation. Notice that in the original population, the red frogs were eliminated and failed to breed. Therefore, their genes were not passed on to the next generation. As a result, the frequencies of the genes change in the gene pool.

## The Importance of Population Size

The *size of the population* has much to do with how effective any mechanism is at generating diversity within a gene pool. The smaller the population, the less genetic diversity it can contain. Therefore, migrations, mutations, and accidental death can have great effects on the genetic makeup of a small population. For example, if a town has a population of 20 people and only 2 have brown eyes and the rest have blue eyes, what happens to those 2 brown-eyed people is more critical than if the town has 20,000 people and 2,000 have brown eyes. Although the ratio of brown eyes to blue eyes is the same in both cases, even a small change in a population of 20 could significantly change the frequency of the brown-eye allele. Often, in small populations, random events can significantly alter the gene pool when rare alleles are lost from the population. This process is called **genetic drift** because the changes are not caused by selection (figure 12.6). This idea will be discussed in greater detail in chapter 13.

## 12.4 Why Genetically Distinct Populations Exist

Many species have wide geographic distribution with reasonably distinct subspecies. There are four reasons that these subspecies developed: adaptation to local environmental conditions, the founder effect, a genetic bottleneck, and barriers to movement.

## Adaptation to Local Environmental Conditions

Because organisms within a population are not genetically identical, some individuals may possess genetic combinations that are valuable for survival in the local environment. As a result, some individuals find the environment less hostile than do others. The individuals with unfavorable genetic combinations leave the population more often, either by death or migration, and remove their genes from the population. Therefore, local populations that occupy sites that differ greatly from conditions at other locations would be expected to consist of individuals having gene combinations suited to local conditions. For example, White Sands National Monument in New Mexico has extensive dunes of white gypsum sand. Several of the animals that live there, such as lizards and mice, have very light coloring, which allows them to blend in with their surroundings. Other populations of the same species that do not live in such a white environment do not have the light coloring.

Many kinds of animals that live in caves lack pigments and eyes, including salamanders, flatworms, shrimp, fish, beetles, and crayfish. A blind Texas salamander (*Eurycea rathbuni*) is at a severe disadvantage when venturing above ground. A blind Texas salamander living in a cave where there is no light, however, is not at the same disadvantage. Thus, these two environments might allow or encourage characteristics to be present in the two populations at different frequencies. Because it takes energy to produce eyes and pigment, individual cave-dwelling Texas blind salamanders that do not produce these characteristics may have an advantage over the individuals that continue to spend the energy to produce these features. (figure 12.7).

## The Founder Effect

The second mechanism that creates genetically distinct populations with unique allele frequencies is the founding of a new population and, so, is called the *founder effect*. The **founder effect** is a form of genetic drift, in which a genetically distinct local population is established by a few colonizing individuals carrying with them alleles that differ in frequencies from those in their original population. The collection of alleles of a small founding population is likely to be different from that present in the larger parent population from which it came. After all, a few pioneering individuals leaving a population would be unlikely to carry copies of all the alleles found within the original population.

**FIGURE 12.7 Specialized Local Populations**
Many populations of animals that live in caves where there is no light lack pigment and functional eyes. If, in the past, the genetic material that directed the production of these traits was lost or mutated, it would not have negatively affected the organism. In fact, it may have been an advantage to not spend the energy to produce such unneeded traits. Hence, in many cave populations, there is a low frequency of genes for the production of eyes and pigment. This is a Texas blind salamander, an endangered species found only in the Edwards Aquifer underneath and near the city of San Marcos, Texas.

**Genetic bottleneck**

in population size due to a chance event that results in a reduction in genetic diversity in subsequent generations. When the size of a population is greatly reduced, some alleles will probably be lost from the population. Any subsequent increase in the size of the population by reproduction among the remaining members of the population will not replace the lost genetic diversity. For example, in the late 1800s the whooping crane population was estimated to be 1300 birds (figure 12.8). Their numbers decreased because of hunting and industrial development. By 1941 there were only 22 wild whooping cranes left in North America. Today there are over 400 birds. However, their lack of genetic diversity puts them at risk of extinction. Thousands of other species are currently undergoing genetic bottlenecks.

They may even carry an unrepresentative mixture of alleles. For example, the water snake *Nerodia sepidon* is found throughout the eastern part of the United States and extends into Canada. The northern water snake subspecies is widespread in the north-central United States and adjacent Canada and is generally brown with light diamond-shaped patches. The Lake Erie water snake subspecies is limited to the islands in the western section of Lake Erie. It is generally a solid color without the lighter patches. The difference in color patterns is related to different allele frequencies for color pattern. The Lake Erie water snake may have been founded by a small number of individuals from the mainland that had a high frequency of alleles for solid coloration rather than the more typical banded pattern. (It is even possible that the island populations could have been founded by one fertilized female.) Once a small founding population establishes itself, it tends to maintain its collection of alleles, because the organisms mate only among themselves. This results in a reshuffling of alleles from generation to generation but does not introduce new genetic information into the population.

## Genetic Bottleneck

The third cause of local, genetically distinct populations relates to the history of the population. A **genetic bottleneck** is a form of genetic drift, in which there is a sharp reduction

**FIGURE 12.8 Whooping Crane**
Today, the only remaining natural, self-sustaining flock of whooping cranes is in Wood Buffalo National Park, Canada and winters in Aransas National Wildlife Refuge, Texas. This flock had only 16 birds during the winter of 1941–1942, and numbered under 35 birds for the next two decades.

Although some endangered species were always rare, most have experienced recent reductions in their populations and a reduction in their genetic diversity, which is a consequence of severely reduced population size.

## Barriers to Movement

The fourth factor that tends to encourage the maintenance of genetically distinct populations is the presence of barriers to free movement. Animals and plants that live in lakes tend to be divided into small, separate populations by barriers of land. Whenever such barriers exist, there will very likely be differences in the allele frequencies from lake to lake, because each lake was colonized separately and the lakes' environments are not identical. Other species of organisms, such as migratory birds (e.g., Canadian geese, mallard ducks), experience few barriers; therefore, subspecies are not as common.

### 12.4  CONCEPT REVIEW

10. List four processes that can lead to local, genetically distinct populations.
11. In what way are the founder effect and a genetic bottleneck similar in their effect on the genetic diversity of a local population?

### 12.5  Genetic Diversity in Domesticated Plants and Animals

Humans often work with small, select populations of plants and animals in order to artificially construct specific genetic combinations that are useful or desirable. This is true of plants and animals used for food. If we can produce domesticated animals and plants with genetic characteristics for rapid growth, high reproductive capacity, resistance to disease, and other desirable characteristics, we can supply ourselves with energy in the form of food. Several processes are used to develop such specialized populations of plants and animals. Most have the side effect of reducing genetic diversity.

## Cloning

Recall that cloning is the process of reproducing organisms asexually, so that large numbers of genetically identical individuals are produced. These individuals are called *clones*.

Plants are easy to work with in this manner, because we can often increase the numbers of specific organisms by asexual (without sex) reproduction. Potatoes, apple trees, strawberries, and many other plants can be reproduced by simply cutting the original plant into a number of parts and allowing these parts to sprout roots, stems, and leaves. If a single potato has certain desirable characteristics, it can be reproduced asexually. All of the individual potato plants reproduced asexually would be genetically identical and would show the same desired characteristics. Figure 12.9 shows how a clone can be developed.

(a)

(b)

(c)

(d)

(e)

**FIGURE 12.9  Cloning Plants from Cuttings**
All the *Peperomia* houseplants in the last figure *(e)* were produced asexually from cuttings and are identical genetically. *(a–c)* The original plant is cut into pieces. Then, *(d)* the cut ends are treated with a growth stimulant and placed in moist soil. *(e)* Eventually, the pieces root and grow into independent plants.

## TABLE 12.2  Cloned Animals

| Animal Cloned | Date First Cloned | Country Where Cloning Occurred |
|---|---|---|
| 1. Camel | 2009 | United Arab Emirates |
| 2. Carp | 1963 | China |
| 3. Cat | 2001 | United States |
| 4. Cattle | 2001 | United States |
| 5. Deer | 2003 | United States |
| 6. Dog | 2009 | South Korea |
| 7. Ferret | 2009 | United States |
| 8. Frog tadpole | 1962 | England |
| 9. Fruit fly | 2004 | Canada |
| 10. Gaur | 2001 | United States |
| 11. Goat | 2009 | Iran |
| 12. Horse | 2003 | Italy |
| 13. Mice | 1986 | Former U.S.S.R. |
| 14. Mouflon | 2001 | Italy |
| 15. Mule | 2003 | United States |
| 16. Pig | 2000 | Scotland |
| 17. Rabbit | 2003 | France |
| 18. Rat | 2003 | France |
| 19. Rhesus monkey | 2000 | United States |
| 20. Sheep | 1996 | Scotland |
| 21. Water buffalo | 2009 | China |
| 22. Wolf | 2009 | Korea |

Through selective breeding, some varieties of chickens have been developed that grow rapidly and are good for meat. Others have been developed to produce large numbers of eggs. Often, the development of new varieties of domesticated animals and plants involves the crossing of individuals from different populations. For this technique to be effective, the desirable characteristics in each of the two varieties should have homozygous genotypes. In small, controlled populations, it is relatively easy to produce individuals that are homozygous for a specific trait. To make two characteristics homozygous in the same individual is more difficult. Therefore, such varieties are usually developed by crossing two different populations to collect several desirable characteristics in one organism. **Intraspecific hybrids** are organisms that are produced by the controlled breeding of separate varieties of the same species.

Occasionally, **interspecific hybrids**—hybrids between two species—are produced as a way of introducing desirable characteristics into a domesticated organism. Because plants can

**Beefalo**

The cloning of most kinds of domesticated animals is much more difficult than the cloning of plants. Even though this is not as yet a practical method of producing animals, in recent years, many kinds of animals have been cloned (table 12.2). The process involves the substitution of a nucleus from a mature animal for the nucleus of an egg. This cell is then stimulated to develop as an embryo. There is a high rate of failure, but the goals of animal cloning are the same as those of plant cloning: the production of genetically identical individuals.

## Selective Breeding

Humans can bring together specific genetic combinations in either plants or animals by selective breeding. Because sexual reproduction tends to generate new genetic combinations rather than preserve desirable combinations, the mating of individual organisms must be controlled to obtain the desirable combination of characteristics. *Selective breeding* involves the careful selection of individuals with specific desirable characteristics and their controlled mating, with the goal of producing a population that has a high proportion of individuals with the desired characteristics.

be reproduced by cloning, it is possible to produce an interspecific hybrid and then reproduce it by cloning. For instance, the tangelo is an interspecific hybrid between a tangerine and a grapefruit. An interspecific hybrid between cattle and the American bison was used to introduce certain desirable characteristics into cattle.

## Genetic Engineering

In recent years, scientific advances in understanding DNA have allowed specific pieces of genetic material to be inserted into cells. This has greatly expanded scientists' ability to modify the characteristics of domesticated plants and animals. The primary goal of genetic engineering is to manipulate particular pieces of DNA and transfer them into specific host organisms, so that they have certain valuable characteristics. These topics were dealt with in greater detail in chapter 11.

## The Impact of Monoculture

Although some of the previously mentioned techniques have been used to introduce new genetic information into domesticated organisms, one of the goals of domestication

**FIGURE 12.10 Monoculture**

This wheat field is an example of monoculture, a kind of agriculture in which large areas are exclusively planted with a single crop with a very specific genetic makeup. Monoculture makes it possible to use large farm machinery, but it also creates conditions that can encourage the spread of disease because the plants have reduced genetic diversity.

is to produce organisms that have uniform characteristics. In order to achieve such uniformity, it is necessary to reduce genetic diversity. Agricultural plants have been extremely specialized through selective breeding to produce the qualities that growers want. Most agriculture in the world is based on extensive plantings of the same varieties of a species over large expanses of land. This agricultural practice is called **monoculture** (figure 12.10). It is certainly easier to manage fields in which only one kind of plant is growing, especially when herbicides, insecticides, and fertilizers are tailored to meet the needs of specific crop species. However, with monoculture comes a significant risk. Because these organisms are so similar, if a new disease comes along, most of them will be affected in the same way and the whole population may be killed or severely damaged.

Our primary food plants and domesticated animal species are derived from wild ancestors that had genetic combinations that allowed them to compete successfully with other organisms in their environment. When humans reduce genetic diversity by developing special populations with certain desirable characteristics, other valuable genetic information is lost from the gene pool. When we select specific, good characteristics, we often get harmful ones along with them. Therefore, these "special" plants and animals require constant attention. Insecticides, herbicides, cultivation, and irrigation are all used to aid the plants and animals we need. In effect, these plants are able to live only under conditions that people carefully maintain (figure 12.11).

Because our domesticated organisms are so genetically similar, there is a great danger that an environmental change or new disease could cause great damage to our ability to produce food. In order to protect against such disasters, gene banks have been established. Gene banks consist of populations of primitive ancestors of modern domesticated plants

**FIGURE 12.11 Cash Crops Require Constant Attention**

The photograph shows a portion of a plantation where native forest has been cleared for the planting of bananas. However, without constant attention, native rainforest plants encroach back into the bananas.

and animals (figure 12.12). By preserving these organisms, their genetic diversity is available for introduction into our domesticated plants and animals if the need arises.

## 12.5 CONCEPT REVIEW

12. How do the genetic combinations in clones and sexually reproducing populations differ?
13. How is a clone developed? What are its benefits and drawbacks?
14. How is an intraspecific hybrid formed? What are its benefits and drawbacks?
15. Why is genetic diversity in domesticated plants and animals reduced?

**FIGURE 12.12 The Banking of Genes**
Plant growers and breeders send genetic material, such as seeds, to the National Seed Storage Laboratory in Ft. Collins, Colorado, where it is stored at extremely cold temperatures to prevent deterioration. Gene banks will play an ever-increasing role in preserving biodiversity as the rate of extinction increases.

**FIGURE 12.13 Sexual Differences Within a Species**
Male and female mallard ducks show strikingly different physical features, yet they are of the same species.

## 12.6 Is It a Species or Not? The Evidence

Scientists must rely on a variety of ways to identify species, because they cannot test every individual by breeding it with another to see if those individuals will have fertile offspring. Furthermore, many kinds of organisms reproduce primarily by asexual means. Because organisms that reproduce exclusively by asexual methods do not exchange genes with any other individuals, they do not fit the *biological species* definition very well. The standards used to identify various species include differences in morphology, behavior, metabolism, and genes.

*Morphological characteristics* are commonly used to differentiate species. Scientists compare the physical features of living and fossilized organisms when trying to identify a species. The idea that organisms can be classified as a species based on their structural characteristics is called the *morphological species concept*. The members of a species usually look alike, and these similarities are useful but not foolproof ways to distinguish among species. For example, the males and females of many birds look different from one another yet are the same species (figure 12.13).

Many plants have color variations or differences in leaf shape that cause them to look quite different, although they are members of the same species. Within the species, the eastern gray squirrel has black members that many people assume to be a different species because they are so different in color. A good example of the genetic diversity within a species is demonstrated by the various breeds of dogs. A Saint Bernard does not look very much like a Basset hound; however, they are members of the same species (figure 12.14).

It is often difficult to distinguish among species based on morphology. For example, to most people all mosquitoes look

(a)   (b)
(c)   (d)

**FIGURE 12.14 Genetic Diversity in Dogs**
Although these four breeds of dogs look quite different, they all have the same number of chromosomes and are capable of interbreeding. Therefore, they are considered to be members of the same species. *(a)* Saint Bernard, *(b)* Australian Shepherd, *(c)* Basset hound, *(d)* Australian dingo. Because the extremes of these breeds rarely interbreed naturally, the question is "How long will it be before they are no longer the same species?"

alike, but there are many species. And, although most people think all zebras are members of the same species, there are actually three species of zebras. In some cases, experts must use detailed morphology traits, such as the vein structure in the wings of insects, to identify species.

*Differences in behavior* are also useful in identifying species. Some species of birds are very similar structurally but can be easily identified by differences in the nature of their songs. Because it is often difficult to distinguish among bacteria, fungi, and other microorganisms on the basis of structure, *metabolic differences* that result in the presence or absence of specific chemicals within the organism are often used to help distinguish among species. The use of *genetic differences*—the analysis of DNA—is an even more precise way of distinguishing one species from another. Technology has allowed genes in many organisms to be sequenced and comparisons to be made. In some situations, this line of evidence has revealed remarkable differences between organisms once considered to be of the same species. In other cases, it has shown extremely similar sequences in what are considered to be very different species.

Because scientists use many standards—morphological, behavioral, metabolic, and genetic differences—to identify various species and none of these standards is perfect, situations frequently exist wherein individuals of two recognized species interbreed to a certain degree. For example, dogs, coyotes, and wolves have long been considered separate species. Differences in behavior and social systems tend to prevent mating among these three species. Wolves compete with coyotes and kill them when they are encountered. However, natural dog-coyote, wolf-coyote, and wolf-dog hybrids occur and the young are fertile (How Science Works 12.1). In fact, people have purposely encouraged mating between dogs and wolves for a variety of reasons. It has been demonstrated that dogs are descendants of wolves that were domesticated, so it should not be surprising that mating between wolves and dogs is easy to accomplish.

The species concept is an attempt to define groups of organisms that are *reproductively isolated* and, therefore, constitute a distinct unit of evolution. Some species are completely isolated from other, closely related species and do fit the definition well; some have occasional exchanges of genetic material between species and do not fit the definition as well; and some groups interbreed so much that they must be considered distinct populations of the same species. In this book, we will use the term *species* as a population of reproductively isolated individuals, complete with the flaws and shortcomings of this definition, because it is a useful way to identify groups of organisms that have great genetic similarity and maintain a certain degree of genetic separateness from all similar organisms.

There is one other thing you need to be careful about when using the word *species*. It is both a singular and plural word, so you can talk about a single species or several species. The only way to tell how the word is being used is by assessing the context of the sentence.

**12.6   CONCEPT REVIEW**

16. List four techniques used to distinguish one species from another.
17. Explain why the terms *reproductively isolated* and *species* are related.

## 12.7  Human Population Genetics

Recall from earlier in this chapter that the human gene pool consists of a number of subgroups. The particular characteristics that set one group apart from another originated many thousands of years ago, before travel was as common as it is today, and we still associate certain physical features with certain geographic areas. Although there is much more movement of people and a mixing of racial and ethnic types today, people still tend to have children with others who are of the same social, racial, and economic background and who live in the same locality.

This non-random mate selection can sometimes bring together two individuals who have alleles that are relatively rare. Information about allele frequencies within specific human subpopulations can be very important to people who wish to know the probability of having children with certain harmful genetic abnormalities. This is important if both individuals are descended from a common ancestral tribal, ethnic, or religious group. For example, Tay-Sachs disease causes degeneration of the nervous system and the early death of children. Because it is caused by a recessive allele, both parents must pass on the allele to their child in order for the child to have the disease. By knowing the frequency of the allele in the backgrounds of both parents, the probability of their having a child with this disease can be determined.

Ashkenazi Jews have a higher frequency of the recessive allele for Tay-Sachs disease than do people of any other group of racial or social origin, and the Jewish population of New York City has a slightly higher frequency of this allele than does the worldwide population of Ashkenazi Jews (figure 12.15). Therefore, people with this background should be aware of the probability that they will have children who will develop Tay-Sachs disease, even though the allele is moving to populations other than the Ashkenazi.

Likewise, sickle-cell anemia is more common in people of specific African ancestry than in any other human subgroup. Because many black slaves were brought to this country from regions where sickle-cell anemia is common, African Americans should be aware that they might carry the allele for this type of defective hemoglobin. If they carry the allele, they should consider their chances of having children with this disease. These and other cases make it very important that trained *genetic counselors* have information about allele frequencies in specific human ethnic groups, so that they can help couples with genetics questions.

## HOW SCIENCE WORKS 12.1

# The Legal Implications of Defining a Species

The red wolf (*Canis rufus*) is an endangered species, so the U.S. Fish and Wildlife Service has instituted a captive breeding program to preserve the animal and reintroduce it to a suitable habitat in the southeastern United States, where it was common into the 1800s. Biologists have long known that red wolves hybridize with both the coyote (*Canis latrans*) and the gray wolf (*Canis lupus*), and many suspect that the red wolf is actually a hybrid between the gray wolf and coyote. Gray wolf-coyote hybrids are common in nature where one of the species is rare. Some have argued that the red wolf does not meet the definition of a species and should not be protected under the Endangered Species Act.

Museums have helped shed light on this situation by providing skulls of all three kinds of animals preserved in the early 1900s. It is known that, during the early 1900s, as the number of red wolves in the southeastern United States declined, they readily interbred with coyotes, which were very common (the gray wolf had been exterminated by the early 1900s). Some scientists believe that the skulls of the few remaining "red

wolves" might not represent the true red wolf but a "red wolf" with many coyote characteristics. Studies of the structure of the skulls of red wolves, coyotes, and gray wolves show that the red wolves were recognizably different and intermediate in structure between coyotes and gray wolves. This supports the hypothesis that the red wolf is a distinct species.

DNA studies were performed using material from preserved red wolf pelts. The red wolf DNA was compared with coyote and gray wolf DNA. These studies showed that red wolves contain DNA sequences of both gray wolves and coyotes but do not appear to have distinct base sequences found only in the red wolf. This evidence supports the opinion that the red wolf is not a species but may be a population that resulted from hybridization between gray wolves and coyotes.

There is still no consensus on the status of the red wolf. Independent researchers disagree with one another and with Fish and Wildlife Service scientists, who have been responsible for developing and administering a captive breeding program and planning the reintroductions of the red wolf.

(a) Gray wolf, *Canis lupus*

(b) Red wolf, *Canis rufus*

(c) Coyote, *Canis latrans*

Twenty-eight in 1,000 carry the allele.

Thirty-three in 1,000 carry the allele.

Four in 1,000 carry the allele.

**Total U.S. population**     **Ashkenazi Jews (world)**     **New York City Jews**

**FIGURE 12.15 The Frequency of the Tay-Sachs Allele**
The frequency of an allele can vary from one population to another. Genetic counselors use this information to advise people of their chances of having specific alleles and of passing them on to their children.

---

**12.7 CONCEPT REVIEW**

18. Give an example of a human population with a high frequency of a deleterious allele.
19. What is the role of a genetic counselor?

---

## 12.8 Ethics and Human Population Genetics

Misunderstanding the principles of heredity and population genetics has resulted in bad public policy. Often, when there is misunderstanding there is mistrust. Even today, many prejudices against certain genetic conditions persist.

Modern genetics had its start in 1900, with the rediscovery of the fundamental laws of inheritance proposed by Mendel. For the next 40 or 50 years, this rather simple understanding of genetics resulted in unreasonable expectations on the part of both scientists and laypeople. People generally assumed that much of what a person was in terms of structure, intelligence, and behavior was inherited. This led to the passage of *eugenics laws*, whose basic purpose was to eliminate "bad genes" from the human gene pool and encourage "good genes." These laws often prevented the marriage or permitted the sterilization of people who were "known" to have "bad genes" (figure 12.16). Often, these laws were promoted as a way to save money, because sterilization would prevent the birth of future "defectives" and, therefore, would reduce the need for expensive mental institutions and prisons. Some people used these laws to legitimize racism and promote prejudice.

The writers of eugenics laws (How Science Works 12.2) overestimated the importance of genetics and underestimated the significance of environmental factors such as disease and poor nutrition. They also overlooked the fact that many genetic abnormalities are caused by recessive alleles. In most cases, the negative effects of recessive alleles can be recognized only in homozygous individuals. Removing only the homozygous individuals from the gene pool would have little influence on the frequency of the "bad genes" in the population. Many recessive alleles would be masked by dominant alleles in heterozygous individuals and would continue to show up in future generations. In addition, we now know that most characteristics are not inherited in a simple dominant/recessive fashion; and that often many alleles at different loci cooperate in the production of a phenotypic

**FIGURE 12.16 A Eugenics Law**
**720.301 Sterilization of mental defectives; statement of policy**

Sec. 1. It is hereby declared to be the policy of the state to prevent the procreation and increase in number of feebleminded and insane persons, idiots, imbeciles, moral degenerates and sexual perverts, likely to become a menace to society or wards of the state. The provisions of this act are to be liberally construed to accomplish this purpose. As amended 1962, No. 160, § 1, Eff. March 28, 1963.

This state law was enacted in 1929 and is typical of many such laws passed during the 1920s and 1930s. A basic assumption of this law is that the conditions listed are inheritable; therefore, the sterilization of affected persons would decrease the frequency of these conditions. Prior to 1962, the law also included epileptics. It was repealed in 1974.

# HOW SCIENCE WORKS 12.2

## Bad Science: A Brief History of the Eugenics Movement

- **1885:** Francis Galton, cousin to Charles Darwin, proposes that human society could be improved "through better breeding." The term *eugenics* is coined; it is "the systematic elimination of undesirables to improve humanity." This would be accomplished by breeding those with "desirable" traits and preventing reproduction of those with "undesirable" traits. John Humphrey Noyes, an American sexual libertarian, molds the eugenics concept to justify polygamy: "While the good man will be limited by his conscience to what the law allows, the bad man, free from moral check, will distribute his seed beyond the legal limit."
- **1907:** Indiana is the first state to pass an involuntary sterilization law.
- **1919:** Charles B. Davenport, founder of Cold Springs Harbor Laboratory and of the Eugenics Record Office, "proves" that "pauperism" is inherited and "that being a naval officer is an inherited trait." He notes that the lack of women in the navy also "proves" that the gene is unique to males.
- **1920:** Davenport founds the American Eugenics Society. He sponsors "Fitter Families Contests," held at many state fairs around the country. The society persuades 20 state governments to authorize the sterilization of men and women in prisons and mental hospitals. The society also puts pressure on the federal government to restrict the immigration of "undesirable" races into the United States.
- **1927:** Oliver Wendel Holmes argues for the involuntary sterilization of Carrie S. Buck, an 18-year-old resident of the Virginia State Colony for Epileptics and Feeble-Minded. Buck is the first person to be selected for sterilization under the law. Buck is sterilized, even though it is later revealed that neither she nor her illegitimate daughter, Vivian, is feebleminded.
- **1931:** Involuntary sterilization measures are passed by 30 states.
- **1933–1941:** Nazi death camps, with the mass murder of Jews, Gypsies, Poles, and Russians, are established and run, resulting in the extermination of millions of people. According to the *New York Times* (August 29, 1935), "Adolf Hitler, . . . guided by the nation's anthropologists, eugenists and social philosophers, has been able to construct a comprehensive racial policy of population development and improvement. . . . It sets a pattern. . . . These ideas have met stout opposition in the Rousseauian social philosophy, . . . which bases . . . its whole social and political theory upon the patent fallacy of human equality. . . . Racial consanguinity occurs only through endogamous mating or interbreeding within racial stock . . . conditions under which racial groups of distinctly superior hereditary qualities . . . have emerged."
- **1972–1973:** Up to 4,000 sterilizations are still performed in Virginia alone, and the federal government estimates that 25,000 adults are sterilized nationwide.

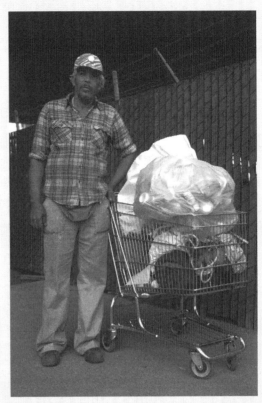

1919 Charles B. Davenport, founder of Cold Springs Harbor Laboratory and of the Eugenics Record Office, "proved" that "*pauperism*" was inherited. Also "proved that being a naval officer is an inherited trait." He noted that the lack of women in the navy also "proved" that the gene was unique to males.

- **1973:** Since March 1973, the American Eugenics Society has called itself The Society for the Study of Social Biology.
- **1987:** Eugenic sterilization of institutionalized retarded persons is still permissible in 19 states, but the laws are rarely carried out. Some states enact laws that forbid the sterilization of people in state institutions.
- **Present:** Some groups and individuals still hold to the concepts of eugenics, claiming that recent evidence "proves" that traits such as alcoholism, homosexuality, and schizophrenia are genetic and, therefore, should be eliminated from the population to "improve humanity." However, the movement lacks the organization and legal basis it held in the past. Modern genetic advances, such as genetic engineering techniques and the mapping of the human genome, allow the identification of individuals with specific genetic defects. Questions about who should have access to such information and how it may be used causes renewed interest in the eugenics debate.

characteristic. Furthermore, mutations occur constantly, adding new alleles to the mix. Usually, these new alleles are recessive and deleterious. Thus, essentially all individuals are carrying "bad genes."

Today, genetic diseases and the degree to which behavioral characteristics and intelligence are inherited are still important social and political issues. The emphasis, however, is on determining the specific method of inheritance and the specific biochemical pathways that result in what is currently labeled as insanity, lack of intelligence, or antisocial behavior. Although progress is slow, several genetic abnormalities have been "cured," or at least made tolerable, by medicines and control of the diet. For example, phenylketonuria (PKU) is a genetic disease caused by an abnormal biochemical pathway. If children with this condition are allowed to eat foods containing the amino acid phenylalanine, they will become mentally retarded. However, if phenylalanine is excluded from the diet, and certain other dietary adjustments are made, the children will develop normally. NutraSweet is a phenylalanine-based sweetener, so people with PKU must use caution when buying products that contain it. This abnormality can be diagnosed very easily by testing the urine of newborn infants.

Effective genetic counseling is the preferred method of dealing with genetic abnormalities. A person known to be a carrier of a "bad gene" can be told the likelihood of passing on that characteristic to the next generation before deciding whether or not to have children. In addition, *amniocentesis* (a medical procedure that samples amniotic fluid) and other tests make it possible to diagnose some genetic abnormalities early in pregnancy. If an abnormality is diagnosed, an abortion can be performed. Because abortion is unacceptable to some people, the counseling process must include a discussion of the facts about an abortion and the alternatives. Although at one time counselors often pushed people toward specific decisions, today it is considered inappropriate for counselors to be advocates; their role is to provide information that allows individuals to make the best decisions possible for them.

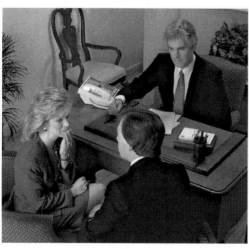

**Genetic counseling**

## 12.8   CONCEPT REVIEW

20. What is amniocentesis?
21. What were eugenics laws? List two facts about human genetics that the advocates of eugenics failed to consider.

## Summary

All organisms with similar genetic information and the potential to reproduce are members of the same species. A species usually consists of several local groups of individuals, known as populations. Groups of interbreeding organisms are members of a gene pool. Although individuals are limited in the number of alleles they can contain, within the population there may be many different kinds of alleles for a trait. Subpopulations may have different allele frequencies from one another.

Genetically distinct populations exist because local conditions may demand certain characteristics, founding populations may have had unrepresentative allele frequencies, and barriers may prevent the free flow of genetic information from one locality to another. Distinguishable subpopulations are known as subspecies, varieties, strains, breeds, or races.

Genetic diversity is generated by mutations, which can introduce new alleles; sexual reproduction, which can generate new genetic combinations; and migration, which can subtract genetic information from, or add genetic information to, a local population. The size of the population is also important, because small populations have reduced genetic diversity.

A knowledge of population genetics is useful for plant and animal breeders and for people who specialize in genetic counseling. The genetic diversity of domesticated plants and animals has been reduced as a result of striving to produce high frequencies of valuable alleles. Clones and intraspecific hybrids are examples. Understanding allele frequencies and how they differ in various populations sheds light on why certain alleles are common in some human populations. Such understanding is also valuable in counseling members of populations with high frequencies of alleles that are relatively rare in the general population.

## Key Terms

*Use the interactive flash cards on the* **Concepts in Biology**, *14/e website to help you learn the meaning of these terms.*

allele frequency 250
biological species
  concept 249

founder effect 254
gene frequency 250
gene pool 248

genetic bottleneck 255
genetic diversity 252
genetic drift 254
interspecific
  hybrids 257
intraspecific hybrids 257

monoculture 258
population 248
population genetics 248
species 248
subspecies (breeds, varieties,
  strains, races) 251

## Basic Review

1. A(n) _____ is all the individuals of the same kind of organism found within a specified geographic region and time.

2. A(n) _____ is all the alleles of all the individuals in a population.
   a. gene pool
   b. population
   c. allele pool
   d. clone

3. Which of the following does not belong?
   a. subspecies
   b. breed
   c. variety
   d. culture

4. Which of the following is a reason that genetically distinct populations exits?
   a. adaptation
   b. the founder effect
   c. cloning
   d. All of the above are correct.

5. Genetic diversity in domesticated plants and animals is affected by
   a. selective breeding.
   b. genetic engineering.
   c. cloning.
   d. All of the above are correct.

6. Morphological, behavioral, metabolic, and genetic differences are all important
   a. standards used to identify species.
   b. ways of generating genetic diversity in a population.
   c. reasons for the existence of gene pools.
   d. sources of mutation.

7. A(n) _____ is a form of genetic drift in which there is a sharp reduction in population size due to a chance event that results in a reduction in genetic diversity in subsequent generations.

8. The organisms that are produced by the controlled breeding of separate varieties of the same species are often referred to as
   a. intraspecific hybrids.
   b. interspecific hybrids.
   c. mutants.
   d. clones.

9. Which of the following causes degeneration of the nervous system and the early death of children?
   a. sickle-cell anemia
   b. Tay-Sachs disease
   c. PKU
   d. eugenics

10. _____ is the term used to describe genetic differences among members of a population.

11. The basic purpose of _____ _____ is to eliminate "bad genes" from the human gene pool and encourage "good genes."

12. If two organisms look different, it means that they are members of different species. (T/F)

13. A "zorse" is the result of breeding between a zebra and a horse and
   a. is an example of an interspecies hybrid.
   b. will no doubt be the beginning of a whole new species.
   c. only happens in zoos.
   d. is an example of intraspecies breeding.

14. Grape plants are grafted onto the stems of already-existing plants to generate more grape plants. This is also known as _____.

15. As a population decreases in size, it is most likely that
   a. genetic diversity will decrease.
   b. extinction is more likely.
   c. the gene pool also decreases in size.
   d. All of the above are true.

**Answers**
1. population  2. a  3. d  4. d  5. d  6. a  7. genetic bottleneck  8. a  9. b  10. genetic diversity  11. eugenics laws  12. F  13. a  14. cloning  15. d

## Thinking Critically

**Is GINA on Your Side?**

"The Genetic Information Nondiscrimination Act of 2008 (Pub.L. 110–233, 122 Stat. 881, enacted May 21, 2008, GINA), is an Act of Congress in the United States designed to prohibit the improper use of genetic information in health insurance and employment. The Act prohibits group health plans and health insurers from denying coverage to a healthy individual or charging that person higher premiums based solely on a genetic predisposition to developing a disease in the future. The legislation also bars employers from using individuals' genetic information when making hiring, firing, job placement, or promotion decisions."

Did you know about his law? What biological information led to the introduction of this bill? On what basis might a person have voted no on this bill? From your perspective, under what kinds of circumstances might a person file suit under this law?

CHAPTER

13

# Evolution and Natural Selection

## CHAPTER OUTLINE

## Study Reveals Information on Human Diversity and Evolution

*To understand the population genetics of any human population, it is necessary to understand Africa first.*

Africa is the birthplace of modern humans and, as a result, Africans have had more time to accumulate changes in their DNA. According to one researcher, ". . . genetically, Africans have been the most neglected and under-represented of any continental group, because the most diverse groups are often remote . . . and don't usually get to clinics."

That is until recently. An international team has analyzed nuclear DNA collected over a decade from 113 populations of Africans from across the continent. The team has found that Africans are descended from 14 ancestral populations, which often correlate with language and cultural groups. They found that all hunter-gatherers and pygmies in Africa today shared ancestors 35,000 years ago and that East Africa was the source of the great migration that populated the rest of the world. They also learned that African-American individuals, on average, have mixed ancestry from all over western Africa. This makes it difficult for African Americans to trace their roots to specific ethnic groups in Africa. The data also support research indicating that the source population for the out-of-Africa migration of modern humans came from east Africa near the Red Sea. These data give us raw material for understanding human evolution that has not been available until now.

- How does separating groups of the same species into different geographic areas affect their diversity?

- What is the ultimate source of genetic variation among different populations?

- What environmental factors might have played roles in generating the genetic differences identified by this research?

## Background Check

**Concepts you should already know to get the most out of this chapter:**
- Traits that make something alive (chapter 1)
- How an allele is involved in protein synthesis (chapter 8)
- The reasons why genetically different populations exist (chapter 12)
- How genetic diversity comes about (chapter 12)

## 13.1 The Scientific Concept of Evolution

People use the term *evolution* in many ways. We talk about the evolution of economies, fashion, and musical tastes. From a biological perspective, the word has a more specific meaning. **Evolution** is a change in the frequency of genetically determined characteristics within a population over time. Evolution can be looked at from two points of view. *Microevolution* occurs when there are minor differences in *allele frequency* between populations of the same species, as when scientists examine genetic differences between subspecies. *Macroevolution* occurs when there are major differences that have occurred over long periods that have resulted in so much genetic change that new *kinds of species* are produced (figure 13.1).

Regardless of the perspective, the ways these differences are brought about are basically the same. The focus of this chapter is on the processes that result in microevolutionary change. Chapter 14 focuses on processes that lead to macroevolutionary change—that is, the development of new species. Evolution, from both perspectives, involves changes in characteristics and the genetic information that produces these characteristics over many generations (Outlooks 13.1).

**(a) Microevolution**

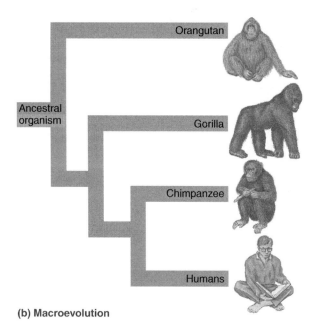

**(b) Macroevolution**

**FIGURE 13.1 Microevolution and Macroevolution**
*(a)* Microevolution occurs when gene frequencies change within the gene pool of a species. Different populations of peppered moths show different gene frequencies based on the color of the bark of the trees they rest on. Black moths are conspicuous on light-colored trunks and light moths are conspicuous on dark colored trunks. Predation by birds removes more of the conspicuous moths and leads to the different gene frequencies in the two populations. These are relatively minor changes, compared with macroevolution changes, which result in new species from common ancestors. *(b)* The macroevolutionary pattern shown here may require tens of millions of years to occur and results in the formation of organisms that are so different that they are unable to interbreed.

## OUTLOOKS 13.1

# Common Misconceptions About the Theory of Evolution

1. **Evolution happened only in the past and is not occurring today.** In fact, there is much evidence that changes in the frequency of alleles are occurring in the populations of current species (e.g., antibiotic resistance, pesticide resistance).

2. **Evolution has a predetermined goal, or "it was meant to be."** Natural selection selects the organisms that best fit the current environment. As the environment changes, so do the characteristics that have value. Random events, such as changes in sea level, major changes in climate, volcanic eruptions, earthquakes, and collisions with asteroids, have had major influences on the subsequent natural selection and evolution.

3. **Changes in the environment cause the mutations that are needed to survive under the new environmental conditions.** Mutations are random events and are not necessarily adaptive. However, mutations that were originally detrimental or neutral may have greater value after the environment changes. The genetic information does not change, but the environmental conditions do. In some cases, the mutation rate may increase, or there may be more frequent genetic exchanges between individuals when the environment changes, but the mutations are still random. They are not directed toward a particular goal.

4. **Individual organisms evolve.** Individuals are stuck with the genes they have inherited from their parents. Although individuals may adapt by changing their behavior or physiology, they cannot evolve; only populations can change gene frequencies.

5. **Many of the current species can be shown to be derived from other present-day species (e.g., apes gave rise to humans).** There are few examples in which it can be demonstrated that one current species gave rise to another. Apes did not become humans, but apes and humans had a common ancestor several million years ago.

6. **Alleles that are valuable to an organism's survival become dominant.** An allele that is valuable may be either dominant or recessive. However, if it has a high value for survival, it will become *common* (more frequent). Commonness has nothing to do with dominance and recessiveness.

---

## 13.1   CONCEPT REVIEW

1. Describe the biological meaning of the word *evolution*.

## 13.2   The Development of Evolutionary Thought

For centuries, people believed that the various species of plants and animals were unchanged from the time of their creation. Although today we know this is not true, we can understand why people may have thought it was true. Because they knew nothing about DNA, meiosis, genetics, or population genetics, they did not have the tools to examine the genetic nature of species. Furthermore, the process of evolution is so slow that the results of evolution are usually not recognized during a human lifetime. It is even difficult for modern scientists to recognize this slow change in many kinds of organisms.

## Early Thinking About Evolution

In the mid-1700s, Georges-Louis Buffon, a French naturalist, wondered if animals underwent change (evolved) over time. After all, if animals didn't change, they would stay the same, and it was becoming clear from the study of fossils that changes had occurred. However, Buffon didn't come up with any suggestions on how such changes might come about. In 1809, Jean-Baptiste de Lamarck, a student of Buffon's, suggested a process by which evolution might occur. He proposed that *acquired characteristics* were transmitted to offspring. **Acquired characteristics** are traits gained during an organism's life and not determined genetically. For example, he proposed that giraffes originally had short necks but because they constantly stretched their necks to get food, their necks got slightly longer (figure 13.2). When these giraffes reproduced, their offspring acquired their parents' longer necks. Because the offspring also stretched to eat, the third generation ended up with even longer necks. And so Lamarck's story was thought to explain why the giraffes we see today have long necks. Although we

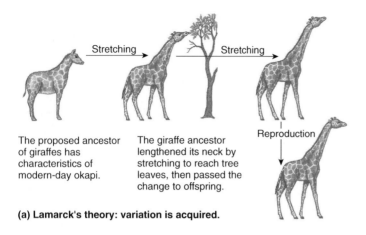

The proposed ancestor of giraffes has characteristics of modern-day okapi.

The giraffe ancestor lengthened its neck by stretching to reach tree leaves, then passed the change to offspring.

Reproduction

**(a) Lamarck's theory: variation is acquired.**

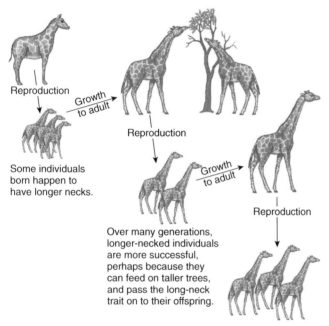

Reproduction

Growth to adult

Some individuals born happen to have longer necks.

Reproduction

Growth to adult

Reproduction

Over many generations, longer-necked individuals are more successful, perhaps because they can feed on taller trees, and pass the long-neck trait on to their offspring.

**(b) Darwin's theory: variation is inherited.**

**FIGURE 13.2 The Contrasting Ideas of Lamarck and the Darwin-Wallace Theory**
*(a)* Lamarck thought that acquired characteristics could be passed on to the next generation. Therefore, he postulated that, as giraffes stretched their necks to get food, their necks got slightly longer. This characteristic was passed on to the next generation, which would have longer necks. *(b)* The Darwin-Wallace theory states that there is variation within the population and that those with longer necks are more likely to survive and reproduce, passing on their genes for long necks to the next generation.

now know Lamarck's theory was wrong (because acquired characteristics are not inherited), it stimulated further thought as to how evolution might occur. From the mid-1700s to the mid-1800s, lively arguments continued about the possibility of evolutionary change. Some, like Lamarck and others, thought that change did take place; many others said that it was not even possible. It was the thinking of two English scientists that finally provided a mechanism for explaining how evolution occurs.

## The Theory of Natural Selection

In 1858, Charles Darwin and Alfred Wallace suggested the theory of *natural selection* as a mechanism for evolution. The **theory of natural selection** is the idea that some individuals whose genetic combinations favor life in their surroundings are more likely to survive, reproduce, and pass on their genes

**Charles Darwin circa 1830**

to the next generation than are individuals who have unfavorable genetic combinations. This theory was clearly set forth in 1859 by Darwin in his book *On the Origin of Species by Means of Natural Selection, or the Preservation of Favored Races in the Struggle for Life* (How Science Works 13.1).

**Alfred Wallace circa 1900**

The theory of natural selection is based on the following assumptions about the nature of living things:

1. All organisms produce more offspring than can survive.
2. No two organisms are exactly alike.
3. Among organisms, there is a constant struggle for survival.
4. Individuals that possess favorable characteristics for their environment have a higher rate of survival and produce more offspring.
5. Favorable characteristics become more common in the species, and unfavorable characteristics are lost.

Using these assumptions, the Darwin-Wallace theory of evolution by natural selection offers a different explanation for the development of long necks in giraffes (figure 13.2b):

1. In each generation, more giraffes would be born than the food supply could support.
2. In each generation, some giraffes would inherit longer necks, and some would inherit shorter necks.
3. All giraffes would compete for the same food sources.
4. Giraffes with longer necks would obtain more food, have a higher survival rate, and produce more offspring.
5. As a result, succeeding generations would show an increase in the number of individuals with longer necks.

## Modern Interpretations of Natural Selection

The logic of the Darwin-Wallace theory of evolution by natural selection seems simple and obvious today, but at the time Darwin and Wallace proposed their theory, the processes of meiosis and fertilization were poorly understood, and the concept of the gene was only beginning to be discussed. Nearly 50 years after Darwin and Wallace suggested their theory, the rediscovery of the work a monk, Gregor Mendel (see chapter 10) provided an explanation for how characteristics could be transmitted from

**Garden Peas**

# HOW SCIENCE WORKS 13.1

## The Voyage of HMS *Beagle*, 1831–1836

Probably the most significant event in Charles Darwin's life was his opportunity to sail on the British survey ship *Beagle*. Surveys were common at that time; they helped refine maps and chart hazards to shipping. Darwin was 22 years old and probably would not have had the opportunity, had his uncle not persuaded Darwin's father to allow him to take the voyage. Darwin was to be a gentleman naturalist and companion to the ship's captain, Robert Fitzroy. When the official naturalist left the ship and returned to England, Darwin replaced him and became the official naturalist for the voyage. The appointment was not a paid position.

The voyage of the *Beagle* lasted nearly 5 years. During the trip, the ship visited South America, the Galápagos Islands, Australia, and many Pacific Islands. The *Beagle's* entire route is shown on the accompanying map. Darwin suffered greatly from seasickness and, perhaps because of it, made extensive journeys by mule and on foot some distance inland from wherever the *Beagle* happened to be at anchor. These inland trips gave

Charles Darwin set forth on a sailing vessel similar to this, the HMS *Beagle*, in 1831 at the age of 22.

of information on them. Also, most other people who had visited these faraway places were military men or adventurers who did not recognize the significance of what they saw. Darwin's notebooks included information on plants, animals, rocks, geography, climate, and the native peoples he encountered. The natural history notes he took during the voyage served as a vast storehouse of information, which he used in his writings for the rest of his life. Because Darwin was wealthy, he did not need to work to earn a living and could devote a good deal of his time to the further study of natural history and the analysis of his notes. He was a semi-invalid during much of his later life. Many people think his ill health was caused by a tropical disease he contracted during the voyage of the *Beagle*. As a result of his experiences, he wrote several volumes detailing the events of the voyage, which were first published in 1839 in conjunction with other information related to the voyage. His volumes were revised several times and eventually were entitled *The Voyage of*

Darwin the opportunity to make many of his observations. His experience was unique for a man so young and very difficult to duplicate because of the slow methods of travel used at that time.

Although many people had seen the places that Darwin visited, never before had a student of nature collected volumes

*the Beagle*. He also wrote books on barnacles, the formation of coral reefs, how volcanoes might have been involved in reef formation, and finally *On the Origin of Species*. This last book, written 23 years after his return from the voyage, changed biological thinking for all time.

**The Voyage of HMS *Beagle*, 1831–1836**

0  1,000  2,000  3,000
Equatorial scale of miles

one generation to the next. Mendel's concepts of the gene explained how traits could be passed from one generation to the next. It also provided the first step in understanding mutations, gene flow, and the significance of reproductive isolation. All of these ideas are interwoven into the modern concept of evolution. If we update the five basic ideas from the thinking of Darwin and Wallace, they might look something like the following:

1. An organism's ability to overreproduce results in surplus organisms.
2. Because of mutation, new, genetically determined traits enter the gene pool. Because of sexual reproduction, involving meiosis and fertilization, new genetic combinations are present in every generation. These processes are so powerful that each individual in a sexually reproducing population is genetically unique. The genetic information present is expressed in the phenotype of the organism.
3. Resources, such as food, soil nutrients, water, mates, and nest materials, are in short supply, so some individuals do without. Other environmental factors, such as disease organisms, predators, and helpful partnerships with other species, also affect survival. All the specific environmental factors that affect survival by favoring certain characteristics are called **selecting agents**.
4. Selecting agents favor individuals with the best combination of alleles—that is, those individuals are more likely to survive and reproduce, passing on more of their genes to the next generation. An organism is selected against if it has fewer offspring than other individuals that have a more favorable combination of alleles. The organism does not need to die to be selected against.
5. Therefore, alleles or allele combinations that produce characteristics favorable to survival become more common in the population and, on the average, the members of the species will be better adapted to their environment.

Evolution results when there are changes in allele frequency in a population. Recall that individual organisms cannot evolve—only populations can. Although evolution is a population process, the mechanisms that bring it about operate at the level of the individual.

Recall that a theory is a well-established generalization supported by many kinds of evidence. The theory of natural selection was first proposed by Charles Darwin and Alfred Wallace. Since the time it was first proposed, the theory of natural selection has been subjected to countless tests yet remains the core concept for explaining how evolution occurs.

## 13.2 CONCEPT REVIEW

2. Why has Lamarck's theory been rejected?
3. List five assumptions about the nature of living things that support the concept of evolution by natural selection.

## 13.3 The Role of Natural Selection in Evolution

Natural selection is a primary process that brings about evolution by selecting which individuals will survive, reproduce, and pass on their genes to the next generation. These processes do not affect genes directly but do so indirectly by selecting individuals for success based on the characteristics an individual displays. Recall that the characteristics displayed by an organism (phenotype) are related to the genes possessed by the organism (genotype). By affecting the reproductive success of

**Road Kill Fox**

individuals, natural selection affects allele frequencies within the population. That change in allele frequency is evolution.

Three factors work together to determine how a species changes over time: *environmental factors* that affect organisms, *sexual reproduction* among the individuals in the gene pool, and the amount of *genetic diversity* within the gene pool. In general, the reproductive success of any individual within a population is determined by how well an individual's characteristics match the demands of the environment in which it lives. **Fitness** is the success of an organism in passing on its genes to the next generation, compared with other members of its population. Just because an organism reproduces doesn't make it "fit." It can be fit only in comparison with others. Individuals whose characteristics enable them to survive and reproduce better than others in their environment have greater fitness (Outlooks 13.2).

Genetic diversity is important because a large gene pool with great genetic diversity is more likely to contain genetic combinations that allow some individuals to adapt to a changing environment. The characteristics of an organism are

## OUTLOOKS 13.2

# Genetic Diversity and Health Care

People turn to their healthcare providers when they experience a medical problem, whether it is the result of an accident, infection, or some abnormality. In many large cities, the emergency rooms (ERs) of large hospitals have become a substitute for a visit to a physician's office or a neighborhood clinic. Medical facilities are thought of as places where everyone always gets better and no one gets sick. However, 2 million people a year get bacterial infections while they are being treated in hospitals as patients. An estimated 90,000 people die from these infections each year.

Many people do not realize that the hospital is a place where patients who have not been able to have their infections resolved by home care bring all of those nasty microbes. Studies have shown that the farther away you are from the hospital, the less dangerous the microbes. What makes this situation worse is the fact that these bacteria are undergoing genetic changes and becoming more unbeatable. Populations of hospital microbes contain mutations that protect them from specific antibiotics—that is, they are antibiotic resistant. If resistant microbes are transmitted, the infected person will find the infection even harder to control. For example, methicillin-resistant *Staphylococcus aureus* (MRSA) was responsible for over 94,000 potentially fatal infections and nearly 19,000 deaths in the United States in 2005. Eighty-five percent of these deaths were associated with healthcare settings.

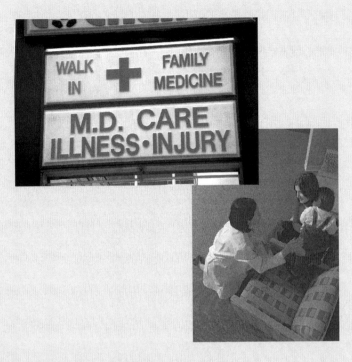

not just its structural traits. Behavioral, biochemical, and metabolic traits are also important. Scientists often use behavior, DNA differences, and other chemical differences to assess evolutionary relationships among existing organisms. However, when looking at extinct species, scientists are usually confined to using structural characteristics to guide their thinking.

### 13.3 CONCEPT REVIEW

4. Define *natural selection*.
5. What is fitness, and how is it related to reproduction?

## 13.4 Common Misunderstandings About Natural Selection

There are several common misinterpretations about the process of natural selection. The first involves the phrase "survival of the fittest." Individual survival is certainly important, because those that do not survive will not reproduce. However, the more important factor is the number of descendants an organism leaves. An organism that has survived for hundreds of years

but has not reproduced has not contributed any of its genes to the next generation and, so, has been selected against. Therefore, the key to being the fittest is not survival alone but, rather, survival and reproduction of the more fit organisms.

Second, the phrase "struggle for life" in the title of Darwin's book does not necessarily refer to open conflict and fighting. It is usually much more subtle than that. When a resource, such as nesting material, water, sunlight, or food, is in short supply, some individuals survive and reproduce more effectively than others. For example, many kinds of birds require holes in trees as nesting places (figure 13.3). If these are in short supply, some birds are fortunate and find a top-quality nesting site, others occupy less suitable holes, and some do not find any. There may or may not be fighting for the possession of a site. If a site is already occupied, a bird may simply fly away and look for other suitable but less valuable sites. Those that successfully occupy good nesting sites will be much more successful in raising young than will those that must occupy poor sites or those that do not find any.

Similarly, on a forest floor where there is little sunlight, some small plants may grow fast and obtain light while shading out plants that grow more slowly. The struggle for life in this instance involves a subtle difference in the rate at which the plants grow. But the plants are, indeed, engaged in a struggle, and a superior growth rate is the weapon for survival.

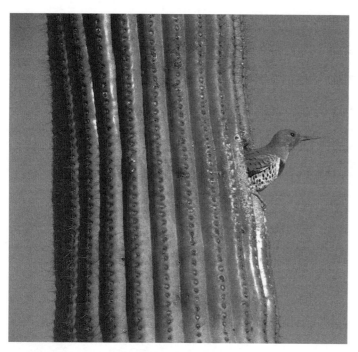

**FIGURE 13.3 Tree Holes as Nesting Sites**
Many kinds of birds, such as this Gilded Flicker (*Colaptes chrysoides*), nest in holes in trees or other plants such as this Saguaro cactus. If such nesting sites are not available, they may not be able to breed. Many people build birdhouses that provide artificial tree holes to encourage birds to nest near their homes.

A third common misunderstanding involves the significance of phenotypic characteristics that are gained during the life of an organism but are not genetically determined. Although such acquired characteristics may be important to an individual's success, they are not genetically determined and cannot be passed on to future generations through sexual reproduction. Therefore, acquired characteristics are not important to the processes of natural selection. Consider an excellent golfer's skill. Although he or she may have inherited the physical characteristics of good eyesight, strength, and muscular coordination that are beneficial to a golfer, the ability to play a good round of golf is acquired through practice, not through genes. An excellent golfer's offspring will not automatically be excellent golfers. They might inherit some of the genetically determined physical characteristics necessary to become excellent golfers, however (figure 13.4).

Humans desire a specific set of characteristics in our domesticated animals. For example, the standard for the breed of dog known as boxers is for them to have short tails. However, the alleles for short tails are rare in this breed. Consequently, their tails are amputated—a procedure called docking. Similarly, most lambs' tails are amputated. These acquired characteristics are not passed on to the next generation. Removing the tails of these animals does not remove the genetic information for tail production from their genomes, and each generation of puppies and lambs is born with long tails.

**FIGURE 13.4 Acquired Characteristics**
The ability to play an outstanding game of golf is learned through long hours of practice. The golf skills acquired by practice cannot be passed on genetically to a person's offspring.

A fourth common misconception involves understanding the relationship between the mechanism of natural selection and the outcomes of the selection process. Although the effects of natural selection appear at the population level, the actual selecting events take place, one at a time, at the level of the individual organism.

| **13.4** | **CONCEPT REVIEW** |
|---|---|

6. Why are acquired characteristics of little interest to evolutionary biologists?
7. In what way are the phrases "survival of the fittest" and "struggle for existence" correct? In what ways are they misleading?

## **13.5** What Influences Natural Selection?

Now that you have a basic understanding of how natural selection works, we can look in more detail at the factors that influence it. *Genetic diversity* within a species, the degree of *genetic expression,* and the ability of most species to *reproduce excess offspring* all exert an influence on the process of natural selection.

### The Mechanisms That Affect Genetic Diversity

For natural selection to occur there must be genetic differences among the individuals of an interbreeding population of organisms. Consider what happens in a population of genetically identical organisms. In this case, it does not matter which individuals reproduce, because the same genes will be passed on to the next generation and natural selection cannot occur. However, when genetic differences exist among individuals in a population and these differences affect fitness, natural selection can take place. Therefore, it is important to identify the processes that generate genetic diversity within a population. Genetic diversity within a population is generated by the *mutation* and *migration* of organisms and by *sexual reproduction* and *genetic recombination*.

## Mutation and Migration

**Spontaneous mutations** are changes in DNA that cannot be tied to a particular factor. Mutations may alter existing genes, resulting in the introduction of entirely new genetic information into a gene pool. It is suspected that cosmic radiation or naturally occurring mutagenic chemicals might be the cause of many of these mutations. Subjecting organisms to high levels of radiation or to certain chemicals increases the rate at which mutations occur. It is for this reason that people who are exposed to mutagenic chemicals or radiation take special safety precautions.

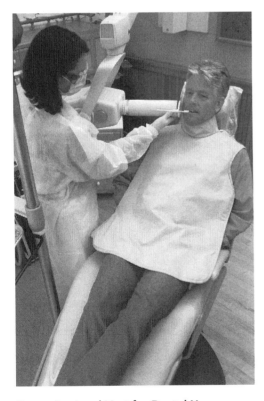

**Protective Lead Vest for Dental X-ray**

Naturally occurring mutation rates are low. The odds of a gene mutating are on the order of 1 in 100,000. Most of these mutations are harmful. Rarely does a mutation occur that is actually helpful. However, in populations of millions of individuals, each of whom has thousands of genes, over thousands of generations it is quite possible that a new, beneficial piece of genetic information will come about as a result of mutation. Remember that every allele originated as a

modification of a previously existing piece of DNA. For example, the allele for blue eyes may be a mutated brown-eye allele, or blond hair may have originated as a mutated brown-hair allele. In a species such as corn (*Zea mays*), there are many different alleles for seed color. Each probably originated as a mutation. Thus, mutations have been very important in introducing genetic material into species over time.

For mutations to be important in the evolution of organisms, they must be in cells that give rise to gametes (eggs or

**Genetic Diversity in Corn**

sperm). Mutations in other cells, such as those in the skin or liver, will affect only those cells and will not be passed on to the next generation.

Recall that migration is another way in which new genetic material can enter a population. When individuals migrate into a population from some other population, they may bring alleles that were rare or absent. Similarly, when individuals leave a population, they can remove certain alleles from the population.

## Sexual Reproduction and Genetic Recombination

Sexual reproduction is important in generating new genetic combinations in individuals. Although sexual reproduction does *not* generate new genetic information, it does allow for the mixing of genes into combinations that did not occur previously. Each individual entering a population by sexual reproduction carries a unique combination of genes—half donated by the mother and half donated by the father. During meiosis, unique combinations of alleles are generated in the gametes through crossing-over between homologous chromosomes and the independent assortment of nonhomologous chromosomes. This results in millions of possible genetic combinations in the gametes of any individual. When fertilization occurs, one of the millions of possible sperm unites with one of the millions of possible eggs, resulting in a genetically unique individual. This genetic mixing that occurs as a result of meiosis and fertilization is known as **genetic recombination**.

The new individual has a set of genes that is different from that of any other organism that ever existed. When genetic recombination occurs, a new combination of alleles may give its bearer a selective advantage, leading to greater reproductive success.

Organisms that primarily use asexual reproduction do not benefit from genetic recombination. In most cases, however, when their life history is studied closely, it is apparent that they also can reproduce sexually at certain times. Organisms that reproduce exclusively by asexual methods are not able to generate new genetic combinations but still acquire new genetic information through mutation.

As scientists have learned more about the nature of species, it has become clear that genes can be moved from one organism to another that was considered to be a different species. In some cases, it appears that whole genomes can be added when the cells of two different species combine into one cell. This process of interspecific hybridization is another method by which a species can have new genes enter its population.

## The Role of Gene Expression

Even when genes are present, they do not always express themselves in the same way. *For genes to be selected for or against, they must be expressed in the phenotype of the individuals possessing them.* There are many cases of genetic characteristics being expressed to different degrees in different individuals. Often, the reason for this difference in expression is unknown.

### Degrees of Expression

**Penetrance** is a term used to describe how often an allele expresses itself. Some alleles have 100% penetrance; others express themselves only 80% of the time. For example, there is a dominant allele that causes people to have a stiff little finger. The expression of this trait results in the tendons being attached to the bones of the finger in such a way that the finger does not flex properly. This dominant allele does not express itself in every person who contains it; occasionally, parents who do not show the characteristic in their phenotype have children that show the characteristic. **Expressivity** is a

**Polydactyly**

term used to describe situations in which an allele is not expressed equally in all individuals who have it. An example of expressivity involves a dominant allele for six fingers or toes, a condition known as polydactyly. Some people with this allele have an extra finger on each hand; some have an extra finger on only one hand. Furthermore, some sixth fingers are well-formed with normal bones, whereas others are fleshy structures that lack bones.

### Why Some Genes May Avoid Natural Selection

There are many reasons a specific allele may not feel the effects of natural selection. Some genetic characteristics can be expressed only during specific periods in the life of an organism. If an organism dies before the characteristic is expressed, it never has the opportunity to contribute to the overall fitness of the organism. Say, for example, a tree has genes for producing very attractive fruit. The attractive fruit is important because animals select the fruit for food and distribute the seeds as they travel. However, if the tree dies before it can reproduce, the characteristic may never be expressed. By contrast, genes such as those that contribute to heart disease or cancer usually have their effect late in a person's life. Because they were not expressed during the person's reproductive years, they were not selected against, because the person reproduced before the effects of the gene were apparent. Therefore, such genes are less likely to be selected against (eliminated from the population) than are those that express themselves early in life.

In addition, many genes require an environmental trigger to be expressed (i.e., they are epigenetic). If the trigger is not encountered, the gene never expresses itself. It is becoming clear that many kinds of human cancers are caused by the presence of genes that require an environmental trigger. Therefore, we try to identify triggers and prevent these negative genes from being turned on and causing disease.

When both dominant and recessive alleles are present for a characteristic, the recessive alleles must be present in a homozygous condition before they have an opportunity to express themselves. For example, the allele for albinism is recessive. There are people who carry this recessive allele but never express it, because it is masked by the dominant allele for normal pigmentation (figure 13.5).

Some genes have their expression hidden because the action of a completely unrelated gene is required before they can express themselves. The albino individual shown in figure 13.5 has alleles for dark skin and hair that will never have a chance to express themselves because of the presence of two alleles for albinism. The alleles for dark skin and hair can express themselves only if the person has the ability to produce pigment, and albinos lack that ability.

### Natural Selection Works on the Total Phenotype

Just because an organism has a "good" gene does not guarantee that it will be passed on. The organism may also have "bad" genes in combination with the good, and the "good" characteristics may be overshadowed by the "bad" characteristics. All individuals produced by sexual reproduction probably have

**FIGURE 13.5 Gene Expression**

Genes must be expressed to allow the environment to select for or against them. The recessive allele *c* for albinism shows itself only in individuals who are homozygous for the recessive characteristic. The man in this photo is an albino who has the genotype *cc*. The characteristic is absent in those who are homozygous dominant and is hidden in those who are heterozygous. The dark-skinned individuals could be either *Cc* or *CC*. However, because the albino individual cannot produce pigment, characteristics for dark skin and dark hair cannot be expressed.

**FIGURE 13.6 Reproductive Potential**

The ability of a population to reproduce greatly exceeds the number necessary to replace those who die. Here are some examples of the prodigious reproductive abilities of some species.

certain genetic characteristics that are extremely valuable for survival and others that are less valuable or harmful. However, natural selection operates on the total phenotype of the organism. Therefore, it is the combination of characteristics that is evaluated—not each characteristic individually. For example, fruit flies may show resistance to insecticides or lack of it, may have well-formed or shriveled wings, and may exhibit normal vision or blindness. An individual with insecticide resistance, shriveled wings, and normal vision has two good characteristics and one negative one, but it would not be as successful as an individual with insecticide resistance, normal wings, and normal vision.

## The Importance of Excess Reproduction

A successful organism reproduces at a rate in excess of that necessary to merely replace the parents when they die (figure 13.6). For example, geese have a life span of about 10 years; on average, a single pair can raise a brood of about eight young each year. If these two parent birds and all their offspring were to survive and reproduce at this rate for a 10-year period, there would be a total of 19,531,250 birds in the family.

However, the size of goose populations and most other populations remains relatively constant over time. Minor changes in number may occur but, if the environment remains constant, a population does not experience dramatic increases in size. A high death rate tends to offset the high reproductive rate and population size remains stable. But this is not a "static population." Although the total number of organisms

in the species may remain constant, the individuals that make up the population change. It is this extravagant reproduction that provides the large surplus of genetically unique individuals that allows natural selection to take place.

If there are many genetically unique individuals within a population, it is highly probable that some individuals will survive to reproduce even if the environment changes somewhat, although the gene frequency of the population may be changed to some degree. For this to occur, members of the population must be eliminated in a non-random manner. Even if they are not eliminated, some may have greater reproductive success than others. The individuals with the greatest reproductive success will have more of their genetic information present in the next generation than will those that die or do not reproduce very successfully. Those that are the most successful at reproducing are those that are, for the most part, better suited to the environment.

### 13.5   CONCEPT REVIEW

8. What factors can contribute to diversity in the gene pool?
9. Why is over-reproduction necessary for evolution?
10. Why is sexual reproduction important to the process of natural selection?
11. How might a harmful allele remain in a gene pool for generations without being eliminated by natural selection?

## 13.6 The Processes That Drive Selection

Several mechanisms allow for the selection of certain individuals for successful reproduction. If predators must pursue swift prey organisms, the faster predators will be selected for, and the selecting agent is the swiftness of available prey. If predators must find prey that are slow but hard to see, the selecting agent is the camouflage coloration of the prey, and keen eyesight is selected for. If plants are eaten by insects, the production of toxic materials in the leaves is selected for. All selecting agents influence the likelihood that certain characteristics will be passed on to subsequent generations.

### Differential Survival

As stated previously, the phrase "survival of the fittest" is often associated with the theory of natural selection. Although this is recognized as an oversimplification of the concept, survival is an important factor in influencing the flow of genes to subsequent generations. If a population consists of a large number of genetically and phenotypically different individuals it is likely that some of them will possess characteristics that make their survival difficult. Therefore, they are likely to die early in life and not have an opportunity to pass on their genes to the next generation.

Charles Darwin described several species of ground finches on the Galápagos Islands (figure 13.7), and scientists have often used these birds in scientific studies of evolution. On one of the islands, scientists studied one of the species of seed-eating ground finches, *Geospiza fortis*. They measured the size of the animals and the size of their bills and related these characteristics to their survival. They found the following: During a drought, the birds ate the smaller, softer seeds more readily than the larger, harder seeds. As the birds consumed the more easily eaten seeds, only the larger, harder seeds remained. During the drought, finch mortality was extremely high. When scientists looked at ground finch mortality, they found that the larger birds with stronger, deeper bills survived better than the smaller birds with weaker, narrower bills. They also showed that the offspring of the survivors tended to show larger body and bill size as well. The lack of small, easily eaten seeds resulted in selection for larger birds with stronger bills, which could crack open larger, tougher seeds. Table 13.1 shows data on two of the parameters measured in this study.

As another example of how differential survival can lead to changed gene frequencies, consider what has happened to many insect populations as humans have subjected them to a variety of insecticides. Because there is genetic diversity within all species of insects, an insecticide that is used for the first time on a particular species kills all the exposed individuals that are genetically susceptible. However, individuals with slightly different genetic compositions and those not exposed may not be killed by the insecticide.

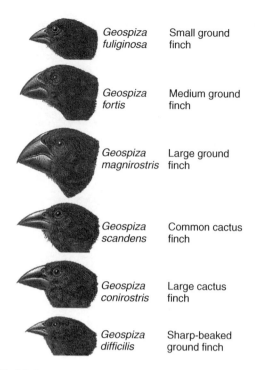

**FIGURE 13.7 A Sample of Darwin's Finches**
Ten species of ground and tree finches were described by Darwin. This figure shows six members of the genus *Geospiza*. The four species of ground finches are primarily seedeaters and use their bills to crush seeds. The two species of cactus finch primarily feed on the fruit and flowers of cactus plants.

**TABLE 13.1** Changes in Body Structure of *Geospiza fortis*

| | Before Drought | After Drought |
|---|---|---|
| *Average Body Weight* | 16.06 g | 17.13 g |
| *Average Bill Depth* | 9.21 mm | 9.70 mm |

Suppose that, in a population of a particular species of insect, 5% of the individuals have genes that make them resistant to a specific insecticide. The first application of the insecticide could, therefore, kill a majority of those exposed. However, tolerant individuals and those that escaped exposure would then constitute the remaining breeding population. This would mean that many more insects in the second generation would be tolerant. The second use of the insecticide on this population would not be as effective as the first. With continued use of the same insecticide, each generation would become more tolerant, because the individuals that were not tolerant were being eliminated and those that could tolerate the toxin passed on their genes for tolerance to their offspring.

Many species of insects produce a new generation each month. In organisms with a short generation time, 99% of the population could become resistant to an insecticide in just 5 years. As a result, the insecticide would no longer be useful in controlling the species. As a new selecting agent (the insecticide) is introduced into the insect's environment, natural selection results in a change in the gene frequency of a population, so that most individuals are tolerant of the insecticide.

The same kind of selection process has occurred with herbicides. Within the past 50 years, many kinds of herbicides have been developed to control weeds in agricultural fields. After several years of use, a familiar pattern develops as more and more species of weeds show resistance to the herbicide. Figure 13.8 shows several kinds of herbicides and the number of weed species that have become resistant over time. In each weed species, there has been selection for the individuals that have the genetic information that allows them to tolerate the presence of the herbicide.

## Differential Reproductive Rates

Survival alone does not always ensure reproductive success. For a variety of reasons, some organisms are better able to use the available resources to produce offspring. If an individual leaves 100 offspring and another leaves only 2, the first organism has passed on more copies of its genetic information to the next generation than has the second. If we assume that all 102 offspring have similar survival rates, the first organism has been selected for, and its genes have become more common in the subsequent population.

Scientists have studied the gene frequencies for the height of clover plants. Two identical fields of clover were planted and cows were allowed to graze in one of them. The cows acted as a selecting agent by eating the taller plants first. These tall plants rarely got a chance to reproduce. Only the shorter plants flowered and produced seeds. After some time, seeds were collected from both the grazed and the ungrazed fields and grown in a greenhouse under identical conditions. The average height of the plants from the ungrazed field was compared with that of the plants from the grazed field. The seeds from the ungrazed field produced some tall, some short, but mostly medium-sized plants. However, the seeds from the grazed field produced many more short plants than medium or tall ones. The cows had selectively eaten the tall plants. Because the flowers are at the tip of the plant, the tall plants were less likely to successfully reproduce, even though they were able to survive grazing by cows.

## Differential Mate Choice—Sexual Selection

**Sexual selection** occurs within animal populations when some individuals are more likely to be chosen as mates than others. Obviously, those that are frequently chosen have more opportunities to pass on more copies of their genetic information than those that are rarely chosen. The characteristics of the more frequently chosen individuals may involve general characteristics, such as body size or aggressiveness, or specific, conspicuous characteristics attractive to the opposite sex.

For example, male red-winged blackbirds establish territories in cattail marshes, where females build their nests. A male will chase out all other males, but not females. Some blackbird territories are large and others are small; some males have none. Although it is possible for any male to mate, those that have no territory are least likely to mate. Those that defend large territories may have two or more females nesting in their territories and are very likely to mate with those females. It is unclear exactly why females choose one male's territory over another, but the fact is that some males are chosen as mates and others are not.

In other cases, it appears that females select males that display specific, conspicuous characteristics. Certain male birds, such as peacocks, have very conspicuous tail feathers

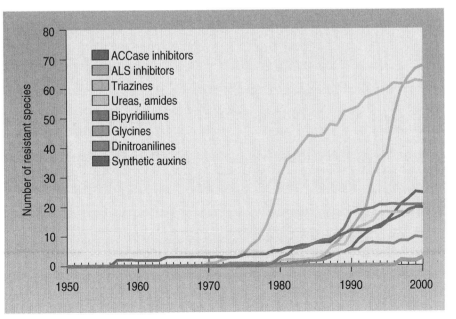

**FIGURE 13.8 Evolutionary Change**
Populations of weed plants that have been subjected repeatedly to herbicides often develop resistant populations. The individual weed plants that have been able to resist the effects of the herbicide have lived to reproduce and pass on their genes for resistance to their offspring; thus, resistant populations of weeds have developed.

**Male Redwing Blackbird**

(figure 13.9). Those with spectacular tails are more likely to mate and have offspring. Darwin was puzzled by such cases, because the large, conspicuous tail should have been a disadvantage to the bird. Long tails require energy to produce, make it more difficult to fly, and make it more likely that predators will capture the individual. The current theory that seeks to explain this paradox involves female choice. If the females have an innate (genetic) tendency to choose the most elaborately decorated males, genes that favor such plumage will be regularly passed on to the next generation.

## 13.6  CONCEPT REVIEW

12.  List three factors that can lead to changed gene frequencies from one generation to the next.
13.  Give two examples of selecting agents and explain how they operate.

## 13.7  Patterns of Selection

Understanding the nature of the environment is key to determining how natural selection will affect how a species will change. In general, three forms of selection have been identified: stabilizing selection, directional selection, and disruptive selection (figure 13.10).

### Stabilizing Selection

**Stabilizing selection** occurs when individuals at the extremes of the range of a characteristic are consistently selected against. This kind of selection is very common. If the environment is stable, most of the individuals show characteristics that are consistent with the demands of the environment. For example, for many kinds of animals, there is a range of color possibilities. Suppose a population of mice has mostly brown individuals and a few white or black ones. If the white or black individuals are more conspicuous and are consistently more likely to be discovered and killed by predators, the elimination of the extreme forms will result in a continued high frequency of the brown form. Many kinds of marine animals, such as horseshoe crabs and sharks, have remained unchanged for thousands of years. The marine environment is relatively constant and probably favors stabilizing selection.

### Directional Selection

**Directional selection** occurs when individuals at one extreme of the range of a characteristic are consistently selected for. This kind of selection often occurs when there is a consistent change in the environment in which the organism exists. For example, when a particular insecticide is introduced to control a certain species of pest insect, there is consistent selection for individuals that have alleles for resistance to the insecticide. Because of

**FIGURE 13.9  Mate Selection**
In many animal species the males display very conspicuous characteristics that are attractive to females. Because the females choose the males they will mate with, those males with the most attractive characteristics will have more offspring and, in future generations, there will be a tendency to enhance the characteristic. With peacocks, those individuals with large colorful displays are more likely to mate.

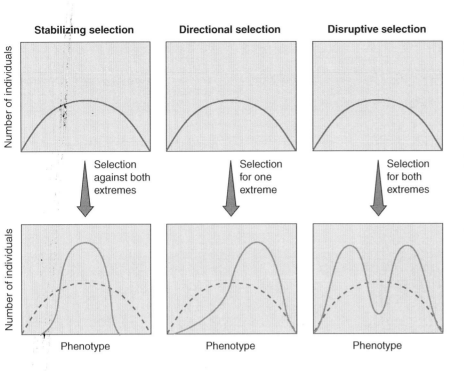

**FIGURE 13.10  Patterns of Selection**
In stabilizing selection, both extremes for a characteristic are selected against. Thus, gene frequencies do not change, and the original range of phenotypes is maintained. In directional selection, one extreme is selected for and the other extreme is selected against. This results in a shift in gene frequency and range of phenotype in a direction toward one extreme and away from the other. In disruptive selection, both extremes are selected for and the intermediate condition is selected against. This leads to the development of two distinct phenotypes with different gene frequencies.

this, there is a shift in the original allele frequency, from one in which the alleles for resistance to the insecticide were rare to one in which most of the population has the alleles for resistance. Similarly, changes in climate, such as long periods of drought, can consistently select for individuals that have characteristics that allow them to survive in the dryer environment, and a change in allele frequency can result. Recent evidence also shows changes resulting from periods of rapid climate warming. The Yukon red squirrel, pitcher-plant mosquito, and European blackcap warbler show genetically based shifts in the timing of their seasonal reproduction, dormancy, or migration.

## Disruptive Selection

**Disruptive selection** occurs when both extremes of a range for a characteristic are selected for and the intermediate condition is selected against. This kind of selection is likely to happen when there are sharp differences in the nature of the environment where the organisms live. For example, there are many kinds of insects that feed on the leaves of trees. Many of these insects have colors that match the leaves they feed on. Suppose the species of insect ranges in color from light green to dark green, and medium green is the most common. If a particular species of insect had some individuals that fed on plants with dark green leaves, whereas other individuals fed on plants with light green leaves, medium green insects could be selected against and the two extremes selected for, depending on the kind of plant they were feeding on.

## 13.7  CONCEPT REVIEW

14. Distinguish among stabilizing, directional, and disruptive selection.

## 13.8  Evolution Without Selection—Genetic Drift

Recall from chapter 12 that genetic drift is a significant change in the frequency of an allele that is not the result of natural selection. Gene-frequency differences that result from chance are more likely to occur in small populations than in large populations. Because they result from random events, such changes are not the result of natural selection or sexual selection. For example, a population of 10 organisms, of which 20% have curly hair and 80% have straight hair, is significantly changed by the death of 1 curly-haired individual. Often, the characteristics affected by genetic drift do not appear to have any adaptive value to the individuals in the population. However, in extremely small populations, vital genes may be lost.

Occasionally, a population has unusual colors, shapes, or behaviors, compared with other populations of the same species. Such unusual occurrences are associated with populations that started as a small founder population or those that have passed through a genetic bottleneck in the past. In large populations, any unusual shifts in gene frequency in one part of the population usually would be counteracted by reciprocal changes in other parts of the population. However, in small populations, the random distribution of genes to gametes may not reflect the percentages present in the population. For example, consider a situation in which there are 100 plants in a population and 10 have dominant alleles for patches of red color, whereas the others do not. If in those 10 plants the random formation of gametes resulted in no red alleles present in the gametes that were fertilized, the allele could be eliminated. Similarly, if all those plants with the red allele happened to be in a hollow that was subjected to low temperatures, they could be killed by a late frost and would not pass on their alleles to

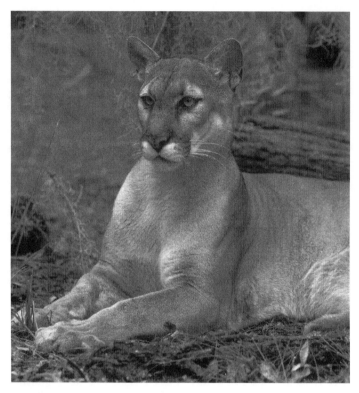

**FIGURE 13.11 The Florida Panther**
The Florida panther (also known as cougar, puma, mountain lion, or catamount) is confined to the Everglades at the southern tip of Florida. The population is small, is isolated from other populations of cougars, and prior to 1995 had lost about 50% of its genetic diversity. In 1995, 8 female cougars from Texas were introduced into the Everglades to increase the genetic diversity of the Florida panther population. The plan seems to be working. By 2002, the population had increased to about 80 adult cougars and the population had shown about 20% genes from the Texas subpopulation. Certain obvious characteristics, such as kinked tails and cowlicks, that were common in the pre-1995 population are now less common.

the next generation. Therefore, the allele would be lost, but the loss would not be the result of natural selection.

Consider the example of cougars in North America. Cougars require a wilderness setting for success. As Europeans settled the land over the past 200 years, the cougars were divided into small populations in the places where relatively undisturbed habitat still existed. The Florida panther is an isolated population of cougars found in the Everglades.

The next nearest population of cougars is in Texas. Because the Florida panther is on the endangered species list, efforts have been made to ensure its continued existence in the Everglades. However, the population is small and studies show that it has little genetic diversity. A long period of isolation and a small population created conditions that led to this reduced genetic diversity. The accidental death of a few key individuals could have resulted in the loss of valuable genes from the population. The general health of the individuals in the population is poor and reproductive success is low. In 1995, wildlife biologists began a program of introducing individuals from the Texas population into the Florida population. The purpose of the program is to reintroduce the genetic diversity lost during the long period of isolation. The program appears to be working, because there has been an increase in genetic diversity within the population (figure 13.11).

## 13.8 CONCEPT REVIEW

15. Why is genetic drift more likely in small populations?
16. Give an example of genetic drift.

## 13.9 Gene-Frequency Studies and the Hardy-Weinberg Concept

In the early 1900s, an English mathematician, G. H. Hardy, and a German physician, Wilhelm Weinberg, recognized that it was possible to apply a simple mathematical relationship to the study of gene frequencies. Their basic idea was that, if certain conditions existed, gene frequencies would remain constant and the distribution of genotypes could be described by the relationship $p^2 + 2pq + q^2 = 1$, where $p^2$ represents the frequency of the homozygous dominant genotype, $2pq$ represents the frequency of the heterozygous genotype, and $q^2$ represents the frequency of the homozygous recessive genotype. Constant gene frequencies over several generations would imply that evolution was *not* taking place. Changing gene frequencies would indicate that evolution was taking place.

The conditions necessary for gene frequencies to remain constant are the following:

1. Mating must be completely random.
2. Mutations must not occur.
3. The migration of individual organisms into and out of the population must not occur.
4. The population must be very large.
5. All genes must have an equal chance of being passed on to the next generation. (Natural selection is not occurring.)

The **Hardy-Weinberg concept** states that gene frequencies will remain constant if these five conditions are met. The concept is important, because it allows a simple comparison of allele

|  |  | Possible female gametes | |
|---|---|---|---|
|  |  | $A = 0.6$ | $a = 0.4$ |
| **Possible male gametes** | $A = 0.6$ | Genotype of offspring $AA = 0.6 \times 0.6 = 0.36 = 36\%$ | Genotype of offspring $Aa = 0.6 \times 0.4 = 0.24 = 24\%$ |
|  | $a = 0.4$ | Genotype of offspring $Aa = 0.4 \times 0.6 = 0.24 = 24\%$ | Genotype of offspring $aa = 0.4 \times 0.4 = 0.16 = 16\%$ |

frequency to indicate if genetic changes are occurring within a population. Two different populations of the same species can be compared to see if they have the same allele frequencies, or populations can be examined at different times to see if allele frequencies are changing.

## Determining Genotype Frequencies

It is possible to apply the Punnett square method from chapter 10 to an entire gene pool to illustrate how the Hardy-Weinberg concept works. Consider a gene pool composed of only 2 alleles, *A* and *a*. Of the alleles in the population, 60% (0.6) are *A* and 40% (0.4) are *a*. In this hypothetical gene pool, we do not know which individuals are male or female and we do not know their genotypes. With these allele frequencies, how many of the individuals would be homozygous dominant (*AA*), homozygous recessive (*aa*), and heterozygous (*Aa*)? To find the answer, we treat these alleles and their frequencies as if they were individual alleles being distributed into sperm and eggs. The sperm produced by the males of the population will be 60% (0.6) *A* and 40% (0.4) *a*. The females will produce eggs with the same relative frequencies. We can now set up a Punnett square as shown at the top of this page. The Punnett square gives the frequency of occurrence of the three possible genotypes in this population: *AA* = 36%, *Aa* = 48%, and *aa* = 16%.

If we use the relationship $p^2 + 2pq + q^2 = 1$, $p^2$ is the frequency of the *AA* genotype, $2pq$ is the frequency of the *Aa* genotype, and $q^2$ is the frequency of the *aa* genotype. Then, $p^2 = 0.36$ and $p$ would be the square root of 0.36, which is 0.6—our original frequency for the *A* allele. Similarly, $q^2 = 0.16$ and $q$ would be the square root of 0.16, which is 0.4. In addition, $2pq$ would equal $2 \times 0.6 \times 0.4 = 0.48$. If this population were to reproduce randomly, it would maintain an allele frequency of 60% *A* and 40% *a* alleles. It is important to understand that Hardy-Weinberg conditions rarely exist; therefore, there are usually changes in gene frequency over time or genetic differences in separate populations of the same species. If gene frequencies are changing, evolution is taking place.

## Why Hardy-Weinberg Conditions Rarely Exist

*Random mating does not occur* for a variety of reasons. Many species are divided into small local populations that are isolated from one another and mating with individuals in other local populations rarely occurs. In human populations, these isolations may be geographic, political, or social. In addition, some individuals may be chosen as mates more frequently than others because of the characteristics they display. Therefore, the Hardy-Weinberg conditions are seldom met, because non-random mating is a factor that leads to changing gene frequencies.

*Spontaneous mutations occur.* Totally new kinds of alleles are introduced into a population, or 1 allele is converted into another, currently existing allele. Whenever an allele is changed, 1 allele is subtracted from the population and a different allele is added, thus changing the allele frequency in the gene pool. Mutations in disease-causing organisms may have significant impacts (Outlooks 13.3).

**Migrating Dandelion Seeds**

*Immigration and emigration of individual organisms are common.* When organisms move from one population to another, they carry their genes with them. Their genes are subtracted from the population they left and added to the population they enter, thus changing the gene pool of both populations. It is important to understand that migration is common for plants as well as animals. In many parts of the world, severe weather disturbances have lifted animals and plants (or their seeds) and moved them over great distances, isolating them from their original gene pool. In other instances, organisms have been distributed by floating on debris on the surface of the ocean. As an example of how important immigration and emigration is, consider the tiny island of Surtsey (3 km²), which emerged from the sea as a volcano near Iceland in 1963 and continued to erupt until 1967. The new island was declared a nature preserve and has been surveyed regularly to record the kinds of organisms present. The nearest possible source of new organisms is about 20 kilometers away. The first living thing observed on the island was a fly seen less than a year after the initial eruption. By 1965, the first flowering plant had been found and, by 1996, 50 species of flowering plants had been recorded on the island. In addition, several kinds of sea birds nest on the island.

*Populations are not infinitely large,* as assumed by the Hardy-Weinberg concept. If numbers are small, random events to a few organisms might alter gene frequencies from what was expected. Consider coin flipping as an analogy. Coins have two surfaces, so, if you flip a coin once, there is a

# OUTLOOKS 13.3

## The Reemerging of Infectious Diseases

Infectious diseases caused by bacteria, viruses, fungi, and parasitic worms continue to be a major cause of suffering and death throughout the world. They are the third leading cause of death in the United States. *Reemerging infectious diseases* (for example, diphtheria, malaria, whooping cough) are diseases that were once major health concerns but then declined significantly. However, they are beginning to increase in frequency.

The reemergence of many kinds of infectious diseases is the result of two primary factors: our failure to immunize against these diseases, and evolutionary changes in the microbes. People who are not being immunized against diseases are susceptible and may become ill with the disease or become asymptomatic carriers of the microbe. A further contributing factor to the reemergence of old diseases is the increased number of people with poorly functioning immune systems. HIV/AIDS has created a huge population of people with compromised immune systems. Famine and malnutrition also impair the immune system. War and the crowding that occurs in refugee camps and prisons enhance the easy spread of disease.

The reemergence of some diseases is also the result of evolution. Mutations are necessary if evolution is to take place. As parasites and their hosts interact, they constantly react to each other in an evolutionary fashion. Hosts develop new mechanisms to combat parasites, and parasites develop new mechanisms to overcome the hosts' defenses (for example, antibiotic resistance).

One of the mechanisms viruses use is a high rate of mutation. This ability to mutate has resulted in many new, serious human diseases. In addition, many new diseases arise when viruses that cause disease in another animal are able to establish themselves in humans. Many kinds of influenza originated in pigs, ducks, or chickens and were passed to humans through close contact with infected animals or by eating infected animals. In many parts of the world, these domesticated animals live in close contact with humans (often in the same building) making conditions favorable for the transmission of animal viruses to humans.

Each year, mutations result in new varieties of influenza and colds, which pass through the human population. Occasionally, the new varieties are deadly. In 1918, a new variety of influenza virus originated in pigs in the United States and spread throughout the world. During the 1918–1919 influenza pandemic that followed, 20 to 40 million people died. In 1997 in Hong Kong, a new kind of influenza was identified that killed 6 of the 18 people infected. When public health officials discovered the virus had come from chickens, they ordered the slaughter of all the live chickens in Hong Kong, which stopped the spread of the disease.

In early 2003, an outbreak of a new viral disease, known as *severe acute respiratory syndrome (SARS)*, originated in China. SARS is a variation of a coronavirus, a class of virus commonly associated with the common cold, but it causes severe symptoms and, if untreated, can result in death. In June 2003, the SARS virus was isolated from an animal known as the masked palm civet (*Paguma larvata*). This animal is used for food in China and is a possible source of the virus that caused SARS in humans. However, other animals have also tested positive for the virus. The disease spread rapidly to several countries as people traveled by airplane from China to other parts of the world. A recognition of the seriousness of the disease and the isolation of infected persons prevented further spread, and this new disease was brought under control. However, if the virus still exists in some unknown wild animal host, it could reappear in the future.

In addition to cold and influenza, other kinds of diseases often make the leap from nonhuman to human hosts. The swine flu virus outbreaks of 2009 were traced to a population of pigs in Mexico. It is likely that genetic mixing occurred in the pigs' cells, resulting in a new kind of virus containing bird, human, and swine genes. The emergence of these new kinds of viruses enables them to more easily move from one species to another.

(a) Influenza Viruses at 295,000 Magnification

(b) Three SARS Virus Particles

**What are the chances?**

50:50 chance that the coin will turn up heads. If you flip two coins, you may come up with two heads, two tails, or one head and one tail. Only one of these possibilities gives the theoretical 50:50 ratio. To come closer to the statistical probability of flipping 50% heads and 50% tails, you would need to flip many coins at the same time. The more coins you flip, the more likely it is that you will end up with 50% of all the coins showing heads and the other 50% showing tails. The number of coins flipped is important. The same is true of gene frequencies. The smaller the population, the more likely it is that random events will alter the gene pool—that is, the more likely it is that genetic drift will occur.

Finally, *genes are not all equally likely to be passed to the next generation.* It is important to understand that genes differ in their value to the species. Some genes result in characteristics that are important to survival and reproductive success. Other genes reduce the likelihood of survival and reproduction. For instance, many animals have cryptic color patterns that make them difficult to see. The genes that determine the cryptic color pattern would be selected for (favored), because animals that are difficult to see are not killed and eaten as often as those that are easy to see. Recall that albinism is the inability to produce pigment, so that the individual's color is white. White animals are conspicuous, so we might expect them to be discovered more easily by predators (figure 13.12). Because not all genes have equal value, natural selection will operate and some genes will be more likely to be passed on to the next generation.

## Using the Hardy-Weinberg Concept to Show Allele-Frequency Change

We can return to our original example of alleles *A* and *a* to determine how natural selection based on differences in survival can result in allele-frequency changes in only one generation. Again, assume that the parent generation has the following genotype frequencies: *AA* = 36%, *Aa* = 48%, and *aa* = 16%, with a total population of 100,000 individuals. Suppose that 50% of the individuals having at least one *A* allele do not reproduce because they are more susceptible to disease. The parent population of 100,000 would have 36,000 individuals with the *AA* genotype, 48,000 with the *Aa* genotype, and 16,000 with the *aa* genotype. Because only 50% of those with an *A* allele reproduce, only 18,000 *AA* individuals and 24,000 *Aa* individuals will reproduce. All 16,000 of the *aa* individuals will reproduce, however. Thus, there is a total

(a)

(b)

**FIGURE 13.12 Albino Animals Are More Conspicuous**
Pythons rely on camouflage coloring to help them catch prey. This albino form *(a)* is more likely to be spotted than a member of the species with normal coloration *(b)*.

reproducing population of only 58,000 individuals out of the entire original population of 100,000. What percentage of *A* and *a* will go into the gametes produced by these 58,000 individuals?

The percentage of *A*-containing gametes produced by the reproducing population will be 31% from the *AA* parents and 20.7% from the *Aa* parents (table 13.2). The frequency of the *A* allele in the gametes is 51.7% (31% + 20.7%). The percentage of *a*-containing gametes is 48.3% (20.7% from the *Aa* parents plus 27.6% from the *aa* parents). The original parental allele frequencies were *A* = 60% and *a* = 40%. These have changed to *A* = 51.7% and *a* = 48.3%. More individuals in the population will have

**TABLE 13.2** Differential Reproduction

The percentage of each genotype in the offspring differs from the percentage of each genotype in the original population as a result of differential reproduction.

| Original Frequency of Genotypes | Total Number of Individuals Within a Population of 100,000 with Each Genotype | Number of Each Genotype Not Reproducing Subtracted from the Total | Total of Each Genotype in the Reproducing Population of 58,000 Following Selection | New Percentage of Each Genotype in the Reproducing Population |
|---|---|---|---|---|
| $AA = 36\%$ | 36,000 | 36,000<br>$-18,000$<br>18,000 | 18,000 | $\dfrac{18,000}{58,000} = 31.0\%$ |
| $Aa = 48\%$ | 48,000 | 48,000<br>$-24,000$<br>24,000 | 24,000 | $\dfrac{24,000}{58,000} = 41.4\%$ |
| $aa = 16\%$ | 16,000 | 16,000<br>$-\quad 0$<br>16,000 | 16,000 | $\dfrac{16,000}{58,000} = 27.6\%$ |
| | 16,000 | 16,000 | | |
| 100% | 100,000 | | 58,000 | 100.0% |

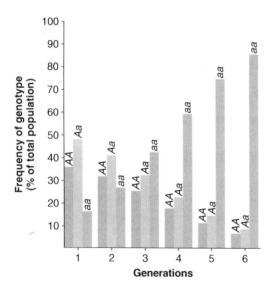

**FIGURE 13.13 Changing Allele Frequency**
If 50% of all individuals with the genotypes *AA* and *Aa* do not reproduce in each generation, the frequency of the *a* allele will increase, whereas the frequency of the *A* allele will decrease. Consequently, the *aa* genotype will increase in frequency, whereas that of the *AA* and *Aa* genotypes will decrease.

the *aa* genotype, and fewer will have the *AA* and *Aa* genotypes.

If this process continued for several generations, the allele frequency would continue to shift until the *A* allele became rare in the population (figure 13.13). This is natural selection in action. Differential reproduction rates have changed the frequency of the *A* and *a* alleles in this population.

**13.9 CONCEPT REVIEW**

17. A gene pool has equal numbers of alleles *B* and *b*. Half of the *B* alleles mutate to *b* alleles in the original generation. What will the allele frequencies be in the next generation?
18. Hardy-Weinberg is a theoretical concept that describes gene frequencies. List five reasons why the conditions of the Hardy-Weinberg concept are rarely met.
19. The smaller the population, the more likely it is that random changes will influence gene frequencies. Why is this true?

**13.10 A Summary of the Causes of Evolutionary Change**

At the beginning of this chapter, evolution was described as a change in allele frequency over time. It is clear that several mechanisms operate to bring about this change. Mutations can either change one allele into another or introduce an entirely new piece of genetic information into the population. Immigration can introduce new genetic information if the entering organisms have genetic information that was not in the population previously. Emigration and death remove genes from the gene pool. Natural selection systematically filters some genes from the population, allowing other genes to remain and become more common. The primary mechanisms involved in natural selection are differences in death rates, reproductive rates, and the rate at which individuals are selected as mates (figure 13.14). In addition, gene frequencies are more easily

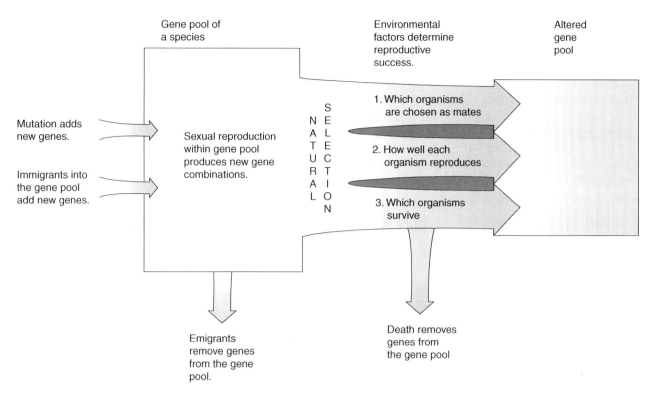

**FIGURE 13.14 Processes That Influence Evolution**
Several processes cause gene frequencies to change. New genetic information enters populations through immigration and mutation. Genetic information leaves populations through emigration and death. Natural selection operates within populations through death, mate selection, and rates of reproduction. Genetic drift can also result in evolutionary change but is not shown in this diagram.

changed in small populations, because events such as death, immigration, emigration, and mutation can have a greater impact on a small population than on a large population.

## 13.10 CONCEPT REVIEW

20. Why is each of the following important for an understanding of evolution: mutation, migration, sexual reproduction, selective agents, and population size?

## Summary

At one time, people thought that all organisms were unchangeable. Lamarck suggested that change does occur and thought that acquired characteristics could be passed from generation to generation. Darwin and Wallace proposed the theory of natural selection as the mechanism that drives evolution. All populations of sexually reproducing organisms naturally exhibit genetic diversity among individuals as a result of mutation and the genetic recombination resulting from meiosis and fertilization. The genetic differences are reflected in

phenotypic differences among individuals. These genetic differences are important in changing environments, because natural selection must have genetic diversity to select from. Natural selection by the environment results in better-suited organisms having greater numbers of offspring than those that are less well off genetically. Not all genes are equally expressed. Some express themselves only during specific periods in the life of an organism, and some are recessive alleles that show themselves only when in the homozygous state. Characteristics that are acquired during the life of an individual and are not determined by genes cannot be raw material for natural selection. Sexual selection occurs when specific individuals are chosen as mates to the exclusion of others. In addition to natural selection and sexual selection, genetic drift in small populations can lead to evolutionary change.

Selecting agents change the gene frequencies of the population if the conditions of the Hardy-Weinberg concept are violated. The conditions required for the Hardy-Weinberg equilibrium are random mating, no mutations, no migration, large population size, and no selective advantage for any genes. These conditions are met only rarely, however, so that, after generations of time, the genes of the more favored individuals will make up a greater proportion of the gene pool. The process of natural selection allows the maintenance of a species in its environment, even as the environment changes.

# Key Terms

*Use the interactive flash cards on the* **Concepts in Biology,** *14/e website to help you learn the meaning of these terms.*

acquired characteristics 269
directional selection 280
disruptive selection 281
evolution 268
expressivity 276
fitness 272
genetic recombination 275
Hardy-Weinberg concept 282

penetrance 276
selecting agents 272
sexual selection 279
spontaneous
  mutations 275
stabilizing selection 280
theory of natural
  selection 270

# Basic Review

1. Which of the following is not true?

   a. All organisms produce more offspring than can survive.

   b. All organisms of the same species are exactly alike.

   c. Among organisms, there is a constant struggle for survival.

   d. Individuals that possess favorable characteristics for their environment have a higher rate of survival and produce more offspring.

2. _____ characteristics are traits gained during an organism's life and not determined genetically.

   a. Genetic          c. Sexual

   b. Acquired        d. Dominant

3. Who proposed the theory of natural selection?

   a. Darwin and Wallace    c. Lamarck

   b. Buffon                d. Hardy and Weinberg

4. _____ is the success of an organism in passing on its gene to the next generation, compared with other members of its population.

5. _____ occurs within animal populations when some individuals are chosen as mates more frequently than others.

   a. Stabilizing selection    c. Sexual selection

   b. Disruptive selection     d. Normative selection

6. _____ is how often an allele expresses itself when present.

   a. Expressivity      c. Fitness

   b. Dominance        d. Penetrance

7. Specific environmental factors that favor certain characteristics are called

   a. selecting agents.     c. mutations.

   b. hurricanes.           d. disruptive factors.

8. _____ _____ is a significant change in the frequency of an allele that is not the result of natural selection.

9. The conditions necessary for gene frequencies to remain constant include all the following except

   a. mating must be completely random.

   b. mutations must not occur.

   c. the migration of individual organisms into and out of the population must not occur.

   d. the population must be very small.

10. _____ occurs when there are minor differences in allele frequency between populations of the same species, as when genetic differences between subspecies are examined.

11. Natural selection can take place when genetic differences exist among individuals in a population and these differences affect the overall health or _____.

12. _____-evolution has taken place when the percentage of dark peppered moths in a population increases as a result of allele-frequency changes.

13. A change in allele _____ can result from changes resulting from rapid periods of climate warming.

14. _____ diseases were thought to be controlled but have become common in recent years.

    a. Reemerging infectious    c. Recurring infectious

    b. Genetic abnormalities    d. Incidental

15. A high _____ _____ tends to offset the high _____ _____ and population size remains stable.

**Answers**
1. b  2. b  3. a  4. Fitness  5. c  6. d  7. a  8. Genetic drift  9. d  10. Microevolution  11. fitness  12. Micro-13. frequency  14. a  15. death rate/reproductive rate

# Thinking Critically

**Microevolution and Sexually Transmitted Diseases**
Penicillin was introduced as an antibiotic in the early 1940s. Since that time, it has been found to be effective against the bacteria that cause gonorrhea, a sexually transmitted disease. The drug acts on dividing bacterial cells by preventing the formation of a new protective cell wall. Without the wall, the bacteria can be killed by normal body defenses. As time passed, a new strain of this disease-causing bacterium developed. This bacterium produces an enzyme that metabolizes penicillin. How can gonorrhea be controlled now that this organism is resistant to penicillin? How did a resistant strain develop? Include the following in your consideration: DNA, enzymes, selecting agents, and gene-frequency changes.

# The Formation of Species and Evolutionary Change

## CHAPTER 14

**Another Piece of the Human Evolution Puzzle Unearthed**

*The newest fossil may reveal more information about our origins.*

Just where would you expect to find a 47-million-year-old primate fossil? Africa, of course! But not this time. "Ida" (*Darwinius masillae*) was found in Messel Pit, a pit created by an oil shale mining operation in Germany in 1983, and not by a professional paleontologist, but an amateur collector. Fossil exploration began after the mining operation was completed and the pit was authorized to become a garbage dump. Ida was kept in a private collection for 25 years before she was acquired by the Natural History Museum of the University of Oslo for scientific study.

Ida is the most complete primate skeleton known in the fossil record. She has a complete skeleton, a soft body outline, and food in her digestive tract. Preliminary evidence reveals that she lived during the Eocene Epoch, after the extinction of dinosaurs and when primates split into two major groups: prosimians and anthropoids. The region was experiencing continental drift and just beginning to take on features we would recognize as Germany's landscape today. During the Eocene, many modern plants and animals were evolving in a subtropical, jungle-like environment. Evolutionarily, Ida and her relatives are thought to have been the evolutionary base of the anthropoid branch that led to monkeys, apes, and humans.

Ida lacks traits found in lemurs, such as a grooming claw on the second toe of the foot, a fused row of teeth in the middle of her lower jaw (known as a toothcomb), and claws. Her more advanced traits include the presence of fingernails, forward-facing eyes (allowing her to have 3-D vision and the ability to judge distance), and teeth similar to those of monkeys. Ida also has a talus bone in her feet. This bone allows her entire weight to be transmitted to the foot, an important feature in bipedal animals.

- **What role have fossils played in understanding species evolution?**
- **What factors are important to the formation of a new species?**
- **What do scientists know about the evolution of humans?**

## Background Check

**Concepts you should already understand to get the most out of this chapter:**
- The fundamentals of meiosis, genes, and alleles (chapter 10)
- Traits that make a population a species (chapter 12)
- The role natural selection plays in evolution (chapter 13)

## 14.1 Evolutionary Patterns at the Species Level

Chapter 13 focused on the concept of microevolution—that is, minor differences in allele frequency between populations of the same species, as when genetic differences between subspecies are examined. This chapter focuses on macroevolution, the major differences that have occurred over long periods that have resulted in so much genetic change that new kinds of species are produced. Furthermore, the present situation is not the end of the evolutionary process because evolution is still occurring today. Recall from chapter 12 that a species is a population of organisms whose members have the potential to interbreed naturally and to produce fertile offspring but *do not* interbreed with other groups. This inability of a species to generate fertile offspring after breeding with other more genetically different organisms is a key to understanding how a new species can originate from a preexisting ancestral species.

**California condor**

There are three key ideas within this definition. First, a species is a population of organisms. An individual is not a species. An individual can only be a member of a group that is a species. The human species, *Homo sapiens*, consists of over 7 billion individuals, whereas the endangered California condor species, *Gymnogyps californianus*, currently consists of about 322 individuals, 179 of which live in the wild.

Second, the definition takes into consideration the ability of individuals within the group to produce fertile offspring. Obviously, not every individual can be checked to see if it is capable of mating with any other individual that is similar to it, so we must make some judgment calls. Can most individuals within the population interbreed to produce fertile offspring? Although all humans are of the same species, some individuals are sterile and cannot reproduce. However, we don't exclude them from the human species because of this. If they were not sterile, they would have the potential to interbreed. Although humans normally choose mating partners from their own local ethnic groups, humans from all parts of the world are potentially capable of interbreeding. This is known to be true because of the large number of instances of reproduction involving people of different ethnic backgrounds. The same is true for many other species that have local subpopulations but have a wide geographic distribution.

Third, the species concept also takes into account an organism's evolutionary history. A species is a group of organisms that shares a common ancestor with other species, but is set off from those others by having newer, genetically unique traits.

So how do we know if two populations really do belong to the same species?

### Gene Flow

One way to find out if two populations belong to the same species is to investigate *gene flow*. **Gene flow** is the movement of genes from one generation to the next as a result of reproduction or from one region to another by migration. Two or more populations that demonstrate gene flow among them constitute a single species. On the other hand, two or more populations that do not have gene flow through reproduction, when given the opportunity, are generally considered to be different species. Some examples will clarify this working definition.

Donkeys (also called asses) and horses are thought to be two different species, even though they can be mated and produce offspring, called mules (figure 14.1). Because mules are nearly always sterile and do not produce offspring, this is not considered to be gene flow, so donkeys and horses are considered separate species. Similarly, lions and tigers can be mated in zoos to produce offspring. However, this does not happen in nature, so gene flow does not occur naturally; thus, they are also considered two separate species.

**Liger**

### Genetic Similarity

Another way to find out if two organisms belong to different species is to determine their degree of genetic similarity. Advances in molecular genetics have allowed scientists to examine the sequence of bases in the genes present in individuals from a variety of populations. Those that have a great deal of similarity in their nitrogenous base sequences are assumed to have resulted from populations that have exchanged genes through sexual reproduction in the recent past. If there are significant differences, the two populations have probably not exchanged genes recently and are more likely to be members of separate species. There is no universal rule that states the smallest allowable genetic difference between two species. For example, genetic similarity between two South American field

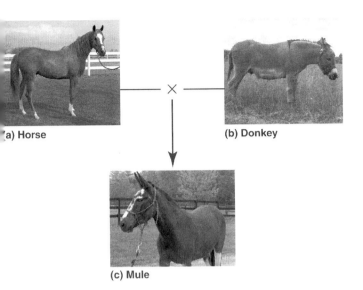

**FIGURE 14.1 Hybrid Sterility**
Even though they do not do so in nature, *(a)* horses *(Equus caballus)* and *(b)* donkeys *(Equus asinus)* can be mated. The offspring produced by mating a female horse with a male donkey is called a *(c)* mule *(Equus asinus* x *caballus)* and is sterile. Because all mules are sterile, the horse and the donkey are considered to be of different species.

mice, *Akodon dolores* and *A. molinae,* have been analyzed to determine if they are, in fact, members of the same species located in different geographic regions. Experts examining the genetic differences concluded that they are the same species but different geographic subspecies. The interpretation of the results obtained by examining genetic differences still requires the judgment of experts. Although this technique is probably not the ultimate method to settle every dispute related to the identification of species, it is an important tool.

---

**14.1   CONCEPT REVIEW**

1. How is the concept of gene flow related to the species concept?
2. Why aren't mules considered a species?

---

**14.2   How New Species Originate**

**Speciation** is the process of generating new species. When biologists look at the evolutionary history of living things, they see that new species have arisen continuously for as long as life has been on Earth. *Fossils* are often used as evidence of the past evolution of organisms. A **fossil** is any evidence of an organism of a past geologic age, such as a preserved skeleton or body imprint. The fossil record shows that huge numbers of new species have originated and that most species have

gone extinct. Two mechanisms are probably responsible for the vast majority of speciation events: geographic isolation, and polyploidy (instant speciation).

## Speciation by Geographic Isolation

**Geographic isolation** occurs when a portion of a species becomes totally cut off from the rest of the gene pool by geographic distance. In order for geographic isolation to lead to speciation, the following steps are necessary: (1) *population isolation* of a subpopulation of a species; (2) *genetic divergence*—that is, a change in the allele frequencies of the isolated subpopulation compared to the rest of the species; and (3) *reproductive isolation* of the new species from its parent species.

### Population Isolation

There are at least three ways that populations can become geographically isolated (figure 14.2). First, the *colonization of a distant area* by one or only a few individuals can lead to

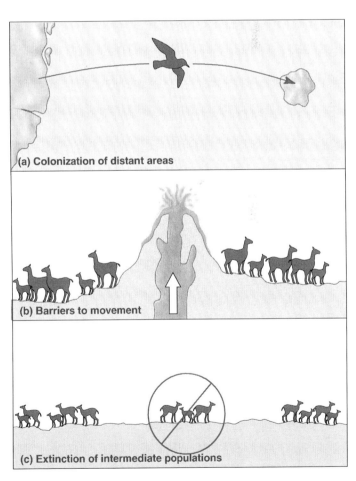

(a) Colonization of distant areas

(b) Barriers to movement

(c) Extinction of intermediate populations

**FIGURE 14.2 Geographically Isolated Populations**
*(a)* The colonization of distant areas by one or a few individuals can cut off a population far from the center of their home population. *(b)* Barriers to movement can split an ancestral population into two isolated groups. *(c)* Extinction of intermediate populations can leave the remaining populations reproductively isolated from one another.

the establishment of a population far from the center of their home population. If these colonies are so far from their home populations that there is no gene flow between them, they are genetically isolated.

Second, speciation occurs if a *geographic barrier* totally isolates a subpopulation from the rest of the species. The uplifting of mountains, the rerouting of rivers, and the formation of deserts may separate one portion of a gene pool from another. For example, two kinds of squirrels are found on opposite sides of the Grand Canyon. The canyon is a barrier that prevents interbreeding among members of the two populations. Some people consider the two types of squirrels to be separate species; others consider them to be different, isolated sub-populations of the same species. Even small changes can cause geographic isolation in species that have little ability to move. A fallen tree, a plowed field, or even a new freeway may effectively isolate populations within such species. Snails in two valleys separated by a high ridge have been found to be closely related but different species. The snails cannot get from one valley to the next because of the height and climatic differences presented by the ridge.

Third, the *extinction of intermediate populations* can leave the remaining populations reproductively isolated from one another for periods that are long enough for them to develop into separate species. For example, the *range* of an organism is the geographic area over which a species can be found. As a species expands its range, some intermediate populations may go extinct so that portions of the original population become separated from the rest. Thus, many species are made up of several, smaller populations that display characteristics significantly different from those of other local populations. Many of these differences are adaptations to local environmental conditions. If the smaller subpopulation in the middle becomes extinct, the distance between the more extreme isolated populations may be too great for gene flow to occur.

### Genetic Divergence

*Genetic divergence* is necessary for new species to develop. Differences in environments and natural selection play very important roles in the process of forming new species. Following separation from the main portion of the gene pool by geographic isolation, the organisms within a small, local population are likely to experience different environmental conditions. If, for example, a mountain range has separated a species into two populations, one population may receive more rain or more sunlight than the other. These environmental differences act as natural selecting agents on the two gene pools and, over a long period of time, account for different genetic combinations in the two places. Furthermore, different mutations may occur in the two isolated populations, and each may generate unique combinations of genes as a result of sexual reproduction. This is particularly true if one of the populations is very small. As a result, the two populations may show differences in color, height, enzyme production, time of seed germination, or many other genetic characteristics.

Over a long period of time, the genetic differences that accumulate may result in subspecies that are significantly modified structurally, physiologically, or behaviorally. In some cases the changes may be so great that new species result.

### Reproductive Isolation

*Reproductive isolation*, or *genetic isolation*, has occurred if the genetic differences between the two populations have become so great that reproduction cannot occur between members of the two populations if they are brought together. At this point, speciation has occurred. In other words, the process of speciation can begin with the geographic isolation of a portion of the species, but new species are generated only if isolated populations become separate from one another *genetically* and gene flow is not reestablished if the geographic barrier is removed.

## Polyploidy: Instant Speciation

Another important mechanism known to generate new species is polyploidy. **Polyploidy** is a condition of having multiple sets of chromosomes, rather than the normal haploid or diploid number. The increase in the number of chromosomes can result from abnormal mitosis or meiosis in which the chromosomes do not separate properly. For example, if a cell had the normal diploid chromosome number of 6 ($2n = 6$), and the cell went through mitosis but did not divide into two cells, it would then contain 12 chromosomes. It is also possible that a new polyploid species could result from crosses between two species followed by a doubling of the chromosome number (figure 14.3). Because the number of chromosomes of the polyploidy is different from that of the parent, successful reproduction between the polyploid and the parent is usually not possible. This is because meiosis would result in gametes that had chromosome numbers different from those of the original parent organism. In one step, the polyploid could be isolated reproductively from its original species.

A single polyploid plant does not constitute a new species. However, because most plants can reproduce asexually, they can create an entire population of organisms that have the same polyploid chromosome number. The members of this population would probably be able to undergo normal meiosis and would be capable of sexual reproduction among themselves. In effect, a new species can be created within a couple of generations. Some groups of plants, such as the grasses, may have 50% of their species produced as a result of polyploidy. Many economically important species are polyploids. Cotton, potatoes, sugarcane, broccoli, wheat, and many garden flowers are examples. Although it is rare in animals, polyploidy is found in some insects, fishes, amphibians, and reptiles. Certain lizards have only female individuals and lay eggs, which develop into additional females. Various species of these lizards appear to have developed by polyploidy. To date, the only mammal found to be polyploid is a rat (*Tympanoctomys barrerae*) found in Argentina and is tetraploid, $4n = 204$.

(a)                     (b)                              (c)                              (d)

**FIGURE 14.3 Polyploidy**
*(a)* The chromosome number of this diploid cell is $2n = 12$. *(b)* What happens when it undergoes polyploidy and doubles its chromosome count—that is, $4n = 24$. Polyploidy has been found in many kinds of plants including grasses and ferns. *(c)* Hibiscus plants (*Hibiscus rosa-sinensis*), and *(d)* many varieties of goldfish (*Carassius auratus*).

## Other Speciation Mechanisms

Speciation can also occur without geographic isolation or polyploidy. Any process that can result in the reproductive isolation of a portion of a species can lead to the possibility of speciation. For example, within populations, some individuals may breed or flower at a somewhat different time of the year. If the difference in reproductive time is genetically based, different breeding populations could be established that could eventually lead to speciation. Among animals, variations in the genetically determined behaviors related to courtship and mating could effectively separate one species into two or more separate breeding populations. In plants, genetically determined incompatibility of the pollen of one population of flowering plants with the flowers of other populations of the same species could lead to separate species. Although there are many examples of these kinds of speciation mechanisms, geographic isolation and polyploidy are considered the primary mechanisms for speciation.

### 14.2 CONCEPT REVIEW

3. How does speciation differ from the formation of subspecies?
4. Can you always tell by looking at two organisms whether or not they belong to the same species?
5. Why is geographic isolation important in the process of speciation?
6. How does a polyploid organism differ from a haploid or diploid organism?
7. List the series of events necessary for speciation to occur.

### 14.3 The Maintenance of Reproductive Isolation Between Species

For a new species to continue to exist, it must reproduce and continue to remain genetically isolated from other, similar species. The speciation process involves the development of **reproductive, or genetic, isolating mechanisms**. These mechanisms prevent matings between members of two different species and, therefore, help maintain distinct species. There are several mechanisms for maintaining reproductive (genetic) isolation:

1. **Habitat preference, or ecological, isolating mechanisms,** occur when two species do not have the opportunity to interbreed because they typically live in different ecological settings. For example, in central Mexico, two species of robin-sized birds, called *towhees,* live in the same general region. However, the collared towhee lives on the mountainsides in the pine forest, whereas the spotted towhee is found at lower elevations in oak forests. Geography presents no barriers to these birds. They are capable of flying to each other's habitats, but they do not. Therefore, they are reproductively isolated because of the habitats they prefer. Similarly, areas with wet soil have different species of plants than nearby areas with drier soils.

2. **Seasonal isolating mechanisms** (differences in the time of year at which reproduction takes place) are effective genetic isolating mechanisms. Some plants flower only in the spring, whereas other species that are closely related flower in midsummer or fall; therefore, the two species are not very likely to pollinate one another. Among insects, there are examples of similar spacing of the reproductive periods of closely related species, so that they do not overlap.

3. **Behavioral isolating mechanisms** occur when inborn behavior patterns prevent breeding between species. The mating calls of frogs and crickets are highly specific. The sound pattern produced by the males is species-specific and invites only females of the same species to engage in mating. The females have a built-in response to the particular species-specific call and mate only with those that produce the correct call. The courtship behavior of birds involves both sound and visual signals that are species-specific. For example, groups of male prairie chickens gather on meadows shortly before dawn in the early summer and begin their dances. The air sacs on both sides of the neck are inflated, so that the brightly colored skin is exposed. Their feet move up and down very rapidly and their wings are spread out and quiver slightly (figure 14.4).

**FIGURE 14.4 Courtship Behavior (Behavioral Isolating Mechanism)**
The dancing of a male prairie chicken attracts female prairie chickens, but not females of other species. This behavior tends to keep prairie chickens reproductively isolated from other species.

This combination of sight and sound is attractive to females. When the females arrive, the males compete for the opportunity to mate with them. Other, related species of birds conduct their own similar, but distinct, courtship displays. The differences among the dances are great enough that a female can recognize the dance of a male of her own species. Behavioral isolating mechanisms such as these occur among other types of animals as well. The strutting of a peacock, the fin display of a beta (Siamese fighting) fish, and the flashing light patterns of "lightning bugs"/"fireflies" (they are actually beetles) of various species are all examples of behaviors that help individuals identify members of their own species and prevent different species from interbreeding (figure 14.5).

4. **Mechanical**, or **morphological**, **isolating mechanisms** involve differences in the structure of organisms. The specific shapes of the structures involved in reproduction may prevent different species from interbreeding. Among insects, the structure of the penis and the reciprocal structures of the female fit like a lock and key; therefore, breeding between different species is very difficult. Similarly, the shapes of flowers may permit only certain animals to carry pollen from one flower to the next.

5. **Biochemical isolating mechanisms** occur when molecular incompatibility prevents successful mating. A vast number of biochemical activities take place around the union of egg and sperm. Molecules on the outside of the egg or sperm may trigger events that prevent their union if they are not from the same species. Among plants, biochemical interactions between the pollen and the receiving flower prevent the germination of the pollen grain and, therefore, prevent sexual reproduction between two closely related species.

6. **Hybrid inviability**, or **infertility**, **mechanisms** prevents the offspring of two different species from continuing to

(a) Species-specific sounds

(b) Species-specific displays

**FIGURE 14.5 Animal Communication—Identifying Members of Their Own Species**
Most animals use specific behaviors to communicate with others of the same species. *(a)* The trilling of a male American toad is specific to its species and is different from that of males of other species. *(b)* The visual displays of this orange octopus communicate to others of the same species.

reproduce. This can occur in three ways: (a) the embryos of such a mating may not develop properly and die; (b) if offspring are produced, they die before they can reproduce; or (c) such hybrids may be sterile or have greatly reduced fertility (review figure 14.1).

back into an earlier stage in its development. Furthermore, because species are reproductively isolated from one another, they usually do not combine with other species to make something new; they can only diverge further. When life in the past is compared with our current diversity of life, many different evolutionary patterns emerge.

## Divergent Evolution

**Divergent evolution** is a basic evolutionary pattern in which individual speciation events cause successive branches in the evolution of a group of organisms. This basic pattern is well illustrated by the evolution of the horse, shown in figure 14.6 Each of the many branches of the evolutionary history of the horse began with a speciation event that separated one species into two species as each separately adapted to local conditions. Changes in the environment from moist forests to drier grasslands would have set the stage for change. The modern horse, with its large size, single toe on each foot, and teeth designed for grinding grasses, is thought to be the result of accumulated genetic changes beginning from a small, dog-sized animal with four toes on its front feet, three toes on its hind feet, and teeth designed for chewing leaves and small twigs. Even though we know much about

## 14.4 Evolutionary Patterns Above the Species Level

A species is the smallest irreversible unit of evolution. Because the exact conditions present when a species came into being will never exist again, it is highly unlikely that it will evolve

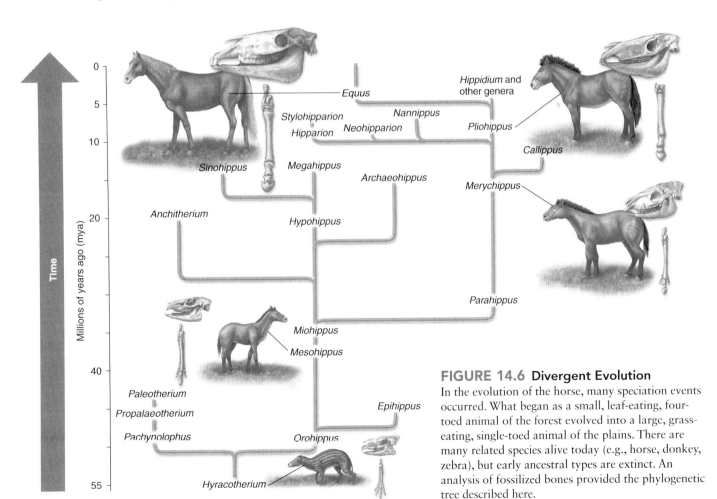

**FIGURE 14.6 Divergent Evolution**
In the evolution of the horse, many speciation events occurred. What began as a small, leaf-eating, four-toed animal of the forest evolved into a large, grass-eating, single-toed animal of the plains. There are many related species alive today (e.g., horse, donkey, zebra), but early ancestral types are extinct. An analysis of fossilized bones provided the phylogenetic tree described here.

evolution, there are still many gaps that need to be filled before we have a complete evolutionary history of any organism (Outlooks 14.1).

## Extinction

**Extinction** is the loss of a species. It is a common pattern in the evolution of organisms. Notice in figure 14.6 that most of the species that developed during the evolution of the horse are extinct. Only members of the genus *Equus* remain. This is typical. Most of the species that have ever existed are extinct. Estimates of extinction are around 99%; that is, 99% or more of all the species that ever existed are extinct. Given this high rate of extinction, we can picture current species of organisms as the product of much evolutionary experimentation. This is not the complete picture, though. Recall from chapter 13 that organisms are continually being subjected to selection pressures that lead to a high degree of adaptation to a particular set of environmental conditions. Organisms become more and more specialized. However, the environment does not remain constant; it often changes in such a way that the species that were originally present are unable to adapt to the new set of conditions. The early ancestors of the modern horse were well adapted to a moist tropical environment, but, when the climate became drier, most were no longer able to survive. Only some kinds had the genes necessary to lead to the development of modern horses and their relatives.

Furthermore, many extinct species were very successful organisms for millions of years. They were not failures for their time but simply did not survive to the present. It is also important to realize that many currently existing organisms will eventually become extinct—perhaps even *Homo sapiens*. Thus, the basic evolutionary pattern is one of divergence with a great deal of extinction. Although divergence and extinction are dominant themes in the evolution of life, adaptive radiation and convergent evolution are two other important evolutionary patterns.

## Adaptive Radiation

**Adaptive radiation** is an evolutionary pattern characterized by a rapid increase in the number of kinds of closely related species. Adaptive radiation results in an evolutionary explosion of new species from a common ancestor. There are basically two situations thought to favor adaptive radiation. One is a condition in which an organism invades a previously unexploited environment. For example, at one time, there were no animals on the landmasses of the Earth. The amphibians were the first vertebrate animals able to spend part of their lives on land. Fossil evidence shows that a variety of amphibians evolved rapidly and exploited several kinds of lifestyles.

Another good example of adaptive radiation is found among the finches of the Galápagos Islands, located 1,000 kilometers west of Ecuador in the Pacific Ocean. These birds were first studied by Charles Darwin. Because these islands are volcanic and arose from the ocean floor, it is assumed that they have always been isolated from South America and originally lacked finches and other land-based birds. It is thought that one kind of finch arrived from South America to colonize the islands and that adaptive radiation from the common ancestor resulted in the many kinds of finches found on the islands today (figure 14.7). Although the islands are close to one another, they are quite diverse. Some are dry and treeless, some have moist forests, and others have intermediate conditions. Conditions were ideal for several speciation events. Because the islands were separated from one another,

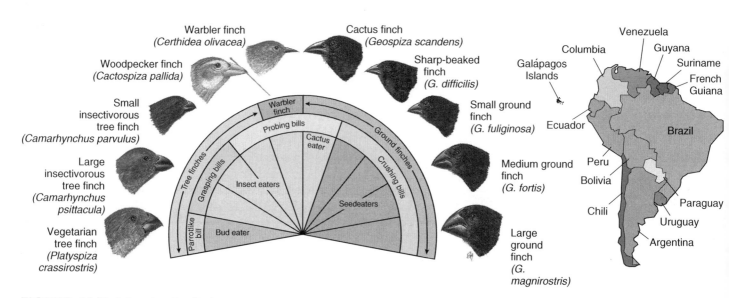

**FIGURE 14.7 Adaptive Radiation**
When Darwin discovered the finches of the Galápagos Islands, he thought they might all have derived from one common ancestor that arrived on these relatively isolated islands. If they were the only birds to inhabit the islands, they could have evolved very rapidly into the many types shown here. The drawings show the specializations of beaks for different kinds of food.

## OUTLOOKS 14.1

# Evolution and Domesticated Cats

The evolutionary history of the domestic cat (*Felis silvestris lybica*) has been unclear because of incomplete fossil records. However, an international team sampling both mitochondrial DNA and the DNA from both X and Y sex chromosomes has finally come up with an evolutionary tree for felines. The group proposes that about 11 million years ago, a single, ancestral feline-like species migrated from Asia throughout the world except Australia.

Researchers believe that 10 to 3 million years ago (MYA) land bridges between continents were created when sea levels fell. The common ancestor to all of today's cats probably migrated south to Africa from Asia. The cats also moved north crossing the Bering land bridge (as wide as 1,000 miles) to North America and migrated to South America by the Panamanian land bridge. When sea levels rose, they covered the land bridges and cut off cat species from their original groups. These isolated subpopulations genetically drifted apart, each adapting

to its unique environment. When the subpopulations had the chance of coming back together, they were no longer able to interbreed and, at that point, found themselves to be different species. Ancestral felines, originally a Eurasian genus, successfully migrated throughout the globe because they encountered little or no competition from other carnivores. They continue to be one of the most successful of carnivore families.

Traditionally, domestication was thought to have occurred about 3,600 years ago in Egypt. Archeological evidence in Egyptian hieroglyphics portrays cats, and bones of cats have been found buried with humans in tombs. However, more recent archeological and genetic evidence strongly suggests that cats were domesticated about 9,500 years ago in the Fertile Crescent, the Middle East. Today, this region includes Egypt, Israel, the West Bank, Gaza strip, and Lebanon; and parts of Jordan, Syria, Iraq, southeastern Turkey, and southwestern Iran and Kuwait.

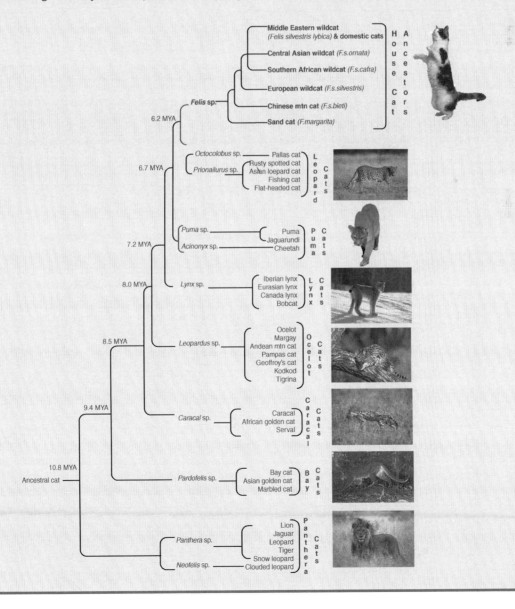

**Historical record of the vertebrates**

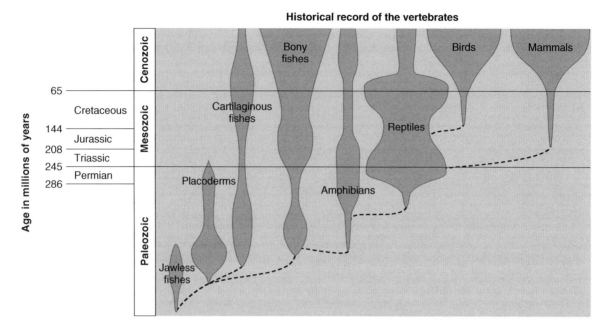

**FIGURE 14.8 Adaptive Radiation in Terrestrial Vertebrates**
The amphibians were the first vertebrates to live on land. They were replaced by the reptiles, which were better adapted to land. The reptiles, in turn, were replaced by the adaptive radiation of birds and mammals. (Note: The width of the colored bars indicates the number of species present.)

the element of geographic isolation was present. Because environmental conditions on the islands were quite different, particular characteristics in the resident birds would have been favored. Furthermore, the absence of other kinds of birds meant that there were many lifestyles that had not been exploited.

In the absence of competition, some of these finches took roles normally filled by other kinds of birds elsewhere in the world. Although finches are normally seed-eating birds, some of the Galápagos finches became warblerlike insect-eaters, others became leaf-eaters, and one uses a cactus spine as a tool to probe for insects.

The second situation that can favor adaptive radiation is one in which a type of organism evolves a new set of characteristics that enables it to displace organisms that previously filled specific roles in the environment. For example, although amphibians were the first vertebrates to occupy land, they lived only near freshwater, where they would not dry out and could lay eggs, which developed in the water. They were replaced by reptiles with such characteristics as dry skin, which prevented the loss of water, and an egg that could develop on land. The adaptive radiation of reptiles was extensive. They invaded most terrestrial settings and even evolved forms that flew and lived in the sea. With the extinction of dinosaurs and many other reptiles, birds and mammals went through a similar radiation. Perhaps the development of homeothermism (the ability to maintain a constant body temperature) had something to do with the success of birds and mammals. Figure 14.8 shows the radiations that occurred within the vertebrate group. The number

of species of bony fishes has increased as the number of other kinds of fishes (jawless fishes, placoderms, cartilaginous fishes) declined and the number of species of birds and mammals has increased as the number of reptiles and amphibians decreased.

## Convergent Evolution

**Convergent evolution** is an interesting evolutionary pattern that involves the development of similar characteristics in organisms of widely different evolutionary backgrounds. This pattern often leads people to misinterpret the evolutionary history of organisms. For example, many kinds of plants that live in desert situations have sharp, pointed structures, such as spines or thorns, and lack leaves during much of the year. Superficially, the sharp, pointed structures may resemble one another to a remarkable degree but may have a completely different evolutionary history. Some of these structures are modified twigs, others are modified leaves, and still others are modifications of the surface of the stem. The presence of sharp, pointed structures and the absence of leaves are adaptations to a desert type of environment: The thorns and spines discourage herbivores and the absence of leaves reduces water loss.

Another example is animals that survive by catching insects while flying. Bats, swallows, and dragonflies all obtain food in this manner. They have wings, good eyesight or hearing to locate flying insects, and great agility and speed in flight, but they are evolved from quite different ancestors (figure 14.9). At first glance, they may appear very similar

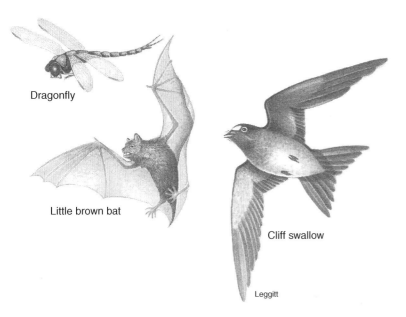

**FIGURE 14.9 Convergent Evolution**
All of these animals have evolved wings as a method of movement and capture insects for food as they fly. However, flight originated independently in each of them.

and perhaps closely related, but a detailed study of their wings and other structures shows that they are different kinds of animals. They have simply converged in structure, the type of food they eat, and their method of obtaining food. Likewise, whales, sharks, and the barracuda appear to be similar—they all have a streamlined shape, which aids in rapid movement through the water; a dorsal fin, which helps prevent rolling; fins or flippers for steering; and a large tail,

which provides power for swimming. However, they are quite different kinds of animals that happen to live in the open ocean, where they pursue other animals as prey. Their structural similarities are adaptations to being fast-swimming predators.

## Homologous or Analogous Structures

To help evolutionary biologists distinguish between structures that are the result of convergent evolution and those that are not, they try to determine if the structures evolved from a common ancestor. **Homologous structures** are structures in different species that have been derived from a common ancestral structure. Thus, the wing of a bat, the front leg of a horse, and the arm of a human show the same basic pattern of bones, but they are extreme modifications of the same basic evolutionary structure (figure 14.10). On the other hand, structures that have the same function (such as the wing of a butterfly and the wing of a bird) but different evolutionary backgrounds are called **analogous structures** and are the result of convergent evolution (review figure 14.9).

## 14.4   CONCEPT REVIEW

10. Describe convergent evolution and adaptive radiation.
11. What are the two dominant evolutionary patterns?
12. How are analogous and homologous structures different?

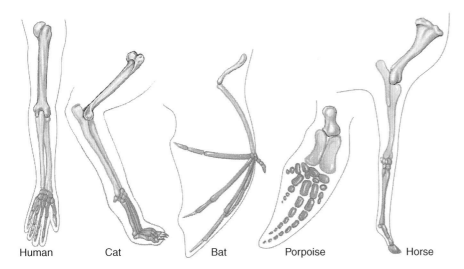

**FIGURE 14.10 Maintaining Traits Through Time—Homologous Structures**
Although these body parts are considerably different in structure and function, the same bones are present in the forelimbs of humans, cats, bats, porpoises, and horses.

## 14.5   Rates of Evolution

Although it is commonly thought that evolutionary change takes long periods of time, rates of evolution can vary greatly. Remember that natural selection is driven by the environment. If the environment is changing rapidly, changes in organisms should be rapid. Periods of rapid environmental change also result in extensive episodes of extinction. During some periods in the history of the Earth when little environmental change was taking place, the rate of evolutionary change was probably slow. Nevertheless, when we talk about evolutionary time, we are generally thinking in thousands or millions of years. Although both of these time periods are long compared with the human life span, the difference between thousands of years and millions of years in the evolutionary time scale is still significant.

The fossil record shows many examples of gradual changes in the physical features of organisms over time. For example, the extinct humanoid fossil *Homo erectus* shows a gradual increase in the size of the skull, a reduction in the size of the jaw, and the development of a chin over about a million years. The accumulation of these changes could result in such extensive change from the original species that we would consider the current organism to be a different species from its ancestor. (Many believe that *Homo erectus* became modern humans, *Homo sapiens*.) This is such a common feature of the evolutionary record that biologists refer to this kind of evolutionary change as *gradualism* (figure 14.11a).

**Gradualism** is a model for evolutionary change that evolution occurred slowly by accumulating small changes over a long period of time. Charles Darwin's view of evolution was based on gradual changes in the features of specific species he observed in his studies of geology and natural history. However, as early as the 1940s, some biologists began to challenge gradualism as the only model for evolutionary change. They pointed out that the fossils of some species were virtually unchanged over millions of years. If gradualism were the only explanation for how species evolved, then gradual changes in the fossil record of a species would always be found. Furthermore, some organisms appear suddenly in the fossil record and show rapid change from the time they first appeared. There are many modern examples of rapid evolutionary change; the development of pesticide resistance in insects and antibiotic resistance in various bacteria has occurred recently.

In 1972, two biologists, Niles Eldredge of the American Museum of Natural History and Stephen Jay Gould of Harvard University, proposed a very different idea. **Punctuated equilibrium** is their hypothesis that evolution occurs in spurts of rapid change, followed by long periods with little evolutionary change (figure 14.11b). The punctuated equilibrium concept is a companion hypothesis to gradualism and suggests a different way of achieving evolutionary change. Punctuated equilibrium proposes that, rather than one species slowly accumulating changes to become a different descendant species, there is a rapid evolution of several closely related species from isolated populations. This would produce a number of species that would compete with one another as the environment changed. Many of these species would become extinct and the fossil record would show change.

Another way to look at gradualism and punctuated equilibrium is to assume that both occur. It is clear from the fossil record that there were periods in the past when there was very rapid evolutionary change, compared with other times. Also, some environments, such as the ocean, have been relatively stable, whereas others, such as the terrestrial environment, have changed significantly. Many marine organisms have remained unchanged for hundreds of millions of years,

**(a) Gradualism**

Speciation occurs gradually.

Fossils will show changes over time.

An ancestral species can be transformed into a new species.

**(b) Punctuated Equilibrium**

Occurs rapidly and then a species remains unchanged.

Fossils showing intermediate characteristics will not necessarily be found.

A subpopulation of the ancestral species becomes a new species.

**FIGURE 14.11 Gradualism vs. Punctuated Equilibrium**
*(a)* Gradualism is the evolution of new species from the accumulation of a series of small changes over a long period of time. *(b)* Punctuated equilibrium is the evolution of new species from a large number of changes in a short period of time.

but there has been great change in the kinds of terrestrial organisms in the past few million years. Thus, it is possible that both gradualism and punctuated equilibrium have operated. The important contribution of punctuated equilibrium is that there can be alternative ways of interpreting the fossil record and that the pace of evolution can be quite variable. However, both approaches take into account the importance of genetic diversity as the raw material for evolution and the mechanism of natural selection as the process of determining which gene combinations fit the environment. The gradualists point to the fossil record as proof that evolution is a slow, steady process. Those who support punctuated equilibrium point to the gaps in the fossil record as evidence that rapid change occurs.

## 14.5 CONCEPT REVIEW

13. What is the difference between gradualism and punctuated equilibrium?

## 14.6 The Tentative Nature of the Evolutionary History of Organisms

Tracing the evolutionary history of an organism back to its origins is a very difficult task, because most of its ancestors no longer exist. Scientists act as "time detectives" when they study fossils of extinct organisms but must keep in mind that the fossil record is incomplete and provides only limited information about the biology of the organism represented in that record. However, new fossils are always being discovered.

There are three reasons that the fossil record is incomplete. First, the likelihood that an organism will become a fossil is low. Most organisms die and decompose, leaving no trace of their existence. (Today, road-killed opossums are not likely to become fossils because they will be eaten by scavengers, repeatedly run over, or decompose by the roadside.) Second, in order to form a fossil, the dead organism must be covered by sediments, dehydrated, or preserved in some other way.

Several factors increase the likelihood that an organism will be found in the fossil record:

- The presence of hard body parts resist decomposition.
- Marine organisms can be covered by sediment on the bottom.
- Fossils of more recent organisms are less likely to have been destroyed by geological forces.
- Fossils of large organisms are easier to find.
- Organisms that were extremely common are more likely to show up in the fossil record.

For example, trilobites are very common in the fossil record. They were relatively large marine organisms, with hard body parts, that were extremely abundant. However, fossils of soft-bodied, extremely ancient, wormlike organisms are rare.

Third, the discovery of fossils is often accidental. It is impossible to search through all the layers of sedimentary rock on the entire surface of the Earth. Therefore, scientists will continue to find new fossils that will extend the known information about ancient life into the foreseeable future. But there can be no question that evolution occurred in the past and continues to occur today (How Science Works 14.1).

Scientists may know a lot about the structure of the bones and teeth or the stems and leaves of an extinct ancestor from fossils but know almost nothing about its behavior, physiology, and natural history. Biologists must use a great deal of indirect evidence to piece together the series of evolutionary steps that led to a current species.

### 14.6 CONCEPT REVIEW

14. Why is it difficult to determine the evolutionary history of a species?

## 14.7 Human Evolution

There is intense curiosity about how our species (*Homo sapiens*) came to be, and the evolution of the human species remains an interesting and hot topic. Human beings are classified as mammals belonging to a group known as primates. Primates are thought to have come into existence approximately 66 million years ago. They include animals with enlarged, complex brains; five digits, with nails, on the hands and feet; and hands and feet adapted for grasping. Their bodies, except those of humans, are covered with hair. There are two groups of primates, the prosimians—lemurs and tarsiers—and the anthropoids—monkeys, apes, and humans (figure 14.12).

You cannot shake hands with any other species belonging to the genus *Homo*. All other versions of our close evolutionary relatives are extinct. This makes it difficult to visualize our evolutionary development. Therefore we tend to think we are not subject to the laws of nature. However, humans show genetic diversity, experience mutations, and are subject to the same evolutionary forces as other organisms.

Scientists use several kinds of evidence to try to sort out our evolutionary history. Fossils of various kinds of prehuman and ancient human ancestors have been found, but many of these are only fragments of skeletons, which are difficult to interpret and are hard to date. Stone tools of various kinds have also been found that are associated with prehuman and early human sites. Finally, other aspects of the culture of our ancestors have been found in burial sites, including cave paintings and ceremonial objects. Various methods have been used to date these findings. When fossils are examined, anthropologists can identify differences in the structures of bones that are consistent with changes in species. Based on the amount of change they see and the ages of the fossils, scientists make judgments about the species to which the fossil belongs.

As new discoveries are made, experts' opinions will change, and our evolutionary history may become clearer as old ideas are replaced. Scientists must also review and make changes in the terminology they use to refer to our ancestors. The term *hominin* now refers to humans and their humanlike ancestors, whereas previously the term *hominid* was used. The term *hominid* now refers to the broader group that includes all humanlike organisms plus the great apes—gorillas, orangutans, chimpanzees, and bonobos. When you read material about this topic, you will need to determine how the terms are being used. Although there is no clear picture of how humans evolved, the fossil record shows that humans are a relatively recent addition to the forms of life. Members of the genus *Homo* are believed to have evolved at least 2.2 million to 2.5 million years ago (Table 14.1).

# HOW SCIENCE WORKS 14.1

## Accumulating Evidence for Evolution

The theory of evolution has become the major unifying theory of the biological sciences. Those in medicine understand the dangers of mutations, the similarity in function of the same organ in related species, and the way in which the environment can interfere with the preprogrammed process of embryological development. Agricultural science has demonstrated the importance of selecting specific genetically determined characteristics for passage into new varieties of crop plants and animals. The concepts of mutation, selection, and evolution are so fundamental to an understanding of what happens in biology that we often forget to take note of the many kinds of observations that support the theory of evolution. The following list describes some of the more important pieces of evidence that support the idea that evolution has been a major force in shaping the nature of living things.

1. Species and populations are not genetically fixed. Change occurs in individuals and populations.
   a. Mutations cause slight changes in the genetic makeup of an individual organism.
   b. Different populations of the same species show adaptations suitable for their local conditions.
   c. Changes in the characteristics displayed by species can be linked to environmental changes.
   d. The selective breeding of domesticated plants and animals indicates that the shape, color, behavior, metabolism, and many other characteristics of organisms can be selected for.
   e. The extinction of poorly adapted species is common.
2. All evidence suggests that, once embarked on a particular evolutionary road, structures, behaviors, or physiological processes are not abandoned, only modified. New organisms are formed by the modification of ancestral species, not by major changes. The following list supports the concept that evolution proceeds by the modification of previously existing structures and processes, rather than by catastrophic change.
   a. All species use the same DNA code.
   b. All species use the same left-handed (levorotary) amino acid building blocks.
   c. It is difficult to eliminate a body part when it is part of a developmental process controlled by genes. A vestigial structure is an organ that is functionless and generally reduced in size. It resembles the fully functioning organs found in related organisms. Structures such as the human appendix, whale pelvic bones, and human tailbone are vestigial structures and evidence of genetic material from previous stages in evolution.
   d. The embryological development of related animals is similar, regardless of the peculiarities of adult anatomy. All vertebrate embryos have an early stage that contains gill-like structures.
   e. Species of organisms that are known to be closely related show greater similarity in their DNA than do those that are distantly related.

**Fossil of sequoia twig**

3. Several aspects of the fossil record support the concept of evolution.
   a. The nature of the Earth has changed significantly over time.
   b. The fossil record shows vast changes in the kinds of organisms present on Earth. New species appear and most go extinct. This is evidence that living things change in response to changes in their environment.
   c. The fossils found in old rocks do not reappear in younger rocks. Once an organism goes extinct, it does not reappear, but new organisms arise that are modifications of previous organisms.

***Archaeopteryx*, fossil skeleton with feathers**

# HOW SCIENCE WORKS 14.1 (*Continued*)

4. New techniques and discoveries invariably support the theory of evolution.
   a. The recognition that the Earth was formed billions of years ago supports the slow development of new kinds of organisms.
   b. The recognition that the continents of the Earth have separated helps explain why organisms on Australia are so different from those elsewhere.
   c. The discovery of DNA and how it works helps explain mutation and demonstrates the genetic similarity of closely related species.
   d. Similarities in protein structure can indicate the degree of relatedness among organisms. For example, the greater the evolutionary distance from humans, the greater is the number of amino acid differences in the vertebrate hemoglobin polypeptide.

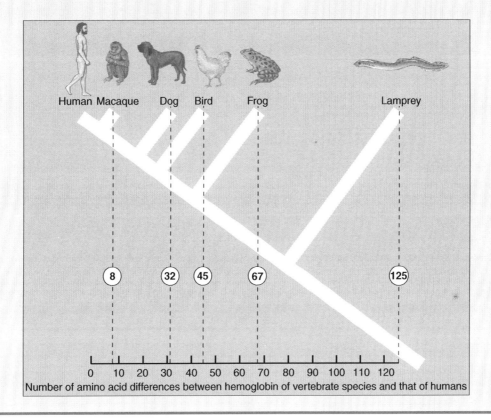

Number of amino acid differences between hemoglobin of vertebrate species and that of humans

1. There is a great deal of fossil evidence that several species of the genera *Australopithecus* and *Paranthropus* were common in Africa beginning at about 4 million years ago. These organisms walked upright and are often referred to collectively as australopiths.
2. Based on fossil evidence, it appears that the climate of Africa was becoming drier during much of the time during which the evolution of humans was occurring.
3. The earliest *Australopithecus* fossils are from about 4.2 million years ago. Earlier fossils, such as *Ardipithecus* (which could have included a number of species), *Orrorin*, and *Sahelanthropus* may be ancestral to the genus *Australopithecus*. *Ardipithecus* would most likely be a "distant cousin" to human beings rather than a direct ancestor. *Australopithecus* and *Paranthropus* were herbivores and walked upright. Their fossils and those of earlier organisms, such as *Ardipithecus*, *Orrorin*, and *Sahelanthropus*, are found only in Africa.
4. The australopiths were sexually dimorphic, with the males much larger than the females, and they had relatively small brains (a cranial capacity of 530 cm³ or less—about the size of a standard softball).
5. Several species of the genus *Homo* became prominent in Africa beginning at about 2.2 million years ago and appear to have made a change from a primarily herbivorous diet to a carnivorous or omnivorous diet.
6. All members of the genus *Homo* have relatively large brains compared with the australopiths. The cranial capacity ranges from about 650 cm³ for early fossils of *Homo* to about 1,450 cm³ for modern humans. These organisms are also associated with various degrees of

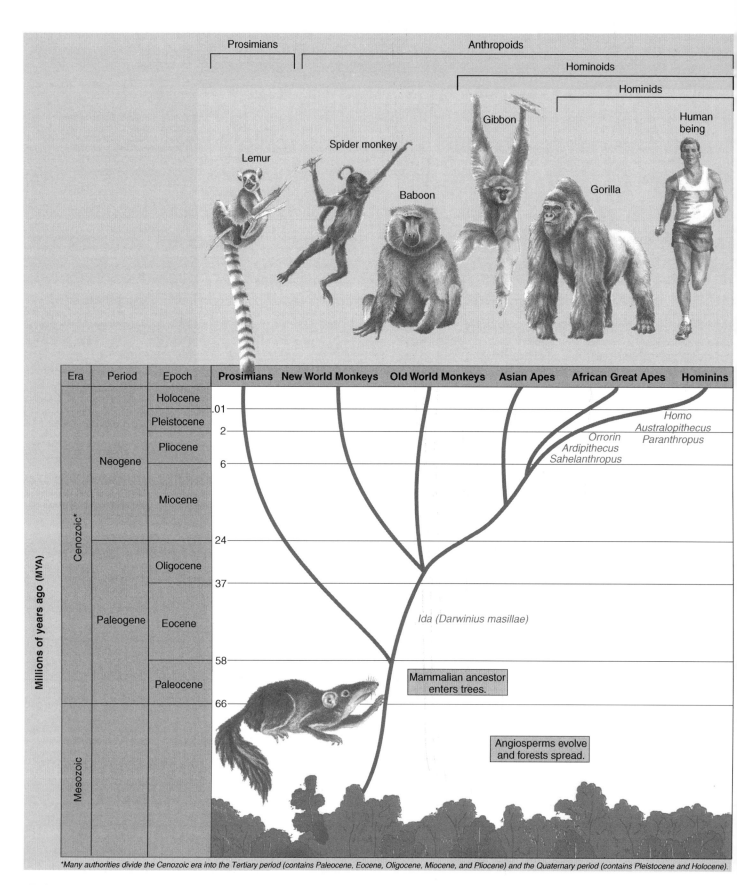

The following labels appear across the top of the figure:

Prosimians | Anthropoids

Hominoids

Hominids

Lemur · Spider monkey · Baboon · Gibbon · Gorilla · Human being

Column headers in the chart:

| Era | Period | Epoch | Prosimians | New World Monkeys | Old World Monkeys | Asian Apes | African Great Apes | Hominins |

Millions of years ago (MYA)

Cenozoic*

Neogene — Holocene, Pleistocene, Pliocene, Miocene

Paleogene — Oligocene, Eocene, Paleocene

Mesozoic

Time markers: .01, 2, 6, 24, 37, 58, 66

Homo
Australopithecus
Paranthropus
Orrorin
Ardipithecus
Sahelanthropus

Ida (Darwinius masillae)

Mammalian ancestor enters trees.

Angiosperms evolve and forests spread.

*Many authorities divide the Cenozoic era into the Tertiary period (contains Paleocene, Eocene, Oligocene, Miocene, and Pliocene) and the Quaternary period (contains Pleistocene and Holocene).

**FIGURE 14.12 Where We Are on the Primate Tree**

As new evidence is uncovered, scientists reconsider how that information best fits into the hypothesis on the evolution of humans. As the pieces of the puzzle are reexamined and rearranged, we see a clearer picture of where human beings fit in the scheme of life.

**TABLE 14.1  Primate Classification— Order to Subfamily**

| Classification Category | Name | Members |
|---|---|---|
| Order | Primates (*Primates*) | Prosimians, tarsiers, monkeys, gibbons, orangutans, gorillas, chimps, humans |
| Suborder | Anthropoidea (*Anthropoid*) | Tarsiers, monkeys, gibbons, orangutans, gorillas, chimpanzee, humans |
| Superfamily | Hominoidea (*Hominoid*) | Gibbons, orangutans, gorillas, chimps, humans |
| Family | Hominidae (*Hominid*) | Orangutans, gorillas, chimps, humans |
| Subfamily | Homininae (*Hominin*) | Humans and direct ancestors |

stone tool construction and use. Some of the australopiths may also have constructed stone tools.

7. The fossils of australopiths, several early species of *Homo*, and the fossils of earlier organisms such as *Ardipithecus*, *Orrorin*, and *Sahelanthropus* are found only in Africa. Fossils of several later species of the genus *Homo* have larger brains and are found in Africa, Europe, and Asia but not in Australia or the Americas. Only *Homo sapiens* is found in Australia and the Americas.

8. Since the fossils of *Homo* species found in Asia and Europe are generally younger than the early *Homo* species found in Africa, it is assumed that species of *Homo* migrated from Africa to Europe and Asia from Africa.

9. Differences in size between males and females are less prominent in the members of the genus *Homo*, so perhaps there were fewer sexual differences in activities than with the australopiths.

When scientists put all these bits of information together, they constructed the following scenario for the likely evolution of our species. Rather than humans evolving from a chimpanzee-like ancestor, chimps and humans evolved from a common primate ancestor. Early primates, ancestors to modern monkeys, chimpanzees, and apes, were adapted to living in forested areas, where their grasping hands, opposable thumbs, big toes, and wide range of shoulder movement, allow them to move freely in the trees. As the climate became drier, grasslands replaced the forests. Early hominins were adapted to drier conditions. Walking upright was probably an adaptation to these conditions. Most later hominins had large brains and used tools. A recent find, however, illustrates just how tentative the understanding of human evolution really is.

The discovery of fossils of a small human—known as the "hobbit"—in the sediments of a cave on an Indonesian island in 2003 has led to much speculation about a possible new species of *Homo*; *Homo floresiensis*. The fossils were dated to about

18,000 years ago. There has been much discussion among scientists about the significance of this discovery. Some feel that the small size indicates a developmental abnormality and that the remains could be that of an abnormally small *H. sapiens*. Others suggest that there are many examples of island animals that show small size and that these fossils were adapted to island conditions. Research continues and a more complete understanding will develop as more information is gathered. Like other human relatives, *H. floresiensis* is extinct. Therefore, *the sole surviving member of our evolutionary line is* Homo sapiens. We are now going to look at several organisms important to understanding the evolution of human beings.

## The Genus *Ardipithecus*

*Ardipithecus ramidus* lived in woodlands and was able to walk upright when on the ground as well as navigate on branches of trees. The fossils from the best-studied site have been aged at about 4.4 million years ago. Studies of these fossils indicate that *Ardipithecus ramidus* was about 120 cm (4 ft) tall when standing, weighed about 50 kg (110 lb), and had a brain capacity of less than 400 cm³. It was able to walk and run on its hindlimbs but had an opposable big toe and was able to climb and walk on the tops of branches on all fours. Males and females were about the same size. They ate a variety of plant and animal materials in their woodland habitat.

## The Genera *Australopithecus* and *Paranthropus*

Both *Australopithecus* and *Paranthropus* are important evolutionary links in understanding our evolutionary past. Various species of *Australopithecus* and *Paranthropus* were present in Africa from about 4.4 million years ago until about 1 million years ago. Various members of these two extinct genera are often referred to as australopiths. *Australopithecus* is the genus to which the famed 3.2 million-year-old "Lucy" belongs, together with a 3.3 million-year-old *A. afarensis*, dubbed "Lucy's baby." Lucy's baby, Selam, is estimated to have been about 3 years of age when she died and is the most complete hominin skeleton ever found. There are few fossils of these early humanlike organisms, however, and many fossils are fragments of organisms. This has led to much speculation and argument among experts about the specific position each fossil has in the evolutionary history of humans. However, from examinations of the fossil bones of the leg, pelvis, and foot, it is apparent that the australopiths were relatively short (males, 1.5 meters or less; females, about 1.1 meters) and stocky and walked upright, as humans do. They had relatively small brains (cranial capacity 530 cm³ or less—about the size of a standard softball).

An upright posture had several advantages in a world that was becoming drier. It allowed for more rapid movement over long distances and the ability to see longer distances, and it reduced the amount of heat gained from the sun. In addition, upright posture freed the arms for other uses, such as carrying and manipulating objects and using tools. The various species of *Australopithecus* and *Paranthropus* shared these characteristics and, based on the structure of their skulls, jaws, and teeth, appear to have been herbivores with relatively small brains.

## The Genus *Homo*

About 2.5 million years ago, the first members of the genus *Homo* appeared on the scene. There is considerable disagreement about how many species there were, but *Homo habilis* is one of the earliest. *H. habilis* had a larger brain (650 cm³) and smaller teeth than the australopiths and made much more use of stone tools. Some experts feel that it was a direct descendant of *Australopithecus africanus*. Many experts feel that *H. habilis* persisted until about 1.44 million years ago. *H. habilis* made use of group activities, tools, and higher intelligence to take over the kills made by other carnivores. The higher-quality diet would have supported the metabolic needs of the larger brain.

About 1.8 million years ago, *Homo ergaster* appeared. It was much larger, up to 1.6 meters tall, than *H. habilis*, which was about 1.3 meters tall and had a much larger brain (a cranial capacity of 850 cm³). A little later, a similar species (*Homo erectus*) appeared in the fossil record and for awhile, coexisted with *H. habilis*. Some consider *H. ergaster* and *H. erectus* to be variations of the same species. Along with their larger brains and body size, *H. ergaster* and *H. erectus* are distinguished from earlier species by their extensive use of stone tools. Hand axes were manufactured and used to cut the flesh of prey and crush the bones to obtain the fatty marrow. These organisms appear to have been predators, whereas *H. habilis* was a scavenger. The use of meat as food allows animals to move about more freely, because appropriate food is available almost everywhere. By contrast, herbivores are often confined to places that have foods appropriate to their use: fruits for fruit eaters, grass for grazers, forests for browsers, and so on. In fact, fossils of *H. erectus* have been found in the Middle East and Asia, as well as Africa. Most experts feel that *H. erectus* originated in Africa and migrated through the Middle East to Asia.

At about 800,000 years ago, another hominin, classified as *Homo heidelbergensis*, appeared in the fossil record. Since fossils of this species are found in Africa, Europe, and Asia, it appears that they constitute a second wave of migration of early *Homo* from Africa to other parts of the world. Both *H. erectus* and *H. heidelbergensis* disappeared from the fossil record as two new species (*Homo neanderthalensis* and *Homo sapiens*) become common.

The Neandertals were primarily found in Europe and adjoining parts of Asia and were not found in Africa. Since Neandertals were common in Europe, many people feel Neandertals are descendants of *H. heidelbergensis*, which also was common in Europe and preceded Neandertals (How Science Works 14.2).

## Two Points of View on the Origin of *Homo sapiens*

*Homo sapiens* is found throughout the world and is now the only species remaining of a long line of ancestors. Two theories seek to explain the origin of *Homo sapiens*. One theory, known as the **out-of-Africa hypothesis**, states that modern humans (*Homo sapiens*) originated in Africa, as did several other similar species (figure 14.13). They migrated

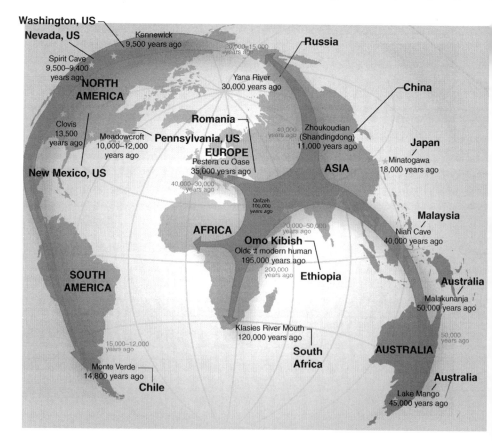

**FIGURE 14.13 Out-of Africa Hypothesis**
Most scientists favor this explanation on the origin and dispersal of *Homo sapiens* that arose in Africa about 200,000 years ago. The first to leave ventured out some 70,000 to 50,000 years ago, reaching Asia and Australia about 50,000 years ago. Speculation is that they moved into the Americas about 20,000 to 15,000 years ago taking advantage of low sea levels and a land bridge that connect Siberia to Alaska.

## HOW SCIENCE WORKS 14.2

# Neandertals—*Homo neanderthalensis* or *Homo sapiens*??

An ongoing controversy surrounds the relationship between the Neandertals and other forms of prehistoric humans. One position is that the Neandertals were a small, separate race or subspecies of human that lived in Europe and western Asia from more than 350,000 years ago to about 30,000 years ago. They could have interbred with other humans and may have disappeared because their subspecies was eliminated by interbreeding with more populous, more successful groups. (Many small, remote tribes have been lost as distinct cultural and genetic entities in the same way in recent history.) Others maintain that the Neandertals showed such great difference from other early humans that they must have been a different species and became extinct because they could not compete with more successful *Homo sapiens* immigrants from Africa. (The names of these ancient people typically are derived from the place where the fossils were first discovered. For example, the Neandertals were first found in the Neander Valley of Germany, and the Cro-Magnons, considered to be modern *Homo sapiens*, were initially found in the Cro-Magnon caves in France.)

The use of molecular genetic technology has shed some light on the relationship of the Neandertals to other kinds of humans. Examination of the mitochondrial DNA obtained from the bones of a Neandertal individual reveals that there are significant differences between the Neandertals and other kinds of early humans. This greatly strengthens the argument that the Neandertals were a separate species, *Homo neanderthalensis*.

In 2006, U.S. and German scientists began a two-year project to decipher Neandertals' genetic code. They used samples from a 38,000-year-old Neandertal fossil. They filtered out

*Homo neanderthalensis*

non-Neandertal DNA that had contaminated the samples following the death of the Neandertal individual. The hope is that this investigation will reveal the genetic differences in cognitive abilities (the process of being aware, knowing, thinking, learning, and judging) between *Homo neanderthalensis* and *H. sapiens*. To date, they have evidence suggesting that Neandertals and modern humans may have interbred, most likely *H. sapiens* fathering children with *H. neanderthalensis* females. Using the latest biotech techniques, scientists have found Neandertal and human genomes are between 99.5% and 99.9% identical. Some researchers believe that the most recent common ancestor of the two human species (*H. sapiens* and *H. neanderthalensis*) lived about 800,000 years ago. Others believe a more recent divergence time, about 465,000 to 569,000 years ago.

---

from Africa to Asia and Europe and displaced species such as *H. erectus* and *H. heidelbergensis*, which had previously migrated into these areas. The other theory, known as the **multiregional hypothesis**, states that *H. erectus* evolved into *H. sapiens*. During a period of about 1.7 million years, fossils of *Homo erectus* showed a progressive increase in the size of the cranial capacity and reduction in the size of the jaw, so it is difficult to distinguish *H. erectus* from *H. heidelbergensis* and *H. heidelbergensis* from *H. sapiens*. Proponents of this hypothesis believe that *H. heidelbergensis* is not a distinct species but, rather, an intermediate between the earlier *H. erectus* and *H. sapiens*. According to this theory, various subgroups of *H. erectus* existed throughout Africa, Asia, and Europe and interbreeding among the various groups gave rise to the various races of humans we see today.

Another continuing puzzle is the relationship of *Homo sapiens* to the Neandertals. Some people consider the Neandertals to be a subgroup of *Homo sapiens* specially

adapted to life in the harsh conditions found in postglacial Europe. Others consider them to be a separate species, *Homo neanderthalensis*. The Neandertals were muscular, had a larger brain capacity than modern humans, and had many elements of culture, including burials. The cause of their disappearance from the fossil record at about 25,000 years ago remains a mystery. Perhaps a change to a warmer climate was responsible. Perhaps contact with *Homo sapiens* resulted in their elimination either through hostile interactions or interbreeding with *H. sapiens*, resulting in their absorption into the larger *H. sapiens* population.

Large numbers of fossils of prehistoric humans have been found in all parts of the world. Many of these show evidence of a collective group memory, called *culture*. Cave paintings, carvings in wood and bone, tools of various kinds, and burials are examples. These are also evidence of a capacity to think and invent, as well as "free time" to devote to things other than gathering food and other necessities of life. We may never know how we came to be, but

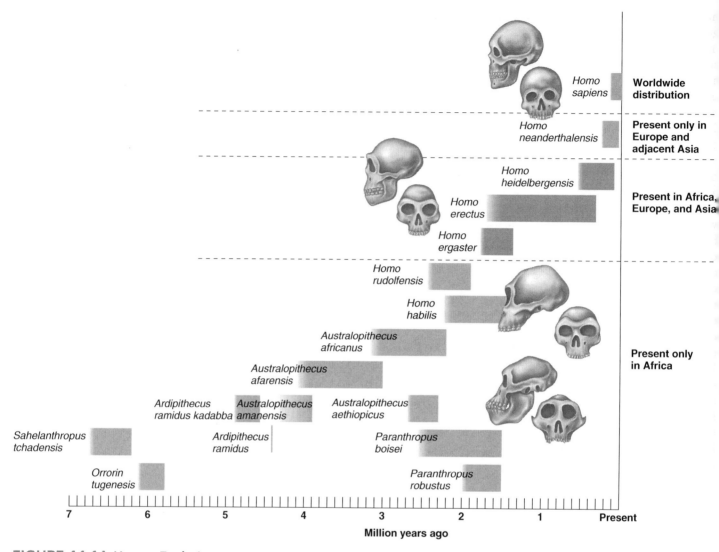

**FIGURE 14.14 Human Evolution**
This diagram shows the various organisms thought to be relatives of humans. The bars represent approximate times the species are thought to have existed. Notice that (1) all species are extinct today except for modern humans, (2) several species of organisms coexisted for extensive periods, (3) all the older species are found only in Africa, and (4) more recent species of *Homo* are found in Europe and Asia, as well as Africa.

we will always be curious and will continue to search and speculate about our beginnings. Figure 14.14 summarizes the current knowledge of the historical record of humans and their relatives.

## 14.7 CONCEPT REVIEW

15. List three differences between australopiths and members of the genus *Homo*.
16. Compare the out-of-Africa hypothesis with the multiregional hypothesis of the origin of *Homo sapiens*.
17. Diagram the relationship among anthropoids, hominoids, and hominids.

## Summary

Populations are usually genetically diverse. Mutations, meiosis, and sexual reproduction tend to introduce genetic diversity into a population. Organisms with wide geographic distribution often show different gene frequencies in different parts of their range. A species is a group of organisms that can interbreed to produce fertile offspring. The process of speciation usually involves the geographic separation of the species into two or more isolated populations. While they are separated, natural selection operates and each population adapts to its environment. If this generates enough change, the two populations may become so different that they cannot interbreed. Similar organisms that have recently evolved into separate species normally have genetic (reproductive) isolating mechanisms to prevent interbreeding. Some of these are habitat preference, seasonal isolating mechanisms, and behavioral isolating mechanisms. Many plants and some animals have a special way of generating new species by increasing their chromosome numbers as a result of abnormal mitosis or meiosis. Organisms that have multiple sets of chromosomes are called polyploids.

Evolution is basically a divergent process on which other patterns can be superimposed. Adaptive radiation is a very rapid divergent evolution; convergent evolution involves the development of superficial similarities among widely different organisms. The rate at which evolution has occurred probably varies. The fossil record shows periods of rapid change interspersed with periods of little change. This has caused some to look for mechanisms that could cause the sudden appearance of large numbers of new species in the fossil record, which challenge the traditional idea of slow, steady change accumulating enough differences to cause a new species to be formed. The early evolution of humans has been difficult to piece together because of the fragmentary evidence. Beginning about 4.4 million years ago, the earliest forms of *Australopithecus* and *Paranthropus* showed upright posture and other humanlike characteristics. The structure of the jaw and teeth indicates that the various kinds of australopiths were herbivores. *Homo habilis* had a larger brain and appears to have been a scavenger. Several other species of the genus *Homo* arose in Africa. These forms appear to have been carnivores. Some of these migrated to Europe and Asia. The origin of *Homo sapiens* is in dispute. It may have arisen in Africa and migrated throughout the world or evolved from earlier ancestors found throughout Africa, Asia, and Europe.

# Key Terms

*Use the interactive flash cards on the **Concepts in Biology**, 14/e website to help you learn the meaning of these terms.*

adaptive radiation 296

analogous structures 299

behavioral isolating
  mechanisms 294

biochemical isolating
  mechanisms 294

convergent evolution 298

divergent evolution 295

extinction 296

fossil 291

gene flow 290

geographic isolation 291

gradualism 300

habitat preference
  (ecological isolating
  mechanisms) 293

homologous
  structures 299

hybrid inviability (infertility
  mechanisms) 294

mechanical (morphological)
  isolating mechanisms 294

multiregional
  hypothesis 307

out-of-Africa hypothesis 306

polyploidy 292

punctuated equilibrium 300

reproductive (genetic)
  isolating mechanisms 293

seasonal isolating
  mechanisms 293

speciation 291

# Basic Review

1. _____ _____ is the movement of genes from one generation to the next as a result of reproduction or from one region to another by migration.

2. A(n) _____ is any remains of an organism of a past geologic age, such as a preserved skeleton or body imprint.

3. Which of the following steps are not necessary for speciation to occur?
   a. geographic isolation
   b. genetic divergence
   c. reproductive isolation
   d. hybrid viability

4. The _____ of an organism is the geographic area over which a species can be found.
   a. range
   b. region
   c. pasture
   d. geographic location

5. If individuals from separate populations overcome the geographic barrier, they may not have accumulated enough _____ to prevent reproductive success.
   a. mutations
   b. genetic differences
   c. barriers
   d. sexual differences

6. _____ is a condition of having multiple sets of chromosomes, rather than the normal haploid or diploid number.

7. Differences in the time of the year at which reproduction takes place are called
   a. geographic isolating mechanisms.
   b. hybrid isolating mechanisms.
   c. seasonal isolating mechanisms.
   d. physical isolating mechanisms.

8. A _____ is a group of organisms that shares a common ancestor with other species, but is set off from those others by having newer, genetically unique traits.

9. The term _____ is now used to refer to humans and their humanlike ancestors.

   a. *hominid*

   b. *anthropoid*

   c. *hominoid*

   d. *hominin*

10. The scientific name for modern human beings is

    a. *Homo habilis.*

    b. *Homo neanderthalensis.*

    c. *H. erectus.*

    d. *Homo sapiens.*

11. Fossil of which small human found in Indonesia are speculated to be a new species of *Homo?*

    a. the "hobbit"

    b. Ida

    c. *Australopithecus* sp.

    d. *Paranthropus* sp.

12. Genetic _____ is a change in the allele frequencies of the isolated subpopulation compared to the rest of the species.

13. The _____ _____ concept is a companion hypothesis to gradualism and suggests a different way of achieving evolutionary change.

14. Which factor will not increase the likelihood that an organism is found in the fossil record?

    a. The soft body parts decompose.

    b. Marine organisms can be covered by sediment on the bottom.

    c. Fossils of more recent organisms are less likely to have been destroyed by geological forces.

    d. Fossils of large organisms are easier to find.

15. _____ structures are similar structures in different species that have been derived from a common ancestor.

**Answers**
1. Gene flow  2. fossil  3. d  4. a  5. b  6. Polyploidy
7. c  8. species  9. d  10. d  11. a  12. divergence
13. punctuated equilibrium  14. a  15. Homologous

## Thinking Critically

**Speciation Has Many Dimensions**
Explain how all of the following are related to the process of speciation: mutation, natural selection, meiosis, geographic isolation, fossils, continental drift, and gene pool.

CHAPTER

# 15

# Ecosystem Dynamics
## The Flow of Energy and Matter

## Fertilizer on Lawns Causes Water Pollution

*You may be able to help solve the problem.*

I n urban areas, lawn care is big business. Millions of dollars are spent annually for fertilizer and pesticides and landscape services to maintain lawns. It is estimated that 15–30% of the fertilizer applied to lawns is washed from the soil and ends up in local streams, ponds, and lakes. Most fertilizers contain nitrogen, phosphorus, and potassium. Of these three components, phosphorus is the most detrimental to aquatic ecosystems because it stimulates the growth of algae and aquatic plants that foul the water and make it unappealing for recreational purposes. Furthermore, in the winter the algae and plants die and decay. The bacteria that bring about their decomposition use oxygen from the water and often lower the oxygen level of the water so much that aquatic animals die from a lack of oxygen.

In order to control pollution of local water bodies in urban areas, the State of Minnesota ("Land of 10,000 Lakes") has passed a law that prohibits the use of phosphorus in fertilizer that is to be applied to lawns. This ban does not extend to agriculture.

- **Can lawns be maintained without the use of fertilizer?**

- **Why does phosphorus stimulate the growth of algae and aquatic plants more than nitrogen?**

- **In order to improve local water quality, would you vote to restrict the use of fertilizer on lawns?**

## Background Check

**Concepts you should already know to get the most out of this chapter:**
- What energy is and how it is related to matter (chapter 2)
- How the atoms of various elements differ in structure (chapter 2)

## 15.1  What Is Ecology?

People often use the terms *ecology* and *environment* as if they meant the same thing. Students, homeowners, politicians, planners, and union leaders speak of "environmental issues" and "ecological concerns." They speak of products that are "green" or "environmentally friendly" and activities that will do "ecological damage." However, scientists use the terms *ecology* and *environment* in a more restricted way.

**Ecology** is the branch of biology that studies the relationships between organisms and their environments. This is a very simple definition for a very complex branch of science. Throughout the next four chapters, we will explore many of the aspects of this interesting topic. Because the word *environment* is included in this definition of *ecology*, it is important to have a clear understanding of how an ecologist uses the term. Most ecologists define the word **environment** very broadly as anything that affects an organism during its lifetime. These environmental influences can be divided into two broad categories: biotic environmental factors and abiotic environmental factors.

The field of environmental science is related to ecology. While environmental science is based on ecology, it is an applied science that looks at the impact of humans on their surroundings. Thus, politics, social interactions, economics, and other aspects of human behavior are important aspects of environmental science.

### Biotic and Abiotic Environmental Factors

**Biotic factors** are living things that affect an organism. You are affected by many different biotic factors. Your classmates, disease organisms, the food you eat, and the trees you seek for shade are all biotic factors. **Abiotic factors** are nonliving things that affect an organism. Common abiotic factors are wind, rain, the composition of the atmosphere, minerals in the soil, sunlight, temperature, and elevation above sea level (figure 15.1).

Characterizing the environment of an organism is a complex and challenging process. There are many things to be considered, and everything seems to be influenced or modified by other factors. For example, consider a fish in a stream; many environmental factors are important to its life. The temperature of the water is extremely important as an abiotic factor, but the temperature may be influenced by the presence of trees (biotic factor) along the stream bank that shade the stream and

**(a) Biotic factor (nesting material and tree)**

**(b) Abiotic factor (wind-driven snow)**

**FIGURE 15.1  Biotic and Abiotic Environmental Factors**
*(a)* The sticks and branches bald eagles use to build their nest are part of their biotic environment. The pine tree in which this nest is built is also part of the eagle's biotic environment. *(b)* The irregular shape of the tree is the result of wind, an abiotic factor that tends to sandblast one side of the tree and prevent limb growth on that side.

prevent the Sun from heating it. Obviously, the kind and number of food organisms in the stream are important biotic factors as well. The type of material that makes up the stream bottom—mud, sand, or gravel—and the amount of oxygen dissolved in the water are other important abiotic factors, both of which are related to how rapidly the water is flowing.

Similarly, a plant is influenced by many factors during its lifetime. The types and amounts of minerals in the soil, the amount of sunlight hitting the plant, and the amount of rainfall are important abiotic factors. The animals that eat the plant and the fungi that cause disease are important biotic factors. Each item on this list can be further subdivided. For instance, because plants obtain water from the soil, rainfall is studied in plant ecology. But even the study of rainfall is not simple. In some places, it rains only during one part of the year; in other places, it rains throughout the year. Some places experience hard, driving rains, whereas others experience long, misty showers. The kind of rainfall affects how much water soaks into the ground—heavy rains tend to run off into streams and be carried away, whereas gentle rain tends to sink into the soil.

## Levels of Organization in Ecology

Ecologists study ecological relationships at several levels of organization. Some ecologists focus on what happens to individual organisms and how they interact with their surroundings. Others are interested in groups of organisms of the same species, called **populations,** and how they change. Interacting populations of different species are called **communities,** and community ecologists are interested in how various kinds of organisms interact in a specific location. The highest level of ecological organization is the **ecosystem,** which consists of all the interacting organisms in an area and their interactions with their abiotic surroundings. Figure 15.2 shows how these levels of organization are related to one another.

Understanding the ecological relationships of any species of organism involves the accumulation of large amounts of detailed information about the organism and how it interacts

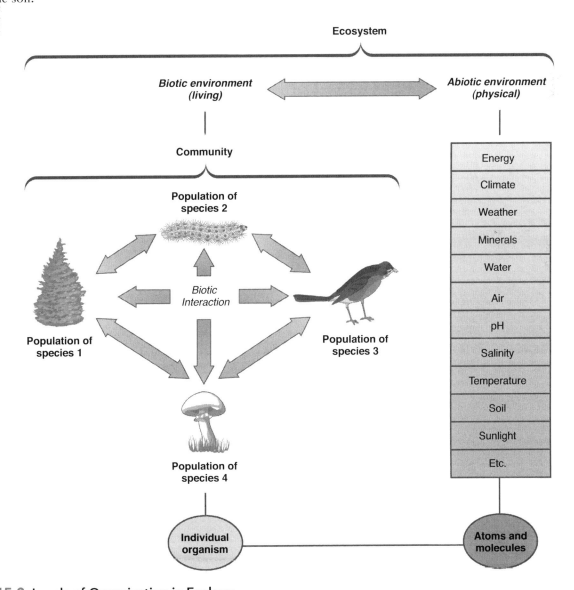

## FIGURE 15.2  Levels of Organization in Ecology
Ecology is the branch of biology that studies the interactions between organisms and their environments. This study can take place at several levels, from the broad ecosystem level through community interactions to population studies and the study of individual organisms. Ecology also involves the study of the physical environment, which makes up the nonliving parts of an ecosystem.

with its surroundings. Although this task may seem impossible, ecologists recognize three broad concepts that help simplify the task:

1. Each organism is part of one or more food chains.
2. The organisms in food chains can be separated into functional units called *trophic levels* based on how they obtain energy.
3. It is possible to trace the flow of energy and matter through ecosystems.

## 15.1  CONCEPT REVIEW

1. List three abiotic factors in the environment of a fish.
2. List three biotic factors in the environment of a songbird.
3. How do an ecosystem, a population, and a community differ?

## 15.2  Trophic Levels and Food Chains

One of the broad concepts of ecology is that organisms fit into categories, based on how they satisfy their energy requirements. There is a pattern in the way energy moves through an ecosystem. In general, energy flows from the Sun to plants and from plants to animals. However, there are recognizable steps in this flow of energy. Each stage in the flow of energy through an ecosystem is known as a **trophic level**. The series of organisms feeding on one another is known as a **food chain** (figure 15.3).

### Producers

**Producers** are organisms that trap sunlight and use it to produce organic molecules from inorganic molecules through the process of photosynthesis. Green plants and other photosynthetic organisms, such as algae and cyanobacteria, in effect, convert sunlight energy into the energy contained within the chemical bonds of organic compounds. Because producers are the first step in the flow of energy, they occupy the *first trophic level*.

### Consumers

Only producers are capable of using sunlight to make organic molecules. All other organisms are directly or indirectly dependent on the organic molecules generated at the producer trophic level to meet their energy needs. Because these organisms must consume organic matter as a source of energy, they are called **consumers**. Consumers can be subdivided into several categories, based on how they obtain food.

**Herbivores** are animals that obtain energy by eating plants. Because herbivores obtain their energy from eating

**FIGURE 15.3 Trophic Levels in a Food Chain**
As one organism feeds on another organism, energy flows from one trophic level to the next. This illustration shows six trophic levels.

plants, they are also called **primary consumers,** and they occupy the *second trophic level.*

**Carnivores** are animals that eat other animals. They are also referred to as **secondary consumers.** Carnivores can be subdivided into different trophic levels, depending on what animals they eat. Animals that feed on herbivores occupy the *third trophic level* and are known as **primary carnivores.** Animals that feed on the primary carnivores are known as **secondary carnivores,** and they occupy the *fourth trophic level.* For example, a human may eat a fish that ate a frog that ate a spider that ate an insect that consumed plants for food.

**Omnivores** are animals that have generalized food habits and act as carnivores sometimes and herbivores other times. They are classified into different trophic levels depending on what they are eating at the moment. Most humans are omnivores.

## Decomposers

**Decomposers** are a special category of consumers that obtain energy when they decompose the organic matter of dead organisms and the waste products of living organisms. Decomposers are usually not assigned to a trophic level, because they break down the organic matter produced by all trophic levels. Furthermore, the decomposer category includes a wide variety of organisms, such as bacteria, fungi, and other microorganisms, that feed on one another. Thus, there are food chains of decomposers.

Decomposers efficiently convert nonliving organic matter into simple inorganic molecules, which producers can reuse in the process of trapping energy. Thus, decomposers are very important components of ecosystems that cause materials to be recycled. As long as the Sun supplies the energy, elements are cycled repeatedly through ecosystems. Table 15.1 summarizes the categories of organisms within an ecosystem. Outlooks 15.1 describes changes in food chains that result from the introduction of exotic, invasive species.

## 15.3  Energy Flow Through Ecosystems

The ancient Egyptians constructed elaborate tombs we call *pyramids.* The broad base of the pyramid is necessary to support the upper levels of the structure, which narrows to a point at the top. The same kind of relationship exists for the various trophic levels of ecosystems. Biologists have adopted this pyramid model as a way to think about how ecosystems are organized. Most ecosystems have large quantities of producers, small quantities of herbivores, and still smaller quantities of carnivores. Because this is so common, ecologists have sought reasons to explain the relationship.

### Laws of Thermodynamics

Two fundamental physical laws of energy are important when looking at ecological systems from an energy point of view. The first law of thermodynamics states that energy is neither created nor destroyed. That means that we should be able to describe the amounts of energy in each trophic level and follow energy as it flows through successive trophic levels. The second law of thermodynamics states that, when energy is converted from one form to another, some energy escapes to the surroundings as heat. This means that, as

**TABLE 15.1  Categories in an Ecosystem**

| Category | Description | Examples |
|---|---|---|
| Producers | Organisms that convert simple inorganic compounds into complex organic compounds by photosynthesis | Trees, flowers, grasses, ferns, mosses, algae, cyanobacteria |
| Consumers | Organisms that rely on other organisms as food, animals that eat plants or other animals | |
| Herbivore | Eats plants | Deer, goose, cricket, vegetarian human, many snails |
| Carnivore | Eats meat | Wolf, pike, dragonfly |
| Omnivore | Eats plants and meat | Rat, most humans |
| Scavenger | Eats food left by others | Coyote, skunk, vulture, crayfish |
| Parasite | Lives in or on another organism, using it for food | Tick, tapeworm, many insects |
| Decomposer | Returns organic compounds to inorganic compounds, is an important component in recycling | Bacteria, fungi |

# OUTLOOKS 15.1

## Changes in the Food Chain of the Great Lakes

Many kinds of human activity aid the distribution of species from one place to another. Today there are over 100 exotic species in the Great Lakes. Some, such as smelt, brown trout, and several species of salmon, were purposely introduced. However, most exotic species entered accidentally as a result of human activity.

Prior to the construction of locks and canals, the Great Lakes were effectively isolated from invasion of exotic fish and other species by Niagara Falls. Beginning in the early 1800s, the construction of canals allowed small ships to get around the falls. This also allowed some fish species such as the sea lamprey and alewife to enter the Great Lakes. The completion of the St. Lawrence Seaway in 1959 allowed ocean-going ships to enter the Great Lakes. Because of the practice of using water as ballast, ocean-going vessels are a particularly effective means of introducing species. They pump water into their holds to provide ballast when they do not have a full load of cargo. (Ballast adds weight to empty ships to make their travel safer.) Ballast water is pumped out when cargo is added. Since these vessels may add water as ballast in Europe and empty it in the Great Lakes, it is highly likely that organisms will be transported to the Great Lakes from European waters. Some of these exotic species have caused profound changes in the food chain of the Great Lakes.

The introduction of the zebra and quagga mussels is correlated with several changes in the food web of the Great Lakes. Both mussels reproduce rapidly and attach themselves to any hard surface, including other mussels. They are very efficient filter feeders that remove organic matter and small organisms from the water. Measurements of the abundance of diatoms and other tiny algae show that they have declined greatly—up to 90% in some areas where zebra or quagga mussels are common. There has been a corresponding increase in the clarity of the water. In many places, people can see objects two times deeper than they could in the past.

*Diporeia* is a bottom-dwelling crustacean that feeds on organic matter. Populations of *Diporeia* have declined by 70% in many places in the Great Lakes. Many feel that this decline is the result of a reduction in their food sources, which are being removed from the water by zebra and quagga mussels. Since *Diporeia* is a major food organism for many kinds of bottom-feeding fish, there has been a ripple effect through the food chain. Recently, whitefish that rely on *Diporeia* as a food source have shown a decline in body condition. Other bottom-feeding fish that eat *Diporeia* serve as a food source for larger predator fish and there have been recent declines in the populations and health of some of these predator fish.

Another phenomenon that is correlated with the increase in zebra and quagga mussels is an increased frequency of toxic algal blooms in the Great Lakes. Although there are no clear answers to why this is occurring, two suggested links have been tied to mussels. The clarity of the water may be encouraging the growth of the toxic algae or the mussels may be selectively rejecting toxic algae as food, while consuming the nontoxic algae. Thus, the toxic algae have a competitive advantage.

Finally, wherever zebra or quagga mussels are common, species of native mussels and clams have declined. There may be several reasons for this correlation. First, the zebra and quagga mussels are in direct competition with the native species of mussels and clams. Zebra and quagga mussels are very efficient at removing food from the water and may be out-competing the native species for food. Secondly, since zebra and quagga mussels attach to any hard surface, they attach to native clams, essentially burying them.

A new threat to the Great Lakes involves the potential for exotic Asian carp (bighead and silver carp) to enter through a canal system that connects Lake Michigan at Chicago to the Mississippi River. These and other species of carp were introduced into commercial fish ponds in the southern United States. However, they soon escaped and entered the Mississippi River and have migrated upstream and could easily enter Lake Michigan. Both bighead and silver carp are filter-feeders that consume up to 40% of their body weight in plankton per day. They could have a further impact on the base of the Great Lakes food web, which has already been greatly modified by zebra and quagga mussels.

Phytoplankton

Sport fish (trout, salmon, walleye, whitefish)

Zebra mussels Quagga mussels

Forage fish (alewife, smelt, sculpin)

*Diporeia*

Actual Size 7.6 mm

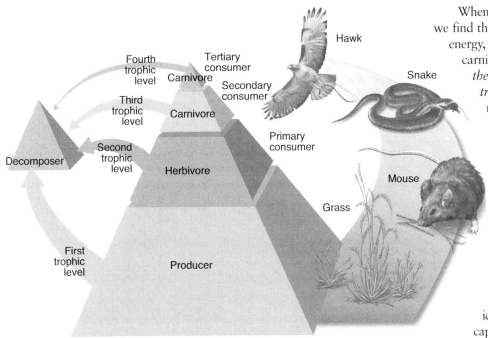

**FIGURE 15.4  Energy and Trophic Levels**
The producer trophic level has the greatest amount of energy and matter. At each successive trophic level, there is less energy and matter.

When we examine a wide variety of ecosystems, we find that the producer trophic level has the most energy, the herbivore trophic level has less, and the carnivore trophic level has the least. *In general, there is about a 90% loss of energy from one trophic level to the next higher level.* Actual measurements vary from one ecosystem to another. Some may lose as much as 99%, whereas other, more efficient systems may lose only 70%, but 90% is a good rule of thumb. This loss in energy content at the second and subsequent trophic levels is primarily due to the second law of thermodynamics. (Whenever energy is converted from one form to another, some energy is lost to the surroundings as heat.)

In addition to the loss of energy as a result of the second law of thermodynamics, there is an additional loss involved in the capture and processing of food material by herbivores and carnivores. Although herbivores don't need to chase their food, they do need to travel to where food is available, then gather, chew, digest, and metabolize it (figure 15.5). All of these processes require energy. Just as the herbivore trophic level experiences a 90% loss in energy content, the higher trophic levels of primary carnivores, secondary carnivores, and tertiary carnivores also experience a 90% reduction in the energy available to them. Figure 15.6 shows the flow of energy through an ecosystem.

energy passes from one trophic level to the next, there is a reduction in the amount of energy in living things and an increase in the amount of heat in their surroundings (figure 15.4).

Think of any energy-converting machine; a certain amount of energy enters the machine and a certain amount of work is done. However, it also releases a great deal of heat energy. For example, an automobile engine must have a cooling system to get rid of the heat energy produced. Similarly, electrical energy is used in an incandescent lightbulb to produce light, but the bulb also produces large amounts of heat. Although living systems are somewhat different, they follow the same energy rules.

## The Pyramid of Energy

The energy within an ecosystem can be measured in several ways. One simple way is to collect all the organisms present at any trophic level and burn them. For example, all the plants in a small field (producer trophic level) can be harvested and burned. The number of calories of heat produced by burning is equivalent to the energy content of the organic material collected. Similarly, all the herbivores in the second trophic level could be collected and burned. Then you could compare the amount of heat generated by producers and herbivores and get an idea of how much energy is lost as you go from the producer to the herbivore trophic level.

Another way of determining the energy present is to measure the rate of photosynthesis and respiration of a group of producers. The difference between the rates of respiration and photosynthesis is the amount of energy trapped in the living material of the plants.

## The Pyramid of Numbers

Because it is difficult to measure the amount of energy at any one trophic level of an ecosystem, scientists often use other methods to quantify trophic levels. One method is simply to count the number of organisms at each trophic level. This

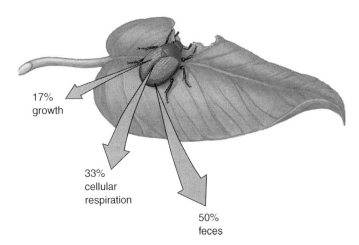

**FIGURE 15.5  Energy Losses in an Herbivore**
When an insect eats a plant to obtain energy, only a small amount is actually converted to new biological tissue in the insect.

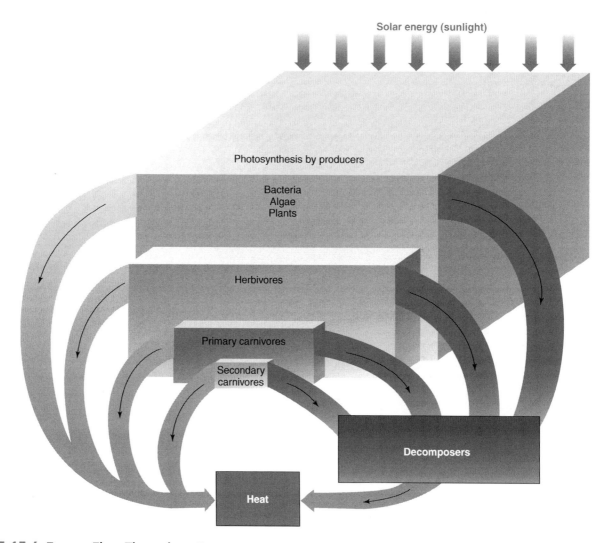

Solar energy (sunlight)

Photosynthesis by producers

Bacteria
Algae
Plants

Herbivores

Primary carnivores

Secondary
carnivores

**Decomposers**

**Heat**

**FIGURE 15.6 Energy Flow Through an Ecosystem**

Energy from the Sun is captured by organisms that carry on photosynthesis. These are the producers at the first trophic level. As energy flows from one trophic level to the next, approximately 90% of it is lost. This means that the amount of energy at the producer level must be 10 times larger than the amount of energy at the herbivore level. Ultimately, all the energy used by organisms is released to the surroundings as heat.

generally gives the same pyramid relationship, called a *pyramid of numbers* (figure 15.7). This is not a very good method to use if the organisms at the different trophic levels are of greatly differing sizes. For example, if you counted all the small insects feeding on the leaves of one large tree, you would actually get an inverted pyramid.

## The Pyramid of Biomass

One way to overcome some of the problems associated with simply counting organisms is to measure the *biomass* at each trophic level. **Biomass** is the amount of living material present; it is usually determined by collecting all the organisms at one trophic level and measuring their dry weight. This eliminates the size-difference problem associated with a pyramid of numbers, because all the organisms at each trophic level are combined and weighed. The *pyramid of biomass* also shows the typical 90% loss at each trophic level.

Although a pyramid of biomass is better than a pyramid of numbers in measuring some ecosystems, it has some

shortcomings. Some organisms tend to accumulate biomass over long periods of time, whereas others do not. Many trees live for hundreds of years; their primary consumers, insects, generally live only 1 year. Likewise, a whale is a long-lived animal, whereas its food organisms are relatively short-lived. Figure 15.8 shows two pyramids of biomass.

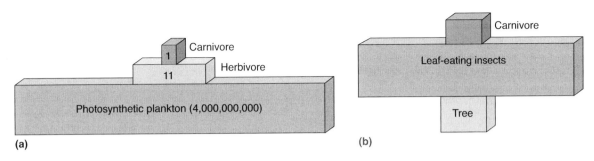

**FIGURE 15.7  Pyramid of Numbers**

One of the easiest ways to quantify the various trophic levels in an ecosystem is to count the number of individuals in a small portion of the ecosystem. As long as all the organisms are of similar size and live about the same length of time, this method gives a good picture of how the trophic levels are related. *(a)* The relationship among photosynthetic plankton in the ocean, the herbivores that eat them, and the carnivores that eat the herbivores is a good example. However, if the organisms at one trophic level are much larger or live much longer than those at other levels, the picture of the relationship may be distorted. *(b)* This is the relationship between forest trees and the insects that feed on them. This pyramid of numbers is inverted.

**FIGURE 15.8  Pyramid of Biomass**

Biomass is determined by collecting and weighing all the organisms in a small portion of an ecosystem. *(a)* This method of quantifying trophic levels eliminates the problem of different-sized organisms at different trophic levels. However, it does not always give a clear picture of the relationship among trophic levels if the organisms have widely different lengths of life. *(b)* For example, in aquatic ecosystems, many of the small producers divide several times per day. The tiny animals (zooplankton) that feed on them live much longer and tend to accumulate biomass over time. The single-celled algae produce much more living material but are eaten as fast as they are produced and, so, do not accumulate a large biomass.

## 15.4 The Cycling of Materials in Ecosystems— Biogeochemical Cycles

Except for small amounts of matter added to the Earth from cosmic dust and meteorites, the amount of matter that makes up the Earth is essentially constant. However, energy comes to the Earth in a continuous stream as sunlight, and even this is ultimately returned to space as heat energy. It is this flow of energy that drives all biological processes. Living systems use this energy to assemble organic matter and continue life through growth and reproduction. Because the amount of matter on Earth does not change, the existing atoms must be continually reused as organisms grow, reproduce, and die. In this recycling process, photosynthesis is involved in combining inorganic molecules to form the organic compounds of living things. The process of respiration by all organisms breaks down organic molecules to inorganic molecules. Decomposer organisms are particularly important in breaking down the organic remains of waste products and dead organisms. If there were no way of recycling this organic matter back into its inorganic forms, organic material would build up as the bodies of dead organisms.

Deposits of organic material do build up if decomposers are prevented from doing their job. This occurred millions of years ago, when the present deposits of coal, oil, and natural gas were formed. Today, new organic deposits are forming in swamps and bogs where acid conditions or lack of oxygen prevent decomposers from breaking down submerged vegetation.

One way to get an appreciation of how various kinds of organisms interact to cycle materials is to look at a specific kind of atom and follow its progress through an ecosystem. Carbon, nitrogen, oxygen, hydrogen, phosphorus, and many other atoms are found in all living things and are recycled when an organism dies.

### The Carbon Cycle

All living things are composed of organic molecules that contain atoms of the element carbon. The **carbon cycle** includes the processes and pathways involved in capturing inorganic carbon-containing molecules, converting them into organic

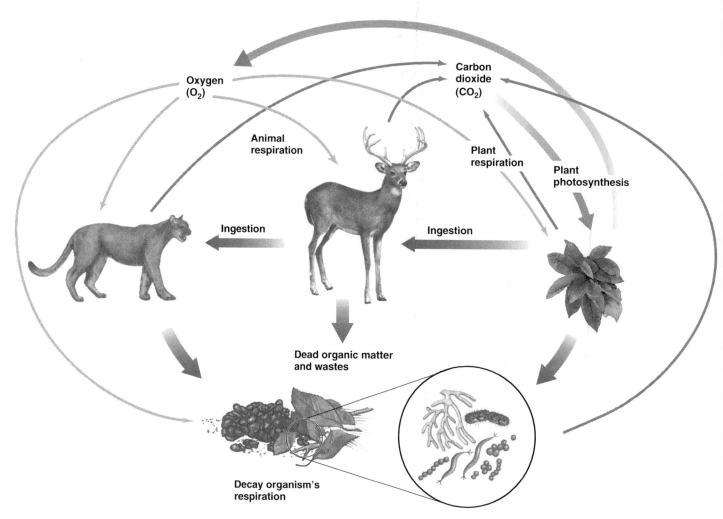

**FIGURE 15.9 The Carbon Cycle**
Carbon atoms are cycled through ecosystems. Carbon dioxide (green arrows) produced by respiration is the source of the carbon that plants incorporate into organic molecules when they carry on photosynthesis. These carbon-containing organic molecules—carbohydrates, fats, and proteins—(black arrows) are passed to animals when they eat plants and other animals. Organic molecules in waste products or dead organisms are consumed by decomposers. In the process, decomposers break down organic molecules into inorganic molecules. All organisms (plants, animals, and decomposers) return carbon atoms to the atmosphere as carbon dioxide when they carry on cellular respiration. Oxygen (blue arrows) is being cycled at the same time that carbon is. The oxygen is released during photosynthesis and taken up during cellular respiration.

molecules that are used by organisms, and the ultimate release of inorganic carbon molecules back to the abiotic environment (figure 15.9).

The same carbon atoms are used over and over again. In fact, you are not exactly the same person today that you were yesterday. Some of your carbon atoms are different. Furthermore, those carbon atoms have been involved in many other kinds of living things over the past several billion years. Some of them were temporary residents in dinosaurs, extinct trees, or insects, but at this instant, they are part of you. Other organic molecules have become part of fossil fuels.

### 1. The Role of Producers

Carbon and oxygen combine to form the molecule carbon dioxide ($CO_2$), which is present in small quantities as a gas in the atmosphere and dissolved in water. During photosynthesis, carbon dioxide from the atmosphere is taken into the leaves of plants where it is combined with hydrogen from water molecules ($H_2O$), which are absorbed from the soil by the roots and transported to the leaves. Many kinds of aquatic organisms such as algae and some bacteria also perform photosynthesis but absorb carbon dioxide and water molecules from the water in which they live. (Actually about 50% of photosynthetic activity on Earth takes place in the oceans due to the activity of algae and photosynthetic bacteria.)

The energy needed to perform photosynthesis is provided by sunlight. As a result of photosynthesis, complex organic molecules such as carbohydrates (sugars) are formed. Producer organisms use these sugars to provide themselves with energy and to make other kinds of organic molecules needed for growth and reproduction. At the same time that carbon is being incorporated into organic molecules, oxygen molecules ($O_2$) are released into the atmosphere or water—because during the process of photosynthesis, water molecules are split to provide hydrogen atoms necessary to manufacture carbohydrate molecules.

2. **The Role of Consumers**
Herbivores can use the complex organic molecules of producers as food. When an herbivore eats plants or algae, the complex organic molecules in their food are broken down into simpler organic molecular building blocks, such as simple sugars, amino acids, glycerol, and fatty acids, which then can be reassembled into the specific organic molecules that are part of the herbivore's chemical structure. Thus, the atoms in the herbivore's body can be traced back to the plants it ate. Nearly all organisms also carry on the process of respiration, in which oxygen from the atmosphere is used to break down organic molecules into carbon dioxide and water. Much of the chemical-bond energy released by respiration is lost as heat, but the remainder is used by the herbivore for movement, growth, and other activities.

In similar fashion, when an herbivore is eaten by a carnivore, some of the carbon-containing molecules of the herbivore become incorporated into the body of the carnivore. The remaining organic molecules are broken down in the process of respiration to obtain energy, and carbon dioxide and water are released.

3. **The Role of Decomposers**
The organic molecules contained in animal waste products and dead organisms are acted upon by decomposers that use these organic materials as a source of food. The decay process of decomposers involves respiration and releases carbon dioxide and water so that organic molecules are typically recycled. (Many human-made organic compounds—plastics, industrial chemicals, and pesticides—are not readily broken down by decomposers.) How Science Works 15.1 describes how human alteration of the carbon cycle has affected climate.

## The Hydrologic Cycle

Water molecules are the most common molecules in living things. Because all the metabolic reactions that occur in organisms take place in a watery environment, within cells or body parts, water is essential to life. During photosynthesis, the hydrogen atoms (H) from water molecules ($H_2O$) are added to carbon atoms to make carbohydrates and other organic molecules. At the same time, the oxygen atoms in water molecules are released as oxygen molecules ($O_2$). The movement of water molecules can be traced as a hydrologic cycle (figure 15.10).

Most of the forces that cause water to be cycled do not involve organisms but, rather, are the result of normal physical and geologic processes. Because of the kinetic energy possessed by water molecules, at normal Earth temperatures liquid water evaporates into the atmosphere as water vapor. This can occur wherever water is present; it evaporates from lakes, rivers, soil, and the surfaces of organisms. Because the oceans contain most of the world's water, an extremely large amount of water enters the atmosphere from the oceans.

Water molecules also enter the atmosphere as a result of *transpiration* by plants. **Transpiration** is a process whereby water is lost from leaves through small openings called stomates. The water that is lost is absorbed from the soil into roots and transported from the roots to leaves, where it is used in photosynthesis or evaporates. This movement of water carries nutrients to the leaves, and the evaporation of the water from the leaves assists in the movement of water upward in the stem. Thus, transpired water can be moved from deep layers of the soil to the atmosphere.

Once the water molecules are in the atmosphere, they are moved along with other atmospheric gases by prevailing wind patterns. If warm, moist air encounters cooler temperatures, which often happens over landmasses, the water vapor condenses into droplets and falls as rain or snow. When the precipitation falls on land, some of it runs off the surface, some of it evaporates, and some penetrates into the soil. The water that runs off the surface makes its way through streams and rivers to the ocean. The water in the soil may be taken up by plants and transpired into the atmosphere, or it may become groundwater. Much of the groundwater eventually makes its way into lakes and streams and ultimately arrives at the ocean, from which it originated.

## The Nitrogen Cycle

The **nitrogen cycle** involves the cycling of nitrogen atoms between the abiotic and biotic components and among the organisms in an ecosystem. Nitrogen is essential in the formation of amino acids, which are needed to form proteins, and in the formation of nitrogenous bases, which are a part of ATP and the nucleic acids, DNA and RNA. Nitrogen is found as molecules of nitrogen gas ($N_2$) in the atmosphere. Although nitrogen gas ($N_2$) makes up approximately 80% of the earth's atmosphere, it is not readily available to most organisms because the two nitrogen atoms are bound very tightly to each other and very few organisms are able to use nitrogen in this form. Since plants and other producers are at the base of nearly all food chains, they must make new nitrogen-containing molecules, such as proteins and DNA. Plants and other producers are unable to use the nitrogen in the atmosphere and must get it in the form of nitrate ($—NO_3$) or ammonia ($NH_3$).

1. **The Role of Nitrogen-Fixing Bacteria**
Because atmospheric nitrogen is not usable by plants, nitrogen-containing compounds are often in short supply, and the availability of nitrogen is often a factor

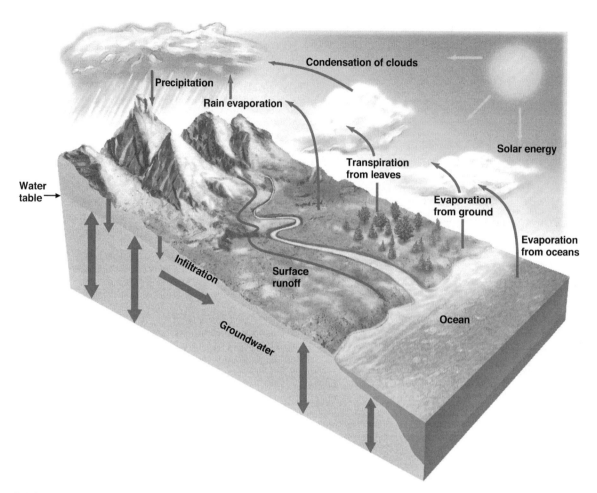

**FIGURE 15.10 The Hydrologic Cycle**
The cycling of water through the environment follows a simple pattern. Moisture in the atmosphere condenses into droplets, which fall to the Earth as rain or snow. Organisms use some of the water and some of it evaporates from soil and organisms, but much of it flows over the Earth as surface water or through the soil as groundwater. It eventually returns to the oceans, where it evaporates back into the atmosphere to begin the cycle again.

that limits the growth of plants. (Most aquatic ecosystems are limited by the amount of phosphorus rather than the amount of nitrogen.) Certain kinds of soil bacteria are the primary source of the nitrogen-containing molecules plants need to make proteins and DNA.

Some bacteria, called **nitrogen-fixing bacteria,** are able to convert the nitrogen gas ($N_2$) that enters the soil into ammonia ($NH_3$) that plants can use. Certain kinds of these bacteria live freely in the soil and are called **free-living nitrogen-fixing bacteria.** Others, known as **symbiotic nitrogen-fixing bacteria,** have a cooperative relationship with certain plants and live in nodules in the roots of plants such as legumes (peas, beans, and clover) and certain trees such as alders. Some grasses and evergreen trees appear to have a similar relationship with certain root fungi that seem to improve the nitrogen-fixing capacity of the plant.

2. **The Role of Producers and Consumers**
Once plants and other producers have nitrogen available in a form they can use, they can construct proteins,

DNA, and other important nitrogen-containing organic molecules. When herbivores eat plants, the plant protein molecules are broken down to smaller building blocks called amino acids. These amino acids are then reassembled to form proteins typical for the herbivore. Nucleic acids and other nitrogen-containing molecules are handled similarly. During the animal's manipulation and transformation of amino acids, and some other molecules, some nitrogen is lost in the organism's waste products as ammonia, urea, or uric acid. These same processes occur when carnivores eat herbivores.

3. **The Role of Decomposers and Other Soil Bacteria**
Bacteria and other types of decay organisms are involved in the nitrogen cycle also. Dead organisms and their waste products contain molecules, such as proteins, urea, and uric acid, that contain nitrogen. Decomposers break down these nitrogen-containing organic molecules, releasing ammonia ($NH_3$), which can be used directly by many kinds of plants. Still other kinds of soil

# HOW SCIENCE WORKS 15.1

## Scientists Accumulate Knowledge About Climate Change

Humans have significantly altered the carbon cycle. As we burn fossil fuels, the amount of carbon dioxide in the atmosphere continually increases. Carbon dioxide allows light to enter the atmosphere but does not allow heat to exit. Because this is similar to what happens in a greenhouse, carbon dioxide and the other gases that have similar effects are called greenhouse gases. Therefore, many scientists are concerned that increased carbon dioxide levels are leading to a warming of the planet, which will cause major changes in our weather and climate.

In science, when a new discovery is made or a new issue is raised, it stimulates a large number of observations and experiments that add to the body of knowledge about the topic. Concerns about global climate change and the role that carbon dioxide plays in causing climate change have resulted in scientists studying many aspects of the problem. This has been a worldwide effort and has involved many different branches of science. This effort has resulted in critical examination of several basic assumptions about climate change, the collection of much new information, and new predictions about the consequences of global climate change.

Several significant studies include:

- Examination of gas bubbles trapped in the ice of glaciers has allowed scientists to measure the amount of carbon dioxide in the atmosphere at the time the ice formed. This provides information about carbon dioxide concentrations prior to human-caused carbon dioxide releases and allows scientists to track the rate of change.
- Long-term studies of the atmosphere at various locations throughout the world show that carbon dioxide levels are increasing.
- Measurements show that sea level is rising almost 2 millimeters per year.
- Measurements of the temperature of the Earth's atmosphere have allowed tracking of temperature. According to NASA, 10 of the warmest years on record occurred in the 12-year period between 1998 and 2009.
- Satellite images of the Arctic Ocean show reduced ice cover.
- Observations of bird migration in Europe document that birds that migrate long distances are arriving in Europe earlier in the spring.

- Many studies of the rate at which different ecosystems take up carbon dioxide have been done to determine if assumptions about the carbon dioxide trapping role of natural ecosystems are correct.
- Warming of the Arctic has resulted in less permafrost.
- Increased water temperatures have been linked to increases in the number and extent of blooms of cyanobacteria in lakes and oceans.
- Studies suggest that an increase in the level of carbon dioxide in the atmosphere could result in increased amounts of dissolved carbon dioxide in the ocean. Increased carbon dioxide will lower the pH of the ocean, which could have a negative effect on animals that make shells.
- Warming of the oceans is linked to more intense hurricanes.
- Earlier arrival of spring is linked to increased numbers and intensity of forest fires in the western United States.

The United Nations established the Intergovernmental Panel on Climate Change (IPCC)—a panel of scientists, political leaders, and economists—to analyze the large amount of information generated on the topic of climate changes. The IPCC has issued several reports about the nature, causes, and the impacts of climate change on ecosystems and culture.

Graph from NASA

---

bacteria, called **nitrifying bacteria,** are able to convert ammonia to nitrite ($-NO_2$), which can be converted by other bacteria to nitrate ($-NO_3$). The production of nitrate is significant because plants can use nitrate as a source of nitrogen for synthesis of nitrogen-containing organic molecules.

Finally, bacteria known as **denitrifying bacteria** are, under conditions where oxygen is absent, able to convert nitrite to nitrogen gas ($N_2$), which is ultimately released

into the atmosphere. Atmospheric nitrogen can reenter the cycle with the aid of nitrogen-fixing bacteria.

4. **Unique Features of the Nitrogen Cycle**

Although a cyclic pattern is present in both the carbon cycle and the nitrogen cycle, the nitrogen cycle shows two significant differences. First, most of the difficult chemical conversions are made by bacteria and other microorganisms. Without the activities of bacteria, little nitrogen would be available and the world would be a very different place. Second, although nitrogen is made available to organisms by way of nitrogen-fixing bacteria and returns to the atmosphere through the actions of denitrifying bacteria, there is a secondary loop in the cycle that recycles nitrogen compounds from dead organisms and wastes directly back to producers. Figure 15.11 summarizes the roles of various organisms in the nitrogen cycle.

5. **Agriculture and the Nitrogen Cycle**
In naturally occurring soil, nitrogen is often a limiting factor of plant growth. To increase yields, farmers provide extra sources of nitrogen in several ways. Inorganic fertilizers are

a primary method of increasing the nitrogen available These fertilizers may contain ammonia, nitrate, or both.

Since the manufacture of nitrogen fertilizer requires a large amount of energy and uses natural gas as a raw material, fertilizer is expensive. Therefore, farmers use alternative methods to supply nitrogen and reduce their cost of production. Several different techniques are effective. Farmers can alternate nitrogen-yielding crops such as soybeans with nitrogen-demanding crops such as corn. Since soybeans are legumes that have symbiotic nitrogen-fixing bacteria in their roots, if soybeans are planted one year, the excess nitrogen left in the soil can be

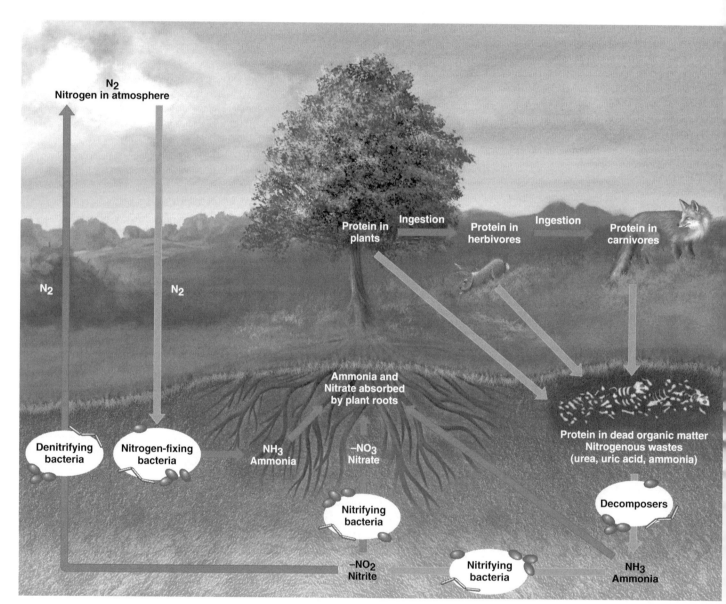

**FIGURE 15.11 The Nitrogen Cycle**
Nitrogen atoms are cycled through ecosystems. Atmospheric nitrogen is converted by nitrogen-fixing bacteria to nitrogen-containing compounds, which plants can use to make proteins and other compounds. Proteins are passed to other organisms when one organism is eaten by another. Dead organisms and their waste products are acted upon by decay organisms to form ammonia, which can be reused by plants and converted to other nitrogen compounds by nitrifying bacteria. Denitrifying bacteria return nitrogen as a gas to the atmosphere.

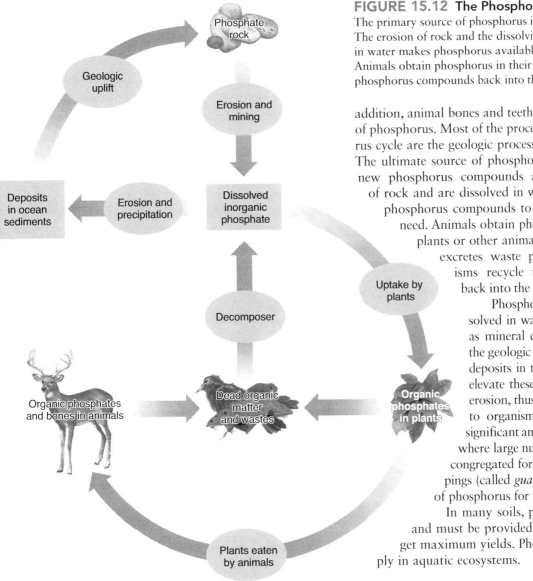

**FIGURE 15.12  The Phosphorus Cycle**
The primary source of phosphorus is phosphorus-containing rock. The erosion of rock and the dissolving of phosphorus compounds in water makes phosphorus available to the roots of plants. Animals obtain phosphorus in their food. Decomposers recycle phosphorus compounds back into the soil.

addition, animal bones and teeth contain significant quantities of phosphorus. Most of the processes involved in the phosphorus cycle are the geologic processes of erosion and deposition. The ultimate source of phosphorus atoms is rock. In nature, new phosphorus compounds are released by the erosion of rock and are dissolved in water. Plants use the dissolved phosphorus compounds to construct the molecules they need. Animals obtain phosphorus when they consume plants or other animals. When an organism dies or excretes waste products, decomposer organisms recycle the phosphorus compounds back into the soil, where they can be reused.

Phosphorus compounds that are dissolved in water are ultimately precipitated as mineral deposits. This has occurred in the geologic past and typically has involved deposits in the oceans. Geologic processes elevate these deposits and expose them to erosion, thus making phosphorus available to organisms. Animal wastes often have significant amounts of phosphorus. In places where large numbers of seabirds or bats have congregated for hundreds of years, their droppings (called *guano*) can be a significant source of phosphorus for fertilizer (figure 15.12).

In many soils, phosphorus is in short supply and must be provided to crop plants in fertilizer to get maximum yields. Phosphorus is also in short supply in aquatic ecosystems.

## Nutrient Cycles and Geologic Time

The nutrient cycles we have just discussed act on a short-term basis in which elements are continually being reused among organisms and on a long-term basis in which certain elements are tied up for long time periods and are not part of the active nutrient cycle. In our discussion of the phosphorus cycle it was mentioned that the source of phosphorus is rock. While phosphorus moves rapidly through organisms in food chains, phosphorus ions are not very soluble in water and tend to precipitate in the oceans to form sediments that eventually become rock on the ocean floor. Once this has occurred, it takes the process of geologic uplift followed by erosion to make phosphorus ions available to terrestrial ecosystems. Thus, we can think of the ocean as a place where phosphorus is removed from the active nutrient cycle (this situation is known as a *sink*).

There are also long-term aspects to the carbon cycle. Organic matter in soil and sediments are the remains of once-living organisms. Thus, these compounds constitute a sink for carbon,

used by the corn plants grown the next year. Some farmers even plant alternating strips of soybeans and corn in the same field. A slightly different technique involves growing a nitrogen-fixing crop for a short period of time and then plowing the crop into the soil and letting the organic matter decompose. The ammonia released by decomposition serves as fertilizer to the crop that follows. This is often referred to as green manure. Farmers can also add nitrogen to the soil by spreading manure from animal production operations or dairy farms on the field and relying on the soil bacteria to decompose the organic matter and release the nitrogen for plant use.

## The Phosphorus Cycle

Phosphorus is another atom common in the structure of living things. It is present in many important biological molecules, such as DNA, and in the membrane structure of cells. In

326 PART IV Evolution and Ecology

particularly in ecosystems in which decomposition is slow (tundra, northern forests, grasslands, swamps, marine sediments). These materials can tie up carbon for hundreds to thousands of years. Fossil fuels (coal, petroleum, and natural gas), which were also formed from the remains or organisms, are a longer-term sink that involves hundreds of millions of years. The carbon atoms in fossil fuels at one time were part of the active carbon cycle but were removed from the active cycle when the organisms accumulated without decomposing. The organisms that formed petroleum and natural gas are thought to be the remains of marine organisms that got covered by sediments. Coal was formed from the remains of plants that were buried by sediments. Once the organisms were buried, their decomposition would be slowed, and heat from the Earth and pressure from the sediments helped to transform the remains of living things into fossil fuels. The carbon atoms in fossil fuels have been locked up for hundreds of millions of years. Thus, the formation of fossil fuels was a sink for carbon atoms.

Oceans are a major carbon sink. Carbon dioxide is highly soluble in water. Many kinds of carbonate sedimentary rock are formed from the precipitation of carbonates from solution in oceans. In addition, many marine organisms form skeletons or shells of calcium carbonate. These materials accumulate on the ocean floor as sediments that over time can be converted to limestone. Limestone typically contains large numbers of fossils. The huge amount of carbonate rock is an indication that there must have been higher amounts of carbon dioxide in the Earth's atmosphere in the past.

Since fossil fuels are the remains of once-living things and living things have nitrogen as a part of protein, nitrogen that was once part of the active nitrogen cycle was removed when the fossil fuels were formed. In ecosystems in which large amounts of nonliving organic matter accumulates (swamps, humus in forests, and marine sediments), nitrogen can be tied up for relatively long time periods. In addition, some nitrogen may be tied up in sedimentary rock and, in some cases, is released with weathering. However, it appears that the major sink for nitrogen is as nitrogen in the atmosphere. Nitrogen compounds are very soluble in water, so when sedimentary rock is exposed to water, these materials are dissolved and reenter the active nitrogen cycle.

## 15.4 CONCEPT REVIEW

10. Trace the flow of carbon atoms through a community that contains plants, herbivores, decomposers, and parasites.
11. Describe four roles that bacteria play in the nitrogen cycle.
12. Describe the flow of water through the hydrologic cycle.
13. List three ways the carbon and nitrogen cycles are similar and three ways they differ.
14. Describe the major processes that make phosphorus available to plants.

## 15.5 Human Use of Ecosystems

The extent to which humans use an ecosystem is tied to its *productivity*. **Productivity** is the rate at which an ecosystem can accumulate new organic matter. Because plants are the producers, it is their activities that are most important. Ecosystems in which the conditions are the most favorable for plant growth are the most productive. Warm, moist sunny areas with high levels of nutrients in the soil are ideal. Some areas have low productivity because one of these essential factors is missing. Deserts have low productivity because water is scarce, arctic areas because temperature is low, and the open ocean because nutrients are in short supply. Some terrestrial ecosystems, such as forests and grasslands, have high productivity. Aquatic ecosystems, such as marshes and estuaries, are highly productive, because the waters running into them are rich in the nutrients that aquatic photosynthesizers need. Furthermore, these aquatic systems are usually shallow, so that light can penetrate through most of the water column.

### The Conversion of Ecosystems to Human Use

The way humans use ecosystems has changed dramatically over the past several thousand years. Initially, humans fit into ecosystems as just another consumer. These kinds of societies are known as hunter-gatherer societies because they collect food and other needed materials directly from the plants and animals that are a natural part of the ecosystem. There are still examples of peoples who live this way (figure 15.13).

However, the development of agriculture has changed how humans interact with other organisms in ecosystems. We have altered certain ecosystems substantially to increase productivity for our own purposes. In so doing, we have destroyed the original ecosystem, with all of its complexity, and have replaced it with a simpler agricultural ecosystem. In addition, many of the crops we plant are not native to the region. For example, nearly all of the Great Plains region of North America has been converted to agriculture. The original ecosystem included the Native Americans, who used buffalo and other plants and animals as a source of food. There was much grass, many buffalo, and few humans. Therefore, in the Native Americans' pyramid of energy, the base was more than ample. However, with the exploitation and settling of America, the population in North America increased at a rapid rate. The food chain (prairie grass–buffalo–human) could no longer supply the food needs of the growing population. Because wheat and corn yield more biomass for humans than the original prairie grasses could, the settlers' domestic grain and cattle replaced the prairie grass and buffalo. This was fine for the settlers, but devastating for the buffalo and Native Americans (figure 15.14). In similar fashion, the deciduous forests of the East were cut down and burned to provide land for crops. The crops were able to provide more food than did harvesting game and plants from the forest.

Associated with modern agriculture is the use of fertilizer and other agricultural chemicals. Fertilizers usually contain nitrogen, phosphorus, and potassium compounds. The numbers on a fertilizer bag indicate the percentage of each in the fertilizer. For example, a 6-24-24 fertilizer has 6% nitrogen, 24% phosphorus, and 24% potassium compounds. In addition to nitrogen, phosphorus, and potassium, other elements including calcium, magnesium, sulfur, boron, copper, and zinc are cycled within ecosystems. In an agricultural ecosystem, these elements are removed when the crop is harvested. Therefore, farmers must not only return the nitrogen, phosphorus, and potassium to the soil but also analyze for other, less-prominent elements and add them to their fertilizer mixture. Aquatic ecosystems are also sensitive to nutrient levels. High levels of nitrates or phosphorus compounds often result in the rapid growth of aquatic producers. In aquaculture, such as that used to raise catfish, fertilizer is added to the body of water to stimulate the production of

**FIGURE 15.13 A Hunter-Gatherer**
This Australian aboriginal hunter functions as a carnivore and uses the natural ecosystem as a source of energy and materials.

**Prairie converted to raising crops**

**Original prairie ecosystem**

**Prairie converted to grazing livestock**

**FIGURE 15.14 The Conversion of Prairie to Agricultural Production**
North America's Great Plains changed from a natural prairie ecosystem to an agricultural ecosystem either for raising crops or for grazing livestock.

## OUTLOOKS 15.2

# Dead Zones

Dead zones are regions of the ocean bottom that have little or no oxygen dissolved in the water. Throughout the world there are about 400 such zones; most located near the mouths of rivers. Two things contribute to the development of dead zones: poor mixing of the water in the area and an input of nutrients from rivers. Rivers carry nutrients from the lands they drain and the nutrients stimulate the growth of phytoplankton (microscopic, single-celled, photosynthetic organisms) in the upper regions of the water column. When these organisms die they sink to the bottom where bacteria bring about their decay. The bacteria use oxygen from the water in the decay process and the amount of oxygen falls. As the oxygen level falls, animals are stressed. Those that are able to swim or crawl leave the area, and those that cannot, die. The result is an area on the ocean floor that is devoid of life.

Dead zones typically develop in the summer months when the water is warm. The combination of warm water and abundant nutrients results in rapid growth of phytoplankton. It appears that the primary source of the excess nutrients is related to the way humans use the land drained by rivers. Fertilizer from agriculture and lawns runs off the land into streams and rivers. Animal waste from cattle feedlots, hog farms, and chicken-raising facilities is often spread on land as fertilizer and washes into streams and rivers. Other animal waste enters streams as a result of poorly designed containment lagoons that fail. Nutrients from human wastes can also enter from sewage treatment plants. All of these sources of nutrients contribute to the problem. A major dead zone develops

*Approximate dead zone in the Gulf of Mexico.*

every year in the Gulf of Mexico near the mouth of the Mississippi River. Most years the area affected is about the size of the state of New Jersey.

The problem is not just of concern to those worried about the environmental impact. It is important economically, since large dead zones impact commercial and recreational fishing.

---

algae, which is the base of most aquatic food chains (see Outlooks 15.2).

Many ecosystems, particularly the drier grasslands, cannot support the raising of crops. However, they can still be used as grazing land to raise livestock. Like the raising of crops, grazing often significantly alters the original grassland ecosystem. Some attempts have been made to harvest native species of animals from grasslands, but the primary species raised on grasslands are domesticated cattle, sheep, and goats. The substitution of the domesticated animals displaces the animals that are native to the area and alters the kinds of plants present, particularly if too many animals are allowed to graze.

Even aquatic ecosystems have been significantly altered by human activity. The Food and Agriculture Organization of the United Nations states that nearly all the fisheries of the world are being fished at capacity or overfished. Overfishing in many areas of the ocean has resulted in the loss of some important commercial species. For example, the codfishing industry along the East Coast of North America has been destroyed by overfishing.

## The Energy Pyramid and Human Nutrition

Anywhere in the world the human population increases, natural ecosystems are replaced with agricultural ecosystems. In many parts of the world, the human demand for food is so large that it can be met only if humans occupy the herbivore trophic level, rather than the carnivore trophic level. Humans are omnivores able to eat both plants and animals as food, so they have a choice. However, as the size of the human population increases, it cannot afford the 90% loss that occurs when plants are fed to animals that are in turn eaten by humans. In much of the less-developed world, the primary food is grain; therefore, the people are already at the herbivore level. It is only in the developed countries that people can afford to eat large quantities of meat. This is true from both an energy point of view and a monetary point of view. Meat, fish, poultry and other sources of animal protein are more expensive than grains. (Most of the corn raised in the United States is used as cattle feed). Figure 15.15 shows a pyramid of biomass having a producer base of 100 kilograms of grain. The second trophic level has only 10 kilograms of cattle because of the 90% energy loss typical when energy is transferred from one trophic level to the next. The consumers at the third trophic level—humans, in this case—experience a similar 90% loss. Therefore, only 1 kilogram of humans can be sustained by the two-step energy transfer. There has been a 99% loss in energy: 100 kilograms of grain are necessary to sustain 1 kilogram of humans. Because much of the world's population is already feeding at the second trophic level, we cannot expect food production to increase to the extent that we could feed 10 times as many people as exist today.

It is difficult for most people to fulfill all their nutritional needs by eating only grains. Although protein is available from plants, the concentration is greater from animal sources and people who rely primarily on plants for food often experience protein deficiency. People in major parts of Africa and Asia have diets that are deficient in both calories and protein. These people have very little food, and what food they do have is mainly from plant sources. These are also the parts of the world where human population growth is the most rapid. In other words, these people are poorly nourished, and as the population increases they will probably experience greater calorie and protein deficiency. It is important to realize that currently there is enough food in the world to feed everyone, but it is not distributed equitably for a variety of reasons. The primary reasons for starvation are political and economic. Wars and civil unrest disrupt the normal food-raising process. People leave their homes and migrate to areas unfamiliar to them. Poor people and poor countries cannot afford to buy food from the countries that have a surplus.

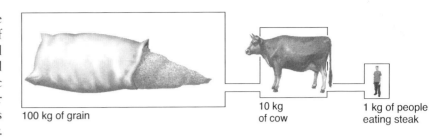

100 kg of grain       10 kg of cow       1 kg of people eating steak

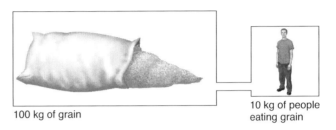

100 kg of grain       10 kg of people eating grain

**FIGURE 15.15  Human Pyramids of Biomass**
Because approximately 90% of the energy is lost as energy passes from one trophic level to the next, more people can be supported if they eat producers directly than if they feed on herbivores. Much of the less-developed world is in this position today. Rice, corn, wheat, and other producers provide most of the food for the world's people.

biomass. Consumers (herbivores, carnivores, and omnivores) eat other organisms. Herbivores feed on producers and are, in turn, eaten by carnivores, which may be eaten by other carnivores. Each level in the food chain is known as a trophic level. Other kinds of organisms involved in food chains are omnivores, which eat both plant and animal food, and decomposers, which break down dead organic matter and waste products.

All ecosystems have a large producer base with successively smaller amounts of energy at the herbivore, primary carnivore, and secondary carnivore trophic levels. This is because, each time energy passes from one trophic level to the next, about 90% of the energy is lost from the ecosystem.

The amount of matter in the world does not change but, rather, is recycled. The carbon cycle involves the processes of photosynthesis and respiration in the cycling of carbon through ecosystems. Water is essential to living things, most of the cycling of water involves the physical processes of evaporation and condensation. The nitrogen cycle relies on the activities of nitrogen-fixing bacteria, nitrifying bacteria, and decomposers to cycle nitrogen through ecosystems. The phosphorus cycle involves the deposition of phosphorus-containing compounds into oceans and the geologic processes of uplift and erosion to make phosphorus available to organisms.

Humans use ecosystems to provide themselves with necessary food and raw materials. As the human population increases, most people will be living as herbivores at the second trophic level, because they cannot afford to lose 90% of the energy by first feeding it to an herbivore, which they then eat. Humans have converted most productive ecosystems to agricultural production and continue to seek more agricultural land as populations increase.

## 15.4  CONCEPT REVIEW

15. Explain why poor people in countries with limited food must eat primarily grains. Explain this from both an economic and ecological point of view.
16. Define the term *productivity.*
17. What is the primary reason for humans destroying natural ecosystems like prairies and deciduous forests?

## Summary

Ecology is the study of how organisms interact with their environment. The environment consists of biotic and abiotic components, which are interrelated in an ecosystem. All ecosystems must have a constant input of energy from the Sun. Producer organisms are capable of trapping the Sun's energy, through photosynthesis, and converting it into the energy in

## Key Terms

*Use the interactive flash cards on the* **Concepts in Biology,** *14/e website to help you learn the meaning of these terms.*

abiotic factors 312

biomass 318

biotic factors 312

carbon cycle 319

carnivores 315

community 313

consumers 314

decomposers 315

denitrifying bacteria 323

ecology 312

ecosystem 313

environment 312

food chain 314

free-living nitrogen-fixing
  bacteria 322

herbivores 314

nitrifying bacteria 323

nitrogen cycle 321

nitrogen-fixing
  bacteria 322

omnivores 315

population 313

primary carnivores 315

primary consumers 315

producers 314

productivity 326

secondary carnivores 315

secondary consumers 315

symbiotic nitrogen-fixing
  bacteria 322

transpiration 321

trophic level 314

## Basic Review

1. Which one of the following is an abiotic factor?

    a. a nest in a tree

    b. the water in a pond

    c. the producers in an ecosystem

    d. the fish in a pond

2. Which one of the following categories of organisms has the largest total energy and biomass?

    a. eagles, which eat fish

    b. herbivores, which eat plants

    c. organisms that carry on photosynthesis

    d. fish that eat insects

3. The carbon that plants need for photosynthesis comes from _____.

4. Symbiotic nitrogen-fixing bacteria

    a. live in association with the roots of certain plants.

    b. convert ammonia to nitrate.

    c. are found in the atmosphere.

    d. are rare.

5. The process of absorbing water from the soil and releasing it from leaves is called _____.

6. In the phosphorus cycle, phosphorus enters plants through the roots. (T/F)

7. When energy flows from one trophic level to the next, about _____ percent of the energy is lost.

8. An herbivore is at the second trophic level. (T/F)

9. Nitrogen is important in which one of the following organic molecules?

    a. sugars                    c. water

    b. fats                       d. proteins

10. Decomposers break down organic matter and release _____ and _____.

11. Which one of the following is a producer?

    a. earthworm                 c. yeast

    b. algae                      d. fungus

12. Which of the following populations in an ecosystem would have the highest biomass?

    a. insect-eating birds       c. fungi

    b. fish-eating birds         d. plants

13. A vegetarian is at the _____ trophic level.

14. Which of the following is the largest conceptual unit?

    a. ecosystem                 c. decomposers

    b. community                 d. producers

15. Humans have altered most ecosystems of the world. (T/F)

**Answers**

1. b   2. c   3. carbon dioxide   4. a   5. transpiration   6. T
7. 90%   8. T   9. d   10. carbon dioxide and water.   11. b
12. d   13. herbivore   14. a   15. T

## Thinking Critically

**Understanding Interrelationships**

Construct a diagram on a piece of paper that includes the following items to show their levels of interaction. Which is the most important item? Which items are dependent on others?

People are starving.

Commercial fertilizer production requires temperatures of 900°C.

Geneticists have developed plants that grow very rapidly and require high amounts of nitrogen to germinate during the normal growing season.

Fossil fuels are stored organic matter.

The rate of the nitrogen cycle depends on the activity of bacteria.

The sun is expected to last for several million years.

Crop rotation is becoming a thing of the past.

The clearing of forests for agriculture changes the weather in the area.

# Community Interactions

## Alien Invasion

*Scientists concerned about survival of native plants.*

Yard and garden centers often sell plant species that are not native to the area in which you live. Furthermore, homeowners often want unusual plants that are particularly colorful or have other striking characteristics. Some of these exotic plants are invasive. They have characteristics such as fruits or seeds that are easily spread from place to place. When this occurs, the exotic plant may become a pest because it competes with local native plants and replaces them, causing local extinctions of native species.

In the United States, there are many examples of exotic invasive species. Glossy buckthorn and autumn olive have replaced understory species in forests of the Northeast. Tamarisk (salt cedar) has become a dominant species along rivers in the Southwest. Brazilian pepper and *Melaleuca* have become major problems in south Florida. Kudzu (a vine) and water hyacinth have become significant problems in areas of the South. Purple loosestrife (see photo) has taken over wetlands in many areas of the northern parts of the United States and southern parts of Canada.

- **What are the invasive exotic species found in your area?**

- **Why do some exotic species spread so rapidly?**

- **Should the kinds of plants you select to plant in your yard be regulated by state laws and/or local ordinances?**

## Background Check

**Concepts you should already know to get the most out of this chapter:**
- The nature of food chains (chapter 15)
- The role of natural selection in shaping the evolution of organisms (chapter 13)

## 16.1 The Nature of Communities

Scientists approach the study of ecological interactions in different ways. For example, in chapter 15, we looked at ecological relationships from the point of view of ecosystems and the way energy and matter flow through them. But we can also study relationships at the community level and focus on the kinds of interactions that take place among organisms. Recall that a community consists of all the populations of different kinds of organisms that interact in a particular location.

### Defining Community Boundaries

One of the first things a community ecologist must do is determine the boundaries of the community to be studied. A small pond is an example of a community with easily determined natural boundaries (figure 16.1). The water's edge naturally defines the limits of this community. We would expect to find certain animals and plants living in the pond, such as fish, frogs, snails, insects, algae, pondweeds, bacteria, and fungi. But you might ask at this point, What about the plants and animals that live at the water's edge? Are they part of the pond community? Or what about great blue herons that catch fish and frogs in the pond but build nests atop some tall trees away from the pond? Or should we include in this community the ducks that spend the night but fly off to feed elsewhere during the day? Should the deer that comes to the pond to drink at dusk be included? What originally seemed to be a clear example of a community has become less clear-cut.

The point of this discussion is that all community boundaries are artificial. However, defining boundaries—even if they are artificial—is important, because it allows us to focus on the changes that occur in a particular area, recognize patterns and trends, and make predictions.

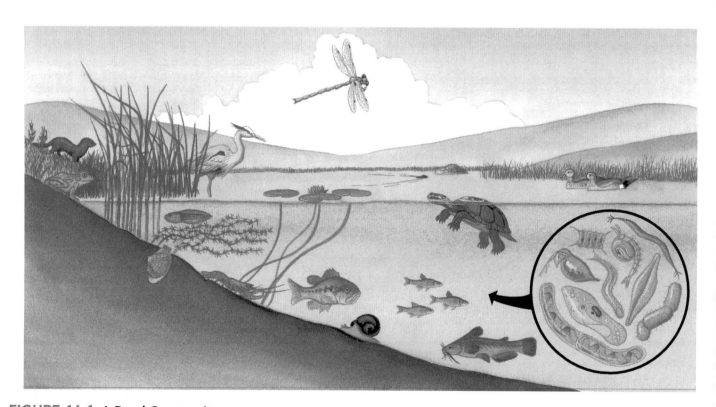

**FIGURE 16.1 A Pond Community**
Although a pond seems an easy community to characterize, it interacts extensively with the surrounding land-based communities. Some of the organisms associated with a pond community are always present in the water (e.g., fish, pondweeds, clams); others occasionally venture from the water to the surrounding land (e.g., frogs, dragonflies, turtles, muskrats); still others are occasional or rare visitors (e.g., minks, heron, ducks).

## Complexity and Stability

Each community has a particular combination of producers, consumers, and decomposers, which interact in many ways. Within the community, each species is a specialist in certain aspects of community function. One of the ways that organisms interact is by feeding on one another. Most organisms in

a community participate in several food chains. When we recognize that many food chains in an area overlap, we see a pattern of interactions we can call a **food web** (figure 16.2).

One of the common features of such a complex set of interrelationships is that natural communities are relatively stable. This stability allows us to identify and name various kinds of communities. In fact, there is a relationship between

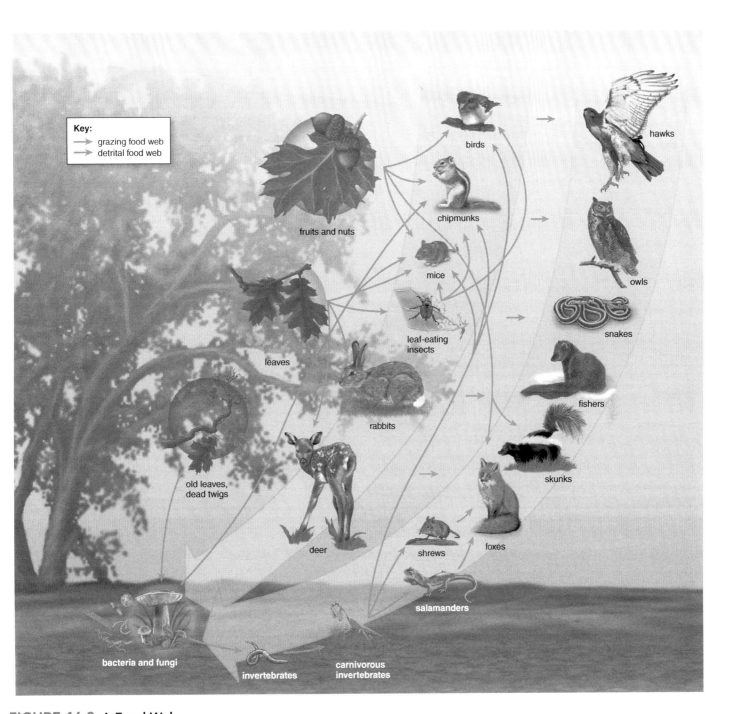

**FIGURE 16.2  A Food Web**

As organisms feed on one another they establish a web of relationships known as a food web. This illustration shows the interactions between grazing and detrital food webs. In grazing food webs, photosynthesis by plants provides the energy for grazing animals that eat plants, which in turn provide energy for carnivores. Since all organisms die, they ultimately become part of a detrital food web in which dead organic matter and waste products supply the energy for a series of bacteria, fungi, and animals.

the degree of complexity and the stability of a community. Complex communities with many kinds of organisms interacting in numerous ways tend to be more stable than those that have few organisms and interactions. In other words, over hundreds of years, you would see the same kinds of organisms living in a woodlot, prairie, or ponderosa pine forest. On the other hand, many human-influenced communities are very unstable. Agricultural ecosystems tend to have very few kinds of organisms and cannot maintain themselves without human involvement.

## Communities Are Dynamic

Although many kinds of communities are stable, that does not mean that there is no activity going on within the community. For example, while the human body is relatively stable, its stability results from the constant activity of various organs. Although at the broad level communities may appear to be unchanging, there is much change occurring among the organisms present. Producers are capturing sunlight, herbivores are eating plants, carnivores are eating animals, and decomposers are recycling materials. Populations of many organisms may rise and fall as well.

However, if the numbers of a particular kind of organism in a community increase or decrease significantly, some adjustment usually occurs in the populations of other organisms within the community. For example, the populations of many kinds of small mammals (mice, voles, lemmings, and so on) vary from year to year. If there are few small mammals to eat, the populations of their predators decrease. In addition, predators switch to different prey species, affecting other parts of the community.

---

**16.1 CONCEPT REVIEW**

1. Why is a food web better than a food chain as a way to describe a community?
2. As the number of insects declines in the autumn as the leaves fall from trees and the grass stops growing, what would you expect to happen to bird populations?

---

## 16.2 Niche and Habitat

One of the ways scientists learn how communities work is by focusing on the activities and impacts of certain species. Each organism has a role to play and is involved in a complex set of interactions with other organisms.

### The Niche Concept

The **niche** of an organism is its specific functional role in its community. A complete description of an organism's niche involves a detailed understanding of the impacts an organism has on its biotic and abiotic surroundings, as well as all the

factors that affect the organism. Therefore, a complete description of the niche of an organism is probably impossible. If we look hard enough, we discover something new we didn't understand before.

For example, the niche of an earthworm includes how an earthworm is affected by abiotic factors such as the size of soil particles, soil texture, moisture, pH, and temperature. Its niche also includes biotic factors such as parasites that infect earthworms; birds, moles, and shrews that eat earthworms; dead plant material that earthworms use for food, and anglers who use worms as bait (figure 16.3). In addition, earthworms perform several important functions in their communities. They (1) transport minerals and nutrients from deeper soil layers to the surface, (2) bury seeds, (3) incorporate organic matter into the soil, and (4) create burrows, which allow air and water to penetrate the soil more easily. And this entire discussion represents only a limited sample of all the aspects of an earthworm's niche.

Some organisms have rather broad niches; others, with very specialized requirements and limited roles to play, have niches that are quite narrow. The opossum (figure 16.4a) is an animal with a very broad niche. It eats a wide variety of plant and animal foods, can adjust to a wide variety of climates, is used as food by many kinds of carnivores (including humans), and produces large numbers of offspring. By contrast, the koala of Australia (figure 16.4b) has a very narrow niche. It can live only in areas of Australia that have specific species of *Eucalyptus* trees, because it only eats the leaves of these trees. Furthermore, it cannot tolerate low temperatures and does not produce many offspring. As you might guess, the opossum is expanding its range, and the koala is endangered in much of its range.

Because an organism's niche includes a complex set of interactions with its surroundings, it is often easy to overlook important roles played by some organisms. For example, Europeans introduced cattle into Australia where there had previously been no large, hoofed mammals. When this was done, no one thought about the effects of cow manure on the biotic community or the significance of *dung beetles*. In parts of the world where dung beetles exist, they rapidly colonize fresh dung and cause it to be broken down. Although there were dung beetles in Australia, they were adapted to feeding on the dung of native marsupials and did not colonize cow dung. Therefore, in areas of Australia where cattle were raised, a significant amount of land became covered with accumulated cow dung. This reduced the area where grass could grow and reduced productivity. The problem was eventually solved by the importation of several species of dung beetles from Africa and Europe, where large, hoofed mammals are common. The dung beetles made use of what the cattle did not digest, returning it to a form that plants could recycle more easily into plant biomass.

### The Habitat Concept

The **habitat** of an organism is the kind of place or community in which it lives. Each organism has particular requirements for life and lives where the environment provides what it

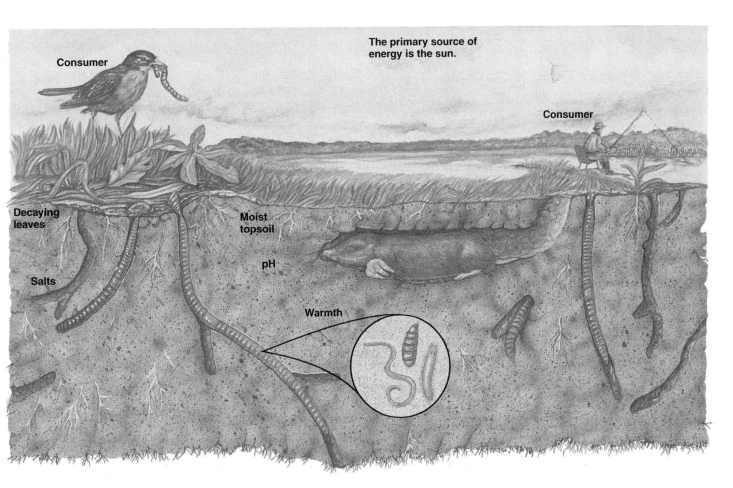

## FIGURE 16.3  The Niche of an Earthworm

The niche of an earthworm involves a great many factors. It includes the fact that the earthworm is a consumer of dead organic matter, a source of food for other animals, a host to parasites, and bait for an angler. Furthermore, the earthworm loosens the soil by burrowing and "plows" the soil when it deposits materials on the surface. Additionally, the pH, texture, and moisture content of the soil have an impact on the earthworm. This is but a small part of what the niche of the earthworm includes.

(a) The opossum has a very broad niche

(b) The koala has a narrow niche

## FIGURE 16.4  Broad and Narrow Niches

(a) The opossum has a very broad niche. It eats a variety of foods, is able to live in a variety of habitats, and has a large reproductive capacity. It is generally extending its range in the United States. (b) The koala has a narrow niche. It feeds on the leaves of only a few species of *Eucalyptus* trees, is restricted to relatively warm, forested areas, and is generally endangered in much of its habitat in Australia.

needs. Habitats are usually described in terms of a conspicuous or particularly significant feature. For example, the habitat of a prairie dog is usually described as grassland and the habitat of a tuna is described as the open ocean. The habitat of a fiddler crab is sandy ocean shores and the habitat of various kinds of cacti is the desert. It is possible to describe the habitat of the bacterium *Escherichia coli* as the gut of humans and other mammals and the habitat of a fungus as a rotting log. Organisms that have very specific places in which they live simply have more restricted habitats.

## 16.2 CONCEPT REVIEW

3. List 10 items that are a part of your niche.
4. What is the difference between habitat and niche?

## 16.3 Kinds of Organism Interactions

One of the important components of an organism's niche is the other living things with which it interacts. Some interactions are harmful to one or both of the organisms, whereas other interactions are beneficial. Ecologists have classified the kinds of interactions between organisms into broad categories.

### Competition

**Competition** is an interaction between organisms in which both organisms are harmed to some extent. This is the most common kind of interaction among organisms. Organisms are constantly involved in competition. Competition occurs whenever two organisms need a vital resource that is in short supply (figure 16.5). The vital resource may be such things as soil nutrients, sunlight, or pollinators for plants; or food, shelter, nesting sites, water, mates, or space for animals.

**Intraspecific competition** takes place between members of the *same* species. It can involve a snarling tug-of-war between two dogs over a scrap of food or a silent struggle between pine seedlings for access to available light. **Interspecific competition** occurs between members of *different* species. The interaction between weeds and tomato plants in a garden is an example of interspecific competition. If the weeds are not removed, they compete with the tomatoes for available sunlight, water, and nutrients, resulting in poor growth of both the tomatoes and weeds. Similarly, there is interspecific competition among species of carnivores (e.g., hawks, owls, coyotes, foxes) for the small mammals and birds they use for food. Competition does not necessarily involve a face-to-face confrontation. For example, if a coyotes kills and eats a rodent, it has had a competitive effect on foxes, hawks, and other carnivores as well as other members of its own species, because there is now one less rodent available to be caught and eaten by others.

**(a) Intraspecific competition between pine trees for light**

**(b) Interspecific competition between vultures and lion for food (zebra)**

**FIGURE 16.5 Competition**
Whenever a needed resource is in limited supply, organisms compete for it. Competition between members of the same species is called *intraspecific competition.* (a) Intraspecific competition for sunlight among these pine trees has resulted in the tall, straight trunks. Those trees that did not grow fast enough died. Competition between different species is called *interspecific competition.* (b) The lion and vultures are competing for the lion's zebra kill.

### Competition and Natural Selection

Competition is a powerful force for natural selection. Although competition results in harm to both organisms, there can still be winners and losers. The two organisms may not be harmed to the same extent, with the result that one gains greater access to the limited resource. Biologists have recognized that, the more similar the requirements of two species of organisms, the more intense the competition between them. This has led to the development of a general rule known as the *competitive exclusion principle.* According to the **competitive exclusion principle,** no two species of organisms can occupy the same niche at the same time. If two species of organisms do occupy the same niche, the competition will be so intense that one or more of the following processes will occur: (1) one of the two species will become extinct, (2) one will migrate to a different area where competition is less intense, or (3) the two species will evolve into slightly different niches, so that the intensity of the competition is reduced. For example, a study of the feeding habits of several kinds of warblers shows that, although they live in the same place and feed on similar organisms, their niches are slightly different, because they feed in different places on trees (figure 16.6).

Another example involves the competition of various species of flowering plants for pollinators. Some have bright red tubular flowers that are attractive to hummingbirds. Some have foul odors that attract flies or beetles. Others are open only at night and are pollinated by moths or bats. A few kinds of orchid flowers mimic female wasps and are pollinated when the male wasp tries to mate with the fake female wasp. Many flowers attract several kinds of bees, butterflies, or beetles, but the flowers open only at certain times of the day. All of these differences are niche specializations that reduce competition for pollinators.

## Predation

**Predation** is an interaction in which one animal captures, kills, and eats another animal. The organism that is killed is the **prey,** and the one that does the killing is the **predator.** Predators

benefit from the relationship because they obtain a source of food; obviously, prey organisms are harmed. Most predators are relatively large, compared to their prey, and have specific adaptations to aid them in catching prey. There are many different styles of predation. Many predators, such as leopards, lions, cheetahs, hawks, squid, sharks, and salmon, use speed and strength to capture their prey. Dragonflies, bats, and swallows use a technique that involves flying around in an area where they can capture flying insects. Predators such as frogs, many kinds of lizards, and insects (e.g., praying mantis) blend in with their surroundings and strike quickly when a prey organism happens by. Wolf spiders and jumping spiders have large eyes, which help them find prey, which they pounce on and kill. The webs of other kinds of spiders serve as nets to catch flying insects. The prey are quickly paralyzed by the spider's bite and wrapped in a tangle of silk threads (figure 16.7). Many kinds of birds, insects, and mammals simply search for slow-moving prey, such as caterpillars, grubs, aphids, slugs, snails, and similar organisms. Many kinds of marine snails and starfish are predators of other slow-moving sea creatures.

Often predators are useful to humans because they control populations of organisms that do us harm. For example, snakes eat rats and mice that eat stored grain and other agricultural products. Birds and bats eat insects that are agricultural pests.

It is even possible to think of a predator as having a beneficial effect on the prey species. Certainly, the *individual* organism that is killed is harmed, but the *population* can benefit. Predators can control the size of a prey population and thus, prevent large populations of prey organisms from

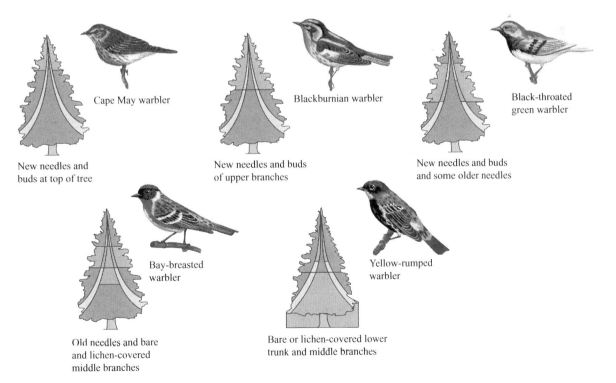

**FIGURE 16.6 Niche Specialization**
Although all of these warbler species have similar feeding habits, they limit the intensity of competition by feeding on different parts of the tree.

(a) Lions use speed and strength to capture their prey

(b) Chameleons use stealth and camouflage to capture prey

(c) Spiders use webs to capture prey

**FIGURE 16.7 The Predator-Prey Relationship**
*(a)* Many predators, such as lions and cheetahs, use speed and strength to capture prey. *(b)* Other predators, such as frogs and chameleons, blend in with their surroundings, lie in wait, and ambush their prey. *(c)* Some spiders use nets to capture prey. Obviously, predators benefit from the food they obtain, to the detriment of the prey.

destroying their habitat or they can reduce the likelihood of epidemic disease by eating sick or diseased individuals. Furthermore, predators act as selecting agents. The individuals that fall prey to them are likely to be less well-adapted than the ones that escape predation. Predators usually kill slow, unwary, poorly hidden, sick, or injured individuals. Thus, the genes that may have contributed to slowness, inattention, poor camouflage, illness, or the likelihood of being injured are removed from the gene pool.

## Symbiotic Relationships

**Symbiosis** means "living together." Unfortunately, this word is used in several ways, none of which is very precise. However, the term symbiosis is usually used for interactions that involve a close physical relationship between two kinds of organisms. The three kinds of relationships discussed in the following sections—parasitism, commensalism, and mutualism—are often referred to as symbiotic relationships because they usually involve organisms that are physically connected to one another.

## Parasitism

In **parasitism**, one organism lives in or on another living organism, from which it derives nourishment. The **parasite** derives benefit and harms the **host**, the organism it lives in or on. Parasites are smaller than their hosts. In general, they do not kill their host quickly but, rather, use it as a source of food for a long time. However, the parasite's activities may weaken the host so that it eventually dies. Parasitism is a very common kind of interrelationship. Nearly every category of living thing has species that are parasites. There are parasitic bacteria, fungi, protozoa, plants, fish, insects, worms, mites, and ticks. In fact, there are more species of parasites in the world than there are nonparasites.

There are many styles of parasitism. Parasites that live on the outside of their hosts are called **external parasites.** For example, ticks live on the outside of the bodies of animals, such as rats, turtles, and humans, where they suck blood and do harm to their hosts. **Internal parasites** live on the inside of their hosts. For example, tapeworms live in their hosts' intestines. Several kinds of plants are parasitic; mistletoe invades the tissues of the tree it is living on to derive its nourishment. Some flowering plants, such as beech drops and Indian pipe, lack chlorophyll and are not able to do photosynthesis. They derive their nourishment by obtaining nutrients from the roots of trees or soil fungi and grow aboveground for a short period when they flower. Indian pipe is interesting in that it is parasitic on the fungi that assist tree roots in absorbing water. The root fungi receive nourishment from the tree and the Indian pipe obtains nourishment from the fungi. So, the Indian pipe is an indirect parasite on trees (figure 16.8).

Many kinds of fungi are parasites of plants, including commercially valuable plants. Farmers spend millions of dollars each year to control fungus parasites. Many kinds of insects, worms, protozoa, bacteria, and viruses are important human parasites.

Many parasites have extremely complicated life cycles (chapter 23 discusses the life cycle of several kinds of worm parasites). In many of these life cycles, some species carry the parasite from one host to the next. Such a carrier organism is known as a **vector.** For example, the protozoan that causes malaria is carried from one human to another by certain species of mosquitos, and the bacterium *Borrelia burgdorferi,* which causes lyme disease, is carried by certain species of ticks (figure 16.9).

## Special Kinds of Predation and Parasitism

Both predation and parasitism are relationships in which one member of the pair is helped and the other is harmed. But there are many kinds of common interactions in which one is harmed and the other aided that don't fit neatly into the categories of interactions dreamed up by scientists. For example, when a deer eats the leaves off a tree or a goose eats grass, they are doing harm to the plant they are eating while deriving a benefit. In essence, these herbivores are *plant predators or parasites* (figure 16.10). In aquatic habitats there are many kinds of organisms (sponges, clams, barnacles, shrimp, etc.) that live as filter-feeders. They are essentially grazers on tiny organisms in the water around them. Most consume a mixture of algae and tiny animals, but they consume the entire organism and can be considered a kind of predator. In addition, there are many animals, such as mosquitoes, biting flies, vampire bats, and ticks, that take blood meals but don't usually live permanently on the host or kill it. Are they temporary parasites or specialized predators?

**(a) A tapeworm is an internal parasite**

**(b) A black-legged tick is an external parasite**

**(c) Indian pipe is a plant that is a parasite**

**FIGURE 16.8 The Parasite-Host Relationship**
Parasites benefit from the relationship because they obtain nourishment from the host. *(a)* Tapeworms are internal parasites in the guts of their host, where they absorb food from the host's gut. *(b)* The tick is an external parasite that sucks body fluids from its host. *(c)* Indian pipe (*Monotropa uniflora*) is a flowering plant that lacks chlorophyll and is parasitic on fungi that have a mutualistic relationship with tree roots. The host in any of these three situations may not be killed directly by the relationship, but it is often weakened, becoming more vulnerable to predators and diseases.

**FIGURE 16.9 Lyme Disease—Hosts, Parasites, and Vectors**
Lyme disease is a bacterial disease originally identified in a small number of people in the Old Lyme, Connecticut, area. Today, it is found throughout the United States and Canada. The parasite *Borrelia burgdorferi*, is a bacterium that can live in a variety of mammalian hosts (e.g., humans, mice, horses, cattle, domestic cats, and dogs). Certain ticks are vectors that suck blood from an infected animal and carry the disease to another animal when the tick feeds on it.

Finally, birds such as cowbirds and some species of European cuckoos do not build nests but, rather, lay their eggs in the nests of other species of bird, which raise these foster young rather than their own. The adult cowbird and cuckoo often remove eggs from the host nest. In addition, cowbird and cuckoo offspring typically push the hosts' eggs or young out of the nest. For these reasons, typically only the cowbird or cuckoo chick is raised by the foster parents. This kind of relationship has been called *nest parasitism*. The surrogate parents (hosts) are harmed, and the cowbird or cuckoo is aided by having others expend the energy needed to raise its young (figure 16.11).

## Commensalism

**Commensalism** is a relationship in which one organism benefits and the other is not affected. For example, sharks often have another fish, the remora, attached to them. The remora has a sucker on the top side of its head, which allows it to attach to the shark for a free ride (figure 16.12a). Although the remora benefits from the free ride and by eating leftovers from the shark's meals, the shark does not appear to be troubled by this uninvited guest, nor does it benefit from its presence.

Another example of commensalism is the relationship between trees and epiphytic plants. **Epiphytes** are plants that live on the surface of other plants but that do not derive nourishment from them (figure 16.12b). Many kinds of plants (e.g., orchids, ferns, and mosses) use the surfaces of trees as places to live. These kinds of organisms are particularly common in tropical rainforests. Many epiphytes derive a benefit from the relationship because they are able to be located in the tops of the trees, where they receive more sunlight and moisture. The trees derive no benefit from the relationship, nor are they harmed; they simply serve as support surfaces for the epiphytes.

**Is a monarch caterpillar eating milkweed, a parasite on milkweed?**

**Is a caribou eating willow, a predator on willow?**

**Is a mosquito sucking blood, a parasite or a specialized carnivore?**

**FIGURE 16.10 Special Kinds of Predation and Parasitism**
Herbivores have a relationship with plants that is very similar to that of carnivores with their prey and parasites with their hosts. The herbivores are aided and the plants they feed on are harmed. Mosquitoes and other kinds of blood-sucking animals can be considered temporary parasites or predators. They do harm to the animal they feed on and benefit from the relationship.

**(a) A remora hitching a ride on a shark**

**FIGURE 16.11 Nest Parasitism**
This cowbird chick in the nest is being fed by its host parent, a yellow warbler. The cowbird chick and its cowbird parents both benefit but the host is harmed because it is not raising any of its own young.

## Mutualism

**Mutualism** is an interrelationship in which two species live in close association with one another, and both benefit. Many kinds of animals that eat plants have a mutualistic relationship with the bacteria and protozoa that live in their guts. One of the major components of plant material is the cellulose material that makes up the cell wall. Most animals are unable to digest cellulose but rely on a collection of microorganisms in their guts to perform that function. For example, mammals such as cows, goats, camels, giraffes, and sheep have specialized portions of their guts, called a rumen, in which microorganisms live. These microbes produce enzymes, known as *cellulases*, that break down the cellulose in the food the animal eats. The microorganisms benefit because the gut provides them with a moist, warm, nourishing environment in which to live. The animals benefit because the breakdown of cellulose provides nutrients the animal could not get otherwise. Termites, plant-eating lizards, and many other kinds of herbivores have similar relationships with the bacteria and protozoa living in their digestive tracts which help them digest cellulose.

Lichens and corals exhibit a more intimate kind of mutualism. The bodies of lichens and corals are composed of the intermingled cells of two different kinds of organisms. Lichens consist of fungal cells and algal cells in a partnership; corals consist of the cells of the coral organism intermingled with algal cells. In both, the algae carry on photosynthesis and provide nutrients, and the fungus or coral provides a moist, fixed structure for the algae to live in.

Another kind of mutualistic relationship exists between flowering plants and insects. Bees and other insects visit flowers to obtain nectar from the blossoms (figure 16.13). Usually, the flowers are constructed so that the bees pick

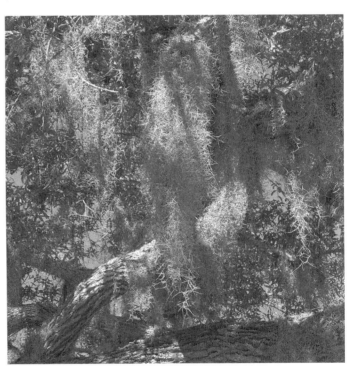

**(b) Spanish moss is an epiphyte that benefits from living on the surface of trees**

**FIGURE 16.12 Commensalism**
In commensalism, one organism benefits and the other is not affected. *(a)* The remora shown here hitchhikes a ride on the shark. It eats scraps of food left over from the shark's messy eating habits. The shark does not seem to be hindered in any way. *(b)* The grey Spanish moss hanging on this oak tree is a good example of an epiphyte. The spanish moss does not harm the tree but benefits from using the tree surface as a place to grow.

up pollen (sperm-containing packages) from the plant on their hairy bodies, which they transfer to the female part of the next flower they visit. Because bees normally visit many individual flowers of the same species for several minutes and ignore other species of flowers, they can

(a) British soldier lichen

(b) Ruminants

(c) Pollination

**FIGURE 16.13 Mutualism**

Mutualism is an interaction between two organisms in which both benefit. *(a)* The British soldier lichen in this photograph consists of a mutualistic association between a fungus and an alga. *(b)* Ruminant animals have a mutualistic relationship with the microorganisms in their gut that helps them obtain nutrients from the plants they eat. *(c)* Insects obtain nectar from plants; the plants benefit by being pollinated. (Note the yellow pollen on the bee.)

**TABLE 16.1  Summary of Kinds of Organism Interactions**

| Kinds of Interaction | Organism 1 | Organism 2 | Comments |
|---|---|---|---|
| Competition | Harmed | Harmed | Usually one is harmed more than the other. |
| Predation | Predator benefited | Prey harmed | Predators have special adaptations for capturing prey. Prey organisms have adaptations to avoid predators. |
| Parasitism | Parasite benefited | Host harmed | Usually the host and parasite are in physical contact. |
| Commensalism | Commensal benefited | Host unaffected | Usually the host and commensal are in physical contact. |
| Mutualism | Benefited | Benefited | Usually the two organisms are in physical contact. |

serve as pollen carriers between two flowers of the same species. Plants pollinated in this manner produce less pollen than do plants that rely on the wind to transfer pollen. This saves the plant energy, because it doesn't need to produce huge quantities of pollen. It does, however, need to transfer some of its energy savings into the production of showy flowers and nectar to attract the bees. The bees benefit from both the nectar and the pollen; they use both for food.

Some plants use birds, bats, mice, beetles, flies, and other kinds of organisms to get their pollen distributed. Each kind of flower is specialized to the kind of pollinating animal. Flowers that are pollinated by bats flower at night; and many of those that are pollinated by hummingbirds have long, tubular flowers. Table 16.1 summarizes features of these various kinds of organism interactions.

Another way in which plants and animals participate in a mutually beneficial relationship is in the production and consumption of fruit. The fruit that plants produce contains its seeds. The fruit is attractive to animals that eat it. When the seeds pass through the gut of the animal, they are typically deposited some distance from the plant that produced the fruit. Similarly animals that bury fruits typically carry the fruit away from the plant that produced it.

Although they may eat some of the seeds, animals like squirrels do not find all of the fruits they buried and thus are involved in planting new plants. Therefore, animals serve as dispersal agents for the seeds of the plant. The plant encourages this activity by providing a nutritious fruit for the animal.

**16.3  CONCEPT REVIEW**

5. What do parasites, commensal organisms, and mutualistic organisms have in common? How are they different?
6. Describe two situations in which competition can involve combat and two that do not involve combat.
7. How is the competitive exclusion principle related to the theory of natural selection?
8. In what way are predators and parasites similar in the way they interact with other species? How do they differ in how they interact with other species?

## 16.4  Types of Communities

Ecologists recognize that the world can be divided into large, regional, terrestrial communities known as *biomes*. **Biomes** are communities of organisms with widespread geographic distribution that are adapted to particular climatic conditions. The primary climatic factors that determine the kinds of organisms that can live in an area are the amount and pattern of *precipitation* and the *temperature* ranges typical for the region (figure 16.14). The map in figure 16.15 shows the distribution of the major terrestrial biomes of the world.

### Temperate Deciduous Forest

*Temperate deciduous forest* exists in the parts of the world that have moderate rainfall (75 to 130 centimeters per year) spread over the entire year and a relatively long summer growing season (130 to 260 days without frost). This biome, like other land-based biomes, is named for a major feature of the community, its dominant vegetation. The predominant plants are large trees that lose their leaves during the fall. Thus, they are called deciduous (figure 16.16). The temperate deciduous forest covers a large area from the Mississippi River to the Atlantic Coast and from Florida to southern Canada. This type of biome is also found in much of Europe and parts of eastern Asia.

Because the trees are the major producers and new leaves are produced each spring, the important primary consumers

**FIGURE 16.14 The Influence of Precipitation and Temperature on Vegetation**
Temperature and moisture influence the kind of vegetation that can live in an area.

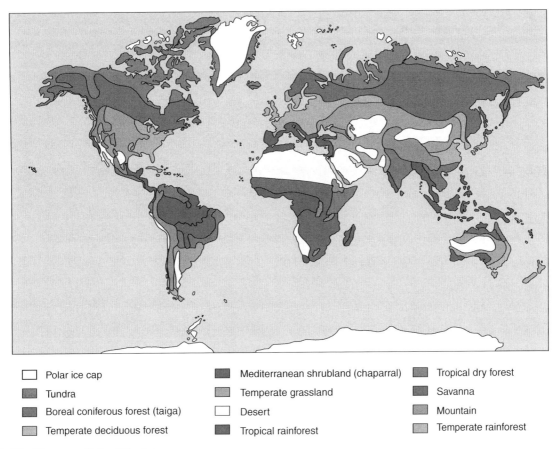

**FIGURE 16.15 Biomes of the World**
Major climatic differences determine the kinds of plants and animals that can live in a region. These regional communities are called biomes.

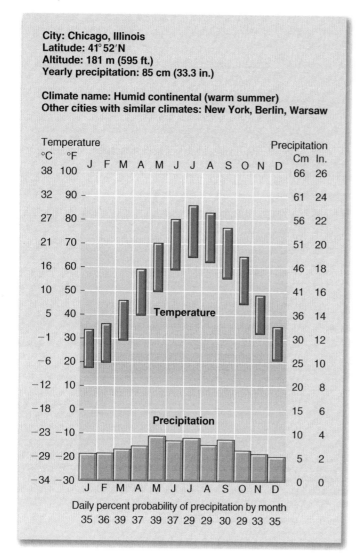

City: Chicago, Illinois
Latitude: 41°52′N
Altitude: 181 m (595 ft.)
Yearly precipitation: 85 cm (33.3 in.)

Climate name: Humid continental (warm summer)
Other cities with similar climates: New York, Berlin, Warsaw

Daily percent probability of precipitation by month
35 36 39 37 39 37 29 29 30 29 33 35

(a)

(b) Temperate deciduous forest in summer

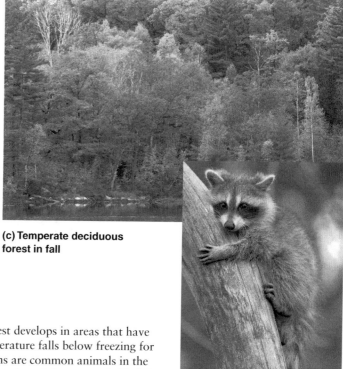

(c) Temperate deciduous forest in fall

(d) Raccoon

**FIGURE 16.16 Temperate Deciduous Forest**
(a) Climagraph for Chicago, Illinois. (b & c) A temperate deciduous forest develops in areas that have significant amounts of moisture throughout the year but where the temperature falls below freezing for parts of the year. During this time, the trees lose their leaves. (d) Raccoons are common animals in the temperate deciduous forest of North America. This kind of forest once dominated the eastern half of the United States and southeastern Canada.

in this biome are leaf-eating insects. These insects are food for a variety of birds that raise their young in the forest during the summer and migrate to more moderate climates in the fall. Many other animals, such as squirrels, some birds, and deer, use the trees' fruits for food. Carnivores, such as foxes, hawks, and owls, eat many of the small mammals and birds typical of the region. Another feature of the temperate deciduous forest is an abundance of spring woodland wildflowers, which emerge early in the spring before the trees have leafed out.

The region where temperate deciduous forests exist encompasses a large geographic area with somewhat different climatic conditions in different locations. Therefore, there are differences in the species of trees (and other organisms) usually

found in different areas within this biome. For instance, in Maryland the tulip tree is one of the state's common large trees, whereas in Michigan it is so unusual that people plant it in lawns and parks as a decorative tree. Aspen, birch, cottonwood, oak, hickory, beech, and maple are typical trees of the temperate deciduous forest. Typical animals of this biome are many kinds of leaf-eating insects, wood-boring beetles, migratory birds, skunks, porcupines, deer, frogs, opossums, owls, and mosquitoes.

In much of this region, the natural vegetation has been removed to allow for agriculture, so the original character of the biome is gone, except where farming is not practical or the original forest has been preserved or allowed to regenerate.

# Temperate Grassland (Prairie)

*Temperate grassland,* or *prairie,* exists where the rainfall (30 to 85 centimeters per year) is not adequate to support the growth of trees; the dominant vegetation consists of various species of grasses (figure 16.17). Typical are long periods during the year when there is no rainfall. Trees are common in this biome only along streams, where they can obtain sufficient water. Interspersed among the grasses are many kinds of prairie wildflowers. The dominant animals are those that use grasses as food; large, grazing mammals (bison and pronghorn antelope); small insects (e.g., grasshoppers and ants); and rodents (e.g., mice and prairie dogs). A variety of carnivores (e.g., meadowlarks, coyotes, and snakes) feed on the herbivores. Most of the bird species are seasonal visitors to the prairie. At one time, fire was a common feature of the prairie during the dry part of the year.

In North America, temperate grasslands are found throughout much of the region between the Mississippi River and the Rocky Mountains. This biome is also common in parts of Eurasia, Africa, Australia, and South America.

Today, most of the original grasslands, like the temperate deciduous forest, have been converted to agricultural uses. Grasslands with adequate rainfall or where irrigation is possible are used to grow crops like corn and wheat. Grasslands that are too dry to allow for farming typically have been used as grazing land for cattle and sheep. The grazing of these domesticated animals has modified the natural vegetation, as has farming in the moister grassland regions.

(a)

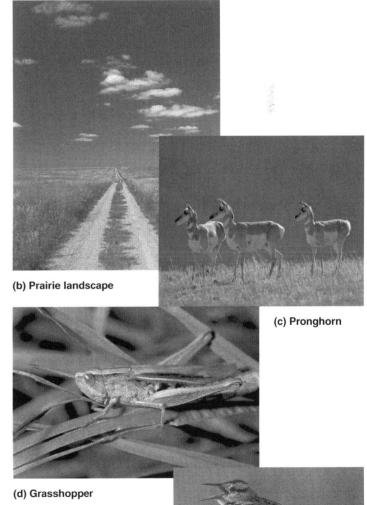

(b) Prairie landscape

(c) Pronghorn

(d) Grasshopper

(e) Meadowlark

**FIGURE 16.17 Temperate Grassland**
*(a)* Climagraph for Tehran, Iran. *(b)* Grasses are better able to withstand low rainfall than are trees. Therefore, in areas that have moderate rainfall, grasses are the dominant plants. *(c & d)* Pronghorns and grasshoppers are common herbivores and *(e)* meadowlarks are common consumers of insects in North American grasslands.

# Savanna

*Savannas* are tropical biomes of central Africa, northern Australia, and parts of South America; they have distinct wet and dry seasons (figure 16.18). Although these regions may receive 100 centimeters of rainfall per year, there is an extended dry season of 3 months or more. Because of the extended period of dryness, the dominant vegetation consists of grasses. In addition, a few thorny, widely spaced, drought-resistant trees dot the landscape. Many kinds of grazing mammals are found in this biome—various species of antelope, wildebeest, and zebras in Africa; various kinds of kangaroos in Australia; and a large rodent, the capybara, in South America. Another animal common to the savanna is the termite, a colonial insect that typically builds mounds above the ground.

During the wet part of the season, the trees produce leaves, the grass grows rapidly, and most of the animals raise their young. In the African savanna, seasonal migration of the grazing animals is typical. Many of these tropical grasslands have been converted to grazing for cattle and other domesticated animals.

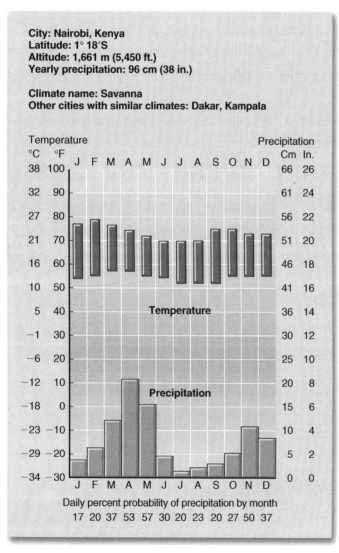

**City: Nairobi, Kenya**
**Latitude: 1° 18′S**
**Altitude: 1,661 m (5,450 ft.)**
**Yearly precipitation: 96 cm (38 in.)**

**Climate name: Savanna**
**Other cities with similar climates: Dakar, Kampala**

Temperature — Precipitation

Daily percent probability of precipitation by month
17  20  37  53  57  30  20  23  20  27  50  37

(a)

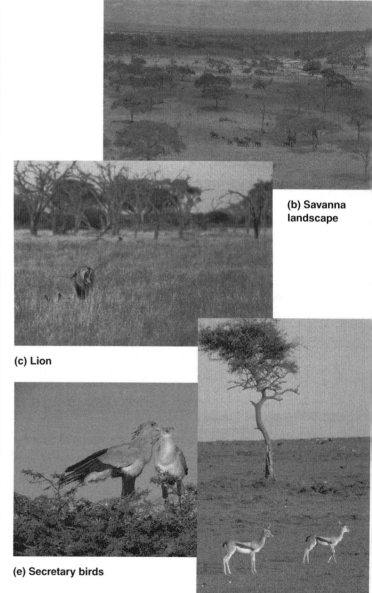

(b) Savanna landscape

(c) Lion

(e) Secretary birds

(d) Thomson's gazelles

## FIGURE 16.18 Savanna

*(a)* Climagraph for Nairobi, Kenya. *(b)* Savannas develop in tropical areas that have seasonal rainfall. They typically have grasses as the dominant vegetation with drought and fire-resistant trees scattered through the area. Grazing animals such as elephants and gazelles *(b & d)* are common herbivores and lions and secretary birds *(c, e)* are common carnivores in African savannas.

## Mediterranean Shrublands (Chaparral)

The *Mediterranean shrublands* are located near an ocean and have a climate with wet, cool winters and dry, hot summers. Rainfall is 40 to 100 centimeters per year. As the name implies, this biome is typical of the Mediterranean coast and is also found in coastal southern California, the southern tip of Africa, a portion of the west coast of Chile, and southern Australia.

The vegetation is dominated by woody shrubs that are adapted to withstand the hot, dry summer. Often the plants are dormant during the summer. Fire is a common feature of this biome, and the shrubs are adapted to withstand occasional fires. The kinds of animals vary widely in the different regions of the world with this biome. Many kinds of insects, reptiles, birds, and mammals are found in

these areas. In the chaparral of California, rattlesnakes, spiders, coyotes, lizards, and rodents are typical inhabitants (figure 16.19).

Very little undisturbed Mediterranean shrubland still exists. The combination of moderate climate and closeness to the ocean has resulted in all Mediterranean shrublands being heavily altered by human activity. Agriculture is common, often with the aid of irrigation, and many major cities such as Los Angeles and San Diego are located in this biome.

## Tropical Dry Forest

The *tropical dry forest* is another biome that is heavily influenced by seasonal rainfall. Tropical dry forests are found in parts of Central and South America, Australia, Africa, and Asia (particularly India and Myanmar). Many of the tropical

**(a)**

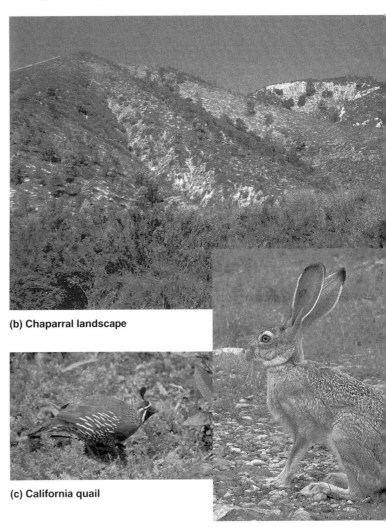

**(b) Chaparral landscape**

**(c) California quail**

**(d) Black-tailed jack rabbit**

**FIGURE 16.19  Mediterranean Shrubland (Chaparral)**
*(a)* Climagraph for Rome, Italy. *(b)* Mediterranean shrublands are characterized by a period of winter rains and a dry, hot summer. The dominant plants are drought-resistant, woody shrubs. *(c & d)* Common animals in the Mediterranean shrubland (chaparral) of California are the California quail and black-tailed jack rabbit.

dry forests have a monsoon climate in which several months of heavy rainfall are followed by extensive dry periods ranging from a few to as many as eight months. (See figure 16.20.) The rainfall may be as low as 50 centimeters or as high as 200 centimeters.

Since the rainfall is highly seasonal, many of the plants have special adaptations for enduring drought. In regions that have long dry periods, many of the trees drop their leaves during the dry part of the year. Many of the species of animals found here are also found in more moist tropical forests of the region. However, there are fewer kinds in dry forests than in rainforests.

Many of these forests occur in areas of very high human population. Therefore, harvesting wood for fuel and building materials have heavily impacted these forests. In addition, many of these forests have been converted to farming or the grazing of animals.

## Desert

*Deserts* are very dry areas found throughout the world wherever rainfall is low and irregular. Typically, the rainfall is less than 25 centimeters per year. Some deserts are extremely hot; others can be quite cold during much of the year. The distinguishing characteristic of desert biomes is low rainfall, not high temperature. Furthermore, deserts show large daily fluctuations in air temperature. When the Sun goes down at night, the land cools off very rapidly, because there is no insulating blanket of clouds to keep the heat from radiating into space.

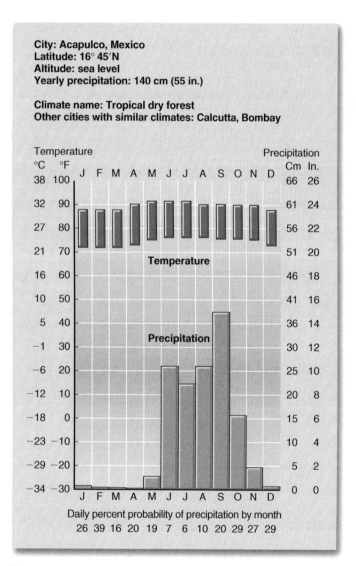

City: Acapulco, Mexico
Latitude: 16° 45′N
Altitude: sea level
Yearly precipitation: 140 cm (55 in.)

Climate name: Tropical dry forest
Other cities with similar climates: Calcutta, Bombay

Daily percent probability of precipitation by month
26 39 16 20 19 7 6 10 20 29 27 29

(a)

(b) Tropical dry forest landscape

(c) White-faced c in Costa Rica

(d) Rhinoceros in Indian tropical dry forest

## FIGURE 16.20 Tropical Dry Forest

*(a)* Climagraph for Acapulco, Mexico. *(b)* Tropical dry forests typically have a period of several months with no rain. In places where the drought is long, many of the larger trees lose their leaves. The coati *(c)* is a common animal in the tropical dry forests of the Americas. The endangered one-horned rhinoceros *(d)* is an inhabitant of the tropical dry forest of Asia.

A desert biome is characterized by scattered, thorny plants that have few or no leaves. However, often the stems are green and carry on photosynthesis (figure 16.21). Because leaves tend to lose water rapidly, the lack of leaves is an adaptation to dry conditions. Many of the plants, such as cacti, can store water in their fleshy stems. Others store water in their roots. Although this is a very harsh environment, many kinds of flowering plants, insects, reptiles, and mammals live there. The animals usually avoid the hottest part of the day by staying in burrows or other shaded, cool areas. Staying underground or in the shade also allows animals to conserve water. Many annual plants also live in this biome, but the seeds germinate and grow only after the infrequent rainstorms. When it does rain, the desert blooms.

## Boreal Coniferous Forest

*Boreal coniferous forest*—also known as the *northern coniferous forest* or the *taiga*—is dominated by evergreen trees (conifers) that are especially adapted to withstand long, cold winters with abundant snowfall. This biome is found throughout the world in northern regions, including parts of southern Canada, extending southward along the Appalachian and Rocky Mountains of the United States, much of northern Europe, and Asia.

Typically, the growing season is less than 120 days, and rainfall ranges between 40 and 100 centimeters per year. However, because of the low average temperature, evaporation is low and the climate is humid. Most of the

City: Cairo, Egypt
Latitude: 29°52′N
Altitude: 116 m (381 ft.)
Yearly precipitation: 1.8 cm (0.7 in.)

Climate name: Hot desert
Other cities with similar climates: Mecca, Karachi

Daily percent probability of precipitation by month
3 3 3 0 0 0 0 0 0 0 3 3

(a)

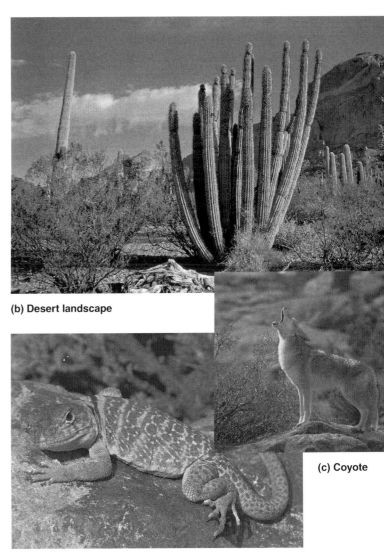

(b) Desert landscape

(c) Coyote

(d) Collared lizard

**FIGURE 16.21 Desert**
*(a)* Climagraph for Cairo, Egypt. *(b)* The desert receives less than 25 centimeters of precipitation per year, yet it teems with life. Cacti, sagebrush, lichens, snakes, small mammals, birds, and insects inhabit the desert. *(c)* Coyotes are common in North American deserts. Because daytime temperatures are often high, most animals are active only at night, when the air temperature drops significantly. Cool deserts also exist in many parts of the world, where rainfall is low but temperatures are not high. *(d)* Collared lizards are common reptiles in many deserts of the United States.

trees in the wetter, colder areas are spruces and firs, but some drier, warmer areas have pines. The wetter areas generally have dense stands of small trees intermingled with many other kinds of vegetation and many small lakes and bogs (figure 16.22). The animals characteristic of this biome include mice, snowshoe hare, lynx, bears, wolves, squirrels, moose, midges, and flies. These animals can be divided into four general categories: those that become dormant in winter (e.g., insects and bears); those that are adapted to withstand the severe winters (e.g., snowshoe hare, lynx); those that live in protected areas (e.g., mice under the snow); and those that migrate south in the fall (most birds).

## Temperate Rainforest

*Temperate rainforest* exists in the coastal areas of northern California, Oregon, Washington, British Columbia, and southern Alaska. Temperate rainforest is also found in New Zealand and the southwest coast and tip of South America. In these coastal areas, the prevailing winds from the west blow over the ocean and bring moisture-laden air to the coast. As the air meets the coastal mountains and is forced to rise, it cools and the moisture falls as rain or snow. Most of these areas receive 200 centimeters or more precipitation per year. This abundance of water, along with fertile soil and mild temperatures, results in a lush growth of plants.

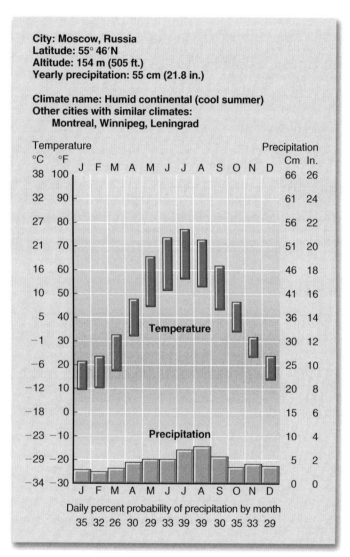

City: Moscow, Russia
Latitude: 55° 46′N
Altitude: 154 m (505 ft.)
Yearly precipitation: 55 cm (21.8 in.)

Climate name: Humid continental (cool summer)
Other cities with similar climates:
    Montreal, Winnipeg, Leningrad

Daily percent probability of precipitation by month
35 32 26 30 29 33 39 39 30 35 33 29

(a)

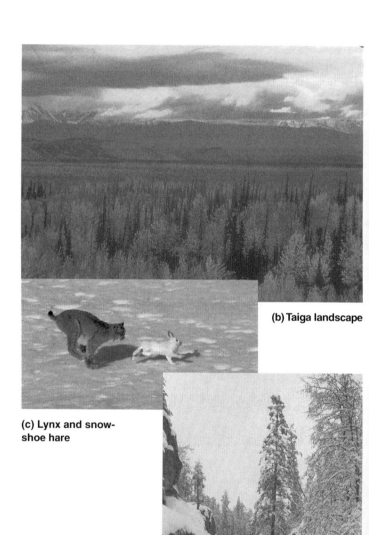

(b) Taiga landscape

(c) Lynx and snow-shoe hare

(d) Taiga in winter

## FIGURE 16.22 Boreal Coniferous Forest, or Taiga

*(a)* Climagraph for Moscow, Russia. *(b & d)* The boreal coniferous forest, or taiga occurs in areas with long winters and heavy snowfall. The trees have adapted to these conditions and provide food and shelter for the animals that live there. *(c)* In North America the lynx and snowshoe hare are common animals.

Sitka spruce, Douglas fir, and western hemlock are typical evergreen coniferous trees in the temperate rainforest of North America. Undisturbed (old growth) forests of this region have trees as old as 800 years that are nearly 100 meters tall. Deciduous trees of various kinds (e.g., red alder, big leaf maple, black cottonwood) also exist in open areas where they can get enough light. All the trees are covered with mosses, ferns, and other plants that grow on the surface of the trees. The dominant color is green, because most of the surfaces have a photosynthetic organism growing on them (figure 16.23).

When a tree dies and falls to the ground, it rots in place and serves as a site for the establishment of new trees. This is such a common feature of the forest that the fallen, rotting trees are called nurse trees. Fallen trees also serve as food for

a variety of insects, which are food for a variety of larger animals.

Because of the rich resource of trees, 90% of the original temperate rainforest has already been logged. Many of the remaining areas have been protected, because they are home to the endangered northern spotted owl and marbled murrelet (a seabird).

## Tundra

*Tundra* is the most northerly biome (figure 16.24). It is characterized by extremely long, severe winters and short, cool summers. The growing season is less than 100 days and, even during the short summer, the nighttime temperatures approach 0°C. Rainfall is low (10 to 25 centimeters per year). The deeper layers

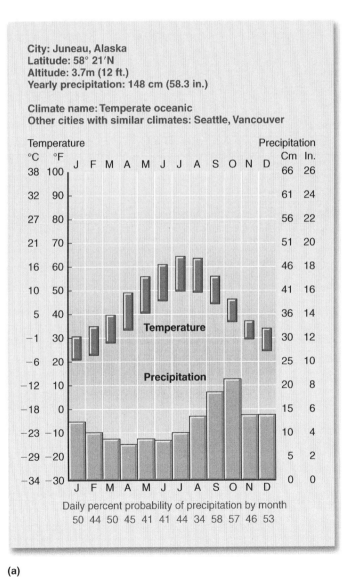

City: Juneau, Alaska
Latitude: 58° 21′N
Altitude: 3.7m (12 ft.)
Yearly precipitation: 148 cm (58.3 in.)

Climate name: Temperate oceanic
Other cities with similar climates: Seattle, Vancouver

Daily percent probability of precipitation by month
50  44  50  45  41  41  44  34  58  57  46  53

(a)

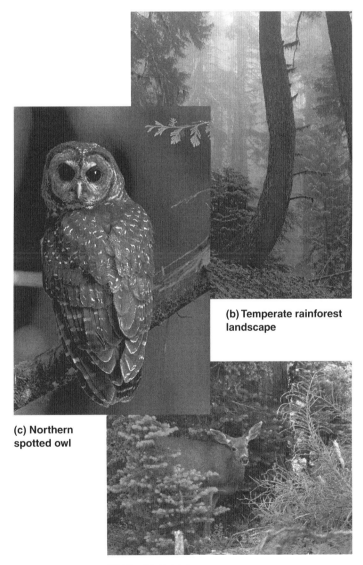

(b) Temperate rainforest landscape

(c) Northern spotted owl

(d) Blacktail deer

**FIGURE 16.23  Temperate Rainforest Biome**
*(a)* Climograph for Juneau, Alaska. *(b)* The temperate rainforest is characterized by high levels of rainfall that support large evergreen trees and the many mosses and ferns that grow on the surface of the trees. *(c & d)* The blacktail deer is common in this biome, which is also the home of the endangered northern spotted owl.

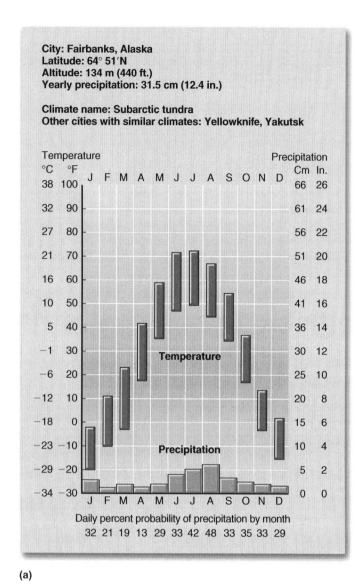

City: Fairbanks, Alaska
Latitude: 64° 51′N
Altitude: 134 m (440 ft.)
Yearly precipitation: 31.5 cm (12.4 in.)

Climate name: Subarctic tundra
Other cities with similar climates: Yellowknife, Yakutsk

Daily percent probability of precipitation by month
32  21  19  13  29  33  42  48  33  35  33  29

(a)

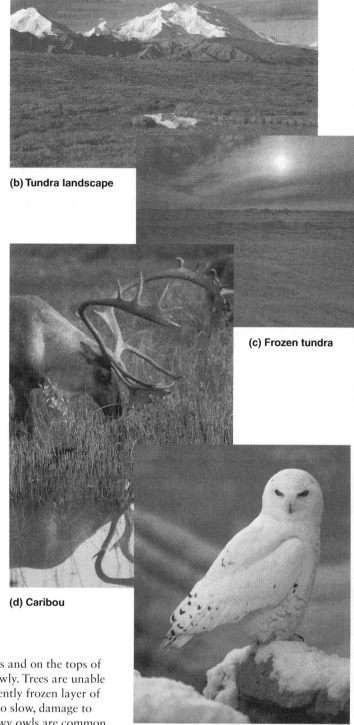

(b) Tundra landscape

(c) Frozen tundra

(d) Caribou

(e) Snowy owl

**FIGURE 16.24 Tundra**

(a) Climagraph for Fairbanks, Alaska. (b & c) In the northern latitudes and on the tops of some mountains, the growing season is short and plants grow very slowly. Trees are unable to live in these extremely cold areas, in part because there is a permanently frozen layer of soil beneath the surface, known as the permafrost. Because growth is so slow, damage to the tundra can still be seen generations later. (d & e) Caribou and snowy owls are common in the tundra.

of the soil remain permanently frozen, forming a layer called the *permafrost*. Because the deeper layers of the soil are frozen, when the surface thaws the water forms puddles on the surface.

Under these conditions of low temperature and short growing season, very few kinds of animals and plants can survive. No trees can live in this region. The typical plants and animals of the area are grasses, sedges, dwarf willow, some other shrubs,

reindeer moss (actually a lichen), caribou, wolves, musk oxen, fox, snowy owls, mice, and many kinds of insects. Many kinds of birds are summer residents only. The tundra community is relatively simple, so any changes have drastic and long-lasting effects. The tundra is easy to injure and slow to heal; therefore, it must be treated gently—the construction of the Alaskan pipeline has left scars that might still be there 100 years from now.

# Tropical Rainforest

*Tropical rainforest* is at the other end of the climate spectrum from the tundra. Tropical rainforests are found primarily near the equator in Central and South America, Africa, parts of southern Asia, and some Pacific islands (figure 16.25). The temperature is high (averaging about 27°C), rain falls nearly every day (typically, 200 to 1,000 centimeters per year), and there are thousands of species of plants in a small area. Balsa (a very light wood), teak (used in furniture), and ferns the size of trees are plants from the tropical rainforest. Every plant has other plants growing on it. Tree trunks are likely to be covered with orchids, many kinds of vines, and mosses. Tree frogs, bats, lizards, birds, monkeys, and an almost infinite variety of insects inhabit the rainforest. These forests are very dense, and little sunlight reaches the forest floor. When the forest is opened up (by a hurricane or the death of a large tree) and sunlight reaches the forest floor, the opened area is rapidly overgrown with vegetation.

(a)

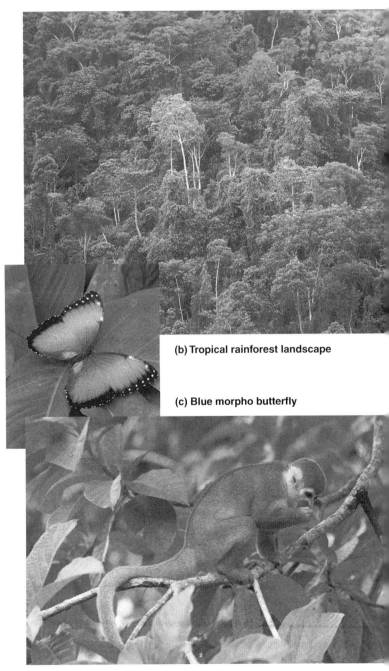

(b) Tropical rainforest landscape

(c) Blue morpho butterfly

(d) Squirrel monkey

**FIGURE 16.25 Tropical Rainforest**
*(a)* Climagraph for Singapore. *(b, c, & d)* Tropical rainforests develop in areas with high rainfall and warm temperatures. They have an extremely diverse mixture of plants and animals such as birds, butterflies, and monkeys.

**TABLE 16.2  Summary of Kinds of Terrestrial Biomes**

| Biome | Temperature | Precipitation | Dominant Vegetation |
|---|---|---|---|
| Temperate deciduous forest | Periods of time with temperatures below freezing | Moderate precipitation throughout the year; greater than 75 cm/year | Trees that drop their leaves in the fall |
| Temperate grassland | Periods of time with temperatures below freezing | Low precipitation; less than 85 cm/year | Grasses and other herbaceous plants; trees uncommon |
| Savanna | Tropical climate without frost | Abundant rainfall but with extensive dry periods | Grasses and other herbaceous plants; scattered trees |
| Dry tropical forest | Tropical climate without frost | Abundant rainfall but with extensive dry periods | Trees that drop their leaves during dry periods |
| Mediterranean shrubland (chaparral) | Moderate temperatures near large oceans | Winter rains and summer drought | Woody shrubs with leathery leaves |
| Desert | Hot or cold | Very little rainfall; less than 25 cm/year | Woody shrubs with reduced leaves |
| Boreal coniferous forest | Long periods with temperatures below freezing | Moderate precipitation with much coming as snow in the winter | Coniferous trees |
| Temperate rainforest | Mild temperatures associated with proximity to ocean | High rainfall; greater than 200 cm/year | Coniferous and deciduous trees |
| Tundra | Long, cold winters; and short, cool summers; permafrost | Low precipitation; less than 25 cm/year; most comes as snow | No trees; ground-hugging shrubby vegetation |
| Tropical rainforest | Warm temperatures; no frost | High rainfall throughout the year; greater than 200 cm/year | Tall, broad-leafed trees that do not lose their leaves all at once |

Because plants grow so quickly in these forests, people assume the soils are fertile, and many attempts have been made to bring this land under cultivation. In reality, the soils are poor in nutrients. The nutrients are in the organisms; as soon as an organism dies and decomposes, its nutrients are reabsorbed by other organisms. Typical North American agricultural methods, which require the clearing of large areas, cannot be used with the soil and rainfall conditions of the tropical rainforest. The constant rain falling on these fields quickly removes the soil's nutrients, so that heavy applications of fertilizer are required. Often, these soils become hardened when exposed in this way. Although most of these forests are not suitable for agriculture, large expanses of tropical rainforest are being cleared yearly because of the pressure for more farmland in the highly populated tropical countries and the desire for high-quality lumber from many of the forest trees.

Table 16.2 summarizes the distinguishing features of each of the biomes. Outlooks 16.1 describes a special kind of tropical forest that involves periodic flooding.

## The Relationship Between Elevation and Climate

The distribution of terrestrial communities is primarily related to temperature and precipitation. Air temperatures are warmest near the equator and become cooler toward the poles. Similarly, air temperature decreases as elevation increases. This means that, even at the equator, cold temperatures are possible on the peaks of tall mountains. Therefore, as one proceeds from sea level to the tops of mountains, it is possible to pass through a series of biomes that are similar to what one would encounter traveling from the equator to the North Pole (figure 16.26).

### 16.4 CONCEPT REVIEW

9. List a predominant abiotic factor in each of the following biomes: temperate deciduous forest, boreal coniferous forest, temperate grassland, Mediterranean shrubland, tropical dry forest, desert, tundra, temperate rainforest, tropical rainforest, and savanna.
10. List a dominant producer organism typical of each of the following biomes: temperate deciduous forest, boreal coniferous forest, temperate grassland, Mediterranean shrubland, tropical dry forest, desert, tundra, temperate rainforest, and savanna.

# Varzea Forests—Seasonally Flooded Amazon Tropical Forests

The Amazon River and it many tributaries constitute the largest drainage basin (about 40% of South America) and the highest volume of flow of any river system in the world—about 20 percent of worldwide river flow. The water is supplied by abundant rainfall. Many areas receive over 300 cm of rain per year—in the basin and snowmelt from the Andes. Since the snowmelt and, to a certain extent the rainfall, is seasonal, the Amazon and its tributaries are characterized by seasonal flooding. Much of the river basin is flat. The city of Iquitos is about 3,600 kilometers from the ocean but the river at that point is only 100 meters above sea level. Because of the flat terrain, extensive areas along the river are often flooded under several meters of water. The area flooded extends several kilometers from the river. This creates a seasonal wetland forest known as the *varzea*. The land farther from the river that does not flood is known as the *terra firme*.

This seasonally flooded area accounts for about 4% of the total area of the Amazon rainforest. The vegetation of the varzea is different from that of the terra firme because the trees and other vegetation must be able to withstand extensive periods of flooding.

The animals of the river and the varzea are greatly affected by the flooding. Animals of the river move into the forest with the flood and use forest resources as food. Varzea forest areas are critical to the freshwater fisheries of the Amazon Basin. Many fish actually change their diet and become fruit eaters when they are able to enter the flooded forest. In the drier portions of the year when the river recedes, they return to the main river channel and are carnivores. In addition to using the forest for food, the fish also distribute the seeds of fruits in their feces. Other river animals such as the caimans and the giant river otter also move into the forest with the flood.

The terrestrial animals of the forest face a different problem. As the river rises they are forced to retreat to higher ground and often become trapped on islands. This results in intense competition for food. Monkeys and birds are less troubled by the flooding. Many of them rely on fruits of trees, which is available even during the flood, as their primary food source. The monkeys can simply travel from tree to tree and the birds can fly over the water.

The periodic flooding of the area deposits silt, which provides a fertile soil. Therefore, the varzea is affected by human activity as people use the land along the river during the dry season to raise crops. Often the crops are a mixture of normal forest plants along with crops like bananas, rice, and root crops. Because of the flooding, people who live along the river build their houses on high ground and often on stilts. The rivers are also the primary highways of the region and small boats are the most common form of transportation.

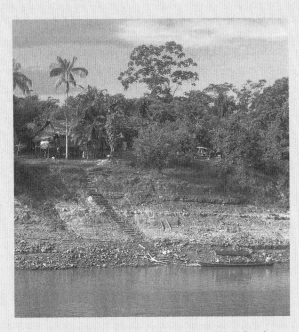

**The river nearly reaches to the top of this bank during floods that occur every year**

**Varzea forest**

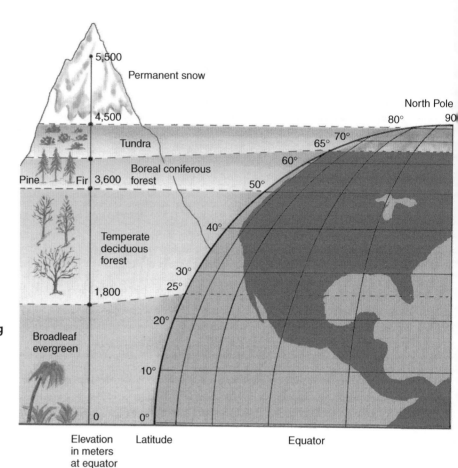

**FIGURE 16.26  The Relationship Among Elevation, Latitude, and Vegetation**
As one travels up a mountain, one experiences changes in climate. The higher the elevation, the cooler the climate. Even in the tropics, tall mountains can have snow on the top. Thus, it is possible to experience the same change in vegetation by traveling up a mountain as one would experience traveling from the equator to the North Pole.

## 16.5  Major Aquatic Ecosystems

Terrestrial biomes are determined by the amount and kind of precipitation and by temperatures. Other factors, such as soil type and wind, also play a part. Aquatic ecosystems also are shaped by key environmental factors. Several important factors are: how far the sun's rays penetrate the water, the depth of the water, currents, the nature of the bottom substrate, the water temperature, and the amount of dissolved salts.

An important determiner of the nature of aquatic ecosystems is the amount of salt dissolved in the water. Those that have a high salt content (35 parts per thousand or greater) are called *marine ecosystems,* and those that have little dissolved salt (less than 0.5 parts per thousand) are called *freshwater ecosystems.*

### Marine Ecosystems

Just like terrestrial ecosystems, marine ecosystems are quite diverse. Ecologists recognize several categories of marine ecosystems.

### Pelagic Marine Ecosystems

In the open ocean, many kinds of organisms float or swim actively. Shrimp, squid, fish, and whales swim actively as they pursue food. Organisms that are not attached to the bottom are called **pelagic** organisms, and the ecosystem they are a part of is called a **pelagic ecosystem.**

The term **plankton** is used to describe aquatic organisms that are so small and weakly swimming that they are simply carried from place to place by currents. As with all ecosystems, organisms that carry on photosynthesis are the base of the energy pyramid. **Phytoplankton** are planktonic organisms that carry on photosynthesis. Most phytoplankton are microscopic, single-celled algae and bacteria. The upper layer of the ocean, where the sun's rays penetrate, is known as the **euphotic zone.** It is in this euphotic zone where phytoplankton are most common. The thickness of the euphotic zone varies with the degree of clarity of the water but in clear water can be up to 150 meters (500 feet) in depth.

**Zooplankton** are small, weakly swimming animals of many kinds (crustaceans, jellyfish, and juvenile fish), and several kinds of protozoa, that feed on the phytoplankton by filtering the phytoplankton from the water. Zooplankton are often located at a greater depth in the ocean than the phytoplankton but migrate upward at night and feed on the large population of phytoplankton. The zooplankton are in turn eaten by larger animals such as fish and larger shrimp, which are eaten by larger animals such as salmon, tuna, sharks, squid, whales and seals. (See figure 16.27.)

A major factor that influences the nature of a marine community is the kind and amount of material dissolved in the water.

## FIGURE 16.27 Marine Ecosystems

All of the photosynthetic activity of the ocean occurs in the shallow water called the euphotic zone, either by attached algae near the shore or by minute phytoplankton in the upper levels of the open ocean. Consumers are either free-swimming pelagic organisms or benthic organisms that live on the bottom. Small animals that feed on phytoplankton are known as zooplankton.

Of particular importance is the amount of dissolved, inorganic nutrients available to the organisms carrying on photosynthesis. Phosphorus, nitrogen, and carbon are all required for the construction of new living material. In water, these are often in short supply. Therefore, the most productive aquatic ecosystems are those in which these essential nutrients are most common. These areas include places in oceans where currents bring up nutrients that have settled to the bottom and places where rivers deposit their load of suspended and dissolved materials.

### Benthic Marine Ecosystems

Organisms that live on the ocean bottom, whether attached or not, are known as **benthic** organisms, and the ecosystem of which they are a part is called a **benthic ecosystem.** Some fish, clams, oysters, various crustaceans, sponges, sea anemones, and many other kinds of organisms live on the bottom. In shallow water, sunlight can penetrate to the bottom, and a variety of attached photosynthetic organisms commonly called seaweeds are common. Since they are attached and some, such as kelp, can grow to very large size, many other bottom-dwelling

organisms, such as sea urchins, worms, and fish, are associated with them.

The material that makes up the bottom is very important in determining the kind of benthic community that develops. Sand tends to shift and move, making it difficult for large plants or algae to become established, although some clams, burrowing worms, and small crustaceans find sand to be a suitable habitat. Clams filter water and obtain plankton and detritus or burrow through the sand, feeding on other inhabitants. Mud may provide suitable habitats for some kinds of rooted plants, such as mangrove trees or sea grasses. Although mud usually contains little oxygen, it still may be inhabited by a variety of burrowing organisms that feed by filtering the water above them or that feed on other animals in the mud. Rocky surfaces in the ocean provide a good substrate for many kinds of large algae. Associated with this profuse growth of algae is a large variety of animals.

Temperature also has an impact on the kind of benthic community established. Some communities, such as coral reefs or mangrove swamps, are found only in areas where the water is warm.

**Coral reef ecosystems** are produced by coral animals that build cup-shaped external skeletons around themselves. Corals protrude from their skeletons to capture food and expose themselves to the sun. Exposure to sunlight is important because corals contain single-celled algae within their bodies. These algae carry on photosynthesis and provide both themselves and the coral animals with the nutrients necessary for growth. This mutualistic relationship between algae and coral is the basis for a very productive community of organisms.

The skeletons of the corals provide a surface upon which many other kinds of animals live. Some of these animals feed on corals directly, while others feed on small plankton and bits of algae that establish themselves among the coral organisms. Many kinds of fish, crustaceans, sponges, clams, and snails are members of coral reef ecosystems. Because they require warm water, coral ecosystems are found only near the equator. Coral ecosystems also require shallow, clear water since the algae must have ample sunlight to carry on photosynthesis. Coral reefs are considered one of the most productive ecosystems on Earth (see figure 16.28).

An **abyssal ecosystem** is a benthic ecosystem that occurs at great depths in the ocean. In such deep regions of the ocean there is no light to support photosynthesis. Therefore, the animals must rely on a continuous rain of organic matter from the euphotic zone above them. Essentially, all of the organisms in this environment are scavengers that feed on

whatever drifts their way. Many of the animals are small an generate light that they use for finding or attracting food.

### Estuaries

An **estuary** is a special category of aquatic ecosystem tha consists of shallow, partially enclosed areas where freshwate enters the ocean. The saltiness (0.5–30 parts per thousand) c the water in the estuary changes with tides and the flow o water from rivers. The organisms that live here are speciall adapted to this set of physical conditions, and the number o species is less than in the ocean or in freshwater.

Estuaries are particularly productive ecosystems becaus of the large amounts of nutrients introduced into the basi from the rivers that run into them. This is further enhance by the fact that the shallow water allows light to penetrate t most of the water in the basin. Phytoplankton and attache algae and plants are able to use the sunlight and the nutrient for rapid growth. This photosynthetic activity supports man kinds of organisms in the estuary.

Estuaries are especially important as nursery sites for fish and crustaceans such as flounder and shrimp. The adult enter these productive, sheltered areas to reproduce and the return to the ocean. The young spend their early life in th estuary and eventually leave as they get larger and are mor able to survive in the ocean. Estuaries also trap sediment. Thi activity tends to prevent many kinds of pollutants from

Coral reef organisms

The Great Barrier Reef–Australia

**FIGURE 16.28 Coral Reef**
Corals are small sea animals that secrete external skeletons. They have a mutualistic relationship with certain algae, which allows both kinds of organisms to be very successful. The skeletal material serves as a substrate upon which many other kinds of organisms live.

eaching the ocean and also results in the gradual filling in of the estuary, which may eventually become a salt marsh and then part of a terrestrial ecosystem.

## Human Impact on Marine Ecosystems

Since the oceans cover about 70% of the Earth's surface, it is hard to imagine that humans can have a major impact on them. However, we use the oceans in a wide variety of ways. The oceans provide a major source of protein in the form of fish, shrimp, and other animals. However, overfishing has destroyed many of the traditional fishing industries of the world such as cod fishing off the east coast of North America. Fish farming in the ocean involves the use of pens to enclose fish. The dense populations in the pens result in pollution of the ocean from the food that is provided to the fish and the waste products the fish produce. These captive populations have also caused diseases to spread from farmed species to wild fish. Estuaries are important fishing areas but are impacted by the flow of fertilizer, animal waste, and pesticides down the rivers that drain farmland and enter estuaries. The use of the oceans as transportation results in oil pollution, and trash regularly floats onto the shore. Coral reefs are altered by fishing and siltation from rivers. Mangrove swamps are destroyed as they are converted to areas for the raising of fish. It is clear that humans have a great impact on marine ecosystems.

# Freshwater Ecosystems

Freshwater ecosystems differ from marine ecosystems in several ways. The amount of salt present is much less, the temperature of the water can change greatly, the water is in the process of moving to the ocean, oxygen can often be in short supply, and the organisms that inhabit freshwater systems are different.

Freshwater ecosystems can be divided into two categories: those in which the water is relatively stationary, such as lakes, ponds, and reservoirs, and those in which the water is running downhill, such as streams and rivers.

## Lakes and Ponds

Large lakes have many of the same characteristics as the ocean. If the lake is deep, there is a euphotic zone at the top, with many kinds of phytoplankton, and zooplankton that feed on the phytoplankton. Small fish feed on the zooplankton and are in turn eaten by larger fish. The species of organisms found in freshwater lakes are different from those found in the ocean, but the roles played are similar, so the same terminology is used.

Along the shore and in the shallower parts of lakes, many kinds of flowering plants are rooted in the bottom. Some have leaves that float on the surface or protrude above the water and are called *emergent plants*. Cattails, bulrushes, arrowhead plants, and water lilies are examples. Rooted plants that stay submerged below the surface of the water are called *submerged plants*. *Elodea* and *Chara* are examples. This region,

with rooted vegetation, is known as the **littoral zone,** and the portion of the lake that does not have rooted vegetation is called the **limnetic zone.** (See figure 16.29.)

Many kinds of freshwater algae also grow in the shallow water, where they may appear as mats on the bottom or attached to vegetation and other objects. Associated with the plants and algae are a large number of different kinds of animals. Adult and larval insects are particularly common in freshwater ecosystems along with fish, crayfish, clams, and many birds and mammals.

Although the water molecule ($H_2O$) has oxygen as part of its structure, this oxygen is not available to organisms. The oxygen that they need is dissolved molecular oxygen ($O_2$), which enters water from the air or when it is released as a result of photosynthesis by aquatic plants and other photosynthetic organisms. When water tumbles over rocks in a stream or crashes on the shore as a result of wave action, air and water mix, which allows more oxygen to dissolve in the water. The amount of dissolved oxygen affects the kind of organisms that live in the water.

## Streams and Rivers

Streams and rivers are a second category of freshwater ecosystem. Since the water is moving, planktonic organisms are less important than are attached organisms because plankton are swept downstream. Most algae grow attached to rocks and other objects on the bottom. Since the water is shallow, light can penetrate easily to the bottom (except for large or extremely muddy rivers). Even so, it is difficult for photosynthetic organisms to accumulate the nutrients necessary for growth, and most streams are not very productive. As a matter of fact, the major input of nutrients is from organic matter that falls into the stream from terrestrial sources. These are primarily the leaves from trees and other vegetation, as well as the bodies of living and dead insects. Within streams there is a community of organisms that is specifically adapted to use the debris from terrestrial sources as a source of food. Bacteria and fungi colonize the organic matter, and many kinds of insects shred and eat this organic matter along with the fungi and bacteria living on it. The feces (intestinal wastes) of these insects and the tiny particles produced during the eating process become food for other insects that build nets to capture the tiny bits of organic matter that drift their way. These insects are in turn eaten by carnivorous insects and fish.

Organisms in larger rivers and muddy streams, which have less light penetration, rely in large part on the food that drifts their way from the many streams that empty into the river. These larger rivers tend to be warmer and to have slower moving water. Consequently, the amount of oxygen is usually less, and the species of plants and animals change. Any organic matter added to the river system reduces the oxygen in the water as it decays. Plants may become established along the river bank and contribute to the ecosystem by carrying on photosynthesis and providing hiding places for animals.

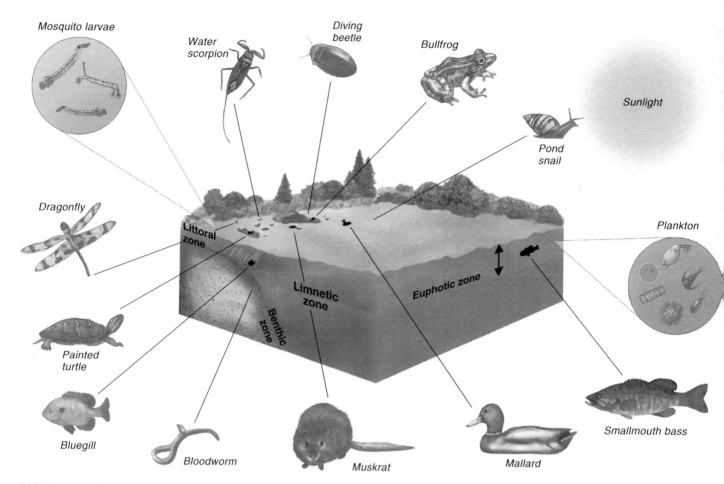

**FIGURE 16.29 Lake Ecosystem**
Lakes are similar in structure to oceans except that the species are different because most marine organisms cannot live in freshwater. Insects are common organisms in freshwater lakes, as are many kinds of fish, zooplankton, and phytoplankton.

## Human Impact on Freshwater Ecosystems

Freshwater resources in lakes and rivers account for about 0.02% of the world's water. Most freshwater ecosystems have been heavily impacted by human activity. Any activity that takes place on land ultimately affects freshwater because of runoff from the land. Agricultural runoff, sewage, sediment, and trash all find their way to streams and lakes.

### 16.5 CONCEPT REVIEW

11. How do phytoplankton and zooplankton differ?
12. Describe how the producers of benthic and pelagic ecosystems differ.
13. List two ways in which the kinds of organisms present in lakes differ from those in shallow parts of the ocean.
14. Describe two abiotic differences between an estuary and the ocean.

### 16.6 Succession

Biomes consist of communities that are relatively stable over long periods of time. A relatively stable, long-lasting community is called a **climax community**. The word *climax* implies the final step in a series of events. That is just what the word means in this context, because communities can go through a series of predictable, temporary stages, which eventually result in a long-lasting, stable community. The process of changing from one type of community to another is called **succession**, and each intermediate stage leading to the climax community is known as a **successional stage** or **successional community**.

Scientists recognize two kinds of succession. **Primary succession** occurs when a community of plants and animals develops where none existed previously. **Secondary succession** occurs when a community of organisms is disturbed or destroyed by a natural or human-related event (e.g., a hurricane, volcano, fire, forest harvest, farming) and is returned to an earlier stage in the process of succession.

## Primary Succession

Primary succession is much more difficult to observe than secondary succession because there are relatively few places on Earth that lack communities of organisms. The tops of mountains, newly formed volcanic rock, and rock newly exposed by erosion or glaciers can be said to lack life. However, bacteria, algae, fungi, and lichens quickly begin to grow on the bare rock surface, beginning the process of succession. The first organisms to colonize an area are often referred to as **pioneer organisms,** and the community is called a **pioneer community.**

### Terrestrial Primary Succession

Lichens are frequently important in pioneer communities. They are unusual organisms consisting of a combination of algae cells and fungi cells—a very hardy combination that is able to grow on the surface of bare rock (figure 16.30). Because algae cells are present, the lichen is capable of photosynthesis and can form new organic matter. Furthermore,

**FIGURE 16.30 Pioneer Organisms**
The orange or black lichens growing on rock begin the process of soil formation that is necessary for the development of later successional stages. They carry on photosynthesis, trap organic matter, and break down the surface of the rock.

many tiny consumer organisms can use the lichen as a food source and a sheltered place to live. The lichen's action also tends to break down the rock surface on which it grows. This fragmentation of rock by lichens is aided by the physical weathering processes of freezing and thawing, dissolution by water, and wind erosion. Lichens also trap dust particles, small rock particles, and the dead remains of lichens and other organisms that live in and on lichens. These processes of breaking down rock and trapping particles result in the formation of a thin layer of soil.

As the soil layer becomes thicker, small plants, such as mosses, may become established, increasing the rate at which energy is trapped and adding more organic matter to the soil. Eventually, the soil may be able to support larger plants that are even more efficient at trapping sunlight, and the soil-building process continues at a more rapid pace. Associated with the producers in each successional stage are a variety of small animals, fungi, and bacteria. Each change in the community makes it more difficult for the previous group of organisms to maintain itself. Tall plants shade the smaller ones they replace; consequently, the smaller plants become less common, and some disappear entirely. Only shade-tolerant species are able to grow and compete successfully in the shade of the taller plants. As this takes place, one stage succeeds the other. Figure 16.31 summarizes these changes.

Depending on the physical environment and the availability of new colonizing species, succession from this point can lead to different kinds of climax communities. If the area is dry, it might stop at a grassland stage. If it is cold and wet, a coniferous forest might be the climax community. If it is warm and wet, it may become a tropical rainforest. The rate at which succession takes place is also variable. In some warm, moist, fertile areas, the entire process might take place in less than 100 years. In harsh environments, such as mountaintops and very dry areas, it may take thousands of years.

### Aquatic Primary Succession

Primary succession also occurs in the progression from an aquatic community to a terrestrial community. Lakes, ponds, and slow-moving parts of rivers accumulate organic matter. Where the water is shallow, this organic matter supports the development of rooted plants. In deeper water, only plants with floating leaves, such as water lilies, send their roots down to the mucky bottom. In shallower water, upright, rooted plants, such as cattails and rushes, develop. As the plants contribute more organic matter to the bottom, the water level becomes shallower. Eventually, a mat of mosses, grasses, and even small trees may develop on the surface along the edge of the water. If this continues for perhaps 100 to 200 years, an entire pond or lake will become filled in. More organic matter accumulates because of the large number of producers and because the depression that was originally filled with water becomes drier. This usually results in a wet grassland, which in many areas is replaced by the climax forest community typical of the area (figure 16.32).

**FIGURE 16.31 Primary Succession**
The formation of soil is a major step in primary succession. Until soil is formed, the area is unable to support large amounts of vegetation. The vegetation modifies the harsh environment and increases the amount of organic matter that can build up in the area. As the kinds of plants change, so do the animals. As taller plants become established, the shorter plants that were part of earlier successional stages are eliminated. If given enough time, a climax community may develop.

**FIGURE 16.32 Succession from a Pond to a Wet Meadow**
A shallow pond will slowly fill with organic matter from producers in the pond. Eventually, a floating mat will form over the pond and grasses will become established. In many areas, this will be succeeded by a climax forest.

## Secondary Succession

Secondary succession occurs when a climax community is altered or destroyed by natural events or human activity. For example, when land is converted to agriculture, the original forest or grassland community is destroyed and replaced by crops. However, when agricultural land is abandoned, it returns to something like the original climax community. One obvious difference between primary succession and secondary succession is that, in secondary succession, there is no need to develop a soil layer. Another difference is that there is likely to be a reservoir of seeds from plants that were part of the original climax community. The seeds can survive in the soil for years in a dormant state, or they might be transported to the disturbed site from undisturbed sites nearby.

If we begin with bare soil the first year, it is likely to be invaded by a pioneer community of annual weed species. Within a year or two, perennial plants, such as grasses, become established. Because most of the weed species need bare soil for seed germination, they are replaced by the perennial grasses and other plants that live in association with grasses. The more permanent grassland community is able to support more insects, small mammals, and birds than the weed community could. In regions where rainfall is low, succession is likely to stop at this grassland stage. In regions with adequate rainfall, several species of shrubs and fast-growing trees that require lots of sunlight (e.g., birch, aspen, juniper, hawthorn, sumac, pine, spruce, and dogwood) become common. As the trees become larger, the grasses fail to get sufficient sunlight and die out. Eventually, shade-tolerant species of trees (e.g., beech, maple, hickory, oak, hemlock, and cedar) replace the shade-intolerant species, and a climax community results (figure 16.33).

## Modern Concepts of Succession and Climax

The discussion of the nature of succession and climax communities in the Succession section is an oversimplification of the true nature of the process. Some historical perspective will help to clarify how ecologists have altered their concept of successional change. When European explorers traveled across the North American continent, they saw huge expanses of land dominated by specific types of communities: hardwood forests in the east, evergreen forests in the north, grasslands in central North America, and deserts in the southwest. These regional communities came to be considered the steady-state or normal situation for those parts of the world. When ecologists began to explore the way in which ecosystems developed over time, they began to think of these ecosystems as the end point or climax of a long journey, beginning with the formation of soil and its colonization by a variety of plants and other organisms.

As settlers removed the original forests or grasslands and converted the land to farming, the original "climax" community was destroyed. Eventually, as poor farming practices destroyed the soil, many farms were abandoned and the land was allowed to return to its "original" condition. This secondary succession often resulted in forests that resembled those that had been destroyed. However, in most cases, these successional forests contained fewer species and in some cases were entirely different kinds of communities from the originals. These new stable communities were also called climax communities, but they were not the same as the original climax communities.

In addition, the introduction of species from Europe and other parts of the world changed the mix of organisms that

| Mature oak/hickory forest destroyed | Farmland abandoned | Annual plants | Grasses and biennial herbs | Perennial herbs and shrubs begin to replace grasses and biennials. | Pines begin to replace shrubs. | Young oak and hickory trees begin to grow. | Pines die and are replaced by mature oak and hickory trees. | Mature oak/hickory forest |
|---|---|---|---|---|---|---|---|---|
| | | **1–2 years** | **3–4 years** | **4–15 years** | **5–15 years** | **10–30 years** | **50–75 years** | |

**FIGURE 16.33 Secondary Succession on Land**
When agricultural land is abandoned, it goes through a series of changes. The general pattern is for annual weeds to become established in the first year or two following abandonment. These weeds are replaced by grasses and other perennial herbs, which are replaced by shrubs, which are replaced by trees. As the plant species change, so do the animal species.

might colonize an area. Many grasses and herbs that were introduced either on purpose or accidentally have become well established. Today, some communities are dominated by these introduced species. Even diseases have altered the nature of climax communities. Chestnut blight and Dutch elm disease have removed tree species that were at one time dominant species in certain plant communities.

Ecologists began to recognize that there was no fixed, predetermined community for each part of the world, and they began to modify the way they looked at the concept of climax communities. The concept today is a more plastic one. It is still used to talk about a stable stage following a period of change, but ecologists no longer feel that land will eventually return to a "preordained" climax condition. They have also recognized in recent years that the type of climax community that develops depends on many factors other than simply climate. One of these is the availability of seeds to colonize new areas. Some seeds may lie dormant in the soil for a decade or more, while others may be carried to an area by wind, water, or animals. Two areas with very similar climate and soil characteristics may develop very different successional and "climax" communities because of the seeds that were present in the area when the lands were released from agriculture.

Furthermore, we need to recognize that the only thing that differentiates a "climax" community from a successional one is the time scale over which change occurs. "Climax" communities do not change as rapidly as successional ones. However, all communities are eventually replaced, as were the swamps that produced coal deposits, the preglacial forests of Europe and North America, and the pine forests of the northeastern United States.

Many human activities alter the nature of the successional process. Agricultural practices obviously modify the original community to allow for the raising of crops. However, several other management practices have also significantly altered communities. Regular logging returns a forest to an earlier stage of succession. The suppression of fire in many forests has also changed the mix of organisms present. When fire is suppressed, those plants that are killed by regular fires become more common and those that are able to resist fire become less common. Changing the amount of water present will also change the kind of community. Draining an area makes it less suitable for the original inhabitants and more suitable for those that live in drier settings. Similarly, irrigation and flooding increase the amount of water present and change the kinds of organisms that can live in an area.

So what should we do with these concepts of succession and climax communities? Although the climax concept embraces a false notion that there is a specific end point to succession, it is still important to recognize that there is an identifiable, predictable pattern of change during succession and that later stages in succession are more stable and longer lasting than early stages. Whether we call a specific community of organisms a climax community is not really important.

## Succession and Human Activity

Most agricultural use of ecosystems involves replacing the natural climax community with an artificial early successional stage. Therefore, it requires considerable effort on our part to prevent succession back to something like the original climax community. This is certainly true if remnants of the original natural community are still locally available to colonize agricultural land. Small woodlots in agricultural areas of the eastern United States serve this purpose. Much of the work and expense of farming (e.g., tilling, herbicides) is necessary to prevent succession to the natural climax community. It takes a lot of energy to fight nature.

Many human-constructed lakes and farm ponds have weed problems, because they are shallow and provide ideal conditions for the normal successional processes that lead to their being filled in. Often, humans do not recognize what a powerful force succession is.

### 16.6 CONCEPT REVIEW

15. How does primary succession differ from secondary succession?
16. How does a climax community differ from a successional community?
17. Describe the steps in the secondary succession of abandoned farmland to a climax community.
18. Describe the steps in the succession of a pond to a climax community.
19. Describe three important factors that determine the kind of climax community that will develop in an area.

## 16.7 The Impact of Human Actions on Communities

There is very little of the Earth's surface that has not been altered by human activity. Often, the changes we cause have far greater impact than we might think (How Science Works 16.1). All organisms are interlinked in a complex network of relationships. Therefore, before changing a community, it is wise to analyze how its organisms are interrelated. This is not always easy, because there is much we still do not know about how organisms interact and how they use molecules from their environment. Several lessons can be learned from studying the effects of human activity on communities.

### Introduced Species

One of the most far-reaching effects humans have had on natural communities involves the introduction of foreign species. Many of these introductions have been conscious

# HOW SCIENCE WORKS 16.1

## Whole Ecosystem Experiments

Many environmental issues are difficult to resolve because, although there are hypotheses about what is causing a problem, the validity of the hypotheses has not been tested by experiments. Therefore, when governments seek to set policy, there are always those who argue that there is little hard evidence that the problem is real or that the cause of the problem has not been identified. Several examples include: What causes eutrophication of lakes? What causes acidification of lakes and rivers? What are the causes of global climate change? What is the likelihood that emissions from coal-fired power plants are causing increased in mercury in fish? The most powerful tests of hypotheses related to these problems are experiments that take place on a large scale in natural settings. Several such experiments have been crucial in identifying causes of environmental problems and led to policy changes that have alleviated environmental problems.

Beginning in 1966, the Canadian government established the Experimental Lakes Area in western Ontario. Many lakes were designated for experiments that would help answer questions about environmental issues. One experiment tested the hypothesis that phosphorus was responsible for eutrophication (excessive growth of algae and plants) of lakes. Laboratory studies had suggested that carbon, nitrogen, or phosphorus could be responsible. To help answer which of these three nutrients was the cause of eutrophication, a dumb-bell-shaped lake was divided in two at its narrow "waist" by placing a plastic curtain across the lake. One portion had carbon, nitrogen, and phosphorus added to it and the other portion had only carbon and nitrogen added. The results were clear. The portion of the lake with the added phosphorus had an abundant growth of algae and turned green. The other portion of the lake with carbon and nitrogen but no phosphorus did not (see photo). As a result of this experiment, governments were justified in requiring detergent manufacturers to remove phosphorous compounds from their products and requiring sewage treatment plants to eliminate phosphorus from their effluent.

Other experiments on whole lakes have investigated:

- The effects of acid deposition on food webs in lakes—predator fish starve as their prey disappear.
- The effects of flooding of land by dams—there is an increase in the mercury content of fish and carbon dioxide and methane are released into the atmosphere.
- The effects of removal of aquatic vegetation—northern pike populations declined.

After each experiment, the Canadian government requires that the lake be returned to its pristine condition.

decisions. Nearly all domesticated plants and animals in North America are introductions from elsewhere. Corn, beans, sunflowers, squash, and turkeys are exceptions. Cattle, horses, pigs, goats, and many introduced grasses have significantly altered the original communities present in the Americas. Cattle have replaced the original grazers on grasslands. Pigs have become a major problem in Hawaii and many other places in the world, where they destroy the natural community by digging up roots and preventing the reproduction of native plants. The introduction of grasses as food for cattle has resulted in the decline of many native species of grasses and other plants that were originally part of grassland communities. In Australia, the introduction of domesticated plants and animals—as well as wild animals, such as rabbits and foxes—has severely reduced the populations of many native marsupial mammals.

Accidental introductions have also significantly altered communities. Chestnut blight has essentially eliminated the American chestnut from the forests of eastern North America. Similarly, a fungal disease (Dutch elm disease) has severely reduced the number of elms. The accidental introduction of zebra mussels has significantly altered freshwater communities in eastern North America and has severely reduced the populations of native clams. Figure 16.34 shows two introduced species that have significantly altered communities in North America.

**Dandelions**

**Mute swans**

**FIGURE 16.34 Introduced Species**
Many introduced species become pests. Dandelions and mute swans are two examples.

## Predator Control

Many kinds of large predators were actively destroyed to protect livestock. Predator control was also thought to be important in the management of game species. During the formative years of wildlife management, it was thought that populations of game species could be increased if the populations of their predators were reduced. For these reasons, many states passed laws to encourage the killing of foxes, eagles, hawks, owls, coyotes, cougars, and other predators that could kill livestock or use game animals as a source of food. Often, bounties were paid to people who killed these predators (figure 16.35).

The absence of predators can lead to many kinds of problems. In many metropolitan areas, deer have become pests. This is due to several reasons, including the fact that there are no predators, and hunting (predation by humans) either is not allowed or is impractical because of the highly urbanized nature of the area. Some municipalities have instituted programs of chemical birth control for their deer populations.

Only a few years ago, the alligator was on the endangered species list and all hunting was suspended. However, today increased numbers of alligators present a danger, particularly to pets and children. Hunting is now allowed in an effort to control the numbers of alligators, because humans are the only effective predators of large alligators.

Similarly, in Yellowstone National Park, elk, bison, and moose populations had become very large, because hunting is not allowed and predator populations had been small. In 1995, wolves were reintroduced to the park in the hope that they would help bring the elk and moose populations under control (figure 16.36). This was a controversial decision, however, because ranchers in the vicinity did not want a return of large predators that might prey on their livestock. They are also opposed to having bison, many of which carry a disease that can affect cattle, stray onto their land. The wolf population has increased significantly in Yellowstone and is having an effect on the populations of bison, elk, and moose. Regardless of the politics involved in the decision, Yellowstone is in a more natural condition today, with wolves present, than it was prior to 1995.

By contrast, the state of Alaska allows the hunting of wolves because many Alaskans believe the wolves are reducing caribou populations below optimal levels. Caribou hunting is an important source of food for Alaskan natives, and hunters who visit the state provide a significant source of income. Many groups oppose the killing of wolves in Alaska, however. They consider the policy misguided and believe it will not have a positive effect on the caribou population.

As wolf populations have increased in parts of the northern Rocky Mountains and the Great Lakes region, they have been removed from the federal endangered species list. Several states have re-established hunting seasons for wolves. The primary justification is to minimize the impact of wolf predation on livestock.

(a)                                                    (b)

**FIGURE 16.35 Predator Control**
At one time, people were paid to kill various kinds of predators. *(a)* These men receive $35 for each wolf killed. *(b)* This coyote was killed and hung on a fence because it was considered a threat to livestock.

A captured Canadian wolf                               Wolf in its habitat

**FIGURE 16.36 The Reintroduction of Wolves to Yellowstone**
In 1995, wolves were captured in Canada and moved to Yellowstone National Park to reestablish a wolf population. Now, there is a large, healthy wolf population in Yellowstone.

## Habitat Destruction

Some communities are fragile and easily destroyed by human activity, whereas others seem able to resist human interference. Communities with a wide variety of organisms that show a high level of interaction are more resistant than are those with few organisms and little interaction. In general, the more complex a community, the more likely it is to recover after being disturbed. The tundra biome is an example of a community with relatively few organisms and interactions. It is not very resistant to change and, because of its slow rate of repair, damage caused by human activity may persist for hundreds of years.

Some species are more resistant to human activity than are others. Rabbits, starlings, skunks, and many kinds of insects and plants are able to maintain high populations despite human activity. Indeed, some may even be encouraged by human activity. By contrast, whales, condors, eagles, and many plant and insect species are not able to resist human interference very well. For most of these endangered species, it is not humans' acting directly with the organisms that cause their endangerment. Very few organisms have been driven to extinction by hunting or direct exploitation. Usually, the cause of extinction or endangerment is an indirect effect of habitat destruction as humans exploit natural communities. As humans convert land to farming, grazing, commercial forestry, development, and special wildlife management areas, natural communities are disrupted, and plants and animals with narrow niches tend to be eliminated, because they lose critical resources in their environment. Figure 16.37 shows various kinds of habitat destruction, and table 16.3 lists eight endangered and threatened species and the probable causes of their difficulties.

## Pesticide Use

Humans have developed a variety of chemicals to control specific pests. These chemicals have a variety of names. *Herbicides* are used to kill plants. *Insecticides* are used to kill insects. *Fungicides* are used to kill fungi. Often, all these kinds of chemicals are lumped together into one large category—*pesticides*—because they are used to control various kinds of pests. Although various kinds of pesticides are valuable in controlling disease in human and domesticated animal populations and in controlling pests in agriculture, they have some negative community effects as well.

One problem associated with continual pesticide use is that pests become resistant to these chemicals. When a pesticide is used, most of the pests are killed. However, some may be able to resist its effects. When these survivors reproduce, they pass on their genes for resistance to their offspring, and the next generation is less susceptible to the pesticide. Ultimately, resistant populations develop and the pesticide is no longer useful.

Another problem associated with pesticide use is the effects they have on valuable nontarget organisms. Insecticides typically kill a wide variety of organisms other than the targeted pest species. Often, other species in the community have a role in controlling pests. Predators kill pests and parasites use them as hosts. Generally, predators and parasites reproduce more slowly than their prey or host species. Because of this, the use of a nonspecific insecticide may indirectly make controlling a pest more difficult. If such an insecticide is applied to an area, the pest is killed, but so are its predators and parasites. Because the herbivore pest reproduces faster than its predators and parasites, the pest population rebounds quickly, unchecked by natural predation and parasitism (figure 16.38).

**Urban development**

**Conversion to agriculture**

**Logging**

**FIGURE 16.37 Habitat Destruction**
Habitat destruction by the building of cities, conversion of land to agriculture, and commercial forest practices has a major impact on the kinds of organisms that can survive in our world.

Today, a more enlightened approach to pest control is *integrated pest management*, which uses a variety of approaches to reduce pest populations. Integrated pest management includes the use of pesticides as part of a pest control program, but it also includes strategies such as encouraging the natural

## TABLE 16.3  Endangered and Threatened Species

| Species | Reason for Endangerment |
|---|---|
| Hawaiian crow (*Corvis hawaiinsis*) | Predation by introduced cat and mongoose, disease, habitat destruction |
| Sonora chub (*Gila ditaenia*) | Competition with introduced species in streams in Arizona and Mexico |
| Black-footed ferret (*Mustela nigripes*) | The poisoning of prairie dogs (their primary food) |
| Snail kite (*Rostrhamus sociabilis*) | Specialized eating habits (they eat only apple snails), the draining of marshes in Florida |
| Grizzly bear (*Ursus arctos*) | The loss of wilderness areas |
| California condor (*Gymnogyps californianus*) | Slow breeding, lead poisoning |
| Ringed sawback turtle (*Graptemys oculifera*) | The modification of habitat by the construction of a reservoir in Mississippi that reduced their primary food source |
| Scrub mint (*Dicerandra frutescens*) | The conversion of their habitat to citrus groves and housing in Florida |

**Preparing an herbicide mixture**

**Aerial application of pesticide**

**FIGURE 16.38  Pesticide Use**
Pesticides are used to control pests that injure or compete with crops and domesticated animals. Their use has several effects on the communities of plants and animals where they are used.

enemies of pests, changing farming practices to discourage pests, changing the mix of crops grown, and accepting low levels of crop damage as an alternative to costly pesticide applications.

## Biomagnification

The use of persistent chemicals has an effect on the food chain. Chemicals that do not break down are passed from one organism to the next, and organisms at higher trophic levels tend to accumulate larger amounts than the organisms they feed on. This situation is known as **biomagnification.**

The history of DDT use illustrates the problems associated with persistent organic molecules. DDT was a very effective insecticide because it was extremely toxic to insects but not very toxic to birds and mammals. It is also a very stable compound, which means that, once applied, it remained effective for a long time. However, when an aquatic area was sprayed with a small concentration of DDT, many kinds of organisms in the area can accumulate tiny quantities in their bodies. Because marshes and other wet places are good mosquito habitats, these areas were often sprayed to control these pests. Even algae and protozoa found in aquatic ecosystems accumulate persistent pesticides. They may accumulate concentrations in their cells that are 250 times more concentrated than the amount sprayed on the

ecosystem. The algae and protozoa are eaten by insects, which in turn are eaten by frogs, fish, and other carnivores.

The concentration in frogs and fish may be 2,000 times the concentration sprayed. The birds that feed on the frogs and fish may accumulate concentrations that are as much as 80,000 times the original amount. Because DDT is relatively stable and is stored in the fat deposits of the organisms that take it in, what was originally a dilute concentration becomes more concentrated as it moves up the food chain (figure 16.39).

Before DDT use was banned in the United States in 1972, many animals at higher trophic levels died as a result of lethal concentrations of the pesticide accumulated from the food they ate. Each step in the food chain accumulated some DDT; therefore, higher trophic levels had higher concentrations. Even if they were not killed directly by DDT, many birds at higher trophic levels, such as eagles, pelicans, and osprey, suffered reduced populations. This occurred because the DDT

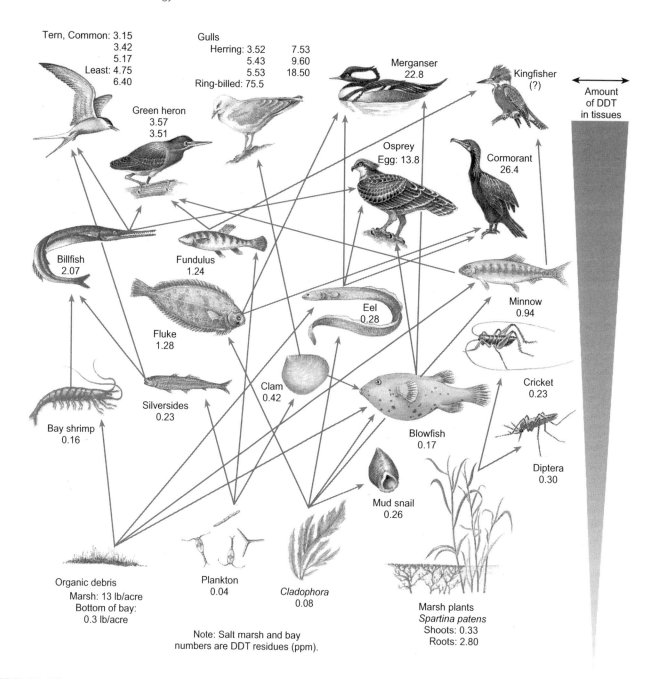

**FIGURE 16.39  The Biomagnification of DDT**
All the numbers shown are in parts per million (ppm). A concentration of one part per million means that, in a million equal parts of the organism, one of the parts would be DDT. Notice how the amount of DDT in the bodies of the organisms increases from producers to herbivores to carnivores. Because DDT is persistent, it builds up in the top trophic levels of the food chain.

interfered with the female birds' ability to produce eggshells. Thin eggshells are easily broken; thus, no live young hatched. Both the bald eagle and the brown pelican were placed on the endangered species list because their populations had dropped dramatically as a result of DDT poisoning. The ban on DDT use in the United States and Canada has resulted in an increase in the populations of both kinds of birds. Because the populations have recovered, the bald eagle was removed from the endangered species list in 2007 and the brown pelican in 2009.

Several other chemical compounds are also of concern today because they are biomagnified in food chains. These include polychlorinated biphenyls (PCBs), dioxins, methylmercury, and many other compounds. Because these compounds can reach high concentrations in fish that are at the top of the food chain, many states and countries publish advisories that caution people not to eat large quantities of these fish. When the production of PCBs was halted in 1979, the level of contamination in fish declined.

## 16.7 CONCEPT REVIEW

20. Why do DDT and PCBs increase in concentration in the bodies of organisms at higher trophic levels?
21. What is the most common form of habitat destruction practiced by humans?
22. List three introduced species that have become pests, and explain why they became pests.
23. What happens to a community of organisms when predators are eliminated?
24. Describe two negative consequences of using pesticides.

## Summary

Each organism in a community occupies a specific space, known as its habitat, and has a specific functional role to play, known as its niche. An organism's habitat is usually described in terms of a conspicuous element of its surroundings. The niche is difficult to describe, because it involves so many interactions with the physical environment and other living things.

Interactions between organisms fit into several categories. Predation is one organism benefiting (predator) at the expense of the organism killed and eaten (prey). Parasitism is one organism benefiting (parasite) by living in or on another organism (host) and deriving nourishment from it. Organisms that carry parasites from one host to another are called vectors. Commensal relationships exist when one organism is helped but the other is not affected. Mutualistic relationships benefit both organisms. Symbiosis is any interaction in which two organisms live together in a close physical relationship. Competition causes harm to both of the organisms involved, although one may be harmed more than the other and may become extinct, evolve into a different niche, or be forced to migrate.

A community consists of the interacting populations of organisms in an area. The organisms are interrelated in many ways in food chains, which interlock to create food webs. Because of this interlocking, changes in one part of the community can have effects elsewhere.

Major land-based regional communities are known as biomes. The temperate deciduous forest, boreal coniferous forest, tropical rainforest, temperate grassland, desert, savanna, temperate rainforest, and tundra are biomes.

Aquatic ecosystems can be divided into marine and freshwater systems. Several kinds of marine ecosystems are: pelagic, benthic, coral reef, abyssal, and shoreline ecosystems. Freshwater ecosystems are generally separated into streams and rivers in which the water is running downhill and lakes and ponds in which it is not.

Communities go through a series of predictable changes that lead to a relatively stable collection of plants and animals. This process of change is called succession, and the resulting stable unit is called a climax community.

Organisms within a community are interrelated in sensitive ways; thus, changing one part of a community can lead to unexpected consequences. The introduction of foreign species, predator-control practices, habitat destruction, pesticide use, and biomagnification of persistent toxic chemicals all have caused unanticipated changes in communities.

## Key Terms

*Use the interactive flash cards on the **Concepts in Biology**, 14/e website to help you learn the meaning of these terms.*

abyssal ecosystem 358
benthic 357
benthic ecosystem 357
biomagnification 369
biomes 343
climax community 360
commensalism 340
competition 336
competitive exclusion principle 337
coral reef ecosystem 358
epiphytes 340
estuary 358
euphotic zone 356
external parasites 338
food web 333
habitat 334
host 338
internal parasites 338
interspecific competition 336
intraspecific competition 336
limnetic zone 359

littoral zone 359
mutualism 341
niche 334
parasite 338
parasitism 338
pelagic 356
pelagic ecosystem 356
phytoplankton 356
pioneer community 361
pioneer organisms 361
plankton 356
predation 337
predator 337
prey 337
primary succession 360
secondary succession 360
succession 360
successional stage (successional community) 360
symbiosis 338
vector 339
zooplankton 356

## Basic Review

1. The role an organism plays in its surroundings is its
   a. niche.
   b. habitat.
   c. community.
   d. food web.

2. The kind of interrelationship between two organisms in which both are harmed is _____.

3. A desert is always characterized by
   a. high temperature.
   b. low amounts of precipitation.
   c. few kinds of plants and animals.
   d. sand.

4. When a community is naturally changing with the addition of new species of organisms and the loss of others, _____ is occurring.

5. When two organisms cooperate and both derive benefit from the relationship, it is known as commensalism. (T/F)

6. Most of the plants and animals involved in agriculture are introduced from other parts of the world. (T/F)

7. A biome that has trees adapted to long winters is known as a
   a. tundra.
   b. temperate deciduous forest.
   c. boreal coniferous forest.
   d. temperate rainforest.

8. If a forest is destroyed by a fire, it will eventually return to being a forest. This process is known as _____ succession.

9. A collection of organisms that interact with one another in an area is known as a
   a. community.
   b. biome.
   c. succession.
   d. biomagnification.

10. The idea that no two organisms can occupy the same niche is known as the competitive exclusion principle. (T/F)

11. The tundra biome has permafrost. (T/F)

12. Plankton organisms are strong swimmers. (T/F)

13. Which of the following organisms are common in freshwater ecosystems and rare in marine ecosystems?
    a. algae
    b. fish
    c. zooplankton
    d. insects

14. Which of the following have resulted in reductions in species native to an ecosystem?
    a. introduced species
    b. habitat destruction
    c. pesticide use
    d. all of the above

15. In marine ecosystems, pelagic organisms are located on the bottom. (T/F)

**Answers**
1. a   2. competition   3. b   4. succession   5. F   6. T   7. c
8. secondary   9. a   10. T   11. T   12. F   13. d   14. d
15. F

## Thinking Critically

**Natural and Managed Ecosystems**
Farmers are managers of ecosystems. Consider a cornfield in Iowa. Describe five ways in which the cornfield ecosystem differs from the original prairie it replaced. At what trophic level does the farmer exist?

CHAPTER

# 17

# Population Ecology

## White-tailed Deer Are Becoming Urban Pests

*Residents look for solutions.*

Many urban areas in eastern North America have a white-tailed deer population problem. Suburban areas with parks, nature preserves, and large lots are particularly hard-hit. The deer eat shrubs and other plantings in parks and in the yards of homes. Car-deer collisions result in millions of dollars of damage yearly and many human and deer deaths. In some areas there is concern about the role deer play in the spread of lyme disease.

Biologists point out that large urban deer populations are a case of "nature out of balance." There are few predators of deer in these areas and hunting is not allowed. So, with low mortality, populations have increased greatly. In more rural areas, there is some natural predation and hunters also play the role of predators.

There are few options to alleviate the problem. Currently, the administration of birth control measures to female deer is too expensive and difficult to achieve. Removal by trapping is expensive and has the additional problem of finding a suitable place to release the deer. Some cities have trapped deer and slaughtered them. More and more metropolitan areas have come to the conclusion that the most cost-effective method of population control is to allow controlled hunting or to hire specially trained sharpshooters to harvest deer. This is particularly effective in lowering populations if the females and young are harvested. In addition, the meat from the deer harvest is often donated to organizations that provide emergency food aid to local residents.

- **What conditions allow these populations to become so large that they become a public nuisance and cause serious economic damage?**

- **If increased mortality is not allowed, what methods could be used to reduce the number of births?**

- **Should cost be an issue in choosing the method used to control these populations?**

## Background Check

**Concepts you should already know to get the most out of this chapter:**
- The difference between sexual and asexual reproduction (chapter 9)
- Organisms acquire matter and energy from their surroundings (chapter 16)
- Organisms change their surroundings (chapter 16)

## 17.1 Population Characteristics

A **population** is a group of organisms of the same species located in the same place at the same time. Examples are the dandelions in a yard, the rat population in your city sewer, and the number of students in a biology class. On a larger scale, all the people of the world constitute the world human population.

The terms *species* and *population* are interrelated, because a species is a population—the largest possible population of a particular kind of organism. The term *population,* however, is often used to refer to portions of a species by specifying a space and time. For example, the size of the human population in a city changes from hour to hour during the day and varies according to the city's boundaries. Because each local population is a small portion of its species, and each population is adapted to its local conditions, it is common that local populations differ from one another in the characteristics they display.

### Gene Flow and Gene Frequency

Recall from chapter 12 that a species is a group of organisms capable of interbreeding and producing fertile offspring. Thus, within a species, genes flow from one generation to the next through reproduction. In addition to gene flow from one generation to the next, genes also can flow from one place to another as organisms migrate or are carried from one locality to another. Typically, both kinds of gene flow happen together as individuals migrate to new regions and reproduce, passing on their genes to the next generation in the new area (figure 17.1).

As genes flow from generation to generation by reproduction or from one location to another by migration, it is possible that separate populations may develop differences in the frequency of specific genes. For example, many populations of bacteria have high frequencies of antibiotic-resistance genes whereas others do not. Methicillin-resistant *Staphylococcus aureus* (MRSA) has become a serious health problem, since this strain (population) of bacterium is resistant to methicillin and many other similar antibiotics. Populations of this strain of *S. aureus* are most common in hospitals and other health-care facilities. The frequency of the genes for tallness in humans is greater in certain African tribes than in any other human population. The frequency of the allele for type B

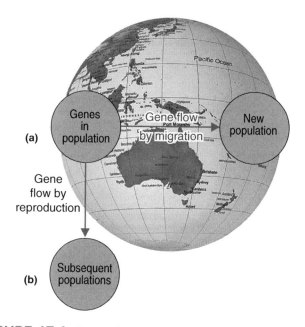

**FIGURE 17.1  Gene Flow**
Gene flow within a species occurs in two ways. *(a)* Genes flow from place to place when organisms migrate. *(b)* Genes flow from generation to generation as a result of reproduction.

blood differs significantly from one human population to another (figure 17.2).

### Age Distribution

**Age distribution** is the number of organisms of each age in a population (figure 17.3). Often, organisms are grouped into three general categories based on their reproductive status:

1. Prereproductive juveniles (e.g. insect larvae, plant seedlings, and babies)
2. Reproductive adults (e.g. mature insects, plants producing seeds, and humans in early adulthood)
3. Postreproductive adults no longer capable of reproduction (e.g. annual plants that have shed their seeds, salmon that have spawned, and many elderly humans)

A population does not necessarily have an age distribution that is divided into equal thirds. Some populations are made up of a majority of one age group (figure 17.4).

Many populations of organisms that live only a short time have high reproductive rates. Thus, they have population

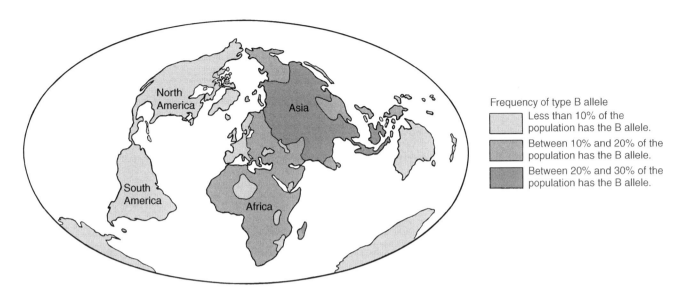

## FIGURE 17.2  Distribution of the Allele for Type B Blood

The allele for type B blood is not evenly distributed in the world. This map shows that the type B allele is most common in parts of Asia and has been dispersed to the Middle East and parts of Europe and Africa. There has been very little flow of the allele to the Americas.

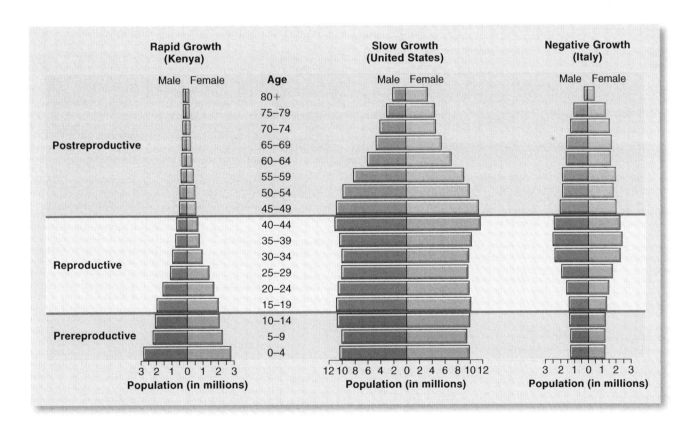

## FIGURE 17.3  Age Distribution in Human Populations

The relative numbers of individuals in each of the three categories (prereproductive, reproductive, and postreproductive) are good clues to the future growth of a population. Kenya has a large number of young individuals who will become reproducing adults. Therefore, this population is likely to grow rapidly. The United States has a large proportion of reproductive individuals and a moderate number of prereproductive individuals. Therefore, this population is likely to grow slowly. Germany has a declining number of reproductive individuals and a very small number of prereproductive individuals. Therefore, its population has begun to decline.

Caterpillars

Sheep

Bladderpod

**FIGURE 17.4 Age Distribution in Selected Populations**
Some populations are composed of many individuals of the same general age. The caterpillars are a population of prereproductives. The flock of sheep has a small number of reproductive adults and a large number of prereproductive juveniles. The population of yellow bladderpod plants is dominated by reproductive adults.

age distributions that change significantly in a matter of weeks or months. For example, many birds have a flurry of reproductive activity during the summer months. Therefore, samples of the population of a particular species of bird at different times during the summer would show widely different proportions of reproductive and prereproductive individuals. In early spring before they have started to nest, all the birds are reproductive adults. In late spring through midsummer, there is a large proportion of prereproductive juveniles.

Similarly, in the spring, annual plants germinate from seeds and begin to grow—all of the individuals are prereproductive juveniles. Later in the year, all the plants flower—they become reproducing adults. Finally, all the plants become postreproductive adults and die. But they have left behind seeds—prereproductive juveniles—which will produce the next generation.

Age distribution can have a major effect on how the population grows. If most of the population is prereproductive, a rapid increase in its size can be anticipated in the future as the prereproductive individuals reach sexual maturity. If most of the population is reproductive, the population should be growing rapidly. If most of the population is postreproductive, a population decline can be anticipated.

## Sex Ratio

The **sex ratio** of a population is the number of males in a population compared with the number of females. In many kinds of animals, such as bird and mammal species in which strong pair-bonding occurs, the sex ratio may be nearly 1 to 1 (1:1). Among mammals and birds that do not have strong pair-bonding, sex ratios may show a larger number of females than males. This is particularly true among game species in which more males than females are shot. This hunting practice leads to a higher proportion of surviving females. Because one male can fertilize several females, the population can remain large even though the females outnumber the males. In addition to these examples, many species of animals, such as bison, horses, elk, and sea lions, have mating systems in which one

**FIGURE 17.5 Sex Ratio**
In some species of animals, males defend a harem of females; therefore, the sex ratio in these groups is several females per male. This male Steller sea lion is defending a harem of several females.

male maintains a harem of females. The sex ratio in these small groups is quite different from a 1:1 ratio (figure 17.5).

In many kinds of insect populations, such as bees, ants, wasps, and termites, there are many more females than males. Generally, in a colony of these organisms there is one or a few reproductive females, a large number of worker females, and very few males.

There are very few situations in which the number of males exceeds the number of females. In some human and other populations, there may be sex ratios in which the males dominate if female mortality is unusually high or if a special mechanism separates most of one sex from the other.

Many kinds of animals and plants are hermaphroditic, having both kinds of sex organs in the same body (e.g. earthworms and many flowering plants). Thus, the concept of sex ratio does not apply to them. Also, some species of animals—oysters, some fish, and others—change their sex at different times of their lives. They spend part of their lives as males and part as females.

## Population Distribution

**Population distribution** is the way individuals within a population are arranged with respect to one another. There are basically three kinds of arrangements: even, random, and clumped. Even distributions occur under circumstances in which the organisms arrange themselves by very specific rules. In many birds that form dense breeding colonies, each nest is just out of reach of the neighbors. Random distributions are typical for many kinds of organisms that do not form social groups and have widely dispersed individuals. Many plants—particularly those that have seeds that are distributed by wind—have random distribution. Clumped distributions are typical for many kinds of plants and animals. In plants that have large seeds, the seeds are likely to fall near the parent plant and a clumped distribution results. In addition, plants that reproduce asexually produce local collections of organisms. Animals that form family groups, social groups, herds, or flocks typically show clumped distributions as do organisms that congregate near valuable resources, such as food or water (figure 17.6).

## Population Density

**Population density** is the number of organisms of a species per unit area. For example, the population density of dandelions in a park can be measured as the number of dandelions per square meter; the population density of white-tailed deer can be measured as the number of deer per square kilometer. Depending on the reproductive success of individuals in the population and the resources available, the density of populations can vary considerably. Some populations are extremely concentrated in a limited space; others are well dispersed. As reproduction occurs, the population density increases, which leads to increased competition for the necessities of life. Intense competition in dense populations is likely to lead to the death of some individuals and dispersal of individuals into less-populated areas.

    **Population pressure** is the concept that increased intensity of competition, resulting from increased population size, causes changes in the environment and leads to the dispersal of individuals to new areas or the death of some individuals. Dispersal can relieve the pressure on the home area and lead to the establishment of new populations. Among animals, it is often the juveniles that participate in dispersal. For example, female bears generally mate every two years and abandon their nearly grown young the summer before the next set of cubs is to be born. The abandoned young bears tend to wander and disperse to new areas. Similarly, young turtles, snakes, rabbits, and many other common animals disperse during certain times of the year. That is one of the reasons so many animals are killed on the roads in the spring and fall.

    If dispersal cannot relieve population pressure, there is usually an increase in the rate at which individuals die

**Even**

**Random**

**Clumped**

**FIGURE 17.6  Population Distribution**
The way organisms are distributed in their habitat varies. A few are evenly distributed. Some are randomly distributed. Many show some degree of clumped distribution.

because of predation, parasitism, starvation, and accidents. For example, plants cannot relieve population pressure by dispersal. Instead, the death of weaker individuals usually results in reduced population density, which relieves population pressure. Following a fire, large numbers of lodgepole

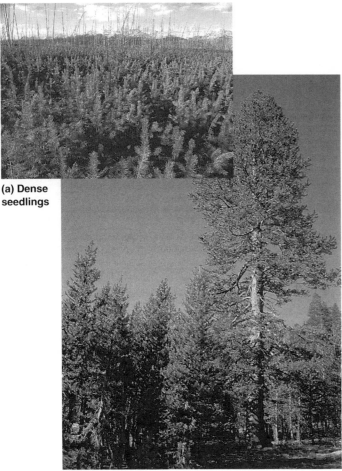

**(a) Dense seedlings**

**(b) Less dense adults**

**FIGURE 17.7 Changes in Population Density**
*(a)* This population of lodgepole pine seedlings consists of a large number of individuals very close to one another. *(b)* As the trees grow, many of the weaker trees will die, the distance between individuals will increase, and the population density will be reduced.

pine seeds germinate. The young seedlings form dense thickets of young trees. As the stand ages, many small trees die and the remaining trees grow larger as the population density drops (figure 17.7).

## 17.1 CONCEPT REVIEW

1. Describe two ways that gene flow occurs.
2. Give an example of a population with a high number of prereproductive individuals and another with a high number of reproductive individuals.
3. Describe two situations that can lead to a clumped distribution of organisms.
4. How is population pressure related to population density?

## 17.2 Reproductive Capacity

Sex ratios and age distributions within a population have a direct bearing on the rate of reproduction. A population's **reproductive capacity,** or **biotic potential,** is the theoretical number of offspring that could be produced. Some species produce huge numbers of offspring, whereas others produce few per lifetime. In some cases, the reproductive capacity is generally much larger than the number of offspring needed simply to maintain the population. For example, a female carp may produce 1 million to 3 million eggs in her lifetime; this is her reproductive capacity. However, only two or three of these offspring ever develop into sexually mature adults. Therefore, her reproductive rate is two or three offspring per lifetime and is much smaller than her reproductive capacity.

In general, there are two strategies for assuring that there will be enough offspring that live to adulthood to ensure the continuation of the species. One strategy is to produce huge numbers of offspring but not provide any support for them. For example, an oyster may produce a million eggs a year, but not all of them are fertilized, and most that are fertilized die. An apple tree with thousands of flowers may produce only a few apples because the pollen that contains the sperm cells was not transferred to the female part of each flower in the process of pollination. Even after offspring are produced, mortality is usually high among the young. Most seeds that fall to the Earth do not grow, and most young animals die. Usually, however, enough survive to ensure the continuance of the species. Organisms that reproduce in this way spend large amounts of energy on the production of gametes and young, but no energy caring for the young. Thus, the probability that any individual will reach reproductive age is small.

The second way of approaching reproduction is to produce relatively fewer individuals but provide care and protection, which ensures a higher probability that the young will become reproductive adults. Humans generally produce a single offspring per pregnancy, but nearly all of them live. In effect, with this strategy, energy has been channeled into the care and protection of the young, rather than into the production of incredibly large numbers of potential young. Even though fewer young are produced by animals such as birds and mammals, their reproductive capacity still greatly exceeds the number required to replace the parents when they die.

## 17.2 CONCEPT REVIEW

5. In what way do the activities of species that produces few young differ from those that produce huge numbers of offspring?
6. How does reproductive capacity compare to the reproductive rate?

# 17.3 The Population Growth Curve

Because most species have a high reproductive capacity, populations tend to grow if environmental conditions permit. The change in the size of a population depends on the rate at which new organisms enter the population, compared with the rate at which they leave. **Natality** is the number of individuals added to the population by reproduction per thousand individuals in the population. **Mortality** is the number of individuals leaving a population by death per thousand individuals in the population. If a species enters a previously uninhabited area, its population will go through a typical pattern of growth. Figure 17.8 shows a **population growth curve**, which is a graph of change in population size over time. There are four recognizable portions in a population growth curve: the *lag phase*, the *exponential growth phase*, the *deceleration phase*, and the *stable equilibrium phase*.

## The Lag Phase

The **lag phase** of a population growth curve is the period of time immediately following the establishment of a population, when the population remains small and fairly constant. During the lag phase, both natality and mortality are low.

The lag phase occurs because reproduction is not an instantaneous event. Even after animals enter an area, they must mate and produce young. This may take days or years, depending on the animal. Similarly, new plant introductions must grow to maturity, produce flowers, and set seed. Some annual plants do this in less than a year, whereas some large trees take several years of growth before they produce flowers. In organisms that take a long time to mature and produce young, such as elephants, deer, and many kinds of plants, the lag phase may be measured in years.

## The Exponential Growth Phase

The **exponential growth phase** of a population growth curve is the period of time when a population is growing rapidly. Exponential growth results in a population increasing by the same percent each year. For example, if the population were to double each year we would have 2, 4, 8, 16, 32, etc. individuals in the population. A population of mice is a good example of why populations can increase rapidly. Assuming that the population is started by a single pair—a male and female—it will take some time for them to mate and produce their first litter of offspring. This is the lag phase. However, once the first litter of young has been produced, the population is likely to increase rapidly. The first litter of young will become sexually mature and able to reproduce in a matter of weeks. If the usual litter size for a pair of mice is 4, the 4 produce 8, which in turn produce 16, and so forth. Furthermore, the original parents will probably produce an additional litter or two during this time period. Now, several pairs of mice are reproducing more than just once. With several pairs of mice reproducing, natality increases while mortality remains low; therefore, the population begins to grow at an ever-increasing rate. However, the population cannot continue to increase indefinitely. Eventually, the rate at which the population is growing will begin to level off.

## The Deceleration Phase

A **deceleration phase** eventually occurs during which the population growth rate begins to slow. The number entering the population by

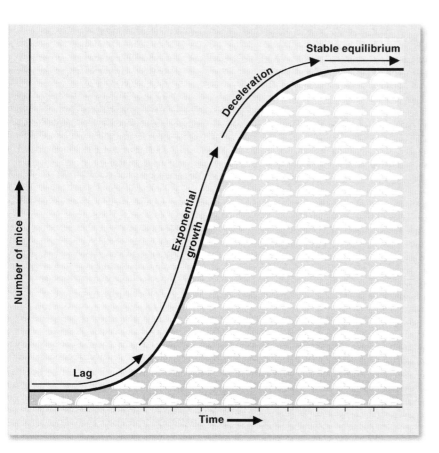

**FIGURE 17.8  A Typical Population Growth Curve**
In this mouse population, the period of time in which there is little growth is known as the lag phase. This is followed by a rapid increase in population as the offspring of the originating population begin to reproduce themselves; this is known as the exponential growth phase. Eventually, the population growth rate begins to slow during the deceleration phase and the population reaches a stable equilibrium phase, during which the birthrate equals the death rate.

reproduction remains high but the number leaving by death increases and the population growth rate begins to slow. The size of the population continues to grow but at a slower and slower rate until natality and mortality become equal. At this point, the population will enter the stable equilibrium phase.

## The Stable Equilibrium Phase

The **stable equilibrium phase** of a population growth curve is the period of time when a population stops growing and maintains itself at a reasonably stable level. This occurs because the number of individuals entering the population by birth will come to equal the number of individuals leaving it by death or migration. The number of organisms cannot continue to increase indefinitely, because eventually something in the environment will become limiting and cause an increase in the number of deaths. For animals, food, water, or nesting sites may be in short supply, or predators or disease may kill many individuals. Plants may lack water, soil nutrients, or sunlight. Often, there is both a decrease in natality and an increase in mortality as a population reaches the stable equilibrium phase. Although the size of the population is stable, the individuals in the population are changing. Birth, death, and migration are still going on, resulting in a changing mix of individuals. The size of the population is stable because there is an equilibrium between those entering and those leaving the population.

## Alternate Population Growth Strategies

When ecologists look at many kinds of organisms and how their populations change, they recognize two general types of reproductive strategies. These are often referred to as K-strategists and r-strategists. The $K$ and $r$ notations come from a mathematical formula where the $K$ represents the carrying capacity and the $r$ represents the population growth rate.

1. K-strategists are large organisms that live a long time and tend to reach a population size that can be sustained over an extended period. These kinds of organisms follow the pattern of population growth just described.

2. r-strategists are organisms that are small and have short life spans, tend to have fluctuating populations, and do not reach a stable equilibrium phase during population growth. Their populations go through the normal pattern of beginning with a lag phase, followed by an exponential growth phase. However, they typically reach a maximum, followed by a rapid decrease in population often called a "crash" (figure 17.9).

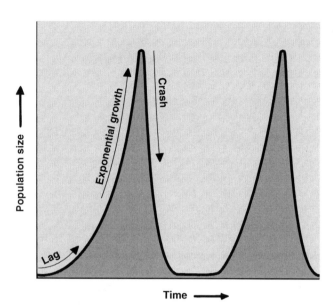

**FIGURE 17.9 A Population Growth Curve for Short-Lived Organisms**
Organisms that are small and live only a short time often show this kind of population growth curve. There is a lag phase, followed by an exponential growth phase. However, instead of entering into a stable equilibrium phase, the population reaches a maximum and crashes.

### 17.3 CONCEPT REVIEW

7. Draw a population growth curve. Label the lag, exponential growth, deceleration, and stable equilibrium phases.
8. What causes a lag phase in a population growth curve? An exponential growth phase? A deceleration phase? A stable equilibrium phase?
9. Describe how the population growth curves of K-strategists and r-strategists differ.

## 17.4 Limits to Population Size

Populations cannot continue to increase indefinitely. Eventually, a factor or combination of factors limits their size. The factors that prevent unlimited population growth are known as **limiting factors**. All the limiting factors that act on a population are collectively known as **environmental resistance**.

### Extrinsic and Intrinsic Limiting Factors

Some factors that control populations come from outside the population and are known as **extrinsic limiting factors.** Predators, the loss of a food source, a lack of sunlight, and accidents of nature are all extrinsic factors. However, the populations of many kinds of organisms appear to be regulated by factors from within the populations themselves. Such limiting factors are called **intrinsic limiting factors.** For example, a study of rats under crowded living conditions showed that, as conditions became more crowded, abnormal social behavior became common. There was a decrease in litter size, fewer litters per year were produced, the mothers were more likely to ignore their young, and many young were killed by adults. Thus, changes in the rats' behavior resulted in lower birthrates and higher death rates, which limit population size. In another example, the reproductive success of white-tailed deer is reduced when the deer experience a series of severe winters. When times are bad, the female deer are more likely to have single offspring than twins.

## Density-Dependent and Density-Independent Limiting Factors

**Density-dependent limiting factors** are those that become more effective as the density of the population increases. For example, the larger a population becomes, the more likely that predators will have a chance to catch some of the individuals. A prolonged period of increasing population allows the size of the predator population to increase as well. Disease epidemics are also more common in large, dense populations, because dense populations allow for the easy spread of parasites from one individual to another. The rat example previously mentioned also illustrates a density-dependent limiting factor in operation—the amount of abnormal behavior increased as the density of the population increased. In general, whenever there is competition among the members of a population, the intensity of competition increases as the population density increases. Large organisms that tend to live a long time and have relatively few young (K-strategists) are most likely to be controlled by density-dependent limiting factors.

    **Density-independent limiting factors** are population-controlling influences that are not related to the density of the population. They are usually accidental or occasional extrinsic factors in nature that happen regardless of the density of a population. A sudden rainstorm may drown many small plant seedlings and soil organisms. Many plants and animals are killed by frosts in late spring or early fall. A small pond may dry up, resulting in the death of many organisms. The organisms most likely to be controlled by density-independent limiting factors are small, short-lived organisms that can reproduce very rapidly (r-strategists).

---

### 17.4 CONCEPT REVIEW

  10. Differentiate between density-dependent and density-independent limiting factors. Give an example of each.
  11. Differentiate between intrinsic and extrinsic limiting factors. Give an example of each.

---

## 17.5 Categories of Limiting Factors

Limiting factors can be placed in four broad categories:

  1. Availability of raw materials
  2. Availability of energy
  3. Production and disposal of waste products
  4. Interaction with other organisms

### Availability of Raw Materials

The availability of raw materials is an extremely important limiting factor. For example, plants require magnesium to manufacture chlorophyll, nitrogen to produce protein and water to transport materials and as a raw material for photosynthesis. If these substances are not present in the soil, the growth and reproduction of plants are inhibited. However, if fertilizer supplies these nutrients, or if irrigation supplies water, the effects of these limiting factors can be removed, and a different factor becomes limiting. For animals, the amount of water, minerals, materials for nesting, suitable burrow sites, and food may be limiting factors.

### Availability of Energy

The availability of energy is a major limiting factor, because all living things need a source of energy. The amount of light available is often a limiting factor for plants, which require light as an energy source for photosynthesis. Because all animals use other living things as sources of energy and raw materials, a major limiting factor for any animal is its food source.

### Accumulation of Waste Products

The accumulation of waste products can significantly limit the size of populations. It does not usually limit plant populations, however, because they produce relatively few wastes. However, the buildup of high levels of self-generated waste products is a problem for bacterial populations and populations of tiny aquatic organisms. As wastes build up, they become more and more toxic, and eventually reproduction stops, or the population dies out. For example, when a few bacteria are introduced into a solution containing a source of food, they go through the kind of population growth curve typical of all organisms. As expected, the number of bacteria begins to increase following a lag phase, increases rapidly during the exponential growth phase, enters a deceleration phase, and eventually reaches stability in the stable equilibrium phase. However, as waste products accumulate, the bacteria drown in their own wastes. When space for disposal is limited, and no other organisms are present that can convert the harmful wastes to less harmful products, a population decline, known as the **death phase,** follows (figure 17.10).

    In small pools, such as aquariums, it is often difficult to keep organisms healthy because of the buildup of ammonia in the water from the animals' waste products. This is the

**FIGURE 17.10 Bacterial Population Growth Curve**
The rate of increase in the size of the population of these bacteria is typical of population growth in a favorable environment. When the environmental conditions worsen as a result of an increase in the amount of waste products, the population first levels off, then begins to decrease. This period of decreasing population size is known as the death phase or decline phase.

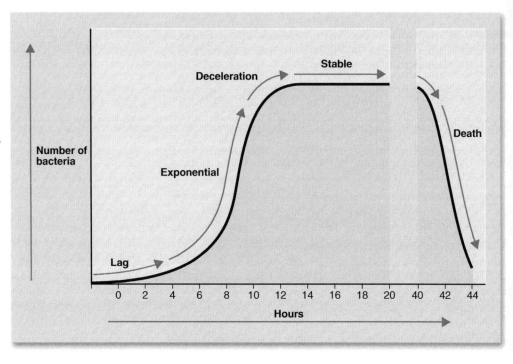

primary reason that activated charcoal filters are used in aquariums. The charcoal removes many kinds of toxic compounds and prevents the buildup of waste products.

## Interaction with Other Organisms

Organism interactions are also important in limiting population size. Recall from chapter 16 that organisms influence each other in many ways. Some interactions are harmful; others are beneficial.

Predation, parasitism, and competition tend to limit the growth of populations and their maximum size. Parasitism and predation usually involve interactions between two different species. Thus, they are extrinsic limiting factors. Competition between members of different species (interspecific competition) is an extrinsic limiting factor. Competition among members of the same species (intraspecific competition) is an intrinsic limiting factor and often is extremely intense.

On the other hand, many kinds of organisms perform beneficial services for others that allow the population to grow more than it would without the help. For example, decomposer organisms destroy toxic waste products, thus benefiting populations of aquatic animals. They also recycle the materials that all organisms need for growth and development. Mutualistic relationships benefit both populations involved. The absence of such beneficial organisms is a limiting factor.

Often, the population sizes of two kinds of organisms are interdependent, because each is a primary limiting factor of the other. This is most often seen in parasite-host relationships and predator-prey relationships.

A study of the population biology of the collared lemming (*Dicrostonyx groenlandicus*) in Greenland illustrates the population interactions between lemmings and four predators. Lemmings have a very high reproductive capacity,

producing two or three litters per year. However, their population is held in check by four predators. Three—the snowy owl, the arctic fox, and the long-tailed skua (a bird that resembles a gull)—are generalist predators, whose consumption of lemmings is directly related to the size of the lemming population. They constitute a density-dependent limiting factor for the lemming population. When lemming numbers are low, these predators seek other prey.

The fourth lemming predator is the short-tailed weasel (*Mustela ermina*); it is a specialist predator on lemmings. The weasels are much more dependent on lemmings for food than are the other three predators. The weasels mate once a year, so their population increases at a slower rate than that of the lemmings. However, as the weasel population increases, it eventually become large enough that it drives down the lemming population. The resulting decrease in lemmings leads to a decline in the number of weasels, which allows for the greater survival of lemmings, which ultimately leads to another cycle of increased weasel numbers (figure 17.11). Outlooks 17.1 provides an example of how interactions between humans and leatherback turtles have negatively affected turtle populations.

## 17.5 CONCEPT REVIEW

12. List four kinds of limiting factors that help set the carrying capacity for a species.
13. Describe an example of how waste products can limit the size of a population.
14. Give an example of how interaction between two species of organisms could allow for populations to be larger than if the interaction did not occur.

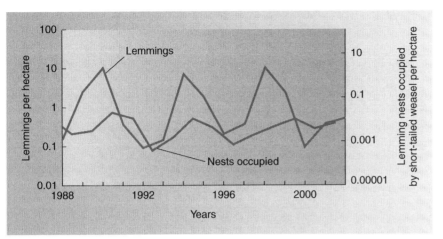

**FIGURE 17.11 Population Cycles**

In many northern regions of the world, population cycles are common. In the case of collared lemmings and short-tailed weasels in Greenland, interactions between the two populations result in population cycles of about 4 years. The graph shows the population of lemmings per hectare and the number of lemming nests occupied by weasels per hectare. The researchers used the number of nests occupied by weasels as an indirect measure of weasel population size.

## OUTLOOKS 17.1

# Marine Turtle Population Declines

Throughout the world, all seven species of marine turtles are endangered. There are several characteristics of their life history and reproductive biology that contribute to this problem. Although there are some differences among the species, in general they are slow to mature and there is high mortality among the young.

Some details about the leatherback turtle (*Dermochelys coriacea*) will help to describe why marine turtles are in trouble. Leatherback turtles are the largest of the marine turtles that are in the range of 1–2 meters in length and between 250 and 700 kg in weight. They reach sexual maturity between 6 and 10 years of age. Once a female turtle reaches sexual maturity she will nearly always return to the beach from which she hatched to lay her eggs. She generally arrives at the beach at night at high tide and drags herself up the sandy beach where she digs a hole in the sand with her rear flippers and deposits up to 100 eggs. She then covers the eggs with sand and leaves. She may lay eggs several times during the breeding season, but it may be two to three years before she returns to lay more eggs.

The eggs hatch after about 60 days. At night the hatchlings crawl up through the sand and migrate down the beach to the ocean. If they are successful in reaching the water they still need to live to maturity. Although large adult turtles have few predators, the hatchlings and small turtles are prey to many birds, mammals, crabs, and fish. In addition, terrestrial mammals may find and eat the eggs. Survival is low. Some researchers estimate that about 1 hatchling per 1,000 makes it to adulthood.

Several kinds of human activities reduce survival. Although marine turtles are a protected species worldwide, in many parts of the world people dig up the eggs of the turtles or capture turtles for food. In addition, the building of resorts and other urban development alters the beaches traditionally used by the turtles. Even the lights associated with urban development are a problem. In particular, the hatchlings rely on light stimuli to guide them to the water. In the absence of human lights, the surface of the water reflects light, which the hatchlings follow to the water. If there are other sources of light, the hatchlings

may orient on lights that lead them away from the water. Human fishing activity also results in the death of many young and adult turtles. If turtles become entangled in nets or are caught on a submerged fishing hook, they will be unable to surface to breathe and will drown. Even discarded plastic in the ocean is a problem—plastic bags resemble jellyfish that are the primary food of the turtles. The turtles eat, but cannot digest them, and the bags block their digestive system, causing death.

So, a combination of factors contributes to the endangered status of the leatherback turtle:

1. Sandy beaches are required as a suitable nesting habitat and they need to be isolated or protected from human predation on the eggs and adults.
2. Mortality of the hatchlings and young is very high due to a combination of natural predation and accidental capture by fishers.
3. Many turtle nesting beaches are also desirable as recreation sites. New resort facilities and the lights associated with them lead to inadvertent deaths of the hatchling turtles.

**Female leatherback turtle fitted with a tracking device**

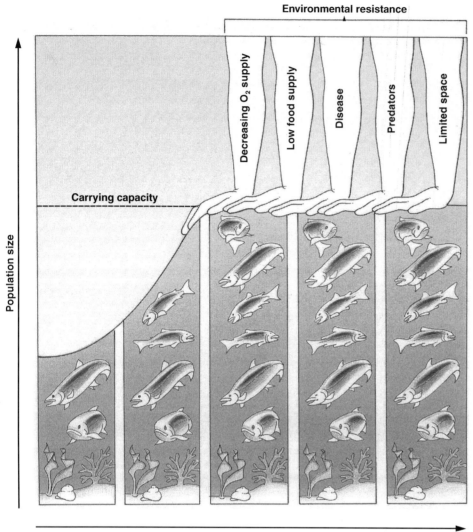

**Environmental resistance**

Decreasing O₂ supply

Low food supply

Disease

Predators

Limited space

Carrying capacity

Population size

Time

**FIGURE 17.12 Carrying Capacity**
A number of factors in the environment, such as food, oxygen supply, diseases, predators, and space, determine the maximum number of organisms that can be sustained in a given area—the carrying capacity of that area. The environmental factors that limit populations are collectively known as environmental resistance.

## 17.6 Carrying Capacity

Many populations reach a maximum size when they reach the stable equilibrium phase. This suggests that the environment sets an upper limit on population size. The **carrying capacity** is the maximum sustainable population for an area. The carrying capacity is determined by a combination of limiting factors. But keep in mind that some limiting factors are more important than others (figure 17.12).

Carrying capacity is not an inflexible number, however. Often, such environmental differences as successional changes, climatic variations, disease epidemics, forest fires, and floods can change the carrying capacity of an area for specific species. In aquatic ecosystems, one of the major factors that determine the carrying capacity is the quantity of nutrients in the water.

Where nutrients are abundant, the numbers of various kinds of organisms are high. Often, nutrient levels fluctuate with changes in current or runoff from the land, and plant and animal populations fluctuate as well. In addition, a change that negatively affects the carrying capacity for one species may increase the carrying capacity for another. For example, the cutting down of a mature forest followed by the growth of young trees increases the carrying capacity for deer and rabbits, which use the new growth for food, but decreases the carrying capacity for squirrels, which need mature, fruit-producing trees as a source of food and old, hollow trees for shelter.

Wildlife management practices often encourage modifications to the environment that will increase the carrying capacity for the designated game species. The goal of wildlife managers is to have the highest sustainable population available for harvest by hunters. Typical habitat modifications include creating water holes, cutting forests to provide young growth, planting food plots, and building artificial nesting sites.

In some cases, the size of the organisms in a population also affects the carrying capacity. For example, an aquarium of a certain size can support only a limited number of fish, but the size of the fish makes a difference. If all the fish are tiny, a large number can be supported, and the carrying capacity is high; however, the same aquarium may be able to support only one, large fish. In other words, the biomass of the population makes a difference (figure 17.13). Similarly, when an area is planted with small trees, the population size is high; however, as the trees get larger, competition for nutrients and sunlight becomes more intense, and the number of trees declines as the biomass increases.

### 17.6 CONCEPT REVIEW

15. How is the carrying capacity of an environment related to the stable equilibrium phase of a population growth curve?
16. How are the concepts of carrying capacity and limiting factors related?
17. Describe an event that could change the carrying capacity for an organism and explain why the event would alter carrying capacity.

1 fish—2 kg

2 fish—1.3 kg
0.7 kg
2.0 kg

8 fish, each 250 g = 2 kg

6 fish—2 (500 g)
4 (250 g)
2,000 g, or 2.0 kg

**FIGURE 17.13  The Effect of Biomass on Carrying Capacity**
Each aquarium can support a biomass of 2 kilograms of fish. The size of the population is influenced by the body size of the fish in the population.

## 17.7  Limiting Factors to Human Population Growth

Today we hear differing opinions about the state of the world's human population. On one hand we hear that the population is growing rapidly. By contrast we hear that some countries are afraid that their populations are shrinking. Other countries are concerned about the aging of their populations, because birthrates and death rates are low. In magazines and on television, we see that there are starving people in the world. At the same time, we hear discussions about the problem of food surpluses and obesity in many countries. Some have even said that the most important problem in the world today is the rate at which the human population is growing. Others maintain that the growing population will provide markets for goods and be an economic boon. How do we reconcile this mass of conflicting information?

It is important to realize that human populations follow the same patterns of growth and are acted on by the same kinds of limiting factors as are populations of other organisms. The growth of the human population over the past several thousand years follows a pattern that resembles the lag and exponential growth phases of a population growth curve. It is estimated that the human population remained low and constant for thousands of years but has increased rapidly in the past few hundred years (figure 17.14). For example, it has been estimated that before European discovery, the Native American population was at or near its

carrying capacity. Although it is impossible to know the Native American population at that time, various experts estimate it was between 1 million and 18 million. Today, the population of the United States is nearly 310 million people. Does this mean that humans are different from other animal species? Can the human population continue to grow forever?

The human species has an upper limit set by the carrying capacity of the environment, as does any other species. However, the human population has been able to increase astronomically because technological changes and the displacement of other species have allowed us to shift the carrying capacity upward. Much of the exponential growth phase of the human population can be attributed to improved sanitation, the control of infectious diseases, improvements in agricultural methods, and the replacement of natural ecosystems with artificial agricultural ecosystems. But even these conditions have their limits. Some limiting factors will eventually cause a leveling off of our population growth curve. We cannot increase beyond our ability to get raw materials and energy, nor can we ignore the waste products we produce and the other organisms with which we interact.

### Availability of Raw Materials

To many of us, raw materials consist simply of the amount of food available, but we should not forget that, in a technological society, iron ore, lumber, irrigation water, and silicon chips are also raw materials. However, most people of the world have much more basic needs. For the past several decades, large portions of the world's population have not had enough food (figure 17.15). Although it is biologically accurate to say that the world can currently produce enough food for everyone, there are complex political, economic, and social issues related to food production and distribution. Probably most important is the fact that the transportation of food from centers of excess to centers of need is often very difficult and expensive. Societies with excess food have been unwilling to bridge these political and economic gaps.

However, a more fundamental question is whether the world can continue to produce enough food. In 2010, the world population was growing at a rate of 1.2% per year. This amounts to about 150 new people added to the population every minute. This would result in an increase from our current population of nearly 6.9 billion to about 9.5 billion by 2050. With a continuing increase in the number

**FIGURE 17.14 Human Population Growth**
The number of humans doubled from A.D. 1800 to 1930 (from 1 billion to 2 billion), had doubled again by 1975 (4 billion), and is projected to double again (8 billion) by about 2025. How long can the human population continue to double before the Earth's ultimate carrying capacity is reached?

**FIGURE 17.15 Food Is a Raw Material**

of mouths to feed, it is unlikely that food production will be able to keep pace with the growth in human population (How Science Works 17.1).

A primary indicator of the status of the world food situation is the amount of grain produced for each person in the world (per capita grain production). World per capita grain production peaked in 1984.

## Availability of Energy

The availability of energy also affects human populations. All species on Earth ultimately depend on sunlight for energy. All energy—whether power from a hydroelectric dam, fossil fuels, or solar cell—is derived from the Sun. Energy is needed for transportation, the construction and maintenance of homes, and food production. It is very difficult to develop unbiased, reasonably accurate estimates of global energy reserves in the form of petroleum, natural gas, and coal. Therefore, it is difficult to predict how long these reserves might last. However, the quantities are limited and the rate of use has been increasing (figure 17.16).

If the less-developed countries were to attain a standard of living equal to that of the developed nations, the global

# HOW SCIENCE WORKS 17.1

## Thomas Malthus and His Essay on Population

In 1798, Thomas Robert Malthus, an Englishman, published an essay on human population, presenting an idea that was contrary to popular opinion. His basic thesis was that the human population increased in a geometric, or exponential, manner (2, 4, 8, 16, 32, 64, etc.), whereas the ability to produce food increased only in an arithmetic manner (1, 2, 3, 4, 5, 6, etc.). The ultimate outcome of these different rates would be that the population would outgrow the land's ability to produce food. He concluded that wars, famines, plagues, and natural disasters would be the means (limiting factors) of controlling the size of the human population. His predictions were hotly debated by the intellectual community of his day, and his assumptions and conclusions were attacked as erroneous and against the best interest of society. At the time he wrote the essay, the popular opinion was that human knowledge and "moral constraint" would be able to create a world that would supply all human needs in abundance. One of Malthus's basic postulates was that "commerce between the sexes" (sexual intercourse) would continue unchanged. Other philosophers of the day believed that sexual behavior would take less procreative forms and the human population would be limited. Only within the past 50 years, however, have effective conception-control mechanisms become widely accepted and used. However, even today they are used primarily in the more developed countries of the world.

**Thomas Robert Malthus**

Malthus did not foresee the use of contraception, major changes in agricultural production techniques, or the exporting of excess people to colonies in the Americas. These factors, as well as high death rates, prevented the most devastating of his predictions from coming true. However, in many parts of the world, people are experiencing the forms of population control (famine, epidemic disease, wars, and natural disasters) that Malthus predicated in 1798. Many people believe that his original predictions were valid—only his time scale was not correct—and that his predictions are coming true today.

Another important impact of Malthus's essay was its effect on young Charles Darwin. When Darwin read it, he saw that what was true for the human population could be applied to the whole of the plant and animal kingdoms. As overreproduction took place, there would be increased competition for food, resulting in the death of the less-fit organisms. This was an important part of his theory of natural selection.

---

**FIGURE 17.16  Humans' Energy Use**

energy reserves would disappear overnight. People should realize that there is a limit to our energy resources; we are living on solar energy that was stored over millions of years, and we are using it at a rate that could deplete it in hundreds of years.

## Accumulation of Wastes

One of the most talked about aspects of human activity is the problem of waste disposal. We have normal biological wastes, which can be dealt with by decomposer organisms. However, we also generate a variety of technological wastes and by-products that cannot be degraded efficiently by decomposers (figure 17.17). Most of what we call pollution results from the waste products of technology. The biological wastes usually can be dealt with fairly efficiently by building wastewater treatment plants and other sewage facilities. Certainly, these facilities take energy to run, but they rely on decomposers to degrade unwanted organic matter to carbon dioxide and water. Earlier in this chapter, we discussed the problems

**FIGURE 17.17 Human Waste Production**

**FIGURE 17.18 Interaction with Other Organisms**

aquarium organisms face when their metabolic waste products accumulate. In this situation, the organisms so "befoul their nest" that their wastes poison them. Are humans in a similar situation on a much larger scale? Are we dumping so much technological waste, much of it toxic, into the environment that we are being poisoned? Is carbon dioxide from the burning of fossil fuels changing our climate?

## Interactions with Other Organisms

Humans interact with other organisms in as many ways as other animals do. We have parasites and, occasionally, predators. We are predators in relation to a variety of animals, both domesticated and wild. We have mutualistic relationships with many of our domesticated plants and animals, because they could not survive without our agricultural practices, and we would not survive without the food they provide. Competition is also very important. Insects and rodents compete for the food we raise, and we compete directly with many other kinds of animals for the use of ecosystems.

As humans convert more and more land to agriculture and other purposes, many other organisms are displaced (figure 17.18). Many of these displaced organisms are not able to compete successfully and must leave the area, reduce their populations, or become extinct. The American bison (buffalo), African and Asian elephants, panda, and grizzly bear are a few species that have reduced populations because they were not able to compete successfully with the human species. The passenger pigeon, Carolina parakeet, and great auk are a few that have become extinct. Our parks and natural areas have become tiny refuges for plants and animals that once occupied vast expanses of the world. If these refuges are lost, many organisms will become extinct. What today might seem to be an insignificant organism may tomorrow be seen as a link to our very survival. We humans have been extremely successful in our efforts to convert ecosystems to our own uses at the expense of other species.

Competition with one another (intraspecific competition), however, is a different matter. Because competition is negative for both organisms, competition between humans harms humans. We are not displacing another species; we are displacing our own kind. Certainly, when resources are in short supply, there is competition. Unfortunately, it is usually the young who are least able to compete, and high infant mortality is the result.

---

### 17.7 CONCEPT REVIEW

18. As the human population continues to grow, what should we expect to happen to other species?
19. How does the shape of the population growth curve of humans compare with that of other kinds of animals?

---

## 17.8 The Control of the Human Population—A Social Problem

Humans are different from most other organisms in a fundamental way: We are able to predict the outcome of a specific course of action. Current technology and medical knowledge are available to control the human population and improve the health and well-being of the people of the world. Why, then, does the human population continue to grow, resulting in human suffering and stressing the environment in which we live? Because we are social animals with freedom of choice, we frequently do not do what is considered best from an unemotional, unselfish, biological point of view. People make decisions based on historical, social, cultural, ethical, and personal considerations. In order to control the human population, individuals may need to set aside some of their wants and desires.

The biggest problems associated with the control of the human population are not biological problems; rather, they require the efforts of philosophers, theologians, politicians, and sociologists. As the population increases, so do political, social, and biological problems; individual freedom diminishes, intense competition for resources intensifies, and famine and starvation become more common. The knowledge and technology necessary to control the human population are available, but the will is not. What will eventually limit the size of our population? Will it be lack of resources, lack of energy, accumulated waste products, competition among ourselves, or rational planning of family size?

Studies of the changes in the population growth rates of various countries indicated that a major factor in determining the size of families is the educational status of women. Regardless of other cultural differences, as girls and women become educated, they have fewer children. Several reasons have been suggested for this trend. Higher levels of education enable women to get jobs with higher pay, which makes them less dependent on males for their support. Being able to read may lead to better comprehension of how methods of birth control work. Regardless of the reasons, increasing the educational levels of women has become a major technique used by rapidly growing countries that hope to control their populations.

## 17.8 CONCEPT REVIEW

20. How does human population growth differ from the population growth of other kinds of organisms?
21. What forces will ultimately lead to the control of human population growth?

## Summary

A population is a group of organisms of the same species in a particular place at a particular time. Populations differ from one another in gene frequency, age distribution, sex ratio, population distribution, and population density. Organisms typically have a reproductive capacity that exceeds what is necessary to replace the parent organisms when they die. This inherent capacity to overreproduce causes a rapid increase in population size when a new area is colonized. A typical population growth curve consists of a lag phase, in which the population rises very slowly, followed by an exponential growth phase in which the population increases at an accelerating rate, followed by a leveling off of the population during the deceleration phase, which leads to a relatively constant population size in a stable equilibrium phase as the carrying capacity of the environment is reached. In some populations, a fifth phase, the death phase, occurs.

The carrying capacity is the maximum sustainable number of organisms an area can support. It is set by a variety of limiting factors. The availability of energy, the availability of raw materials, the accumulation of wastes, and interactions with other organisms are limiting factors. Because organisms are interrelated, population changes in one species sometimes affect the size of other populations. This is particularly true when one organism uses another as a source of food. Some limiting factors operate from outside the population and are known as extrinsic limiting factors; others are properties of the species itself and are called intrinsic limiting factors. Some limiting factors become more intense as the density of the population increases; these are known as density-dependent limiting factors. Limiting factors that are more accidental and unrelated to population density are called density-independent limiting factors.

Humans as a species have the same limits and influences that other organisms do. Our current problems of food production, energy needs, pollution, and habitat destruction are outcomes of uncontrolled population growth. However, humans can reason and predict, thus offering the possibility of population control through conscious population limitation.

## Key Terms

*Use the interactive flash cards on the* **Concepts in Biology,** *14/e website to help you learn the meaning of these terms.*

age distribution 374
carrying capacity 384
death phase 381
deceleration phase 379
density-dependent limiting factors 381
density-independent limiting factors 381
environmental resistance 380
exponential growth phase 379
extrinsic limiting factors 380
intrinsic limiting factors 381
lag phase 379

limiting factors 380
mortality 379
natality 379
population 374
population density 377
population distribution 377
population growth curve 379
population pressure 377
reproductive capacity (biotic potential) 378
sex ratio 376
stable equilibrium phase 380

## Basic Review

1. The number of reproducing adults in a population compared with the number of juveniles is the
   a. population density.
   b. age distribution.
   c. population distribution.
   d. gene frequency.

2. The period of time when a population is growing rapidly is known as the _____.

3. Populations grow
   a. because most species have a high reproductive capacity.
   b. when birthrates are greater than death rates.
   c. when there are high numbers of reproductive and juvenile individuals in the population.
   d. All of the above are correct.

4. The maximum size of a population is set by limiting factors of the environment. (T/F)

5. A limiting factor that becomes more intense as the size of a population increases is known as a density-independent limiting factor. (T/F)

6. The carrying capacity
   a. for the human population has been reached.
   b. is determined by the limiting factors of the environment.
   c. is the same for all organisms.
   d. None of the above is correct.

7. When the size of a population is caused to stop growing because of competition among its members, there are _____ in action.
   a. extrinsic limiting factors
   b. density-independent limiting factors
   c. intrinsic limiting factors
   d. population distribution factors

8. The populations of all species eventually reach a stable equilibrium phase. (T/F)

9. Which one of the following populations would grow most rapidly?
   a. a population of mice in which there were twice as many males as females
   b. a population of mice that had reached its carrying capacity
   c. a population of mice in which density-dependent limiting factors were acting strongly
   d. a population that was in the lag phase

10. The human population has been increasing rapidly for the past 200 years because
    a. humans have displaced other organisms.
    b. humans have controlled many disease organisms.
    c. humans have developed improvements in agriculture.
    d. All of the above are correct.

11. Gene flow occurs when individuals _____ to new places.

12. Pollution can be considered to be a waste product. (T/F)

13. Which of the following is an extrinsic limiting factor?
    a. the number of siblings in a bird nest
    b. competition among individuals for food
    c. rainstorms that kill many plant seedlings
    d. None of the above is correct.

14. A K-strategist
    a. lives a short time.
    b. gives care to its young.
    c. is always a tiny organism.
    d. None of the above is correct.

15. The lag phase of a population growth curve results in
    a. a reduction in the size of the population.
    b. little increase in the size of the population.
    c. a rapidly growing population.
    d. None of the above is correct.

**Answers**
1. b   2. exponential growth phase   3. d  4. T  5. F  6. b  7. c  8. F  9. d  10. d  11. travel/migrate/move  12. T  13. c  14. b  15. b

## Thinking Critically

**Understanding Human Population Growth**
Review figure 17.14; note that this population growth curve has very little in common with the population growth curve shown in figure 17.8. What factors have allowed the human population to grow so rapidly? What natural limiting factors will eventually bring our population under control? What is the ultimate carrying capacity of the world? What alternatives to the natural processes of population limitation could bring human population under control? Consider the following in your answers: reproduction, death, diseases, food supply, energy, farming practices, food distribution, cultural biases, and anything else you consider relevant.

# CHAPTER

# 18

# Evolutionary and Ecological Aspects of Behavior

## Urban Coyotes Kill Pets
*What can be done to solve the problem?*

Coyotes have adapted to urban and suburban locations where there are natural areas such as parks, golf courses, drainage ditches, and similar places that provide suitable habitat. Reports of coyotes killing pets, particularly cats and small dogs, are common throughout the United States. What has happened to make this wary animal lose its fear of humans?

Humans have contributed to this problem by providing several sources of food that are attractive to wild animals. Animals like coyotes learn to associate food with humans. The three most common sources of food are (1) garbage that is not in a secure container; (2) pet food provided outdoors; and (3) bird feeders. Coyotes are scavengers as well as carnivores and will use these sources of food. Once coyotes become habituated to finding food around homes, they are likely to encounter pets that are outside the home. Cats that roam at night are particularly vulnerable to predation by coyotes.

- Why do coyotes lose their fear of humans?

- Can coyotes be trained to avoid humans?

- In areas with a coyote problem, should homeowners be required to place garbage in a secure container, stop feeding birds, and keep their pets indoors?

## Background Check

Concepts you should already know to get the most out of this chapter:
- How natural selection shapes the evolution of organisms (chapter 13)
- The difference between a scientific test of a hypothesis and an opinion (chapter 1)

## 18.1    Interpreting Behavior

**Behavior** is how an animal acts—what it does and how it does it. When you watch a bird, a squirrel, or any other animal, its activities appear to have a purpose. Birds search for food, take flight as you approach, and build nests in which to raise young. Usually, the nests are inconspicuous or placed in difficult-to-reach spots. Likewise, squirrels collect and store nuts and acorns, "scold" when you get too close, and learn to visit sites where food is available.

### Discovering the Significance of Behavior

It is not always easy to identify the significance of a behavior without careful study of the behavior pattern and its impact on other organisms. For example, a baby herring gull pecks at a red spot on its parent's bill. What possible value can this behavior have for either the chick or the parent? If we watch, we see that, when the chick pecks at the spot, the parent regurgitates food onto the ground, and feeds it to the chick (figure 18.1). This looks like a simple behavior, but there is more to it than meets the eye. Why did the chick peck to begin with? How did it "know" to peck at that spot? Why did the pecking cause the parent to regurgitate food? These questions are not easy to answer. Many people assume that the actions have the same motivation and direction as similar human behaviors, but this is not necessarily a correct assumption. For example, when a little girl points to a piece of candy and

makes appropriate noises, she is indicating to her parent that she wants some candy. Is that what the herring gull chick is doing? We don't know. Although both kinds of young may get food, we don't know what the baby gull is thinking because we can't ask it.

### Behavior Is Adaptive

When we observe behavior, we must keep in mind that behavior is adaptive just like any other characteristic displayed by an animal. Behaviors are important for survival and appropriate for the environment in which an animal lives. As with animals' highly adaptive structural characteristics, behaviors are the result of a long evolutionary process. Birds that do not take flight at the approach of another animal are eaten by predators. Squirrels that do not find deposits of food are less likely to survive, and birds that build obvious nests on the ground are more likely to lose their young to predators.

Because the nervous system of animals is the product of genes, many aspects of behavior have a genetic component. In this respect, behavioral characteristics are no different from physical characteristics, such as eye structure, wing shape, or tail length. However, the evolution of behavior is much more difficult to study than structural characteristics. This is because behavior is temporary, and it is difficult to find fossils that show the development of behavior, the way fossils allow us to follow changes in structures. Fossils of footprints, nests, and specific structures such as teeth adapted for grinding give clues about the behavior of extinct animals (How Science Works 18.1). However, these examples represent only a few fragments of the total behavior that must have been a part of the lives of extinct animals. When scientists compare the behavior of closely related animals living today, they can see inherited behaviors that are slightly different from one another. This strongly suggests that these behaviors have evolved, just as the wings of different species of birds have evolved for different kinds of flight. In both cases (structural and behavioral) a basic pattern has been modified as the organisms adapted to their environments.

**FIGURE 18.1 Understanding Behavior**
A herring gull chick causes its parent to regurgitate food onto the ground by pecking at the red spot on its parent's bill. This behavior is instinctive. The parent then picks up the food and feeds it to the chick.

### 18.1    CONCEPT REVIEW

1. Why is it more difficult to study the evolution of behavior than the evolution of structural characteristics?
2. List two animal behaviors and state their significance to the animal's reproductive success.

# HOW SCIENCE WORKS 18.1
## Males Raised the Young in Some Species of Dinosaurs

Sometimes it is possible to use fossils to gain insight into the behavior of extinct animals. In 2008, scientists published a study that suggests that some kinds of theropod dinosaurs (*Oviraptor, Troodon, Citipati*) had a mating system in which the male dinosaurs were the primary caregivers for young. The male dinosaurs guarded the eggs in the nest and cared for the young after the eggs hatched. They based their assertion on several lines of evidence. Fossils of adult dinosaurs have been found associated with nests of eggs and the position of the adult is consistent with it protecting the nest. The dinosaurs that show this behavior show many birdlike characteristics and are closely related to species of birds that show male brooding of young—kiwi, ostrich, and emu. The number of eggs in the nest is large. Birds in which males brood the eggs and raise the young have large numbers of eggs. They compared the number of eggs in the nest of the dinosaurs with that of modern dinosaur relatives—crocodiles, alligators, and birds—and found that the number of eggs in the nest closely matched that of birds in which males brood the eggs. Finally, they compared the bone structure of the dinosaurs found guarding the nest and determined that the bones lacked a layer of spongy bone inside their long bones. Female birds produce this spongy bone during reproduction. The absence of this feature strengthens the argument that the individual guarding the nest were males.

This has significant implications for our understanding of the evolution of bird behavior. Perhaps the first birds were those in which males cared for the young, and the common pattern we see today—both parent birds caring for the young—has evolved from the more primitive condition found in ostriches and their relatives.

## 18.2 The Problem of Anthropomorphism

**Anthropomorphism** is the idea that we can assign human feelings, meanings, and emotions to the behavior of animals (figure 18.2). Poets, composers, and writers have often described birdsong as the act of a "joyful songster," but is a bird singing on a warm, sunny spring day making a beautiful sound because it is happy? Students of animal behavior do not accept this idea and have demonstrated that a bird sings primarily to attract mates and to tell other birds to keep out of its territory. The barbed stinger of a honeybee remains in your skin after you are stung, and the bee tears the stinger out of its body when it flies away. The damage to its body is so great that it dies. Has the bee performed a noble deed of heroism and self-sacrifice? Was it defending its hive from you? Scientists need to know a great deal more about the behavior of bees to understand the value of such behavior to the success of the bee species. The fact that bees are social animals, like humans, makes it tempting to think that they are doing things for the same reasons we are.

If you chase a squirrel in a park it will run up a tree and chatter at you. This is often referred to as scolding; however, this is a human interpretation based on what we might do if someone disturbed us. We might yell at the other person to go away and leave us alone. However, several other possible

**FIGURE 18.2 Anthropomorphism**
It is tempting to think that both the girl and the dog are having the same experience. However, that would be anthropomorphic thinking. We really don't know what the dog is experiencing. We can't ask the dog what it is thinking.

interpretations are equally reasonable. Perhaps the purpose of the squirrel's noise-making is directed at driving you away. Or perhaps its vocalizations warn other squirrels of the presence of a predator. Or perhaps it is simply a nervous reaction to being disturbed. We cannot crawl inside the brain of another animal and see what it is thinking.

In order to evaluate behavior objectively, we need to avoid anthropomorphic assumptions. A scientific study of this scolding behavior would attempt to determine what triggers the behavior, rather than jump to a conclusion that it must be for the same reasons we humans do things. Furthermore, a scientific study of this behavior would seek to determine the effect of the behavior. A scientific study of an organism's behavior looks at the behavior of an animal during its lifetime and seeks to determine the behavior's value to the animal and how that behavior may have evolved. This scientific way of thinking requires the testing of hypotheses; an anthropomorphic approach does not.

---

## 18.2 CONCEPT REVIEW

3. Why do students of animal behavior reject the idea that a singing bird is happy?
4. Define *anthropomorphism*.

---

## 18.3 Instinctive and Learned Behavior

There are two major kinds of behaviors: instinctive and learned. **Instinctive behavior** is behavior that is inherited, automatic, and inflexible. **Learned behavior** is behavior that changes as a result of experience. Both are involved in the behavior patterns of most organisms. Learning allows an organism to generate a completely new behavior or to slightly modify existing behavior patterns. Most animals (e.g., jellyfish, clams, insects, worms, frogs, turtles) have a high proportion of instinctive behavior and very little learning. Others, such as many birds and mammals, have a great deal of learned behavior in addition to many instinctive behaviors.

### The Nature of Instinctive Behavior

Instinctive behavior makes up most of the behavior in animals that have short life cycles, simple nervous systems, and little contact with their parents. These behaviors are performed correctly the first time without previous experience. Such behaviors are found in a wide range of organisms, from simple, one-celled protozoans to complex vertebrates.

#### Stimulus and Response

Instinctive behaviors occur as a result of a specific *response* to a particular *stimulus*. A **stimulus** is a change in the organism's internal or external environment that an animal is able to detect. A **response** is an organism's reaction to a stimulus.

In our example of the herring gull chick, the red spot on the parent's bill serves as a stimulus for the chick. The chick

responds to this spot in a genetically programmed way. The behavior is instinctive—it is done correctly the first time without prior experience. The chick's pecking behavior, in turn, is the stimulus for the adult bird to regurgitate food. Obviously, these behaviors have adaptive value for the survival of the young, because they leave little to chance. The young will get food automatically from the adult. Instinctive behavior has great value to a species, because it allows correct, appropriate, and necessary behavior to occur without prior experience.

An organism can respond only to stimuli it can recognize. For example, it is difficult for humans to appreciate what the world is like to a bloodhound. The bloodhound is able to identify individuals by smell, whereas we have great difficulty detecting, let alone distinguishing among, many odors. Some animals, such as dogs, deer, and mice, can see only shades of gray. Others, such as honeybees, see ultraviolet light, which is invisible to us. Some birds and other animals are able to detect the magnetic field of the Earth. And some, such as rattlesnakes, are able to detect infrared radiation (heat) from distant objects.

### Instinctive Behavior Cannot Be Modified

Instinctive behaviors can be very important for the survival of individuals of a species. This is especially true for fundamental, essential activities that do not require modification. The major drawback of instinctive behavior is that it cannot be modified when a new situation presents itself.

Over long periods of evolutionary time, genetically determined behaviors have been selected for and have been useful to most individuals of the species. However, instances of inappropriate behavior may be generated by unusual stimuli or unusual circumstances in which the stimulus is given. For example, many kinds of insects fly toward a source of light. Over the millions of years of insect evolution, this has been a valuable, useful behavior. It allows them easily to find their way to open space. However, the human species invented artificial lights and transparent windows, which cause the animals to engage in totally inappropriate behavior. We have all seen insects drawn to lights at night or insects inside houses, constantly flying against window panes through which sunlight is entering. This mindless, mechanical behavior seems incredibly stupid to us. Although *individual* animals die, the general behavior pattern of flying toward light is still valuable because *most* of the individuals of the species do not encounter artificial lights or get trapped inside houses, and they complete their life cycles normally.

Geese and other birds sit on nests. This behavior keeps the eggs warm and protects them from other dangers. During this incubation period, the eggs may roll out of the nest as the parents get on and off the nest. When this happens, certain species of geese roll the eggs back into the nest. If the developing young within the egg are exposed to extremes of heat or cold, they are killed; thus, the egg-rolling behavior has a significant adaptive value. If, however, the egg is taken from

**FIGURE 18.3  Inflexible Instinctive Behavior**
Geese use a specific set of head movements to roll any reasonably round object back to the nest. There are several components of this instinctive behavior, including recognition of the object and head-tucking movements. If the egg is removed during the head-tucking movements, the behavior continues as if the egg were still there. This demonstrates the inflexible nature of instinctive behavior.

the goose when it is in the middle of egg-rolling behavior, the goose will continue its egg rolling until it gets back to the nest, even though there is no egg to roll (figure 18.3). This is typical of the inflexible nature of instinctive behaviors. It has also been found that many other, somewhat egg-shaped structures can stimulate egg-rolling behavior. For example, beer cans and baseballs trigger egg-rolling behavior. Thus, not only are the birds unable to stop the egg rolling in mid-stride, but also nonegg objects can generate inappropriate behavior because they resemble eggs.

## Instinctive Behavior Can Be Complex

Some activities are so complex that it seems impossible for an organism to be born with such abilities. For example, a spider web is not just a careless jumble of silk threads; it is so precisely made that scientists can recognize what species of spider made it by the pattern of threads in the web. However, web spinning is not a learned ability. A spider has no opportunity to learn how to spin a web, because it never observes others doing it. Furthermore, spiders do not practice several times before they get a proper, workable web. It is as if a "program" for making a particular web were in the spider's "computer" (figure 18.4).

Might these behavior patterns be the result of natural selection? Many kinds of behaviors are controlled by genes. The "computer" in our example is really the spider's DNA, and the "program" is a specific package of genes. Through the millions of years that spiders have been in existence, natural selection has modified the web-making program to refine the process. Certain genes of the program have undergone mutation, resulting in changes in behavior. Imagine various ancestral spiders, each with a slightly different program. The inherited program that gives individuals the best chance of living long enough to produce a new generation is the program selected for, and the most likely to be passed on to the next generation.

(a)

(b)

**FIGURE 18.4  Complex Instinctive Behavior**
*(a)* The kind of web constructed by a spider is determined by instinctive behavior patterns. *(b)* Instinctive behavior by this masked weaver is responsible for its construction of this complex nest.

**TABLE 18.1** Comparison of Instinct and Learning

| Instinct | Learning |
|---|---|
| The animal is born with the behavior. | The animal is not born with the behavior. |
| Instinctive behavior is genetically determined. | Learned behavior is not genetically determined, but the way in which learning occurs is at least partly hereditary. |
| No experience is required; the behavior is done correctly the first time. | Performance improves with experience; learning the behavior requires practice. |
| The behavior cannot be changed. | The behavior can be changed. |
| Memory is not important. | Memory is important. |
| New instinctive behavior can evolve as gene frequencies change and new species evolve. | The *ability* to learn can evolve as gene frequencies change and new species evolve. However, changes in the actual behaviors learned are not the result of genetic changes. |
| Instinct is more common in simple animals with short lives and little contact with their parents. | Learning is typical of more complex animals with long lives and extensive contact with parents. |
| Instinctive behaviors can be passed from parents to offspring only by genetic means. | Learning allows acquired behaviors to be passed from parents to offspring by cultural means. |

## The Nature of Learned Behavior

The alternative to preprogrammed, instinctive behavior is learned behavior. **Learning** is a change in behavior as a result of experience.

Learning is very significant in long-lived animals that care for their young. Animals that live many years are highly likely to benefit from an ability to recognize previously encountered situations and to modify their behavior accordingly. Furthermore, because the young spend time with their parents, they can imitate their parents and develop behaviors that are appropriate to local conditions. These behaviors take time to develop but have the advantage of adaptability. For learning to become a dominant feature of an animal's life, the animal must also have a memory, which requires a relatively large brain in which to store new information. This is probably why learning is a major part of the lives of only a few kinds of animals, such as the vertebrates. Nearly all human behavior is learned. Even such important behaviors as walking, communicating, feeding oneself and sexual intercourse must be learned. Table 18.1 compares instinctive and learned behaviors.

**FIGURE 18.5  Habituation**
These elephants in a national park are habituated to the presence of vehicles containing tourists.

## 18.4  Kinds of Learning

Scientists who study learning recognize that there are various kinds of learning: *habituation, association, exploratory learning, imprinting,* and *insight.*

### Habituation

**Habituation** is a change in behavior in which an animal ignores an insignificant stimulus after repeated exposure to it. There are many examples of this kind of learning. Typically, wild animals flee from humans. Under many conditions, this is a valuable behavior. Wild animals that frequently encounter humans and never experience negative outcomes may learn to ignore humans. Many wild animals, such as the deer, elk, and bears in parks, have been habituated to the presence of humans and behave in a way that would be totally inappropriate in areas near the park where hunting is allowed (figure 18.5).

**18.3  CONCEPT REVIEW**

5. List two ways in which learned and instinctive behaviors differ.
6. Briefly describe an example of unlearned behavior in a particular animal. Explain why you know it is unlearned.
7. Briefly describe an example of learned behavior in a particular animal. Explain why you know it is learned.

Similarly, loud noises usually startle humans and other animals. However, constant exposure to such sounds cause the individuals to ignore them. As a matter of fact, the sound may become so much a part of the environment that the stopping of the sound causes a response. Habituation is valuable because the animal does not waste time and energy responding to a stimulus that does not have a beneficial or negative impact on the animal. Animals that respond continually to inconsequential stimuli have less time to feed and may miss other, more important stimuli.

## Association

**Association** occurs when an animal makes a connection between a stimulus and an outcome. Associating a particular outcome with a particular stimulus is important to survival, because it allows an animal to avoid danger or take advantage of a beneficial event. If association allows the animal to get more food, avoid predators, or protect its young more effectively, this kind of learning is advantageous to the species. The association of certain shapes, colors, odors, or sounds with danger is especially valuable. There are three common kinds of association: *classical conditioning, operant (instrumental) conditioning,* and *observational learning (imitation).*

### Classical Conditioning
**Classical conditioning** occurs when an involuntary, natural, reflexive response to a natural stimulus is transferred from the natural stimulus to a new stimulus. The response provoked by the new stimulus is called a **conditioned response.** During the period when learning is taking place, the new stimulus is given *before* or *at the same time as* the normal stimulus.

A Russian physiologist, Ivan Pavlov (1849–1936), was investigating the physiology of digestion when he discovered that dogs can transfer a natural response to a new stimulus. He was studying the production of saliva by dogs and knew that a natural stimulus, such as the presence or smell of food, would cause the dogs to start salivating. Then, he rang a bell just before presenting them with food. After a training period, the dogs began to salivate when the bell was rung even though no food was presented. The natural response (salivating) was transferred from the natural stimulus (the smell or taste of food) to a new stimulus (the sound of a bell).

Animals can also be conditioned unintentionally. Many pets anticipate their mealtimes because their owners go through a certain set of behaviors, such as going to a cupboard or opening a can of pet food prior to putting food in a dish. It is doubtful that this kind of learning is common in wild animals, because it is hard to imagine such tightly controlled sets of stimuli in nature.

### Operant (Instrumental) Conditioning
**Operant (instrumental) conditioning** also involves the association of a particular outcome with a specific stimulus, but it differs from classical conditioning in several ways. First, during operant conditioning, the animal learns to repeat acts that bring good results and avoid those that bring bad results.

Second, the animal receives a reward or punishment *after* engaging in a particular behavior. Third, the animal's response is typically a more complicated behavior than a simple reflex. A reward that encourages a behavior is known as positive reinforcement, and a punishment that discourages a behavior is known as negative reinforcement.

The training of many kinds of animals involves this kind of conditioning. If a dog being led on a leash is given the command *heel* and is then vigorously jerked into the correct position, it eventually associates the word *heel* with assuming the correct position slightly behind and to the side of the trainer. This is negative reinforcement, because the animal avoids the unpleasantness of being jerked about if it assumes the correct position. Similarly, petting or giving food to a dog when it has done something correctly will positively reinforce the desired behavior. For example, placing the dog into the sitting position on the command *sit* and rewarding the dog when it performs the behavior on command is positive reinforcement.

Wild animals have many opportunities to learn through positive or negative reinforcement. As animals encounter the same stimulus repeatedly, there is an opportunity to associate the stimulus with a particular outcome. For example, many kinds of birds eat berries and other small fruits. If a distinctly colored berry has a good flavor, birds will return repeatedly to eat them. Pigeons in cities have learned to associate food with people in parks. They can even identify specific individuals who feed them regularly. Their behavior is reinforced by being fed. Many birds in urban areas have associated automobiles with food and are seen picking smashed insects from the grills and bumpers of cars. When a car drives into the area, birds immediately examine it for food.

In some national parks, bears have associated backpacks with food. In some cases, attempts have been made to use negative reinforcement to condition the bears to avoid humans. Usually, the bears are exposed to loud or painful stimuli if they approach backpacks. Some bears that cannot be trained to avoid humans and their "equipment" are killed. Conversely, in areas where bears are hunted, they have generally been conditioned to avoid contact with humans. Similarly, if certain kinds of fruits or insects have unpleasant tastes, animals learn to associate the bad tastes with the colors and shapes of the offending objects and avoid them in the future (figure 18.6). Each species of animal has a distinctive smell. If a deer or rabbit has several bad experiences with a predator that has a particular smell, it can avoid places where the smell of the predator is present.

Animals also engage in trial-and-error learning, which includes some elements of conditioning. When confronted with a problem, they try one option after another until they achieve a positive result. Once they have solved the problem, they can use the same solution repeatedly. For example, if a squirrel has a den in a hollow tree on one side of a stream and is attracted to a source of food on the other side, it may explore several routes to get across the stream. It may jump from a tree on one side of the stream to another on the opposite side. It may run across a log that spans the stream. It may wade a shallow portion of the stream. Once it has found a

**(a) Positive reinforcement**

**(b) Negative reinforcement**

**FIGURE 18.6 Association Learning Positive and Negative Reinforcement**

*(a)* These geese have frequently received food from people who come to the water's edge. Therefore, they have associated people with the food. *(b)* The monarch butterfly this blue jay is eating contains a chemical that makes the blue jay sick. After one or two such experiences, blue jays learn not to eat monarchs.

good pathway, it is likely to use the same pathway repeatedly. Similarly, many hummingbirds visit many different flowers during the course of a day. When they have found a series of nectar-rich flowers, they follow a particular route and visit the same flowers several times a day.

**FIGURE 18.7 Observational Learning**
By following and observing their mother, these cubs will learn how to fish for salmon.

### Observational Learning (Imitation)

**Observational learning (imitation)** is a form of association; it consists of a complex set of associations formed while watching another animal being rewarded or punished after performing a particular behavior. The animal does not receive the reward or punishment itself but, rather, observes the positive outcomes of the other's behavior. Subsequently, the observing animal may show behaviors that receive rewards and avoid behaviors that lead to punishment. It is likely that conditioning is involved in imitation, because an animal that imitates a beneficial behavior is rewarded. Observing a negative outcome to another animal is also beneficial, because it allows the observer to avoid negative consequences. Many kinds of young birds and mammals follow their parents and sample the same kinds of foods their parents eat (figure 18.7). If the foods taste good, they are positively reinforced. They may also observe warning and avoidance behaviors associated with particular predators and mimic these behaviors when the predators are present. For example, crows will mob predators, such as hawks and owls. As young crows observe older ones cawing loudly and chasing an owl, they learn the same behavior. They associate a certain kind of behavior (mobbing) with a certain kind of stimulus (owl or hawk).

## Exploratory Learning

Animals are constantly moving about and sampling their environment. For animals that rely primarily on instinctive behaviors, this movement increases the likelihood that they will find food or other valuable resources but does not result in learning because they do not increase their efficiency at finding resources. Animals that have a significant amount of memory can store information about their surroundings as they wander about. In some cases, the new information may have immediate value—for example, many kinds of birds and mammals remember where certain physical features are located in their environment. They may find a food source during their wanderings and can return to it repeatedly in the future.

When you put up a bird feeder, it does not take very long before many birds are visiting the feeder on a regular basis (figure 18.8). Birds certainly find suitable nesting sites by exploring; then, they store the location in memory. Even invertebrate animals with limited ability to store information engage in exploratory learning. For example, in spring, a queen bumblebee will fly about, examining holes in the ground. Eventually, she will find a hole in which she will lay eggs and begin to raise her first brood of young. Once she has selected a site, she must learn to recognize that spot so that she can return to it each time she leaves to find food, or her young will die.

In other cases, the information learned is not used immediately but might be of use in the future. If an animal has an inventory of its environment, it can call on the inventory to solve problems later in life. Many kinds of animals hide food items when food is plentiful and are able to find them later when food is scarce. Even if they don't remember exactly

**FIGURE 18.8 Exploratory Learning**
As a result of traveling about, these goldfinches located this bird feeder. Once they found this food source, they could return repeatedly to obtain food.

where the food is hidden, if they always hide food in a particular kind of place, they are likely to find it later. (For example, if you needed to drive a car that you have never seen before, you would know that you need to use a key, and you would search in a particular place in the car to insert the key.) Having a general knowledge of its environment is very useful to an animal.

Many kinds of small mammals, such as mice and ground squirrels, avoid predators by scurrying under logs or other objects or into holes in the ground. Experiments with mice and owl predators show that mice that are familiar with their surroundings are more likely to escape predators than are those that are not.

## Imprinting

**Imprinting** is a special kind of irreversible learning in which a very young animal is genetically primed to learn a specific behavior in a very short period during a specific time in its life. The time during which imprinting is possible is known as the **critical period.** This type of learning was originally recognized by Konrad Lorenz (1903–1989) in his experiments with geese and ducks. He determined that, shortly after hatching, goslings and ducklings would follow an object if the object was fairly large, moved, and made noise. The critical period was short—minutes to hours immediately following hatching.

Imprinting is irreversible. Ducklings will follow only the object on which they are originally imprinted. Under normal conditions, the first large, noisy, moving object newly hatched ducklings see is their mother. Imprinting ensures that the immature birds will follow her and may learn appropriate feeding, defensive tactics, and other behaviors by example. Because they are always near their mother, she can also protect them from enemies or bad weather. If animals imprint on the wrong objects, they are not likely to survive (figure 18.9a).

Since these experiments by Lorenz in the early 1930s, scientists have discovered that many young animals can be imprinted on several types of stimuli and that there are responses other than following. The way song sparrows learn their song appears to be a kind of imprinting. The young birds must hear the correct song during a specific part of their youth, or they will never be able to perform the song correctly as adults. This is true even if later in life they are surrounded by other adult song sparrows that are singing the correct song. Furthermore, the period of time when they learn the song is before they begin singing. Recognizing and performing the correct song is important, because it has a particular meaning to other song sparrows. For males, it conveys that a male song sparrow has reserved a space for himself. For females, the male's song is an announcement of the location of a male of the correct species that is a possible mate.

Mother sheep and many other kinds of mammals imprint on the odor of their offspring. They are able to identify their

**(a) Following response**

**(b) Imprinted on odor**

**FIGURE 18.9** **Imprinting**
Imprinting is irreversible learning that occurs during a very specific part of the life of an animal. *(a)* Ducklings exhibit the "following response" to their mother. *(b)* Female sheep imprint on the odor of their lambs and will only let their lambs nurse.

offspring among a group of lambs and allow only their own lambs to suck milk (figure 18.9b). Shepherds have known for centuries that they can sometimes get a mother that has lost her lambs to accept an orphan lamb if they place the skin of the mother's dead lamb over the orphan.

Many fish appear to imprint on odors in the water. Salmon are famous for their ability to return to the freshwater streams where they were hatched. Fish that are raised in artificial hatcheries can be imprinted on minute amounts of specific chemicals and be induced to return to any stream that contains the chemical.

## Insight

**Insight** is learning in which past experiences are reorganized to solve new problems. When faced with a new problem, whether it is a crossword puzzle, a math problem, or any

other, everyday problem, we sort through our past experiences to find those that apply. We may not even realize we are doing it, but we put these past experiences together in a new way that may solve the current problem. Because this process is internal and can be demonstrated only through a response, it is very difficult to understand exactly what goes on when insight occurs. Behavioral scientists have explored this area for many years, but the study of insight is still in its infancy.

Insight is very difficult to study, because it is impossible to know for sure whether a novel solution to a problem is the result of thinking it through or simply an accident. For example, a small group of Japanese macaques (monkeys) was studied on an island. They were fed by simply dumping food, such as sweet potatoes or wheat, onto the beach. Eventually, one of the macaques discovered that she could get the sand off the sweet potato by washing it in a nearby stream. She also discovered that she could sort the wheat from the sand by putting the mixture into water because the wheat would float. Are these examples of insight? We will probably never know, but it is tempting to think so. In addition, in the colony of macaques, the others soon began to display the same behavior, probably imitating the female that had first made the discovery. Table 18.2 summarizes the characteristics and significance of each of the kinds of learning discussed here.

---

**18.4** **CONCEPT REVIEW**

8. Give an example of a conditioned response. Describe one that is not mentioned in this chapter.
9. How are classical conditioning and operant conditioning different?
10. What is imprinting, and what value does it have to an organism?
11. Give an example of habituation in a wild animal.
12. In what kinds of animals is observational learning common?
13. Why is insight difficult to demonstrate in animals?
14. Give an example of the value of exploratory learning.

---

**18.5** **Instinct and Learning in the Same Animal**

It is important to recognize that all animals have both learned and instinctive behaviors, and that a single behavior pattern can include both instinctive and learned elements. For example, biologists have raised young song sparrows in the absence of any adult birds, so that there was no song for the young birds to imitate. These isolated birds sang a series of notes similar to the normal song of the species, but not exactly correct. Birds from the same nest that were raised with their parents developed a song nearly identical to that of their parents. If birdsongs were totally instinctive, there would be no

## TABLE 18.2  Kinds of Learning

| Kind of Learning | Defining Characteristic | Ecological Significance | Example |
|---|---|---|---|
| Habituation | An animal ignores a stimulus to which it is subjected continually. | An animal does not waste time or energy by responding to unimportant stimuli. | Wild animals raised in the presence of humans lose their fear of humans. |
| Association | An animal learns that a particular outcome is connected with a particular stimulus. | An animal can avoid danger or anticipate beneficial events by connecting a particular outcome with a specific stimulus when that stimulus is frequently tied to a particular outcome. | Many mammalian predators associate prey with high-pitched, squealing sounds. |
| Classical conditioning | A new stimulus is presented in combination with a natural stimulus. The animal transfers its response from the natural stimulus to the new stimulus. | Classical conditioning probably does not happen in natural settings. | Pets can anticipate when they will be fed, because their owners' food-preparation behavior occurs shortly before food is presented. |
| Operant (instrumental) conditioning | An animal responds to a new stimulus. It is rewarded or punished following its response. Eventually, the animal associates the reward or punishment with the stimulus and responds appropriately to the stimulus. | Animals can avoid harmful situations that are associated with particular stimuli. They can learn to repeat behaviors that bring benefits. | Animals that associate a shape, color, smell, or sound with a predator can take refuge. Animals that associate a shape, color, smell, or sound with the presence of food will find food more readily. |
| Observational learning (imitation) | An animal imitates the behaviors of others. | The animal can acquire the knowledge of others by watching. This can be more rapid than learning by trial and error. | Young animals run when their mothers do and feed on the food their parents do. |
| Exploratory learning | An animal moves through and observes the elements of its environment. | Information stored in memory may be valuable later. | An awareness of hiding places can allow an animal to escape a predator. |
| Imprinting | An animal learns specific, predetermined activity at a specific time in life. | The animal quickly gains a completely developed behavior that has immediate value to its survival. | Many kinds of newborn animals follow their mothers. |
| Insight | An animal understands the connection between things it had no way of experiencing previously. | Information stored in an animal's memory can be used to solve new problems. | The manufacture and use of tools by humans and some other primates suggests insight is involved. |

difference between these two groups. It appears that all these birds inherited the ability to produce appropriate notes but the refinements of the song's melody came from experience. Therefore, the characteristic song of that species is partly learned behavior (a change in behavior as a result of experience) and partly unlearned (instinctive). This is probably true of the behavior of many organisms; they show complex behaviors that are a combination of instinct and learning. It is important to note that many kinds of birds learn most of their songs with very few innate components. Mockingbirds are very good at imitating the songs of a wide variety of bird species in their region. They even imitate the sounds made by inanimate objects, such as the screeching of a rusty hinge.

This mixture of learned and instinctive behavior is not the same for all species. Many invertebrate animals rely on instinct for most of their behavior patterns, whereas many of the vertebrates (particularly birds and mammals) make use of a great deal of learning (figure 18.10).

When a behavior pattern has both instinctive and learned components, typically the learned components have particular

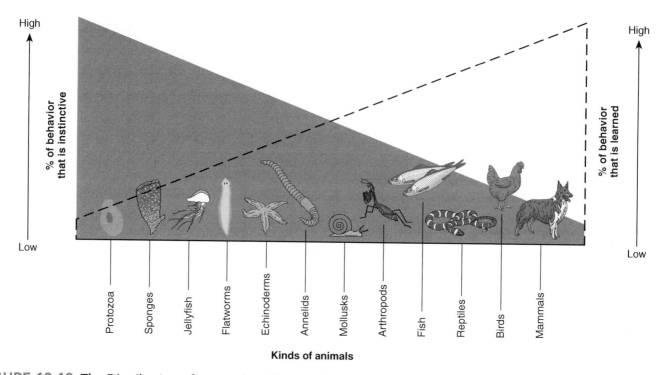

**FIGURE 18.10  The Distribution of Learned and Instinctive Behaviors**
Different groups of animals show different proportions of instinctive and learned behaviors in their behavior patterns.

value for the animal's survival. For example, most of a honeybee's behavior is instinctive; however, when it finds a new food source, it can remember the route between the hive and the food source. A bird's style of nest is instinctive, but the skill with which it builds may improve with experience. Birds' food-searching behavior is probably instinctive, but the ability to modify the behavior to exploit unusual food sources, such as bird feeders, is learned. On the other hand, honeybees cannot be taught to make products other than honey and beeswax, a robin will not build a nest in a birdhouse, and most insect-eating birds will not learn to visit bird feeders.

### 18.5  CONCEPT REVIEW

15. Which one of the following animals—goose, shark, or grasshopper—is likely to have the highest proportion of learning in its behavior? List two reasons for your answer.

### 18.6  Human Behavior

We tend to think of human behavior as different from that of other animals, and it is. However, we are different only in the degree to which we demonstrate different kinds of behavior.

1. *Instinctive behavior* is rare in humans. We certainly have reflexes that cause us to respond appropriately without thinking. Touching a hot object and rapidly pulling your hand away is a good example. Newborns grasp objects

and hang on tightly with both their hands and feet. This kind of grasping behavior in our primitive ancestors would have allowed the child to hang onto its mother's hair as the mother and child traveled from place to place. But do we have more complicated instinctive behaviors? Newborns display several behaviors that can be considered instinctive. If you stroke the side of an infant's face, the child will turn its head toward the side touched and begin sucking movements. This is not a simple reflex behavior but, rather, requires the coordination of several sets of muscles and involves the brain. It is hard to see how this is a learned behavior, because the child does the behavior without prior experience. Therefore, it is probably instinctive. This behavior may be associated with nursing, because carrying the baby on its back would place the child's cheek against the mother's breast. Other mammals, even those whose eyes do not open for several days following birth, are able to find nipples and begin nursing shortly after birth.

2. *Habituation* is a common human experience. We readily ignore sounds that are continuous, such as the sound of air conditioning equipment or the background music in shopping malls. Teachers recognize that it is important to change activities regularly to keep their students' attention.

3. *Association* is extremely common in humans. We associate smells with certain kinds of food, sirens with emergency vehicles, and words with their meanings. Much of the learning we do is by association. We also use positive and negative reinforcement to change behavior. We seek

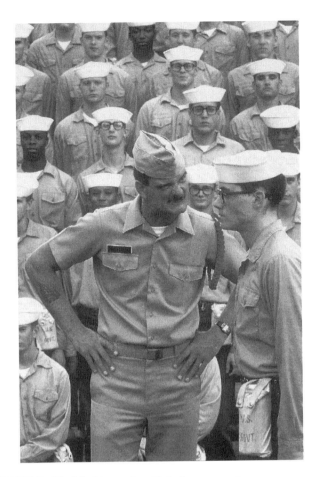

**FIGURE 18.11 Negative Reinforcement**
The reprimand this recruit is receiving is an example of negative reinforcement.

to reward appropriate behavior and punish inappropriate behavior (figure 18.11). We can even experience positive and negative reinforcement without actually engaging in a behavior, because we can visualize its possible consequences. Adults routinely describe consequences for children, so that they will not experience harm: "If you don't study for your biology exam, you'll probably fail it."

4. *Exploratory learning* is extremely common in humans. Children wander about and develop a mental picture of where things are in their environment. Exploration also involves behaviors such as picking things up, tasting things, and making sounds. Even adults explore new ideas and activities.

5. *Imprinting* in humans is more difficult to demonstrate, but there are instances in which imprinting may be taking place. Bonding between mothers and infants is thought to be an important step in the development of the mother-child relationship. Most mothers form very strong emotional attachments to their children; likewise, children are attached to their mothers, sometimes literally, as they seek to maintain physical contact with them. However, it is very difficult to show what is actually happening at this early time in the life of a child.

Language development in children may also be an example of imprinting. All children learn whatever languages are spoken where they grow up. If multiple languages are spoken, they learn them all and they learn them easily. However, adults have more difficulty learning new languages, and many find it impossible to "unlearn" languages they spoke previously, so they speak new languages with an accent. This appears to meet the definition of imprinting. Learning takes place at a specific time in life (critical period), the kind of learning is preprogrammed, and what is learned cannot be unlearned. Recent research using brain-imaging technology shows that those who learn a second language as adults use two different parts of the brain for language—one part for the native language or languages they learned as children and a different part for their second language.

6. *Insight* is what our species prides itself on. We are *thinking* animals. **Thinking** is a mental process that involves memory and an ability to reorganize information. A related aspect of our thinking nature is our concept of self. We can project ourselves into theoretical situations and measure our success by thinking without needing to experience a situation. For example, we can look at the width of a small stream and estimate our ability to jump across it without needing to do the task. We are mentally able to measure our personal abilities against potential tasks and decide if we should attempt them. In the process of thinking, we come up with new solutions to problems. We invent new objects, new languages, new culture, and new challenges to solve. However, how much of what we think is really completely new, and how much is imitation? As mentioned earlier, association is a major core of our behavior, but we also are able to use past experiences, stored in our large brains, to provide clues to solving new problems.

## 18.6 CONCEPT REVIEW

16. Give examples of instinct, habituation, association, and imprinting in humans.

## 18.7 Selected Topics in Behavioral Ecology

The science of animal behavior is a broad one, drawing on information from several fields of study, and it can be used to explore many kinds of questions. Of the examples so far in this chapter, some involved laboratory studies, some were field studies, and some included aspects of both. Often, these studies overlap with the field of psychology. This is particularly true for many of the laboratory studies. The topics that follow concentrate on the significance of behavior from ecological and evolutionary points of view. Now that we have some understanding of how organisms generate behavior, we can look at a variety of behaviors in several kinds of animals and see how they are significant for their ecological niches.

## Communication

**Communication** is the use of signals to convey information from one animal to another. Animals communicate in many ways and for a variety of purposes.

### Sensory Systems

The senses of hearing, sight, taste, smell, and touch are all involved in communication. Regardless of the sensory system used, communication involves the production of signals that can be received and interpreted by others of the same species. For most animals, the communication system is instinctive. However, in humans language is a learned behavior.

1. *Sound* is used by many kinds of animals for communication. Birds, frogs, alligators, crickets, wolves, and many other animals use sound to communicate information.
2. *Sight* is used to communicate in many ways. Colors, lights, body postures, and movements are all involved in communication.
3. *The chemical senses of taste and smell* are important in the communication system of many kinds of animals. **Pheromones** are chemicals produced by animals and released into the environment that trigger behavioral or developmental changes in other animals of the same species. For example, honeybees produce a pheromone that smells like bananas to humans. This pheromone triggers aggressive behavior in the bees of the hive. Many kinds of animals produce odors that communicate information about their reproductive status. Licking or touching with antennae is a way to obtain chemical information about other animals.
4. *Touch* is probably involved in the communication systems of nearly all organisms. If nothing else, the touch of one animal by another announces its presence.

Often, several of the senses are used at the same time in the process of communication. For example, when two dogs meet for the first time, they are likely to communicate by sound, sight, smell, touch, and taste. They bark or growl. They assume special body postures or bare their teeth, which are visual signals. They sniff one another. They may push one another, or one may put a leg over the other's body. Finally, if they are friendly, they are likely to lick one another.

### Purposes of Communication

Animals communicate for several purposes.

1. *Advertising location* is an important function of communication. Information about location can be used to gather individuals together. The calls of frogs in the spring bring animals together at a breeding site (figure 18.12). The calls of crows can call attention to a predator or food source. Many birds use sounds to attract potential mates

**FIGURE 18.12 Communication by Sound**
This tree frog is calling. The inflated vocal sac amplifies the sound he produces.

**FIGURE 18.13 Maintaining Social Order**
Many kinds of body postures and actions are used for communication that reinforces the social status of animals. The wolf on the left is the dominant wolf. It has its ears up, head in an elevated position, and is staring. The wolf on the right is in a submissive position. Its ears are back and its head is lowered. Both wolves are showing aggression with exposed teeth.

to their location. The same sounds can be used to tell others of the same species that a particular piece of the habitat is occupied and to stay away.
2. *Social structure* among animals that live in groups is maintained through communication. The elaborate greeting activities of wolves are an example. There is much posturing, touching, smelling, licking, and vocalization, all of which help reinforce the status of each individual in the group (figure 18.13).
3. *Alarm signals* alert animals to potential danger. The alarm pheromone of honeybees mentioned earlier is an example. The raised tail of a white-tailed deer is a similar signal, but deer also snort and stamp their forefeet when they are disturbed by something in their surroundings.

And many birds and mammals use alarm calls to alert others to the presence of danger.

4. *Reproduction* requires communication. Information about the location and reproductive readiness of individuals is important for reproduction to be successful.

## Reproductive Behavior

The reproductive behavior of many kinds of animals has been studied a great deal. Although each species has its own behaviors, some components of reproductive behavior are common to nearly all animals. In order for an animal to produce offspring that reach adulthood, several events must occur. A suitable mate must be located, mating and fertilization must take place, and the young must be provided for.

### Finding Each Other

To reproduce, an animal must find individuals of the same species that are of the opposite sex. Various species use different methods, but most send signals that can be interpreted by others of the same species. Depending on the species, any of the senses (sound, sight, touch, smell, or taste) may be used to identify the species, sex, and sexual receptiveness of another animal. For instance, different species of frogs produce distinct calls. The call produced by male frogs, which both male and female frogs can hear, results in frogs of both sexes congregating in a limited area. Once they gather in a small pond, it is much easier to have the further communication necessary for mating to take place. Many other animals, including most birds, insects (e.g., crickets), reptiles (e.g., alligators), and some mammals, produce sounds that are important for bringing individuals together for mating.

Chemicals can have the same effect as the sounds made by frogs or birds; they are just a different code system. For example, many kinds of female moths release a chemical into the air. The large, fuzzy antennae of the male moths can receive the chemical in unbelievably tiny amounts. The males fly upwind to the source of the pheromone, which is a female (figure 18.14).

Most mammals rely on odors. Females typically produce distinct odors when they are in breeding condition. When a male happens on such an odor trail, he follows it to the female. Many reptiles also produce distinctive odors that are attractants.

Visual cues are also important for many species. Brightly colored birds, insects, fish, and many other animals use specific patches of color for species identification. Conspicuous movements can also be used to attract the attention of a member of the opposite sex.

The firefly is probably the most familiar organism that uses light signals to bring males and females together. Several species may live in the same area, but each species flashes its own code. The code is based on the length of the flashes, their frequency, and their overall pattern (figure 18.15). There is also a difference between the signals given by males and those given by females. For the most part, males are attracted to

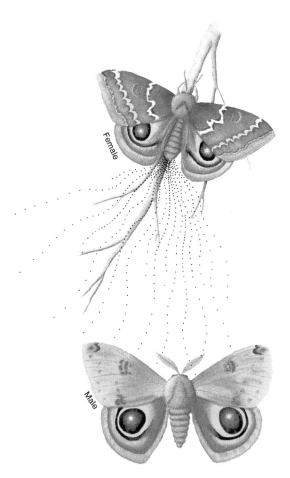

**FIGURE 18.14 Chemical Communication**
The female moth signals her readiness to mate and attracts males by releasing a pheromone, which attracts males from long distances downwind.

and mate with females of their own species. Once male and female animals have attracted one another's attention, the second stage in successful reproduction takes place. However, in one species of firefly, the female has the remarkable ability to signal the correct answering code to species other than her own. After she has mated with a male of her own species, she continues to signal to passing males of other species. She is not hungry for sex, just hungry. The luckless male who responds to her "come-on" will be her dinner.

### Assuring Fertilization

The second important activity in reproduction is fertilizing eggs. Many marine organisms simply release their gametes into the sea simultaneously and allow fertilization and further development to take place without any input from the parents. Sponges, jellyfishes, and many other marine animals fit into this category. Other aquatic animals congregate, so that the chances of fertilization are enhanced by the male and female being near one another as the gametes are shed. This is typical of many fish and some amphibians, such as frogs. Internal fertilization, in which the sperm are introduced into

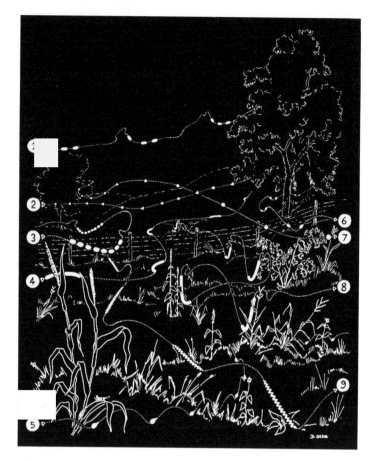

**FIGURE 18.15 Firefly Communication**
The pattern of light flashes, their location, and their duration all
help fireflies identify members of the opposite sex who are of the
appropriate species.
Courtesy of James E. Lloyd.

**FIGURE 18.16 No Parental Care**
The mother of these caterpillars does not provide any care for her
offspring. The only provision she has made for her offspring is to
lay her eggs on a suitable food plant. Most of these larvae will die.

the female's reproductive tract, occurs in most terrestrial
animals. Some spiders and other terrestrial animals produce
packages of sperm, which the female picks up with her reproductive structures. Many of these mating behaviors require
elaborate, species-specific communication prior to the mating act.

## Raising Young
The third element in successful reproduction is providing the
young with the resources they need to live to adulthood.
Many invertebrate animals spend little energy on the care of
the young, leaving them to develop on their own. Usually, the
young become free-living larvae, which eat and grow rapidly.
Many insects lay their eggs on the particular species of plant
that the larva will feed on as it develops. Parasitic species seek
out the required host in which to lay their eggs. The eggs of
others may be placed in spots that provide safety until the
young hatch from the egg (figure 18.16). Turtles, many fish,
and some insects fit into this category. In most of these cases,
however, the female lays large numbers of eggs, and most of
the young die before reaching adulthood. This is an enor-
mously expensive process: The female invests considerable

energy in producing eggs but has a low success rate.
Nevertheless, most species use this strategy, and it has proven
to be very successful.

An alternative strategy to this "wasteful" loss of potential young is to produce fewer young but invest large
amounts of energy in their care. This is not necessarily a
more efficient system, because it still requires large investments by the parents in the production and care of the
young. This strategy is typical of birds and mammals. Parents
build nests, share in the feeding and protection of the young,
and often assist the young in learning appropriate behaviors.
Caring for the young requires many complex behavior
patterns (figure 18.17). Most of the animals that feed and
raise young are able to distinguish their own young from
those of other nearby families and may even kill the young of
another family unit. Elaborate greeting ceremonies are usually performed when animals return to the nest or the den.
Perhaps this has something to do with being able to identify
individual young. Often, this behavior is shared among
adults as well. This is true for many colonial nesting birds,
such as gulls and penguins, and for many carnivorous mammals, such as wolves, dogs, and hyenas.

Care of the young also occurs in several species of fish
and reptiles, such as alligators. Certain kinds of insects, such
as bees, ants, and termites, have elaborate social organizations in which one or a few females (queens) produce large
numbers of young, which are cared for by the queen's sterile
offspring. Most of the offspring are sterile workers, but a few
become new queens.

a)

**FIGURE 18.18 Territorial Behavior**
This clown fish lives with a sea anemone. It will defend its small territory against other clown fish.

(b)

**FIGURE 18.17 Parental Care**
Mammals and birds typically invest a great deal of energy in caring for their young. (a) Zebras protect their young and provide food in the form of milk. (b) Robins and other birds build nests away from most predators, and provide food until the young are able to fend for themselves.

## Territorial Behavior

A **territory** is the space used for food, mating, or other purposes, that an animal defends against others of the same species. **Territorial behaviors** are activities performed to secure and defend a space. These behaviors are widespread in the animal kingdom and can be seen in such diverse groups as insects, spiders, fish, reptiles, birds, and mammals (figure 18.18).

On the other hand, many kinds of animals do not establish fixed territories. For example, most insects, worms, and many other invertebrates do not form territories. In addition, many kinds of migratory animals, such as tuna and wildebeest, do not establish territories or do so only during the breeding season.

### Territorial Behavior Reduces Conflict
When territories are first being established, there is often much conflict among individuals. However, this eventually gives way to their use of signals that define the territory and communicate to others that the territory is occupied. For example, the male redwing blackbird has red shoulder patches, but the female does not. The male will perch on a high spot, flash his red shoulder patches, and sing to other males that venture into his territory. Most other males get the message and leave his territory; those that do not leave are attacked. He will also attack other red objects such as people wearing red caps. Clearly, the spot of red is the characteristic that stimulates the male to defend his territory. Once the initial period of conflict is over, the birds tend to respect one another's boundaries. All that is required is to frequently announce that the territory is still occupied. They do so by singing from a conspicuous position in the territory. After territorial boundaries have been established, little time is required to prevent other males from venturing close. Thus, the animal may spend a great deal of time and energy securing the territory initially, but doesn't need to expend much to maintain it.

### Territorial Behavior Involves Special Signals
For redwing blackbirds, singing in a conspicuous location and flashing red shoulder patches is a signal warning other male blackbirds to stay away. The use of signals replaces the need for fighting. Much of the singing behavior of other species of birds is also territorial. Many carnivorous mammals, such as foxes, weasels, cougars, coyotes, and wolves, use urine

**FIGURE 18.19 Territory Size**
Colonial nesting seabirds typically have very small nest territories. Each territory is just out of pecking range of the neighbors.

**FIGURE 18.20 Advertising One's Territory**
The howling of this wolf has several functions. One is to advertise its presence in its territory.

or other scents to mark the boundaries of their territories. Territorial fish use color patterns and threat postures to defend their territories. Crickets use sound and threat postures. Male bullfrogs engage in shoving matches to displace males that invade their small territories along the shoreline.

### Territorial Behavior Allocates Resources

A territory has great importance, because it reserves exclusive rights to the use of a certain space for an individual or small group of individuals, such as a pair of robins or a wolf pack. These resources may include sources of food or water, nest or den sites, or access to potential mates. Thus, establishing and maintaining a territory is a way to allocate resources among the members of a species. This is also likely to have an effect on population size, because animals that are not able to establish a territory or are forced to accept poor-quality territories will be less likely to survive and reproduce.

### Territory Size

Different species of animals maintain territories for different purposes. Some species maintain small territories of a few square meters, whereas others maintain territories of several square kilometers. For example, many seabirds build nests in colonies. Each pair of birds maintains an extremely small nesting territory of about 1 square meter within the colony. Each territory is just beyond the reach of the bills of the neighbors (figure 18.19). When one bird invades the nesting territory of another, the resident bird uses threat postures to drive the intruder away. If the intruder does not take the hint, it is attacked. Many kinds of fish also maintain small territories.

Many other birds maintain territories for both nesting and gathering food resources. These territories range from a few hundred square meters, such as for robins, to several square kilometers, such as for owls.

Many large carnivores have territories that cover several square kilometers. In such cases, the signals they use must be perceived over great distances or last for a long time. The howling of wolves and the roaring of lions are signals that can be heard over long distances (figure 18.20). The use of scent posts—places where animals urinate, defecate, or deposit other scents, transmits long-lasting signals. The "owner" of the territory does not need to be present all the time to defend its territory, but it must visit these sites regularly to renew the signal.

## Dominance Hierarchy

In social animals, a kind of organization known as a *dominance hierarchy* is often observed. A **dominance hierarchy** is a relatively stable, mutually understood order of priority within the group. One individual in the group dominates all the others. A second-ranking individual dominates all but the highest-ranking individual, and so forth; the lowest-ranking individual must give way to all others within the group. Generally, the initial establishment of a dominance hierarchy involves fighting. The best fighters take the top places. However, once the hierarchy is established, it results in a more stable social unit with little conflict, because the positions of the individuals within the hierarchy are reinforced by various kinds of threats without the need for fighting. This kind of behavior is seen in barnyard chickens and is known as a *pecking order*. Figure 18.21 shows a dominance hierarchy; the lead animal has the highest rank and the last animal has the lowest rank.

A dominance hierarchy gives certain individuals preferential treatment when resources are scarce. The dominant individual has first choice of food, mates, shelter, water, and other resources because of its position. Animals low in the hierarchy may be malnourished or fail to mate in times of scarcity. In many social animals, such as wolves, usually only the dominant male and female reproduce. If the dominant male and female have achieved their status because they have superior characteristics, their favorable genes will probably be passed on to the next generation. Poorly adapted animals

(a)

(b)

**FIGURE 18.21 A Dominance Hierarchy**
Many animals maintain order within their groups by establishing a dominance hierarchy. For example, in a group of cows or sheep walking in single file, the dominant animal is probably at the head of the line and the lowest-ranking individual is at the end.

with low rank may never reproduce. Such a hierarchy frequently results in low-ranking individuals emigrating from the area. Such migrating individuals are often subject to heavy predation.

## Behavioral Adaptations to Seasonal Changes

Most animals live in environments that change from time to time. There may be differences in temperature, rainfall, or availability of food. In some areas, the dry part of the year is the most stressful. In temperate areas, winter reduces many sources of food and forces organisms to adjust. Animals have several behavioral means for coping with these changes.

1. *Metabolic changes* allow many animals to avoid seasonal changes or times of environmental stress. Where drought occurs, many animals become inactive until water becomes available. Frogs, toads, and many insects remain inactive (*estivate*) underground during long periods of drought and emerge to mate when it rains. *Hibernation* in mammals is a response to cold, seasonal temperatures in which the body temperature drops and all the body processes slow down. The slowing of body processes allows an animal to survive on the food it has stored within its body as fat prior to the onset of severe environmental conditions and low food availability. Hibernation is typical of bats, marmots, and some squirrels. Animals such as insects, reptiles, and amphibians are not able to regulate their temperatures the way birds and mammals do. Because their body temperatures drop when the

**FIGURE 18.22 Seasonal Migration**
*(a)* Snow geese and many other birds migrate from their northern breeding grounds to milder climates during the winter. In this way, they are able to use the north for breeding and avoid the harsh winter climate. *(b)* Wildebeest migrate annually to find better grazing.

environmental temperature drops, their activities are slowed during the winter and they require less food.

2. *Migration* allows many animals simply to move to areas that are less stressful. Migratory birds fly hundreds or thousands of kilometers. Many birds that nest in the north avoid winter by migrating to more southerly regions (figure 18.22). Many migratory mammals move from drier areas where food has been depleted to other moister areas where food is more available. In many cases, the migrations are triggered by instinctive responses to environmental clues, and the same migration routes are used generation after generation.

3. *Storing food* during seasons of plenty for periods of scarcity is a common behavior pattern. These behaviors are instinctive and are seen in a variety of animals. Squirrels bury nuts, acorns, and other seeds. (They also

plant trees because they never find all the seeds they bury.) Chickadees stash seeds in cracks and crevices when food is plentiful and spend many hours during the winter exploring similar places for food. Some of the food they find is food they stored. Honeybees store honey, which allows them to live through the winter when nectar is not available. This requires a rather complicated set of behaviors that coordinates the activities of thousands of bees in the hive.

## Navigation and Migration

Because animals move from place to place to meet their needs, it is useful for them to be able to return to a nest, water hole, den, or favorite feeding spot. This requires some memory of their surroundings (a mental map) and a way of determining direction. Direction can be determined by such things as magnetic fields, landmarks, scent trails, or reference to the Sun or stars. If the Sun or stars are used for navigation, some sort of time sense is also needed because these bodies move in the sky. It is valuable to have information about distance as well.

Animals often use the ability to sense changes in time to prepare for seasonal changes. Away from the equator, the length of the day—the **photoperiod**—changes as the seasons change. Many birds prepare for migration and have their migration direction determined by the changing photoperiod. For example, in the fall, many birds instinctively change their behavior, store up fat, and begin to migrate from northern areas to areas closer to the equator. This seasonal migration allows them to avoid the harsh winter conditions signaled by the shortening of days. The return migration in the spring is triggered by the lengthening photoperiod. This migration requires a lot of energy, but it allows many birds to exploit temporary food resources in the north during the summer months.

In honeybees, navigation also involves communication among the various individuals that are foraging for nectar. The bees are able to communicate information about the direction and distance of the nectar source from the hive. If the source of nectar is some distance from the hive, the scout bee performs a "wagging dance" in the hive. The bee walks in a straight line for a short distance, wagging its rear end from side to side. It then circles around back to its starting position and walks the same path as before (figure 18.23). This dance is repeated many times. The direction of the straight-path portion of the dance indicates the direction of the nectar relative to the position of the Sun. For instance, if the bee walks straight upward on a vertical surface in the hive, this tells the other bees to fly directly toward the Sun. If the path is 30° to the left of vertical, the source of the nectar is 30° to the left of the Sun's position.

The duration of the entire dance and the number of waggles in its straight-path portion are positively correlated with the length of time the bee must fly to get to the nectar source. So the dance communicates the duration of flight as well as the direction. Because the recruited bees have picked up the scent of the nectar source from the dancer, they also have information about the kind of flower to visit when they

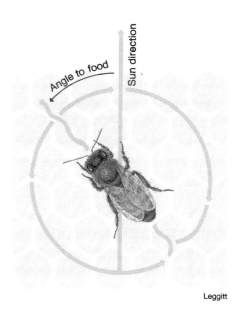

Leggitt

### FIGURE 18.23 Honeybee Communication and Navigation

The direction of the straight, tail-wagging part of the dance of the honeybee indicates the direction to a source of food. The angle that this straight run makes with the vertical is the same angle the bee must fly in relation to the Sun to find the food source. The length of the straight run and the duration of each dance cycle indicate the flying time necessary to reach the food source.

arrive at the correct spot. Because the Sun is not stationary in the sky, the bee must constantly adjust its angle to the Sun. It appears that they do this with an internal clock. Bees that are prevented from going to the source of nectar or from seeing the Sun still fly in the proper direction sometime later, even though the position of the Sun is different.

Like honeybees, some daytime-migrating birds use the Sun to guide them. For nighttime migration, some birds use the stars to help them find their way. In one interesting experiment, warblers, which migrate at night, were placed in a planetarium. The pattern of stars as they appear at any season could be projected onto a large, domed ceiling. In autumn, when these birds would normally migrate southward, the stars of the autumn sky were shown on the ceiling. The birds responded with much fluttering activity at the south side of the cage, as if trying to migrate southward. Then, the experimenters projected the stars of the spring sky, even though it was autumn. The birds then attempted to fly northward, although there was less unity in their efforts to head north; the birds seemed somewhat confused. Nevertheless, the experiment showed that the birds recognized star patterns and were influenced by them.

Some birds navigate by compass direction—that is, they fly as if they had a compass in their heads. They seem to be able to sense magnetic north. Their ability to sense magnetic fields was proven at the U.S. Navy's test facility in Wisconsin. The weak magnetism radiated from this test site has changed the flight patterns of migrating birds, but it is yet to be proved that birds use the Earth's magnetism to guide their migration. Homing pigeons are famous for their ability to find their way home. They make use of a wide variety of clues, but it has been shown that one of the clues they use is magnetism. In one study, birds with tiny magnets glued to the sides of their heads were very poor navigators; others, with nonmagnetic objects attached to the sides of their heads, did not lose their ability to navigate.

## Social Behavior

A **society** is a group of animals of the same species that interact with one another and in which there is a division of labor.

Animal societies exhibit many levels of complexity, and the types of social organization differ from species to species. Some societies show little specialization of individuals other than that determined by sexual differences and differences in physical size and endurance. The African wild dog illustrates such a flexible social organization. These animals are nomadic and hunt in packs. Although an individual wild dog can kill prey about its own size, groups are able to kill fairly large animals if they cooperate in the chase and kill. Young pups are unable to follow the pack. When adults return from a successful hunt, they regurgitate food if the proper begging signal is presented to them (figure 18.24). Therefore, the young and the adults that remained behind to guard the young are fed by the returning hunters. The young are the responsibility of the entire pack, which cooperates in their feeding and protection. While the young are at the den site, the pack must give up its nomadic way of life. Therefore, the young are born during the time of year when prey are most abundant. Only the dominant female in the pack has young each year. If every female had young, the pack couldn't feed them all. At about

2 months of age, the young begin to travel with the pack, and it can return to its nomadic way of life.

Honeybees have a social organization with a high degree of specialization. A hive may contain thousands of individuals, but under normal conditions only the queen bee and the male drones are capable of reproduction. None of the thousands of workers, who are also females, reproduce. The large number of sterile female worker honeybees collect food, defend the hive, and care for the larvae. As they age, the worker honeybees move through a series of tasks over a period of weeks. When they first emerge from their wax cells, they clean the cells. Several days later, their job is to feed the larvae. Next, they build cells. Later, they become guards, challenging all insects that land near the entrance to the hive. Finally, they become foragers, finding and taking back nectar and pollen to the hive to feed the other bees and to be stored for the winter. Foraging is usually the workers' last job before they die. Although this progression of tasks is the normal order, workers can shift from their main task to others if there is a need. Both the tasks performed and the progression of the tasks are instinctively (genetically) determined (figure 18.25).

### Altruism

**Altruism** is behavior in which an individual animal gives up an advantage or puts itself in danger to aids others. In honeybee societies, the workers give up their right to reproduce and help raise their sisters. Is this a kind of self-sacrifice by the workers, or is there another explanation? In general, the workers are the daughters or sisters of the queen and, therefore, share a large number of her genes. This means that they are helping a portion of their genes get to the next generation by helping raise their own sisters, some of whom will become new queens. This argument has been used to partially explain behaviors in societies that might be bad for the individual but advantageous for the society as a whole.

In other cases, it is not clear that there is any advantage to altruistic behavior. Alarm calls may alert others to a danger

**FIGURE 18.24  African Wild Dog Society**
African wild dogs hunt in groups and share food, which they take back to the den. Only the dominant male and female mate and raise offspring.

**FIGURE 18.25  Honeybee Society**
Within the hive, the queen lays eggs, which the sterile workers care for. The workers also clean and repair the hive and forage for food.

**FIGURE 18.26** Tree-Climbing Lions
In most of Africa, lions do not climb trees; however, in some areas, they do. The difference is cultural.

but do not benefit the one who gives the alarm. In fact, the one giving the alarm may call attention to itself.

## Culture

Culture often develops among social organisms. Extensive contact between parents and offspring allows the offspring to learn certain behavior patterns from their parents. Thus, there are behavioral differences among groups within species. This is obvious in humans, who have various languages, patterns of dress, and many other cultural characteristics. But it is even possible to see similar differences in other social animals. Different groups of chimpanzees use different kinds of tools to get food. Some groups of lions climb trees; others do not (figure 18.26).

## Sociobiology

In many ways, honeybee and African wild dog societies are similar. Not all the females reproduce, raising the young is a shared responsibility, and there is some specialization of roles. The analysis and comparison of animal societies has led to the thought that there may be fundamental processes that shape all societies. **Sociobiology** is the systematic study of all forms of social behavior, both human and nonhuman.

How did various types of societies develop? What selective advantage does a member of a social group have? In what ways are social groups better adapted to their environment than nonsocial organisms? How does social organization affect the way populations grow and change? These are difficult questions because, although evolution occurs at the population level, it is individual organisms that are selected. Thus, new ways of looking at evolutionary processes are needed when describing the evolution of social structures.

The ultimate step is to analyze human societies according to sociobiological principles. Such an analysis is difficult and controversial, however, because humans have a much greater ability to modify behavior than do other animals. However, there are some clear parallels between human and nonhuman

social behaviors. This implies that there are certain fundamental similarities among social organisms, regardless of their species. Do we see territorial behavior in humans? "No trespassing" signs and fences between neighboring houses seem to be clear indications of territorial behavior in our social species. Do groups of humans have dominance hierarchies? Most business, government, and social organizations have clear dominance hierarchies, in which those at the top get more resources (money, prestige) than those lower in the organization. Do human societies show division of labor? Our societies clearly benefit from the specialized skills of certain individuals. Do humans treat their own children differently than other children? Studies of child abuse indicate that abuse is more common between stepparents and their nongenetic stepchildren than between parents and their biological children. Although these few examples do not prove that human societies follow certain rules typical of other animal societies, it bears further investigation. Sociobiology will continue to explore the basis of social organization and behavior and will continue to be an interesting and controversial area of study.

## 18.7   CONCEPT REVIEW

17. Describe why communication is important to successful reproduction.
18. Describe two alternative strategies for assuring that some offspring will survive to continue the species.
19. How do territorial behavior and dominance hierarchies provide certain individuals with an advantage?
20. What distinguishes societies from simple aggregations of individuals?
21. How do animals use chemicals, light, and sound to communicate?
22. What is sociobiology?

## Summary

Behavior is how an organism acts, what it does, and how it does it. The kinds of responses organisms make to environmental changes (stimuli) include simple reflexes, very complex instinctive behavior patterns, or learned responses.

From an evolutionary viewpoint, behaviors represent adaptations to the environment. They increase in complexity and variety the more highly specialized and developed the organism is. All organisms have inborn, or instinctive, behavior, but higher animals also have one or more ways of learning. These include habituation, association, exploratory learning, imprinting, and insight. Communication for purposes of courtship and mating is accomplished through sounds, visual displays, touch, and chemicals, such as pheromones. Many animals have behavior patterns that are useful in the care and raising of their young.

Territorial behavior is used to obtain exclusive use of an area and its resources. Both dominance hierarchies and territorial behavior are involved in the allocation of scarce resources. To escape from seasonal stress, some animals estivate or hibernate, others store food, and others migrate. Migration to avoid seasonal extremes requires a timing sense and a way of determining direction. Animals navigate by means of sound, celestial light cues, and magnetic fields.

Societies consist of groups of animals in which individuals specialize and cooperate. Sociobiology attempts to analyze all social behavior in terms of evolutionary principles, ecological principles, and population dynamics.

## Key Terms

*Use the interactive flash cards on the* **Concepts in Biology,** *14/e website to help you learn the meaning of these terms.*

altruism 411
anthropomorphism 393
association 397
behavior 392
classical conditioning 397
communication 404
conditioned response 397
critical period 399
dominance hierarchy 408
habituation 396
imprinting 399
insight 400
instinctive behavior 394
learned behavior 394

learning 396
observational learning
  (imitation) 398
operant (instrumental)
  conditioning 397
pheromones 404
photoperiod 410
response 394
society 411
sociobiology 412
stimulus 394
territorial behaviors 407
territory 407
thinking 403

## Basic Review

1. Instinctive behavior differs from learned behavior in that instinctive behavior
   a. is inherited.
   b. is flexible.
   c. is found only in simple animals.
   d. is less valuable than learned behavior.

2. The thought that your dog is happy to see you is an example of _____.

3. Imprinting is different from other kinds of learning in that imprinting
   a. is of little value to an organism.
   b. is not reversible.
   c. can be changed easily.
   d. can occur at any time during the life of an individual.

4. Learning is a change in behavior as a result of experience. (T/F)

5. All of the following are typical of territorial behavior EXCEPT
   a. territorial behavior reserves resources for particular individuals or groups.
   b. territorial behavior involves the use of signals to denote territorial boundaries.
   c. territorial behavior is found only in higher animals, such as birds and mammals.
   d. territorial behavior reduces conflict after territories are established.

6. Social behavior typically involves individuals assuming specialized roles. (T/F)

7. Most methods of communication used by animals are learned. (T/F)

8. A social system in which each animal has a particular ranking in the group is a(n) _____.

9. Most kinds of animals provide no care for their offspring. (T/F)

10. Which of the following provide navigational clues to migrating animals?
    a. landmarks, such as rivers and shorelines
    b. the magnetic fields of the Earth
    c. the stars
    d. All of the above are correct.

11. Instinctive behaviors are simple. (T/F)

12. Humans do not learn through association. (T/F)

13. The concept of sociobiology
    a. supposes that social behavior has common characteristics in all animals, including humans.
    b. does not apply to humans.
    c. is applied only to birds and mammals.
    d. None of the above is correct.

14. If an organism has instinctive behavior, it probably also has the ability to learn. (T/F)

15. Exploratory learning
    a. provides information that an animal can use later in life.
    b. is evidence of imprinting.
    c. is instinctive.
    d. None of the above is correct.

**Answers**
1. a  2. anthropomorphism  3. b  4. T  5. c  6. T  7. F  8. dominance hierarchy  9. T  10. d  11. F  12. F  13. c  14. T  15. a

## Thinking Critically

**Talk to the Animals**
If you were going to teach an animal to communicate a message new to that animal, what message would you select? How would you teach the animal to communicate the message at the appropriate time?

CHAPTER

19

# The Origin of Life and the Evolution of Cells

## Scientists Create Virus from Simple Chemicals

*Could this be a step toward creating life in a test tube?*

In 2004, scientists used off-the-shelf chemicals to synthesize the poliovirus. They had to use several highly technical procedures, but they were able to create a poliovirus from scratch. The process involved several steps. The genetic code of the poliovirus is in the form of RNA and the sequence of RNA nucleotides is known. The first step involved using this known RNA sequence to assemble a DNA molecule from individual DNA nucleotides. RNA viruses, like the poliovirus, do not make copies of their RNA from RNA but use the enzymes and other structures of the host cell to make a DNA copy of its RNA. The DNA copy is then transcribed in the host cell to produce multiple copies of the poliovirus RNA.

Because polioviruses are normally parasites in human cells, the researchers then placed the newly synthesized RNA into a culture made from human cells. The cells were ground up and large structures, such as nuclei, were removed. However, the ribosomes, enzymes, amino acids, and other materials necessary for protein synthesis were still present. When the newly synthesized viral RNA was placed in this juice, it was able to direct the synthesis of the protein coat that surrounds the RNA of the virus. To show that the poliovirus they produced was functional, they infected mice with the virus and the mice developed the disease.

The scientists started with individual chemical units they obtained from chemical suppliers and produced a functional poliovirus. Although viruses are not cells, they show some similarities to living things and may be similar to some of the earliest forms of life.

- **What conditions on Earth billions of years ago could have allowed for the creation of the first living thing?**

- **What additional steps would be necessary to get *cells* from simple chemicals?**

- **Do you think it is ethical for scientists to go one step further and try to create living cells from scratch?**

## Background Check

**Concepts you should already know to get the most out of this chapter:**
- Carbohydrates, lipids, proteins, and nucleic acids are components of living things (chapter 3)
- Chemical reactions are either exothermic or endothermic (chapter 2)
- Basic cell structure of both prokaryotic and eukaryotic cells (chapter 4)

## 19.1 Early Thoughts About the Origin of Life

For centuries, people have asked the question "How did life originate?" Scientists are still trying to answer that question today. One hypothesis for the origin of life is *spontaneous generation*. **Spontaneous generation** is the concept that living things arise from nonliving material. Aristotle (384–322 B.C.) proposed this concept and it was widely accepted until the seventeenth century. People believed that maggots arose from decaying meat; mice developed from wheat stored in dark, damp places; lice formed from sweat; and frogs originated from damp mud. However, as time passed, people began to question this long-held belief and proposed an alternative idea, called *biogenesis*. **Biogenesis** is the concept that living things develop only from other living things and not from nonliving matter. For several hundred years, proponents of these two alternative concepts about how life originated argued and performed scientific experiments to test their ideas.

In 1668, Francesco Redi, an Italian physician, performed an experiment that challenged the concept of spontaneous generation. He set up a controlled experiment to test the hypothesis that maggots arose spontaneously from rotting meat (figure 19.1). He used two sets of jars that were identical except for one aspect. Both sets of jars contained decaying meat, and both were exposed to the atmosphere. However, one set of jars was covered by gauze while the other was uncovered. Redi observed that flies settled on the meat in the open jars, but the gauze blocked their access to the meat in the covered jars. When maggots appeared on the meat in the uncovered jars but not on the meat in the covered ones, Redi concluded that the maggots arose from the eggs of the flies (biogenesis), not from spontaneous generation in the meat.

However, Redi's experiment did not settle the question. Eighty years later, in 1748, John T. Needham, an English priest, performed an experiment that led him to conclude that spontaneous generation did happen. He placed a solution of boiled mutton broth in containers, which he sealed with corks. Needham reasoned that boiling would kill any organisms in the broth and that the corks would prevent any living thing from entering. Thus, if the broth was found to contain living things, it must be the result of spontaneous generation. Conversely, if no life appeared, the concept of biogenesis would be supported. When, after several days, the broth became cloudy with a large population of microorganisms, he concluded that life in the broth was the result of spontaneous generation.

Experimental group                                   Control group

**FIGURE 19.1 Redi's Experiment**
Francesco Redi performed an experiment in which he prepared two sets of jars that were identical in every way except one. One set of jars had a gauze covering. The uncovered set was the control group; the covered set was the experimental group. Any differences seen between the control and the experimental groups were the result of a single variable—being covered by gauze. In this manner, Redi concluded that the presence of maggots in meat was due to flies laying their eggs on the meat and not spontaneous generation.

A short time later, in 1767, another Italian scientist and Catholic priest, Abb'e Lazzaro Spallanzani, challenged Needham's findings. He thought that Needham's experimental design may have allowed something to enter the broth and devised a slightly different experiment that made certain that nothing accidentally entered the broth. Spallanzani boiled a meat and vegetable broth, placed this mixture in clean glass containers, and sealed the openings by melting the glass over a flame. This would prevent anything from entering the flask. He placed the sealed containers in boiling water to kill any living things that might have been in the broth. As a control, he set up the same conditions but did not seal the necks, allowing air to enter the flasks (figure 19.2). Two days later, the open containers had a large population of microorganisms, but there were none in the sealed containers. He concluded that spontaneous generation did not occur and that something had entered the unsealed flasks from the air that caused the growth in the broth.

Spallanzani's experiment did not completely disprove spontaneous generation to everyone's satisfaction, however. The supporters of spontaneous generation attacked Spallanzani by stating that he excluded air from his sealed flasks, a factor believed necessary for spontaneous generation. Supporters of spontaneous generation also argued that

**FIGURE 19.2 Spallanzani's Experiment**
Spallanzani boiled a meat and vegetable broth and placed this mixture into clean flasks. He sealed one and put it in boiling water. As a control, he subjected another flask to the same conditions, except he left it open. Within 2 days, the open flask had a population of microorganisms. Spallanzani maintained that this demonstrated that spontaneous generation did not occur and that something from the air was responsible for the growth in the broth.

boiling had destroyed a "vital element." In 1774, when Joseph Priestly discovered oxygen, the proponents of spontaneous generation claimed that oxygen was the "vital element" that Spallanzani had excluded from his sealed containers.

In 1861, French chemist Louis Pasteur convinced most scientists that spontaneous generation could not occur. He designed an experiment that would allow air to enter a flask but would prevent tiny living things from entering. He placed a fermentable sugar solution and yeast mixture in a flask that had a long swan neck. The mixture and the flask were boiled for a long time. The flask was left open to allow oxygen, the "vital element," to enter, but no organisms developed in the mixture. Organisms did not enter the part of the flask with the sugar mixture because they settled on the bottom of the curved portion of the neck and could not reach the sugar-water mixture. As a control, he cut off the swan neck (figure 19.3). This allowed microorganisms from the air to fall into the flask, and within 2 days the fermentable solution was supporting a population of microorganisms. In his address to the French Academy, Pasteur stated, "Never will the doctrine of spontaneous generation arise from this mortal blow."

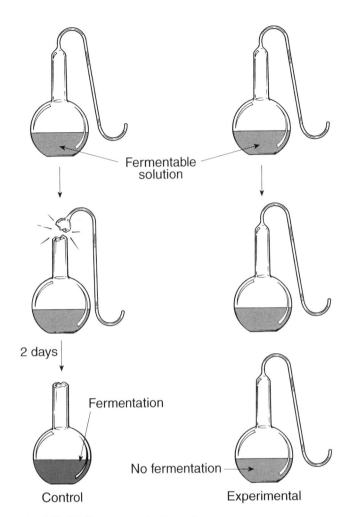

**FIGURE 19.3 Pasteur's Experiment**
Louis Pasteur conducted an experiment designed to test the idea that a "vital element" (oxygen) from the air was necessary to produce life. He boiled a mixture of sugar and yeast in swan-neck flasks that allowed oxygen, but not airborne organisms, to enter them. He left some flasks intact (the experimental group) and broke the neck off others (the control group). Within 2 days, there was growth in the flasks that had their swan necks removed but none in the intact flasks. Thus, Pasteur concluded that it was not oxygen in the air that caused growth in the flasks but that the growth resulted from living things, which entered the flask when the swan neck was broken off. This supported the concept of biogenesis and argued against the concept of spontaneous generation.

## 19.1 CONCEPT REVIEW

1. What is meant by the term *spontaneous generation*?
2. What is meant by the term *biogenesis*?
3. Describe the contribution of each of the following scientists to the biogenesis/spontaneous generation debate: Redi, Needham, Spallanzani, and Pasteur.

## 19.2 Current Thinking About the Origin of Life

Today, it is clear that current living things are the result of biogenesis. New living things come from other living things as a result of either sexual or asexual reproduction. But that does not answer the question of how the *first* living thing developed. Because the evidence is strong that the universe had a time of origin, life must have originated spontaneously from nonliving material at least once. It is clear that we will never really know how the first living thing developed, because we cannot repeat the "original" experiment that led to the first living thing. However, that does not prevent scientists from speculating on the origin of life and evaluating relevant scientific information. There are many different hypotheses that have some supporting evidence.

### An Extraterrestrial Origin for Life on Earth

Early in the 1900s, Swedish scientist Svante Arrhenius popularized the idea of *panspermia*. **Panspermia** is the concept that life arose outside Earth and that living things were transported to Earth to seed the planet with life. However, this idea does not explain *how* life arose originally. It sees Earth as similar to one of Spallanzani's or Pasteur's open flasks. Although Arrhenius's ideas had little scientific support at that time, his basic concept has since been revived and modified as a result of new evidence gained from examinations of meteorites and space explorations.

#### Evidence from Meteorites

Since all life forms that we know about are based on organic molecules, the presence of organic molecules in space and in extraterrestrial objects such as meteorites suggest that life or the conditions necessary for life may have existed in other worlds.

In 1996, a meteorite found in Antarctica generated excitement about the possibility of life on other planets. Its chemical makeup suggested it had been a portion of the planet Mars that had been ejected from that planet as a result of a collision with an asteroid. Analysis of the meteorite showed the presence of complex organic molecules and tiny, microscopic objects that were thought to be ancient microorganisms. While scientists no longer think these objects are microorganisms or were formed by living things, many still think conditions on Mars may have been able to support life in the past.

#### Evidence from Mars and Beyond

In June and July 2003, two spacecrafts were launched by the National Aeronautics and Space Administration (NASA) to explore the surface of Mars. One of the important goals of these missions is to search for signs of present or past life. The robotic rover vehicles from these two spacecrafts have gathered much information about the surface of Mars. One important piece of information is that it is highly likely that in the past, liquid water existed in large enough quantities to form rivers, lakes, and perhaps salty oceans. In 2009 it was discovered that methane (a simple organic molecule) exists on Mars. However, methane can be produced by either geochemical or biological means and at this point, it is not clear which processes are responsible.

In recent years, astronomers have been able to detect the presence of planets in other solar systems. By 2010 over 400 such planets have been identified orbiting stars in other solar systems. Although many are large gas planets like Jupiter, a few appear to be smaller rocky planets like Earth or Mars.

Although none of these discoveries proves that life exists or existed elsewhere in the universe, they keep open the possibility that life may have originated elsewhere and arrived on Earth.

### An Earth Origin for Life on Earth

A popular alternative explanation for the origin of life on Earth focuses on chemical evolution. This hypothesis proposes that chemical reactions between simple, inorganic chemicals produced complex, carbon-containing organic molecules. These organic molecules, in turn, combined to form the first living cell. Furthermore, it is possible to perform experiments that test scientists' hypotheses about these processes. Several pieces of evidence support the idea that life could have arisen on Earth.

1. The temperature range on Earth allows for water to exist as a liquid on its surface. This is important, because water is the most common compound of living things.
2. Analysis of the atmospheres of the other planets in our solar system shows that they all lack oxygen. The oxygen in Earth's current atmosphere is the result of photosynthesis by living organisms. Therefore, before there was life on Earth, the atmosphere probably lacked oxygen.
3. Experiments demonstrate that organic molecules can be generated in an atmosphere that lacks oxygen.
4. Because it is assumed that all of the planets have been cooling off as they age, it is very likely that Earth was much hotter in the past. The large portions of Earth's surface that are of volcanic origin strongly suggest a hotter past.
5. The discovery of specialized Bacteria and Archaea that live in extreme environments of high temperature, high salinity, low pH, or the absence of oxygen suggests that they may have been adapted to life in a world that is very different from today's Earth. These kinds of organisms are found today in unusual locations, such as hot springs and around thermal vents in the ocean floor, and may retain characteristics that were essential to the first organisms formed on the primitive Earth.

### 19.2 CONCEPT REVIEW

4. Provide two kinds of evidence that support the idea that life could have originated on Earth.
5. Provide two kinds of evidence that support the idea that life could have arrived on Earth from space.

## 19.3 The "Big Bang" and the Origin of the Earth

An understanding of how Earth formed and what conditions were like on early Earth will help us think about how life may have originated.

### The "Big Bang"

Astronomers note that the current stars and galaxies are moving apart from one another. This and other evidence has led to the concept that our universe began as a very dense mass of matter that had a great deal of energy. This dense mass of matter exploded in a "big bang" about 13 billion years ago, resulting in the formation of simple atoms, such as hydrogen and helium. When huge numbers of these atoms collected in one place, stars formed. Stars consist primarily of hydrogen and helium atoms. The light from stars is the result of nuclear fusion, in which these atoms combine to form larger atoms. According to this theory, all of the chemical elements were formed as a result of nuclear fusion.

### The Formation of the Planet Earth

Many scientists believe that Earth—along with other planets, meteors, asteroids, and comets—was formed at least 4.6 billion years ago. The *protoplanet nebular model* proposes that the solar system was formed from a large cloud of gases and elements produced by previously existing stars (figure 19.4). The simplest and most abundant gases were hydrogen and helium, but other, heavier elements had been formed by nuclear fusion and were present as well. A gravitational force was created by the collection of particles within this cloud, which caused other particles to be pulled from the outer edges to the center. As the particles collected into larger bodies, gravity increased and more particles were attracted to the bodies. Ultimately, a central body (the Sun) was formed, with several other bodies (planets) moving around it. Like other stars, the Sun consists primarily of hydrogen and helium atoms that are being fused together to form larger atoms, with the release of large amounts of thermonuclear energy.

Thermonuclear reactions also occurred as the particles became concentrated to form Earth. Thus, the early Earth would have been a very hot place. Geologically, this period in the history of Earth is called the "Hadean Eon." The term *Hadean* means "hellish." Although not as hot as the Sun, the material of Earth formed a molten core, which became encased by a thin outer crust as it cooled. (How Science Works 19.1). In Earth's early stages of formation, about 4 billion years ago, there probably was a considerable amount of volcanic activity.

### Conditions on the Early Earth

The high temperature of the early Earth would have prevented an atmosphere from forming, because light gases such as hydrogen and helium would have escaped into space. Over hundreds of millions of years, Earth is thought to have changed slowly. As it cooled, volcanic activity would have released gases, and an atmosphere would have formed. Studies of current volcanoes show that they release water vapor ($H_2O$), carbon dioxide ($CO_2$), carbon monoxide (CO), methane ($CH_4$), nitrogen ($N_2$), ammonia ($NH_3$), hydrochloric acid (HCl), and various sulfur compounds. These gases would have formed a **reducing atmosphere**—an atmosphere that did not contain molecules of oxygen ($O_2$). Any oxygen would have quickly combined with other atoms to form compounds. Further cooling enabled the water vapor in the atmosphere to condense into droplets of rain, which ran over the land and collected to form oceans.

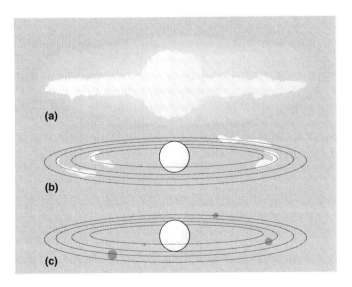

**FIGURE 19.4  The Formation of Our Solar System**
*(a)* As gravity pulled gases and other elements toward the center, the accumulating matter resulted in the formation of the Sun. *(b)* In other regions, smaller gravitational forces caused the formation of the Sun's planets. *(c)* Finally, the solar system was formed.

### 19.3  CONCEPT REVIEW

6. How did the atmosphere, the temperature, and the surface of the newly formed Earth differ from what exists today?
7. What is the approximate age of Earth?

## 19.4 The Chemical Evolution of Life on Earth

When we consider the nature of the simplest forms of life today, we find that living things have certain characteristics. They have an outer membrane, which separates the cell from its surroundings; genetic material in the form of nucleic acids; and many kinds of enzymes, which control the activities of the cell. Therefore, when we speculate about the origin of life

# HOW SCIENCE WORKS 19.1

## The Oldest Rocks on Earth

Determining events that happened in Earth's distant past are difficult to achieve. The early Earth would have been molten and, as it cooled, the outer layer of Earth would have solidified into a thin crust of igneous rock. Earth is not static—it consists of geologic plates that are moving across the surface and in many places are being forced below the surface where they melt to reemerge at some other place. Thus, finding really old rock is rare.

In September 2008, scientists at McGill University in Montreal, Canada, announced they had found, on the eastern shore of Hudson Bay in northern Canada, the oldest Earth rocks yet discovered. To determine the age of the rocks they compared the amounts of specific isotopes of the element neodymium. This analysis led them to conclude that the rocks are about 4.28 billion years old. Since Earth is thought to have originated about 4.57 billion years ago, these rocks would have formed about 290 million years after the origin of Earth. These rocks are presumed to be some of the first formed on Earth as it cooled. The age of these rocks also suggests that Earth cooled faster than previously thought.

As with all new discoveries, other scientists are being cautious about accepting this new information. They would like to see additional evidence to confirm the date.

---

from inorganic material, it seems logical that several events or steps were necessary:

1. Simple organic molecules must first have been formed from inorganic molecules.
2. Simple organic molecules must have combined to form larger organic molecules, such as RNA, proteins, carbohydrates, and lipids.
3. A molecule must have served as genetic material.
4. Genetic material must have become self-replicating.
5. Some molecules must have functioned as enzymes.
6. The molecules serving as genetic material and other large organic molecules must have been collected and segregated from their surroundings by a membrane.
7. The first life-forms would have needed a way to obtain energy from their surroundings in order to maintain their complex structure.

## The Formation of the First Organic Molecules

In the 1920s, a Russian biochemist, Alexander I. Oparin, and a British biologist, J. B. S. Haldane, working independently, proposed that the first organic molecules were formed spontaneously in the reducing atmosphere thought to be present on the early Earth. According to their theory, inorganic molecules in the primitive atmosphere supplied the atoms of carbon, hydrogen, oxygen, and nitrogen needed to build organic molecules. Lightning, heat from volcanoes, and ultraviolet radiation furnished the energy needed for the synthesis of simple organic molecules from inorganic molecules (figure 19.5).

It is important to understand the significance of a reducing atmosphere to this proposed mechanism for the origin of life. The absence of oxygen in the atmosphere would have allowed these organic molecules to remain and combine with one another. This does not happen today because organic molecules are either consumed by organisms or oxidized to simpler inorganic compounds because of the oxygen present in our atmosphere. For example, today many kinds of organic air pollutants (hydrocarbons) eventually oxidize into smaller molecules in the atmosphere. Unfortunately, they participate in the formation of photochemical smog as they are broken down.

Recognize that all the ideas discussed so far in this section cannot be confirmed by direct observation, because we cannot go back in time. However, several assumptions central to this model for the origin of life have been laboratory tested.

In 1953, Stanley L. Miller conducted an experiment to test the idea that organic molecules can be synthesized in a reducing environment. He constructed a simple model of the early Earth's atmosphere (figure 19.6). In a glass apparatus, he placed distilled water to represent the early oceans. Adding hydrogen ($H_2$), methane ($CH_4$), and ammonia ($NH_3$) to the water ($H_2O$) simulated the reducing atmosphere. Electrical sparks provided the energy needed to produce organic compounds. By heating parts of the apparatus and cooling others, he simulated the rains that are thought to have fallen into the early oceans. After a week of operation, he removed some of the water from the apparatus. When he analyzed this water, he found that it contained many simple organic compounds.

- Carbon
- Nitrogen
- Oxygen
- Hydrogen

**FIGURE 19.5  The Formation of Organic Molecules in the Atmosphere**
The environment of the primitive Earth was harsh and lifeless. But many scientists believe that it contained the necessary molecules and sources of energy to fashion the first living cell. The energy furnished by volcanoes, lighting, and ultraviolet light could have broken the bonds in the simple inorganic molecules in the atmosphere. New bonds could have formed as the atoms from the smaller molecules were rearranged and bonded to form simple organic compounds in the atmosphere. Rain and runoff from the land would have carried these chemicals into the oceans, where they could have reacted with each other to form more complex organic molecules.

Water vapor

Electrodes discharge sparks (lightning simulation)

Stopcocks for testing samples

Mixture of gases ("primitive atmosphere")

Condenser

Water

Condensed liquid with complex molecules

Heated water ("ocean")

**FIGURE 19.6  Miller's Apparatus**
Stanley Miller developed this apparatus to demonstrate that the spontaneous formation of organic molecules from inorganic molecules could take place in a reducing atmosphere.

The idea that organic molecules could have formed on Earth is further supported by the discovery of many kinds of organic molecules in interstellar clouds and in the structure of meteorites. These pieces of evidence show that organic molecules form without the presence of living things.

## The Formation of Macromolecules

Although Miller demonstrated the nonbiological synthesis of simple organic molecules, such as amino acids and simple sugars, his results did not account for complex organic molecules, such as proteins and nucleic acids (e.g., DNA).

After simple organic molecules were formed in the atmosphere, they probably would have been washed from the air and carried into the newly formed oceans by rain and runoff from the land. There, the molecules could have reacted with one another to form the more complex molecules of simple sugars, amino acids, and nucleic acids. The accumulation of larger organic molecules is thought to have occurred over half a billion years, resulting in oceans that were a dilute organic soup.

Several ideas have been proposed to explain how simple organic molecules could have been concentrated and caused to combine to form larger macromolecules. One hypothesis suggests that a portion of the early ocean could have been separated from the main ocean by geologic changes. The evaporation of water from this pool could have concentrated the molecules, which might have led to the formation of macromolecules by dehydration synthesis. Second, it has been proposed that freezing may have been the means of concentration. When a mixture of alcohol and water is placed in a freezer, the water freezes solid and the alcohol becomes concentrated into a small portion of liquid. A similar process could have occurred on Earth's early surface, resulting in the concentration of simple organic molecules. In this concentrated solution, dehydration synthesis in a reducing atmosphere could have occurred, resulting in the formation of macromolecules. A third theory proposes that clay particles may have been a factor in concentrating simple organic molecules. Small particles of clay have electrical charges, which can attract and concentrate organic molecules, such as proteins, from a watery solution. Once the molecules became concentrated, it would have been easier for them to interact to form larger macromolecules.

## RNA May Have Been the First Genetic Material

As you know from chapter 8, the genetic system of most current organisms involves the replication of DNA and the distribution of the copied DNA to subsequent cells. Furthermore, DNA is responsible for the manufacture of RNA, which is responsible for the manufacture of proteins. Some of the proteins produced serve as enzymes that control chemical reactions. However, it is difficult to see how this complicated sequence of events, which involves many steps and the assistance of several enzymes, could have been generated spontaneously, so scientists have looked for simpler systems that could have led to the current DNA system.

In recent years many people have come to look at RNA as the prime candidate for the first genetic material. In order to serve as genetic material, a molecule must store information, mutate, and make copies of itself:

1. **RNA can store genetic information.** Scientists involved in studying the structure and function of viruses discovered that many viruses do not contain DNA but, rather, store their genetic information in the structure of RNA. In order for these RNA-viruses to reproduce, they must enter a cell. The cell makes copies of the RNA and the proteins necessary to make more of the virus. Certain plant diseases are caused by pieces of naked RNA known as viroids, which enter cells and cause the cells to make copies of the RNA. In other words, in both of these cases, RNA serves as genetic material.
2. **RNA can mutate.** Scientists who study viral diseases find that it is difficult to develop vaccines for many viral diseases because their genetic material mutates easily. Because of this, researchers have been studying the nature of viral DNA or RNA to see what causes the high rate of mutation.
3. **RNA can make copies of itself.** RNA can be assembled from simpler subunits that could have been present on the early Earth. Scientists have also shown that RNA molecules are able to make copies of themselves without the need for enzymes, and they can do so without being inside cells. Furthermore, some RNA molecules serve as

enzymes for specific reactions. Such molecules are called *ribozymes*. Because RNA is a much simpler molecule than DNA, contains genetic information, can mutate, and can make copies of itself without the aid of enzymes, perhaps it was the first genetic material. Once a primitive life-form had the ability to copy its genetic material, it would be able to reproduce. Reproduction is one of the most fundamental characteristics of living things.

If RNA was the first genetic material, many subsequent changes would have been necessary to get to the kind of genetic system we see in most organisms today:

1. DNA must have replaced RNA as the self-replicating genetic material of the cell.
2. DNA must have become the molecule responsible for making RNA.
3. RNA must have taken over control of protein synthesis.
4. Proteins must have become the catalysts (enzymes) of the cells.
5. Membranes and other cellular structures involved in cell reproduction and protein synthesis would have developed.

Obviously, there is much still to learn about the how this genetic system developed.

## The Development of Membranes

One of the defining features of any living thing is the presence of a membrane surrounding its cells which regulates what enters and leaves them. Consider the formation of bubbles in water. Bubbles are particularly common when organic molecules are present in water. Perhaps the first membranes were formed because of an interaction between water and organic molecules similar to the formation of bubbles. There are several theories about what the first membranes were like. Some suggest that they were made of proteins, others that they were lipids or other organic molecules. Several kinds of experiments have sought to clarify what the first membrane might have been like. Alexander I. Oparin mentioned earlier, speculated that a structure could have formed consisting of a collection of organic macromolecules surrounded by a film of water molecules. This arrangement of water molecules, although not a membrane, could have functioned as a physical barrier between the organic molecules and their surroundings. He called these structures *coacervates*.

Coacervates have been synthesized in the laboratory (figure 19.7). They can selectively absorb molecules from the surrounding water and incorporate them into their structure. Also, the chemicals within coacervates have a specific arrangement—they are not random collections of molecules. Some coacervates contain proteins (enzymes) that direct a specific type of chemical reaction. Because they lack a definite membrane, no one claims that coacervates are alive, but these structures do exhibit some lifelike traits: They can increase in size and can split into smaller particles if the right conditions exist.

**FIGURE 19.7   Coacervates**
One hypothesis proposes that a film of water, which acted as a primitive cell membrane, could have surrounded organic molecules, forming a structure that resembles a living cell. Such a structure can easily be produced in the lab. This view shows one large and several small spherical coacervates.

An alternative hypothesis is that the early, cell-like structure could have consisted of a collection of organic macromolecules with a double-layered outer boundary. These structures have been called *microspheres*. Microspheres can be formed in the laboratory by heating simple, proteinlike compounds in boiling water and slowly cooling them. Some of the protein material produces a double-boundary structure enclosing the microsphere. Although these boundaries do not contain lipids, they exhibit some membranelike characteristics and suggest the structure of a cellular membrane.

Microspheres swell or shrink, depending on the osmotic potential in the surrounding solution. They also display a type of internal movement (streaming) similar to that exhibited by living cells and contain some molecules that function as enzymes. Using ATP as a source of energy, microspheres can direct the formation of polypeptides and nucleic acids. They can absorb material from the surrounding medium and form buds, resulting in a second generation of microspheres.

A third possibility is that a membrane forms as a result of lipid materials interacting with water. Lipids do not dissolve in water and whenever lipids are mixed with water, spherical structures form, as in vinegar and oil salad dressing.

There is no way to know if any of these models represents what really happened in the origin of living things. However, some kind of structure was necessary to separate the complex, organized molecules from the watery environment in which they were dissolved. Once organic molecules were separated from their watery surroundings by a membrane, these structures were similar to primitive cells.

## The Development of Metabolic Pathways

Fossil evidence indicates that there were primitive forms of life on Earth about 3.5 billion years ago. Regardless of how they developed, these first primitive cells would have needed a way to add new organic molecules to their structures as previously existing molecules were lost or destroyed. There are two ways to accomplish this. Heterotrophs capture organic molecules, such as sugars, amino acids, or organic acids, from their surroundings, which they use to make new molecules and provide themselves with energy. Autotrophs use an external energy source, such as sunlight or the energy from inorganic chemical reactions, to combine simple inorganic molecules, such as water and carbon dioxide, to make new organic molecules. These new organic molecules can then be used as building materials for new cells or can be broken down at a later date to provide energy.

### The Heterotroph Hypothesis

Many scientists support the idea that the first living things on Earth were heterotrophs, which lived off organic molecules in the oceans. There is evidence to suggest that a wide variety of compounds were present in the early oceans, some of which could have been used, unchanged, by primitive cells. The earliest cells appear in the fossil record over 2 billion years before there is evidence of oxygen in the atmosphere. Therefore, these early heterotrophs would have been anaerobic organisms. However, as their populations increased through reproduction, they would have begun to consume organic molecules faster than they were being spontaneously produced in the atmosphere.

The compounds that could be used easily by these cells would have been the first to become depleted. However, some of the heterotrophs may have contained a mutated form of nucleic acid, which allowed them to convert previously unusable material into something they could use. Heterotrophic cells with such mutations could have survived, whereas those without such mutations would have become extinct as the compounds they used for food became scarce. It has been suggested that, through a series of mutations in the early heterotrophic cells, a more complex series of biochemical reactions originated within some of the cells. Such cells could use chemical reactions to convert unusable chemicals into usable organic compounds. Thus, additional steps would have been added to their metabolic processes, and new metabolic pathways would have evolved.

### The Autotroph Hypothesis

The heterotroph hypothesis for the origin of living things was the prevailing theory for many years. However, recent discoveries have caused many scientists to consider an alternative—that the first organisms were autotrophs. Several kinds of information support this theory. There is much evidence that Earth was a much hotter place in the past. Today, many different kinds of prokaryotic organisms are autotrophic and live in extremely hostile environments resembling the conditions that may have existed on the early Earth. These organisms are found in hot springs—such as those found in Yellowstone National Park; in Kamchatka, Russia (Siberia); and near thermal vents—areas where hot, mineral-rich water enters seawater from the deep ocean floor. They use energy released from inorganic chemical reactions to synthesize organic molecules from inorganic components. Because of this, they are called *chemoautotrophs*. If their ancient ancestors had similar characteristics, the first organisms may have been autotrophs.

If the first organisms were autotrophs, there would have been competition among different cells for the inorganic raw materials they needed for their metabolism, and there would have been changes in the metabolic processes as mutations occurred. There could have been subsequent evolution of a variety of cells, both autotrophic and heterotrophic, which could have led to the diversity of prokaryotic organisms seen today.

### Summary

As a result of this discussion you should understand that we do not know how life on Earth originated. Scientists look at many kinds of evidence and continue to explore new avenues of research. Thus, currently there are three competing theories of the origin of life on Earth:

1. Life arrived here from an extraterrestrial source.
2. Life originated on Earth as a heterotroph.
3. Life originated on Earth as an autotroph.

Figure 19.8 summarizes the steps that are thought to have been necessary for primitive cells to evolve from inorganic molecules.

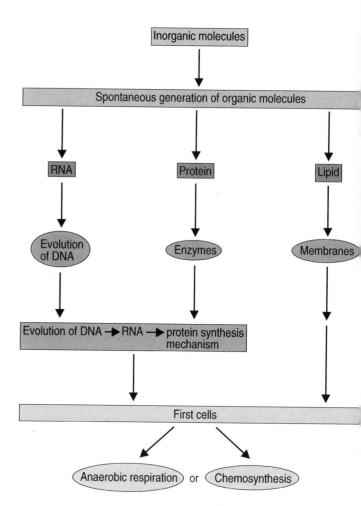

**FIGURE 19.8  The Chemical Evolution of Life**
This diagram summarizes the steps necessary for primitive cells to evolve from inorganic molecules.

## 19.5  Major Evolutionary Changes in Early Cellular Life

Once living things had genetic material that stored information and could mutate, they could evolve. Thus, living things could have proliferated into a variety of kinds that were adapted to specific environmental conditions. Remember that Earth has not been static but has been changing as a result of its cooling, volcanic activity, and encounters with asteroids. In addition, the presence of living organisms has had an impact on the way in which Earth has developed. Regardless of the way in which life originated on Earth, there have been several major events in the subsequent evolution of living things.

### The Development of an Oxidizing Atmosphere

Since its formation, Earth has undergone constant change. In the beginning, it was too hot to support an atmosphere. Later, as it cooled and as gases escaped from volcanoes, a reducing

**19.4  CONCEPT REVIEW**

8. List two kinds of evidence that suggest that organic molecules could have formed before there were living things.
9. List two kinds of evidence that suggest that RNA was the first genetic material.
10. Describe two models that suggest how collections of organic molecules could have been segregated from other molecules.
11. Why must the first organism of Earth have been anaerobic?
12. How do heterotrophs and chemoautotrophs differ in how they obtain organic molecules?

atmosphere (one lacking oxygen) was likely to have been formed. The earliest life-forms would have lived with a reducing atmosphere. However, now we have an **oxidizing atmosphere** which contains 20 percent oxygen. Today, most organisms use the oxygen to extract energy from organic molecules through a process of aerobic respiration. But what caused the atmosphere to change? It is clear that the oxygen in our current atmosphere is the result of the process of photosynthesis.

### The Origin of Photosynthesis

Today, we find that several kinds of Bacteria perform some form of photosynthesis in which sunlight is used to synthesize organic molecules from inorganic molecules. Several of these perform a type of photosynthesis that does not result in the release of oxygen. However, one major group, the cyanobacteria, use a form of photosynthesis that results in the release of oxygen. Therefore, it seems plausible that the first organisms, regardless of whether they were heterotrophs or chemoautotrophs, accumulated many mutations over time, resulting in photosynthetic autotrophs. Because oxygen is released from the most common form of photosynthesis, this would have resulted in the development of an oxidizing atmosphere.

The development of an oxidizing atmosphere created an environment *unsuitable* for the continued spontaneous formation of organic molecules. Organic molecules tend to break down (oxidize) when oxygen is present. The presence of oxygen in the atmosphere would make it impossible for life to spontaneously originate in the manner described earlier in this chapter because an oxidizing atmosphere would not allow the accumulation of organic molecules in the seas. However, once living things existed, new life could be generated through reproduction, and new *kinds* of life could be generated through mutation and evolution. The presence of oxygen in the atmosphere had one other important outcome: It opened the door for the evolution of aerobic organisms.

Geologic evidence suggests that oxygen was present in small amounts in the atmosphere about 2.4 billion years ago. However, oxygen-releasing photosynthesis would have been present some time earlier, since the first oxygen produced would have immediately combined with elements in Earth's crust to form oxides of various kinds. Once oxygen became a significant component of the atmosphere, the oxygen molecules also would have reacted with one another to form ozone ($O_3$). Ozone collected in the upper atmosphere and acted as a screen to prevent most of the ultraviolet light from reaching Earth's surface. The reduction of ultraviolet light diminished the spontaneous formation of complex organic molecules. It also reduced the number of mutations in cells. In an oxidizing atmosphere, it was no longer possible for organic molecules to accumulate over millions of years to be later incorporated into living material.

### The Origin of Aerobic Respiration

The appearance of oxygen in the atmosphere also allowed for the evolution of aerobic respiration. Because the first heterotrophs were, of necessity, anaerobic organisms, they did not derive large amounts of energy from the organic materials

available as food. With the evolution of aerobic heterotrophs, there could be a much more efficient conversion of food into usable energy. Aerobic organisms would have a significant advantage over anaerobic organisms. They could use the newly generated oxygen as a final hydrogen acceptor and, therefore, generate many more adenosine triphosphates (ATPs) from the food molecules they consumed.

## The Establishment of Three Major Domains of Life

Biologists have traditionally divided organisms into kingdoms, based on their structure and function. However, because of their small size, it is very difficult to do this with microscopic organisms. However, advances in the ability to decode the sequence of nucleic acids made it possible to look at the genetic nature of organisms without being confused by their external structures. Biologist Carl Woese studied the sequences of nucleotides in the ribosomal RNA of many kinds of prokaryotic cells commonly known as bacteria and compared their similarities and differences. As a result of his studies and those of many others, a new concept of the relationships between various kinds of organisms has emerged. It is now clear that the bacteria that previously had been considered a group of similar organisms, are actually two very different kinds of organisms: the Bacteria and the Archaea. Furthermore, the Archaea have unique characteristics that differentiate them from other living things and share some characteristics with eukaryotic organisms.

Thus, today biologists recognize three main kinds of living things—Bacteria, Archaea, and Eucarya—that are called domains. The domains Bacteria and Archaea are both prokaryotic organisms that lack a nucleus. The domain Eucarya contains organisms that have eukaryotic cells. Within each domain are several kingdoms. In the domain Eucarya, there are four kingdoms: Animalia, Plantae, Fungi, and Protista. The process of identifying kingdoms within the Bacteria and Archaea is currently ongoing.

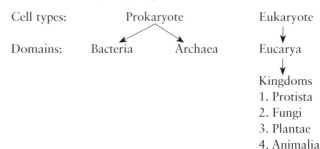

The oldest living things gave rise to two major types of prokaryotic organisms (Bacteria and Archaea). Strangely, the domains Archaea and Eucarya share many characteristics, suggesting that they are more closely related to each other than either is to the domain Bacteria.

It appears that each domain developed specific abilities. The Archaea have very diverse metabolic abilities. Some are chemoautotrophic and use inorganic chemical reactions to generate the energy they need to make organic matter. Often, these reactions result in the production of methane ($CH_4$), and these organisms are known as methanogens. Others use sulfur and produce hydrogen sulfide ($H_2S$). Others use reactions with ammonia, hydrogen gas, or metals to provide themselves with energy. Some do a form of photosynthesis but do not release oxygen. Many of these organisms are found in extreme environments, such as hot springs, or in extremely salty or acidic environments. However, it is becoming clear that they also inhabit soil, the guts of animals, and are particularly abundant in the ocean.

The Bacteria developed many different metabolic abilities. Today, many Bacteria are heterotrophic and use organic molecules as a source of energy. Some of these heterotrophs use anaerobic respiration, whereas others use aerobic respiration. Other Bacteria are autotrophic. Some, such as the cyanobacteria, carry on photosynthesis, whereas others are chemosynthetic and get energy from inorganic chemical reactions similar to Archaea.

The Eucarya are the most familiar and appear to have exploited the metabolic abilities of other organisms by incorporating them into their own structure. Chloroplasts and mitochondria are both bacteria-like structures found inside eukaryotic cells.

## The Origin of Eukaryotic Cells

Biologists generally believe that eukaryotes evolved from prokaryotes. Two major characteristics distinguish eukaryotic cells from prokaryotic cells. Eukaryotic cells have their DNA in a nucleus surrounded by a membrane and have many kinds of membranous organelles. The most widely accepted theory of how eukaryotic cells originated is the *endosymbiotic theory*. The **endosymbiotic theory** states that present-day eukaryotic cells evolved from the uniting of several types of primitive prokaryotic cells. It is thought that some organelles found in eukaryotic cells may have originated as free-living prokaryotes. For example, mitochondria and chloroplasts contain DNA and ribosomes that resemble those of bacteria. They also reproduce on their own and synthesize their own enzymes. Therefore, it has been suggested that mitochondria were originally free-living prokaryotes that carried on aerobic respiration and chloroplasts were free-living photosynthetic prokaryotes. If the combination of two different cells in this symbiotic relationship were mutually beneficial, the relationship could have become permanent (figure 19.9).

Although endosymbiosis explains how many of the membranous organelles may have arisen in eukaryotic cells, the origin of the nucleus is less clear. There are currently two ideas about how the nucleus came to be. One suggests that the nucleus formed in the same way as other organelles. An invading cell with a membrane around it became the nucleus

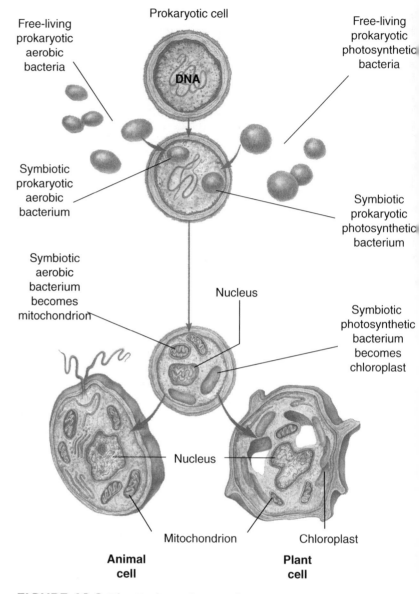

**FIGURE 19.9 The Endosymbiotic Theory**
This theory proposes that some free-living prokaryotic bacteria entered a host cell and a symbiotic relationship developed. Mitochondria appear to have developed from certain aerobic bacteria and chloroplasts from photosynthetic cyanobacteria. Once eukaryotic cells were present, the subsequent evolution of more complex protozoa, algae, fungi, plants, and animals could take place.

when it took over the running of the cell from the cell's original DNA. The alternative hypothesis is that prokaryotic cells developed a nuclear membrane on their own from membranes in the cell. In other words, an increase in the number of membranes within prokaryotic cells could have produced an envelope that enclosed the DNA of the cell.

When the endosymbiotic theory was first suggested, it met with a great deal of criticism. However, continuing research has uncovered several other instances of the probable joining of two different prokaryotic cells to form one. In addition, it appears that endosymbiosis occurred among eukaryotic organisms as well. Several kinds of eukaryotic red and brown algae contain chloroplast-like structures, which appear to have originated as free-living eukaryotic cells.

The endosymbiotic theory is further supported by DNA studies. It is now clear that over their long evolutionary history, the genes within any one species of organism may appear to have arisen from several sources. We know that viruses carry genes from one organism to another, different species of bacteria can exchange genetic information, and parasitic organisms use their DNA to manipulate their hosts. The incorporation of entire cells with their DNA into other cells would also bring about the transfer of genes from one species to another and result in cells that have DNA from a variety of sources. Figure 19.10 summarizes current thinking about how endosymbiosis has been involved in the evolution of various kinds of organisms. Table 19.1 summarizes the major characteristics of these three domains.

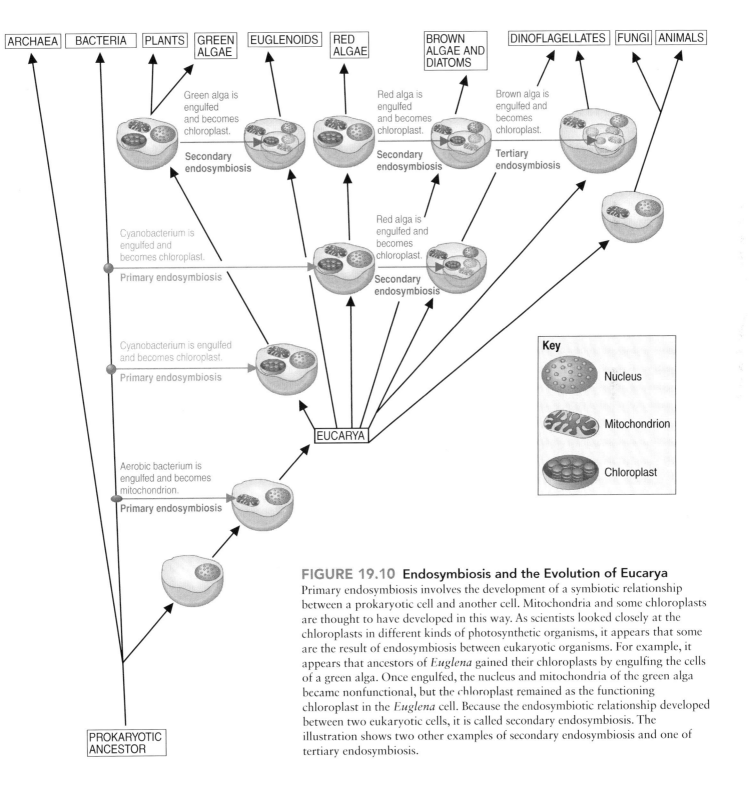

**FIGURE 19.10  Endosymbiosis and the Evolution of Eucarya**
Primary endosymbiosis involves the development of a symbiotic relationship between a prokaryotic cell and another cell. Mitochondria and some chloroplasts are thought to have developed in this way. As scientists looked closely at the chloroplasts in different kinds of photosynthetic organisms, it appears that some are the result of endosymbiosis between eukaryotic organisms. For example, it appears that ancestors of *Euglena* gained their chloroplasts by engulfing the cells of a green alga. Once engulfed, the nucleus and mitochondria of the green alga became nonfunctional, but the chloroplast remained as the functioning chloroplast in the *Euglena* cell. Because the endosymbiotic relationship developed between two eukaryotic cells, it is called secondary endosymbiosis. The illustration shows two other examples of secondary endosymbiosis and one of tertiary endosymbiosis.

**TABLE 19.1    Summary of Characteristics of the Three Major Domains of Life**

DOMAIN

| Characteristics | Bacteria | Archaea | Eucarya |
|---|---|---|---|
| *Cell Structure* | Few membranous structures | Few membranous structures | Many kinds of membranous organelles are present in cells. |
| | There is no nuclear membrane. | There is no nuclear membrane. | A nuclear membrane is present. |
| | | | Chloroplasts are probably derived from cyanobacteria and entered cells through endosymbiosis. |
| | | | Mitochondria are probably derived from certain aerobic bacteria and entered cells through endosymbiosis. |
| *Metabolic Activity* | Some Bacteria are chemoautotrophs that use energy from inorganic chemical reactions to produce organic molecules. | Most Archaea are chemoautotrophs that obtain energy from inorganic reactions to make organic matter. | |
| | Most Bacteria are anaerobic heterotrophs. | There are few heterotrophs. | A few Eucarya use only anaerobic respiration—fungi, some protozoa |
| | | | Many Eucarya have tissues that use anaerobic respiration—muscle |
| | Some Bacteria are aerobic heterotrophs. | | Nearly all Eucarya have mitochondria and use aerobic respiration. |
| | Chlorophyll-based, oxygen-generating photosynthesis was an invention of the cyanobacteria. | | Plants and algae have chloroplasts and use photosynthesis in addition to aerobic respiration. |
| *Evolutionary Status* | Probably related to the first living thing | | |
| | Some live at high temperatures and are probably ancestral to Archaea. | Probably derived from Bacteria | |
| | | Archaea probably have a common ancestor with Eucarya. | Eucarya probably have a common ancestor with Archaea. |
| | | | The common evolutionary theme is the development of complex cells through endosymbiosis of other organisms. |
| *Ecological Status* | Major role as photosynthesizers in aquatic environments | | Major role as photosynthesizers on terrestrial and in aquatic environments |
| | Major category of decomposers | Archaea are typically found in extreme environments. | Dominant form of life today |
| | Many are pathogenic. | None have been identified as pathogenic. | Various eukaryotes fill ecological roles of producer, consumer, pathogen, and decomposers. |

## The Development of Multicellular Organisms

Following the development of eukaryotic cells, there was a long period in which single-celled organisms (both prokaryotic and eukaryotic) were the only ones on Earth. Eventually, organisms developed that consisted of collections of cells. At first, these collections may have been very similar to modern algae in which there was very little specialization of cells (figure 19.11a).

**(a) Zygnema**

**(b) Kelp**

### FIGURE 19.11  Simple and Complex Algae

*(a) Zygnema* is a simple alga, which forms long, hairlike strands a few millimeters long, in which all the cells are identical. *(b)* The kelp, *Macrocystis,* is a much more complex alga, with specialized structures, such as stalks, leaf-like blades, and gas-filled bladders. It can be several meters long.

However, eventually some cells within organisms became specialized for specific tasks, and the many kinds of multicellular algae, fungi, plants, and animals developed (figure 19.11b).

### 19.5   CONCEPT REVIEW

13. What organisms were probably responsible for the development of an oxygen-containing atmosphere?
14. What evidence supports the theory that eukaryotic cells arose from the development of an endosymbiotic relationship between primitive prokaryotic cells?
15. Why is it unlikely that organic molecules would accumulate in the oceans today?
16. List two significant biologically important effects caused by the increase of oxygen in Earth's atmosphere.
17. In what sequence did the following things happen: living cell, oxidizing atmosphere, respiration, photosynthesis, reducing atmosphere, first organic molecule?
18. List two distinguishing characteristics of each of the following domains: Bacteria, Archaean, and Eucarya.

### 19.6   The Geologic Timeline and the Evolution of Life

A geologic timeline shows a chronological history of living organisms based on the fossil record. The largest geologic time units are called *eons.* From earliest to most recent, the geologic eons are the Hadean, Archaean, Proterozoic, and Phanerozoic. The Phanerozoic eon is divided into the *eras* Paleozoic, Mesozoic, and Cenozoic. Each of these eras is subdivided into smaller time units called *periods.* For example, Jurassic is the period of the Mesozoic era that began 208 million years ago (figure 19.12).

Note on the geological time chart in figure 19.12 that its divisions are associated with the major events in the evolutionary history of living things. For example, the Ordovician period is characterized by the appearance of the first primitive land plants and a major extinction of marine animals. The Carboniferous period is characterized by large swamps of primitive plants and cone-bearing plants, and reptiles arose by the end of the period. The Tertiary period is the time when most forms of modern terrestrial organisms arose. In each instance, the dominance of a particular plant or animal group resulted from adaptive radiation. It is also important to note that the ends of many geologic time designations are associated with major extinctions. These extinctions appear to be related to major changes in climate or sea level or asteroid impacts. Following each major extinction, a new group of organisms became dominant.

| Eon | Era | Period | Epoch | Million Years Ago | Major Events and Characteristics |
|---|---|---|---|---|---|
| Phanerozoic | Cenozoic | Quaternary | Holocene (Recent) | 0.01 to present | Dominance of modern humans<br>Much of Earth modified by humans |
| | | | Pleistocene | 1.8–0.01 | Extinction of many large mammals<br>Most recent period of glaciation |
| | | Tertiary | Pliocene | 5–1.8 | Cool, dry period<br>Grasslands and grazers widespread<br>Origin of ancestors of humans |
| | | | Miocene | 23–5 | Warm, moist period<br>Grasslands and grazers common |
| | | | Oligocene | 38–23 | Cool period—tropics diminish<br>Woodlands and grasslands expand |
| | | | Eocene | 54–38 | All modern forms of flowering plants present<br>All major groups of mammals present |
| | | | Paleocene | 65–54 | Warm period<br>Many new kinds of birds and mammals |
| | Mesozoic | Cretaceous | | 144–65 | Meteorite impact causes mass extinction<br>Dinosaurs dominant<br>Many new kinds of flowering plants and insects |
| | | Jurassic | | 208–144 | Giant continent begins to split up<br>Dinosaurs dominant<br>First flowering plants and birds |
| | | Triassic | | 245–208 | Giant continent—warm and dry<br>Explosion in reptile and cone-bearing plant diversity<br>First dinosaurs and first mammals |
| | Paleozoic | Permian | | 286–245 | 90% of species go extinct at end of Permian<br>New giant continent forms<br>Modern levels of oxygen in atmosphere<br>Gymnosperms, insects, amphibians, and reptiles dominant |
| | | Carboniferous | | 360–286 | Gymnosperms and reptiles present by end<br>Vast swamps of primitive plants—formed coal<br>Amphibians and insects common |
| | | Devonian | | 408–360 | Glaciation the probable cause of extinction of many warm-water marine organisms<br>Abundant fish, insects, forests, coral reefs |
| | | Silurian | | 436–408 | Melting of glaciers caused rise in sea level<br>Numerous coral reefs<br>First land animals (arthropods), jawed fish, and vascular plants |
| | | Ordovician | | 505–436 | Sea level drops causing major extinction of marine animals at end of Ordovician<br>Primitive plants present—jawless fish common |
| | | Cambrian | | 540–505 | Major extinction of organisms at end of Cambrian<br>All major phyla of animals present<br>Continent splits into several parts and drift apart |
| Proterozoic | This period of time is also known as the Precambrian | | | 2,500–540 | First multicellular organisms about 1 billion years ago<br>First eukaryotes about 1.8 billion years ago<br>Increasing oxygen in atmosphere<br>Single large continent about 1.1 billion years ago |
| Archaean | | | | 3,800–2,500 | Continents form—no oxygen in atmosphere<br>Fossil prokaryotes—about 3.5 billion years ago |
| Hadean | | | | 4,500–3,800 | Crust of Earth in process of solidifying<br>Origin of the Earth |

## FIGURE 19.12 A Geologic Time Chart

This chart shows the various geologic time designations, their time periods, and the major events and characteristics of each time period.

# An Aquatic Beginning

Recent evidence suggests that the first living thing most likely came into existence in the ocean approximately 3.8 billion years ago during the Archaean eon. Prokaryotic cell types (domain Bacteria) appear about 3.5 billion years ago in the fossil record. One of the common fossils is of stromatolites, photosynthetic Bacteria that grew in layers and formed columns in shallow oceans. Modern-day stromatolites still exist in western Australia (figure 19.13). Also about this time, the Archaea diverged from the Bacteria. For approximately 2 billion years, the only organisms on Earth were Bacteria and Archaea that lived in the ocean. For most of its existence Earth was dominated by prokaryotic organisms. The photosynthetic cyanobacteria are thought to have been responsible for the production of the molecular oxygen ($O_2$) that began to accumulate in the atmosphere about 2.4 billion years ago. The presence of oxygen made conditions favorable for the evolution of other types of cells. The first members of the Domain Eucarya, the eukaryotic organisms, appeared approximately 1.8 billion years ago.

There is fossil evidence of multicellular algae at about 1 billion years ago and multicellular animals at about 0.6 billion years ago. During the Cambrian period of the Paleozoic era, an evolutionary explosion of multicellular animals occurred. Examples of most of the present-day kinds of marine invertebrate animals (e.g., echinoderms, arthropods, mollusks) are found in the fossil record at this time.

Several other "evolutionary explosions," or *adaptive radiations*, followed.

**FIGURE 19.13  Stromatolites in Australia**
This photo of stromatolites was taken at Hamelin Pool, Western Australia, a marine nature preserve. The dome-shaped structures are composed of cyanobacteria and materials they secrete, they grow to 60 centimeters tall. Similar structures are known from the fossil record. Taking samples from fossil stromatolites and cutting them into thin slices produces microscopic images that show some of the world's oldest cells.

# Adaptation to a Terrestrial Existence

For about 90% of Earth's history, life was confined to the sea. Primitive land plants probably arose about 430 million years ago and the first land animals (ancestors to present-day centipedes and millipedes) at about 420 million years ago. In order to live on land, organisms needed several characteristics:

1. an ability to exchange gases (particularly oxygen and carbon dioxide) with the air,
2. a way to prevent dehydration,
3. some sort of skeleton for support, and
4. an ability to reproduce out of water.

Modern plants exchange gases through openings in their leaves. Plants with vascular tissue were able to obtain water from the soil and regulate its loss with a waxy coating on their exterior. The cellulose cell walls allowed for support. The development of pollen grains allowed sperm to be transferred to the egg through the air. More primitive plants like mosses and ferns have swimming sperm and need water for sexual reproduction.

The first major group of land animals to become abundant was the insects, followed by vertebrates. Both groups are very successful but solved the problems associated with life on land in different ways. The marine ancestors of insects already had two characteristics that were valuable. They had an external skeleton and they had legs that they could use to walk on the ocean bottom or on land. In this sense they were somewhat preadapted for life on land. Marine ancestors of insects would have had gills, and some terrestrial arthropods (spiders and land crabs) have modified gills that work on land. However, modern insects have a system of tubes that permeate their bodies and carry oxygen to each cell. A waxy coating on the exterior reduces water loss and internal fertilization and an egg that resists drying allow for reproduction on land.

The conquest of a terrestrial environment by vertebrates appears to have involved several steps. Among the vertebrates, the first land animals most likely evolved from a lobe-finned fish of the Devonian period. They possessed two important adaptations: lungs and paired, lobed fins which had a skeletal structure. The lobe fins allowed the organisms to pull themselves onto land and travel to new water holes during times of drought. They were probably the ancestors of the first amphibians. Early amphibians would have found a variety of unexploited terrestrial niches, resulting in the rapid evolution of new amphibian species and their dominance during the Carboniferous period. Although early amphibians had a skeleton with legs and could breathe air, they probably lost water through their skin and returned to water to reproduce as modern amphibians do.

Reptiles are the first truly terrestrial vertebrate organisms. In addition to having lungs and a supportive skeleton like their amphibian ancestors, they also had a relatively impermeable skin that reduced water loss and two reproductive adaptations that allowed for reproduction on land. One change allowed males to deposit sperm directly within females. Because the sperm could directly enter females and remain in a moist interior, it was no longer necessary for the animals to return to the water to mate, as the amphibians still had to do. However, the developing young still required a moist environment for early growth. A second modification, the amniotic egg, solved this problem. An amniotic egg, such as a chicken egg, protected the developing young from injury and dehydration while allowing for the exchange of gases with the external environment. See chapter 23 for a discussion of the nature of an amniotic egg. With these adaptations, the reptiles were able to outcompete the amphibians in most terrestrial environments. The amphibians that did survive were the ancestors of present-day frogs, toads, and salamanders. With extensive adaptive radiation, the reptiles took to the land, sea, and air. A particularly successful group of reptiles was the dinosaurs, which were the dominant terrestrial vertebrates for more than 100 million years.

Both birds and mammals are descendants of reptiles. They have a relatively impermeable skin and internal fertilization but have diverged somewhat in the way they reproduce. All birds lay eggs and most mammals have a uterus in which the young develop prior to birth. A more complete discussion of terrestrial adaptations can be found in chapter 22 for plants and chapter 23 for animals.

## 19.6 CONCEPT REVIEW

19. Describe four problems organisms had to overcome to be successful on land.
20. For each of the following pairs of terms, select the one that is the earliest in geologic time.
    a. eukaryote—prokaryote
    b. marine—terrestrial
    c. vertebrate—invertebrate
    d. flowering plant—cone-bearing plant
    e. aerobic respiration—photosynthesis
    f. plants—animals

## Summary

Current theories on the origin of life speculate that either the primitive Earth's environment led to the spontaneous organization of organic chemicals into primitive cells or primitive forms of life arrived on Earth from space.

The spontaneous origin of living things on Earth would require:

- the formation of organic molecules,
- a genetic system,
- a membrane that separated the organic molecules from their surroundings, and
- a method of obtaining energy.

There are two different theories about the way in which the first living things would have obtained energy. They were either anaerobic heterotrophs or chemosynthetic autotrophs. Regardless of how the first living things came to be on Earth, these basic units of life were probably similar to present-day prokaryotes. The primitive cells could have changed through time as a result of mutation. A changing environment would have selected for new combinations of characteristics.

The recognition that prokaryotic organisms can be divided into two distinct types has led to the development of the concept that there are three major domains of life: the Bacteria, the Archaea, and the Eucarya. The Bacteria and Archaea are similar in structure, but the Archaea have metabolic processes that are distinctly different from those of the Bacteria.

The origin of the Eucarya is more clear-cut. Similarities between cyanobacteria and chloroplasts and between aerobic bacteria and mitochondria suggest that they have a common origin. The endosymbiotic theory proposes that eukaryotic cells are the result of combining two or more ancient cell ancestors into one cellular unit and that both of the original separate cells benefit from the new combination.

The accumulation of geologic information has allowed several key events in the history of life to be placed in sequence (figure 19.14).

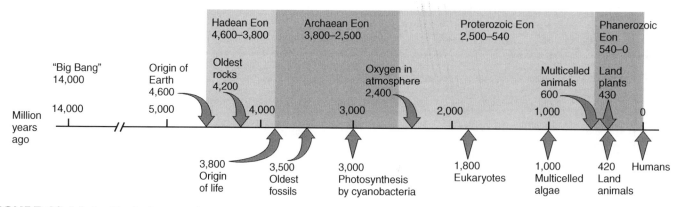

**FIGURE 19.14 An Evolutionary TimeLine**
This chart displays how science sees the order of major, probable events in the origin and evolution of life from the "Big Bang" to the present day.

## Key Terms

*Use the interactive flash cards on the **Concepts in Biology,** 4/e website to help you learn the meaning of these terms.*

biogenesis 416

endosymbiotic theory 426

oxidizing atmosphere 425

panspermia 418

reducing atmosphere 419

spontaneous generation 416

## Basic Review

1. The reproduction of an apple tree by seeds is an example of
    a. spontaneous generation.
    b. biogenesis.
    c. endosymbiosis.
    d. None of the above is correct.
2. The first organisms on Earth would have carried on aerobic respiration. (T/F)
3. Endosymbiosis involves one cell invading and living inside another cell. (T/F)
4. Which of the following suggests that organic molecules may have formed on Earth from inorganic molecules?
    a. Experiments that simulated the early Earth's atmosphere have produced organic molecules.
    b. Organic molecules have been detected in interstellar gases in space.
    c. Meteorites contain organic molecules.
    d. All of the above are correct.
5. Oxygen in today's Earth atmosphere is the result of the process of _____.
6. The oldest fossils of living things are about _____ years old.
    a. 3.5 million
    b. 3.5 billion
    c. 4.5 billion
    d. 4.5 million
7. The first genetic material was probably
    a. protein.
    b. DNA.
    c. RNA.
    d. enzymes.
8. An organism that requires organic molecules for food is known as a(n) _____.
9. A prokaryotic organism that is a chemoautotroph and lives in a very hot environment is probably in the domain
    a. Archaea.
    b. Extremophile.
    c. Eucarya.
    d. Any of these are correct.

10. Which one of the following evolved before all of the others?
    a. terrestrial plants and animals
    b. prokaryotic cells
    c. eukaryotic cells
    d. multicellular organisms
11. The first terrestrial organisms were
    a. vertebrates.
    b. insects.
    c. simple plants.
    d. amphibians.
12. Chloroplasts are probably derived from
    a. Archaea.
    b. cyanobacteria.
    c. Eucarya.
    d. None of the above is correct.
13. Louis Pasteur performed an experiment that showed that _____ did not occur.
14. Stanley Miller performed an experiment that showed that
    a. life originated on Earth.
    b. life originated in outer space.
    c. membranes form around cells.
    d. organic molecules can be formed from inorganic molecules in a rather than a reducing atmosphere.
15. In order to be successful as a terrestrial organism, any organism must be able to retain water. (T/F)

**Answers**
1. b   2. F   3. T   4. d   5. photosynthesis   6. b   7. c   8. heterotroph   9. a   10. b   11. c   12. b   13. spontaneous generation   14. d   15. T

## Thinking Critically

**Thinking Like an Astrobiologist**
Imagine that there is life on another planet in our galaxy (Planet X). Using the following data concerning the nature of this life, determine what additional information is necessary and how you would verify the additional data needed to develop a theory of the origin of life on Planet X.

1. The age of the planet is 5 billion years.
2. Water is present in the atmosphere.
3. The planet is farther from its Sun than our Earth is from our Sun.
4. The molecules of various gases in the atmosphere are constantly being removed.
5. Chemical reactions on this planet occur at approximately half the rate at which they occur on Earth.

CHAPTER

# 20

# The Classification and Evolution of Organisms

## Taxonomists Needed

*Taxonomists are important in medical discoveries.*

M any scientists are concerned that there is a lack of scientific specialists who identify and classify living things. Although this may seem like a skill with limited value to the general public, it is extremely important to medicine and many other aspects of our modern society. Many of our medicines were originally discovered in other living organisms. Digitalis, which is used to stimulate the heart, comes from the foxglove plant. Chemicals in marijuana are used to treat nausea. Many kinds of antibiotics are derived from fungi. Taxol, which is used to treat ovarian and other forms of cancer, is an extract from the bark of the Pacific yew, *Taxus brevifolia* (see photo) which has a rather limited distribution along the northwest coast of the United States.

Proper identification of organisms is important because the beneficial chemical may be found in only one species within a group of closely related species that basically all look alike to the general public. Initially taxol was produced by harvesting Pacific yews and extracting taxol from the bark. This was not sustainable and an alternative source of the drug was sought. It was logical to look at closely related but more common species of yews to see if they also produced the drug. Eventually, it was discovered that the common yew, *Taxus baccata*, which is widely grown throughout the world as an ornamental, produced a compound similar to taxol that could be modified to produce taxol. This discovery greatly increased the source of supply for this valuable drug and protected the Pacific yew from overharvesting. Subsequently, a cell culture method was developed that allows for the production of the drug without harvesting trees.

- Why is precise identification of organisms important?
- What tools do taxonomists use to classify organisms?
- Should governments subsidize the education of taxonomists?

## Background Check

Concepts you should already know to get the most out of this chapter:
- The processes of natural selection and evolution (chapter 13)
- Prokaryotic organisms have a simpler cellular structure than eukaryotic organisms (chapter 4)

## 20.1 The Classification of Organisms

In order to talk about items in our world, we must have names for them. As new items come into being or are discovered, we devise new words to describe them. For example, the words *laptop*, *palm pilot*, and *text message* describe technology that did not exist 30 years ago. Similarly, in the biological world, people have given names to newly discovered organisms so they can communicate to others about the organism.

### The Problem with Common Names

The common names people use vary from culture to culture. For example, *dog* in English is *chien* in French, *perro* in Spanish, and *cane* in Italian. Often different names are used in different regions within a country to identify the same organism. For example, the common garter snake is called a garden snake or gardner snake, depending on where you live (figure 20.1). Actually, there are several species of garter snakes that have been identified as distinct from one another. Thus, common names can be confusing, so scientists sought a more acceptable way to name organisms, one that all scientists would use that would eliminate confusion.

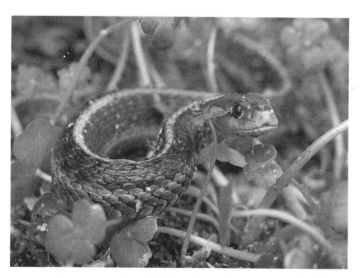

**FIGURE 20.1 Names for the Common Garter Snake**
Depending on where you live, you may call this organism a garter snake, a garden snake, or a gardner snake. These common names can lead to confusion. However, the scientific name (*Thamnophis sirtalis*) is recognized worldwide by the scientific community.

The naming of organisms is a technical process, but it i extremely important. When biologists are describing thei research, common names, such as robin or maple tree, or gar ter snake are not good enough. They must be able to identify the organisms involved accurately, so that everyone who read the report, wherever they live in the world, knows wha organism is being discussed. The scientific identification o organisms involves two different but related activities. One *taxonomy*, is the naming of organisms; the other, *phylogeny* involves showing how organisms are related evolutionarily. I reality, no taxonomic decisions are made without considering the evolutionary history of the organism.

### Taxonomy

**Taxonomy** is the science of naming organisms and grouping them into logical categories. The root of the word *taxonomy* is the Greek word *taxis*, which means arrangement.

During the Middle Ages, Latin was widely used as the scientific language. As new species were identified, they were given Latin names, often using as many as 15 words to describe a single organism. Although using Latin meant that most biologists, regardless of their native language, could understand a species name, it did not completely do away with duplicate names. Because many of the organisms were found over wide geographic areas and communication was slow, there could still be two or more Latin names for a species. To make the situation even more confusing, ordinary people used common local names.

#### The Binomial System of Nomenclature

The modern system of classification began in 1758, when Carolus Linnaeus (1707–1778), a Swedish doctor and botanist, published his tenth edition of *Systema Naturae* (figure 20.2). (Linnaeus's original name was Carl von Linné, which he "latinized" to Carolus Linnaeus.) In the previous editions of his book, Linnaeus had used the polynomial Latin system of classification, which required many words to identify a species. However, in the tenth edition, he introduced the *binomial system of nomenclature*. The **binomial system of nomenclature**, uses only two Latin names—the *genus* name and the *specific epithet* (epithet = descriptive word) for each species of organism. Recall that a species is a population of organisms capable of interbreeding and producing fertile offspring. Individual organisms are members of a species. A **genus** (plural, *genera*) is a group of closely related organisms. The **specific epithet** is a word added to the genus name to identify which one of several species within the genus is being referred to.

**FIGURE 20.2  Carolus Linnaeus (1707–1778)**
Carolus Linnaeus, a Swedish doctor and botanist, originated the modern system of taxonomy known as binomial nomenclature.

This is similar to the naming system we use with people. When we look in the phone book, we look for a last name (surname), the correct general category. Then, we look for a first name (given name) to identify the specific individual we wish to call. The unique name given to an organism is its species name, or scientific name. In order to clearly distinguish the scientific name from other words, binomial names are either *italicized* or <u>underlined</u>. The first letter of the genus name is capitalized. The specific epithet is always written in lowercase. For example, *Thamnophis sirtalis* is the binomial name for the common garter snake.

When biologists adopted Linnaeus's binomial method, they simplified the names of organisms and eliminated the confusion of using common local names. Since the adoption of Linnaeus's system, international rules have been established to assure that an orderly system is maintained. The three primary sets of rules are the International Rules for Botanical Nomenclature, the International Rules for Zoological Nomenclature, and the International Bacteriological Code of Nomenclature. Although approximately 1.5 million species have been named, no one knows how many species of organisms live on Earth, but most biologists estimate that several million are yet to be identified.

## The Organization of Species into Logical Groups

In addition to assigning a specific name to each species, Linnaeus recognized a need for placing organisms into groups. He originally divided all organisms into two broad groups, which he called the plant and animal kingdoms, and subdivided each kingdom into smaller units. Since Linnaeus's initial attempts to place all organisms into categories, there have been many changes. One of the most fundamental is the recent recognition that there are three major categories of organisms, called *domains*.

Recall that a domain is the largest category into which organisms are classified, and there are three domains: Bacteria, Archaea, and Eucarya (figure 20.3). Organisms are separated into these three domains based on the specific structural and biochemical features of their cells. The Bacteria and Archaea are prokaryotic and the Eucarya are eukaryotic.

A **kingdom** is a subdivision of a domain. There are several kingdoms within the Bacteria and Archaea based primarily on differences in the metabolism and genetic composition of

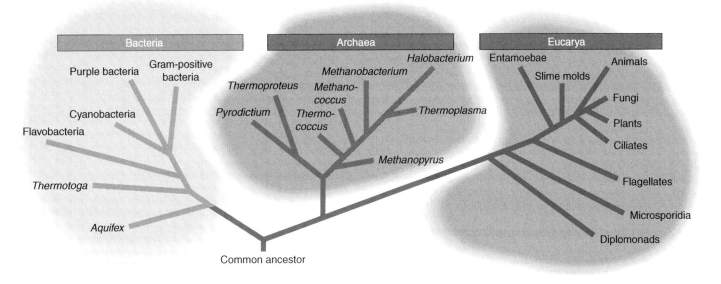

**FIGURE 20.3  The Three Domains of Life**
The three domains of living things are related to one another evolutionarily. The domain Bacteria is the oldest group. The domains Archaea and Eucarya are derived from the Bacteria.

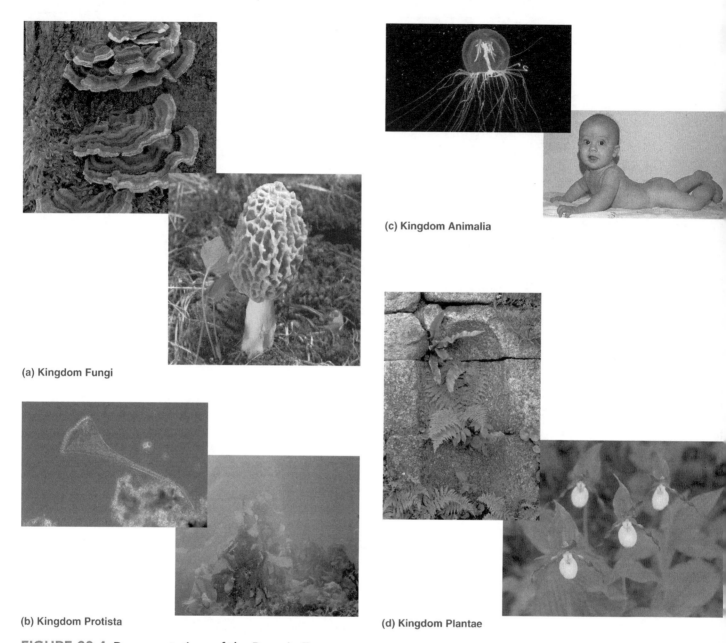

(a) Kingdom Fungi

(b) Kingdom Protista

(c) Kingdom Animalia

(d) Kingdom Plantae

**FIGURE 20.4 Representatives of the Domain Eucarya**
There are four kingdoms in the domain Eucarya, represented by the following organisms: *(a)* The bracket fungus *Trametes versicolor,* and the edible mushroom *Morchella esculenta* of the kingdom Fungi; *(b)* The protozoan *Stentor* and the a large alga of the kingdom Protista; *(c)* The moon jellyfish, and *Homo sapiens* of the kingdom Animalia; and *(d)* Ferns and the orchid *Cypripedium calceolus* of the kingdom Plantae.

the organisms. Within the domain Eucarya, there are four kingdoms: Plantae, Animalia, Fungi, and Protista (protozoa and algae) (figure 20.4).

A **phylum** is a subdivision of a kingdom. However, microbiologists and botanists often use the term *division* rather than *phylum*. All kingdoms have more than one phylum. For example, the kingdom Plantae contains several phyla that include flowering plants, conifer trees, mosses, ferns and several other less-common groups. Organisms are placed in phyla based on careful investigation of the specific nature of their

structure, metabolism, and biochemistry. An attempt is made to identify natural groups, rather than artificial or haphazard arrangements. For example, although nearly all plants are green and carry on photosynthesis, only flowering plants have flowers and produce seeds; conifers lack flowers but have seeds in cones; ferns lack flowers, cones, and seeds; and mosses are so simple in structure that they even lack tissues for transporting water.

A **class** is a subdivision within a phylum. For example, within the phylum Chordata within the kingdom Animalia, there

## TABLE 20.1  Classification of Humans

| Taxonomic Category | Taxonomic Name | Characteristics | Other Representatives |
|---|---|---|---|
| Domain | Eucarya | Cells containing a nucleus and many other kinds of organelles | Plants, animals, fungi, protozoa, algae |
| Kingdom | Animalia | Eukaryotic heterotrophs that are usually motile and have specialized tissues | Sponges, jellyfish, worms, clams, insects, snakes, cats |
| Phylum | Chordata | Animals with a stiffening rod down their back | Fish, amphibians, reptiles, birds, mammals |
| Class | Mammalia | Animals with hair and mammary glands | Platypus, kangaroos, mice, whales, skunks, monkeys |
| Order | Primates | Mammals with a relatively large brain and opposable thumbs | Monkeys, gorillas, chimpanzees, baboons |
| Family | Hominidae | Primates that lack a tail and have upright posture | Humans and extinct relatives in several genera (*Australopithecus, Paranthropus, Homo*) |
| Genus | *Homo* | Hominids with large brains | Humans and extinct relatives such as *Homo erectus* and *Homo neanderthalensis* |
| Species | *Homo sapiens* | Humans | |

are seven classes: mammals, birds, reptiles, amphibians, and three classes of fishes.

An **order** is a category within a class. The order Carnivora is an order of meat-eating animals within the class Mammalia. There are other orders of mammals, including horses and their relatives, cattle and their relatives, rodents, rabbits, bats, seals, whales, humans, and many others.

A **family** is a subdivision of an order that consists of a group of closely related genera, which in turn are composed of groups of closely related species. Felidae is a family composed of various kinds of cats within the order Carnivora. It includes many species in several genera, including the Canada lynx and bobcat (genus *Lynx*); the cougar (genus *Puma*); the leopard, tiger, jaguar, and lion (genus *Panthera*); the house cat (genus *Felis*); and several other genera. Thus, in the present-day science of taxonomy, each organism that has been classified has a unique binomial name. In turn, it is assigned to larger groupings that are thought to have a common evolutionary history. Table 20.1 classifies humans to show how the various categories are used.

## Phylogeny

**Phylogeny** is the science that explores the evolutionary relationships among organisms, seeking to reconstruct evolutionary history. Taxonomists and phylogenists work together, so that the products of their work are compatible. A taxonomic ranking should reflect the phylogenetic (evolutionary) relationships among the organisms being classified. New organisms and new information about organisms are discovered constantly. Therefore, taxonomic and phylogenetic relationships are constantly being revised. During this revision process, scientists often have differences of opinion about the significance of new information.

## The Evidence Used to Establish Phylogenetic Relationships

Phylogenists use several lines of evidence to develop evolutionary histories: fossils, comparative anatomy, life cycle information, and biochemical and molecular evidence.

1. *Fossils* are physical evidence of previously existing life. There are several forms of fossils. Some fossils are preserved whole and relatively undamaged. For example, mammoths and humans have been found frozen in glaciers, and bacteria and insects have been preserved after becoming embedded in plant resins. Other fossils are only parts of once living organisms. The outlines or shapes of extinct plant leaves are often found in coal deposits, and individual animal bones that have been chemically altered over time are often dug up. Animal tracks have also been discovered in the dried mud of ancient riverbeds (figure 20.5).

   When looking for fossils it is important to understand how various kinds of rocks were formed. Sedimentary rocks are formed by the depositing of eroded particles in layers on the bottom of an ocean, lake, or river. Sedimentary rock is not subject to high temperatures and is usually relatively undisturbed. Thus, sedimentary rock can contain evidence of organisms that were covered by sediments and modified into fossils. Igneous rocks are formed from molten material that cooled and solidified. Metamorphic rocks are formed when a previously existing rock (igneous, metamorphic, or sedimentary) is subjected to high temperature and pressure, causing the form of the rock to change. Thus, fossils are not found in igneous or metamorphic rock.

   It is important to understand that some organisms are more easily fossilized than others. Those that have hard parts, such as cell walls, skeletons, and shells, are

**(a)**

**(b)**

**(c)**

**FIGURE 20.5 Fossil Evidence**
A fossil is any evidence of previously existing life. Fossils can be the intact, preserved remains of organisms, as in *(a)* the remains of an ancient fly preserved in amber or the preserved parts of an organism, as in *(b)* the fossilized skeleton and body outline of a bony fish. It is even possible to have evidence of previously existing living things that are not the remains of organisms, as in *(c)* a dinosaur footprint.

more likely to be preserved than are tiny, soft-bodied organisms. Aquatic organisms are more likely to be buried in the sediments at the bottom of the oceans or lakes than are their terrestrial counterparts. Later, when sedimentary rock is pushed up by geologic forces, aquatic fossils are found in layers of sediments on dry land.

Evidence obtained from the discovery and study of fossils allows biologists to place organisms in a time sequence. This can be accomplished by comparing the sedimentary layers in which a fossil is found. As geologic time passes and new layers of sediment are laid down, the older organisms should be in deeper layers, assuming that the sequence of layers has not been disturbed (figure 20.6). In addition, it is possible to age-date certain kinds of rocks by comparing the amounts of certain radioactive isotopes they contain. Older rocks have less of these specific radioactive isotopes than do younger rocks. Fossils associated with rocks of a known age are usually of a similar age to the rocks.

It is also possible to compare subtle changes in particular kinds of fossils over time. For example, in studies of a certain kind of fossil plant, the size of the leaf changed extensively through long geologic periods. If one only looked at the two extremes, they would be classified into different categories. However, because there are fossil links that show intermediate stages between the extremes, scientists conclude that the younger plant is a descendant of the older.

2. *Comparative anatomy studies* of fossils or currently living organisms can be very useful in developing a phylogeny. Because the structures of an organism are determined by its genes, organisms having similar structures are thought to be related. For example, plants can be divided

**FIGURE 20.6 Rock Layers and the Age of Fossils**
Because new layers of sedimentary rock are formed on top of older layers of sedimentary rock, it is possible to determine the relative ages of fossils found in various layers. The layers of rock shown here represent millions of years of formation. The fossils of the lower layers are millions of years older than the fossils in the upper layers.

into several categories: All plants that have flowers are thought to be more closely related to one another than they are to plants that do not have flowers, such as ferns. In the animal kingdom, all organisms that have hair and mammary glands are grouped together, and all animals in the bird category have feathers, wings, and beaks.

3. *Life cycle information* is another line of evidence useful to phylogenists and taxonomists. Many organisms have complex life cycles, which include many completely different stages. After fertilization, some kinds of organisms grow into free-living developmental stages that do not resemble the adults of their species. These are called *larvae* (singular, *larva*). Larval stages often provide clues to the relatedness of organisms. For example, adult barnacles live attached to rocks and other solid marine objects and look like small, hard cones. Their outward appearance does not suggest that they are related to shrimp; however, the larval stages of barnacles and shrimp are very similar. Detailed anatomical studies of mature barnacles confirm that they share many structures with shrimp, such as legs and an external skeleton; their outward appearance tends to be misleading (figure 20.7).

Both birds and reptiles lay eggs with shells. However, reptiles lack feathers and have scales covering their bodies. The fact that these two groups share this fundamental eggshell characteristic implies that they are more closely related to each other than they are to other groups, but they can be divided into two groups based on their anatomical differences.

This kind of evidence also applies to the plant kingdom. Many kinds of plants, such as peas, peanuts, and lima beans, produce large, two-parted seeds in pods. Even though peas grow as vines, lima beans grow as bushes, and peanuts have their seeds underground, all these plants are considered to be related.

4. *Biochemical and molecular studies* are recent additions to the toolbox of phylogenists. Like all aspects of biology, the science of phylogeny is constantly changing as new techniques develop. Recent advances in DNA analysis are being used to determine genetic similarities among species. In the field of ornithology, the study of birds, there are those who believe that storks and flamingos are closely related; others believe that flamingos are more closely related to geese. An analysis of the DNA points to

**(a) Barnacle**

**(c) Nauplius larva of barnacle**

**(b) Shrimp**

**(d) *Nauplius* larva of shrimp**

**FIGURE 20.7  Developmental Stages and Phylogeny**
The adult barnacle *(a)* and shrimp *(b)* are very different from each other, but their early larval stages *(c* and *d)* look very much alike.

a closer evolutionary relationship between flamingos and storks than between flamingos and geese.

There are five kinds of chlorophyll found in algae and plants: chlorophyll *a*, *b*, *c*, *d*, and *e*. Most photosynthetic organisms contain a combination of two of these chlorophyll molecules. Members of the kingdom Plantae have chlorophyll *a* and *b*. The large seaweeds, such as kelp, superficially resemble terrestrial plants, such as trees and shrubs. However, a comparison of their chlorophylls shows that kelp has chlorophyll *a* and *d*. Another group of algae, called the *green algae*, has chlorophyll *a* and *b*. Along with other anatomical and developmental evidence, this biochemical information has helped establish an evolutionary link between the green algae and plants. All the kinds of evidence (fossils, comparative anatomy, life cycle information, and biochemical evidence) have been used to develop phylogenetic relationships and taxonomic categories.

### A Current Phylogenetic Tree

Given all the sources of evidence, biologists have developed a picture of how they think all organisms are related (figure 20.8). The three domains—Bacteria, Archaea, and Eucarya—diverged early in the history of life. Subsequently, many new kinds of organisms have evolved. It is important to remember that this diagram is a work in progress. As new information is discovered, there will be changes in the way biologists think organisms are related (How Science Works 20.1). Biologists have also developed new techniques that help in determining phylogenies. One such technique is cladistics (How Science Works 20.2).

### 20.1    CONCEPT REVIEW

1. List two ways that scientific names are different from common names for organisms.
2. Who designed the present-day system of classification? How does this system differ from the previous system?
3. What are the goals of taxonomy and phylogeny?
4. Name the categories of the classification system.
5. Describe four kinds of evidence scientists use to place organisms into a logical phylogeny.

## 20.2    A Brief Survey of the Domains of Life

Members of the domains Bacteria and Archaea are all tiny, prokaryotic cells that are difficult to distinguish from one another. Because of this, in the past it was assumed that the members of these groups were closely related. However, recent evidence gained from studying DNA and RNA nucleotide sequences and a comparison of the amino acid sequences of proteins indicate that there are major differences between the Bacteria and Archaea. The Bacteria evolved first and then gave rise to the Archaea; finally, the Eucarya evolved.

### The Domain Bacteria

The Bacteria are small, prokaryotic, single-celled organisms ranging in size from 1 to 10 micrometers (μm). Their cell walls contain a complex organic molecule known as peptidoglycan. Peptidoglycan is found only in the Bacteria and is composed of two kinds of sugars linked together by amino acids. One of these sugars, muramic acid, is found only in the cell walls of Bacteria. The most common shapes of the cells are spheres, rods, and spirals.

Because they are prokaryotic, Bacteria have no nucleus. Their genetic material consists of a single loop of DNA. When Bacteria reproduce, the loop of DNA replicates to form two loops, and the cell divides into two, each having one copy of the DNA loop. This method of reproduction is known as binary fission (figure 20.9). Since the two cells have the same DNA, this is a form of asexual reproduction. Many Bacteria are also known to show a kind of sexual reproduction, in which two bacteria exchange pieces of DNA. Although no additional individuals were formed, both individuals have new combinations of genes.

Some Bacteria move by secreting a slime that glides over their surface, causing them to move through the environment.

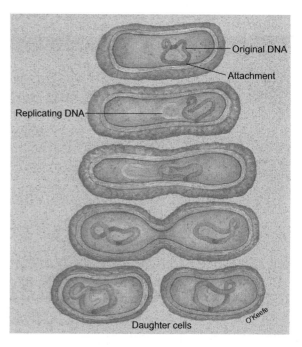

**FIGURE 20.9 Asexual Reproduction (Binary Fission) in Bacteria and Archaea**
When Bacteria and Archaea reproduce, the loop of DNA replicates and the cell divides, with each cell having one of the two loops of DNA. This form of asexual reproduction is known as binary fission.

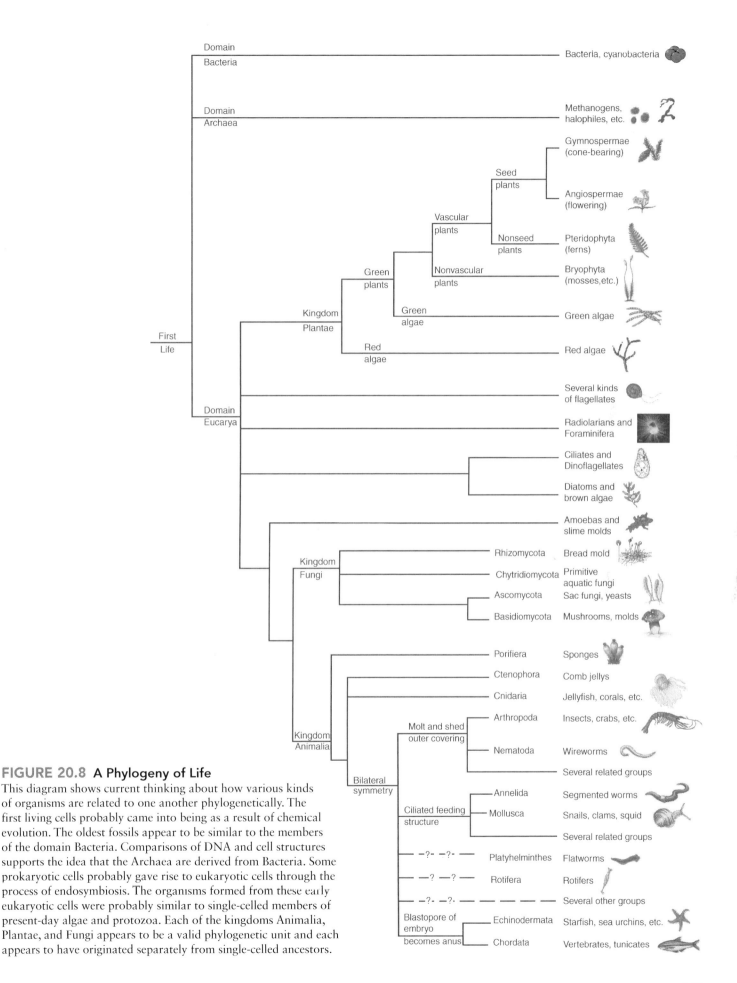

**FIGURE 20.8** **A Phylogeny of Life**

This diagram shows current thinking about how various kinds of organisms are related to one another phylogenetically. The first living cells probably came into being as a result of chemical evolution. The oldest fossils appear to be similar to the members of the domain Bacteria. Comparisons of DNA and cell structures supports the idea that the Archaea are derived from Bacteria. Some prokaryotic cells probably gave rise to eukaryotic cells through the process of endosymbiosis. The organisms formed from these early eukaryotic cells were probably similar to single-celled members of present-day algae and protozoa. Each of the kingdoms Animalia, Plantae, and Fungi appears to be a valid phylogenetic unit and each appears to have originated separately from single-celled ancestors.

# HOW SCIENCE WORKS 20.1

## New Information Causes Changes in Taxonomy and Phylogeny

The taxonomy and phylogeny of groups of organisms are constantly changing as new information and new tools become available. In his initial classification of organisms, Linnaeus identified two kingdoms—the plant and animal kingdoms. Plants included all kinds of organisms that were not motile and had cell walls. Animals lacked cell walls and moved. Several major scientific and technical developments over the intervening years allowed for a better understanding of the nature of organisms and how they are related. These developments led to changes in taxonomy:

• Advances in the development of microscopes that could look at the smallest of cells made it clear that some of the smallest organisms previously called bacteria and classified as plants, lacked a nucleus. They were, therefore, reclassified into a separate kingdom, Monera.
• A better understanding of the chemical nature of cell walls led to the discovery that a major group of "plants" had cell walls containing chitin and did not have cellulose. Those with chitin in their cell walls were reclassified into the kingdom Fungi.
• Based on the cellular specialization of organisms, multicellular plants and animals that have specialized groups of cells were separated from protozoa and algae that do not have specialized groups of cells. The

protozoa and algae were placed in a separate kingdom, Protista.
• Studies of the structure of DNA and ribosomes led to the development of an entirely new way of looking at living things. A new category—domain—was established above the kingdom level. The prokaryotic organisms, "bacteria," which had formerly been in the kingdom Monera, were divided into two major groups, the domains Bacteria and Archaea, and all the remaining kinds of living things that were eukaryotic were placed in the domain Eucarya.
• Although most people agree that kingdoms Plantae and Animalia are valid collections of organisms with a common ancestry, most people recognize that the kingdom Protista is not a valid phylogenetic unit. In the future, this group of organisms will be divided into distinct categories that will be more phylogenetically meaningful.
• The kingdom Fungi will probably undergo some revision. Some organisms are likely to be moved to other kingdoms or placed in an entirely new kingdom.
• The recognition that endosymbiosis occurs and that many organisms of widely different evolutionary backgrounds have shared genes has further complicated the science of taxonomy.
• Stay tuned.

## Changes in Taxonomy with Increase in Knowledge

| Introduced in 1735 | | Introduced in 1969 | | Introduced in 1990 | | Future Developments |
|---|---|---|---|---|---|---|
| **Two Kingdoms** | | **Five Kingdoms** | | **Three Domains** | | |
| **Kingdom** | **Kinds of Organisms** | **Kingdom** | **Kinds of Organisms** | *Domain/* **Kingdom** | **Kinds of Organisms** | |
| **Plantae** | Bacteria | **Monera** | Bacteria | *Bacteria* | Bacteria | Kingdoms currently being developed |
| | Archaea | | | | Archaea | *Archaea* | Archaea | Kingdoms currently being developed |
| | | | | *Eucarya* | | |
| | Plants | **Plantae** | Plants | **Plantae** | Plants | Probably a valid group—little change |
| | Fungi | **Fungi** | Fungi | **Fungi** | Fungi | Some reclassification to other kingdoms |
| | Algae | **Protista** | Algae Protozoa | **Protista** | Algae Protozoa | Will be reorganized into several kingdoms |
| **Animalia** | Protozoa Animals | **Animalia** | Animals | **Animalia** | Animals | Probably a valid group—little change |

# HOW SCIENCE WORKS 20.2

## Cladistics: A Tool for Taxonomy and Phylogeny

Classification, or taxonomy, is one part of the much larger field of phylogenetic systematics. Classification involves placing organisms into logical categories and assigning names to those categories. Phylogeny, or *systematics*, is an effort to understand the evolutionary relationships of living things in order to interpret the way in which life has diversified and changed over billions of years of biological history. Phylogeny attempts to understand how organisms have changed over time. *Cladistics* (*klados* = branch) is a method biologists use to evaluate the degree of relatedness among organisms within a group, based on how similar they are genetically. The basic assumptions behind cladistics are that

1. Groups of organisms are related by descent from a common ancestor.
2. The relationships among groups can be represented by a branching pattern, with new evolutionary groups arising from a common ancestor.
3. Changes in characteristics occur in organisms over time.

Several steps are involved in applying cladistics to a particular group of organisms. First, you must select characteristics that vary and collect information on the characteristics displayed by the group of organisms you are studying. The second step is to determine which expression of a characteristic is ancestral and which is more recently derived. Usually, this involves comparing the group in which you are interested with an *outgroup* that is related to, but not a part of, the group you are studying. The characteristics of the outgroup are then considered to be ancestral. Finally, you must compare the characteristics displayed by the group you are studying and construct a diagram known as a *cladogram*. For example, if you were interested in studying how various kinds of terrestrial vertebrates are related, you could look at the following characteristics:

| Characteristic Organism | Lungs Present | Skin Dry | Warm- Blooded | Hair Present |
|---|---|---|---|---|
| Shark | 0 | 0 | 0 | 0 |
| Frog | + | 0 | 0 | 0 |
| Lizard | + | + | 0 | 0 |
| Crow | + | + | + | 0 |
| Bat | + | + | + | + |

In this example, the shark is the outgroup, and the ancestral conditions are lungs absent, skin not dry, cold-blooded, and hair absent. Using this information, you could construct the following cladogram.

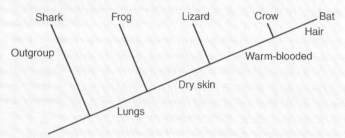

All of the organisms, except sharks, have lungs. Lizards, crows, and bats have dry skin, as well as lungs and so on. Crows and bats share the following characteristics; they have lungs, they have dry skin, and they are warm-blooded. Because they share more characteristics with each other than with the other groups, they are considered to be more closely related.

It is important to recognize that cladistics is a tool and, like any tool, it can be used appropriately or inappropriately. The choice of the outgroup and the characteristics chosen to be evaluated are important to the validity of the process. If a person mistakenly used a whale as the outgroup, they would come to completely different conclusions about how the various kinds of terrestrial vertebrates are related.

It is also important to carefully select the characteristics to be used in making the comparison. Two organisms may share many characteristics but not be members of the same evolutionary group if the characteristics being compared are not from the same genetic background. For example, if you were to compare butterflies, birds, and squirrels using the presence or absence of wings and the presence or absence of bright colors as your characteristics, you would conclude that butterflies and birds are more closely related than birds and squirrels. However, this is not a valid comparison, because the wings of birds and butterflies are not of the same evolutionary origin.

---

Others move by means of a kind of flagellum. The structure of the flagellum is different from the flagellum found in eukaryotic organisms.

Because the early atmosphere is thought to have been a reducing atmosphere, the first Bacteria were probably anaerobic organisms. Today, there are both anaerobic and aerobic Bacteria. Many heterotrophic Bacteria are **saprophytes,** organisms that obtain energy by the decomposition

of dead organic material; others are parasites that obtain energy and nutrients from living hosts and cause disease (Outlooks 20.1); still others are mutualistic and have a mutually beneficial relationship with their host; finally, some are commensalistic and derive benefit from a host without harming it. Several kinds of Bacteria are autotrophic. Many are called cyanobacteria because they contain a blue-green pigment, which allows them to capture sunlight and

## OUTLOOKS 20.1

# A Bacterium that Controls Animal Reproduction

*Wolbachia* is a small kind of bacterium called a rickettsia. It is an intracellular parasite that only lives in the cells of its hosts—many kinds of insects, other arthropods, and nematode worms. *Wolbachia* is extremely common—at least 20% of all insects are infected with this parasite. Because it is an intracellular parasite, it is most easily transmitted from one generation of its host to the next during reproduction. Since the eggs of the host species carry *Wolbachia* but the sperm do not, *Wolbachia* is passed from one generation of its host to the next only in the egg of the host as if it were an organelle in the egg. *Wolbachia* manipulates the reproductive biology of its host in several ways that enhance the likelihood that *Wolbachia*-infected female hosts will produce large numbers of *Wolbachia*-infected female offspring.

1. **Egg/sperm incompatibility**
   When a female insect **uninfected** with *Wolbachia* mates with a male **infected** with *Wolbachia*, some or all of her fertilized eggs die. This means that **uninfected** female insects produce fewer offspring than **infected** females. Thus, there is a bias toward producing *Wolbachia*-infected offspring.
2. **Killing of host males**
   In some cases, infected male hosts are killed by the presence of the parasite. The killing of male hosts means that only infected females are produced.

3. **Changing the sex of genetic male hosts**
   In some cases, genetic male host offspring that are infected with *Wolbachia* are converted to females. If they are fertile females, they will produce *Wolbachia*-containing eggs. If they are infertile pseudofemales, they do not reproduce.
4. **Parthenogenetic development**
   In certain species of wasps, it appears that infection with *Wolbachia* has resulted in the complete elimination of males. The female wasps reproduce by parthenogenesis, which is a form of reproduction in which unfertilized eggs develop into only female offspring. Thus, all of the female wasps offspring are infected with *Wolbachia*.
5. **Mutualism**
   Some species of nematode worms are unable to reproduce without the presence of *Wolbachia*.

These examples suggest that the *Wolbachia* DNA has taken over some of the functions of its host. In fact, examination of the DNA of the eukaryotic host species shows that they contain *Wolbachia* genes in their nucleus.

---

carry on photosynthesis. They can become extremely numerous in some polluted waters where nutrients are abundant. Others use inorganic chemical reactions for their energy sources and are called chemosynthetic.

## The Domain Archaea

The term *archaea* comes from the Greek word *archaios*, meaning ancient. This is a little misleading, because the Archaea are thought to have branched off from the Bacteria between 2 and 3 billion years ago.

The Archaea are similar to the Bacteria in that they both have a prokaryotic cell structure. However, the Archaea differ from the Bacteria in several fundamental ways. The Archaea do not have peptidoglycan in their cell walls, and the structure of their DNA is different from that of the Bacteria. Although the DNA of the Archaea is a loop, like that of the Bacteria, the DNA of the Archaea appears to have a large proportion of genes that are different from either the Bacteria or the Eucarya. Archaea reproduce asexually by binary fission, as do the Bacteria. They also exchange pieces of DNA between individuals, as do Bacteria. Also, the cell membranes of the Archaea have a unique chemical structure, found in neither the Bacteria nor the Eucarya. Members of the Archaea exist in many shapes, including rods, spheres, spirals, filaments, and flat plates.

Because many members of the Archaea are found in extreme environments, they have become known as *extremophiles*. However,

as more species are discovered and organisms that were once thought to be Bacteria are reclassified as Archaea, it is becoming clear there are many that do not live in extreme environments. Archaea use a variety of ways of obtaining energy. Many are autotrophs that use inorganic chemical reactions (chemoautotrophs) or light (photoautotrophs) as sources of energy and carbon dioxide as a source of carbon. Some are heterotrophs and use organic molecules as a source of energy and carbon.

Members of the Archaea are extremely diverse. Based on the particular habitats they occupy and the kind of metabolism they display, Archaea are divided into several functional groups:

1. *Methanogens* are anaerobic, methane-producing organisms. They can be found in sewage, swamps, and the intestinal tracts of termites and ruminant animals, such as cows, sheep, and goats. They are even found in the intestines of humans.
2. *Halobacteria* (*halo* = salt) live in very salty environments, such as the Great Salt Lake (Utah), salt ponds, and brine solutions. Many have a reddish pigment and can be present in such high numbers that they color the water red. Some contain a special kind of chlorophyll and are therefore capable of generating their ATP by a kind of photosynthesis but they do not release oxygen.
3. *Thermophilic* Archaea live in environments that normally have very high temperatures and high concentrations of sulfur (e.g., hot sulfur springs and around deep-sea hydrothermal vents). Over 500 species of thermophiles

have been identified at the openings of hydrothermal vents in the open oceans. One such thermophile, *Pyrolobus fumarii*, grows in a hot spring in Yellowstone National Park (figure 20.10). It grows best at 106°C and can grow at temperatures up to 113°C but will not grow below 90°C. Another species that survives at 122°C has been discovered. Some of these heat-loving Archaea also live in extremely acid conditions.

4. *Marine*, *freshwater*, and *soil Archaea* have recently been discovered to be extremely abundant, but little is yet known about their role in these habitats.

5. Recently an archeon has been discovered that appears to be parasitic on another archeon.

## The Domain Eucarya

Most biologists now believe that eukaryotic cells evolved from prokaryotic cells through endosymbiosis (see chapter 19). This hypothesis proposes that structures such as mitochondria, chloroplasts, and several other membranous organelles found in eukaryotic cells were originally separate living organisms that were incorporated into another cell. Once inside another cell, these structures and their functions became integrated with the host cell and ultimately became essential to its survival. This new type of cell was the forerunner of present-day eukaryotic cells.

Eukaryotic cells are usually much larger than prokaryotic cells, typically having more than a thousand times the volume of prokaryotic cells. Their larger size was made possible by the presence of specialized membranous organelles, such as the endoplasmic reticulum, mitochondria, chloroplasts, and nuclei.

### Kingdom Protista

The changes in cell structure that led to eukaryotic organisms probably gave rise to single-celled organisms similar to those currently grouped in the kingdom Protista.

There is a great deal of diversity among the approximately 60,000 known species of Protista. Many species live in freshwater; others are found in marine or terrestrial habitats, and some are parasitic, commensalistic, or mutualistic. All species can undergo mitosis, resulting in asexual reproduction. Some species can also undergo meiosis and reproduce sexually. Many are autotrophs that have chloroplasts and carry on photosynthesis. These are commonly called algae. Others are heterotrophs that require organic molecules as sources of energy. These are commonly called protozoa. Both autotrophs and heterotrophs have mitochondria and respire aerobically.

Because members of this kingdom are so diverse with respect to details of cell structure, metabolism, and reproductive methods, most biologists do not think that the Protista form a valid phylogenetic unit and should be divided into several distinct kingdoms. However, it is still a convenient taxonomic grouping. By placing these organisms together in this group, it is possible to gain a useful perspective on how they relate to other kinds of organisms. After the origin of eukaryotic organisms,

**FIGURE 20.10 Habitat for Thermophilic Archaea**
Thermophilic Archaea are found in hot springs like these at Yellowstone National Park and around thermal vents on the ocean floor.

evolution proceeded along several pathways. Three major lines of evolution within the Protista can be seen. There are plantlike autotrophs (algae), animal-like heterotrophs (protozoa), and funguslike heterotrophs (slime molds). *Amoeba* and *Paramecium* are commonly encountered examples of protozoa. Many seaweeds and pond scums are collections of large numbers of algal cells. Slime molds are seen less frequently, because they live in and on the soil in moist habitats; they are most often encountered as slimy masses on decaying logs. Figure 20.11 shows some examples of this diverse group of organisms.

## Kingdom Fungi

**Fungus** is the common name for members of the kingdom Fungi. The ancestors of fungi were probably related to some of the heterotrophic protozoa. They have evolved several distinct characteristics. Most fungi are nonmotile. They have a rigid, thin cell wall, which contains chitin, a complex carbohydrate containing nitrogen. The members of the kingdom Fungi are non-photosynthetic, eukaryotic organisms. Most of the approximately 70,000 species (mushrooms and molds) are multicellular, but a few, such as yeasts, are single-celled. In the multicellular fungi, the basic structural unit is a network of multicellular filaments.

Because all of these organisms are heterotrophs, they must obtain nutrients from organic sources. Most are saprophytes and secrete enzymes that digest large molecules into smaller units, which are absorbed as food for the organism. They are very important as decomposers in all ecosystems. They feed on a variety of nutrients ranging from dead organisms to such products as shoes, foodstuffs, and clothing. Most synthetic organic molecules are not attacked as readily by fungi; this is why plastic bags and foam cups are slow to decompose.

Some fungi are parasitic. Many of the parasitic fungi are important plant pests. Some (e.g., chestnut blight, Dutch elm disease) attack and kill plants; others injure the fruit, leaves, roots, or stems. In crop plants, fungi are important pests that kill or weaken plants and reduce yields. The fungi that are human parasites are responsible for athlete's foot, vaginal yeast infections, valley fever, "ringworm," and other diseases.

Other fungi are mutualistic. Lichens are common organisms that consist of a mutualistic relationship between fungal and algal cells. Another important group of mutualistic fungi form an association with the roots of plants and improve the nutrient and water capturing capacity of plants. Indeed many species of plants will not grow without their fungal associates. Figure 20.12 shows examples of several kinds of fungi.

## Kingdom Plantae

The members of the kingdom Plantae are nonmotile, terrestrial (mostly), multicellular organisms that contain chlorophyll and produce their own organic compounds by photosynthesis. All plant cells have a cellulose cell wall.

Most biologists believe that the evolution of this kingdom began nearly 500 million years ago, when the green algae gave rise to nonvascular plants, such as mosses. The development of vascular (water-transporting) tissue was a major step in the evolution of plants, because it allowed plants to increase in size and to live in drier environmental conditions. Ferns, cone-bearing plants, and flowering plants all have vascular tissue. Some of the vascular plants evolved into seed-producing plants, which today are the cone-bearing and flowering plants, whereas the ferns never developed seeds (figure 20.13). Over 300,000 species of plants have been classified; about 85% are flowering plants, 14% are mosses and ferns, and the remaining 1% are cone-bearers and several other small groups within the kingdom.

**Green Algae**

**Kelp**

**Slime mold**

**Protozoan**

**Diatom**

**FIGURE 20.11  A Diversity of Protista**
The kingdom Protista includes a wide variety of organisms that are simple in structure. They are not a phylogenetic group.

**Several kinds of mold**

**Puffball**

**Mushroom**

**FIGURE 20.12  Examples of Fungi**
Molds, mushrooms, and puffballs are common examples of this kingdom.

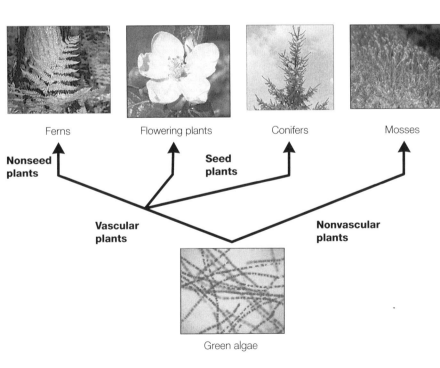

Ferns

Flowering plants

Conifers

Mosses

**Nonseed plants**

**Seed plants**

**Vascular plants**

**Nonvascular plants**

Green algae

**FIGURE 20.13  Plant Evolution**
Two lines of plants are thought to have evolved from the green algae of the kingdom Protista. The nonvascular mosses evolved as one type of plant. The second type, the vascular plants, evolved into more complex plants. The early vascular plants did not produce seeds, like present-day ferns. Eventually, the evolution of the ability to produce seeds resulted in two distinct lines: the cone-bearing plants and the flowering plants.

A major unifying theme in the plants and their green alga ancestors is the presence of a unique life cycle with two distinct generation or stages. They have a haploid **gametophyte generation**, which produces haploid sex cells by mitosis. The sex cells unite to form a diploid zygote that grows into a diploid **sporophyte generation**. The sporophyte generation produces haploid spores by meiosis and the haploid spores germinate and grow into the gametophyte generation. This kind of life cycle is referred to as **alternation of generations**. In addition to sexual reproduction, plants are able to reproduce asexually.

## Kingdom Animalia

Over a million species of animals have been classified, ranging from microscopic types, such as mites and the aquatic larvae of marine animals, to huge animals, such as elephants and whales. All animals have some common traits. All are composed of eukaryotic cells and all species are heterotrophic and multicellular. All animals are motile, at least during some portion of their lives, although some, such as the sponges, barnacles, mussels, and corals, are sessile (i.e., nonmotile) as adults. All animals are capable of sexual reproduction, but many of the less complex animals also reproduce asexually.

The ancestors of the kingdom Animalia are thought to be certain kinds of flagellated protozoa. It is thought that colonies of flagellated protozoa gave rise to simple, multicellular forms of animals such as the ancestors of present-day sponges. These first animals lacked specialized tissues and organs. As cells became more specialized, organisms developed special tissues, organs, and systems of organs, and the variety of kinds of animals increased (figure 20.14).

**Sponge**

**Sea anemone**

**Earthworm**

**Insect**

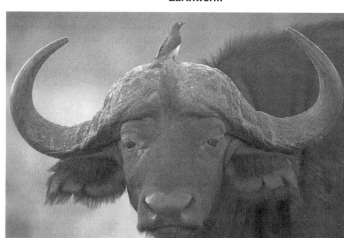
**Mammal and bird**

## FIGURE 20.14 Animal Diversity
Animals range in complexity from simple, marine sponges and sea anemones to complex, terrestrial insects, birds, and mammals.

6. List two ways that Bacteria and Archaea differ.
7. Describe two distinctly different ways that Bacteria obtain energy.
8. Describe two distinctly different ways that Archaea obtain energy.
9. List the four kingdoms of the domain Eucarya and give two distinguishing characteristics for each.
10. Which of the following groups of organisms contain members that are autotrophic: Bacteria, Archaea, Protista, Fungi, Plantae, Animalia?

## 20.3   Acellular Infectious Particles

All of the groups discussed so far are cellular forms of life. They all have at least the following features in common. They have (1) cells that have an outer plasma membrane and contain organelles, (2) DNA as genetic material that is involved in reproduction, (3) enzyme-controlled metabolic pathways, (4) an ability to reproduce, and (5) an ability to adapt to their environment physiologically and evolutionarily.

However, some particles show some characteristics of life and cause disease but do not have a cell structure and cannot perform some life functions without the assistance of living cells. Because they lack a cell structure, they are referred to as *acellular* (a = lacking). Because they enter cells, cause disease, and can be passed from one organism to another, they are often called infectious particles. In causing disease, they make copies of themselves. There is no clear explanation of how these particles came to be. Therefore, they are not included in the classification system for cellular organisms. There are three kinds of acellular infectious particles: *viruses*, *viroids*, and *prions*.

### Viruses

A **virus** is an acellular infectious particle consisting of a nucleic acid core surrounded by a coat of protein (figure 20.15). Viruses are often called *obligate intracellular parasites*,

which means they are infectious particles that can function only when inside a living cell. Viruses are not considered to be living because they are not capable of living and reproducing by themselves and because they show some characteristics of life only when inside living cells.

Viruses vary in size and shape, which helps in classifying them. Some are rod-shaped, others are spherical, and still others are in the shape of a coil or helix. Most are too small to be visible through a light microscope and require an electron microscope to make them visible. Most viruses are identified by the disease symptoms they cause when they infect cells. It is very likely that all species on Earth serve as hosts to viruses (table 20.2).

### How Did Viruses Originate?

Soon after viruses were discovered in the late nineteenth century, biologists began to speculate on how they originated. One early hypothesis was that they were descendents of the first precells that did not evolve into cells. This idea was discarded as biologists learned more about the complex relationship between viruses and host cells. The recent discovery of a giant virus—mimivirus—in amoebas has added evidence that in their evolutionary past, viruses were more complex. The mimivirus is as large as some bacteria and has as many genes. It has both DNA and RNA. All other known viruses have only DNA or RNA as genetic material—not both. However, its structure is similar to that of other viruses and it shows a typical virus life cycle.

A second hypothesis was that viruses developed from intracellular parasites that became so specialized that they needed only their nucleic acid to continue their existence. Once inside a cell, this nucleic acid can take over and direct the host cell to provide for all of the virus's needs.

A third hypothesis is that viruses are runaway genes that have escaped from cells and must return to a host cell to replicate. Regardless of how the viruses came into being, today they are important as parasites in all forms of life.

**FIGURE 20.15 Typical Viruses**
Viruses consist of a core of nucleic acid, either DNA or RNA, surrounded by a protein coat. Some have an additional layer, called an envelope, surrounding the protein coat.

| TABLE 20.2 | Viral Diseases |
| --- | --- |
| **Type of Virus** | **Disease** |
| Papovaviruses | Warts in humans |
| Paramyxoviruses | Mumps and measles in humans; distemper in dogs |
| Adenoviruses | Respiratory infections in most mammals |
| Poxviruses | Smallpox |
| Wound-tumor viruses | Diseases in corn and rice |
| Potexviruses | Diseases in potatoes |
| Bacteriophage | Infections in many types of bacteria |

## How Do Viruses Cause Disease?

Viruses are typically host-specific, which means that they usually attack only one kind of cell. The host is a specific kind of cell that provides what the virus needs to function. Viruses can infect only the cells that have the proper receptor sites to which the virus can attach. This site is usually a glycoprotein molecule on the surface of the cell membrane. For example, the virus responsible for measles attaches to the membranes of skin cells, hepatitis viruses attach to liver cells, and mumps viruses attach to cells in the salivary glands. Host cells for the human immunodeficiency virus (HIV) include some types of human brain cells and several types belonging to the immune system.

Once it has attached to the host cell, the virus either enters the cell intact or injects its nucleic acid into the cell. If it enters the cell, the virus loses its protein coat, releasing the nucleic acid. Once released into the cell, the virus's nucleic acid may remain free in the cytoplasm, or it may link with the host's genetic material. Some viruses contain as few as 3 genes; others contain as many as 500. A typical eukaryotic cell contains tens of thousands of genes. Most viruses need only a small number of genes, because they rely on the host to perform most of the activities necessary for viral multiplication.

Some viruses have DNA as their genetic material but many have RNA. Many RNA viruses can be replicated directly, but others must have their RNA reverse-transcribed to DNA before they can reproduce. Reverse transcriptase, the enzyme that accomplishes this has become very important in the new field of molecular genetics, because its use allows scientists to make large numbers of copies of a specific molecule of DNA.

Viruses do not divide like true cells; they are *replicated*. Virus particles are replicated by using a set of genetic instructions from the virus and new building materials and enzymes from the host cell. Viral genes take command of the host's metabolic pathways and use the host's available enzymes and ATP to make copies of the virus. When enough new viral nucleic acid and protein coat are produced, complete virus particles are assembled and released from the host (figure 20.16). In many cases, this process results in the death of the host cell. When the virus particles are released, they can infect adjacent cells and the infection spreads. The number of viruses released ranges from 10 to thousands. The virus that causes polio affects nerve cells and releases about 10,000 new virus particles from each human host cell. Some viruses remain in cells and are only occasionally triggered to reproduce, causing symptoms of disease. Herpes viruses, which cause cold sores, genital herpes, and shingles, reside in nerve cells and occasionally become active.

Some viruses cause serious disease; others cause mild symptoms. It is also highly likely that there are viruses that require cells for reproduction but go unrecognized because they do not cause the death of cells or cause disease symptoms.

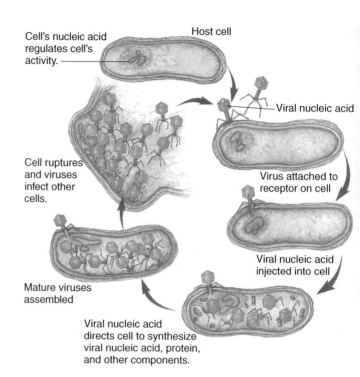

**FIGURE 20.16 Viral Invasion of a Bacterial Cell**
The viral nucleic acid takes control of the activities of the host cell. Because the virus has no functional organelles of its own, it can become metabolically active only while it is within a host cell. The viral genetic material causes the host cell to make copies of the virus, ultimately resulting in the destruction of the host cell.

## Viroids: Infectious RNA

A **viroid** is an infectious particle composed solely of a small, single strand of RNA in the form of a loop. To date, no viroids have been found to infect animal cells. The hosts in which they have been found are cultivated crop plants, such as potatoes, tomatoes, and cucumbers. Viroid infections result in stunted or distorted growth and may cause the plant to die. Pollen, seeds, and farm machinery can transmit viroids from one plant to another. Some scientists believe that viroids are parts of normal RNA from plant cells that have gone wrong.

## Prions: Infectious Proteins

**Prions** are thought to be proteins that can be passed from one organism to another and cause disease. All the diseases of this type cause changes in the brain that result in a spongy appearance called spongiform encephalopathies. Because these diseases can be transmitted from one animal to another, they are often called transmissible spongiform encephalopathies. The symptoms typically involve abnormal behavior and eventually death. There are many scientists who are still cautious about accepting prions as a cause of disease. Although it appears that proteins are involved in these diseases, they suggest that environmental factors may be causing changes in the proteins rather than having the proteins passed from organism to organism.

## Examples of Prion Diseases

In animals, the most common examples are scrapie in sheep and goats and mad cow disease in cattle. Scrapie got its name because one of the symptoms of the disease is an itching of the skin associated with nerve damage that causes the animals to rub against objects and scrape their hair off.

In humans, there are several similar diseases. Kuru is a disease known to have occurred in the Fore people of the highlands of Papua New Guinea. The disease was apparently spread because the people ate small amounts of the brain tissue of dead relatives. (This ritual was performed as an act of love and respect for their relatives.) When the Fore people were encouraged to discontinue this ritual, the incidence of the disease declined. Creutzfeldt-Jakob disease (CJD) is found throughout the world. Its spread is associated with medical treatment; contaminated surgical instruments and tissue transplants, such as corneal transplants, are the most likely causes of transfer from infected to uninfected persons.

The occurrence of mad cow disease (bovine spongiform encephalopathy—BSE) in Great Britain in the 1980s and 1990s was apparently caused by the spread of prions from sheep to cattle. This occurred because of the practice of processing unusable parts of sheep carcasses into a protein supplement that was fed to cattle. It now appears that the original form of BSE has changed to a variety that is able to infect humans. This new form is called vCJD; scientists believe that BSE and CJD are, in fact, caused by the same prion.

A form of transmissible spongiform encephalopathy called *chronic wasting disease* is present in elk and deer in parts of the United States and Canada. It is called chronic wasting disease because the animals lose muscle mass and weight as a result of the prion infection. Similar diseases occur in mink, cats, and dogs.

## How Prions Cause Disease

How are prions formed and how do they multiply? Prion multiplication appears to result from the disease-causing prion protein coming in contact with a normal body protein and converting it into the disease-causing form, a process called *conversion*. Because this normal protein is produced as a result of translating a DNA message, scientists looked for the genes that make the protein and have found it in a wide variety of mammals. The normal allele produces a protein that does not cause disease but is able to be changed by the invading prion protein into the prion form. Prions do not reproduce or replicate as do viruses and viroids. A prion protein (pathogen) presses up against a normal (not harmful) body protein and may cause it to change shape to that of the dangerous protein. When this conversion happens to a number of proteins, they stack up and interlock, as do the individual pieces of a Lego toy. When enough link together, they have a damaging effect—they form plaques (patches) of protein on the surface of nerve cells, disrupting the flow of the nerve impulses and eventually causing nerve cell death. Brain tissues taken from animals that have died of such diseases appear to be full of holes, thus the name spongiform encephalopathy.

A person's susceptibility to acquiring a prion disease, such as CJD, depends on many factors, such as his or her genetic makeup. If a person produces a functional protein with a particular amino acid sequence, the prion may not be able to convert it to its dangerous form. Other people may produce a protein with a slightly different amino acid sequence that can be converted to the prion form. Once formed, these abnormal proteins resist being destroyed by enzymes and most other agents used to control infectious diseases. Therefore, individuals with the disease-causing form of the protein can serve as the source of the infectious prions. There is still much to learn about the function of the prion protein and how the abnormal, infectious protein can cause copies of itself to be made. A better understanding of the alleles that produce proteins that can be transformed by prions will eventually lead to the prevention and effective treatment of these serious diseases in humans and other animals.

## 20.3 CONCEPT REVIEW

11. Why do viruses invade only specific types of cells?
12. Describe how viruses reproduce.
13. Describe how viruses and viroids differ in structure.
14. What is the chemical structure of a prion?
15. How does a prion cause disease?

## Summary

To facilitate accurate communication, biologists assign a specific name to each species that is cataloged. The various species are cataloged into larger groups on the basis of similar traits.

Taxonomy is the science of classifying and naming organisms. Phylogeny is the science of trying to figure out the evolutionary history of a particular organism. The taxonomic ranking of organisms reflects their evolutionary relationships. Fossil evidence, comparative anatomy, developmental stages, and biochemical evidence are used in taxonomy and phylogeny.

The first organisms thought to have evolved were prokaryotic, single-celled organisms of the domain Bacteria. Current thinking is that the domain Archaea developed from the Bacteria and, ultimately, more complex, eukaryotic, many-celled organisms evolved. These organisms have been classified into the kingdoms Protista, Fungi, Plantae, and Animalia within the domain Eucarya.

There are three kinds of acellular infectious particles: viruses, viroids, and prions. Viruses consist of pieces of genetic material surrounded by a protein coat. Viroids consist of naked pieces of RNA. Prions are proteins. Viruses and viroids can be replicated within the cells they invade. Prions cause already existing proteins within an organism to deform, resulting in disease.

## Key Terms

*Use the interactive flash cards on the* **Concepts in Biology,** *14/e website to help you learn the meaning of these terms.*

alternation of
  generations 450
binomial system of
  nomenclature 436
class 438
family 439
fungus 448
gametophyte generation 450
genus 436
kingdom 437

order 439
phylogeny 439
phylum 438
prions 452
saprophytes 445
specific epithet 436
sporophyte generation 450
taxonomy 436
viroid 452
virus 451

## Basic Review

1. In the binomial system for naming organisms, an organism is given two names: the _____ and the specific epithet.

2. The most inclusive group into which an organism can be classified is the
   a. phylum.
   b. genus.
   c. domain.
   d. kingdom.

3. Phylogeny is the study that attempts to
   a. name organisms.
   b. organize organisms into groups based on how they evolved.
   c. decide on the names of phylums.
   d. classify organisms.

4. Closely related organisms should have very similar reproductive stages. (T/F)

5. Fossils
   a. provide information about when organisms lived.
   b. are found in sediments that form rock.
   c. of soft-bodied animals are rare, compared with those with hard body parts.
   d. All of the above are true.

6. The Bacteria and Archaea are prokaryotic. (T/F)

7. Which one of the following organisms has not been placed in the kingdom Protista?
   a. protozoa
   b. algae
   c. yeast
   d. slime mold

8. Which one of the following kinds of plants does not have seeds?
   a. ferns
   b. pine trees
   c. roses
   d. apple trees

9. All viruses have DNA. (T/F)

10. Prions are proteins. (T/F)

11. The kingdom Protista is a valid phylogenetic category. (T/F)

12. All of the following are members of the domain Eucarya EXCEPT
   a. cows
   b. mushrooms
   c. algae
   d. Bacteria

13. The Archaea
   a. are eukaryotic.
   b. have ribosomes.
   c. have a nucleus.
   d. All of the above are correct.

14. Plants have a life cycle that shows alternation of _____.

15. All animals and fungi are heterotrophs. (T/F)

**Answers**

1. genus 2. c 3. b 4. T 5. d 6. T 7. c 8. a 9. F 10. T 11. F 12. d 13. b 14. generations 15. T

## Thinking Critically

**Examine Life**

A minimum estimate of the number of species of insects in the world is 750,000. Perhaps, then, it would not surprise you to see a fly with eyes on stalks as long as its wings, a dragonfly with a wingspread greater than 1 meter, an insect that can revive after being frozen at –35°C, and a wasp that can push its long, hairlike, egg-laying tool directly into a tree. Only the dragonfly is not presently living, but it once was. What other curious features of this fascinating group can you discover? Have you looked at a common beetle under magnification? It will hold still if you chill it.

# The Nature of Microorganisms

## CHAPTER OUTLINE

## Are We Killing the Oceans?

*Fertilizer may be the cause.*

Dead zones are areas in the world's oceans where the oxygen level is so low that most organisms die. In 2006, the United Nations published a list of over 200 places in the world's oceans where dead zones developed for at least part of each year. Similar dead zones occur in some lakes. Dead zones normally develop at the mouths of rivers as a result of human action and the activity of various kinds of microorganisms. One of the largest dead zones is in the Gulf of Mexico off the mouth of the Mississippi River. Fertilizer from agricultural runoff, waste from large industrial livestock operations, and the effluent from poorly controlled municipal and industrial sewage flow into rivers that ultimately empty into an ocean (see photo). These nutrients stimulate the growth of single-celled and multi-cellular algae during the warmer months of the year. Eventually, these organisms die and sink to the bottom, where decomposer bacteria use oxygen in the process of aerobic respiration to break down the dead organic matter. This lowers the amount of dissolved oxygen in the water, causing the death of bottom-dwelling animals.

- Why are bacteria able to live in regions of low oxygen when animals cannot?

- Why do dead zones occur off the mouths of rivers?

- Should the amount of fertilizer farmers apply to their fields to increase yields be regulated?

## Background Check

**Concepts you should already know to get the most out of this chapter:**
- The processes of natural selection and evolution (chapter 13)
- Prokaryotic organisms have a simpler cellular structure than eukaryotic organisms (chapter 4)
- How structural and life history characteristics are used to classify organisms (chapter 20)

## 21.1 What Are Microorganisms?

A **microorganism,** or **microbe,** is a tiny organism that usually cannot be seen without the aid of a microscope. These are terms of convenience for a wide variety of organisms, including the domains Bacteria and Archaea and the kingdoms Protista and Fungi in the domain Eucarya. Often, tiny animals, particularly those that cause disease (mites, worms, etc.), are considered microorganisms as well. Viruses are also treated as microbes. However, we will not consider animals or viruses in this chapter. Viruses were discussed in chapter 20 and animals are discussed in chapter 23.

In a very general sense, microorganisms share several characteristics. These organisms generally consist of cells, which function independently. Many are single-celled organisms, although some single-celled microbes form loose aggregations, called colonies. Others are multicellular and have some specialization of cells for certain functions. Their primary method of reproduction is asexual reproduction, in which one cell divides to become two cells, although most kinds are also capable of sexual reproduction. Many have special structures involved in the production of gametes. Many microbes, particularly Bacteria, have the ability to exchange pieces of genetic material, which creates new combinations of genes. In some cases this even involves gene exchange between organisms that are considered to be of different species.

Microbes are extremely common organisms. It is estimated that the total biomass of microbes is larger than the biomass of all other kinds of organisms combined. They live in any aquatic or moist environment and occur in huge numbers in the oceans and other bodies of water and in soil. It has been suggested that if one were able to instantly remove all living things from Earth except microbes, everything on Earth would still be visible in outline form because microbes cover all surfaces, including living things. Because they are small, their moist habitat does not need to be large. Microbes can maintain huge populations in places such as human skin or intestine, temporary puddles, and soil. Your skin, mouth, and gut each contains trillions of microbes. Most die if they dry out, but some have the special ability to become dormant and survive long periods without water. When moistened, they become actively growing cells again.

### 21.1 CONCEPT REVIEW

1. What taxonomic groups are included in the category known as microorganisms?
2. List three general characteristics the various kinds of microbes share.

## 21.2 The Domains Bacteria and Archaea

At one time, all prokaryotic organisms were lumped into one group of microorganisms called bacteria. Today, scientists recognize that there are two, very different kinds of prokaryotic organisms: the domains Bacteria and Archaea. The Bacteria and Archaea differ in several ways: Bacteria have a compound called peptidoglycan, in their cell walls, which Archaea do not have. The chemical structure of the cell membranes of Archaea is different from that of all other kinds of organisms. When the DNA of Archaea is compared with that of other organisms, it is found that a large proportion of their genes are unique.

Today, most scientists still use the terms *bacterium* and *bacteria.* However, they are used in a restricted sense to refer to members of the domain Bacteria. The term *archeon* is frequently used to refer to members of the Domain Archaea.

### The Domain Bacteria

The Bacteria are an extremely diverse group of organisms. Although only about 2,000 species of Bacteria have been named, most biologists feel that there are probably millions still to be identified (How Science Works 21.1). They occupy every conceivable habitat and have highly diverse metabolic abilities. They are typically spherical, rod-shaped, or spiral-shaped. They are often identified by the characteristics of their metabolism or the chemistry of their cell walls. Many have a kind of flagellum, which rotates and allows for movement. Figure 21.1 shows the general structure of a bacterium. Some form resistant spores, which can withstand dry or other harsh conditions. Bacteria play several important ecological roles and interact with other organisms in many ways.

#### Decomposers

Many kinds of bacteria are heterotrophs that are saprophytes. They break down organic matter to provide themselves with energy and raw materials for growth. Therefore, they function as decomposers in all ecosystems. Decomposers are a diverse group and use a wide variety of metabolic processes. Some are anaerobic and break down complex organic matter to simpler organic compounds. Others are aerobic and degrade organic matter to carbon dioxide and water. In nature, this decomposition process is important in the recycling of carbon, nitrogen, phosphorus, and many other elements.

The actions of decomposers have been harnessed for human purposes. Sewage treatment plants rely on bacteria and other organisms to degrade organic matter (figure 21.2) (How Science Works 21.2).

# HOW SCIENCE WORKS 21.1

## How Many Microbes Are There?

Biologists have long suspected that there are large numbers of undiscovered species of microbes in the world. One of the major problems associated with identifying microbes is that they must be isolated and grown to be characterized. Unfortunately, it appears that most microbes cannot be grown in the lab and therefore cannot be studied in detail.

However, the technology of DNA sequencing has provided a better estimate of the number of kinds of microbes in our world. J. Craig Venter, one of the scientists who developed techniques for sequencing the human genome, has applied the DNA sequencing techniques to the ocean ecosystem. Water samples were collected from many parts of the ocean. The samples were filtered to collect the microbes. The DNA from these mixtures of organisms was then sequenced. The result was a "metagenome," a picture of the DNA of an ecosystem.

Once this composite of DNA was known, pieces of it could be compared to known genes and new, unique sequences could be identified. The result was the identification of 1.2 million new genes and a doubling of the number of kinds of proteins produced from those genes. Many new genes appear to be related to molecules responsible for trapping sunlight by autotrophic microbes. The identification of new genes and the proteins they produce implies that there are many new species in the ocean responsible for their production.

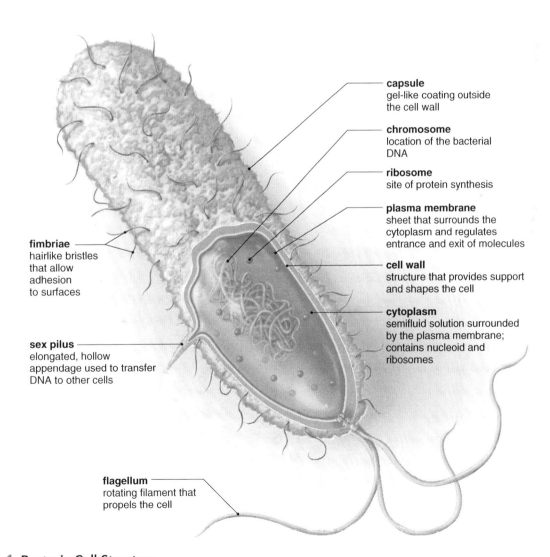

capsule
gel-like coating outside
the cell wall

chromosome
location of the bacterial
DNA

ribosome
site of protein synthesis

plasma membrane
sheet that surrounds the
cytoplasm and regulates
entrance and exit of molecules

cell wall
structure that provides support
and shapes the cell

cytoplasm
semifluid solution surrounded
by the plasma membrane;
contains nucleoid and
ribosomes

fimbriae
hairlike bristles
that allow
adhesion
to surfaces

sex pilus
elongated, hollow
appendage used to transfer
DNA to other cells

flagellum
rotating filament that
propels the cell

**FIGURE 21.1 Bacteria Cell Structure**
The plasma membrane regulates the movement of material between the cell and its environment. A rigid cell wall protects the cell and determines its shape. Some bacteria, usually pathogens, have a capsule to protect them from the host's immune system. The genetic material consists of a loop of DNA.

# HOW SCIENCE WORKS 21.2

## Bioremediation

Bioremediation involves the use of naturally occurring microbes to break down unwanted or dangerous materials. In many ways we have been using bioremediation for centuries. Composting, sewage treatment plants, and the activities of soil bacteria to break down animal manure are common examples of how microbes break down unwanted organic matter. However, modern society has invented other kinds of pollution that are more resistant to the activities of microbes. Oil spills and the release of synthetic organic compounds such as polychlorinated biphenyls (PCBs), trichloroethylene (TCE), and many other persistent organic molecules have created a new kind of pollution that also can be treated with microbes.

Several types of activities are commonly involved when bioremediation is attempted. In order to find the microbes with the desired abilities, scientists screen many kinds. In some cases, genetic engineering techniques have been used to introduce genes into microbes that allow the microbes to survive in toxic situations. When bioremediation is to be attempted, several actions are commonly taken. Specific microbes with desirable properties may be added to break down the pollutant. Nutrients such as nitrogen or phosphorus may be added to stimulate the growth of microorganisms already present. In some cases, the concentration of the pollutant may be diluted so that the pollutant will not kill the microbes that will eventually metabolize it.

Bioremediation has been used to clean up oil spills, degrade pesticides, detoxify metallic contaminants, and in many other ways.

**FIGURE 21.2 Decomposers in Sewage**
A sewage treatment plant is designed to encourage the growth of bacteria and other microorganisms that break down organic matter. The tank in the foreground contains a mixture of sewage and microorganisms, which is being agitated to assure the optimal growth of microbes.

The food industry uses lactic acid fermentation by certain bacteria to produce cheeses, yogurt, sauerkraut, and many other foods. Alcohols, acetones, acids, and other chemicals are produced by bacterial cultures. Some bacteria can even metabolize oil and are used to clean up oil spills.

Unfortunately, decomposer bacteria do not distinguish between items that we want to decompose and those that we don't want to decompose. Bacteria in food can cause milk to turn sour or vegetables and meat to spoil. Thus, it is often necessary to control the populations of some decomposer bacteria, so that foods and other valuable materials are not destroyed by rotting or spoiling.

## Commensal Bacteria

Many kinds of bacteria have commensal relationships with other organisms. They live on the surface or within other organisms and cause them no harm, but neither do they perform any valuable functions. Most organisms are lined and covered by populations of bacteria called *normal flora* (table 21.1). In fact, if an organism lacks bacteria, it is considered abnormal. The bacterium *Escherichia coli* (commonly called *E. coli*) is common in the intestinal tract of humans, other mammals, and birds. A large proportion of human feces is composed of *E. coli* and other bacteria. Many of the odors humans produce from the skin and gut are the result of commensal bacteria.

## Photosynthetic Bacteria

Several kinds of Bacteria carry on a form of photosynthesis. A group called the cyanobacteria carries out a form of photosynthesis that is essentially the same as that in plants and algae. They use carbon dioxide and water as raw materials and release oxygen. In fact, the chloroplasts of eukaryotic organisms are assumed to be cyanobacteria that, in the past, formed an endosymbiotic relationship with other cells. Cyanobacteria are thought to be the first oxygen-releasing organisms; thus, their activities led to the presence of oxygen in the atmosphere and the subsequent evolution of aerobic respiration. Cyanobacteria are extremely common and are found in fresh and marine waters and soil and other moist environments. When conditions are favorable, asexual reproduction can result in what is called a **bloom**— a rapid increase in the population of microorganisms in a body of water (figure 21.3). Many cyanobacteria form filaments or other kinds of colonies, which produce large masses when a bloom occurs. Some species of cyanobacteria produce toxins. When blooms occur, the levels of toxins

**TABLE 21.1** Common Bacteria in or on Humans

| | |
|---|---|
| Skin | *Corynebacterium* sp., *Staphylococcus* sp., *Streptococcus* sp., *Escherichia coli*, *Mycobacterium* sp. |
| Eye | *Corynebacterium* sp., *Neisseria* sp., *Bacillus* sp., *Staphylococcus* sp., *Streptococcus* sp. |
| Ear | *Staphylococcus* sp., *Streptococcus* sp., *Corynebacterium* sp., *Bacillus* sp. |
| Mouth | *Streptococcus* sp., *Staphylococcus* sp., *Lactobacillus* sp., *Corynebacterium* sp., *Fusobacterium* sp., *Vibrio* sp., *Haemophilus* sp. |
| Nose | *Corynebacterium* sp., *Staphylococcus* sp., *Streptococcus* sp. |
| Intestinal tract | *Lactobacillus* sp., *Escherichia coli*, *Bacillus* sp., *Clostridium* sp., *Pseudomonas* sp., *Bacteroides* sp., *Streptococcus* sp. |
| Genital tract | *Lactobacillus* sp., *Staphylococcus* sp., *Streptococcus* sp., *Clostridium* sp., *Peptostreptococcus* sp., *Escherichia coli* |

**Staphylococcus**

**Escherichia coli**

**Lactobacillus**

**Pseudomonas**

**FIGURE 21.3 Bloom of Cyanobacteria**
Many kinds of cyanobacteria reproduce rapidly in nutrient-rich waters and produce masses of organisms known as a bloom.

in the water may be high enough to poison humans and other animals.

Within the filaments of many cyanobacteria are specialized, larger cells capable of nitrogen fixation which converts atmospheric nitrogen, $N_2$, to ammonia, $NH_3$. This provides a form of nitrogen usable to other cells in the colony—an example of division of labor.

Two kinds of Bacteria, known as purple and green bacteria, carry on different forms of photosynthesis that do not release oxygen. Many of these organisms release sulfur as a result of their photosynthesis.

## Mutualistic Bacteria

Mutualistic relationships occur between bacteria and other organisms. Some intestinal bacteria benefit humans by producing antibiotics, which inhibit the development of disease-causing bacteria. They also compete with disease-causing bacteria for nutrients, thereby helping keep them in check. They aid digestion by releasing various nutrients. They produce and release vitamin K. Mutualistic bacteria establish this symbiotic relationship when humans ingest them along with food or drink. When people travel, they consume local bacteria with their food and drink and may have problems establishing a new symbiotic relationship with these foreign bacteria. Both the host and the symbionts must adjust to their new environment, which can result in a very uncomfortable situation for both. Some people develop traveler's diarrhea as a result.

There are many other examples of mutualistic relationships between bacteria and other organisms. Many kinds of plants have nitrogen-fixing bacteria in their roots in a symbiotic relationship. Some fish and other aquatic animals have bioluminescent bacteria in their bodies, allowing them to produce light. Many kinds of lichens contain cyanobacteria as symbionts with their fungal cells.

## Bacteria and Mineral Cycles

Many different bacteria are involved in the nitrogen cycle. In addition to symbiotic nitrogen-fixing bacteria, free-living nitrogen-fixing bacteria in the soil convert $N_2$ to $NH_3$. Other bacteria convert ammonia to nitrite and nitrate. These bacteria are chemoautotrophs that use inorganic chemical reactions involving nitrogen to provide themselves with energy. All of these bacteria are extremely important ecologically, because they are ultimately the source of nitrogen for plant growth. Finally, some bacteria convert nitrite to atmospheric nitrogen.

In addition to nitrogen; iron, sulfur, manganese, and many other inorganic materials are cycled by chemoautotrophic bacteria with specialized metabolic abilities. Some of these are important ecologically, because they produce acid mine drainage or convert metallic mercury to methylmercury, which can enter animals and cause health problems.

## Disease-Causing Bacteria

Disease-causing bacteria are heterotrophs that use the organic matter of living cells as food. Bacteria and other kinds of organisms that are capable of causing harm to their host are called **pathogens.** Only a small minority of bacteria fall into this category; however, because historically they have been responsible for huge numbers of deaths and continue to be a serious problem, they have been studied intensively and many pathogens are well understood.

Pathogenic bacteria can cause disease in several ways. Many are normally harmless commensals but cause disease when their populations increase to excessively high numbers. For example, *Streptococcus pneumoniae* can grow in the throats of healthy people without any pathogenic effects. But if a person's resistance is lowered, as after a bout with viral flu, *Streptococcus pneumoniae* can invade the lungs and reproduce rapidly, causing pneumonia. The relationship changes from commensalistic to parasitic.

Other bacteria invade the healthy tissue of their host and cause disease by altering the tissue's normal physiology. Bacteria living in the host release a variety of enzymes that cause the destruction of tissue. The disease ends when the pathogens are killed by the body's defenses or an outside agent, such as an antibiotic. Examples are the infectious diseases strep throat, syphilis, anthrax, pneumonia, tuberculosis, and leprosy.

Many other illnesses are caused by toxins or poisons produced by bacteria. Some of these bacteria release toxins that may be consumed with food or drink. In this case, disease can be caused even though the pathogens never enter the host. For example, botulism is a deadly disease caused by bacterial toxins in food or drink. Other bacterial diseases are the result of toxins released from bacteria growing inside the host tissue; tetanus and diphtheria are examples. In general, toxins cause tissue damage, fever, and aches and pains.

Bacterial pathogens are also important factors in certain plant diseases. Bacteria cause many types of plant blights, wilts, and soft rots. Apples and other fruit trees are susceptible to fire blight, a disease that lowers the fruit yield because it kills the tree's branches. Citrus canker, a disease of citrus fruits that causes cancerlike growths on stems and lesions on leaves and fruit, can generate widespread damage. Federal and state governments have spent billions of dollars controlling this disease (figure 21.4).

Probably all species of organisms have bacterial pathogens. Plants and animals get sick and die all the time. However, scientists are not likely to spend time and money studying these diseases unless the organisms have economic value to us.

**FIGURE 21.4 A Bacterial Plant Disease**
Citrus canker is a disease of citrus trees caused by the bacterium *Xanthomonas axonopodis*. This photograph shows the typical lesions on the fruit and leaves of an orange tree.

Therefore, scientists know much about bacterial diseases in humans, domesticated animals, and crop plants but know very little about the diseases of jellyfish, squid, or most plants.

## Control of Bacterial Populations

The diseases and many kinds of environmental problems caused by bacteria are actually population control problems. Small numbers of bacteria cause little harm. However, when the population increases, their negative effects are multiplied. Despite large investments of time and money, scientists have found it difficult to control bacterial populations. Three factors operate in favor of the bacteria: their reproductive rate, their ability to form resistant stages, and their ability to mutate and produce strains that resist antibiotics and other control agents.

Under ideal conditions, some bacteria can grow and divide every 20 minutes. If one bacterial cell and all its offspring were to reproduce at this ideal rate, in 48 hours there would be $2.2 \times 10^{43}$ cells. In reality, bacteria cannot achieve such incredibly large populations, because they would eventually run out of food and be unable to dispose of their wastes. However, many of the methods used to control pathogenic bacteria are those that control their numbers by interfering with their ability to reproduce. Many antibiotics interfere with a certain aspect of bacterial physiology so that the bacteria are killed or become unable to divide and reproduce. This allows the host's immune system to gain control and destroy the disease-causing organism. Without the antibiotic, the immune system may be overwhelmed and the person may die.

Although antibiotics can save lives, they don't always work because bacteria mutate and produce individuals that are resistant to the effects of an antibiotic. Because bacteria reproduce so rapidly, a few antibiotic-resistant cells in a bacterial population can increase to dangerous levels in a very short time. This requires the use of stronger doses or new types of antibiotics to bring the bacteria under control. Furthermore, these resistant strains can be transferred from one host to another, making it difficult to control the spread of disease. For example, sulfa drugs and penicillin, once widely used to fight infections, are now ineffective against many strains of pathogenic bacteria. Methicillin has been a valuable antibiotic for many years. However, some strains of *Staphylococcus aureus*, a common skin bacterium, have become resistant to methicillin. As a result, common skin infections that should be controlled easily have become life-threatening. These strains have become known as methicillin-resistant *Staphylococcus aureus* (MRSA). As with methicillin, when any new antibiotic is developed, natural selection encourages the development of resistant bacterial strains. Therefore, humans are constantly waging battles against new strains of resistant bacteria.

In addition to antibiotics, various kinds of *antiseptics* are used to control the numbers of pathogenic bacteria. Antiseptics are chemicals able to kill or inhibit the growth of microbes. They can be used on objects or surfaces that have colonies of potentially harmful bacteria. Certain antiseptics are used on the skin or other tissues of people who are receiving injections or undergoing surgery. Reducing the numbers of bacteria lessens the likelihood that the microbes on the skin will be carried into the body, causing disease. We all are constantly in contact with pathogenic bacteria; however, as long as their numbers are controlled, they do not become a problem.

Another factor that enables some bacteria to survive a hostile environment is their ability to form *endospores*. An **endospore** is a unique bacterial structure with a low metabolic rate that can withstand hostile environmental conditions and germinate later, when there are favorable conditions to form a new, actively growing cell (figure 21.5). Endospores thought to be *Bacillus sphaericus* and estimated to be 25 million to 40 million years old have been isolated from the intestinal tract of a bee fossilized in amber. When placed in an optimum growth environment, they have germinated and grown into numerous colonies.

Some spore-forming bacteria are important disease-causing organisms. People who preserve food by canning often boil the food in the canning jars to kill the bacteria, but not all are killed by boiling, because some form endospores. The endospores of *Clostridium botulinum*, the bacterium that causes botulism, can withstand boiling and remain for years in the endospore state. However, endospores do not germinate and produce botulism toxin if the pH of the canned goods is in the acid range; in that case, the food remains preserved and edible. If conditions become favorable for *Clostridium* endospores to germinate, they become actively growing cells and produce toxin. Using a pressure cooker and heating the food to temperatures higher than 121°C for 15 to 20 minutes destroys both the botulism toxin and the endospores.

**(a)** *Bacillus thuringiensis*

**(b)** *Bacillus* bacteria with endospores

**FIGURE 21.5** **Bacterial Endospore**
*(a)* The body at the top end of the cell is an endospore. It contains the bacterial DNA, as well as a concentration of cytoplasmic material surrounded and protected by a thick wall. *(b)* The photo shows a *Bacillus* bacterium that has formed endospores in some cells.

Anthrax is an acute infectious disease caused by the spore-forming bacterium *Bacillus anthracis*. Anthrax spores can live in the soil as spores for long periods and cause disease when they are inhaled, are swallowed, or invade the skin. Because anthrax spores can survive dry conditions, they were used to contaminate mail as an agent of bioterrorism.

Contaminated food and water are common ways that people encounter bacteria that cause them harm. These disease episodes are commonly referred to as food poisoning or stomach flu (Outlooks 21.1).

**OUTLOOKS 21.1**

## Food Poisoning/Foodborne Illness/Stomach Flu

Many people talk about a disease experience they call stomach flu but it is not caused by the influenza virus. The disease usually involves nausea, vomiting, and diarrhea. It may also involve headache, fever, and abdominal cramping. The Centers for Disease Control and Prevention estimates that food poisoning causes about 75 million cases of illness in the United States each year. The U.S. population is about 310 million, so we all have about a 1 in 4 chance of having this uncomfortable experience each year.

Food poisoning is not caused by the virus that causes influenza and should more properly be called gastroenteritis. In addition, it is not a single disease but is caused by a variety of organisms and mechanisms. The typical way of contracting the disease is through food or water contaminated with viruses, bacteria, or protozoa that, when ingested, multiply and cause the symptoms—hence the name *food poisoning*. Furthermore, these diseases are usually contagious because those who are sick pass the organism in their feces and can transmit it to those around them if those infected do not practice good hygiene.

Norovirus is responsible for about 50% of cases in United States and generally is contracted as a result of fecally contaminated food. Rotavirus is the most common cause of severe diarrhea in infants and young children. Nearly every child in the world has been infected with rotavirus at least once, but they develop partial immunity following infection and subsequent infections tend to be mild. Many kinds of bacteria are involved in cases of food poisoning: *Salmonella, Escherichia coli, Shigella,* and *Staphylococcus* are examples.

An additional cause that leads to similar symptoms involves changes in the kinds and numbers of bacteria normally found in your intestine. Your gut is an ecosystem in which there are many different kinds of Bacteria, Archaea, and protozoa. Each has specific metabolic requirements and produces specific kinds of metabolic waste products. Some of these products may be gases. If you change the kind of food you eat, or if the water you drink has different kinds of minerals in it, some of your intestinal microbes may experience population increases that lead to symptoms similar to those of food poisoning.

Treatment usually does not involve medication. One simply waits until the illness runs its course. The most serious health concern is dehydration from vomiting and diarrhea. Consequently, providing liquids is important and, in severe cases, intravenous fluids may be required.

## The Domain Archaea

The Archaea are distinct from the Bacteria. They differ from Bacteria in the nature of their cell walls, cell membranes, DNA, and other details of structure and physiology. In addition to the spherical, rod-shaped, and spiral-shaped forms found in the Bacteria, some Archaea are lobed, platelike, or irregular in shape. Like the Bacteria, the Archaea are extremely diverse and extremely common. Only a couple hundred species have been described, but DNA sampling of the ocean and soil suggests that there is a huge number of undescribed species. Some species are found in extreme habitats—high temperature, high acid, high salt—and are referred as extremophiles (lovers of extremes).Others are very common in the ocean, freshwater, soil, and the digestive tract of animals where they play a variety of ecological roles. To date only one archeon has been identified as a parasite and it is a parasite on other Archaea.

### Extreme Halophiles

Extreme halophiles (salt lovers) are Archaea that can live only in extremely salty environments—such as the Great Salt Lake in Utah and the Dead Sea, located between Israel and Jordan. They require a solution of at least 8% salt and grow best in solutions that are about 20% salt. The Atlantic Ocean is about 3.5% salt. The Dead Sea is about 15% salt. They also live in artificial salt ponds used to evaporate seawater to produce salt. Because they contain the reddish pigment carotene, they color these salt ponds pinkish or red.

Most of these organisms are aerobic heterotrophs. They use organic matter from their environment as a source of food. Some have been found growing on food products, such as salted fish, causing spoilage. However, some of them are also photosynthetic autotrophs that have a carotene-containing pigment, called bacteriorhodopsin, which absorbs sunlight and allows the cells to make ATP.

### Thermophiles

The thermophiles (heat lovers) are a diverse group of the Archaea that live in extremely hot environments, such as the hot springs found in Yellowstone National Park and hydrothermal vents on the ocean floor (figure 21.6). All require high environmental temperatures—typically, above 50°C (122°F)—and some grow well at temperatures above 100°C (212°F). They are diverse metabolically; some are aerobic whereas others are anaerobic. Some can reduce sulfur or sulfur-containing compounds by attaching hydrogen to sulfur ($S + 2H \rightarrow H_2S$). Thus, they release hydrogen sulfide gas ($H_2S$). Some live in extremely acidic conditions, with a pH of 1–2 or even less.

### Acidophiles and Alkaliphiles

Some Archaea live at extreme pHs. One acidophile is known to live at a pH of 0. Another acidophile has been identified as important in the acid drainage from abandoned mines where they oxidize iron. Alkalophiles live in lakes with basic pHs of 9–11 and maintain a near normal internal pH by pumping hydrogen ions from their environment into their cells.

**FIGURE 21.6 Hydrothermal Vents**
Extremely hot, mineral-rich water enters the ocean from hydrothermal vents on the ocean floor. Many kinds of specialized Archaea live in these places, where they use sulfur as a source of energy. These archeons are, in turn, eaten by other organisms that live in the vicinity.

## Methanogens

Methanogens are members of the Archaea that are strict anaerobes (do not live where there is oxygen) and release methane as a waste product of cellular metabolism. Most are chemosynthetic autotrophs that produce methane by transferring hydrogen to carbon dioxide ($4H_2 + CO_2 \rightarrow CH_4 + 2H_2O$). Others are heterotrophic decomposers that break down simple organic molecules, such as acetate, to produce methane ($CH_3COOH \rightarrow CO_2 + CH_4$). They live in a variety of environments where oxygen is absent. Many live in mud at the bottom of lakes and swamps, and some live in the intestinal tracts of animals, including humans, where they generate methane gas. The digestive system of cattle and some other organisms involves a complex mixture of microorganisms. Some are Bacteria that break down cellulose to simpler molecules, such as acetate, and release hydrogen. Others are methane-producing Archaea that convert the breakdown products of the Bacteria to methane (Outlooks 21.2). Methanogens are also present in certain kinds of waste treatment systems used to manage animal and human waste. Anaerobic digesters containing methanogens can be used to produce methane from human or animal waste. Methanogens are also common in flooded rice paddies. The two most common sources of methane released to the atmosphere are rice paddies and the digestive tracts of animals.

Methane is a greenhouse gas tied to the problem of global warming, so scientists have tried to characterize the role of Archaea as producers of methane. However, because they are involved as components of important agricultural activities (rice growing and cattle raising), it is not likely that this source of methane will be controlled.

### Non-Extremophiles

Although at one time it was thought that the Archaea were all extremophiles, that impression is changing. It is becoming clear that archeons are common in most environments where there is moisture, not just in extreme environments. A major problem with characterizing the roles played by Archaea is that they are difficult to isolate and grow in captivity. However, when environments such as the ocean and soil are sampled for DNA, large amounts of Archaea DNA are found. They appear to be extremely common in the ocean, in freshwater, and in the soil, where they perform a variety of functions (Outlooks 21.3). Many are heterotrophs that degrade organic material and thus are decomposers. Some of these decomposers are aerobic whereas others are anaerobic heterotrophs. Other Archaea are chemoautotrophs that use inorganic chemical reactions to make organic matter. In addition, it appears that there are many archeons that are photoautotrophs that use light to produce organic molecules. In the ocean it appears that these two kinds of autotrophs are important contributors to the base of the marine food web. Because of their small size, they are referred to as picoplankton. These autotrophic archeons are eaten by bacteria, protozoa, and other organisms. In the ocean it is becoming clear that some of chemoautotrophic Archaea are involved in several steps in the nitrogen cycle. Since Archaea are also common in the soil, it is likely that they are also involved in the terrestrial part of the nitrogen cycle as well.

## 21.2 CONCEPT REVIEW

3. List three ways that Bacteria and Archaea differ.
4. Give an example of a member of the Bacteria that is
   a. photosynthetic.
   b. involved in the nitrogen cycle.
   c. mutualistic.
   d. commensal.
5. Give two examples of how humans use Bacteria as decomposers.
6. What is meant by the term *bloom?*
7. What is a pathogen? Give two examples.
8. Define the term *saprophyte.*
9. What is a bacterial endospore?
10. What are methanogens?
11. Describe how members of the Archaea are involved in the nitrogen cycle.
12. Describe three roles played by Archaea in the ocean.
13. What is a thermophile? A halophile?

## OUTLOOKS 21.2

# The Microbial Ecology of a Cow

Ruminants are animals, such as cattle, deer, bison, sheep, and goats, that have a special design to their digestive system. These animals have a large, pouchlike portion of the gut, called a rumen, connected to the esophagus. Ruminants eat plant materials that are often dry and consist of large amounts of cellulose from the plants' cell walls. They do not have enzymes (cellulases) that allow them to break down the cellulose. The rumen is essentially a fermentation chamber for a variety of anaerobic microorganisms, including fungi, members of the domains Bacteria and Archaea, and ciliates and other protozoa from the kingdom Protista.

Cows and other ruminants chew their cud. This is a process in which the animal eat grasses and other plant materials, which go into the rumen. Later, they regurgitate the food and chew it again, which further reduces the size of the food particles and thoroughly mixes the food with liquids containing the mixture of microorganisms.

Some of the microorganisms (certain bacteria, fungi, and protozoa) in the rumen produce enzymes that can break down cellulose to short-chain fatty acids. These fatty acids are absorbed into the cow's bloodstream and are used by its cells to provide energy. But the story does not end there. Methanogens (certain Archaea) are common in the gut of ruminants. They metabolize some of the fatty acids to methane. A cow typically releases 200 to 500 liters of methane gas per day. Methane production by ruminants and termites that have a similar gut metabolism contributes significantly to the level of methane in the atmosphere. Because methane is a greenhouse gas, cows and their archeon companions are a factor in global warming.

Agricultural researchers look at methane production by cows as an opportunity to increase the food efficiency of cattle. If the researchers could prevent the methanogens from using some of the fatty acids to make methane, there would be more for the cows to turn into meat or milk. They have experimented with substances that inhibit the growth of methanogens.

The digestive system of ruminants encourages the growth of microorganisms that assist in the breakdown of cellulose.

## 21.3 The Kingdom Protista

The kingdom Protista is a taxonomic category of convenience. Scientists do not actually think that the organisms in this group are closely related to one another. The only characteristic they share is that they are the simplest eukaryotic organisms. Many of them are single-celled, but others are multicellular and show a degree of cellular specialization. The ancestors of this group are thought to have formed about 2 billion years ago.

There is great diversity among the more than 250,000 species. Because of this diversity, it is a constant challenge to separate the kingdom Protista into meaningful subgroups. Furthermore, research continually reveals new evidence about the members of this group and their evolutionary relationships, requiring changes in taxonomy. Usually, the species are divided into three general groups, based on their mode of life: *algae*, autotrophic unicellular organisms; *protozoa*, heterotrophic unicellular organisms; and funguslike protists. These categories are helpful in discussing the major roles of these organisms but do not reflect how the organisms have evolved. For example, many kinds of flagellated protists are photosynthetic, but other, closely related organisms are not. Thus, two closely related organisms would be placed in the categories protozoa or algae, depending on their ability to perform photosynthesis. Figure 21.7 shows some current ideas about how some of these groups are related.

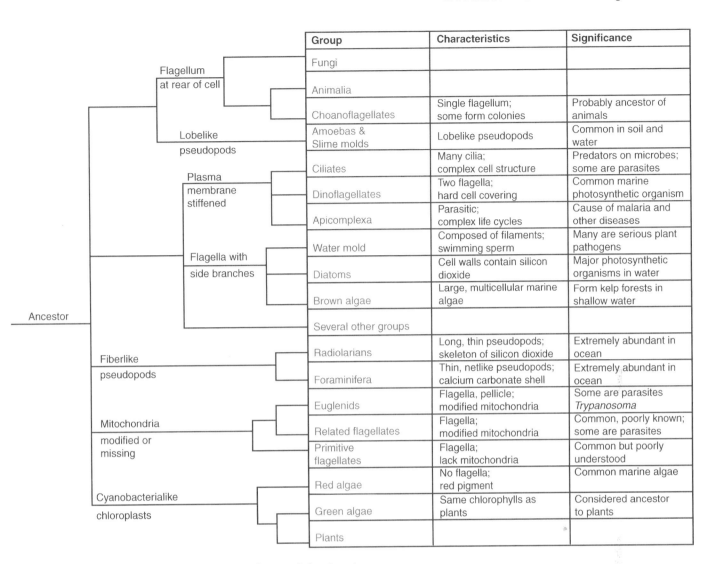

| | Group | Characteristics | Significance |
|---|---|---|---|
| Flagellum at rear of cell | Fungi | | |
| | Animalia | | |
| | Choanoflagellates | Single flagellum; some form colonies | Probably ancestor of animals |
| Lobelike pseudopods | Amoebas & Slime molds | Lobelike pseudopods | Common in soil and water |
| Plasma membrane stiffened | Ciliates | Many cilia; complex cell structure | Predators on microbes; some are parasites |
| | Dinoflagellates | Two flagella; hard cell covering | Common marine photosynthetic organism |
| | Apicomplexa | Parasitic; complex life cycles | Cause of malaria and other diseases |
| Flagella with side branches | Water mold | Composed of filaments; swimming sperm | Many are serious plant pathogens |
| | Diatoms | Cell walls contain silicon dioxide | Major photosynthetic organisms in water |
| | Brown algae | Large, multicellular marine algae | Form kelp forests in shallow water |
| | Several other groups | | |
| Fiberlike pseudopods | Radiolarians | Long, thin pseudopods; skeleton of silicon dioxide | Extremely abundant in ocean |
| | Foraminifera | Thin, netlike pseudopods; calcium carbonate shell | Extremely abundant in ocean |
| Mitochondria modified or missing | Euglenids | Flagella, pellicle; modified mitochondria | Some are parasites *Trypanosoma* |
| | Related flagellates | Flagella; modified mitochondria | Common, poorly known; some are parasites |
| | Primitive flagellates | Flagella; lack mitochondria | Common but poorly understood |
| Cyanobacterialike chloroplasts | Red algae | No flagella; red pigment | Common marine algae |
| | Green algae | Same chlorophylls as plants | Considered ancestor to plants |
| | Plants | | |

Ancestor

**FIGURE 21.7  Relationships Among Members of the Protista**
In this figure, organisms that are photosynthetic are shown in green and are generally known as algae. Those that are shown in red are typically hetertrophs and are generally known as protozoa. Those shown in blue are funguslike. Some groups, such as the Euglenids and Dinoflagellates, have some members that are photosynthetic and others that are not.

## Algae

**Algae** are protists that contain chlorophyll in chloroplasts and therefore carry on photosynthesis. Many of these organisms are single-celled, but some groups are multicellular. Although most live in the ocean and bodies of freshwater, they can also be found in other moist places, such as soil and the surface of other organisms in rainforests and other moist habitats. **Plankton** is a collection of small, floating or weakly swimming organisms. Algae are the major components of the **phytoplankton** that consists of the photosynthetic plankton that is the basis of most aquatic food chains. Cyanobacteria are the other major component of phytoplankton. **Zooplankton** consists of nonphotosynthetic plankton, including aquatic protozoa and tiny animals. **Benthic** organisms live attached to the bottom or to objects in the water. Many benthic algae form denses "forests" of large seaweeds in shallow sea water. The large number of benthic and planktonic algae makes them

an important source of atmospheric oxygen ($O_2$). It is estimated that over 50% of the oxygen in the atmosphere is produced by marine algae. Furthermore, because algae are important producers in marine food chains, disruptions to the marine algal community can have serious implications for the production of fish and shellfish.

Because algae require light, they are found only near the surface of the water. Even in the clearest water, photosynthesis does not usually occur any deeper than 100 meters. Benthic forms are found in shallow water and are common along the ocean shoreline. Some phytoplankton have flagella or other methods of locomotion, which assist them in remaining near the surface. Others maintain their position by storing food as oil, which is less dense than water and enables the cells to float near the surface.

The various kinds of algae reproduce both sexually and asexually. However, their primary method of reproduction is asexual cell division. Like the cyanobacteria, in warm,

## OUTLOOKS 21.3

# The Marine Microbial Food Web

The analysis of terrestrial ecosystems typically involves the categorization of organisms into functional groups based on their metabolic abilities and their position in food chains. Plants are identified as producers, animals as consumers, and fungi and bacteria as decomposers. Scientists have long known that microorganisms were important in marine food webs but have been hampered in their study by the nature of the organisms involved.

There are significant problems in studying microbes. Their small size makes it difficult to identify organisms. A new term, picoplankton, is used to describe aquatic organisms that are in a size range between 0.2 and 2 µm. In addition, once organisms are detected it is often difficult or impossible to grow microbes to study their metabolic abilities and determine how they contribute to food webs.

However, by using new techniques for identifying organisms and indirect methods to get an idea of their metabolic abilities, it is becoming clear that the ocean is dominated by a microbial food web. As with all ecosystems, the base consists of autotrophs that use a source of energy to manufacture organic matter. The majority of photosynthesis in the ocean is the result of cyanobacteria and the eukaryotic dinoflagellates and diatoms. The photosynthetic cyanobacteria are the most common bacteria in the ocean. The Archaea also appear to be important as autotrophs, although many are chemoautotrophs that use inorganic chemical reactions to provide themselves with energy. They are extremely common, particularly in deep ocean waters where sunlight does not penetrate.

Once we get beyond the producer level in the ocean, various kinds of microbes are first in line to consume the cells of autotrophs. Flagellates, ciliates, fungi, and bacteria consume other organisms. Finally, we arrive at the animals that are filter-feeding animals, such as sponges, corals, and crustaceans that sift a mixture of organisms from water. These become food for larger animals such as crabs, snails, fish, and squid.

There is an important subplot to this microbial food web picture. Much of the organic matter never reaches animals at higher trophic levels. It is trapped in a microbial loop that involves many kinds of microbes that simply recycle organic matter. It is thought that bacteria alone process more than half of all the carbon involved in metabolism in the oceans. Dissolved organic carbon is an important part of the microbial food web. Autotrophic microbes produce organic molecules from inorganic molecules. Dissolved organic carbon enters the water as a result of leakage and waste products from microbes (both autotrophs and heterotrophs) and the death and decay of organisms. It is becoming clear that viruses have an important role to play in this process. Studies that sample the DNA in the ocean identify a large virus component. Many scientists estimate that there are millions of viruses per milliliter of seawater. Viruses infect and kill their hosts: Bacteria, Archaea, and eukaryotic microbes. The disintegration of their host cells releases organic matter into the water, which, in turn, becomes food for saprophytic microbes.

These studies are significant to understanding the basis for ecologic interactions in the ocean. These interactions can impact fisheries biology and human health when there are huge increases in the population of certain toxic marine microbes that restrict the use of fish for food and cause the closure of beaches to prevent illness.

---

nutrient-rich waters, various kinds of algae can reproduce rapidly by asexual reproduction and cause an algal bloom. The population can become so large that clumps of algae float on the surface or in the case of single-celled algae, the water may become colored or murky.

## Single-Celled Algae

There are several common kinds of single-celled algae. *Euglenids* are single-celled algae that move by flagella. They have an outer covering, called a pellicle, which gives them shape but is flexible. *Euglenids* vary in terms of their metabolism. Some lack chloroplasts and are heterotrophs. Others have chloroplasts and are autotrophs. However, even among those that have chloroplasts, many are able to consume food and behave as heterotrophs, particularly when light levels are low. Most of them, like the common *Euglena*, are found in freshwater. They are widely studied because they are easy to culture.

*Diatoms* are extremely common single-celled algae found in freshwater, marine, and soil environments. They are a major component of the phytoplankton of the oceans and serve as a food source for zooplankton and many kinds of filter-feeding organisms, such as whales, clams, and barnacles. A few species are heterotrophs or parasites. They are typically brownish in color. Although they do not have cilia or flagella, they are able to move with a sort of gliding motion. They are unique because their cell walls contain silicon dioxide (silica). The walls fit together like the lid and bottom of a shoe box; the lid overlaps the bottom. The silica-containing walls have many pores, which form interesting patterns. Because their cell walls contain silicon dioxide, they readily form fossils. The fossil cell walls have many tiny holes and can be used in a number of commercial processes. They are used as filters for liquids and as abrasives in specialty soaps, toothpastes, and scouring powders.

*Dinoflagellates*, along with diatoms, are important food producers in the ocean's ecosystem. They are also very common in freshwater and brackish water. All members of this group of algae have two flagella, which is the reason for their name (*di* = two), and an outer cellulose covering made up of lates. Although many dinoflagellates are photosynthetic, some are heterotrophs and others are parasites. Some change from autotroph to heterotroph, depending on environmental conditions.

Some species of dinoflagellates have symbiotic relationships with marine animals, such as the reef corals; the dinoflagellates provide a source of nutrients for the reef-building coral. Corals that live in the light and contain dinoflagellates grow 10 times faster than corals without this symbiont. Thus, in coral reef ecosystems, dinoflagellates form the foundation of the food chain.

Some forms of dinoflagellates produce toxins. Because many of the toxin-producing dinoflagellates are reddish in color, a bloom of these organisms is called a *red tide*. Often, fish and other vertebrates such as birds and mammals are killed by exposure to the toxins. Although the toxins do not seem to harm shellfish, such as oysters, consuming the toxin along with the shellfish can cause sickness or death. Red tides usually occur in the warm months and are more common in tropical and semitropical waters. During red tide episodes, people are warned not to swim in areas that have a red tide or harvest fish or shellfish for food. Commercially available shellfish are tested for toxin content; if they are toxic, they are not marketed.

The dinoflagellate *Pfiesteria piscidia* has been responsible for the death of millions of fish in estuaries of the eastern United States. These dinoflagellates release toxins that paralyze fish. The dinoflagellates then feed on the fish. They have also been responsible for human and wildlife poisoning. It appears that blooms of these organisms may be triggered by high amounts of nutrients in the water as a result of runoff from feedlots and agricultural land.

Many marine forms of dinoflagellates are bioluminescent; they are responsible for the glow seen at night in ocean waves or in a boat's wake. Figure 21.8 shows examples of euglenids, diatoms, and dinoflagellates.

## Multicellular Algae

Many kinds of algae are multicellular and can be quite large, with some specialization of cells and body parts. These algae are commonly known as *seaweed*. They are found in shallow water attached to objects. Two types, red algae and brown algae, are mainly marine forms. The green algae are primarily freshwater species.

*Red algae* live in warm oceans and attach to the ocean floor by means of a holdfast structure. They are found from the splash zone, the area where waves are breaking, to depths of 100 meters. Some red algae become encrusted with calcium carbonate and are important in reef building. Other species are commercially important, because they produce agar and carrageenin. *Agar* is widely used as a jelling agent for growth media in microbiology. *Carrageenin* is a gelatinous material used in paints, cosmetics, and baking. It is also used to make gelatin desserts harden faster and ice cream smoother. In Asia and Europe, some red algae are harvested and used as food.

*Brown algae* are found in cooler marine environments. Most species of brown algae have a holdfast organ. Colonies of these algae can reach 100 meters in length. Brown algae produce *alginates*, which are widely used as stabilizers in frozen desserts, as emulsifiers in salad dressings, and as thickeners to give body to foods such as chocolate milk and cream cheeses; they are also used to form gels in such products as fruit jellies.

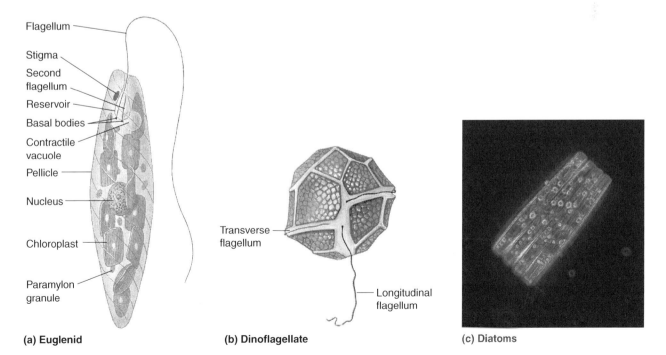

**FIGURE 21.8 Single-Celled Algae**
Three very common kinds of single-celled algae are the euglenids, dinoflagellates, and diatoms.

The Sargasso Sea is a large mat of free-floating brown algae between the Bahamas and the Azores. It is thought that this huge mass (as large as the European continent) is the result of brown algae that have become detached from the ocean bottom, have been carried by ocean currents, and have accumulated in this calm region of the Atlantic Ocean. This large mass of floating algae provides a habitat for a large number of marine animals, such as marine turtles, eels, jellyfish, and innumerable crustaceans. Figure 21.9 shows examples of red and brown algae.

*Green algae* are found primarily in freshwater ecosystems, although a few kinds live in oceans. Some are single-celled and have flagella; some lack flagella and form strings, which either float in the water or grow on surfaces. The members of this group can also be found growing on trees, in the soil, and even on snowfields in the mountains. Like land plants, green algae have cellulose cell walls and store food as starch. Green algae also have the same types of chlorophyll as do plants. Biologists believe that land plants evolved from the green algae. Figure 21.10 shows a variety of green algae.

## Protozoa

**Protozoa** are members of the kingdom Protista; they are eukaryotic, heterotrophic, single-celled organisms that lack cell walls. Generally, protozoa lack all types of chlorophyll, but some organisms may contain chloroplasts at some times in their lives and lack them at others. One common way to classify the protozoa into subgroups is by their method of locomotion. Although this is a convenient way to subdivide the organisms for the purposes of discussion, it is clearly not a valid phylogenic grouping.

### Flagellates

Flagellates are an extremely diverse group of organisms that have flagella and lack cell walls and chloroplasts. They live in any moist environment, including marine waters and freshwater.

**Red algae**

**Brown algae**

**FIGURE 21.9  Red and Brown Algae**
Red and brown algae are primarily marine organisms. Most of them grow attached to the ocean bottom or other organisms in their environment.

*Macrasterias*

*Volvox*

*Ulothrix*

**FIGURE 21.10  Green Algae**
Some green algae are single-celled; others form colonies.

moist soil, and as parasites or symbionts. Some flagellates have an extremely simple structure, suggesting that they may be the most primitive of all eukaryotic organisms. Some feed by absorbing simple organic molecules through their cell membranes; others engulf food particles or other organisms.

Many kinds of flagellates are mutualistic or parasitic. Termites are insects that eat wood but cannot digest it. Their guts contain mutualistic flagellated protozoa capable of digesting cellulose. Thus, the termite benefits from a food source and the flagellate benefits from a good place to live and a continuous supply of food.

There are many examples of parasitic flagellates (figure 21.11). One is *Trichomonas vaginalis*, that can live in the reproductive tract of both men and women and is the cause of a common sexually transmitted disease. Often, it doesn't cause any symptoms but sometimes causes itching and a discharge. The symptoms are more common in women than men. Trypanosomes, which cause sleeping sickness in humans and domestic cattle, primarily in Africa are another example

*Trypanosoma gambiense*

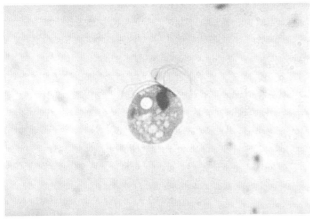

*Trichomonas vaginalis*

**FIGURE 21.11 Flagellates**
Several flagellated protozoa are parasites. *Trypanosoma gambiense* causes sleeping sickness. It is shown here among red blood cells. *Trichomonas vaginalis* is the cause of a common sexually transmitted disease.

of a parasitic flagellate. The parasite develops in the circulatory system and moves to the cerebrospinal fluid surrounding the brain. When this occurs, the infected person develops the "sleeping" condition, which, if untreated, is eventually fatal.

*Giardia lamblia* is a flagellated protozoan that contaminates freshwater throughout the world. Because *Giardia* is a common intestinal parasite of deer, beaver, and many other animals, even "pure" mountain streams in wilderness areas are likely to be contaminated. Infection usually causes diarrhea, intestinal gas, and nausea, although it does not usually cause life-threatening illness. The most effective way to eliminate the spores formed by this protozoan is to filter out particles as small as 1 micrometer from the water or boil it for at least 5 minutes before drinking.

Choanoflagellates are colonial flagellates that many biologists believe are ancestral to all multicellular animals, because the simplest animals, sponges, contain cells that are extremely similar in structure to free-living choanoflagellates.

## Amoeboid Protozoans

Amoeboid protozoans have extensions of their cell surface called pseudopods in which the cytoplasm flows. They range from the well-known *Amoeba*, with its constantly changing, lobelike pseudopods to species with thin, fiberlike pseudopods (figure 21.12). Most amoeboid protozoans are free-living and feed on bacteria, algae, or even small, multicellular organisms. *Amoeba* uses pseudopods to move about and to engulf food.

Some forms are parasitic. *Entamoeba histolytica* is responsible for the disease known as amoebic dysentery. People become infected with this protozoan when they travel to parts of the world that have poor sewage and water treatment facilities and often have contaminated water.

Radiolarians and foraminiferans are two specialized groups of amoeboid protozoans that are extremely common in the oceans. Both kinds have long, thin pseudopods and float in the ocean, feeding on organic material and other living organisms. However, the radiolarians have a kind of skeleton composed of silicon dioxide, and the foraminiferans have a skeleton of calcium carbonate. When these organisms die, their cells disintegrate but their skeletons remain and sink to the bottom of the sea. Extensive limestone deposits were formed from the accumulated skeletons of ancient foraminiferans. The white cliffs of Dover, England, were formed from such shells.

## Apicomplexa

All members of the Apicomplexa are nonmotile parasites with a sporelike stage in their life cycles. The disease malaria, one of the leading causes of disability and death in the world, is caused by members of the Apicomplexa. About 3.3 billion people live in malaria-prone regions of the world. There are about 250 million new cases of malaria each year, and the disease kills about one million people annually.

The organisms that cause malaria have a complex life cycle involving transmission by a mosquito vector (figure 21.13). While in the mosquito vector, the parasite goes through the sexual stages of its life cycle. One of the best ways to control

**FIGURE 21.12 Amoeboid Protozoa**
Amoeboid protozoa have extensions of their cell surface called pseudopods. Pseudopods contain moving cytoplasm. Some, such as *Amoeba,* have large, lobelike pseudopods, which change shape as the cell moves and feeds. Others have long, filamentous pseudopods that trap organisms and transport food molecules to the central cell from the objects they feed on.

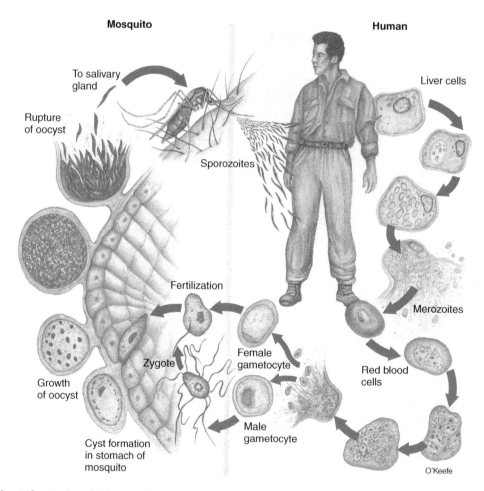

**FIGURE 21.13 The Life Cycle of *Plasmodium vivax***
*Plasmodium vivax* is one of the members of the Apicomplexa that causes malaria. The life cycle requires two hosts, the *Anopheles* mosquito and the human. Humans get malaria when they are bitten by a mosquito carrying the larval stage of *Plasmodium.* The larva undergoes asexual reproduction and releases thousands of individuals, which invade the red blood cell. Their release from massive numbers of infected red blood cells causes the chills, fever, and headache associated with malaria. Inside the red blood cell, more reproduction occurs to form male gametocytes and female gametocytes. When the mosquito bites a person with malaria, it ingests some gametocytes. Fertilization occurs and zygotes develop in the stomach of the mosquito. The resulting larvae are housed in the mosquito's salivary gland. Then, when the mosquito bites someone, some saliva containing the larvae is released into the person's blood and the cycle begins again.

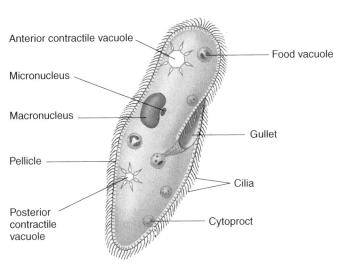

**FIGURE 21.14 Ciliates**
Ciliates, such as *Paramecium*, have a complex cell structure and a large number of cilia on their surface, which propel them through the water. They feed on a variety of organisms.

**FIGURE 21.15 Slime Mold**
Slime molds grow in moist conditions and are important decomposers. As slime molds grow, additional nuclei are produced by mitosis, but there is no cytoplasmic division. Thus, at this stage, a slime mold is a single mass of cytoplasm with many nuclei.

this disease is to eliminate the vector, which usually involves using a pesticide. Many of us are concerned about the harmful effects of pesticides in the environment. However, in the parts of the world where malaria is common, the harmful effects of pesticides are of less concern than the harm generated by the disease. Many diseases of insects, birds, and mammals are also caused by the members of this group.

## Ciliates

Ciliates are a group of protozoans with a complex cellular structure and numerous short, flexible extensions from the cell called *cilia* (figure 21.14). The cilia move in an organized, rhythmic manner and propel the cell through the water. Some types of ciliates, such as *Paramecium*, have nearly 15,000 cilia per cell and move at a rapid speed of 1 millimeter per second. Most ciliates are free-living cells found in freshwater and salt water or damp soil, where they feed on bacteria and other small organisms. Ruminant animals have large numbers of ciliates in their digestive systems, where they are part of the complex ecology of the ruminant gut (see Outlooks 21.2).

Ciliates have a complex cellular structure with two kinds of nuclei. Most have a macronucleus and one or more micronuclei. The macronucleus is involved in the day-to-day running of the cell, whereas the micronuclei are involved in sexual reproduction. Sexual reproduction involves a process called conjugation, in which two cells go through a series of nuclear divisions equivalent to meiosis and exchange some of their nuclear material. Although the exchange does not result in additional cells, it does result in cells that have a changed genetic mixture.

## Funguslike Protists

Funguslike protists have a motile reproductive stage but they do not have chitin in their cell walls, which differentiates them from true fungi. There are two kinds of funguslike protists: slime molds and water molds.

## Slime Molds

Slime molds are amoeba-like organisms that crawl about and digest dead organic matter. Some slime molds look like giant amoebae. They are essentially a large mass several centimeters across, in which the nucleus and other organelles have divided repeatedly within a single large cell (figure 21.15). No cell membranes partition this mass into separate segments. They vary in color from white to bright red or yellow, and they can reach relatively large sizes (45 centimeters in length) when in an optimum environment.

Other kinds of slime mold exist as large numbers of individual, amoeba-like cells. These haploid cells get food by engulfing microorganisms. They reproduce by mitosis. When their environment becomes dry or otherwise unfavorable, the cells come together into an irregular mass. This mass glides along rather like an ordinary garden slug and is labeled the sluglike stage. This sluglike form may flow about for hours before it forms spores. When the mass gets ready to produce spores, it creates a stalk with cells that have cell walls. At the top of this specialized structure, cells are modified to become haploid spores. When released, these spores may be carried by the wind and, if they land in a favorable place, may develop into new amoeba-like cells.

## Water Molds

Water molds were once thought to be fungi. However, they differ from fungi in two fundamental ways. Their cell walls are made of cellulose, not chitin, and water molds have a flagellated reproductive stage. Thus, they are considered to be more closely related to the diatoms and brown algae than to fungi. Although called water molds, they live in many moist environments, not just in bodies of water (figure 21.16).

Water molds are important saprophytes and parasites in aquatic ecosystems. They are often seen as fluffy growths on

**FIGURE 21.16 Water Mold**
Rapidly reproducing water molds quickly produce a large mass of filaments. These filaments cause the fuzzy growth often seen on dead fish and other dead material in the water.

dead fish or other organic matter floating in water. A parasitic form of water mold is well known to people who rear tropical fish; it causes a cottonlike growth on the fish. Although these organisms are usually found in aquatic habitats, they are not limited to this environment. Some species cause downy mildew on plants such as grapes. In the 1880s, this mildew almost ruined the French wine industry when it spread throughout the vineyards. A copper-based fungicide called *Bordeaux mixture*—the first chemical used against plant diseases—was used to save the vineyards. A water mold was also responsible for the Irish potato blight. In the nineteenth century, potatoes were the staple of the Irish diet. Cool, wet weather in 1845 and 1847 damaged much of the potato crop, and more than a million people died of starvation. Nearly one-third of the survivors left Ireland and moved to Canada or the United States.

## 21.3 CONCEPT REVIEW

14. Why is the kingdom Protista not considered a valid phylogenetic group?
15. What is phytoplankton?
16. List three different categories of organisms that are considered algae.
17. List two major kinds of marine phytoplankton.
18. List the two major kinds of multicellular marine algae.
19. Describe a characteristic for each of the following:
    a. apicomplexa
    b. ciliates
    c. flagellates
    d. foraminifera
20. Why are water molds and slime molds not considered to be Fungi?

## 21.4 Multicellularity in the Protista

The three major types of organisms in the kingdom Protista (algae, protozoa, and funguslike protists) include both single-celled and multicellular forms. Biologists believe that there has been a similar type of evolution in all three of these groups. The most primitive organisms in each group are thought to have been single-celled and to have given rise to the more advanced, multicellular forms. Most protozoan organisms are single-celled however, some ciliates are colonial. The multicellular forms of funguslike protists are the slime molds, which have both single-celled and multicellular stages.

Perhaps the most widely known example of this trend from a single-celled to a multicellular condition is found in the green algae. A very common single-celled green alga is *Chlamydomonas*, which has a cell wall and two flagella. It looks just like the individual cells of the colonial green algae *Volvox*. Some species of *Volvox* have as many as 50,000 cells (figure 21.17). All the flagella of each cell in the colony move in unison, allowing the colony to move in one direction. In some *Volvox* species, certain cells have even specialized to produce sperm or eggs. Biologists believe that the division of labor seen in colonial protists represents the beginning of the specialization that led to the development of true multicellular organisms with many kinds of specialized cells. Three types of multicellular organisms—fungi, plants, and animals—eventually developed.

## 21.4 CONCEPT REVIEW

21. Why do biologists think that the ancestors of plants, animals, and fungi could have been Protista?

## 21.5 The Kingdom Fungi

The members of the kingdom Fungi are nonphotosynthetic, eukaryotic organisms with cell walls. The structure of the cell wall differs from that of other organisms because fungal cell walls contain chitin along with other compounds. Some are single-celled, but most are multicellular organisms composed of filaments of cells joined end-to-end. Each filament is known as a hypha. The hyphae form a network known as a mycelium (figure 21.18).

Even though fungi are nonmotile, they are easily dispersed, because they form huge numbers of spores. A **spore** is a cell with a tough, protective cell wall that can resist extreme conditions. Fungi have a variety of kinds of spores. Some spores are produced by sexual reproduction, others by asexual reproduction. An average-sized mushroom can produce over 20 billion spores; a good-sized puffball can produce as many as 8 trillion spores. When released, the spores are transported by wind or water. Because of their small size, spores can remain in the atmosphere a long time and travel thousands of kilometers. Fungal spores have been collected as high as 50 kilometers above Earth.

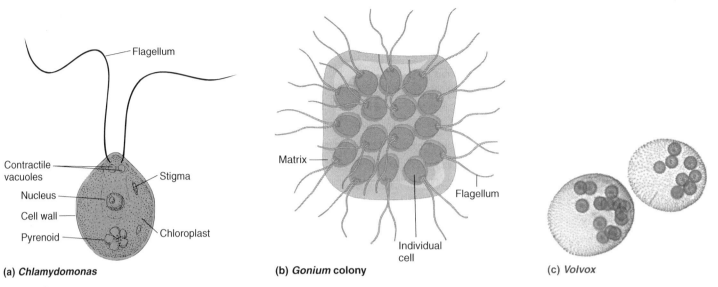

**FIGURE 21.17** **The Development of Multicellular Green Algae**
*(a) Chlamydomonas* is a green, single-celled alga containing the same type of chlorophyll as that found in green plants. *(b) Gonium,* a green alga similar to *Chlamydomonas,* forms colonies composed of 4 to 32 cells that are essentially the same as *Chlamydomonas.* *(c) Volvox* is a colonial green alga that produces daughter colonies and also has specialized cells that produce eggs and sperm.

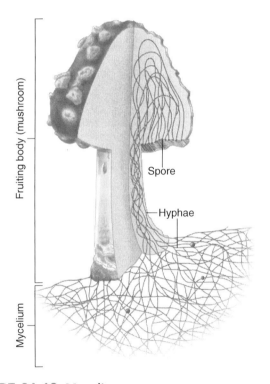

**FIGURE 21.18** **Mycelium**
The basic structure of a fungus is a multicellular filament known as a hypha. A mass of hyphae is collectively known as a mycelium.

All fungi are heterotrophs that must obtain nutrients from organic sources. Most secrete enzymes that digest large molecules into smaller units, which the fungi absorb. Fungi grow by division of the cells at the end of a hypha. In this way they expand into new areas where there are new sources of organic matter. Fungi are free-living, parasitic, or mutualistic. Free-living fungi, such as mushrooms, decompose dead organisms as they absorb nutrients. Parasitic fungi are responsible for many plant diseases and a few human infections, such as athlete's foot, vaginal yeast infections, and ringworm. Mutualistic fungi are commonly associated with the roots of plants.

## The Taxonomy of Fungi

Fungi are divided into subgroups, based on their methods of reproduction (figure 21.19). It is assumed that fungi originated from ancestors that had flagellated swimming reproductive spores and that the most primitive groups of fungi would share this characteristic.

The *Chytridiomycota* are fungi that are aquatic or live in moist soil where they digest organic matter. They are considered one of the most primitive groups of fungi because they have a flagellated spore stage. Infections caused by one member of this group, *Batrachochytrium dendrobatidis,* are thought to be one of the reasons for the decline in frogs and other amphibians throughout the world.

The *Neocallimastigomycota* are fungi that form flagellated spores and live as mutualistic, anaerobic fungi in the rumen of ruminants. They break down cell walls of plants to simpler compounds and contribute to the nutrition of ruminants (see Outlooks 21.2).

The *Zygomycota* are distinguished from other fungi because they form sexual spores when the hyphae of two different strains of the species join. The spores do not have flagella. One common example is bread mold.

The *Glomeromycota* are fungi that form arbuscular mycorrhizae with plants. (Mycorrhizae are discussed later in this chapter.) It appears that most must obtain nutrients from the roots of plants to live. It appears that they only reproduce asexually.

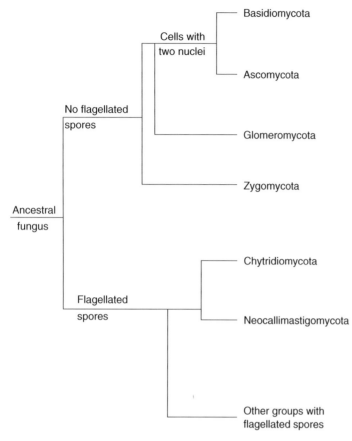

**FIGURE 21.19  Fungus Taxonomy**
There are several subgroups within the kingdom Fungi. They are distinguished from one another primarily by their methods of reproduction.

The *Ascomycota* are distinguished from other fungi because their cells contain two distinct nuclei and they produce spores by sexual reproduction in a saclike structure. They also produce spores asexually. About 75% of all fungi are in this group. Molds, mildews, yeasts, morel mushrooms, and truffles are examples. In recent years a fungus in this group, *Geomyces destructans*, has been identified as the cause of white-nose syndrome in bats. Millions of bats have died because of infections with this fungus.

The *Basidiomycota* are unique in having cells that contain two distinct nuclei and sexual spores produced in sets of four on a club-shaped structure. Bracket fungi, most mushrooms, and puffballs are common examples. Many are parasites on plants; rusts and smuts are examples.

The term *yeast* is not a taxonomic term. A yeast is any fungus that is single-celled and generally reproduces by asexual reproduction. One common method of asexual reproduction is budding in which one cell grows a lobe that eventually pinches off to become a separate organism. Yeasts are found in the Basidiomycota and Ascomycota. The yeasts involved in brewing and baking are in the Ascomycota.

*Mold* and *mildew* are other terms associated with fungi. They are not taxonomic terms but simply describe growths of a fungus that forms a fuzzy growth or discolors a surface. They can be from many different taxonomic categories, not just fungi. They are common everywhere there is a source of organic molecules and moisture.

## The Significance of Fungi

Fungi play many significant roles in ecosystems. They are also economically important to humans in many ways.

### Decomposers

Because fungi produce so many spores, any dead organism is likely be colonized by a fungus. Because all fungi are capable of breaking down organic matter, fungi along with bacteria are the major decomposers of organic matter in ecosystems. This decomposer function recycles elements such as carbon, nitrogen, and phosphorus. However, fungi also colonize and break down organic matter that we do not want to have recycled and cause billions of dollars of damage each year. Clothing, wood, leather, and all types of food are susceptible to damage by fungi. One of the best ways to protect against such damage is to keep the material dry, because fungi grow best in a moist environment.

### Fungi as Food

Fungi and their by-products have been used as sources of food for centuries. When we think of fungi and food, mushrooms usually come to mind. The common mushroom found in the grocer's vegetable section is grown in many countries and has an annual market value in the billions of dollars. But there are other uses for fungi as food. *Shoyu* (soy sauce) was originally made by fermenting a mixture of wheat, soybeans, and an ascomycote fungus for a year. Most of the soy sauce used today is made by a cheaper method of processing soybeans with hydrochloric acid. True connoisseurs still prefer soy sauce made the original way. Another mold is important to the soft-drink industry. The citric acid that gives a soft drink its sharp taste was originally produced by squeezing juice from lemons and purifying the acid. Today, however, a mold is grown on a nutrient medium with table sugar (sucrose) to produce great quantities of citric acid at a low cost.

The primary flavors of blue cheeses, such as Danish, American, and the original Roquefort, are produced because the cheeses have been aged with the mold *Penicillium roquefortii*. Another species of *Penicillium* produces the antibiotic penicillin (How Science Works 21.3).

Yeasts are important organisms in the production of alcoholic beverages and in the making of bread. It is difficult to imagine a world in which these two food materials are not important.

### Mycorrhizae

**Mycorrhizae** are associations between certain fungi and the roots of plants. There are two kinds of mycorrhizae. In one kind, arbuscular mycorrhiza, the cells of fungi actually penetrate the cells of the plant roots. Members of the Glomeromycota are always found as arbuscular mycorrhizae. In the other kind,

## HOW SCIENCE WORKS 21.3

## Penicillin

In 1928, Dr. Alexander Fleming was working at St. Mary's Hospital in London. As he sorted through some old petri dishes on his bench, he noticed something unusual. The mold *Penicillium notatum* was growing on some of the petri dishes. Apparently, the mold had found its way through an open window and onto a bacterial culture of *Staphylococcus aureus*. The bacterial colonies that were growing at a distance from the fungus were typical, but there was no growth close to the mold. Fleming isolated the agent responsible for this destruction of the bacteria and named it *penicillin*.

Through Fleming's research efforts and those of several colleagues, the chemical was identified and used for about 10 years in microbiological work in the laboratory. Many suspected that penicillin could be used as a drug, but the fungus could not produce enough of the chemical to make it worthwhile. When World War II began, and England was being firebombed, there was an urgent need for a drug that would control bacterial infections in burn wounds.

Two scientists from England were sent to the United States to begin research into the mass production of penicillin. Their research in isolating new forms of *Penicillium* and purifying the drug were so successful that cultures of the mold now produce over 100 times more of the drug than the original mold discovered by Fleming. In addition, the price of the drug dropped considerably—from a 1944 price of $20,000 per kilogram to a current price of less than $250.00. The species of *Penicillium* used to produce penicillin today is *P. chrysogenum*, which was first isolated in Peoria, Illinois, from a mixture of molds found growing on a cantaloupe. The species name, *chrysogenum*, means golden and refers to the golden-yellow droplets of antibiotic that the mold produces on the surface of its hyphae. The spores of this mold were isolated and irradiated with high dosages of ultraviolet light, which caused mutations to occur in the genes. When some of these mutant spores were germinated, the new hyphae were found to produce much greater amounts of the antibiotic.

---

ectomycorrhiza, the fungal cells surround the root cells but do not invade them. Ectomycorrhizae are usually formed by members of the Ascomycota and Basidiomycota (figure 21.20). Mycorrhizal fungi are found in 80–90% of all plants, and many plants cannot live without their mycorrhizal fungi. The addition of these fungi to the roots of plants increases the roots' surface area for absorption. Plants with mycorrhizal fungi can absorb as much as 10 times more minerals than those without the fungi. Some types of fungi also supply plants with growth hormones, whereas the plants supply carbohydrates and other organic compounds to the fungi.

### Lichens

**Lichens** are organisms that consist of a symbiotic relationship between a fungus and either an alga or a cyanobacterium. The alga or cyanobacterium does photosynthesis and provides the fungus with organic molecules for food, while the fungus provides the moist environment required by the alga or cyanobacterium.

Because the fungi provide a damp environment and the algae produce the food, lichens require no soil for growth. For this reason, many kinds of lichens are commonly found growing on bare rock and are the pioneer organisms in the process of succession. Some lichens grow as fluffy growths on trees or as fleshy structures on the soil (figure 21.21). Lichens are important in the process of soil formation. They secrete an acid, which weathers the rock and makes minerals available for use by plants. When lichens die and decompose, their organic matter mixes with rock particles to form soil.

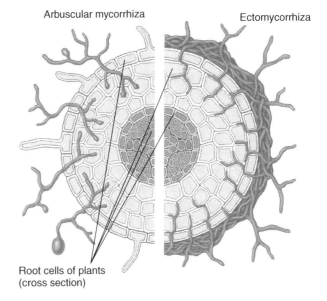

**FIGURE 21.20  Mycorrhizae**

Mycorrhizae are associations between fungi and the roots of plants. Both organisms benefit. The plants have increased absorption of water and minerals, and the fungi receive organic molecules as food from the plants.

Lichens are found in a wide variety of environments, ranging from the frigid Arctic to the scorching desert. Reindeer moss of cold northern regions is actually a lichen. One reason for this success is their ability to withstand

(a) Lichens on a stump

(b) Lichens on tree bark

**FIGURE 21.21 Lichens**
Lichens grow in a variety of habitats. *(a)* There are several kinds of shrubby lichens growing on this stump in Alaska. *(b)* There are several kinds of lichen growing on the bark of this tree. The different colors are due to the different species of algae or cyanobacteria in the lichens.

drought conditions. Some lichens can survive with only 2% water by weight. In this condition, they stop photosynthesis and go into a dormant stage until water becomes available and photosynthesis begins again.

Another factor in the success of lichens is their ability to absorb minerals. However, because air pollution increases the amounts of minerals in the air, many lichens are damaged. Some forms of lichen absorb concentrations of sulfur 1,000 times greater than those found in the atmosphere. This increases the amount of sulfuric acid in the lichen, resulting in damage or death. For this reason, areas with heavy air pollution are "lichen deserts." Because they can absorb minerals, certain forms of lichen have been used to monitor the amount of various pollutants in the atmosphere.

## Pathogenic Fungi

Many kinds of fungi are important pathogens of plants, and a few are human pathogens. Chestnut blight and Dutch elm disease almost caused these two species of trees to become extinct. Wheat rust gets its common name because infected wheat plants look as if they are covered with rust. Corn smut is also due to a fungal pathogen (figure 21.22).

A fungal disease known as *sudden oak death* was identified in Germany, the Netherlands, California, and Oregon. It is caused by the fungus *Phytophthora ramorum*, which also infects rhododendrons, redwoods, and fir trees. Once a tree is infected, an oozing canker develops on the lower trunk; a few weeks later, its leaves turn yellow to brown. Control of the disease will require spending millions of dollars for fungicides. It will also be expensive and difficult to dispose of the millions of infected plants to prevent the spread of the fungus.

Pathogenic fungi that affect domestic crops cost billions of dollars yearly. Farmers and fruit growers must use large amounts of fungicides to control the spread of fungal disease in their fields and orchards.

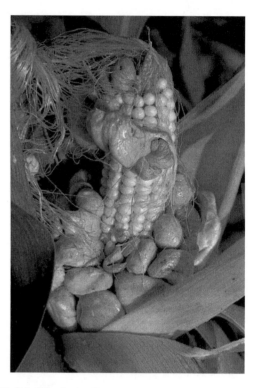

**FIGURE 21.22 Corn Smut**
Most people who raise corn have seen corn smut. Besides being unsightly, it decreases the corn yield.

The most common sites of human fungal infections are the skin, mouth, and lungs. For example, the organism *Pneumocystis* is present in the lungs of most people. However, in people with impaired immune systems, such as AIDS patients, the populations of this organism can increase and cause a form of pneumonia that is often fatal.

The growth of many kinds of molds releases large numbers of spores that are easily inhaled. These can lead to allergic reactions that cause serious illness. The flooding of homes on the Gulf Coast of the United States as a result of hurricanes resulted in many homes developing mold problems. Rehabilitation of these homes requires removal of plaster board to allow the underlying wood structures to dry out and to permit spraying with disinfectants. This costs several thousand dollars.

### Toxic Fungi

A number of fungi produce deadly poisons called **mycotoxins.** The most deadly of these fungi is *Amanita verna,* known as "the destroying angel"; it can be found in woodlands during the summer (figure 21.23). Mushroom hunters must learn to recognize this deadly species. It is believed to be so dangerous that food accidentally contaminated by its spores can cause illness and possibly death.

The mushroom *Psilocybe mexicana* has been used for centuries in religious ceremonies by certain Mexican tribes because of the hallucinogenic chemical it produces. These mushrooms have been grown in culture, and the drug psilocybin has been isolated. In the past, it was used experimentally to study schizophrenia.

*Claviceps purpurea* is a parasite on rye and other grains that affects the flowers of the grasses. It is commonly called ergot. The infection produces a small, hard structure similar in appearance to a seed. The metabolic activity of *C. purpurea* produces a toxin that can cause hallucinations, muscle spasms, insanity, and even death. However, it is also used in controlled doses to treat high blood pressure, to stop bleeding after childbirth, and to treat migraine headaches.

## 21.5 CONCEPT REVIEW

22. Name two beneficial results of fungal growth and activity.
23. Why are spores important in the life cycle of fungi?
24. Describe the role of fungi in lichens and mycorrhizae.
25. How do fungi obtain food?
26. What kinds of organisms are most affected by parasitic fungi?

## Summary

Organisms in the domains Archaea and Bacteria and in the kingdoms Protista and Fungi rely mainly on asexual reproduction, and each cell usually satisfies its own nutritional needs. The Bacteria are prokaryotic and perform a wide variety of functions in ecosystems. Cyanobacteria are major photosynthesizers. Other functions include decomposer, mineral cycling, parasitism, and mutualism. Only a few species are pathogenic.

The Archaea are prokaryotic organisms that differ from Bacteria in the structure of cells and DNA. They are extremely common in aquatic habitats and the soil. Many live in extreme environments. Some live at high temperatures, some in high-salt environments. Many produce methane. Some are chemoautotrophs while others are decomposers. They are involved in the nitrogen cycle. None are pathogenic.

The members of the kingdom Protista are one-celled eukaryotic organisms. In some species, there is minimal cooperation between cells. The protists include: (1) algae with cells that have a cell wall and carry on photosynthesis; (2) protozoa, which lack cell walls and cannot carry on photosynthesis; and (3) funguslike protists that lack chitin and are thus distinguished from true fungi. Some species of Protista are multicellular and have cells specialized for particular functions. It is thought that the multicellular fungi, plants, and animals had Protista-like ancestors.

The kingdom Fungi consists of nonphotosynthetic, eukaryotic organisms with cell walls that contain chitin. Most species are multicellular. Fungi are nonmotile organisms that disperse by producing spores. Lichens are organisms that consist of a combination of organisms involving a mutualistic relationship between a fungus and an algal protist or a cyanobacterium. Mycorrhizae are associations between fungi and plant roots that are beneficial to both organisms.

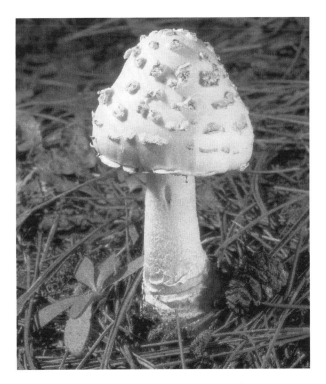

**FIGURE 21.23 Poisonous *Amanita* Mushroom**
The *Amanita* mushroom is deadly poisonous. It destroys the liver cells of those who eat it, causing death.

## Key Terms

*Use the interactive flash cards on the **Concepts in Biology**, 14/e website to help you learn the meaning of these terms.*

| | |
|---|---|
| algae 465 | mycotoxins 477 |
| benthic 465 | pathogens 460 |
| bloom 458 | phytoplankton 465 |
| endospore 461 | plankton 465 |
| lichens 475 | protozoa 468 |
| microorganism (microbe) 456 | spore 472 |
| mycorrhizae 474 | zooplankton 465 |

## Basic Review

1. The domains Bacteria and Archaea differ from the domain Eucarya in that the Eucarya

    a. are eukaryotic and the Bacteria and Archaea are prokaryotic.

    b. are single-celled but the others are not.

    c. carry on photosynthesis but the others do not.

    d. are simpler organisms than the others.

2. Some Archaea are found living in extremely salty or hot environments. (T/F)

3. The Apicomplexa are parasitic species of protozoa. (T/F)

4. Which one of the following groups does not have members that carry on photosynthesis?

    a. the kingdom Protista

    b. the domain Bacteria

    c. the kingdom Fungi

    d. diatoms

5. The primary organisms that make up marine phytoplankton are cyanobacteria, dinoflagellates and _____.

6. Fungi are primarily dispersed by tiny structures called _____.

7. Methanogens are members of the domain Bacteria. (T/F)

8. The Chytridiomycota differ from Zygomycota in that Chytridiomycota

    a. do not have chitin in their cell walls.

    b. have spores with flagella.

    c. do not cause disease.

    d. form mushrooms.

9. Benthic algae live attached to objects. (T/F)

10. Lichens and mycorrhizae are similar in that they both involve symbiotic relationships with fungi. (T/F)

11. Both Bacteria and Archaea are involved in the nitrogen cycle. (T/F)

12. The major kind of Bacteria that carries on photosynthesis is _____.

13. Methanogens are in the domain _____.

14. Which of the following does not have pseudopods?

    a. *Amoeba*

    b. foraminifera

    c. radiolarians

    d. dinoflagellates

15. A mushroom is composed of hyphae. (T/F)

**Answers**
1. a   2. T   3. T   4. c   5. diatoms   6. spores   7. F   8. b
9. T   10. T   11. T   12. cyanobacteria   13. Archaea   14. d
15. T

## Thinking Critically

### A Mushroom Decline

Throughout much of Europe, there has been a severe decline in the mushroom population. On study plots in Holland, data collected since 1912 indicate that the number of mushroom species has dropped from 37 to 12 per plot in recent years. Along with the reduction in the number of species, there has been a parallel decline in the number of individual plants; moreover, the surviving plants are smaller. The phenomenon of the disappearing mushrooms is also evident in England. One study noted that, in 60 fungus species, 20 exhibited declining populations. Mycologists are also concerned about a decline in the United States; however, there are no long-term studies, such as those in Europe, to provide evidence for such a decline. Consider the niche of fungi in the ecosystem. How would an ecosystem be affected by a decline in fungi numbers?

# The Plant Kingdom

**Plants Can Reduce Hurricane Damage**

*Protect our coastal vegetation.*

## CHAPTER OUTLINE

Hurricanes are generated over warm ocean water. Warm air rises, and when the proper conditions exist, the rising warm air contributes to a tight, circular motion of the air and a hurricane forms. Hurricanes cause damage as a result of two things—high winds and a wall of water known as a storm surge that results from the high winds blowing over the surface of the water and the low barometric pressure. Both the strength of the wind and the height of the storm surge are made less severe by vegetation. Hurricanes lose their source of hot air and weaken when they move over land. Although urban areas on the shore are unprotected, urban areas that have healthy marsh between them and the ocean are protected because hurricanes weaken as they pass over the marshlands.

Vegetation provides a porous barrier to the flow of water. It does not stop the water, but reduces the rate at which the water flows into an area and makes the storm surge less severe. Also, the roots of the vegetation tend to bind the soil together and prevent wetlands from being washed away.

Action can be taken to protect current mashes and restore those that have been destroyed. These actions are low in cost compared to the cost of repairing damage to homes, roads, bridges, and other infrastructure. The plants require little maintenance and can reproduce and repair damage done by hurricanes.

More people need to recognize the importance of vegetation and the preservation of coastal wetlands. Various conservation groups are sponsoring revegetation projects to help moderate future damage from hurricanes and need the support of governments and volunteers.

- **Why might plants be better at controlling storm surge than a concrete wall?**

- **Why might plants be a more cost-effective way of controlling storm surge?**

- **Should people be prohibited from destroying coastal vegetation?**

## Background Check

**Concepts you should already know to get the most out of this chapter:**
- The processes of natural selection and evolution (chapter 13)
- Structural and life history characteristics are used to classify organisms (chapter 20)
- Plant cells differ from animal cells (chapter 4)

## 22.1 What Is a Plant?

Plants are eukaryotic, multicellular organisms that have chlorophyll *a* and chlorophyll *b* and carry on photosynthesis. Their cells have cellulose cell walls. They also have specializations for life on land. Plants are, for the most part, terrestrial organisms that can live in just about any environment, including deserts, arctic regions, and swamps (figure 22.1). Many live in shallow freshwater (e.g., water lilies, cattails), and a few live in shallow oceans (e.g., eelgrass, mangroves). Within the estimated 300,000 species, plants show a remarkable variety of form, function, and activity. Plants range in size from tiny, floating duckweed the size of a pencil eraser to redwood trees over 100 meters tall. There are some that lack chlorophyll and are parasites, some that digest animals, and some that have mutualistic relationships with animals.

### 22.1 CONCEPT REVIEW

1. List three characteristics shared by all plants.

## 22.2 Alternation of Generations

Plants have a life cycle that involves two distinctly different generations: the *sporophyte generation* and the *gametophyte generation*. The **sporophyte generation** is diploid (*2n*) and has plant parts in which meiosis takes place to produce haploid (*n*) spores. The word *spore* is used several different ways. There are structures called spores in bacteria, algae, protozoa, fungi, and plants. Each is distinct from the others. In our discussion of plants, the word *spore* refers to a haploid cell produced by meiosis that germinates to give rise to a multicellular haploid

**Desert plants**

**Arctic plants**

**Aquatic plants**

**FIGURE 22.1 Plant Diversity**
Plants are adapted to a wide range of terrestrial habitats, including such extremes as deserts and arctic regions. Many live in freshwater and a few live in shallow marine environments.

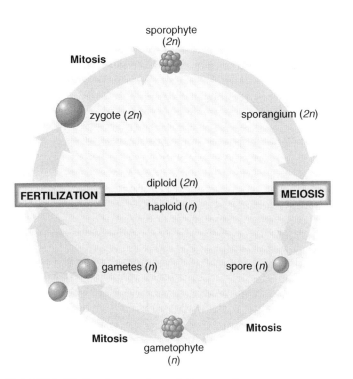

FIGURE 22.2 **Alternation of Generations**
Plants go through two distinctly different generations during their life cycle. The sporophyte generation is diploid and the gametophyte generation is haploid.

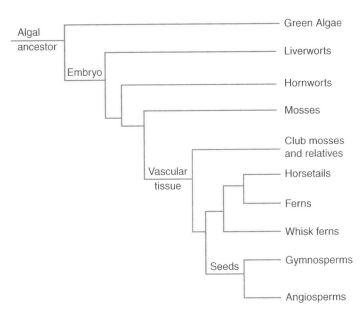

FIGURE 22.3 **The Evolution of Plants**
The evolution of plants involves specializations for living on land and changes in the way they reproduce. Plants differ from their algal ancestors in that they have a multicellular immature stage known as an embryo. Vascular tissue and seeds were important evolutionary steps that allowed plants to be successful away from moist habitats.

generation known as the *gametophyte generation*. The **gametophyte generation** is haploid and develops structures that produce gametes: eggs and sperm. Because the gametophyte is already haploid, eggs and sperm are produced by mitosis. When haploid gametes unite, a diploid zygote is formed. The zygote is the first cell in a new sporophyte generation. The zygote divides by mitosis, and a new multicellular sporophyte generation results. Recall that the term *alternation of generations* is used to describe this kind of life cycle, in which plants cycle between two stages in their life—the diploid sporophyte and the haploid gametophyte (figure 22.2).

## 22.2  CONCEPT REVIEW

2. Which generation in the plant life cycle is haploid and which is diploid?
3. What reproductive cells do sporophytes produce? Are these structures haploid or diploid?
4. What reproductive cells do gametophytes produce? Are these structures haploid or diploid?

## 22.3  The Evolution of Plants

At one time, all life was aquatic. Therefore, it is logical to look for the ancestors of plants among the aquatic, photosynthetic algae. Most scientists feel that the ancestor of plants

was a freshwater member of the green algae. The strongest evidence for this is that green algae have the same kinds of chlorophyll (chlorophyll *a* and chlorophyll *b*) and the same kinds of chloroplasts as plants. Comparison of the DNA of plants and green algae also supports this conclusion. The evolution of plants shows two general trends. One is toward greater specialization for living in a dry environment; the other is toward a more prominent role for the sporophyte generation in the life cycle.

The most primitive plants lack vascular tissue to help carry water. **Vascular tissue** consists of specialized cells arranged end to end that carry water and nutrients from one place to another. Because nonvascular plants lack vascular tissue, most are limited to moist habitats. The more advanced vascular plants have specialized cells that help transport water and other materials throughout the plant. A second major development that allowed advanced plants to exploit terrestrial habitats was the evolution of seeds that could resist drying.

In the more primitive plants, the gametophyte generation is the more conspicuous, and long-lived (dominant) generation, whereas, in more advanced groups, the sporophyte generation is dominant. The taxonomy of plants is based on these trends (figure 22.3). Subsequent sections will discuss the major groups of plants and show how life cycles and the capacity to live in a dry environment evolved.

## 22.4 Nonvascular Plants

The nonvascular plants, which include the mosses, hornworts, and liverworts, are commonly known as *bryophytes*. These three kinds of plants share the following characteristics.

1. They lack vascular tissue.
2. They do not have true roots or leaves.
3. The gametophyte generation is the most prominent part of the life cycle.
4. The sperm swim to the egg.

Because they lack vascular tissue and roots for the absorption and transportation of water, they must rely on the physical processes of diffusion and osmosis to move dissolved materials through their bodies. They have sperm that swim to the egg, so they are similar to their algal ancestors and must have water to reproduce sexually. Thus, most of these organisms are small and live in moist habitats. In other words, they are only minimally adapted to a terrestrial environment.

### The Moss Life Cycle

Although there are differences in details of the life cycle of nonvascular plants, we will use the moss life cycle to represent the group. The moss plant that you commonly recognize is the gametophyte generation. Recall that the gametophyte generation is haploid and is the gamete-producing stage in the plant life cycle. Although the cells of the gametophyte have the haploid number of chromosomes (the same as gametes), not all of them function as gametes. At the top of the moss gametophyte are two kinds of structures that produce gametes: the *antheridium* and the *archegonium* (figure 22.4).

The **antheridium** is a sac-like structure that consists of the developing sperm surrounded by a layer of cells called jacket cells. The **archegonium** is a flask-shaped structure that produces the egg; it has a

tubular channel leading to the egg at its base. There is usually only one egg cell in each archegonium. When the sperm are mature, the outer jacket of the antheridium splits open releasing the flagellated sperm. The sperm swim through a film of dew or rainwater to the archegonium and continue down the channel of the archegonium to fertilize the egg. When the sperm and egg nuclei fuse, a diploid zygote is produced. The zygote is the first cell of the sporophyte generation. The zygote divides by mitosis and the sporophyte generation begins to grow within the archegonium and eventually develops into a mature sporophyte, which grows out of the top of the gametophyte.

The sporophyte consists of a long stalk with a capsule on the end of it. Within the capsule, meiosis takes place, producing haploid spores. These tiny spores are released and distributed by wind and water. When they germinate, they give rise to a multicellular filament known as a protonema. The protonema develops into a mature gametophyte plant. Thus, in mosses and other nonvascular plants, the gametophyte generation is the dominant stage and the sporophyte is dependent on the gametophyte.

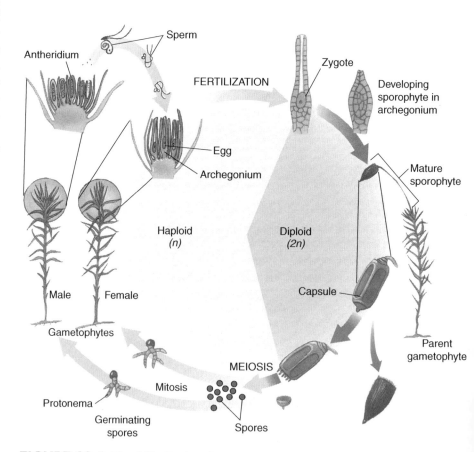

**FIGURE 22.4  The Life Cycle of a Moss**
The haploid gametophyte generation produces eggs in a structure called an archegonium and sperm in a structure called an antheridium. Sperm swim to the egg and fertilization occurs within the archegonium. The zygote is diploid and is the first stage of the sporophyte generation. The sporophyte grows and protrudes from the top of the gametophyte. Meiosis takes place in the capsule of the sporophyte, producing haploid spores. The spores are released and give rise to new gametophyte plants.

**Moss**

**Liverwort**

**Hornwort**

**FIGURE 22.5 Nonvascular Plants**
There are three kinds of nonvascular plants: mosses, liverworts, and hornworts. Because they lack vascular tissue, they are generally small and are usually found in moist environments.

## Kinds of Nonvascular Plants

The mosses are the most common nonvascular plants. Mosses grow as a carpet of many individual gametophyte plants. Each moss plant is composed of a central stalk less than 5 centimeters tall, with short, leaflike structures that are the sites of photosynthesis. There are over 15,000 species of mosses, and they are found anywhere there is adequate moisture.

The gametophytes of liverworts and hornworts are flat sheets only a few layers of cells thick. The name *liverwort* comes from the fact that these plants resemble the moist surface of a liver. There are about 8,000 species of liverworts. Hornworts derive their name from the presence of a long, slender sporophyte, which protrudes from the flat gametophyte plants. Their cells are unusual among plants, because they contain only one, large chloroplast in each cell, whereas other plants have many chloroplasts per cell. There are about 100 species of hornworts found throughout the world. Figure 22.5 shows examples of nonvascular plants.

### 22.4  CONCEPT REVIEW

7. What sex cells are associated with antheridia? With archegonia?
8. List three characteristics shared by nonvascular plants.
9. What are the three major kinds of nonvascular plants?

## 22.5  The Significance of Vascular Tissue

A major step in the evolution of plants was the development of vascular tissue. Plants like ferns, pines, flowering plants, and many others have vascular tissue. Vascular tissue consists of tube-like cells that allow plants to efficiently transport water and nutrients about the plant. The presence of vascular tissue is associated with the development of roots, leaves, and stems. **Roots** are underground structures that anchor the plant and absorb water and minerals. **Leaves** are structures specialized for carrying out the process of photosynthesis. **Stems** are structures that connect the roots with the leaves and position the leaves so that they receive sunlight.

There are two kinds of vascular tissue: *xylem* and *phloem*. **Xylem** is involved in the transport of water and minerals. The primary direction of flow is from the roots to the leaves. Xylem consists of a series of dead, hollow cells arranged end to end to form a tube. The walls of these "cells" are strengthened with extra deposits of cellulose and a complex organic material called lignin. There are two kinds of xylem cells: vessel elements and tracheids. Vessel elements are essentially dead, hollow cells, up to 0.7 mm in diameter, in which the endwalls are missing. Thus, vessel elements form long tubes similar to a series of pieces of pipe hooked together. Tracheids are smaller in diameter and consist of cells with overlapping, tapered ends. Holes in the walls allow water and minerals to move from one tracheid to the next (figure 22.6).

**Phloem** carries the organic molecules (primarily sugars and amino acids) produced in the leaves to other parts of the plant where growth or storage takes place. Growth occurs at the tips of roots and stems and in the production of reproductive structures (cones, flowers, fruits). The roots are typically the place where food is stored, but some plants store food in their stems. The phloem consists of two kinds of cells: sieve tube elements and companion cells. The sieve tube elements lack a nucleus and most organelles but retain a modified granular cytoplasm with strands that extend toward the ends of the cell. In addition, the sieve tube elements have holes in the endwalls that allow the flow of water and dissolved nutrients. The companion cells have direct connections to the sieve tube elements and assist in the movement of sugars and amino acids by active transport from cells in the leaves into the sieve tube elements (figure 22.7).

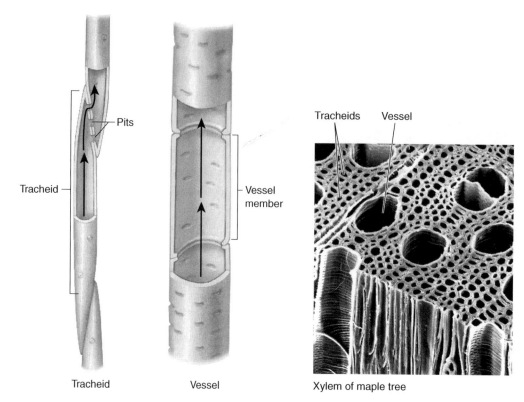

**FIGURE 22.6  Xylem**

Xylem consists of hollow, thick-walled cells. Vessel elements are connected end to end and have no endwalls. Tracheids have overlapping portions and pores that allow water to flow from one tracheid to the next.

**FIGURE 22.7  Phloem**

Phloem consists of cells called sieve tube elements (member) and companion cells. The endwalls of the sieve tube elements have holes that allow the movement of materials from one cell to the next. The cells lack a nucleus but have a form of cytoplasm. Companion cells have nuclei and help sieve tube elements transport materials.

To be well adapted to a dry environment, plants need a waterproof layer on their surface in addition to vascular tissue. This layer reduces the amount of water they lose, and the presence of vascular tissue allows for the easy replacement of the water that is lost. Because vascular tissue allows for the more efficient transport of materials throughout the plant, it allows for an increase in plant size. Although not all vascular plants are large, many are able to become large, because vascular tissue allows them to transport water and nutrients efficiently (Outlooks 22.1).

**22.5  CONCEPT REVIEW**

10. What are the two kinds of vascular tissue, and what do they do?

**22.6  The Development of Roots, Stems, and Leaves**

The development of plant parts that are specialized for particular functions is associated with the presence of vascular tissue because materials can be moved from one specialized plant organ to another by the vascular tissue (figure 22.8). Nearly all vascular plants have plant parts specialized as roots, stems, and leaves.

## Plant Terminology

There are several sets of terminology used to discuss plants that describe their nature but do not have any relationship to their taxonomy or phylogeny.

### Herbaceous and woody

*Herbaceous* plants have few cells with thick cell walls and, thus, are generally small and easily damaged. Mosses, grasses, and many garden plants are herbaceous. *Woody* plants have a great deal of tissue with thick cell walls. The xylem and associated cells are important in strengthening woody plants. There are ferns, gymnosperms, and angiosperms that are woody.

### Annual and perennial

*Annual* plants live one year. They germinate from seeds, grow, produce flowers and seeds, and die within 1 year. The seeds produced germinate the following year and the cycle continues. Most annual plants are angiosperms (flowering plants).

*Perennial* plants live many years. Most kinds of plants are perennials, including mosses, ferns, horsetails, pines, and most flowering plants. Many perennial plants are woody, such as various kinds of trees. Other perennial plants produce above-ground parts that die back at the end of a growing season. The plant regrows above-ground parts from the roots each year, as do tulips, daffodils, rhubarb, and ferns.

### Trees, Shrubs, and Herbs

A *tree* is a large, woody plant that usually has a single main stem with branches. There are tree ferns, most gymnosperms are trees, and many flowering plants are trees. A *shrub* is a perennial woody plant that generally has several main stems and is relatively short. *Herbs* are generally small, herbaceous (non-woody) plants. The word *herb* is also used to indicate plants that have specific food, flavoring, or medicinal value.

## FIGURE 22.8 Vascular Tissue and the Specialization of Plant Parts

Vascular tissue allows for the specialization of leaves for photosynthesis, roots for the absorption of water and minerals, and stems for the positioning of the leaves. The xylem carries water and minerals from the roots to the leaves. The phloem transports organic molecules to places they are needed for growth or storage.

## Roots

Roots are the underground parts of plants that anchor them in the soil and absorb water and nutrients, such as nitrogen, phosphorus, potassium, and other inorganic molecules from the soil. The xylem allows these materials to be distributed for use by other parts of the plant. The phloem transports organic molecules from the leaves and stem to the roots.

Roots grow from their tips. By growing constantly, roots explore new territory for available nutrients and water. As a plant becomes larger, it needs more root surface to absorb water and nutrients and to hold the plant in place. The actively growing portions of the root near the tips have many small, fuzzy, hairlike cell extensions called **root hairs,** which provide a large surface area for the absorption of nutrients and water.

Most roots are important storage places for the food produced by the above-ground parts of the plant. Food is stored in their roots during the growing season and used to stay alive during the winter. The food also provides the raw materials necessary for growth for the next growing season. Although humans do not eat the roots of plants such as maple trees, rhubarb, and grasses, their roots are as important to them in food storage as are those of carrots, turnips, and radishes (figure 22.9).

## Stems

Stems are, in most cases, the above-ground structures of plants that support the light-catching leaves in which photosynthesis occurs. However, they can vary considerably. Trees have stems that support large numbers of branches; vines

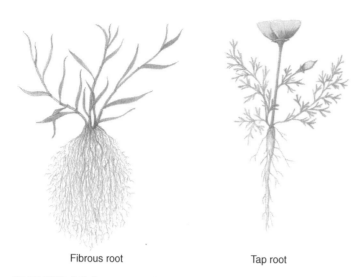

Fibrous root          Tap root

### FIGURE 22.9 Kinds of Roots

The roots of grasses are often in the upper layers of the soil and form a dense network. This form of root is called a fibrous root and is an adaptation to relatively dry conditions. In grasslands, rainfall is infrequent and rarely penetrates very deeply into the soil. The network of roots near the surface efficiently captures the water when it is available. The roots of trees and many other plants typically extend deep into the soil, where they obtain moisture and serve as anchors to hold large plants upright. This kind of root is called a tap root.

have stems that require support; some plants, such as dandelions, have very short stems, with their leaves flat against the ground; and some stems are actually underground. Stems have two main functions:

1. They support the leaves.
2. They transport raw materials from the roots to the leaves and manufactured food from the leaves to the roots.

The support that stems provide is possible because of the nature of plant cell walls. First, all plant cells are surrounded by a cell wall made of cellulose fibers interwoven to form a box, within which the plant cell is contained. Because the cell wall consists of fibers, it is like a wicker basket. There are spaces between cellulose fibers through which materials pass relatively easily. However, the cellulose fibers do not stretch; if the cell is full of water and other cellular materials, it becomes quite rigid. Remember that the process of osmosis results in cells having an internal pressure. It is this pressure against the nonstretchable cell wall that makes the cell rigid. Many kinds of small plants, called *herbaceous plants,* rely primarily on this mechanism for support.

The second way stems provide support involves the thickening of cell walls. *Woody plants* have especially thick cell walls. The xylem of woody plants has thick cell walls and lignin

deposited in the cell walls that provides strength and binds cell walls to one another. This combination of thick cell walls with strengthening lignin is such an effective support mechanism that large trees and bushes are supported against the pull of gravity and can withstand strong winds for centuries. Some of the oldest trees on Earth have been growing for several thousand years.

Another important function of the stem is to transport materials between the roots and the leaves (figure 22.10). A cross section of a stem examined under a microscope reveals that a large proportion of the stem consists of vascular tissue.

In addition to support and transport, the stems of some plants have additional functions. Some stems store food. This is true of sugar cane, yams, and potatoes. (Yams and potatoes are actually highly modified underground stems.) Many plant stems are green and, therefore, are involved in photosynthesis. Cacti and many herbaceous plants are examples. Stems also have a waterproof layer on the outside. In the case of herbaceous plants, it is usually a waxy layer. In the case of woody plants, there is a tough, outer, waterproof bark.

## Leaves

Leaves are the specialized parts of plants that are the major sites of photosynthesis. (See chapter 7 for a discussion of photosynthesis.) To carry out photosynthesis, leaves must have certain characteristics (figure 22.11). Because it is a solar collector, a leaf should have a large surface area. Also,

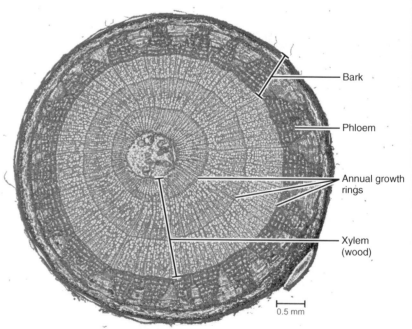

Bark

Phloem

Annual growth rings

Xylem (wood)

0.5 mm

**Cross section of basswood stem**

### FIGURE 22.10 Cross Section of a Stem

This photo shows the cross section of a 3-year-old basswood tree. On the outside is the bark, which contains the phloem. Inside the bark are three layers of xylem tissue. Each layer of xylem constitutes 1 year's growth.

Cuticle

Upper epidermal cell

Palisade mesophyll cells

Air space

Spongy mesophyll cells

Bundle sheath cell

Vascular bundle (vein)

Lower epidermis

Guard cell

Stomate

Cuticle

Xylem

Phloem

Petiole

Blade

## FIGURE 22.11  The Structure of a Leaf

Although a leaf is thin, it consists of several specialized layers. An outer epidermis lacks chloroplasts and has a waxy cuticle on its surface. In addition, the epidermis has openings, called stomates, that can open and close to regulate the movement of gases into and out of the leaf. The internal layers have many cells with chloroplasts, air spaces, and bundles of vascular tissue all organized so that photosynthetic cells can acquire necessary nutrients and transport metabolic products to other locations in the plant.

most leaves are relatively thin, compared with other plant parts. Thick leaves would not allow the penetration of light to the maximum number of photosynthetic cells. Throughout the leaf are bundles of vascular tissue, which transport water and minerals to the photosynthesizing cells and sugars and other molecules from these cells. The thick walls of the cells of vascular tissue also provide support for the leaf. In addition, the leaves of most plants are arranged so that they do not shade one another. This assures that the maximum number of cells in the leaf will be exposed to sunlight.

A drawback to having large, flat, thin leaves is an increase in water loss through evaporation. To help slow water loss, the outermost layer of cells, known as the epidermal layer, has a waxy, waterproof coat on its outer surface. However, some exchange of gases and water must take place through the leaf. When water evaporates from the leaf, it creates a negative pressure, which tends to pull additional water and dissolved minerals through the xylem into the leaf, a process called *transpiration*. Because too much water loss can be deadly, the leaf must regulate transpiration. The amount of water, carbon dioxide, and oxygen moving into and out of the leaves of most plants is regulated by many tiny openings in the epidermis, called *stomates* (figure 22.12). The stomates can close or open to control the rate at which

Closed

Open

## FIGURE 22.12  Stomates

The stomates are located in the covering layer (epidermis) on the outside of leaves. When these two elongated guard cells are swollen, the space between them is open and leaves lose water and readily exchange oxygen and carbon dioxide. In their less rigid and relaxed state, the two stomatal cells close. In this condition, the leaf conserves water but is not able to exchange oxygen and carbon dioxide with the outside air.

water is lost and gases are exchanged. Often during periods of drought or during the hottest, driest part of the day, the stomates are closed, reducing the rate at which the plant loses water.

### 22.6   CONCEPT REVIEW

11. Describe two ways the structure of each of the following is related to its function.
    a. roots
    b. stems
    c. leaves

## 22.7   Seedless Vascular Plants

Seedless vascular plants include the ferns, horsetails, club mosses, and whisk ferns. They share several characteristics:

1. They have vascular tissue.
2. Most have roots, stems, and leaves.
3. The sporophyte generation is the most prominent part of the life cycle.
4. The sperm swims to the egg.
5. They do not have seeds.

With fully developed vascular tissues, these plants are not limited to wet areas, as are the mosses and other nonvascular plants. They can absorb water through their roots and distribute it to above-ground parts of the plant. However, because they have swimming sperm, they must have moist conditions at least for a part of their life cycle.

### The Fern Life Cycle

Although there are differences in the details of the life cycles of seedless vascular plants, we will use the life cycle of ferns as a general model. The conspicuous part of the life cycle is the diploid sporophyte generation. The leaves of most ferns are complex, branched structures commonly called fronds. The sporophyte produces haploid spores by meiosis in special structures of the leaves. The spore-producing parts are typically on the underside of the leaves in structures called sori. However, some species have specialized structures whose sole function is the production of spores. The tiny spores are distributed by the wind or by water and when they fall to the ground, they give rise to a haploid, heart-shaped gametophyte, which has archegonia and antheridia. The sperm swims to the archegonium and fertilizes the egg. Typically, the sperm fertilizes an egg of a different gametophyte plant. Following fertilization of the egg, the diploid zygote derives nourishment from the gametophyte and begins to grow. Eventually, a new sporophyte grows from the gametophyte to begin the life cycle again. Figure 22.13 illustrates the life cycle of the fern.

## Kinds of Seedless Vascular Plants

*Ferns* are the most common of the seedless vascular plants. There are about 12,000 species of ferns in the world. They range from the common bracken fern, found throughout the world, to tree ferns, seen today in some tropical areas (figure 22.14). Along with horsetails and club mosses, tree ferns were important members of the forests of the Carboniferous period, 360–286 million years ago.

*Whisk ferns* are odd plants that lack roots and leaves. They appear to be related to ferns. They are anchored in the soil by an underground stem, which has filaments

Bracken fern

Tree fern

**FIGURE 22.14  Typical Ferns**
There are many different kinds of ferns. The bracken fern is one of the most common. In some places, it is a weed that people try to eliminate from fields. The largest ferns are tree ferns.

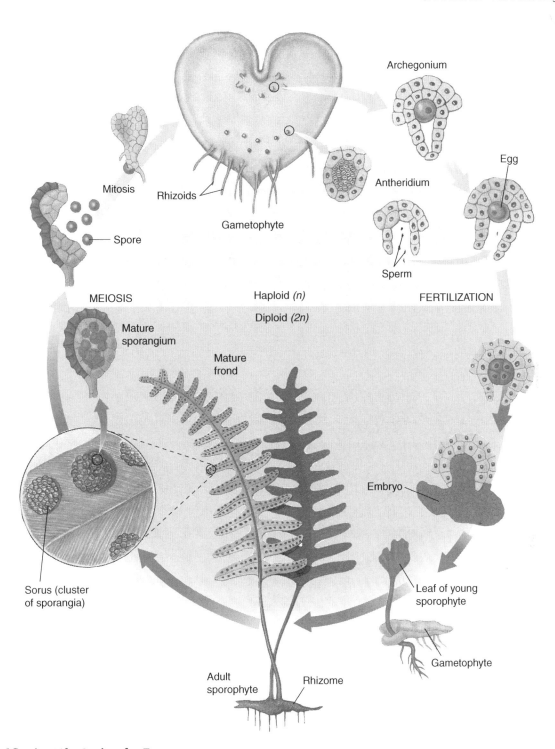

**FIGURE 22.13 The Life Cycle of a Fern**
The sporophyte of a fern consists of an underground stem (rhizome) and roots and above-ground leaves. The leaves are known as fronds. On the back of some fern leaves are small dots called sori. Each sorus contains structures that produce spores by meiosis. These haploid spores develop into the heart-shaped gametophyte. The gametophyte has archegonia, which produce eggs, and antheridia, which produce sperm. The sperm swim to the egg. The fertilized egg (zygote) is diploid and grows into a new sporophyte plant.

growing from it that absorb water and soil nutrients. It has flattened structures similar to leaves, but they are not considered leaves because they lack vascular tissue. Whisk ferns are most common in warm, moist environments. There are about 15 species. The spores are produced at the ends of branches and produce a gametophyte in the soil.

*Horsetails* are low-growing plants with jointed stems. The leaves are tiny and encircle the stem at the joints. Much of the photosynthesis actually occurs in the green stem.

There are about 15 species. They store silicon dioxide in their cell walls and, so, feel rough. They often are called scouring rushes because pioneers used them to clean pots and pans. The spores are produced in structures at the end of the stems. The spores give rise to gametophytes, which produce either eggs or sperm. Tree-sized members of this group are well known from the fossil record of the Carboniferous period.

*Club mosses* are usually evergreen, bright green, low-growing, branching plants. Because they are evergreen and have a slight resemblance to small pine trees, some kinds are called ground pines. Their leaves are small and have only a single bundle of vascular tissue. Over 1,000 species are alive today. Like the whisk ferns and horsetails, they produce spores in structures at the end of stems. The spores give rise to gametophytes. Like the horsetails, these plants were prominent trees like plants in ancient Carboniferous forests. Figure 22.15 shows examples of whisk ferns, horsetails, and club mosses.

### 22.7 CONCEPT REVIEW

12. List three ways that vascular seedless plants differ from nonvascular plants.
13. What kinds of vascular plants do not produce seeds?
14. Describe the life cycle of a fern.

## 22.8 Seed-Producing Vascular Plants

The most successful plants on Earth today are those that produce *seeds*. A **seed** is a specialized structure that contains an embryo, along with stored food, enclosed in a protective covering called the seed coat. The seed coat allows the embryo to resist drying. Thus, the seed is an adaptation that allows plants to live in dry terrestrial settings. Seeds are also important as dispersal devices for

**Whisk fern**

**Horsetail**

**Club moss**

**FIGURE 22.15  Whisk Ferns, Horsetails, and Club Mosses**
In addition to ferns, whisk ferns, horsetails, and club mosses are plants that have vascular tissue but do not have seeds. Whisk ferns are primarily tropical. They are odd plants that lack leaves and roots. Part of the stem is underground; the above-ground part is green and carries on photosynthesis. Horsetails and club mosses are common throughout North America.

plants. Two major groups of plants produce seeds: the **gymnosperms** (conifers and their relatives) and the **angiosperms** (flowering plants). There were also extinct fernlike plants that had a kind of seed.

Another important innovation of seed-producing plants is the development of a life cycle in which *pollen* is produced. **Pollen** is the miniaturized male gametophyte generation. Pollen can be carried from one plant to another by wind or animals, which makes the presence of water for fertilization unnecessary.

## Gymnosperms

Several kinds of woody plants produce seeds that are not enclosed. Typically, their seeds are produced in woody structures called **cones**. However, the seeds are not totally enclosed but are produced on the surface of flat, woody parts of the cone. Because the seeds are not enclosed, they are said to be *naked*. Thus, these cone-producing plants, such as conifers, are called *gymnosperms*, which means naked seed plants. However, there are several distinct kinds of plants in this group: the cycads, ginkgos, and conifers. All are woody perennial plants. We will examine the life cycle of the pine tree to illustrate the life cycle of a gymnosperm.

## The Pine Life Cycle

The dominant portion of the pine life cycle is the large, diploid sporophyte generation. Pines produce two kinds of cones, which are part of the sporophyte generation but produce separate haploid male and female gametophytes. The large cones on pines are the female cones, which produce the female gametophyte generation. The female gametophyte consists of several thousand cells and produces several archegonia, each of which contains an egg.

The small male cones are located on the ends of branches. The male cones produce pollen. Each of these small, dustlike pollen grains is a male gametophyte plant that contains haploid nuclei. Some of these nuclei function as sperm. In order to obtain a fertilized egg, two separate events must occur: pollination and fertilization. **Pollination** is the process of getting the pollen from the male cone to the female cone. Conifers are wind pollinated. Pollen is released in such large quantities that clouds of pollen can be seen in the air when sudden gusts of wind shake the branches of the trees. Once the pollen grain (male gametophyte) is in the vicinity of the female gametophyte in the female cone, it begins to grow a tubelike structure—the pollen tube. The pollen tube enters the archegonium of the female gametophyte and releases a sperm nucleus, which fertilizes the egg. The processes of pollination and fertilization are separate events. Pollination occurs with the transfer of pollen to the female cone. Fertilization occurs when the sperm nucleus from the pollen unites with the egg cell in the archegonium. Fertilization in gymnosperms may occur months or even years following pollination.

The fertilized egg (zygote) is diploid and develops into an embryo within a seed. Many kinds of birds and mammals use the seeds of pines and related trees for food. In most pines, the seeds are released from the cone when the scales of the cone fold back. The winged seeds are carried by wind and fall to the ground. The seed germinates and gives rise to a new sporophyte plant, and the life cycle continues. Figure 22.16 reviews the life cycle of the pine.

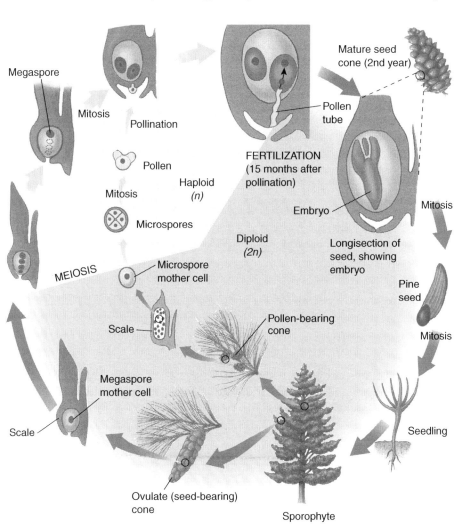

**FIGURE 22.16  The Life Cycle of a Pine**
The pine tree is the sporophyte plant. It produces two kinds of cones: small, male cones, which produce pollen (the male gametophyte), and larger, female cones, which contain the female gametophytes that produce eggs. The pollen is carried to the female cone by wind. After pollination, fertilization of the egg occurs when a pollen tube grows to the vicinity of the egg. The fertilized egg develops into an embryo enclosed within a seed. The seeds are eventually released from the female cone.

Thus, in addition to vascular tissue, the pine life cycle has two significant innovations that reduce the plant's dependence on water. The seed contains an embryo sporophyte plant along with some stored food, surrounded by a seed coat that reduces water loss. Therefore, the seed can withstand dry periods. The production of pollen and the process of pollination also reduce the need for water. The sperm do not need to swim to the egg. The entire male gametophyte (pollen) is transported to the female gametophyte by wind. Then, the male gametophyte transfers the sperm nucleus to the egg, when the pollen grain grows a tube that releases a sperm nucleus to fertilize the egg.

## Kinds of Gymnosperms

*Cycads* are stout, woody gymnosperms that have a ring of fernlike leaves at the top. They live in tropical regions and are minor parts of the landscape. During the Jurassic period (144 to 213 million years ago), cycads were major organisms in the forests. The seeds are produced in tough, woody, conelike structures. There are about 300 species, and half of them are in danger of extinction.

*Ginkgo* trees were common in the Jurassic, but today there is only one species (*Ginkgo biloba*). It is a tree with fan-shaped leaves. Humans eat the seeds, and the leaves are used in many herbal medicines.

*Conifers* are the common trees and shrubs that bear seeds in cones. Most conifers have needle-shaped leaves. Because they retain their leaves throughout the year, they are often called evergreens. Although they have needles throughout the year, they do shed needles a few at a time throughout the year, as evidenced by the mat of needles under a conifer. A few conifers—for example, *Larix* (tamarack) and *Taxodium* (bald cypress), lose their leaves all at once in the fall. There are over 600 species of conifers, and about half are considered threatened. Many kinds of conifers are important in the production of lumber. Figure 22.17 shows the three types of gymnosperms.

**Conifer (pine)**

**Cycad**

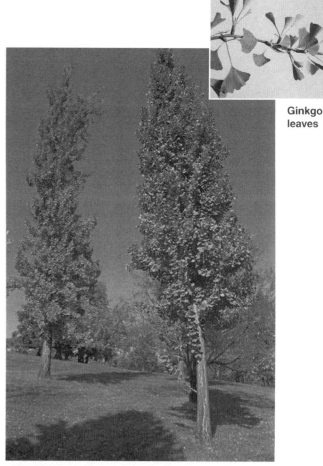

**Ginkgo leaves**

**Ginkgo**

**FIGURE 22.17 Several Gymnosperms**
There are three common types of gymnosperms: conifers, such as pines, cedars, spruces, and firs; cycads, which are tropical and have fernlike leaves; and a single species of ginkgo.

# Angiosperms

*Angiosperms* are plants that produce flowers and have their seeds enclosed in a *fruit*. A **fruit** is a modification of the ovary wall into a special structure that contains the seeds. Like the gymnosperms, the flowering plants are well adapted to terrestrial life with vascular tissue, seeds, and pollen.

## Flower Structure

A **flower** is the structure, composed of highly modified leaves, that is responsible for sexual reproduction. At the center of a typical flower is the **pistil,** which is composed of the *stigma, style,* and *ovary.* The ovary produces the female gametophyte plant. Surrounding the pistil are the **stamens,** which consist of a long *filament* with *anthers* at the top. The anther produces the pollen (male gametophyte plant). **Petals** are a whorl of modified leaves surrounding the stamens and pistil. In many flowering plants, the petals are large and showy. Outside the petals is another whorl of modified leaves, known as **sepals.** Many kinds of flowers produce odors and a sugary liquid, known as nectar. Figure 22.18 shows the arrangement of parts in a typical flower.

There is a great degree of specialization of flowers. Some are large and showy, such as the flowers of roses and magnolias. Others are small and inconspicuous, such as the flowers of grasses and birch trees. In addition, some plants have two kinds of flowers. One kind has a pistil, whereas a different flower has the stamens. Any flower that has both pistil and stamens is called a **perfect flower;** a flower containing just a pistil or just stamens is called an **imperfect flower.**

## The Life Cycle of a Flowering Plant

The life cycle of a flowering plant has both sporophyte and gametophyte generations. The sporophyte is the dominant

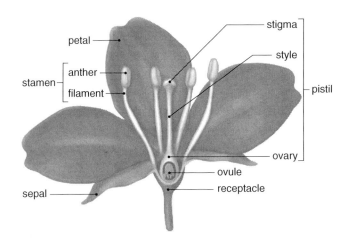

**FIGURE 22.18  Flower Structure**
The flower is the structure in angiosperms that produces gameophyte plants, which produce sex cells. The female gametophyte is produced within the ovary. The pollen (male gametophyte) is produced within the anther. Following fertilization of the egg, the ovary modifies to form the fruit.

stage of the life cycle, and the male and female gametophytes are produced within the flower. As in gymnosperms, the male gametophyte is the pollen. The female gametophyte is found within the ovary of the pistil and consists of only eight cells. One of the cells is an egg cell.

Pollination occurs when pollen is transferred from an anther to the stigma of the pistil. In some cases, pollination must be between flowers of different plants of the same species; this is called cross-pollination. However, some species of plants are able to pollinate themselves; this is called self-pollination.

The pollen grain germinates and produces a pollen tube, which grows down through the tissue of the style to the ovary, where the female gametophyte is located. The pollen tube releases two sperm. One fertilizes the egg nucleus and gives rise to the zygote. The other sperm nucleus combines with two other nuclei in the female gametophyte and produces a triploid nucleus, which develops into endosperm. The endosperm is the stored food of the seed. Because two sperm nuclei are involved, each fertilizing different cells, this is often called *double fertilization*. Both the embryo and the endosperm grow, and a seed coat develops around them to produce the mature seed. The wall of the ovary develops into a specialized seed-containing structure known as a fruit (figure 22.19).

## Pollination Strategies

Plants use several strategies to ensure pollination. Most plants that have inconspicuous flowers are wind pollinated. They produce large numbers of flowers and huge amounts of pollen. This is necessary because the distribution of pollen by wind is a random process. By producing large amounts of pollen, the plant increases the chances that pollen will be transferred successfully. Grasses, sedges, and some other herbaceous plants are wind pollinated. Many trees, such as aspens, birches, and oaks, are also wind pollinated.

It is the pollen from wind-pollinated plants that is responsible for "hay fever," an allergic reaction to the presence of airborne pollen. Most tree species produce pollen in the spring, so people who have hay fever symptoms in the spring are usually reacting to the pollen of certain trees. Grasses and other herbaceous plants typically produce their pollen in late summer or fall. Ragweed is a common plant that produces pollen late in the growing season and is a common cause of hay fever.

Plants with large, showy flowers are typically pollinated by animals. Although many showy flowers are pollinated by insects, such as bees, others are constructed to be pollinated by birds or small mammals. The animals feed on the nectar produced by the flower; in the process, they are dusted with pollen and carry it to another flower of the same species. Many flowers produce odors to help the animals find the plants. This is a mutualistic relationship between the flowers, which are pollinated, and the animals, which receive food in the form of nectar or pollen (figure 22.20).

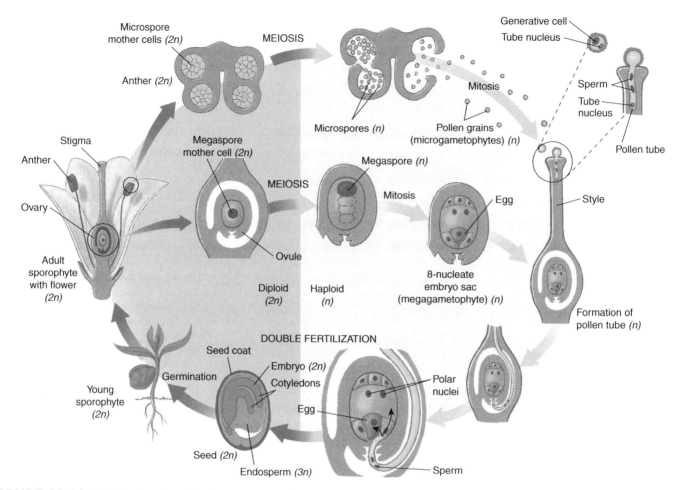

**FIGURE 22.19  Life Cycle of an Angiosperm**
Angiosperms have flowers, which produce eggs in the ovary and pollen in the anther. Pollen is carried to the pistil by wind or animals. A pollen tube releases haploid nuclei, fertilizing the egg. The fertilized egg develops into the embryo, and the remaining cells associated with the egg develop into a food storage material called endosperm. A seed coat develops around the embryo and endosperm. The ovary enlarges and becomes the fruit, which contains the seeds. The seed germinates to produce the next generation of flowering plant.

**Wind pollinated**

**Insect pollinated**

**FIGURE 22.20  Wind and Insect Pollinated Flowers**
The flowers of wind-pollinated plants, such like this oak, are small and inconspicuous. The flowers of plants that are pollinated by animals are typically large and showy, as are these California poppies and lupines.

## Fruit

Because plants cannot move, they must have a method of dispersing their seeds to new locations. Most fruits are involved in the dispersal of plants.

Some fruits—for example, apples, watermelon, tomatoes, and raspberries—contain large amounts of nutritious materials. The nutrients are not for the plant's use but, rather, attract animals that eat the seeds along with the fruit. The seeds pass through the animals' digestive tract unharmed, dispersing the plant's offspring. Other fruits—such as cottonwoods, milkweeds, and dandelions—release fluffy seeds, which are carried by the wind. Many trees—such as maples and ashes—produce fruits with wings, which aid their dispersal by wind. The fruits of some plants have hooks or sticky surfaces, which become attached to the fur or feathers of passing animals. Figure 22.21 shows several kinds of fruits.

## Angiosperm Diversity

Flowering plants are the most diverse group of plants, with about 260,000 species. Botanists classify angiosperms into two groups: *dicots* or *monocots*. The names *dicot* and *monocot* refer to structures in the seeds of these plants called cotyledons. **Cotyledons**, also known as seed leaves, are embryonic leaves that have food stored in them. They are the first leaves that emerge when a seed germinates. A **monocot** has one cotyledon, and a **dicot** has two cotyledons (figure 22.22).

A peanut is a dicot, as are lima beans and apples. Grasses, lilies, palms, and orchids are monocots. Figure 22.23 lists the differences between monocots and dicots.

Even with this separation into monocots and dicots, the diversity is staggering. Although some monocots are woody species, such as yuccas and palms, most monocots are herbaceous.

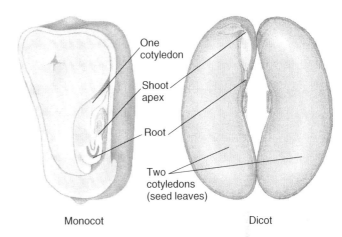

Monocot                              Dicot

**FIGURE 22.22 Embryos in Monocots and Dicots**
The embryos of plants have embryonic leaves, called seed leaves or cotyledons, attached to the embryonic stem. The monocots have one cotyledon and the dicots have two.

Burdock                      Milkweed                            Raspberry

**FIGURE 22.21 Types of Fruits**
From a plant's point of view, fruits are useful as methods of dispersal. Each of these kinds of fruits uses a different method of dispersal. Burdock has hooks, which stick to passing animals. Milkweed fruits open to release seeds, which are carried by the wind. Raspberries are eaten by birds or other animals. The raspberry seeds pass through the gut and are distributed in the feces.

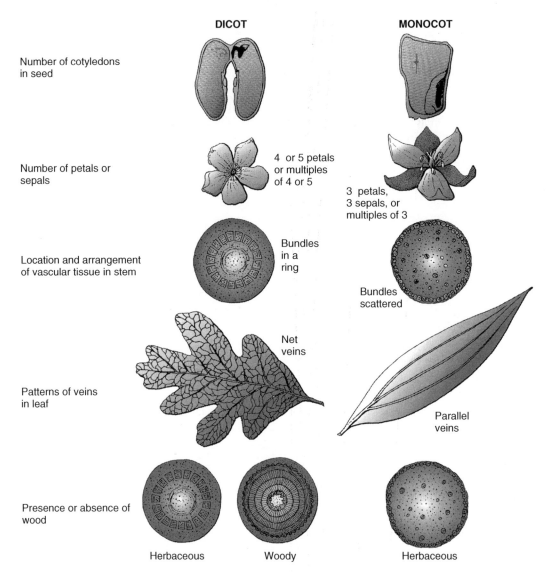

**FIGURE 22.23  A Comparison of Structures in Dicots and Monocots**
Botanists classify angiosperms into the monocots and the dicots. Several general characteristics help differentiate these two groups.

Many of these plants grow from underground structures, in which they store food. Many important food plants are monocots, including wheat, rice, corn, yams, onions, and bananas.

Common herbaceous dicots, such as mints, carrots, cabbages, mustards, tomatoes, potatoes, and peppers, are important food plants. About half of the dicots are woody trees and shrubs, such as aspen trees and sagebrush. These plants add layers of new xylem and phloem each year, as the stem and root of the plant get larger in diameter. The phloem is in the outermost part of the stem called the bark. Dicot trees and shrubs generally produce broad, flat leaves. In colder parts of the world, most woody dicots lose all their leaves during the fall. Such trees are said to be **deciduous** (figure 22.24). However, there are exceptions. Some are **nondeciduous,** keeping their leaves and staying green throughout the winter—for example, American holly (*Ilex opaca*). In tropical and semitropical regions, many of these trees shed leaves one at a time, so they

retain their leaves throughout the year. In areas that have pronounced changes in rainfall, many trees and shrubs lose their leaves during the dry part of the year.

## 22.8   CONCEPT REVIEW

15. How is a seed different from pollen, and how do both of these differ from a spore?
16. Describe how wind and insect pollinated flowers differ.
17. Describe the major kinds of gymnosperms.
18. Describe how monocots and dicots differ.
19. Describe two ways the life cycle of flowering plants differs from that of cone-bearing plants.
20. List the parts of the flower.

**FIGURE 22.24 Deciduous Trees and Fall Colors**
The cells of leaves contain a variety of pigments. In the fall, a layer of waterproof tissue forms at the base of each leaf, cutting off the flow of water and other nutrients. The cells of the leaf die and their chlorophyll disintegrates. The color change seen in leaves in the fall in certain parts of the world is the result of the breakdown of the green chlorophyll. Other pigments (red, yellow, orange, brown) are present but are masked by the green chlorophyll pigments. When the chlorophyll disintegrates, the reds, oranges, yellows, and browns are revealed. It appears that red pigments are synthesized in the fall but most of the other pigments are present throughout the year.

**FIGURE 22.25 A Cross Section of Woody Stem**
Woody stems are composed of xylem in the middle and a covering of bark on the outside. The phloem is located in the bark. Between the xylem and phloem is the vascular cambium. The cells of the vascular cambium divide and add to the diameter of the stem by adding xylem and phloem.

## 22.9 The Growth of Woody Plants

All gymnosperms and a large proportion of the dicots are woody plants. Although these two groups of plants have different evolutionary histories, they share the ability to grow continuously for many years. The trees get taller and larger in diameter each year. Both the stems and the roots grow from their tips and add to their length. In addition, they increase in diameter by adding new xylem and phloem to the outside of the stem.

As a tree becomes larger, the strengthening tissue in the stem becomes more and more important. A layer of cells in the stem, called the **vascular cambium**, is responsible for this increase in diameter. The vascular cambium is between the xylem and the phloem. Xylem tissue is the innermost part of

the tree trunk or limb, and phloem is outside. The bark of the tree, containing the phloem, is important in protecting the underlying tissues. Cambium cells go through a mitotic cell division, and two cells form. One cell remains cambium tissue, and the other specializes to form vascular tissue. If the cell is on the inside of the cambium ring, it becomes xylem; if it is on the outside of the cambium ring, it becomes phloem. As cambium cells divide again and again, one cell always remains cambium, and the other becomes vascular tissue. Thus, the tree constantly increases in diameter (figure 22.25) (How Science Works 22.1).

The accumulation of the xylem in the trunk of gymnosperms and woody angiosperms is called **wood.** Wood is one of the most valuable biological resources of the world. We get lumber, paper products, turpentine, and many other valuable materials from the wood of gymnosperms and angiosperms. In many areas of the world, firewood is the primary fuel for cooking and heating homes.

As you can see from this discussion, both angiosperms and gymnosperms have members that are woody. Therefore the term *woody* cuts across taxonomic lines.

### 22.9 CONCEPT REVIEW

21. What is the significance of the vascular cambium tissue in woody perennials?
22. Wood is composed of what kind of cell?

# HOW SCIENCE WORKS 22.1

## Using Information from Tree Rings

Trees that live in seasonal climates produce a ring of new growth each year. These annual rings are visible in the cut stem because in the spring, when trees start to produce new growth, the xylem cells produced are large. The cells produced later in the year are smaller. The abrupt change between the small cells produced in the fall and the large cells produced the following spring is easy to see.

In the accompanying photograph of a cross section of a Douglas fir tree, we can gather several bits of information:

1. We can count the rings and determine that the tree was about 50 years old when it was harvested.
2. By noticing how close together the annual rings are in the center of the stem, we can see that in the early years of its life, it grew relatively slowly.
3. By examining the width of the annual rings in the darker brown area and counting the rings, we can determine that the tree grew rapidly for about 20 years in the middle of its life.
4. Growth then slowed considerably in the later part of the tree's life as evidenced by the narrow annual rings in the outer portion of the stem.

Scientists can use this information for a variety of purposes. Foresters can bore into a tree and obtain a sample of the tree rings to assess how well the tree is growing. Healthy, rapidly growing trees will show wide annual rings, while poorly growing trees will show narrow annual rings. Based on this information they can make decisions about when to harvest trees to get the greatest production from a forest.

Scientists interested in how climate may have changed in the past can look at tree rings and determine if there were periods of drought or other factors that may have altered a tree's growth pattern. Since some trees live for thousands of years, it is possible to use tree rings to get an idea of climate alterations that occurred before recorded history.

Because the trees used in wooden structures were killed when they were harvested, archaeologists can use tree rings to determine the age of artifacts and ancient structures. The tree ring patterns in wooden structures and implements can be examined for patterns of growth that can be correlated with known events. Thus, it is possible to place precise dates on certain archaeological structures. It is even possible of examine growth patterns in petrified wood (see photo).

— Slow growth

— Rapid growth

— Slow growth

**Tree rings give information about rates of growth.**

**Ancient tree rings in a petrified tree stump.**

## 22.10 Plant Responses to Their Environment

Our casual impression of plants is that they are unchanging objects. However, on closer examination we recognize that plants change over time. They grow, produce flowers and fruits at certain times of the year, and grow toward a source of light. Furthermore, they respond to organisms that harm them and may even mount an attack against competitors.

### Tropisms

A **tropism** is a growth movement toward or away from a stimulus. For example, plants orient themselves toward light.

This is known as *phototropism.* The value of this response is obvious, because plants need light to survive. The mechanism that allows this response involves a hormone known as auxin. The growing tip of the stem produces auxin, which is transported down the stem. Auxin stimulates cells to divide, grow, and elongate. If the growing tip of a plant receives more light on one side, the shaded side produces more auxin than does the lighted side. The larger amount of auxin on the shaded side causes greater growth in that area, and the tip of the stem bends toward the light. When all the sides of the stem are equally illuminated, the stem grows equally on all sides and grows straight. House plants near a window must be turned regularly, or they will grow more on one side than the other (figure 22.26).

**FIGURE 22.26 Phototropism**
These tomato plants were growing in a window and have oriented themselves to the light coming through the window.

Many kinds of climbing vines are able to wrap stringlike *tendrils* around sturdy objects in a matter of minutes. This kind of growth response is called *thigmotropism*. As the tendrils grow, they slowly wave about. When they encounter an object, their tropic response is to wrap around it and anchor the vine. Once attached, the tendrils change into hard structures that bind the vine to its attachment. Sweet peas, grapevines, and ivy attach in this manner (figure 22.27). Ivy can cause great damage to buildings as it grows, and its tendrils loosen siding and serve as a haven for the growth of other destructive organisms.

Plants also have growth responses to gravity and the presence of water. Stems grow up; roots grow down and toward water in the soil.

## Seasonal Responses

Plants live in a seasonal world, and they respond accordingly. Plants that live in temperate regions experience changes in temperature and the amount of sunlight. The days are longest in the summer and shortest in the winter. Plants are able to measure day length and manufacture hormones that cause changes in the growth and development of specific parts of the plant. Some plants produce flowers only when the days are getting longer, some only when the days are getting shorter, and some only after the days have reached a specific length. In deciduous trees, the shortening day length in the fall triggers a response that causes the tree to produce a wall of waterproof tissue between the leaves and the stem. Because the leaves no longer receive water, they die and fall to the ground.

Other plants store food materials in underground structures such as bulbs and tubers during the active growing period in the summer. In the fall the above-ground part of the plant dies back, but the underground portion remains alive in a dormant state. In the spring, as the soil warms, these storage structures send up new growth.

**FIGURE 22.27 Thigmotropism—Clinging Stems**
Some stems are modified to wrap themselves around objects and give support. The tendrils of this grapevine are a good example.

Many parts of the world experience seasonal rainfall. Rain is abundant for several months and totally absent during others. Plants' responses to these conditions are similar to those of plants that respond to seasonal changes in temperature. During the dry season, the leaves fall from trees and many smaller plants become dormant. When it rains, the plants respond by growing, flowering, and fruiting.

## Responses to Injury

Plants are attacked by a variety of disease-causing organisms and by plant-eating herbivores. Plants respond to disease in much the same way as animals do. When infected with a disease organism, they have an innate ability to fight the infection. Plants also repair wounds by growing a form of scar tissue over the wounded area.

Attack by herbivores is handled in a different way. Many plants produce toxic materials, which interfere with the metabolism of animals that eat plants. When the leaves of plants are eaten by animals, the new leaves produced to replace those lost often contain higher amounts of toxic materials than the original leaves.

Plants may even have the ability to communicate with one another. An experiment carried out in a greenhouse produced some interesting results. Some of the plants had their leaves mechanically "eaten" by an experimenter, whereas nearby plants were not harmed. Not only did the cut plants produce new leaves with more toxins, but the new growth on neighboring, nonmutilated plants had increased toxin levels as well. This raises the possibility that plants communicate in some way, perhaps by the release of molecules that cause changes in the receiving plant.

## 22.10 CONCEPT REVIEW

23. Describe phototropism and thigmotropism.
24. Describe two examples of how plants respond to environmental changes.
25. Why might a plant gain an advantage by producing toxic substances in its tissues?

## 22.11 The Coevolution of Plants and Animals

The first terrestrial organisms were plants. Shortly after the plants became established on land, animals, such as insects and amphibians, arrived. Thus, terrestrial plants and animals have a long history of interaction, which has had an influence on the evolution of each group. There are many examples of their coevolution.

Most flowering plants are pollinated by insects or other animals. Insect-pollinated plants produce flowers that are showy, have nectar, and produce odors. Many flowers that are pollinated by birds are red and produce much nectar. Some flowers bloom only at night and are pollinated by moths or bats.

Grasses and grazers have coevolved. Grasses have silica in their cell walls. This is a very hard material, and it tends to wear down the teeth of grazers. Most grazing animals have very long teeth, which can accommodate a lifetime of wear. Grasses also differ from most other plants in that their leaves

and stems grow from the base of the plant rather than from the tip. Thus, they can withstand regularly having the tips of their leaves chewed off.

Many kinds of flowering plants produce large, nutritious fruits, which animals use for food, in the process distributing the seeds. There are even seeds that will not germinate unless they have passed through the gut of an animal. Birds eat small fruits and their seeds, which are dispersed when the birds defecate. In tropical forests, many trees have very large fruits, which are eaten by monkeys. They eat the fleshy part of the fruit and drop the seeds.

Browsers are animals that eat the leaves and small twigs of woody plants. Many kinds of woody plants have thorns, making this task more difficult, but browsers have techniques or structures that allow them to put up with the prickly deterrents.

Plants produce a variety of chemicals. Some of these chemicals are toxic or irritating and deter certain animals from eating portions of the plant. Others chemicals produce odors that help animals locate flowers or fruits. These attractive odors aid the plant by assuring that pollination and seed dispersal will take place. Humans use many of these plants and the chemicals they produce as spices and flavorings (Outlooks 22.2).

## 22.11 CONCEPT REVIEW

26. Describe how the coevolution of grasses and grazing animals affected both kinds of organisms.
27. In what ways do some flowering plants encourage insects to visit them?

## OUTLOOKS 22.2

## Spices and Flavorings

Think about all the plant materials we use to season our foods. Black pepper comes from the hard, dried berries of a tropical plant, *Piper nigrum*. Cayenne pepper is made from the ground-up fruits of *Capsicum annuum*, and the hot, spicy chemical in the fruit and seeds is known as capsaicin. The seeds of the dill plant, *Anethum graveolens*, are used to flavor pickles and many other foods. The dried or fresh leaves of many herbs such as thyme, rosemary, chives, and parsley, are also used as flavorings. Many kitchen cabinets also contain cinnamon from the bark of a tree found in India; cloves, which are the dried flower buds of a tropical tree; ginger from the root of a tropical plant of Africa and China; nutmeg from the seed of a

tropical tree of Asia; and saffron from the dried, fragrant stigmas of the crocus flower (*Crocus sativus*) from Spain. Saffron's small size and difficulty in harvesting the stigmas make it the most expensive spice on Earth.

Centuries ago, spices such as these were so highly prized that fortunes were made in the spice trade. Beginning in the early 1600s, ships from Europe regularly visited the tropical regions of Asia and Africa, returning with cargoes of spices and other rare commodities that could be sold at great profit. Consequently, India has been greatly influenced by Britain, Indonesia has been greatly influenced by the Netherlands, and the development of various portions of Africa has been influenced by Britain and France.

## Summary

The plant kingdom is composed of eukaryotic, multicellular organisms that can manufacture their own food through photosynthesis. All plants have alternation of generations with a haploid, gametophyte generation and a diploid, sporophyte generation. The gametophyte produces sex cells (eggs and sperm) by mitosis and the sporophyte produces haploid spores by meiosis. There is a general trend in the evolution of plants for less dependence on a moist environment and an increase in the importance of the sporophyte generation. The nonvascular plants (mosses and related organisms) lack vascular tissue, have the gametophyte generation as the dominant generation, and have swimming sperm. The seedless vascular plants (ferns and related organisms) have vascular tissue, a dominant sporophyte generation, and swimming sperm. Seed-producing vascular plants (cone-bearing and flowering plants) have vascular tissue, a dominant sporophyte generation, the development of pollen, and seeds.

Vascular tissue consists of xylem, which carries water and inorganic nutrients from the roots to the leaves; and phloem, which carries organic molecules from the leaves to places where they are needed. The presence of vascular tissue is associated with the specialization of body parts into roots, stems, and leaves. Roots anchor the plant and absorb water and nutrients from the soil. Leaves are generally thin, flat structures specialized for photosynthesis. Stems connect the roots to the leaves and position the leaves to receive sunlight.

Pollen is the male gametophyte plant and is either carried by wind or animals from one plant to another. Wind-pollinated plants produce huge amounts of pollen. Some flowering plants are pollinated by animals and produce showy flowers and nectar to attract animals.

Plants respond to their environment in complex and interesting ways. They respond to the position of the sun, day length, contact with other objects, and injury.

## Key Terms

*Use the interactive flash cards on the **Concepts in Biology**, 14/e website to help you learn the meaning of these terms.*

angiosperms 491
antheridium 482
archegonium 482
cones 491
cotyledons 495
deciduous 496
dicot 495
flower 493
fruit 493
gametophyte generation 481
gymnosperms 491
imperfect flower 493
leaf 486
monocot 495
nondeciduous 496
perfect flower 493
petals 493
phloem 483
pistil 493
pollen 491
pollination 491
root 483
root hairs 485
seed 490
sepals 493
sporophyte generation 480
stamens 493
stem 483
tropism 498
vascular cambium 497
vascular tissue 481
wood 497
xylem 483

## Basic Review

1. The sporophyte generation
   a. is diploid.
   b. produces spores.
   c. is the dominant stage in angiosperms.
   d. All of the above are correct.
2. Gymnosperms produce fruits. (T/F)
3. All of the following are vascular plants except
   a. ferns.
   b. mosses.
   c. horsetails.
   d. gymnosperms.
4. There are two kinds of vascular tissue: xylem and _____.
5. The central part of a woody stem consists of
   a. xylem.
   b. phloem.
   c. silica.
   d. bark.
6. Nearly all gymnosperms are woody perennials. (T/F)
7. Plants are able to sense changes in their environment. (T/F)
8. From a plant's point of view, a fruit
   a. is used to feed seeds.
   b. is used to disperse seeds.
   c. requires little energy to produce.
   d. All of the above are correct.
9. The pollination of plants by insects is an example of _____.
10. Which one of the following plant groups has the largest number of species?
    a. conifers
    b. ferns
    c. angiosperms
    d. mosses

11. Which of the following does not have swimming sperm?

    a. moss

    b. fern

    c. gymnosperm

    d. horsetail

12. Phototropism is a response to _____.

13. Phloem

    a. cells are hollow.

    b. is found in the center of a tree.

    c. has companion cells.

    d. is found in mosses.

14. Fossils of mosses that are trees have been found. (T/F)

15. All plants have a gametophyte generation. (T/F)

**Answers**

1. d  2. F  3. b  4. phloem  5. a  6. T  7. T  8. b
9. coevolution  10. c  11. c  12. light  13. c  14. F  15. T

## Thinking Critically

**Potato Facts**

Some people say the ordinary "Irish" potato is poisonous when the skin is green, and they are at least partly correct. A potato develops a green skin if the potato tuber grows so close to the surface of the soil that it is exposed to light. An alkaloid called *solanine* develops under this condition and may be present in toxic amounts. Eating such a potato raw can be dangerous. However, cooking breaks down the solanine molecules and makes the potato as edible and tasty as any other. The so-called Irish potato is of interest historically. Its country of origin is only part of the story. Check your local library to find out about this potato and its relatives. Are all related organisms edible? Where did this group of plants develop? Why is it called the Irish potato?

CHAPTER

# The Animal Kingdom

## Peregrine Falcon Back from the Brink of Extinction

*Urban birds are part of the story.*

The peregrine falcon (*Falco peregrinus*) is a crow-sized bird with a worldwide distribution. It is a predator on smaller birds such as pigeons, doves, shorebirds, and ducks. Its method of hunting is adapted to open spaces where it can spot prey and pursue it. Typically a peregrine will perch on an elevated site or hover while searching for prey. When it spots prey, it dives at speeds of up to 320 kilometers per hour (200 mph) and strikes its prey in the air.

As with many other predatory birds, the population of peregrine falcons was severely reduced by the accumulation of DDT, an insecticide commonly used from about 1940 to 1972. DDT caused egg shells to be thin, and few offspring were raised successfully. Consequently populations of the American subspecies that nests in Canada, the United States, and Mexico fell from an estimated 3,875 pairs in the 1900s to 324 pairs in 1975. The ban on the use of DDT in 1972 and the passage of the Endangered Species Act in the United States helped to save it. Captive breeding programs were instituted to rebuild the population and, in 1999, the peregrine falcon was removed from the list of endangered species. Today, there are between 2,000 and 3,000 nesting pairs in North America.

One of the interesting sidelights to this successful recovery is that many pairs of birds have adapted to urban settings. Some were purposely released in urban settings but wild birds have also taken up an urban lifestyle. Tall buildings and bridges provide nesting sites similar to their normal nesting sites on cliffs. The areas between buildings provide suitable open space for hunting and the abundant supply of urban birds (particularly pigeons and starlings) provides a ready food source.

- Why is the thickness of the egg shell important?

- Why are birds and mammals more likely than insects to be on endangered species lists?

- DDT is still used in some countries to control mosquitoes that carry malaria. Should it be banned in those countries?

## Background Check

**Concepts you should already know to get the most out of this chapter:**
- The processes of natural selection and evolution (chapter 13)
- That structural and life history characteristics are used to classify organisms (chapter 20)
- That cells are specialized to perform certain functions (chapter 4)

## 23.1 What Is an Animal?

Animals are eukaryotic, multicellular organisms whose cells lack cell walls. Like plants, animals have cells that are specialized for specific purposes. Functions such as ingesting food, exchanging gases, and removing wastes are more complicated in animals than in one-celled protists. In one-celled organisms, any exchange between the organism and the external environment occurs through the plasma membrane. However, because animals are multicellular, most of their cells are not on the body surface and, therefore, not in direct contact with the external environment. Thus, animals must have specialized ways to exchange materials between their internal and external environments.

Some simple animals, such as sponges and jellyfish, have a few kinds of specialized cells, whereas other, more complex animals, such as insects and mollusks, have bodies composed of groups of cells organized into tissues, organs, and organ systems. The more complex animals have gills, lungs, or other structures used to exchange gases; various kinds of structures are involved in capturing and digesting food; and there are usually special structures for getting rid of waste products. Like plants, many of the larger animals have a method of transporting materials throughout the body.

Animals are heterotrophs that eat other organisms to obtain organic molecules, and many are specialized for consuming certain kinds of food organisms. Although there are many ways of capturing and consuming food, all of them involve movement.

Movement is a characteristic associated with all animals; it involves specialized muscle cells that shorten. Many animals have appendages (e.g., legs; wings; tentacles; spines; or soft, muscular organs) that bend or change shape. Often, these structures are involved in moving the animal from place to place, but they are also used to capture food, to clean the animals' surfaces, and to move things in the animals' environment.

Sexual reproduction is important in all groups of animals. The methods vary greatly—from the release of sperm and eggs into the water, for many aquatic organisms, to fertilization inside the body, for most terrestrial organisms. A few kinds, such as birds and mammals, provide a great deal of care for their offspring. Asexual reproduction is also an important part of the life cycle of many of the more primitive animals. Those that reproduce asexually also reproduce sexually at other times in their life cycle.

Animals also have sensory structures on their surface that detect changes in the environment. A system of nerve cells integrates information about the environment and coordinates movements, so that movements occur at appropriate times and with a proper orientation. Figure 23.1 shows a variety of animals.

Frog

Jellyfish

Praying mantis

Snail

Starfish

**FIGURE 23.1 Variety of Animals**
Animals show an amazing variety of body forms and lifestyles.

## 23.2   The Evolution of Animals

Scientists estimate that the Earth is at least 4.5 billion years old and that life originated in the ocean about 3.8 to 3.7 billion years ago. The earliest animal-like fossils date to about 600 million years ago. Most of the earliest animals were probably either small organisms that floated or swam in the ocean or wormlike organisms that crawled on the bottom or through the sediment on the ocean floor.

Because they lived in the ocean, these animals did not require special mechanisms to deal with rapid or extreme changes in the environment and they did not have a problem with dehydration. Because the concentration of salts in the early ocean approximated that of the animals' cells, the animals did not need to expend energy to keep their cells in osmotic balance. Furthermore, their body temperature was that of the water in which they lived.

The early evolution of animals was rapid. Scientists have found examples of all the major groups of animals as far back as the Cambrian period, 540 to 490 million years ago. They were all marine animals, and many groups, such as sponges, jellyfish, mollusks, crustaceans, starfish, and many kinds of fish—are still primarily marine animals. The evolution of organisms that inhabit freshwater and terrestrial environments is a more recent development. The first terrestrial animals (arthropods) are found in the fossils of the Silurian period, 443 to 417 million years ago. Major changes in the kinds of terrestrial animals occurred after that time. Two groups—arthropods (particularly the insects) and vertebrates (especially reptiles, birds, and mammals)—were extremely successful in terrestrial habitats.

The evolution of animals led to great diversity, and today animals are adapted to live in just about any environment. They live in all the oceans, on the shores of oceans, and in shallow freshwater. They live in the bitter cold of the Arctic, the dryness of the desert, and the driving rains of tropical forests. Some animals eat only other animals, some are parasites, some eat both plants and other animals, and some feed only on plants. They show a remarkable variety of form, function, and activity. They can be found in an amazing variety of sizes, colors, and body shapes.

It is common to divide animals into two categories. Animals with backbones made of vertebrae are called **vertebrates** and include various kinds of fishes, amphibians, reptiles, birds, and mammals. Those without backbones are called **invertebrates.** All early animals lacked backbones, and invertebrates still constitute 99.9% of all animal species in existence today (Outlooks 23.1).

The evolution of animals is complex and often difficult to interpret. Figure 23.2 shows the current knowledge of how various groups of animals are related.

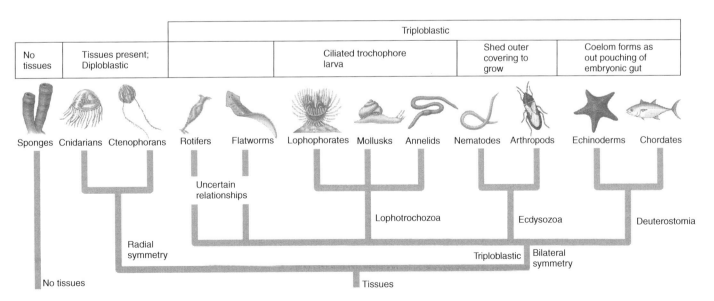

**FIGURE 23.2  Animal Evolution**

This diagram shows the current thinking about how the major groups of animals are related to one another. There are about 30 recognized phyla. Only the major phyla are shown here.

# OUTLOOKS 23.1

## The Problem of Image

We humans are vertebrate mammals. We unconsciously view all other animals by comparing them with ourselves. If other animals are like us, we feel we understand them and can empathize with them. If they are not mammals like us, we often consider them to be weird.

Mammals make up less than 0.04 percent of all the animals that exist; thus, mammals are a minor ingredient in the whole collection of animals in the world in terms of numbers and in significance. Because certain species are able to grab the attention of the public, often they are called charismatic species.

Our narrow, biased view of the world is evidenced in subtle ways. For example, most of the endangered species listed are vertebrate animals like us. About 7% of the known species of vertebrates are designated as endangered. On the other hand,

less than 0.2% of invertebrate species are known to be endangered. The lack of invertebrates on lists of endangered species is primarily because we know so little about them. We don't even know how many different species there are, let alone if species are going extinct or not.

We have organizations to save whales, pandas, and wild horses (which are not endangered), but we do not have organizations to save the poison arrow frog or endangered native crayfish and clams. In actuality, in North America the most vulnerable category of organisms consists of freshwater species of mussels (clams), crayfish, fish, and stoneflies. The least vulnerable are birds and mammals, yet birds and mammals capture most of the public's interest and governmental financial support, and are highlighted by the U.S. Fish and Wildlife Service on its endangered species website.

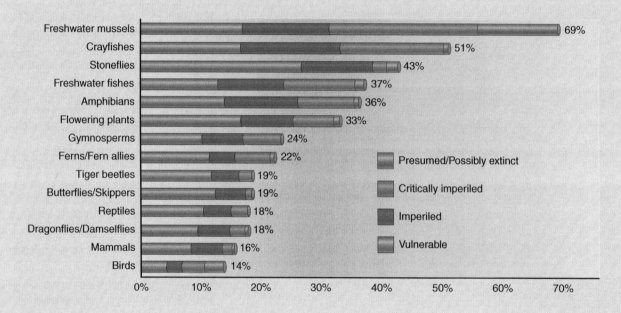

**Source:** Data from Natureserve, Prescious Heritage.

## 23.3 Temperature Regulation

The temperature of an organism affects the rate at which its metabolic reactions take place. Some animals do little to regulate their temperature, whereas others expend considerable energy to maintain a constant temperature.

**Poikilotherms** are organisms whose body temperature varies with the environmental temperature. When the water or air temperature changes, so does the temperature of the organism. All microbes and plants and most animals, including insects, worms, and reptiles, are poikilotherms. This is

significant because, at colder body temperatures, poikilotherms have lower metabolic rates; at higher body temperatures, they have higher metabolic rates. A low metabolic rate means that all of their body functions, such as movement and rate of digestion of food, are slowed. However, an organism with a low metabolic rate requires less food.

**Homeotherms** are animals that maintain a constant body temperature that is generally higher than the environmental temperature, regardless of the external temperature (figure 23.3). These animals—birds and mammals—have high metabolic rates, because they use metabolic energy to maintain their

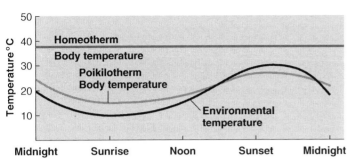

**FIGURE 23.3  Regulating Body Temperature**
The body temperature of a homeotherm remains relatively constant, regardless of changes in environmental temperature. The body temperature of a poikilotherm varies considerably, depending on the environmental temperature.

constant body temperature. This means that homeotherms have higher food demands than poikilotherms but are able to remain active at low environmental temperatures. Among homeotherms, the smaller animals have higher body temperatures and higher metabolic rates than the larger animals. This is in part because small animals lose heat faster than large animals, because small animals have a larger surface area compared to their volume.

Sometimes, the terms *ectotherm* and *endotherm* are used to describe the same relationship from a slightly different point of view. **Ectotherms** are organisms whose body temperatures depend on the external temperature, and **endotherms** are animals that have internal heat-generating mechanisms and can maintain a relatively constant body temperature in spite of wide variations in the temperature of their environment.

However, poikilotherms or ectotherms are not necessarily totally at the mercy of their environment. Many poikilotherms use behavioral means to regulate body temperature. One simple method is to position the body so that it absorbs heat from its surroundings. Many kinds of reptiles and insects "sun" themselves. By placing themselves in the Sun or on rocks or other surfaces that have been heated by the Sun, they can raise their body temperature above that of their environment. Similarly, many poikilotherms can generate heat by contracting their muscles. In cold weather, bumblebees often beat their wings prior to flying, raising their body temperature. Body temperature is important, because the rate at which the wings can beat is determined by body temperature.

## 23.4  Body Plans

Although animals come in a variety of sizes and shapes, you can see certain evolutionary trends and a few basic body plans.

### Symmetry

Symmetrical objects have similar parts that are arranged in a particular pattern. For example, the parts of a daisy flower and a bicycle are arranged symmetrically.

**Asymmetry** is a condition in which there is no pattern to the individual parts. Asymmetrical body forms are rare and occur only in certain species of sponges, which are the simplest kinds of animals.

**Radial symmetry** occurs when a body is constructed around a central axis. Any division of the body along this axis results in two similar halves. Although many animals with radial symmetry are capable of movement, they do not always lead with the same portion of the body; that is, there is no anterior, or head, end. Starfish and jellyfish are examples of organisms with radial symmetry.

**Bilateral symmetry** exists when an animal is constructed with equivalent parts on both sides of a plane. Animals with bilateral symmetry have a head and a tail region. There is only one way to divide bilateral animals into two mirrored halves. Animals with bilateral symmetry move head first, and the head typically has sense organs and a mouth. The feature of having an anterior head end is called *cephalization* (*cephal* = head). It appears that bilateral symmetry was an important evolutionary development since most animals have bilateral symmetry (figure 23.4).

### Embryonic Cell Layers

Animals differ in the number of layers of cells of which they are composed. When we look at the development of embryos we find that the embryos of the simplest animals (sponges) do not form distinct, tissuelike layers. However, jellyfishes and their relatives have embryos that consist of two layers. The **ectoderm** is the outer layer and the **endoderm** is the inner layer. Because their embryos are composed of two layers, these animals are said to be **diploblastic.** In adults, these embryonic cell layers give rise to an outer, protective layer and an inner layer that forms a pouch and is involved in processing food.

All the other major groups of animals have embryos that are *triploblastic.* **Triploblastic** animals have three layers of cells in their embryos. Sandwiched between the ectoderm and endoderm is a third layer, the **mesoderm.** In the adult body, the ectoderm gives rise to the skin or other surface covering, the endoderm gives rise to the lining of the digestive system, and the mesoderm gives rise to muscles, connective tissue, and other organ systems involved in the excretion of waste, the circulation of material, the exchange of gases, and body support (figure 23.5).

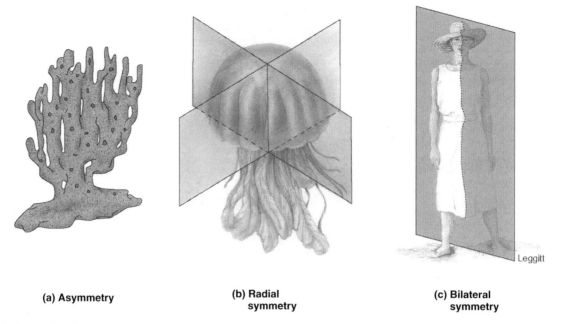

**(a) Asymmetry**  **(b) Radial symmetry**  **(c) Bilateral symmetry**

**FIGURE 23.4  Kinds of Symmetry**

*(a)* This sponge has a body that cannot be divided into symmetrical parts and is therefore asymmetrical. *(b)* In animals such as this jellyfish with radial symmetry, any cut along the central body axis results in similar halves. *(c)* In animals with bilateral symmetry, only one cut along one plane results in similar halves.

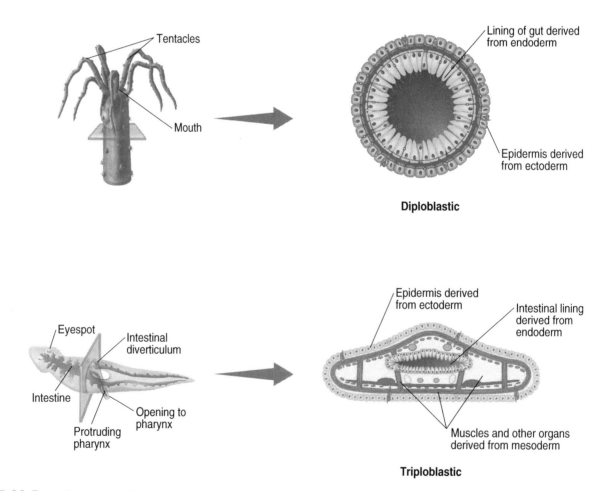

Tentacles

Mouth

Lining of gut derived from endoderm

Epidermis derived from ectoderm

**Diploblastic**

Eyespot

Intestinal diverticulum

Intestine

Protruding pharynx

Opening to pharynx

Epidermis derived from ectoderm

Intestinal lining derived from endoderm

Muscles and other organs derived from mesoderm

**Triploblastic**

**FIGURE 23.5  Embryonic Cell Layers**

Diploblastic organisms have two embryonic cell layers. The outer ectoderm becomes the epidermis and the inner endoderm becomes the lining of the gut. Triploblastic organisms have three embryonic cell layers: the ectoderm, endoderm, and mesoderm. The mesoderm forms most of the tissues and organs of the body.

## Body Cavities

A **coelom** is a fluid-filled body cavity that separates the outer body wall of the organism from the gut and internal organs. The development of a coelom was an important step in animal evolution.

Simple animals, such as jellyfish and flatworms, are **acoelomate,** which means that they have no space separating their outer surface from their internal organs. However, most animals have some form of a coelom. Because organs such as the gut and heart are not embedded in a mass of cells but are suspended in a space (the coelom), they have a greater freedom of movement than the organs of acoelomate animals. Organs are not loose in the coelom; they are held in place by sheets of connective tissue called **mesenteries.** Mesenteries also support the blood vessels connecting the various organs.

It is often difficult to visualize the presence of a coelom as a cavity, because the cavity is filled with organs and a small amount of fluid. Perhaps a common example will help.

The coelom in a turkey is the cavity where you stuff the dressing. In the living bird this cavity contains a number of organs, including those of the digestive, excretory, and circulatory systems.

Some animals do not have a true coelom but have a similar space called a *pseudocoelom.* A **pseudocoelom** differs from a true coelom in that it is located between the lining of the gut and the outer body wall. In other words, animals with a pseudocoelom do not have muscles around their digestive system. In addition, there are no mesenteries suspending the gut from the outer body wall. Nematode worms and several related groups of animals have a pseudocoelom (figure 23.6).

## Segmentation

Many kinds of bilaterally symmetrical organisms have segmented bodies. **Segmentation** is the separation of an animal's body into a number of recognizable units from its anterior to its posterior end. Segmentation is associated with the specialization of certain parts of the body. Three common groups of animals show segmentation: annelid worms, arthropods, and chordates. Annelid worms have a series of very

similar segments with minor differences between them. Segmentation in arthropods is modified so that several segments are specialized as a head region and more posterior segments are less specialized. Many of the posterior segments have legs and other appendages. Among the arthropods, insects show a great deal of specialization of segments. In chordates, the segmentation is of a different sort but is obvious in the arrangement of muscles and the vertebral column (figure 23.7). Studies of the genes that control development show that all bilaterally symmetrical

(a) Acoelomate

(b) Pseudocoelomate

(c) Coelomate

**FIGURE 23.6  Body Cavities**
*(a)* Acoelomate animals, such as flatworms, have no open space between the gut and outer body layer. *(b)* Roundworms, commonly found in soil, have a body cavity called a pseudocoelom. It contains some cells, and there are no muscles surrounding the gut. *(c)* Other animals, including all vertebrates, have a coelom, which is a fluid-filled space that separates internal organs from the outer body wall. In addition, the coelom is lined with connective tissue of mesodermal origin. Organs project into the coelom and are held in place by thin sheets of connective tissue called mesenteries.

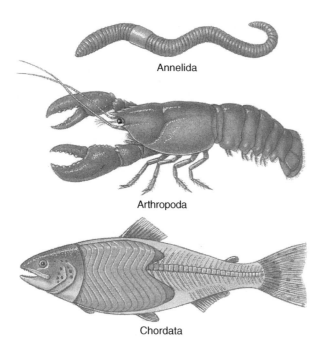

Annelida

Arthropoda

Chordata

**FIGURE 23.7 Segmentation**
Segmentation is associated with the specialization of certain parts of the body. Annelid worms show many segments with little specialization. Arthropods show a highly developed head region, with the more posterior segments less specialized. Chordates show the segmentation of muscles and skeletal structures.

animals have essentially the same genes controlling their development and how different regions or segments of the body develop (How Science Works 23.1).

## Skeletons

A **skeleton** is the part of an organism that provides structural support. Most animals have a skeleton. It serves as strong scaffolding, to which other organs can be attached. In particular, the skeleton provides places for muscle attachment and, if the skeleton has joints, the muscles can move one part of the skeleton with respect to others. Some aquatic organisms, such as sea anemones and many kinds of worms, are generally supported by the dense medium in which they live and lack well-developed skeletons. However, most aquatic animals have a skeleton. Most terrestrial animals have a strong structure that supports them in the thin medium of the atmosphere.

There are two major types of skeletons: internal skeletons (**endoskeletons**) and external skeletons (**exoskeletons**) (figure 23.8). The vertebrates (fish, amphibians, reptiles, birds, mammals), echinoderms (starfish, sea urchins, etc.), and some other groups have internal skeletons. The various organs are attached to and surround the skeleton, which grows in size as the animal grows. Arthropods (crustaceans, spiders, insects, millipedes, centipedes), nematodes, and some

# HOW SCIENCE WORKS 23.1

## Genes, Development, and Evolution

One of the important discoveries of modern molecular genetics is the remarkable similarity in the kinds of genes found in all organisms. This has important implications for understanding the evolution of organisms. It appears that once a new, valuable gene is created through the process of mutation, it is preserved in evolutionary descendants. One example is a group of genes known as *homeotic genes*. These genes regulate how an organism's body is formed by helping to define which end of the developing embryo is the head and which is the tail. As the embryo develops and regular body segments form, the homeotic genes also help define what each segment becomes. In insects, one segment might give rise to antennae, while another gives rise to wings or legs. Homeotic genes were first discovered in the fruit fly (*Drosophila melanogaster*), which has been a favorite species for students of animal genetics for 100 years (see photo). Fruit flies are ideal for genetic studies for several reasons: They are easy and inexpensive to raise in the lab, a new generation can be produced every 10 days, and large numbers of offspring are produced.

It is now known that homeotic genes control the same developmental processes in all organisms that are bilaterally symmetrical (their left side mirrors their right side). This trend is so overwhelming that some scientists have suggested that the presence of one type of homeotic genes, the *Hox* genes, should be used to define the Animal kingdom.

Essentially the same genes with the same functions can be found in widely different animals, such as fruit flies, earthworms, sea urchins, tapeworms, and humans. This means that the study of fruit flies can be used to discover how the same genes function in humans and other animals. Because homeotic genes are involved in regulating embryonic development and cellular differentiation, these studies can be used to help identify the causes of human embryonic development abnormalities and other diseases like cancer.

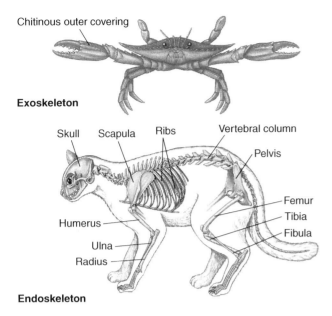

Chitinous outer covering

**Exoskeleton**

Skull  Scapula  Ribs  Vertebral column

Pelvis

Humerus

Femur
Tibia
Fibula

Ulna

Radius

**Endoskeleton**

**FIGURE 23.8 Skeletons**
There are two major types of skeletons; endoskeletons and exoskeletons. Endoskeletons are typical of vertebrates and echinoderms, and exoskeletons are typical of arthropods and their relatives.

other groups have an external skeleton that surrounds all the organs. It is generally hard and has joints. These animals accommodate growth by shedding the old skeleton and producing a new, larger one. This period in the life of an arthropod is dangerous, because for a short period it is without its hard, protective outer layer. Many other animals have structures that have a supportive or protective function (such as clams, snails, and corals) and these are sometimes called skeletons, but they do not have joints.

Some organisms use water as a kind of supportive skeleton. Annelid worms and some other animals have fluid-filled coeloms. Because water is not compressible, but it is movable, compressive forces by muscles can cause the animal's shape to change. This is similar to what happens with a water-filled balloon; compression in one place causes it to bulge out somewhere else.

## 23.5 Marine Lifestyles

All groups of animals originated in the ocean, and most still call the oceans home. Marine animals exhibit several kinds of lifestyles.

### Zooplankton

Zooplankton is a mixture of different kinds of small animals that drift with currents and feed on phytoplankton and other zooplankton. Crustaceans make up approximately 70% of the zooplankton. These include copepods, krill (small, shrimplike organisms), and other kinds of crustaceans. In addition, jellyfish and comb jellies are common. Other kinds of zooplankton include protozoa, several kinds of worms, a group of mollusks, and the larvae (immature, free–living offspring) of many animals, including fish and primitive chordate relatives.

### Nekton

**Nekton** includes many kinds of aquatic animals that are large enough and strong enough to be able to swim against currents and tides and go where they want to. They are carnivores that feed either on plankton or other nekton. Like the zooplankton, this is a diverse group of organisms, including some actively swimming jellyfish, squid and cuttlefish, shrimp, sharks, bony fish, turtles, sea snakes, birds (penguins, cormorants, and other diving birds), and several kinds of mammals (whales, porpoises, seals, sea otters, walruses, and so on).

### Benthic Animals

A major ecological niche in the oceans includes large numbers of bottom-dwelling (benthic) organisms. Among the benthic organisms are such animals as sponges, corals, and sea anemones; segmented worms; clams and snails; lobsters, crabs, and shrimp; starfish and sea urchins; and many kinds of fish. Benthic marine organisms fall into two general categories: those that move about in search of food and those that are filter feeders. Common animals that move about the bottom are crabs, many worms, fish, starfish and some mollusks.

Filter feeders are sessile—permanently attached to the substrate. They feed by creating water currents with cilia or appendages that bring food to them. Sponges, corals, tube worms, clams, barnacles, and crinoids are examples of filter feeders.

Sexual reproduction presents special problems for sessile animals because they cannot move to find mates. However, because they are in an aquatic environment, the sperm can swim to the egg and fertilize it. The fertilized egg develops into a larval stage—the juvenile stage (figure 23.9). The larvae are usually ciliated or have appendages that enable them to move, even though the adults are sessile. The free-swimming larval stages allow the animal to disperse through its environment.

The larva differs from the sessile adult not only because it is free-swimming but also because it usually uses a different source of food and often becomes part of the plankton community. The larval stages of most organisms are subjected

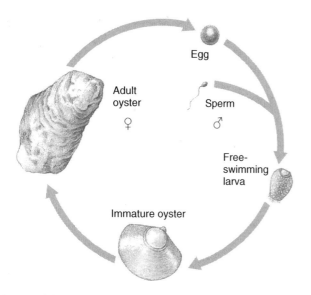

**FIGURE 23.9 The Life Cycle of an Oyster**
Each oyster can be either male or female at different times in its life. Sperm are released and swim to the egg. Fertilization results in the formation of a free-swimming larva. This larva undergoes several changes during the first 12 to 14 days and eventually develops into an immature oyster, which becomes attached and develops into the adult oyster.

to predation, and the mortality rate is high. The larvae move to new locations, settle down, and develop into adults.

Even many marine animals that do not have sessile stages produce free-swimming larvae. For example, crabs, starfish, and eels move about freely and produce free-swimming larvae.

### 23.5 CONCEPT REVIEW

12. What is a sessile filter feeder?
13. How do plankton and nekton organisms differ?
14. What is a benthic organism?

## 23.6 Primitive Marine Animals

Members of the Porifiera (sponges) and Cnidaria (jellyfish, corals, and relatives) are the simplest multicellular animals. Fossils of these kinds of animals have been found that date to about 580 million years ago. Nearly all of the animals in these groups are found in saltwater environments. There are a few freshwater species.

### Porifera—Sponges

Even though sponges are classified as multicellular, in many ways they are similar to colonial protozoa. In particular, a group of flagellated protozoa known as choanoflagellates have a structure that is very similar to the flagellated cells (called choanocytes) found in sponges. Sponges have two layers of cells, with the choanocytes on the inside and flat,

platelike cells (pinacocytes) on the outside. There are also a few other kinds of cells present. There is a jellylike layer between the two kinds of cells. The cells of sponges are rather loosely connected and can move about, and some even change their function. Because of this loosely defined organization, sponges are not considered to have tissues, which are groups of cells with specific functions.

All adult sponges are benthic, sessile (permanently attached) filter feeders. The flagellated choanocytes cause a current of water to circulate through the organism. All the cells engulf entire food particles directly from the water just as most protozoa do (figure 23.10). Although some sponges are radially symmetrical, most sponges are asymmetrical. Sponges have structures, called spicules, in a jellylike material between the two layers of cells. Some species have spicules of calcium carbonate, others of silicon dioxide, and some of a protein material. It is the skeletons composed of protein spicules that are used as bath sponges. (Actually, most sponges we buy are manufactured from various forms of plastic.)

Asexual reproduction in sponges can occur by fragmentation. Wave action may tear off a part of a sponge, which eventually settles down, attaches itself, and begins to grow. Sponges also reproduce by **budding,** a type of asexual reproduction in which the new organism is an outgrowth of the parent. Sexual reproduction involves the release of sperm, which are carried to adjacent sponges where fertilization takes place. The fertilized egg develops into a free-swimming, flagellated larval stage. The larva swims in the plankton and eventually settles to the bottom, attaches, and grows into an adult sponge.

## Cnidaria—Jellyfish, Corals, and Sea Anemones

Members of the Cnidaria (pronounced *nid'-air-e-ah*) include the jellyfish, corals, and sea anemones. They are diploblastic with an outer epidermis and an inner layer that forms digestive cavity. Because the cells of these two layers are specialized, the cnidarians are considered to have a tissue level of development. There is a jellylike material between the two layers of cells; it is very thick in jellyfishes. Cnidarians show radial symmetry, and all species have a single opening leading into a saclike digestive cavity. Surrounding the opening is a series of tentacles (figure 23.11). These long, flexible, armlike tentacles have specialized cells that produce structures called *nematocysts,* which can sting and paralyze small organisms. Nematocysts are unique to the Cnidaria. The cells that produce the nematocysts are known as cnidocytes and are responsible for the name of the group—Cnidaria. Even though they are primitive organisms, cnidarians are carnivorous.

Many species of Cnidaria exhibit alternation of generations and have both sexual and asexual stages of reproduction. The **medusa** is a free-swimming adult stage that reproduces sexually. The **polyp** is a benthic, sessile larval stage that reproduces asexually (figure 23.12). Sea anemones and corals are polyps. Some species lack a medusa stage in their life cycles and the polyps produce eggs and sperm. Corals

**(a) Cellular structure**          **(b) Vase-shaped sponge**          **(c) Asymmetrical sponge**

**FIGURE 23.10   Sponge Structure and Function**

*(a)* Sponges consist of an outer epidermal layer and an inner layer of flagellated cells called choanocytes. These flagella create a current, which brings water in through the openings formed by the porocyte cells, and propels it out through the osculum. The current brings food and oxygen to the inner layer of the cells. The food is filtered from the water as it passes through the animal. *(b)* Some sponges have a "vase shape"; however, *(c)* most sponges are asymmetrical and have no distinct form.

**Jellyfish**                    **Sea anemone**                      **Coral**

**FIGURE 23.11   Phylum Cnidaria**

There are three major types of cnidarians: jellyfish, sea anemones, and corals. The fuzzy appearance of the coral is because the polyps are extended.

secrete an external skeleton of calcium carbonate or other material. The polyp lives in a depression in the skeleton into which it can withdraw. Polyps extend from the depression when they feed. Jellyfish are free-swimming medusas; they often produce small polyp stages during their life cycle.

## Ctenophora—Comb Jellies

Members of Ctenophora (pronounced *tin'-off-er-ah*) are similar to cnidarians in that they are diploblastic and have radial symmetry. They have rows of cilia that allow them to

swim, and many have two long, armlike appendages, which help them gather food (figure 23.13).

### 23.6   CONCEPT REVIEW

15. How do sponges feed?
16. What are spicules?
17. What are the differences between a polyp and a medusa?
18. List three structural characteristics of cnidarians.

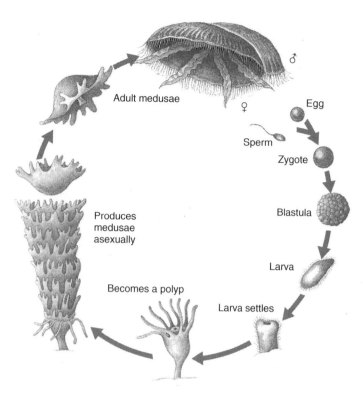

**FIGURE 23.12  A Cnidarian Life Cycle**
The life cycle of *Aurelia* is typical of the alternation of generations seen in most species of Cnidaria. The free-swimming adult medusa (jellyfish) reproduces sexually, and the resulting larva develops into a polyp. The polyp undergoes asexual reproduction, which produces the free-swimming medusa stage.

**FIGURE 23.13  Ctenophora**
Ctenophorans are marine, planktonic organisms that swim with rows of cilia. Many are bioluminescent.

## 23.7  Platyhelminthes—Flatworms

The simplest bilaterally symmetrical animals are the flatworms. Because they are also triploblastic, they represent a major increase in complexity over the sponges and cnidarians. They are considered more primitive than other bilaterally symmetrical, triploblastic animals because they lack a coelom and have only one opening to the gut. They have no circulatory or respiratory system. Their flat structure allows for the diffusion of gases between their environment and the internal cells.

There are three basic types of flatworms. Turbellaria is a class of free-living flatworms (often called *planarians*). The other two groups are parasitic: Trematoda (flukes) and Cestoda (tapeworms). These parasitic kinds constitute the majority of species of flatworms (figure 23.14). We may consider this form of nutrition rather unusual, but of all the kinds of animals in the world, more are parasites than not.

*Turbellarians* are free-living flatworms that are bottom dwellers in marine waters or freshwater. A few species are found in moist terrestrial habitats. They are carnivores or scavengers that feed on dead organisms. The food that enters

**(a) Turbellarian**

**(b) Tapeworm**

**(c) Fluke**

**FIGURE 23.14  Flatworm Diversity**
*(a)* Turbellarians are free-swimming, nonparasitic flatworms that inhabit marine and freshwater. (This is a marine species.) *(b)* Adult tapeworms are parasites found in the intestines of many carnivores. *(c)* Some flukes live attached to the outside surface of animals, but most are internal parasites of the lungs, liver, and intestine of vertebrate animals.

the gut is partly broken down; then, the food particles are engulfed by the cells that line the gut. Many marine species are brightly colored.

*Flukes* are common parasites. Some flukes are external parasites on the gills and scales of fish, but most are internal parasites. Most flukes have a complex life cycle involving more than one host. Typically, the larval stage infects an invertebrate host (usually a mollusk), whereas the adult parasite infects a vertebrate host. They are commonly found in the gut, liver, or lungs of vertebrate hosts.

For example, the disease schistosomiasis is caused by adult *Schistosoma mansoni* flukes, which live in the blood vessels of the human digestive system. This disease is common in tropical countries. The presence of the worms in the body causes diarrhea, liver damage, anemia, and a lowering of the body's resistance to other diseases. Fertilized eggs pass out with the feces. Eggs released into the water hatch into free-swimming larvae. If a larva infects a snail, it undergoes additional asexual reproduction and produces a second larval stage. A single infected snail may be the source of thousands of larvae. These new larvae swim freely in the water. If they encounter a human, the larvae bore through the skin and enter the circulatory system, which carries them to the blood vessels of the intestine (figure 23.15).

In North America, people often encounter this kind of parasite as swimmer's itch. Swimmer's itch is caused by the larval stages of a species of *Schistosoma* burrowing into the skin. However, the normal hosts for the parasite are species of ducks. Humans are not ducks, so the larvae that have burrowed into the skin die and a rash often develops. In sensitive individuals, the reaction can be extreme and require medical attention.

*Tapeworms* are parasites that have a completely different structure and way of life from flukes. The life cycle involves two hosts. One of the hosts is an herbivore and the other is an omnivore or a carnivore. Both hosts are usually vertebrate animals. An herbivore eats tapeworm eggs that have been passed from an infected carnivore host through its feces. The eggs contaminate the vegetation and are eaten along with the vegetation the herbivore uses for food. An egg develops into a larval stage, which migrates to the herbivore's muscle and forms a cyst. When the herbivore is eaten by a carnivore, the tapeworm cyst develops into the adult form in the carnivore's intestine. The adult worm is highly specialized. It has no digestive system, but it has hooks and suckers for holding onto the intestine of its host. It produces a series of sections, called proglottids, by asexual reproduction. Each proglottid has a complete set of reproductive organs. It is important not to confuse proglottids with the segments seen in other kinds of organisms. Proglottids are not segments, but are asexually produced buds. Mating takes place between proglottids within the intestine, and the proglottids become filled with fertilized eggs. The end proglottids break off and pass out with the feces. As the proglottids dry out, they rupture and disperse the eggs into the environment (figure 23.16).

**FIGURE 23.15 The Life History of *Schistosoma mansoni***
*(1)* Cercaria larvae in water penetrate human skin and are carried through the circulatory system to the veins of the intestine. They develop into *(2)* adult worms, which live in the blood vessels of the intestine. *(3)* Copulating worms are shown. The female produces eggs, which enter the intestine and leave with the feces. *(4)* A miracidium larva within an eggshell is shown. *(5)* The miracidium larva hatches in water and burrows into a snail *(6)*, where it develops into a mother sporocyst *(7)*. The mother sporocyst produces many daughter sporocysts *(8)*, each of which produces many cercaria larvae. These leave the snail's body and enter the water, thus completing the life cycle.

Adult tapeworm

Infected
meat eaten

Mature
bladder
worm

Mature cysts
in striated muscle

Gravid (ripe)
proglottid

Eggs

Tapeworm
eggs

O'Keefe

Eggs
eaten

**FIGURE 23.16 The Life Cycle of a Tapeworm**
The adult beef tapeworm lives in the human small intestine. Proglottids, individual segments containing male and female sex organs, are the site of egg production. When the eggs are ripe, the proglottids drop off the tapeworm and pass out in the feces. If a cow eats an egg, the egg will develop into a cyst in the cow's muscles. When humans eat the cyst in raw or poorly cooked meat, the cyst develops into an adult tapeworm.

outer epidermis covered by a thick, flexible cuticle. The cuticle is shed periodically as the animal grows. Nematodes are triploblastic and have a pseudocoelom (figure 23.17). Their gut is continuous, with a mouth at one end and an anus at the other. Few animals are found in as many diverse habitats or in such numbers as the roundworms. They live in marine and freshwater habitats, moist soil, and many live within other organisms as parasites. Soil nematodes are extremely common.

Although most roundworms are free-living, many are economically important parasites. Some are parasitic on plants, whereas others infect animals; collectively, they do billions of dollars worth of damage to crops and livestock. Roundworm parasites of animals range from the relatively harmless human intestinal pinworms *Enterobius*, which may cause irritation but do no serious harm, to *Dirofilaria*, which can cause heartworm disease in dogs. If untreated, this infection can be fatal. Often, the amount of damage inflicted by roundworms is directly proportional to their number. For example, hookworms (figure 23.18) feed on the host's blood. A slight infestation often results in mild anemia, but a heavy infestation of hookworms can result in mental or physical retardation in children because of the severe anemia it causes.

## 23.7   CONCEPT REVIEW

19. List three structural characteristics typical of flatworms.
20. Describe the life cycle of a fluke.
21. Describe the life cycle of a tapeworm.

## 23.8   Nematoda—Roundworms

Members of the Nematoda are extremely common animals, often called roundworms or nematodes. They have a simple, unsegmented, elongated body structure that consists of an

## 23.8   CONCEPT REVIEW

22. Describe the general body structure of a nematode.

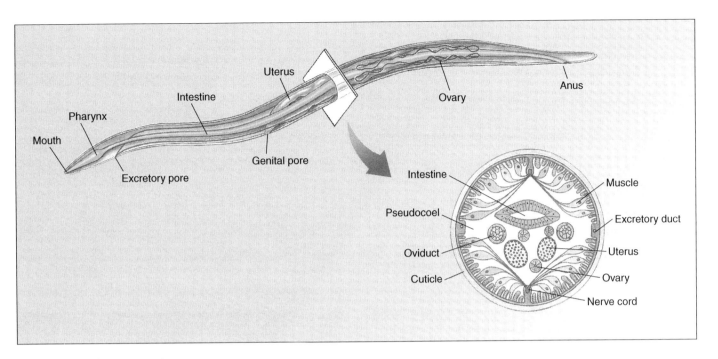

**FIGURE 23.17 Nematode Worms**
Nematode worms have a simple structure but have a complete gut with a mouth and an anus. Their body cavity is a pseudocoelom.

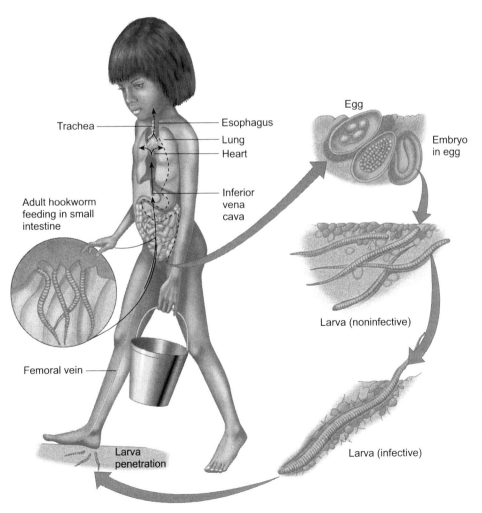

**FIGURE 23.18 The Life Cycle of a Hookworm**
Fertilized hookworm eggs pass out of the body in the feces and develop into larvae. In the soil, the larvae feed on bacteria. The larvae bore through the skin of humans and develop into adults. The adult hookworms live in the digestive system, where they suck blood from the host. The loss of blood can result in anemia, mental and physical retardation, and a loss of energy.

## 23.9 Annelida—Segmented Worms

The annelid worms are bilaterally symmetrical and have a body structure consisting of repeating segments (figure 23.19). Most of the segments are very similar to one another, although there is usually some specialization of anterior segments into a head, and there may be specialization related to reproduction and digestion. Each segment has a coelomic cavity. They have well-developed muscular, circulatory, digestive, excretory, and nervous systems. There are three major types of annelid worms (figure 23.20).

*Polychaetes* are primarily benthic, marine worms that have paddlelike appendages on each segment. They have a well-developed head region with sense organs and a mouth. Some live in tubes and are filter feeders. Others burrow in mud or sand; some swim in search of food. Most polychaetes have separate sexes and release eggs and sperm into the ocean, where fertilization takes place. The fertilized egg develops into a ciliated larva known as a trochophore larva; it is planktonic and eventually metamorphoses into the adult form of the worm.

*Oligochaetes* live in moist soil or freshwater. The most commonly seen members of this group are the various kinds of earthworms. They differ from polychaetes in that they do not have appendages and a well-developed head region. They

Polychaete

Leech

Filter-feeding polychaete

Earthworm

mouth
pharynx
ventral nerve cord
brain
esophagus
ventral blood vessel
coelom
hearts
clitellum
seminal vesicle
nephridium
crop
dorsal blood vessel
anus

### FIGURE 23.19 Annelid Structure

An earthworm shows the major features of annelid structure. Annelids are bilaterally symmetrical, segmented, and have complex organ systems and a coelom.

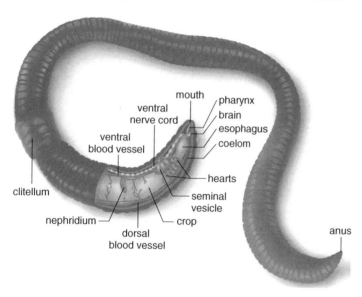

longitudinal muscles
dorsal blood vessel
circular muscles
muscular wall of intestine
coelomic lining
nephridium
typhlosole
setae
coelom
ventral blood vessel
cuticle
ventral nerve cord
excretory pore
subneural blood vessel
gland cell

### FIGURE 23.20 Annelid Diversity

There are three major types of annelid worms. Polychaete worms are primarily marine worms. Some live in tubes and obtain food by filtering water. Others are free to move and are omnivores or carnivores. Oligochaetes (earthworms) burrow through soil and eat organic matter. Leeches either are carnivores or suck the blood of other animals.

are also hermaphroditic (have both sets of sex organs in the same individual). Mating between two earthworms results in each receiving sperm from the other. Earthworms are extremely important soil organisms. They eat organic matter in the soil or come to the surface to eat dead leaves and other organic matter. As they burrow through the soil, they create spaces, which allow water and air to penetrate the soil. They are also important food organisms to many other animals.

*Leeches* live in freshwater or moist terrestrial environments. They have suckers, which allow them to hold on to objects. Some are free-swimming carnivores, but many feed on the blood of various vertebrates. They attach to their victims, rasp a hole through the skin, and suck blood. They produce an anticoagulant, which aids in their blood-feeding lifestyle.

## 23.9  CONCEPT REVIEW

23. List three structural characteristics of annelids.
24. What are the three kinds of segmented worms?

## 23.10  Mollusca

Like most other forms of animal life, the mollusks originated in the ocean, and, even though some forms have made the move to freshwater and terrestrial environments, most still live in the oceans. The members of this phylum display a true body cavity, a coelom. Reproduction is generally sexual; some species have separate sexes and others are hermaphroditic. They range from microscopic organisms to the giant squid, which is up to 18 meters long. A primary characteristic of mollusks is the presence of a soft body enclosed by a hard shell. They are not segmented but have three distinct body regions: the mantle, the foot, and the visceral mass. The mantle produces a shell and is involved in gas exchange, the foot is involved in movement, and the visceral mass contains the organs of digestion, circulation, and reproduction. Most of the mollusks have a tonguelike structure known as a radula, which has teeth on it. They use the radula like a rasp to scrape away at food materials and tear them to tiny particles that are ingested (figure 23.21).

Except for the squids and octopuses, mollusks are slow-moving benthic animals. Some are herbivores and feed on marine algae; others are scavengers and feed on dead organic matter. A few are even predators of other slow-moving or sessile neighbors. As with most other marine animals, the mollusks produce a free-swimming larval stage, which aids in dispersal. It is a ciliated trochophore larva similar to that seen in the annelids.

There are several kinds of mollusks; the most commonly observed are the chitons, bivalves, snails, and octopuses and squids (figure 23.22).

The chitons are a primitive group of marine mollusks that have a series of eight shell plates along their back. They generally live on rocky surfaces and use their radula to scrape algae from the rocks. They can clamp onto their rocky substrate when disturbed. Many species are common along rocky shores.

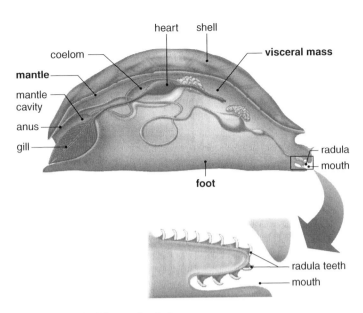

**FIGURE 23.21  Mollusk Structure**
Mollusks are bilaterally symmetrical organisms with a coelom and a body composed of three body regions: the foot, the mantle, and the visceral mass.

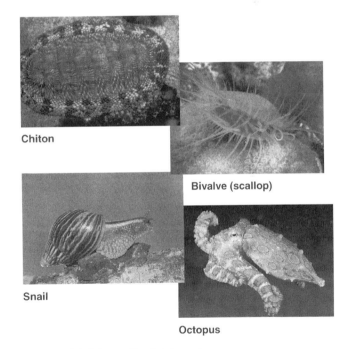

**FIGURE 23.22  Mollusk Diversity**
Mollusks range in complexity from small, slow-moving, grazing animals, such as chitons and snails, to clams, which are filter feeders, to intelligent, rapidly moving carnivores, such as octopuses.

Snails have a coiled shell. Most snails are benthic marine organisms, but some live in freshwater and moist terrestrial habitats. Slugs are a kind of snail that does not have a shell. Snails and slugs are extremely common and there are a huge number of different species. Many marine snails are carnivores.

The bivalves (clams, oysters, and mussels) are benthic marine and freshwater mollusks that have two shells. They also differ from other mollusks in that they are filter feeders and lack a radula.

Squids and octopuses have no external shell although a related organism—the nautilus—has a shell. They are marine animals that are active, rapidly moving predators. Squids are free-swimming predators, whereas octopuses are benthic and use ambushing as a way to capture prey.

## 23.10 CONCEPT REVIEW

25. Describe the general body plan of mollusks.
26. How does the lifestyle of a squid differ from that of a chiton?

## 23.11 Arthropoda

The arthropods are the most successful group of animals on Earth. The earliest arthropods were marine, and today arthropods are found as plankton, nekton, and benthic animals. However, the most successful group of animals is the terrestrial insects. Over three-fourths of the species of animals are arthropods, and over three-fourths of the arthropods are insects.

Arthropods have an external skeleton composed of chitin. Their bodies are segmented, but the segmentation is highly modified, compared with that of the annelids. There is generally a head region, and the segments that follow may be modified into regions as well. Many of the segments have paired appendages. Both the body and the appendages are jointed.

Because they have an exoskeleton, in order to grow they must shed their skeleton and manufacture a new, larger one at intervals. They have well-developed nervous, muscular, respiratory, circulatory, and reproductive systems (figure 23.23).

There are many types of arthropods: crustaceans, millipedes, centipedes, arachnids, and insects (figure 23.24). Nearly all crustaceans are aquatic (both marine and freshwater) but range in size from large crabs and lobsters to tiny, planktonic organisms and sessile barnacles. Crustaceans are typically omnivores, which feed on a variety of living and dead materials.

Millipedes and centipedes have long bodies with many legs, and all the posterior segments are similar to one another. The earliest fossils of terrestrial animals are of this type.

The arachnids are the scorpions, spiders, mites, and ticks. They are very successful as land animals. Mites are extremely common as soil organisms. Spiders are carnivores, and most ticks are blood feeders.

Insects are terrestrial animals with a body divided into three regions: head, thorax, and abdomen. They have three pairs of legs, and most species have wings.

## 23.11 CONCEPT REVIEW

27. List three characteristics typical of all arthropods.
28. How do crustaceans and insects differ structurally?

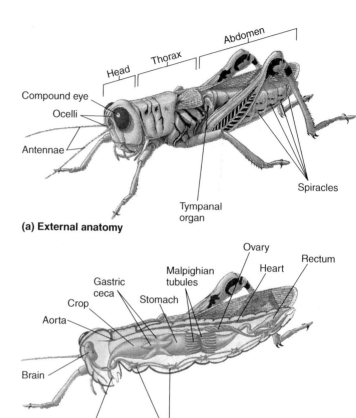

**FIGURE 23.23 Arthropod Structure—Grasshopper**
*(a)* Arthropods have an external skeleton and segments that are modified into special body regions. They have jointed appendages. *(b)* They have complex organ systems.

## 23.12 Echinodermata

The echinoderms represent a completely different line of evolution from other invertebrates. They are actually more closely related to the vertebrates than to other invertebrates. Echinoderms, along with chordates, have an embryological development, in which the anus is the first opening of the gut to form. Such animals are called deuterostomes. In all other triploblastic organisms, the mouth is the first opening of the gut to form; these are called protostomes. All echinoderms are marine benthic animals and are found in all regions, from the shoreline to the deep portions of the ocean. Echinoderms are the most common type of animal on much of the ocean floor. Most species are free-moving and either are carnivores or feed on detritus.

They are unique among the more advanced invertebrates in that they display radial symmetry. They have a five-part radial symmetry; thus, they have five arms or regions of the body that project from a central axis. However, the larval stage has bilateral symmetry, leading many biologists to believe that the echinoderm ancestors were bilaterally symmetrical.

Another unique characteristic of this group is their water vascular system (figure 23.25). In this system, water is taken in

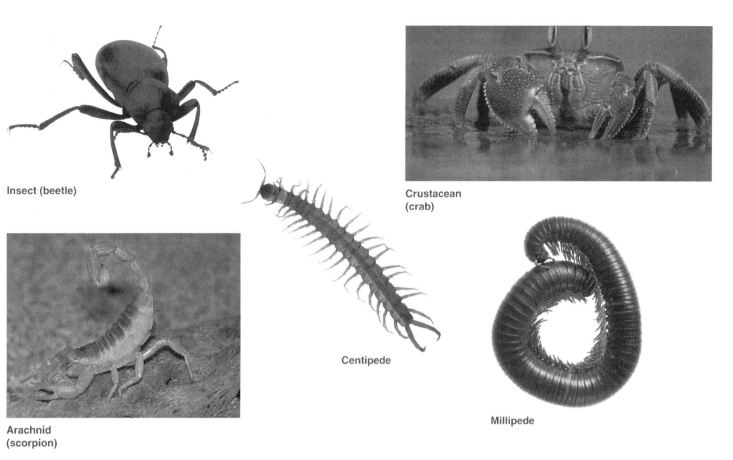

Insect (beetle)

Crustacean
(crab)

Centipede

Arachnid
(scorpion)

Millipede

## FIGURE 23.24  Arthropod Diversity
Arthropods are the most successful group of organisms on Earth.

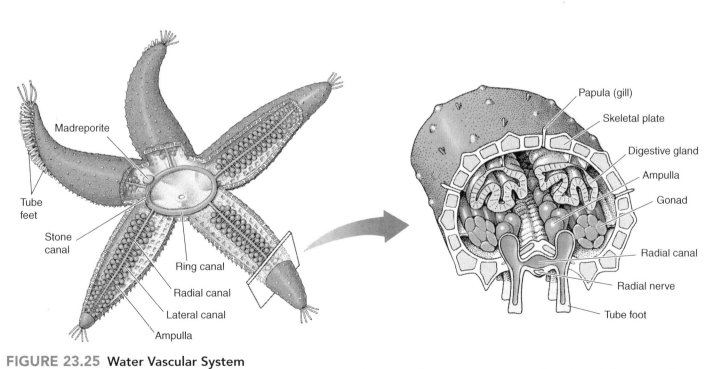

## FIGURE 23.25  Water Vascular System
Echinoderms move by means of a water vascular system. Water enters the system through an opening, travels to the radial canals, and is forced into the tube feet.

Starfish

Brittle star

Sea urchin

Sea cucumber

Feather star

**FIGURE 23.26 Echinoderm Diversity**
Echinoderms have a five-part radial symmetry and an internal skeleton. Many of them have spines that protrude from the surface. There are five major types of echinoderms: starfish, brittle stars, sea urchins, sea cucumbers, and crinoids (feather stars).

through a structure on the top side of the animal and then moves through a series of canals. The passage of water through this water vascular system is involved in the organism's locomotion.

They have a hard, jointed internal skeleton covered by a thin skin. Many of them have spines that are part of the skeleton and project from the animal.

There are five major types of echinoderms: starfish, brittle stars, sea urchins, sea cucumbers, and crinoids (figure 23.26). Starfish, brittle stars, and sea urchins move slowly along the ocean bottom and feed primarily on detritus. Some starfish are carnivores that eat clams. Crinoids are sessile, and many of them are stalked. Because they have five arms that are often feather-like, they are often called sea lilies or feather stars. They are filter feeders. Sea cucumbers are sausage-shaped organisms that lie on the bottom or burrow in the mud. Some are detritus feeders and some are filter feeders.

### 23.12 CONCEPT REVIEW

29. Describe the general body plan of an echinoderm.
30. What is a water vascular system, and what does it do?

### 23.13 Chordata

The chordates are a diverse group of animals. They have a hollow nerve cord down the back of the body; they have a flexible rod just below the nerve cord, known as the notochord; they have a tail, which extends beyond the anus; and they have a region posterior to the mouth, known as a pharynx, that has pouches in it. The most primitive chordates are small marine organisms that have a notochord but no backbone. They are *Branchiostoma* (formerly named *Amphioxus*) and tunicates. *Branchiostoma* has a notochord as an adult, but the tunicates have only a notochord in the tail region during the larval stage (figure 23.27). However, most chordates are vertebrates (animals with a backbone) and only have a notochord during their embryonic stages. In the aquatic chordates the pouches in the pharynx region form gill slits. In terrestrial vertebrates, these pouches are obvious in embryos but are highly modified in the adults.

There are several kinds of vertebrates that have always been aquatic organisms and are commonly called fishes. Hagfish and lampreys lack jaws and are the most primitive of the fish. Hagfish are strictly marine forms and are scavengers; lampreys are mainly marine but can also be found in freshwater (figure 23.28). Adult lampreys suck blood from their larger fish hosts. Lampreys reproduce in freshwater

*Branchiostoma*

**Adult Tunicate**

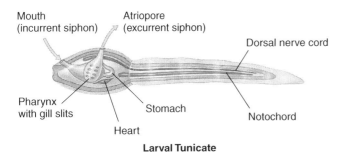

**Larval Tunicate**

**FIGURE 23.27  Invertebrate Chordates**
*Branchiostoma* and tunicates are invertebrate chordates. They have a notochord but no backbone of vertebrae. Tunicates have a larval stage that has a notochord in the tail. Most tunicates change into a saclike body form that is sessile. *Branchiostoma* lives in the sand on the ocean floor. Both organisms are filter feeders.

streams, where the eggs develop into filter-feeding larvae. After several years, the larvae change to adults and migrate to open water.

Sharks and rays are marine animals that have an internal skeleton made entirely of cartilage (figure 23.29). These animals have no swim bladder to adjust their body density in order to maintain their position in the water; therefore, they must constantly swim or they will sink. Rays feed by gliding along the bottom and dredging up food, usually invertebrates.

**(a) Lamprey mouth**

**(b) Lampreys on carp**

**FIGURE 23.28  The Lamprey**
The lamprey uses its round mouth *(a)* to attach to a fish and then *(b)* to suck blood from the fish.

**(a) Silvertip shark**

**(b) Blue-spotted stingray**

**FIGURE 23.29  Cartilaginous Fish**
Although *(a)* sharks and *(b)* rays are large animals, they do not have bones; their skeletal system is made entirely of cartilage.

Sharks are predatory and feed primarily on other fish. They travel great distances in search of food. Most species of sharks grow no longer than a meter. The whale shark, the largest, grows to 16 meters, but it is strictly a filter feeder.

The bony fish are the class most familiar to us (figure 23.30). Their skeleton is composed of bone. Most species have a swim bladder and can regulate the amount of gas in the bladder to control their density. Thus, the fish can remain at a given level in the water without expending large amounts of energy. Bony fish are found in marine and freshwater habitats, and some, such as salmon, can live in both. There are many kinds of bony fish. Some are bottom-dwelling, whereas others are wide-ranging in the open water. Some fish are highly territorial and remain in a small area their entire lives. Of the many kinds, some feed primarily on algae and detritus. However, many are predators.

The remaining groups of vertebrates (amphibians, reptiles, birds, and mammals) all are terrestrial animals. The amphibians are transitional organisms, which must return to water to reproduce and have aquatic larval stages. Reptiles, birds, and mammals have become very successful terrestrial animals. They are discussed in section 23.14.

**23.13  CONCEPT REVIEW**

31. List three characteristics shared by all chordates.
32. How does a shark differ from most freshwater fish?

## 23.14  Adaptations to Terrestrial Life

There is fossil evidence of land plants and fungi at about 480 million years ago, during the Ordovician period, and vascular plants were well established on land by the time terrestrial animals show up in the fossil record at about 420 million years ago. Thus, plants and fungi served as a source of food and shelter for the animals.

All animals that live on land must overcome certain common problems. Terrestrial animals must have:

1. a moist membrane that allows for an adequate gas exchange between the atmosphere and the organism,
2. a means of support and locomotion suitable for land travel,
3. methods to conserve internal water,
4. a means of reproduction and early embryonic development in which large amounts of water are not required, and
5. methods to survive the rapid and extreme climatic changes that characterize many terrestrial habitats.

When the first terrestrial animals evolved, there were many unfilled niches; therefore, much adaptive radiation occurred, resulting in a large number of different animal species. Of all the many phyla of animals in the ocean, only a few made the transition from the ocean to the extremely variable environments found on the land. The annelids (earthworms and leeches) and the mollusks (land snails) have terrestrial species

Lined sweet lips

Sea horse

**FIGURE 23.30  Bony Fish**
Bony fish have a skeleton composed of bone. Most fish have a streamlined body and are strong swimmers. A few, such as the sea horse, have unusual body shapes and are relatively sedentary.

but are confined to moist habitats. Many of the arthropods (centipedes, millipedes, scorpions, spiders, mites, ticks, and insects) and vertebrates (reptiles, birds, and mammals) adapted to a wide variety of drier terrestrial habitats.

### Terrestrial Arthropods

There are five kinds of terrestrial arthropods: crustaceans, millipedes, centipedes, arachnids (mites, ticks, spiders, scorpions), and insects. The few terrestrial crustaceans are generally confined to moist environments. The first terrestrial animals were millipedes, which are known from the fossil record from over 400 million years ago. Flightless insects also are early terrestrial organisms. The exoskeleton of marine arthropods was important in allowing some of their descendents to adapt to land. It provides the support needed in the less buoyant air and serves as a surface for muscle attachment that permits rapid movement. The exoskeleton of most terrestrial arthropods has a waterproof, waxy coating that reduces water loss.

Terrestrial arthropods have an internal respiratory system that prevents the loss of water from their respiratory surface. They have a tracheal system of thin-walled tubes extending into all regions of the body, thus providing a large surface area for gas exchange (figure 23.31a). These tubes have small openings to the outside, which reduce the amount of water lost to the environment. Another important method of conserving water in insects and spiders is the presence of Malpighian tubules, thin-walled tubes that surround the gut and reabsorb water from nitrogenous wastes prior to their excretion (figure 23.31b).

Internal fertilization is typical of terrestrial arthropods. It involves copulation, in which a penis is used to insert the sperm into the reproductive tract of the female (insects, millipedes) or the production of special sperm-containing sacs (spermatophores) that are picked up by the female (spiders, centipedes). This is important because both the sperm and egg are protected from drying.

Terrestrial arthropods have evolved a number of characteristics that assure their survival under hostile environmental conditions. Many seek out sheltered sites and become inactive during periods of cold or drought. Often this involves changes in physiology that protect against freezing or prevent water loss. In addition, their rapid reproductive rate can replace the large number that die. Most of a population may be lost because of an unsuitable environmental change, but, when favorable conditions return, the remaining individuals can quickly increase in number. Many have complex life cycles that involve larval stages that occupy different niches from the adults. For example, butterflies have larval stages that feed on the leaves of plants and grow rapidly. The adults feed on the nectar of flowers and are primarily involved in sexual reproduction that involves mating and laying of the eggs on appropriate host plants (figure 23.32).

The terrestrial arthropods occupy an incredible variety of niches. Many insects are herbivores that compete directly with humans for food. They are capable of decimating plant populations that serve as human food. Many farming practices, including the use of pesticides, are directed at controlling insect populations. Other kinds of insects, as well as spiders and centipedes, are carnivores that feed primarily on arthropods and other small animals. Mites and millipedes feed primarily on decaying material and the fungi and bacteria that are part of decaying material. Insects have evolved in concert with the flowering plants; their role in pollination is well understood. Bees, butterflies, and beetles transfer pollen from one flower to another as they visit the flowers in search

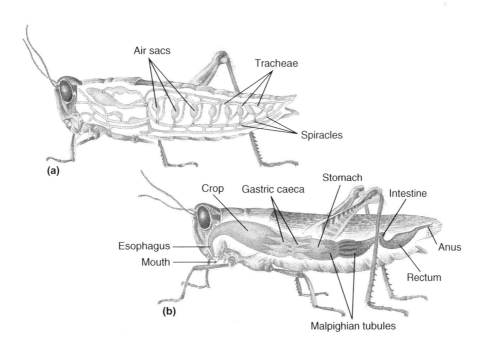

**FIGURE 23.31 Insect Respiratory and Waste-Removal Systems**
*(a)* Spiracles are openings in the exoskeleton of insects and other terrestrial arthropods. These openings connect to a series of tubes (tracheae) that allow for the transportation of gases in the insect's body. *(b)* Malpighian tubules are used in the elimination of waste materials and the reabsorption of water into the arthropod body. Both systems are means of conserving body water.

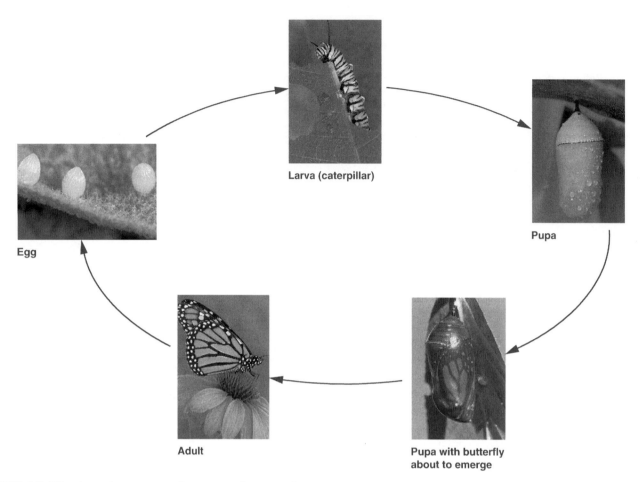

**FIGURE 23.32 The Life History of a Monarch Butterfly**
The adult female lays eggs on a milkweed plant. The fertilized egg hatches into the larval stage, known as a caterpillar, which feeds on the leaves of the milkweed plant. The caterpillar grows and eventually metamorphoses into a pupa. After emerging from the pupa, the adult's wings expand to their full size. The adults feed on the nectar of flowers. After mating, the female lays eggs and the life cycle starts over again.

of food. Many kinds of crops rely on bees for pollination, and farmers even rent beehives to ensure adequate pollination for fruit production.

## Terrestrial Vertebrates

The first vertebrates on land were probably the ancestors of present-day amphibians (frogs, toads, and salamanders). The endoskeleton of vertebrates is an important prerequisite for life on land. It provides the support in the air and provides the places for muscle attachment necessary to movement. However, appendages are needed to move about. Certain bony fishes have lobe-fins, which can serve as primitive legs. It is likely that the amphibians evolved from a fish with modified fins (How Science Works 23.2). The first amphibians made the transition to land about 360 million years ago during the Devonian period. This was 50 million years after plants and arthropods had become established on land. Thus, when the first vertebrates developed the ability to live on land, shelter and food for herbivorous as well as carnivorous

animals were available. But vertebrates faced the same problems that the insects, spiders and other invertebrates faced in their transition to life on land.

### Amphibians

Amphibians are only minimally adapted to a terrestrial life. Although they have lungs they do not have an efficient method of breathing. They swallow air to fill the lungs and are able to accomplish some exchange of oxygen and carbon dioxide. However, most gas exchange occurs through their moist skin. In addition to needing water to keep their skin moist, amphibians must reproduce in water. When they mate, the female releases eggs into the water, and the male releases sperm amid the eggs. External fertilization occurs in the water, and the fertilized eggs must remain in water or they will dehydrate. Thus, amphibians live on "dry" land but are not found far from water, because they lose water through their moist skin and reproduction must occur in water. The most common present-day amphibians are frogs, toads, and salamanders (figure 23.33).

Frog tadpole

Frog

Salamander

Toad

**FIGURE 23.33 Amphibians**
Amphibian larvae (tadpoles) are aquatic organisms that have external gills and feed on vegetation. Most adult salamanders, frogs, and toads feed on insects, worms, and other small animals.

## Reptiles

For 40 million years, amphibians were the only vertebrate animals on land. However, eventually they were replaced by reptiles, which were better adapted to life on land. In addition to having internal lungs, reptiles have a waterproof skin and water-conserving kidneys to reduce water loss. Furthermore, their reproduction involves internal fertilization, which protects the egg and sperm from drying. However, to be truly free of water it is necessary to have a specialized aquatic environment in which the embryo develops. This is accomplished with a special reproductive development known as an amniotic egg.

Reptiles became completely independent of an aquatic environment with the development of the amniotic egg, which protects the developing young from injury and dehydration (figure 23.34). The covering on the egg retains moisture and protects the developing young from dehydration while allowing for the exchange of gases. The reptiles were the first animals to develop such an egg.

The development of a means of internal fertilization and the amniotic egg allowed the reptiles to spread over much of the Earth and occupy a large number of previously unfilled niches. For about 200 million years, they were the only large vertebrate animals on land. The evolution of reptiles increased competition with the amphibians for food and space. The amphibians generally lost in this competition; consequently, most became extinct. Some evolved into present-day frogs, toads, and salamanders.

In a similar fashion, as birds and mammals evolved, many kinds of reptiles became extinct. However, there are still many kinds of reptiles present today. They include turtles, lizards, snakes, crocodiles, and alligators (figure 23.35).

## Birds

The reptiles gave rise to two other groups of vertebrates: birds and mammals. About 65 million years ago, a mass extinction of many kinds of reptiles occurred. At that time, birds and mammals began to diversify and became the

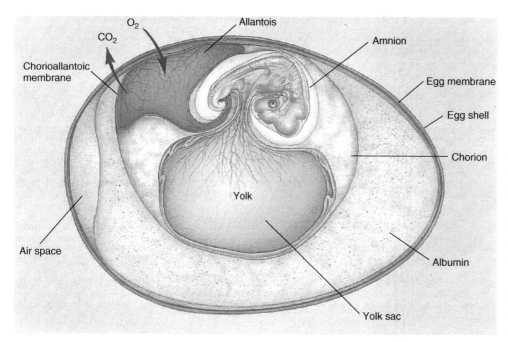

**FIGURE 23.34 The Amniotic Egg**
An amniotic egg has a shell and a membrane that prevent the egg from dehydrating but still allow for the exchange of gases between the egg and the environment. The egg yolk provides a source of nourishment for the developing young. The embryo grows three extraembryonic membranes: the amnion is a fluid-filled sac that allows the embryo to develop in a liquid medium, the allantois collects the embryo's metabolic waste material and exchanges gases, and the chorion is a membrane that encloses the embryo and the other two membranes.

Turtle

Snake

Alligator

Lizard

**FIGURE 23.35 Reptiles**
Present-day reptiles include turtles, crocodiles and alligators, snakes, and lizards.

# HOW SCIENCE WORKS 23.2

## Coelacanth Discoveries

Sometimes, scientific discoveries are made because the right person is in the right place at the right time. In 1938, a coelacanth—a fish that was thought to have been extinct for about 80 million years—was discovered near the mouth of the Chalumna River on the east coast of South Africa. The fishing boat captain who caught the fish contacted Marjorie Courtney-Latimer, the director of the local museum in the town of East London. She immediately contacted a fish biologist, J. L. B. Smith, and the coelacanth became a scientific celebrity. The coelacanth was named *Latimeria chalumnae*, incorporating both Courtney-Latimer's name and the name of the Chalumna River in its name. Subsequently, it was discovered that the fish was probably a stray and that the center of the population was farther north in the waters between Mozambique and the island of Madagascar.

In 1997, a biologist, Mark Erdmann, saw a coelacanth in a market in Indonesia. He photographed the fish and questioned the fishers. He then returned to Indonesia and, over a 5-month period, interviewed over 200 fishers. Eventually, he discovered two fishermen who occasionally caught coelacanths. Eventually, he was rewarded with a live specimen, and it was eventually described as a new species, *Latimeria menadoensis*. Scientists used structural differences and DNA analysis as evidence that the Indonesian coelacanth was a different species from the African species.

What was once thought to have been extinct for 80 million years can now be studied in the flesh. Over 200 specimens have been captured, and diving submarines have been used to observe coelacanths in the wild. They live in deep water and typically stay in caves during the day.

The coelacanth has several characteristics that make it of interest to biologists. Primary among them is the presence of

lobe fins. The fins are on short, limblike appendages that resemble stubby legs. Because of this, many biologists thought that coelacanths may have been the ancestors of terrestrial, four-legged vertebrates. Although most no longer feel this is the case, coelacanths do have several interesting characteristics. When they swim, they move their fins alternately in a manner similar to the way four-legged animals walk. They do not have a vertebral column but have a notochord that serves the same purpose as a spine. They have internal fertilization and the young develop from large eggs that are retained within the body of the mother and are born when they have completed development.

Sometimes accidental discoveries lead to a new body of scientific information.

---

dominant forms of vertebrates on land. Like the structures of their reptile ancestors, the skin, lungs, and kidneys of birds reduce water loss, and reproduction involves internal fertilization and the shelled amniotic egg.

They also have other adaptations that allow them to be successful as land animals. Birds are homeothermic and have feathers. As homeotherms, they have a high body temperature and a more rapid metabolic rate than reptiles. Feathers serve two primary functions in birds. They form an insulating layer, which helps prevent heat loss, and they provide structural surfaces enabling the birds to fly. There are several values to flight. Animals that fly are able to travel long distances in a short time and use less energy than animals that must walk or run. They are able to cross barriers, such as streams, lakes, oceans, bogs, ravines, or mountains, that other animals cannot easily cross. They can also escape many kinds of predators by taking flight quickly.

The exploitation of flight has shaped the entire structure and function of birds. The forelimbs are modified into wings for flight, although it is actually the flight feathers that provide most of the flight surface. Large breast muscles provide the power for flight. Feathers help provide a streamlined shape. Homeothermism enables a high constant temperature, which allows for the rapid wing beats typical of most birds. In addition, the skeleton is reduced in weight and the jaws lack teeth that are heavy. The beak performs some of the functions of the teeth and is lighter. Birds have successfully occupied many niches. Some are nectar feeders, some are carnivores, some are seedeaters, some are aquatic, and some have even lost their ability to fly (figure 23.36).

Because they are homeotherms, birds' eggs must be kept at a warm temperature. Thus, birds build nests, incubate their eggs, and care for their young.

**Hummingbird**

**Eagle**

**Ostrich**

**FIGURE 23.36 Birds**
Birds range in size from the small hummingbird with a rapid wingbeat to the large, flightless ostrich. In food habits, they range from the nectar-feeding hummingbird to the omnivorous ostrich and the carnivorous eagle.

## Mammals

The first mammals appeared about 200 million years ago, when reptiles were at their most diverse. Like birds, mammals are homeotherms, with a high constant body temperature. Like reptiles and birds, they have a waterproof skin and water-conserving lungs and kidneys. However, they differ from birds in several respects. Their insulating covering is hair, rather than feathers, and they provide nourishment to their young with milk produced by special glands.

There are three categories of mammals. Monotremes (platypus and echidna) are egg-laying mammals whose young still develop in an external egg. Following hatching, the mother provides nourishment in the form of milk. The milk glands are widely distributed on her underside, and the young lap up the milk from her fur.

Marsupials (pouched mammals) have internal development of the young. However, the young are born in a very immature state and develop further in an external pouch in the belly region of the female. In the pouch, the young attach to a nipple. They continue their development and eventually begin to leave the pouch for periods of time until they are able to forage for themselves.

Placental mammals have a form of development in which the young remain within the female much longer. The embryo is attached to the wall of the uterus by an organ known as a placenta. In the placenta, capillaries from the circulatory systems of the mother and embryo are adjacent to one another. This allows for the exchange of materials between the developing young and the mother, and the young are born in a more advanced stage of development than is typical for marsupials. The young rely on milk as a source of food for some time before they begin to feed on their own (figure 23.37).

### 23.14 CONCEPT REVIEW

33. List the problems animals had to overcome to adapt to a terrestrial environment.
34. List four adaptations of arthropods that allow them to be successful terrestrial animals.
35. Why can't amphibians live in all types of terrestrial habitats?
36. What is the importance of the amniotic egg?
37. How does a marsupial differ from a placental mammal?

## Summary

The 4 million known species of animals, which inhabit widely diverse habitats, are all multicellular and heterotrophic. Animal body shape is asymmetrical, radial, or bilateral. All animals with bilateral symmetry have a body structure composed of three layers.

Animal life originated in the ocean about 600 million years ago; for the first 200 million years, all animal life remained in the ocean. Many simple marine animals have life cycles that involve alternation of generations.

Many kinds of flatworms and nematodes have a parasitic lifestyle with complicated life cycles. A major ecological niche for many marine animals is the ocean bottom—the benthic zone. Many marine animals are planktonic. These zooplankton feed on phytoplankton and, in turn, are fed upon by larger, free-swimming marine animals—the nekton.

Animals that adapted to a terrestrial environment had to have (1) a moist membrane for gas exchange, (2) support and locomotion suitable for land, (3) a means of conserving body water, (4) a means of reproducing and providing for early embryonic development out of water, and (5) a means of surviving in rapid and extreme climatic changes.

Monotreme (echidna)

Placental mammal (zebra)

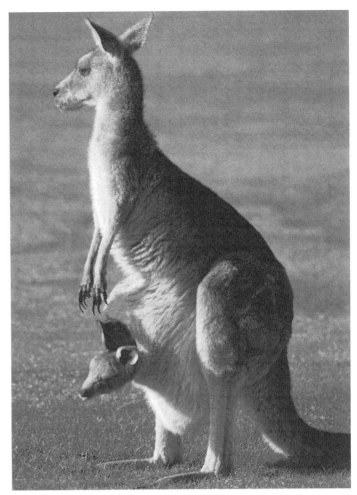

Marsupial (kangaroo)

**FIGURE 23.37  Mammals**

All mammals have hair and produce milk. However, there are three, very different kinds of mammals. Monotremes lay eggs. Marsupials have pouches; the young are born in an immature stage and are carried in the pouch while they finish their development. Placental mammals have a placenta, which connects the mother and embryo; they retain the young in the uterus for a longer period of time.

## Key Terms

*Use the interactive flash cards on the* **Concepts in Biology,** *14/e website to help you learn the meaning of these terms.*

acoelomate 509
asymmetry 507
bilateral symmetry 507
budding 512
coelom 509
diploblastic 507
ectoderm 507
ectotherms 507
endoderm 507

endoskeletons 510
endotherms 507
exoskeletons 510
homeotherms 506
invertebrates 505
medusa 512
mesenteries 509
mesoderm 507
nekton 511

poikilotherms 506
polyp 512
pseudocoelom 509
radial symmetry 507

segmentation 509
skeleton 510
triploblastic 507
vertebrates 505

## Basic Review

1. The most abundant group of terrestrial animals is the
   a. mammals.
   b. birds.
   c. earthworms.
   d. insects.

2. The sponges and cnidarians
   a. reproduce sexually.
   b. are primarily marine.
   c. are not bilaterally symmetrical.
   d. All of the above are correct.
3. Which of the following animal groups shows radial symmetry?
   a. annelids
   b. echinoderms
   c. vertebrates
   d. None of the above is correct.
4. The most successful group of animals based on the number of species is the _____.
5. The three general parts of the mollusk body are the visceral mass, mantle, and _____.
6. Nematode worms are extremely common in soil. (T/F)
7. Which of the following organisms has a body consisting of a linear arrangement of similar segments?
   a. nematodes
   b. mollusks
   c. annelids
   d. cnidarians
8. All of the following animals have an amniotic egg except
   a. monotremes.
   b. marsupials.
   c. reptiles.
   d. birds.
9. Terrestrial animals have
   a. internal fertilization.
   b. a waterproof skin.
   c. a strong skeleton.
   d. All of the above are correct.
10. The two groups of animals that are homeotherms are the _____.
11. Which of the following animals is diploblastic?
    a. jellyfish
    b. starfish
    c. shark
    d. mammal
12. Annelid worms are
    a. diploblastic.
    b. coelomate.
    c. assymetrical.
    d. homeotherms.
13. Most marine animals have a free-swimming developmental stage called a _____.

14. The flatworms are
    a. triploblatic.
    b. acoelomate.
    c. poikilotherms.
    d. All of the above are correct.
15. Nematodes have a body cavity known as a _____.

**Answers**
1. d   2. d   3. b   4. arthropods   5. foot   6. T   7. c   8. b
9. d   10. birds and mammals   11. a   12. b   13. larva   14. d
15. pseudocoelom

## Thinking Critically

**Using Animals in Research**
Animals have been used routinely as models for the development of medical techniques and strategies. They have also been used in the development of pharmaceuticals and other biomedical products, such as heart valves and artificial joints. The techniques necessary to perform heart, kidney, and other organ transplants were first refined using chimpanzees, rats, and calves. Antibiotics, hormones, and chemotherapeutic drugs have been tested for their effectiveness and for possible side effects using laboratory animals that are very sensitive and responsive to such agents. Biologists throughout the world have bred research animals that readily produce certain types of cancers that resemble the cancers found in humans. By using these animals instead of humans to screen potential drugs, the risk to humans is greatly reduced. The emerging field of biotechnology is producing techniques that enable researchers to manipulate the genetic makeup of organisms. Research animals are used to perfect these techniques and highlight possible problems.

Animal rights activists are very concerned about using animals for these purposes. They are concerned about research that seems to have little value in relation to the suffering these animals are forced to endure. Members of the American Liberation Front (ALF), an animal rights organization, vandalized a laboratory at Michigan State University where mink were used in research to assess the toxicity of certain chemicals. Members of this group poured acid on tables and in drawers containing data, smashed equipment, and set fires in the laboratory. This attack destroyed 32 years of research records, including data used for developing water-quality standards. In 1 year, 80 similar actions were carried out by groups advocating animal rights. What type of restrictions or controls should be put on such research? Where do you draw the line between "essential" and "nonessential" studies? Do you support the use of live animals in experiments that may alleviate human suffering?

# Materials Exchange in the Body

CHAPTER

# 24

## CHAPTER OUTLINE

## Leeches Used in Modern Medicine

*An ancient practice returns.*

For thousands of years, bloodletting was an established medical practice. It was thought that "bad blood" or a "disturbance of the humors" was the cause of many diseases and maladies and that removing blood would cure the problem. One of the established methods for removing the blood was to attach blood-sucking leeches to a person. This was such a common practice in the 1700s and 1800s that a slang term for "doctor" was "leech." This method of bloodletting is also preserved in the scientific name of the European leech commonly used for this purpose—*Hirudo medicinalis*.

Today, leeches are used as an effective way to reduce swelling in patients who have had reconstructive and reattachment surgery. During these types of surgery, arteries are reattached to supply blood to the area. However, it is much more difficult to reattach veins that drain blood from the area. Thus, swelling occurs and creates a problem that can cause death of the cells in the affected parts. When fluid builds up and causes swelling, the cells in the area cannot receive oxygen and nutrients and get rid of wastes effectively. The cells die, and the surgery is a failure.

This is where the leech becomes important. An effective way to prevent swelling is to attach leeches to the affected area. The leeches rasp a hole in the skin and have anti-clotting molecules in their saliva, allowing them to feed on blood. As a result of their feeding activity, they remove the blood that builds up. This allows time for the establishment of veins and lymph vessels that carry this fluid away. As one leech becomes filled with blood and drops off, another is added until normal drainage through veins and lymph vessels is established.

- Why does swelling occur with many kinds of surgeries?

- What role do veins play in normal circulation?

- How would you convince patients that the use of leeches is a necessary part of their recovery from surgery?

## Background Check

Concepts you should understand in order to get the most out of this chapter:
- The nature of acids, bases, salts, and buffers (chapter 2)
- The types of organic molecules and the roles they play (chapter 3)
- The structure of prokaryotic and eukaryotic cells (chapter 4)
- The concept of surface area-to-volume ratio (chapter 4)

## 24.1 The Basic Principles of Materials Exchange

Large, multicellular organisms, such as humans, consist of trillions of cells. Because many of these cells are buried within the organism far from the body surface, the body needs ways to solve its materials-exchange problems. Cells are highly organized units that require a constant flow of energy to maintain themselves. The energy they require is provided in the form of nutrient molecules. Oxygen is required for the efficient release of energy from the large, organic molecules that serve as fuel. Inevitably, as oxidation takes place, waste products form that are useless or toxic, and they must be removed. The five organ systems engaged in these efforts are the cardiovascular, lymphatic, respiratory, digestive, and excretory systems. All these organ systems are integrated, affecting one another in many ways. The interactions of these systems require regulation and specialization for them to maintain life.

### 24.1 CONCEPT REVIEW

1. Why do multicellular organisms have materials-exchange problems?

## 24.2 Circulation: The Cardiovascular System

The **cardiovascular system** of all vertebrates, including humans, is the organ system that pumps blood around the body; and consists of the blood, heart, and blood vessels. **Blood** is the fluid tissue that assists in the transport of materials and heat. The **heart** is a muscular pump that forces the blood from one part of the body to another. The heart pumps blood into blood vessels. **Arteries** are the vessels that carry blood away from the heart and distribute it to the organs. The blood flows through successively smaller arteries until it reaches tiny vessels called *capillaries*. **Capillaries** are the thinnest blood vessels where exchange of materials between the blood and tissues that surround the vessels takes place. The blood flows from the capillaries into **veins,** the vessels that return blood to the heart.

## The Nature of Blood

Blood is a fluid tissue consisting of several kinds of cells and platelets, called **formed elements,** suspended in a watery solution called **plasma** (table 24.1). This fluid plasma also contains many kinds of dissolved molecules, including nutrients, wastes, salts and proteins. The blood's primary function is to transport molecules, cells, and heat from one part of the body to another. The major kinds of molecules distributed by the blood are respiratory gases (oxygen and carbon dioxide), nutrients of various kinds, waste products, disease-fighting cells and antibodies, and chemical messengers (hormones). Also, substances in the blood are capable of forming clots or plugs to prevent blood loss.

Heat is generated by metabolic activities and must be removed from the body. To handle excess body heat, blood is moved through the vessels to the surface of the body, where it can be radiated away. In addition, humans and some other animals have the ability to sweat. The evaporation of sweat (released from glands in the skin) from the body surface also gets rid of excess heat. If the body is losing heat too rapidly, blood is moved away from the skin, and metabolic heat is conserved. Vigorous exercise produces an excess of heat, so that, even in cold weather, blood is moved to the skin and the skin feels hot.

### Formed Elements

The most numerous formed elements are **red blood cells (rbcs),** which are small, disk-shaped cells that lack a nucleus. Their primary function is to allow the blood to distribute respiratory gases efficiently (Outlooks 24.1). RBCs have the iron-containing pigment **hemoglobin,** the protein molecule to which oxygen molecules bind readily. Red blood cells transport oxygen around the body attached to their hemoglobin molecules. Very little oxygen is carried as free, dissolved oxygen in the plasma.

Because hemoglobin is inside red blood cells, some health problems can be diagnosed by counting the number of red blood cells a person has. If the number is low, the person's blood cannot carry oxygen efficiently and he or she tires easily. *Anemia* is a condition in which a person has reduced oxygen-carrying capacity. Anemia can also result when a person does not consume enough iron. Because iron is a central atom in hemoglobin molecules, people with an iron deficiency cannot manufacture sufficient hemoglobin; they can be anemic even if their number of red blood cells is normal.

## TABLE 24.1   Components of Blood

| Formed Elements | Function and Description | Source | | Plasma | Function | Source |
|---|---|---|---|---|---|---|
| **Red blood cells** (erythrocytes) | Transport $O_2$ and help transport $CO_2$ | Red bone marrow | | Water (90–92% of plasma) | Maintains blood volume; transports molecules | Absorbed from intestine |
| 4 million–6 million per $mm^3$ blood | 7–8 μm in diameter Bright red to dark purple, biconcave disks without nuclei | | | Plasma proteins (7–8% of plasma) | Maintain blood osmotic pressure and pH | Liver |
| **White blood cells** (leukocytes) 4,000–11,000 per $mm^3$ blood | Fight infection | Red bone marrow | | Albumin | Maintains blood volume and pressure | |
| *Granular leukocytes* | | | | Globulins | Transport; fight infection | |
| • Basophil | 10–12 μm in diameter Spherical cells with lobed nuclei; large, irregularly shaped, deep blue granules in cytoplasm | | | Fibrinogen | Clotting | |
| 20–50 per $mm^3$ blood | | | | Salts (less than 1% of plasma) | Maintain blood osmotic pressure and pH; aid metabolism | Absorbed from intestine |
| • Eosinophil | 10–14 μm in diameter Spherical cells with bilobed nuclei; coarse, deep red, uniformly sized granules in cytoplasm | | | Gases | | |
| 100–400 per $mm^3$ blood | | | | Oxygen Carbon dioxide | Cellular respiration End product of metabolism | Lungs Tissues |
| • Neutrophil | 10–14 μm in diameter Spherical cells with multilobed nuclei; fine, pink granules in cytoplasm | | | Nutrients | Food for cells | Absorbed from intestine |
| 3,000–7,000 per $mm^3$ blood | | | | Fats Glucose Amino acids | | |
| *Agranular leukocytes* | | | | Nitrogenous waste | Excretion by kidneys | Liver |
| • Lymphocyte | 5–17 μm in diameter (average 9–10 μm) Spherical cells with large, round nuclei | | | Urea Uric acid | | |
| 1,500–3,000 per $mm^3$ blood | | | | Other | | |
| • Monocyte | 10–24 μm in diameter Large, spherical cells with kidney-shaped, round, or lobed nuclei | | | Hormones, vitamins, etc. | Aid metabolism | Varied |
| 100–700 per $mm^3$ blood | | | | | | |
| **Platelets** (thrombocytes) | Aid clotting | Red bone marrow | | | | |
| 150,000–300,000 per $mm^3$ blood | 2–4 μm in diameter Disk-shaped cell fragments with no nuclei; purple granules in cytoplasm | | | | | |

Plasma 55%

Formed elements 45%

## OUTLOOKS 24.1

# Blood Doping

The use of performance-enhancing techniques and drugs in sports is not new. For example, one way to increase the amount of oxygen available to muscles is to inhale higher concentrations of the gas. You may have seen athletes breathing from an oxygen tank while on the sidelines during a sporting event. Another approach to increasing the amount of available oxygen is to increase the number of oxygen-carrying red blood cells. This can be accomplished in several ways. An athlete can have a pint of his or her blood removed and put into storage about three weeks before an event. During that time, the

athlete's body replaces the removed red blood cells. Just before the event, the "donated" blood is transfused back into the athlete, increasing the total number of red blood cells. This method of enhancing an athlete's performance has been banned because it is considered to give an unfair advantage and because there can be dangerous side-effects.

Another technique involves artificially stimulating the body to produce more red blood cells by injecting the protein hormone erythropoietin, commonly referred as EPO. The kidney produces EPO, and after it is released into the bloodstream, it binds to receptors on stem cells in the red bone marrow, where it stimulates the production of new red blood cells. The increased red blood cell production in turn increases the oxygen-carrying capacity of the blood. This fact has resulted in some members of the athletic community using EPO as a performance-enhancing drug to artificially increase the amount of red blood cells.

Still another method of increasing available oxygen is the use of synthetic oxygen carriers, such as hemoglobin-based oxygen carriers (HBOCs) or perfluorocarbons (PFCs). These are purified proteins or chemicals that have the ability to carry oxygen. They can be useful in emergencies when human blood is not available, when the risk of blood infection is high, or when there is not enough time to properly cross-match donated blood with a recipient. However, their misuse for doping carries the risk of cardiovascular disease, in addition to other side-effects such as stroke, heart attack, or blood clot.

The use of blood transfusions, EPO, and synthetic oxygen carriers is prohibited under the World Anti-Doping Agency's (WADA) List of Prohibited Substances and Methods.

---

Red blood cells are also important in the transport of carbon dioxide. Carbon dioxide is a result of the normal aerobic cellular respiration of food materials in the cells of the body. If carbon dioxide is not eliminated, it causes the blood to become more acidic (lowers its pH), eventually resulting in death. Carbon dioxide can be carried in the blood in three forms: about 7% is dissolved in the plasma, about 23% is carried attached to hemoglobin molecules, and 70% is carried as bicarbonate ions. The enzyme carbonic anhydrase in red blood cells helps convert carbon dioxide into bicarbonate ions ($HCO_3^-$), which can be carried as dissolved ions in the plasma of the blood. The following reversible chemical equation shows the changes that occur.

$$CO_2 + H_2O \longleftrightarrow H_2CO_3 \longleftrightarrow H^+ + HCO_3^-$$

When the blood reaches the lungs, dissolved carbon dioxide is lost from the plasma, and carbon dioxide is released from the hemoglobin molecules. In addition, the bicarbonate ions reenter the red blood cells and can be converted back into molecular carbon dioxide by the same enzyme-assisted process that converts carbon dioxide to bicarbonate ions. The

importance of this mechanism will be discussed in the section "Gas Exchange: The Respiratory System."

**White blood cells (wbcs)**, also called leukocytes, are formed elements in the blood that lack hemoglobin and are involved in defending the body from disease-causing agents. There are several kinds of wbcs that vary in size and function (see table 24.1). When wbcs are stained with dyes and viewed under the microscope, they all have a conspicuous nucleus, and some kinds have granules in their cytoplasm. The granule-containing leukocytes are basophils, eosinophils, and neutrophils. Those without granules are lymphocytes and monocytes. All of these cells have specific roles to play in protecting the body from bacteria, viruses, fungi, worms, toxins, and cancer cells.

**Platelets** (also called thrombocytes), another kind of formed element in the blood, are actually fragments of a specific kind of white blood cell. Platelets are important in blood clotting. About 200 billion are formed each day. When a wound occurs, they collect at the site of the wound, where they form an initial plug and release compounds that cause other platelets to collect at the site. They also release compounds that begin a series of reactions among chemicals in

## OUTLOOKS 24.2

# Newborn Jaundice

Albumin transports bilirubin, a yellowish molecule that is a breakdown product of hemoglobin from destroyed rbcs. Normally, bilirubin is transported to the liver, where it is destroyed and the broken-down products are released with the bile into the intestine. However, some newborns become jaundiced (a yellowing of the skin and whites of the eyes) because their liver has not matured enough to do this important job. If bilirubin is allowed to accumulate in their blood, jaundiced babies can develop deafness, cerebral palsy, or brain damage. Placing babies under a special ultraviolet ("bili") light helps relieve the problem. The light has a wavelength that helps break down the bilirubin to a form that can be eliminated through the kidneys until the baby's liver matures and can adequately handle the bilirubin.

the plasma called clotting factors. There are at least 13 known clotting factors. The interactions of the various clotting factors ultimately result in the formation of fibers that trap platelets and blood cells and form a stronger plug than the initial platelet plug in the opening of the wound. Blood clots at the site of wounds are sometimes called scabs. They have a reddish or brownish color because they contain the leftovers of destroyed rbcs. Scabs are short-lived and are replaced by healthy tissue as the wound heals.

### Plasma

Recall that plasma is the liquid part of the blood, consisting of water and dissolved materials, such as a variety of salts, proteins, nutrients, and waste products. Salts serve as buffers that help maintain the blood's pH. They also play a role in maintaining the proper osmotic balance between the blood and surrounding tissues.

Plasma proteins perform a variety of functions. The most plentiful plasma protein is albumin. It makes up about 60% of all plasma proteins, is the primary molecule involved in maintaining osmotic balance, and is also important in maintaining the proper blood pH. Albumin also assists in the transport of compounds that enter the blood (Outlooks 24.2). Globulins (antibodies), many of the clotting factors, regulatory proteins, and many other proteins circulate freely in the plasma.

Because the blood is under pressure from the pumping of the heart, it is normal for some fluid to leak from the smallest blood vessels (capillaries) into the surrounding tissues. This fluid that bathes the body's cells is called **tissue fluid**. It is similar to plasma but contains less dissolved albumin because the proteins are too large to pass through the walls of the capillaries, whereas salts can pass. Although the tissue fluid carries nutrients and other materials to the cells, it must be returned to the circulatory system, or swelling will occur. The albumin in the blood maintains the osmotic balance such that tissue fluid tends to return to the circulatory system.

In addition to water, salts, and proteins, plasma carries a variety of other important molecules. Nutrient molecules from the gut are carried to other locations, where they are modified, metabolized, or incorporated into cell structures. Amino acids and simple sugars are carried as dissolved molecules in the blood. Lipids, which are not water-soluble, are combined with proteins and carried as suspended particles called lipoproteins. Some organs manufacture or modify molecules for use elsewhere; therefore, they must constantly receive raw materials and distribute their products to the cells that need them through the blood. In addition, many kinds of hormones are produced by the brain, reproductive organs, digestive organs, and glands. These are secreted into the bloodstream and transported throughout the body. Tissues with appropriate receptors bind to these molecules and respond to these chemical messengers.

## The Heart

Blood can perform its transportation function only if it moves. The heart is responsible for providing the energy to pump the blood throughout the body. For a fluid to flow through a tube, there must be a pressure difference between the two ends of the tube; water flows through pipes because it is under pressure. Because the pressure is higher behind a faucet than at the spout, water flows from the spout when the faucet is opened. The circulatory system can be understood from the same point of view. The heart is the muscular pump that provides the pressure necessary to propel the blood throughout the body. It must continue its cycle of contraction and relaxation or the blood stops flowing and the body's cells cannot obtain nutrients or get rid of wastes. Some cells, such as brain cells, are extremely sensitive to interruptions in the flow of blood, because they require a constant supply of glucose and oxygen. Others, such as muscle cells and skin cells, are much better able to withstand temporary interruptions of blood flow.

The hearts of humans, other mammals, and birds consist of four chambers and four sets of valves, that work together to ensure that blood flows in one direction only. Two of these chambers, the right and left **atria** (singular, *atrium*), are relatively thin-walled structures that collect blood from the major veins and empty it into the larger, more muscular **ventricles** (figure 24.1). Most of the blood is drawn in from the atria to the ventricles by the lowered pressure produced within the ventricles as they relax. The contraction of the thin-walled atria helps empty them more completely.

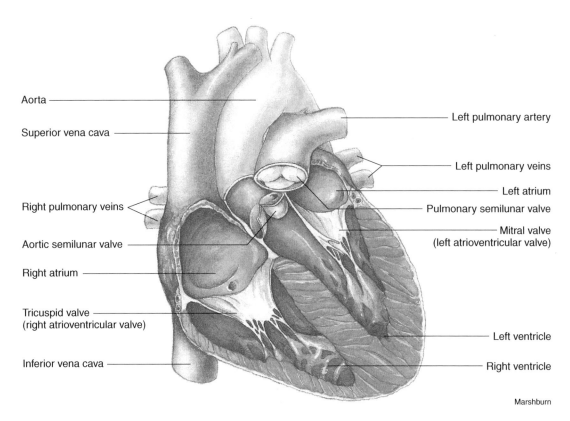

Aorta

Superior vena cava

Right pulmonary veins

Aortic semilunar valve

Right atrium

Tricuspid valve
(right atrioventricular valve)

Inferior vena cava

Left pulmonary artery

Left pulmonary veins

Left atrium

Pulmonary semilunar valve

Mitral valve
(left atrioventricular valve)

Left ventricle

Right ventricle

Marshburn

**FIGURE 24.1 The Anatomy of the Heart**

The heart consists of two thin-walled chambers, called atria, which contract to force blood into the two muscular ventricles. When the ventricles contract, the atrioventricular valves close, and blood is forced into the aorta and pulmonary artery. (The left atrioventricular valve is also known as the mitral or bicuspid valve and the right atrioventricular valve is also known as the tricuspid valve.) Semilunar valves in the aorta and pulmonary artery prevent the blood from flowing back into the ventricles when they relax.

The right and left ventricles are chambers with powerful muscular walls, whose contractions force blood to flow through the arteries to all parts of the body. The valves between the atria and the ventricles, the **atrioventricular valves,** are important one-way valves that allow blood to flow from the atria to the ventricles but prevent flow in the opposite direction. Similarly, there are valves in both the aorta and pulmonary artery, known as the **semilunar valves.** The **aorta** is the large artery that carries blood from the left ventricle to the body, and the **pulmonary artery** carries blood from the right ventricle to the lungs. The semilunar valves act as "check valves" to prevent blood from flowing back into the ventricles. If the atrioventricular or semilunar valves are damaged or function improperly, the heart's efficiency as a pump is diminished, and the person may have insufficient blood flow, which can cause shortness of breath, swelling in the feet, or other symptoms.

Malfunctioning heart valves are often diagnosed because they cause abnormal sounds—called heart murmurs—as the blood passes through them. Similarly, if the muscular walls of the ventricles are weakened because of infection, damage from a heart attack, or lack of exercise, the heart's pumping efficiency is reduced and the person develops symptoms such as shortness of breath, fatigue, or chest pain. Shortness of

breath and fatigue result because the heart is not able to pump blood, and the oxygen and nutrients it contains, efficiently to the lungs, muscles, and other parts of the body. Chest pain is caused by an increase in the amount of lactic acid in the heart muscle, because the muscle is not getting sufficient oxygen to satisfy its needs. The heart receives blood from coronary arteries that are branches of the aorta; it is not nourished by the blood that flows through its chambers. If heart muscle does not get sufficient oxygen for a period of time, the portion of the heart muscle not receiving blood dies.

The right and left sides of the heart have slightly different jobs, because they pump blood to different parts of the body. The right side of the heart receives blood from the general body and pumps it through the pulmonary arteries to the lungs, where the exchange of oxygen and carbon dioxide takes place and the blood returns from the lungs to the left atrium. This is called **pulmonary circulation.** The larger, more powerful left side of the heart receives blood from the lungs, delivers it through the aorta to all other parts of the body, and returns it to the right atrium by way of the veins. This is known as **systemic circulation.** Both circulatory pathways are shown in figure 24.2. The systemic circulation is responsible for gas, nutrient, and waste exchange in all parts of the body except the lungs.

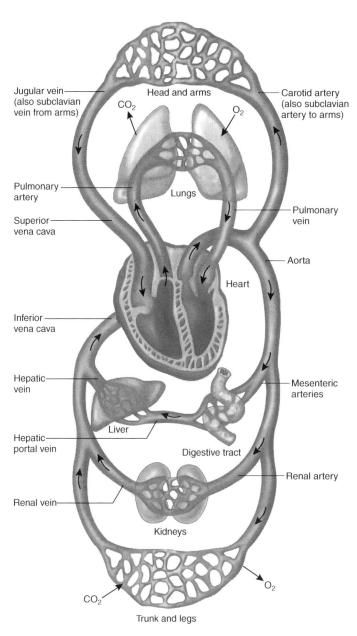

Jugular vein
(also subclavian
vein from arms)

Head and arms

$CO_2$

$O_2$

Carotid artery
(also subclavian
artery to arms)

Pulmonary
artery

Lungs

Pulmonary
vein

Superior
vena cava

Aorta

Heart

Inferior
vena cava

Hepatic
vein

Mesenteric
arteries

Liver

Hepatic
portal vein

Digestive tract

Renal artery

Renal vein

Kidneys

$CO_2$

$O_2$

Trunk and legs

**FIGURE 24.2 Pulmonary and Systemic Circulation**
The right ventricle pumps blood that is poor in oxygen to the lungs by way of the pulmonary arteries, where it receives oxygen and turns bright red. The blood is then returned to the left atrium by way of four pulmonary veins. This part of the circulatory system is known as pulmonary circulation. The left ventricle pumps oxygen-rich blood by way of the aorta to all parts of the body except the lungs. This blood returns to the right atrium, depleted of its oxygen, by way of the superior vena cava from the head region and the inferior vena cava from the rest of the body. This portion of the circulatory system is known as systemic circulation.

## Blood Vessels: Arteries, Veins, and Capillaries

Recall that arteries and veins are the tubes that transport blood from one place to another within the body. Arteries carry blood away from the heart. The contraction of the ventricle walls increases the pressure in the arteries. A typical pressure recorded in a large artery while the heart is in the process of contracting is about 120 millimeters of mercury (mmHg). This is known as the **systolic blood pressure.** The typical pressure recorded while the heart is relaxing is about 80 millimeters of mercury. This is known as the **diastolic blood pressure.** A blood pressure reading includes both numbers—for example, 120/80. (Originally, blood pressure was measured by how high the pressure of the blood caused a column of mercury [Hg] to rise in a tube. Although the devices used today have dials or digital readouts and contain no mercury, they are still calibrated in mmHg.)

### Artery Structure and Function

The walls of arteries are relatively thick and muscular yet elastic (figure 24.3a). Healthy arteries have the ability to expand as blood is pumped into them and return to normal as the pressure drops. This ability to expand absorbs some of the pressure and reduces the peak pressure within the arteries, thus reducing the likelihood that they will burst. If arteries become hardened and less elastic, peak systolic blood pressure rises and the arteries are more likely to rupture. The elastic nature of the arteries also helps in blood flow. When the arteries return to normal from their stretched condition, they give a little push to the blood flowing through them.

Blood is distributed from the large aorta through smaller and smaller blood vessels to millions of tiny capillaries. Some of the smaller arteries, called **arterioles,** contract or relax to regulate the flow of blood to specific parts of the body. The major parts of the body that receive differing amounts of blood, depending on need, are the digestive system, muscles, and skin. When you exercise, blood flow to the muscles increases to accommodate their higher metabolic needs—the muscles need to take in more oxygen and glucose

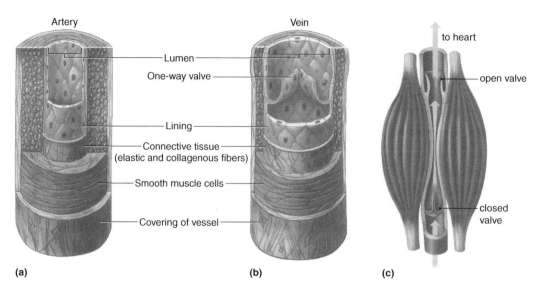

Artery

Vein

to heart

Lumen

One-way valve

open valve

Lining

Connective tissue
(elastic and collagenous fibers)

Smooth muscle cells

closed
valve

Covering of vessel

(a)

(b)

(c)

**FIGURE 24.3 The Structure of Arteries and Veins**
The walls of *(a)* arteries are much thicker than the walls of *(b)* veins. (The pressure in arteries is much higher than the pressure in veins.) The pressure generated by the ventricles of the heart forces blood through the arteries. Veins often have very low pressure. The valves in the veins prevent the blood from flowing backward, away from the heart. *(c)* Contractions of skeletal muscle along with valves in the veins help move blood in the veins back to the heart.

and to get rid of wastes. Exercise also results in an increased blood flow to the skin, which allows your body to get rid of excess heat. At the same time, the amount of blood flowing to the digestive system is reduced. Athletes do not eat a full meal before exercising. The additional blood flow to the digestive system reduces the amount of blood available to the muscles and lungs and they are not able to perform as well. In addition, muscular cramps can result if insufficient blood flows to the muscles.

## Vein Structure and Function

Veins collect blood from the capillaries and return it to the heart. The pressure in veins is very low. Some of the largest veins may have a blood pressure of 0.0 mmHg for brief periods. The walls of veins are not as muscular as those of arteries (figure 24.3b). Because of the low pressure, veins must have valves to prevent the blood from flowing back-wards, away from the heart. Veins are often found on the surface of the body and are seen as blue lines. *Varicose veins* result when veins contain faulty valves, which do not allow the efficient return of blood to the heart. Therefore, blood pools in these veins, and they become swollen, bluish networks.

Because the pressure in veins is so low, muscular move-ments of the body are important in helping return blood to the heart. When the muscles of the body contract, they com-press nearby veins, and this pressure pushes blood along in the veins. Because the valves allow blood to flow only toward the heart, this activity acts as an additional pump to help return blood to the heart (figure 24.3c). People who sit or stand for long periods without using their leg muscles tend to

have a considerable amount of blood pool in the veins of their legs and lower body. Thus, less blood may be available to go to the brain, causing people to faint. Although the arteries are responsible for distributing blood to various parts of the body and arterioles regulate where blood goes, it is the function of capillaries to assist in the exchange of materials between the blood and cells.

## Capillary Structure and Function

Capillaries are tiny, thin-walled tubes that receive blood from arterioles. They are so small that red blood cells must go through them in single file. They are so numerous that each cell in the body has a capillary located near it. It is estimated that there are about 1,000 square meters of capillary surface area in a typical human. Each capillary wall consists of a single layer of cells and, therefore, presents only a thin barrier to the diffusion of materials between the blood and the cells in the surrounding tissue. The flow of blood through these smallest blood vessels is relatively slow. This allows time for the diffusion of such materials as oxygen, glucose, and water from the blood to surrounding cells, and for the movement of waste products such as carbon dioxide, lactic acid, and ammonia from the cells into the blood.

It is also possible for liquid to flow through tiny spaces between the cells of most capillaries. This fluid, tissue fluid, bathes individual cells. This assists in the exchanges of materi-als between the blood and the cells. Ultimately this fluid must be returned to the circulatory system. Some simply diffuses back into the capillaries. The remainder is collected by lymph vessels and moves through these vessels until it empties into veins near the heart (figure 24.4).

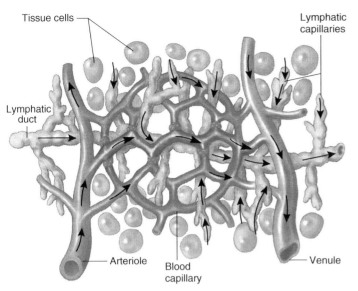

**FIGURE 24.4 Capillaries**
Capillaries are tiny blood vessels. Exchange of molecules between blood and tissues occurs by diffusion through the thin walls of capillaries. Some water and dissolved materials actually pass through the walls of capillaries and bathe cells. The lymph vessels collect any excess fluid and return it to the circulatory system.

## 24.2 CONCEPT REVIEW

2. List the functions of the salts and proteins found in the plasma.
3. What are the functions of the heart, arteries, veins, arterioles, blood, and capillaries?
4. How do red blood cells assist in the transportation of oxygen and carbon dioxide?

## 24.3 The Lymphatic System

The **lymphatic system** is a collection of lymph organs and thin-walled tubes (lymph vessels) that branch throughout the body. The lymphatic system plays three important roles: (1) It moves fat from the intestinal tract to the bloodstream, (2) it transports excess tissue fluid back to the cardiovascular system, and (3) it defends against harmful agents, such as bacteria and viruses (refer to chapter 26, Immunity). **Lymph** is tissue fluid that moves through this system.

Lymph vessels collect lymph and ultimately empty it into two large veins near the heart. Because the lymph vessels have valves to prevent backflow, lymph is moved one way through the vessels as a result of the contraction of the body's muscles. For this system to function properly, the person must be active, or the tissue fluid will not move into the lymph vessels and will build up, causing the tissue to swell, a condition called edema. Edema is common in circulatory disorders. Another cause of edema results from an increase in capillary permeability as a result of injury. Fluid

**FIGURE 24.5 The Lymphatic System**
Lymphatic vessels drain the tissue fluid that surrounds cells and return it to the cardiovascular system near the heart. The enlargement shows that lymphatic vessels have valves to prevent backflow. The lymph nodes, tonsils, spleen, thymus gland, and red bone marrow are lymph organs.

moves from inside the blood vessels into the damaged tissue and is seen as swelling. A swollen sprained ankle or smashed thumb are examples you may have experienced. Figure 24.5 shows the structure of the lymphatic system.

There are five types of lymph organs: (1) lymph nodes, (2) tonsils, (3) spleen, (4) thymus, and (5) red bone marrow.

**Lymph nodes** are small encapsulated bodies found along the lymph vessels that contain large numbers of white blood cells (wbc), particularly macrophages and lymphocytes that remove microorganisms and foreign particles from the lymph. As the lymph makes its way back to the circulatory system, it is filtered by lymph nodes. When nodes are actively engaged in this cleanup, they swell as the wbc population increases. During an examination, physicians palpate or feel the nodes (usually in the neck) to help determine if a person has an infection.

The tonsils are lymph organs located on either side of the throat. Adenoids are lymph organs located at the back of the nasal cavity. Their job, like that of lymph nodes, is to clean the lymph of pathogens. Because they are so close to the mouth and nose, they are likely to encounter pathogens and become swollen as the number of white blood cells increases. In the past, if tonsils repeatedly became "infected" and unable to manage pathogens, they were removed by a surgical procedure called a tonsillectomy. This procedure was performed on children who displayed chronic sore throats or infections. Today, the functions of tonsils are better understood and tonsillectomies are rarely performed.

The spleen also contains large numbers of white blood cells and filters the blood. It is about the size of a small pickle, located in the upper left side of the body just below the diaphragm. Its job is to clean the blood of pathogens and worn-out or damaged rbcs. Should the spleen be ruptured as a result of an accident or a wound, it may have to be removed. In such cases, the person loses an important blood-filtering and disease-fighting organ.

The thymus gland, located beneath the breastbone, is large and active in children. As a person ages, the thymus shrinks and may actually disappear. Its primary function is to produce wbcs, which are vital to the functioning of the immune system. These cells, called T-lymphocytes, are distributed from the thymus throughout the body and establish themselves in lymph nodes. Even though the thymus shrinks in size into adulthood, the descendants of the T-lymphocytes it produced earlier in life are still active throughout the lymphatic system.

The red bone marrow produces red and white blood cells and platelets. Stem cells found inside these bones continue to divide throughout a person's life, providing a continuous supply of rbcs and wbcs. Red bone marrow is found in most of a child's bones. In adults, the red bone marrow is only found in the pelvis (hipbone), sternum (breastbone), skull, clavicle (collarbone), ends of long bones, and vertebrae (backbone).

## 24.3 CONCEPT REVIEW

5. What purposes are served by the lymphatic system?
6. List the organs of the lymphatic system and describe the function of each.

## 24.4 Gas Exchange: The Respiratory System

The **respiratory system** is the organ system that moves air into and out of the body; it consists of the *lungs, trachea, air-transport pathway,* and *diaphragm.* The **lungs** are organs of the body that allow gas exchange to take place between the air and blood. Associated with the lungs is a set of tubes, part of the air-transport pathway, that conducts air from outside the body to the lungs. The single, large-diameter **trachea** is supported by rings of cartilage that prevent its collapse. It branches into two major **bronchi** (singular, *bronchus*), which deliver air to smaller and smaller branches. Bronchi are also supported by cartilage. The smallest tubes, **bronchioles**, contain smooth muscle and are therefore capable of constricting. Finally, the bronchioles deliver air to clusters of tiny sacs, known as **alveoli** (singular, *alveolus*), where the exchange of gases between the air and the blood takes place.

The nose, mouth, and throat are also important parts of the air-transport pathway because they modify the humidity and temperature of the air and clean the air as it passes. The lining of the trachea contains cells with cilia, which beat in one direction to move mucus and foreign materials from the lungs. The foreign matter can then be expelled by swallowing or coughing. Figure 24.6 illustrates the various parts of the respiratory system.

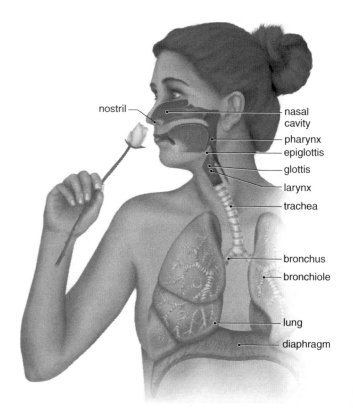

nostril

nasal cavity
pharynx
epiglottis
glottis
larynx
trachea

bronchus
bronchiole

lung
diaphragm

**FIGURE 24.6 Respiratory Anatomy**
Although gas exchange takes place in the alveoli of the lungs, there are many other important parts of the respiratory system. The nasal cavity cleans, warms, and humidifies the air entering the lungs. The trachea is also important in cleaning the air going to the lungs.

## Mechanics of Breathing

**Breathing** is the process of moving air in and out of the lungs. It is accomplished by the movement of several muscles. The **diaphragm** is a muscular organ that separates the chest cavity, which contains the lungs, from the abdominal cavity. In addition, *intercostal* muscles located between the ribs are involved in breathing. During inhalation, the diaphragm contracts, causing it to move downward and the external intercostal muscles of the chest wall contract, causing the chest wall to move outward and upward. Both of these actions cause the volume of the chest cavity to increase. This results in a lower pressure in the chest cavity compared with the outside air pressure. Thus, air flows from the outside high-pressure area through the trachea, bronchi, and bronchioles to the alveoli. During normal, relaxed breathing, exhalation is accomplished by the chest wall and diaphragm simply relaxing and returning to their normal positions. Muscular contraction is not involved (figure 24.7).

When the body's demand for oxygen increases during exercise, the breathing system responds by exchanging the gases in the lungs more rapidly. This can be accomplished both by increasing the breathing rate and by increasing the volume of air exchanged with each breath. An increase in volume exchanged per breath is accomplished in two ways. First, the muscles of inhalation can contract more forcefully, resulting in a greater change in the volume of the chest cavity.

Second, the lungs can be emptied more completely by contracting the muscles of the abdomen, which forces the abdominal contents upward against the diaphragm and compresses the lungs. A set of internal intercostal muscles also helps compress the chest.

## Breathing System Regulation

Several mechanisms can cause changes in the rate and depth of breathing, but the primary mechanism is tied to the amount of carbon dioxide present in the blood. Carbon dioxide, a waste product of aerobic cellular respiration, becomes toxic in high quantities because it combines with water to form carbonic acid:

$$CO_2 + H_2O \rightarrow H_2CO_3$$

As mentioned previously, if carbon dioxide cannot be eliminated, the pH of the blood is lowered. Eventually, this can cause death.

Exercising causes an increase in the amount of carbon dioxide in the blood, because the muscles are oxidizing glucose more rapidly. This lowers the blood's pH. Certain brain cells and specialized cells in the aortic arch and carotid arteries are sensitive to changes in blood pH. When these cells sense a lower blood pH, they cause the brain to send nerve impulses more frequently to the diaphragm and intercostal muscles. These muscles contract more rapidly and

**(a) Inhalation**

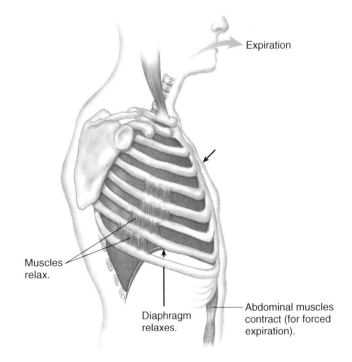

**(b) Exhalation**

### FIGURE 24.7  Breathing Movements

During *(a)* inhalation, the diaphragm and external intercostal muscles between the ribs contract, causing the volume of the chest cavity to increase. During a normal *(b)* exhalation, these muscles relax, and the chest volume returns to normal.

**FIGURE 24.8 Control of Breathing Rate**

The rate of breathing is controlled by cells in the brain, aorta, and carotid arteries that sense the pH of the blood. When the amount of $CO_2$ increases, the pH drops (the blood becomes more acidic) and the brain sends more frequent messages to the diaphragm and intercostal muscles, causing the breathing rate to increase. More rapid breathing increases the rate at which $CO_2$ is lost from the blood; thus, the blood pH rises (it becomes less acidic) and the breathing rate decreases.

more forcefully, resulting in more rapid, deeper breathing. Because more air is being exchanged per minute, carbon dioxide is lost from the lungs more rapidly. When exercise stops, blood pH rises, and breathing eventually returns to normal (figure 24.8).

## Lung Function

The lungs allow blood and air to come into close contact with each other. Air flows in and out of the lungs during breathing. The blood flows through capillaries in the lungs and is in close contact with the air in the alveoli of the lungs. For oxygen to enter or carbon dioxide to exit the body, the molecules must pass through a surface. The efficiency of exchange is limited by the surface area available. This problem is solved in the lungs by the large number of tiny sacs, the alveoli. Each alveolus is about 0.25 to 0.5 millimeters across. However, alveoli are so numerous that the total surface area of all these sacs is about 70 square meters—comparable to the floor space of many standard-sized classrooms. The walls of both the capillaries and the alveoli are very thin, and the close association of alveoli and capillaries in the lungs allows the easy diffusion of oxygen and carbon dioxide across these membranes (figure 24.9).

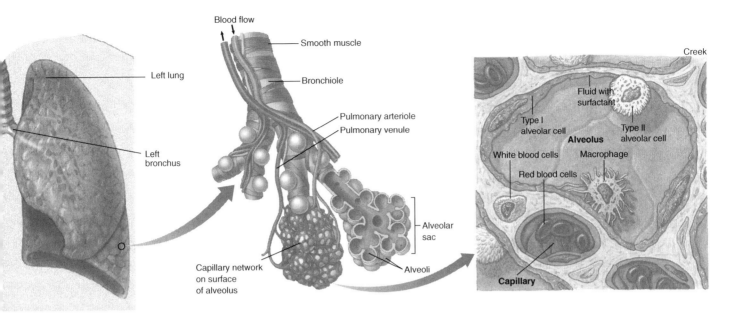

**FIGURE 24.9 The Association of Capillaries with Alveoli**
The exchange of gases takes place between the air-filled alveolus and the blood-filled capillary. The capillaries form a network around the saclike alveoli. The thin walls of the alveolus and capillary are in direct contact with one another; their combined thickness is usually less than 1 micrometer (a thousandth of a millimeter).

Another factor that increases the efficiency of gas exchange is that both the blood and the air are moving. Because blood is flowing through capillaries in the lungs, the capillaries continually receive new blood that is poor in oxygen and high in carbon dioxide. As blood passes by the alveoli, it is briefly exposed to the gases in the alveoli, where it gains oxygen and loses carbon dioxide. Thus, blood that leaves the lungs is high in oxygen and low in carbon dioxide. Although the movement of air in the lungs is not in one direction, as is the case with blood, the cycle of inhalation and exhalation allows air that is high in carbon dioxide and low in oxygen to exit the body and brings in new air that is rich in oxygen and low in carbon dioxide. This oxygen-rich, bright red blood is then sent to the left side of the heart and pumped throughout the body.

Any factor that interferes with the flow of blood or air or alters the effectiveness of gas exchange in the lungs reduces the efficiency of the organism. A poorly pumping heart sends less blood to the lungs, and the person experiences shortness of breath. Similarly, diseases such as asthma, which cause constriction of the bronchioles, reduce the flow of air into the lungs and inhibit gas exchange.

Any process that reduces the number of alveoli also reduces the efficiency of gas exchange in the lungs. For example, *emphysema* is a progressive disease in which some of the alveoli are lost. As the disease progresses, those afflicted have less and less respiratory surface area and experience greater and greater difficulty getting adequate oxygen, even though they may be breathing more rapidly. Often, emphysema is accompanied by an increase in the amount of connective tissue and the lungs do not stretch as easily, further reducing their ability to exchange gases.

### 24.4 CONCEPT REVIEW

7. Describe the muscles involved in breathing and explain how they cause air to flow into and out of the lungs.
8. How are $CO_2$, blood pH, and breathing rate interrelated?
9. How do each of the following affect the efficiency of gas exchange in the lungs: poorly functioning heart, contracted bronchioles, reduced number of alveoli?

## 24.5 Obtaining Nutrients: The Digestive System

The **digestive system** is the organ system responsible for the processing and distribution of nutrients; it consists of a muscular tube and glands that secrete digestive juices into the tube. Four kinds of activities are involved in getting nutrients to the cells that need them: mechanical processing, chemical processing,

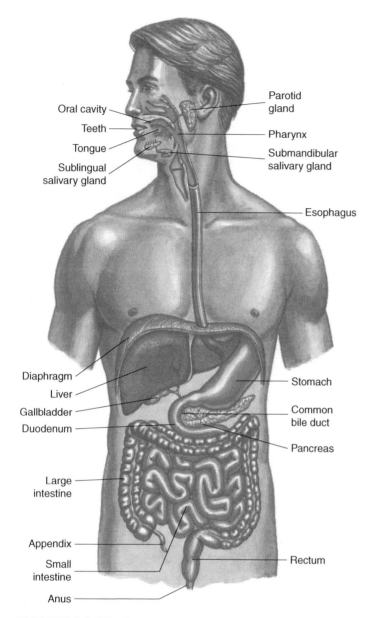

**Oral cavity**

**Teeth**

**Tongue**

**Sublingual salivary gland**

**Parotid gland**

**Pharynx**

**Submandibular salivary gland**

**Esophagus**

**Diaphragm**

**Liver**

**Gallbladder**

**Duodenum**

**Large intestine**

**Appendix**

**Small intestine**

**Anus**

**Stomach**

**Common bile duct**

**Pancreas**

**Rectum**

**FIGURE 24.10 The Digestive System**
The teeth, tongue, and enzymes from the salivary glands modify the food before it is swallowed. The stomach adds acid and enzymes and further changes the food's texture. The food is eventually emptied into the duodenum, where the liver and pancreas add their secretions. The small intestine also adds enzymes and is involved in absorbing nutrients. The large intestine is primarily involved in removing water.

nutrient uptake, and chemical alteration. Figure 24.10 shows the various structures of the digestive system.

## Mechanical and Chemical Processing

The purpose of the digestive system is to break down large chunks of food into small molecules, which the circulatory system can distribute to the body's cells. The first step in the digestive process is mechanical processing.

It is important to grind large particles into small pieces by chewing to increase their surface areas and allow for more efficient chemical reactions. It is also important to add water to the food, which further disperses the particles and provides the watery environment needed for these chemical reactions. Materials also must be mixed so that all the molecules that need to interact with one another have a good chance of doing so. The oral cavity and the stomach are the major body regions involved in reducing the size of food particles. The teeth are involved in cutting and grinding food to increase its surface area. The watery mixture that is added to the food in the oral cavity is called *saliva*, and the three pairs of glands that produce saliva are known as **salivary glands.** Saliva contains the enzyme salivary amylase, which begins the chemical breakdown of starch. Saliva also lubricates the oral cavity and helps bind food before swallowing.

In addition to having taste buds that help identify foods and potentially toxic materials, the tongue performs the important service of helping position the food between the teeth and pushing it to the back of the throat for swallowing. The oral cavity is very much like a food processor, in which mixing and grinding take place.

Once the food has been chewed, it is swallowed and passes down the esophagus to the stomach. The process of swallowing involves a complex series of events. First, a ball of food, known as a *bolus*, is formed by the tongue and moved to the back of the oral cavity. There, it stimulates the walls of the throat, also called the **pharynx.** Nerve endings in the lining of the pharynx are stimulated, causing a reflex contraction of the walls of the esophagus, which transports the bolus to the stomach. Because both food and air pass through the pharynx, it is important to prevent food from getting into the lungs. During swallowing, the larynx is pulled upward, causing a flap of tissue, called the *epiglottis*, to cover the opening to the trachea and preventing food from entering the trachea.

In the stomach, additional liquid, called **gastric juice,** is added to the food. Gastric juice contains enzymes and hydrochloric acid. The major enzyme of the stomach is **pepsin**, which initiates the chemical breakdown of protein. The pH of gastric juice is very low, generally around pH 2. Consequently, very few kinds of bacteria or protozoa emerge from the stomach alive. Those that do survive have characteristics that protect them from the gastric juice as they pass through the stomach. The entire mixture is churned by the contractions of the three layers of muscle in the stomach wall. The combined activities of enzymatic breakdown, chemical breakdown by hydrochloric acid, and mechanical processing by muscular movement result in a thoroughly mixed liquid. This liquid eventually leaves the stomach through a valve known as the **pyloric sphincter** and enters the **small intestine** (How Science Works 24.1).

The first part of the small intestine is called the **duodenum.** In addition to producing enzymes, the duodenum secretes several kinds of hormones that regulate the release of food

# HOW SCIENCE WORKS 24.1

## An Accident and an Opportunity

On the morning of June 6, 1822, on Mackinac Island in northern Lake Huron, a 19-year-old French-Canadian fur trapper named Alexis St. Martin was shot in the stomach by the accidental discharge from a shotgun. The army surgeon at Fort Mackinac, Michigan, Dr. William Beaumont, was called to attend to the wounded man. Part of St. Martin's stomach and body wall had been shot away, and parts of his clothing were embedded in the wound. Although Dr. Beaumont did not expect St. Martin to live, he quickly cleaned the wound, pushed portions of the lung and stomach that were protruding back into the cavity, and dressed the wound. Finding St. Martin alive the next day, Beaumont was surprised and encouraged to do what he could to extend his life. In fact, Dr. Beaumont cared for St. Martin for 2 years. When the wound was completely healed, the stomach had fused to the body wall and a hole allowed Dr. Beaumont to look into the stomach. Fortunately for St. Martin, a flap of tissue from the lining of the stomach closed off the opening, so that what he ate did not leak out.

Dr. Beaumont found that he could look through the opening and observe the activities in the stomach and recognized that this presented an opportunity to study the stomach's function in a way that had not been done before. He gathered gastric juice, had its components identified, introduced food into the hole with a string attached so that he could retrieve the food particles that were partially digested for examination, and observed the effect of emotion on digestion. He discovered many things that were new to science and contrary to the teachings of the time. He recounted many of his observations and experiments in his journal: *"I consider myself but a humble inquirer after truth—a simple experimenter. And if I have been led to conclusions opposite to the opinions of many who have been considered luminaries of physiology, and, in some instances, from all the professors of this science, I hope the claim of sincerity will be conceded to me, when I say that such difference of opinion has been forced upon me by the convictions of experiment, and the fair deductions of reasoning."*

Following are some of his important discoveries.

1. He measured the temperature of the stomach and found that it does not heat up when food is introduced, as was thought at the time: *"But from the result of a great number of experiments and examinations, made with a view to asserting the truth of this opinion, in the empty and full state of the organ, . . . I am convinced that there is no alteration of temperature. . . ."*
2. He found that pure gastric juice contains large amounts of hydrochloric acid. This was contrary to the prevailing opinion that gastric juice was simply water: *"I think I am warranted, from the result of all the experiments, in saying, that the gastric juice, so far from being "inert as water," as some authors assert, is the most general solvent in nature, of alimentary matter—even the hardest bone cannot withstand its action."*

House where Dr. Beaumont treated Alexis St. Martin

3. He observed that gastric juice is not stored in the stomach but, rather, is secreted when food is eaten: *"The gastric juice does not accumulate in the cavity of the stomach, until alimentary matter is received, and excite its vessels to discharge their contents, for the immediate purpose of digestion."*
4. He realized that digestion begins immediately when food enters the stomach. The prevailing opinion of the day was that nothing happened for an hour or more: *"At 2 o'clock P.M.—twenty minutes after having eaten an ordinary dinner of boiled, salted beef, bread, potatoes, and turnips, and drank [sic] a gill of water, I took from his stomach, through the artificial opening, a gill of the contents. . . . Digestion had evidently commenced, and was perceptually progressing, at the time."*
5. He discovered that food in the stomach satisfies hunger even though it is not eaten: *"To ascertain whether the sense of hunger would be allayed without food being passed through the oesophagus [sic], he fasted from breakfast time, til 4 o'clock, P.M., and became quite hungry. I then put in at the aperture, three and a half drachms of lean, boiled beef. The sense of hunger immediately subsided, and stopped the borborygmus, or croaking noise, caused by the motion of the air in the stomach and intestines, peculiar to him since the wound, and almost always observed when the stomach is empty."*

St. Martin did not take kindly to these probings and twice ran away from Dr. Beaumont's care back to Canada, where he married, had two children, and resumed his former life as a voyager and fur trapper. He did not die until the age of 83, having lived over 60 years with a hole in his stomach.

from the stomach and the release of secretions from the pancreas and liver. The **pancreas** produces a number of digestive enzymes and secretes large amounts of bicarbonate ions, which neutralize the acids that enter from the stomach so that the pH of the duodenum is about pH 8. The liver, a large organ in the upper abdomen, performs several functions, one of which is the secretion of **bile.** When bile leaves the liver, it is stored in the **gallbladder** prior to being released into the duodenum. When bile is released from the gallbladder, it assists mechanical processing by breaking large fat globules into smaller particles, much as soap breaks up fat particles into smaller globules that are suspended in water and washed away. This process is called *emulsification.* Emulsification is important because fats are not soluble in water, yet the reactions of digestion must take place in a water solution.

Along the length of the small intestine, additional watery juices are added until the mixture reaches the **large intestine** or colon. The 1.5-meter-long large intestine is primarily involved in reabsorbing the water that has been added to the food tube when saliva, gastric juice, bile, pancreatic secretions, and intestinal juices are introduced into the digestive system. The large intestine is also home to a variety of bacteria. Most live on food that was not absorbed in the small intestine. Some provide additional benefit by producing vitamins that can be absorbed from the large intestine. A few are capable of causing disease.

Several kinds of enzymes have been mentioned in this section. Each is produced by a specific organ and has a specific function. Chapter 5 introduced the topic of enzymes and how they work. Some enzymes, such as those involved in glycolysis, the Krebs cycle, and protein synthesis, are produced and used inside cells; others, such as the digestive enzymes, are produced by cells and secreted into the digestive tract. Digestive enzymes are simply a class of enzymes; they have the same characteristics as all other enzymes. They are protein molecules that speed up chemical reactions and are sensitive to changes in temperature or pH. The various digestive enzymes, the sites of their production, and their functions are listed in table 24.2.

## Nutrient Uptake

Digestion results in a variety of simple organic molecules that are available for absorption from the tube of the gut into the circulatory system. As simple sugars, amino acids, glycerol, and fatty acids move into the circulatory system, surface area again becomes important. The amount of material that can be taken up is limited by the surface area available. There are several ways in which the structure of the intestinal tract provides a large surface area. First, the small intestine is a very long tube; the longer the tube, the greater the internal surface area. In a typical adult human, it is about 6 to 8 meters long. In addition to length, the lining of the small intestine consists of millions of fingerlike projections, called **villi,** which increase the surface area. The cells that make up the villi also have folds in their surface membranes. All of these characteristics increase the surface area available for

| TABLE 24.2 | Digestive Enzymes and Their Functions | | |
|---|---|---|---|
| **Enzyme** | **Site of Production** | **Molecules Altered** | **Molecules Produced** |
| Salivary amylase | Salivary glands | Starch | Smaller polysaccharides |
| Pepsin | Stomach lining | Proteins | Peptides |
| Gastric lipase | Stomach lining | Fats | Fatty acids and glycerol |
| Chymotrypsin | Pancreas | Polypeptides (long chains of amino acids) | Peptides |
| Trypsin | Pancreas | Polypeptides | Peptides |
| Carboxypeptidase | Pancreas | Peptides (several amino acids) | Smaller peptides and amino acids |
| Pancreatic amylase | Pancreas | Polysaccharides (many sugar molecules attached together) | Disaccharides |
| Pancreatic lipase | Pancreas | Fats | Fatty acids and glycerol |
| Nuclease | Pancreas | Nucleic acids | Nucleotides |
| Aminopeptidase | Intestinal lining | Peptides | Smaller peptides and amino acids |
| Dipeptidase | Intestinal lining | Dipeptides | Amino acids |
| Lactase | Intestinal lining | Lactose | Glucose and galactose |
| Maltase | Intestinal lining | Maltose | Glucose |
| Sucrase | Intestinal lining | Sucrose | Glucose and fructose |
| Nuclease | Intestinal lining | Nucleic acids | Nucleotides |

the transport of materials from the gut into the circulatory system. Scientists estimate that the cumulative effect of all these features produces a total intestinal surface area of about 250 square meters. That is equivalent to about the area of a basketball court.

The surface area by itself would be of little value if it were not for the intimate contact of the circulatory system with the intestinal lining. Each villus contains several capillaries and a branch of the lymphatic system called a **lacteal.** The close association between the intestinal surface and the circulatory and lymphatic systems allows for the efficient uptake of nutrients from the cavity of the gut into the circulatory system (figure 24.11).

Several processes are involved in the transport of materials from the small intestine to the circulatory system. Some molecules, such as water and many ions, simply diffuse through the wall of the small intestine into the circulatory system. Other materials, such as amino acids and simple sugars, are assisted across the membrane by carrier molecules. Fatty acids and glycerol are absorbed into the intestinal lining cells, where they are resynthesized into fats and enter lacteals in the villi. Because the lacteals are part of the lymphatic system, which eventually empties its contents into the circulatory system, fats also are transported by the blood. They just reach the blood by a different route.

## Chemical Alteration: The Role of the Liver

When the blood leaves the small intestine, it flows directly to the liver through the **hepatic portal vein.** Portal veins are blood vessels that collect blood from capillaries in one part of the body and deliver it to a second set of capillaries in another part of the body without passing through the heart. Thus, *hepatic portal veins* collect nutrient-rich blood from the small intestine and deliver it directly to the liver. As the blood flows through the liver, enzymes in the liver cells modify many of the molecules and particles that enter them. One of the functions of the liver is to filter any foreign organisms from the blood that might have entered through the intestinal cells.

The liver also detoxifies many dangerous molecules that might have entered with the food. Many foods contain toxic substances that could be harmful if not destroyed by the liver. Ethyl alcohol is one obvious example. Many plants contain various kinds of toxic molecules that are present in small quantities and could accumulate to dangerous levels if the liver did not perform its role of detoxification.

In addition, the liver is responsible for modifying nutrient molecules. The liver collects glucose molecules and synthesizes glycogen, which can be stored in the liver for later use. When glucose is in short supply, the liver can convert some of

**FIGURE 24.11** **The Exchange Surface of the Intestinal Tract**
The surface area of the intestinal lining is increased by the many fingerlike projections known as villi. Within each villus are capillaries and lacteals. Most kinds of materials enter the capillaries, but most fat-soluble substances enter the lacteals, part of the lymphatic system, giving them a milky appearance. Because the lymphatic system empties into the circulatory system, fat-soluble materials also eventually enter the circulatory system. The close relationship between the vessels and the epithelial lining of the villi allows for the efficient exchange of materials from the intestinal cavity to the circulatory system.

its stored glycogen back into glucose. Although amino acids are not stored, the liver can change the relative numbers of various amino acids circulating in the blood. It can remove the amino group from one kind of amino acid and attach it to a different carbon skeleton, generating a different amino acid. The liver can also take the amino group off amino acids, so that what remains of the amino acid can be used in aerobic cellular respiration. The toxic amino groups are then converted to urea by the liver. Urea is secreted back into the bloodstream for disposal in urine.

## 24.5  CONCEPT REVIEW

10. Describe three ways in which the digestive system increases its ability to absorb nutrients.
11. List three functions of the liver.
12. Name five digestive enzymes and describe their functions.
13. What is the role of bile, saliva, enzymes, and hydrochloric acid in digestion?
14. How is fat absorption different from the absorption of carbohydrate and protein?

## 24.6  Waste Disposal: The Excretory System

The **excretory system** is the organ system responsible for the processing and elimination of metabolic waste products; it consists of the kidneys, ureters, urinary bladder, and urethra (figure 24.12). Because cells modify molecules during metabolic processes, harmful waste products are constantly being formed. Urea is a common waste; many other toxic materials must be eliminated as well. Among these are large numbers of hydrogen ions produced by metabolism. This excess of hydrogen ions must be removed from the bloodstream. Other molecules, such as water and salts, may be consumed in excessive amounts and must also be removed.

### Kidney Structure

The **kidneys** are the primary organs involved in regulating the level of toxic or unnecessary molecules in the body. The kidneys consist of about 2.4 million tiny units called **nephrons.** At one end of a nephron is a cup-shaped structure called a **Bowman's capsule,** which surrounds a knot of capillaries known as a **glomerulus** (figure 24.13). In addition to Bowman's capsule, a nephron consists of three distinctly different regions: the **proximal convoluted tubule,** the **loop of Henle,** and the **distal convoluted tubule.** The distal convoluted tubule of a nephron is connected to a collecting duct, which transports fluid to the ureters and ultimately to the urinary bladder, where it is stored until it can be eliminated through the urethra.

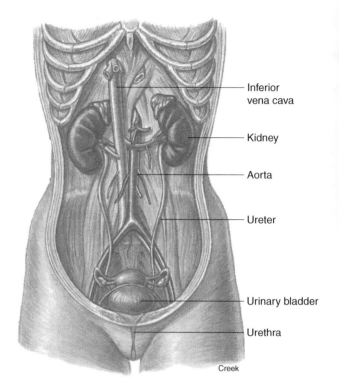

**FIGURE 24.12  The Excretory System**
The primary organs involved in removing materials from the blood are the kidneys. The urine produced by the kidneys is transported by the ureters to the urinary bladder. From the bladder, the urine is emptied to the outside of the body by way of the urethra.

### Kidney Function

As in the other systems discussed in this chapter, the excretory system involves a close connection between the circulatory system and a surface. In this case, the large surface is provided by the walls of the millions of nephrons, which are surrounded by capillaries. Three major activities occur at these surfaces: filtration, reabsorption, and secretion. The glomerulus presents a large surface for the filtering of material from the blood to Bowman's capsule. Blood that enters the glomerulus is under pressure from the muscular contraction of the heart. The capillaries of the glomerulus are quite porous and provide a large surface area for the movement of water and small dissolved molecules from the blood into Bowman's capsule. Normally, only the smaller molecules, such as glucose, amino acids, and ions, are able to pass through the glomerulus into the Bowman's capsule at the end of the nephron. The various kinds of blood cells and larger molecules, such as proteins like albumin, do not pass out of the blood into the nephron. (The chronic presence of albumin in the urine is an indicator of kidney damage or disease.) This physical filtration process allows many kinds of molecules to leave the blood and enter the nephron. The volume of material filtered in this way through the approximately 2.4 million nephrons of the kidneys is about 7.5 liters per hour. Because the entire blood supply is about 5 to 6 liters, there must be a method for recovering much of this fluid.

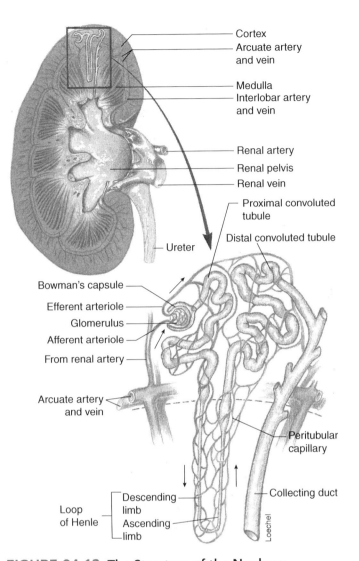

Cortex
Arcuate artery
and vein
Medulla
Interlobar artery
and vein
Renal artery
Renal pelvis
Renal vein
Proximal convoluted
tubule
Distal convoluted tubule
Ureter
Bowman's capsule
Efferent arteriole
Glomerulus
Afferent arteriole
From renal artery
Arcuate artery
and vein
Peritubular
capillary
Collecting duct
Descending
limb
Loop
of Henle
Ascending
limb
Loechel

**FIGURE 24.13  The Structure of the Nephron**
The nephron and the closely associated blood vessels create a system that allows for the passage of materials from the circulatory system to the nephron by way of the glomerulus and Bowman's capsule. Materials are added to and removed from the fluid in the nephron via the tubular portions of the nephron and their associated capillaries.

Surrounding the various portions of the nephron are capillaries that passively accept or release molecules on the basis of diffusion gradients. The walls of the nephron are made of cells that actively assist in the transport of materials. Some molecules are reabsorbed from the nephron and picked up by the capillaries that surround them, whereas other molecules are actively secreted into the nephron from the capillaries. Each portion of the nephron has cells with specific secretory abilities.

The proximal convoluted tubule is primarily responsible for reabsorbing valuable materials from the fluid moving through it. Molecules such as glucose, amino acids, and sodium ions are actively transported across the membrane of the proximal convoluted tubule and returned to the blood. In addition, water moves across the membrane because it follows the

absorbed molecules and diffuses to the area where water molecules are less common. By the time the fluid has reached the end of the proximal convoluted tubule, about 65% of the fluid has been reabsorbed into the capillaries surrounding this region.

The next portion of the tubule, the loop of Henle, is primarily involved in removing additional water from the nephron. Although the details of the mechanism are complicated, the principles are rather simple. The cells of the ascending loop of Henle actively transport sodium ions from the nephron into the space between nephrons where sodium ions accumulate in the fluid that surrounds the loop of Henle. The collecting ducts pass through this region as they carry urine to the ureters. Because the area these collecting ducts pass through is high in sodium ions, water within the collecting ducts diffuses from the ducts and is picked up by surrounding capillaries. However, the ability of water to pass through the wall of the collecting duct is regulated by hormones. Thus, it is possible to control water loss from the body by regulating the amount of water lost from the collecting ducts. For example, if you drank a liter of water or some other liquid, the excess water would not be allowed to leave the collecting duct (it would stay in the collecting duct) and would exit the body as part of the urine. However, if you were dehydrated, most of the water passing through the collecting ducts would be reabsorbed, and very little urine would be produced. The primary hormone involved in regulating water loss is the antidiuretic hormone (ADH). When the body has excess water, cells in the hypothalamus of the brain respond and send a signal to the pituitary, and only a small amount of ADH is released and water is lost in the urine. When you are dehydrated, the same brain cells cause more ADH to be released and water leaves the collecting duct and is returned to the blood.

The distal convoluted tubule is primarily involved in fine-tuning the amounts of various kinds of molecules that are lost in the urine. Hydrogen ions ($H^+$), sodium ions ($Na^+$), chloride ions ($Cl^-$), potassium ions ($K^+$), and ammonium ions ($NH_4^+$) are regulated in this way. Some molecules that pass through the nephron are relatively unaffected by the various activities going on in the kidneys. One of these is urea, which is filtered through the glomerulus into Bowman's capsule. As it passes through the nephron, much of it stays in the tubule and is eliminated in the urine. Many other kinds of molecules, such as minor metabolic waste products and some drugs, are also treated in this manner. Figure 24.14 summarizes the major functions of the various portions of the kidney tubule system.

## 24.6  CONCEPT REVIEW

15. What are the functions of the glomerulus, proximal convoluted tubule, loop of Henle, and distal convoluted tubule?
16. Describe how the kidneys regulate the amount of water in the body.

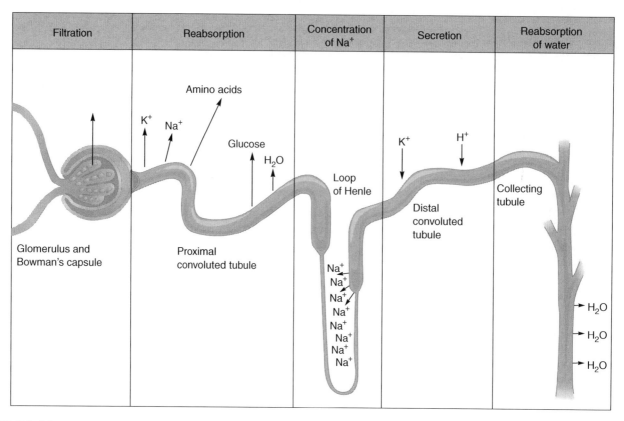

| Filtration | Reabsorption | Concentration of Na$^+$ | Secretion | Reabsorption of water |
|---|---|---|---|---|

**FIGURE 24.14 Specific Functions of the Nephron**
Each portion of the nephron has specific functions. The glomerulus and Bowman's capsule accomplish the filtration of fluid from the bloodstream into the nephron. The proximal convoluted tubule reabsorbs most of the material filtered. The loop of Henle concentrates Na$^+$ so that water will move from the collecting tubule. The distal convoluted tubule regulates pH and ion concentration by differential secretion of K$^+$ and H$^+$ and other ions.

## Summary

The body's systems must be integrated in such a way that the internal environment stays relatively constant. This chapter surveys five systems of the body—the cardiovascular, lymphatic, respiratory, digestive, and excretory systems—and describes how they are integrated. All of these systems are involved in the exchange of materials across membranes.

The cardiovascular system consists of a pump, the heart, and blood vessels that distribute the blood to all parts of the body. The blood is a carrier fluid that transports molecules and heat. The exchange of materials between the blood and body cells takes place through the walls of the capillaries. Because the flow of blood can be regulated by the contraction of arterioles, blood can be sent to different parts of the body at different times. Hemoglobin in red blood cells is very important in the transport of oxygen. Carbonic anhydrase is an enzyme in red blood cells that converts carbon dioxide into bicarbonate ions, which can be easily carried by the blood.

The lymphatic system is a collection of thin-walled tubes (lymph vessels) that branch throughout the body and lymph organs. The lymphatic system moves fat from the intestinal tract to the bloodstream through lacteals, transports excess tissue fluid back to the cardiovascular system, and defends against harmful agents, such as bacteria and viruses. The lymph organs include the lymph nodes, tonsils, spleen, thymus gland, and red bone marrow.

The respiratory system consists of the lungs and the associated tubes that allow air to enter and leave the lungs. The diaphragm and muscles of the chest wall are important in the process of breathing. In the lungs, alveoli provide a large surface area in association with capillaries, which allows for the rapid exchange of oxygen and carbon dioxide.

The digestive system disassembles food molecules. This involves several processes: grinding by the teeth and stomach, the emulsification of fats by bile from the liver, the addition of water to dissolve molecules, and enzymatic action to break complex molecules into simpler molecules for absorption. The small intestine provides a large surface area for the absorption of nutrients, because it is long and its wall contains many tiny projections that increase surface area. Once absorbed, the materials are carried to the liver, where molecules can be modified. The large intestine is primarily involved in reabsorption of water.

The excretory system is a filtering system of the body. The kidneys consist of nephrons, into which the circulatory system filters fluid. Most of this fluid is useful and is reclaimed by the cells that make up the walls of these tubules. Materials that are present in excess and those that are harmful are allowed to escape. Some molecules may be secreted into the tubules before being eliminated from the body.

## Key Terms

*Use the interactive flash cards on the **Concepts in Biology**, 14/e website to help you learn the meaning of these terms.*

alveoli 542
aorta 538
arteries 534
arterioles 539
atria 537
atrioventricular valves 538
bile 548
blood 534
Bowman's capsule 550
breathing 543
bronchi 542
bronchioles 542
capillaries 534
cardiovascular system 534
diaphragm 543
diastolic blood pressure 539
digestive system 545
distal convoluted tubule 550
duodenum 546
excretory system 550
formed elements 534
gallbladder 548
gastric juice 546
glomerulus 550
heart 534
hemoglobin 534
hepatic portal vein 549
kidneys 550
lacteal 549
large intestine 548

loop of Henle 550
lungs 542
lymph 541
lymph nodes 542
lymphatic system 541
nephrons 550
pancreas 548
pepsin 546
pharynx 546
plasma 534
platelets 536
proximal convoluted tubule 550
pulmonary artery 538
pulmonary circulation 538
pyloric sphincter 546
red blood cells (rbcs) 534
respiratory system 542
salivary glands 546
semilunar valves 538
small intestine 546
systemic circulation 538
systolic blood pressure 539
tissue fluid 537
trachea 542
veins 534
ventricles 537
villi 548
white blood cells (wbcs) 536

## Basic Review

1. The vessels that carry blood away from the heart are
   a. veins.
   b. arteries.
   c. capillaries.
   d. lacteals.
2. Which of the following is not a formed element?
   a. rbc
   b. wbc
   c. platelets
   d. plasma
3. _____ is the liquid that baths the body's cells and contains the same chemicals as plasma but smaller amounts of albumin.
4. Which of the following is not a function of the lymphatic system?
   a. It moves fat from the intestinal tract to the bloodstream.
   b. It transports excess tissue fluid back to the cardiovascular system.
   c. It defends against harmful agents, such as bacteria and viruses.
   d. It carries oxygen to cells deep in the body.
5. The stomach
   a. produces hydrochloric acid.
   b. begins digestion of protein.
   c. continues the mechanical breakdown of food begun in the mouth.
   d. All of the above are correct.
6. Saliva contains the enzyme _____, which begins the chemical breakdown of starch.
   a. salivary amylase
   b. pepsin
   c. trypsin
   d. pylorase
7. In the respiratory system, the small sacs in the lungs where gas exchange takes place are called
   a. nephrons.
   b. alveoli.
   c. nodes.
   d. platelets.

8. The lining of the small intestine consists of millions of fingerlike projections, called
   a. nodes.
   b. alveoli.
   c. villi.
   d. glomeruli.

9. The proximal convoluted tubule is primarily involved in
   a. secreting harmful materials into the nephron.
   b. reabsorbing useful materials from the nephron.
   c. removing hydrogen ions from the urine.
   d. None of the above is correct.

10. About 200 billion _____ are formed each day and are important in blood clotting.
   a. nephrons
   b. lacteals
   c. platelets
   d. formed elements

11. The primary waste products released in the urine are _____ and _____.

12. The flow of blood back to the heart through veins is assisted by valves and _____.

13. Breathing rate is primarily determined by the level of the chemical _____ in the blood.

14. Capillaries are intimately associated with the _____ of the lungs, the _____ of the kidneys, and the _____ of the small intestine.

15. The right ventricle pumps blood to the _____.

**Answers**
1. b   2. d   3. Tissue fluid   4. d   5. d   6. a   7. b   8. c   9. b
10. c   11. urea; hydrogen ions   12. contractions of the body's muscles   13. carbon dioxide   14. alveoli, nephrons, villi
15. lungs

## Thinking Critically

**Mechanically Assisted Life**
It is possible to keep a human being alive even if the heart, lungs, kidneys, and digestive tract are not functioning by using heart-lung machines in conjunction with kidney dialysis and intravenous feeding. This implies that the basic physical principles involved in the functioning of these systems is well understood because the natural functions can be duplicated with mechanical devices. However, these machines are expensive and require considerable maintenance. Should society be spending money to develop smaller, more efficient mechanisms that could be used to replace diseased or damaged hearts, lungs, and kidneys?

# Nutrition

## Food and Diet

CHAPTER

25

## Energy Drinks— Hype or Help?

*Check the ingredient list.*

Energy drinks are marketed to appeal to young people. They claim to provide energy for physical activity. What are the facts?

Many energy drinks do contain various kinds of sugar that are a source of Calories. The amount of sugar is generally similar to that in soft drinks. Some energy drinks are sugar-free.

The primary ingredients in all energy drinks are substances that stimulate the nervous system. Caffeine is usually shown as an ingredient and is typically in an amount equivalent to that found in a cup of coffee, although some brands have higher amounts. Two herbal ingredients commonly found in energy drinks are also known to be stimulants—guarana and yerba maté. Because they are herbal products, it is not required that companies provide detailed information about their quantities and effects. Both of these ingredients are extracts of South American plants. So, energy drinks containing guarana or yerba maté have additional stimulants that have effects similar to caffeine.

Taurine is another ingredient commonly found in energy drinks. It is naturally produced by the body and is a major ingredient of liver bile. It is present in meat and fish. Although it is often called an amino acid, it is not. However, it is produced in the body from the amino acid cysteine. It appears to have a variety of effects in the body but it is unclear if additional quantities have any beneficial effect. Its presence in energy drinks is probably related to some evidence that it improves the endurance of muscles. Its name is also of interest. It was first isolated from the bile of an ox, so it was given the name *taurine* after Taurus the bull. It appears that high doses are not harmful.

So, it appears that the primary effect of these drinks is to stimulate the nervous system so that people are more alert. They are not sources of energy in the metabolic sense.

- **What is the nutritional content of an energy drink?**
- **What role does caffeine play in metabolism?**
- **Should marketers of energy drinks be required to prove their claims?**

## Background Check

**Concepts you should understand in order to get the most out of this chapter:**
- The basic principles of chemistry (chapter 2)
- The basic principles of organic chemistry (chapter 3)
- How enzymes work in processing energy and matter (chapter 5)
- The structure and function of the digestive system (chapter 24)

## 25.1 Living Things as Chemical Factories: Matter and Energy Manipulators

Organisms maintain themselves by constantly processing molecules to obtain energy and building blocks for new living material. Autotrophs can manufacture organic molecules from inorganic molecules, but heterotrophs must consume organic molecules to get what they need. **Nutrients** are all the molecules required to support living things. Some nutrients are elements, such as calcium, iron, and potassium; others are organic molecules, such as carbohydrates, proteins, fats, and vitamins. All heterotrophs obtain the nutrients they need from food, and each kind of heterotroph has particular nutritional requirements. This chapter examines the nutritional requirements of humans.

### Diet and Nutrition Defined

The word *nutrition* is used in two contexts. First, **nutrition** is the branch of science that seeks to understand food, its nutrients, how the body uses nutrients, and how inappropriate combinations or quantities of nutrients lead to ill health. The word *nutrition* also refers to all the processes by which we take in food and use it, including *ingestion, digestion, absorption,* and *assimilation*. **Ingestion** is the process of taking food into the body through eating. **Digestion** is the breakdown of complex food molecules to simpler molecules. **Absorption** is the movement of simple molecules from the digestive system to the circulatory system for dispersal throughout the body. **Assimilation** is the modification and incorporation of absorbed molecules into the structure of the organism.

Many of the nutrients that enter living cells undergo chemical changes before they are incorporated into the body. These interconversion processes are ultimately under the control of the cell's genetic material. It is DNA that codes the information necessary to manufacture the enzymes required to extract energy from chemical bonds and to convert raw materials (nutrients) into the structure (anatomy) of the organism.

**Diet** is the food and drink consumed by a person from day to day. It must contain the minimal nutrients necessary to manufacture and maintain the body's structure (e.g., the bones, skin, tendon, muscle) and regulatory molecules (enzymes and hormones) and to supply the energy (ATP) needed to run the body's machinery. If the diet is deficient in nutrients, or if a person's body cannot process nutrients efficiently, a dietary deficiency and ill health may result. A good understanding of nutrition can promote good health; it requires an understanding of the energy and nutrient content in various foods (figure 25.1).

### Energy Content of Food

The *kilocalorie (kcal)* is the unit used to measure the amount of energy in foods. One **kilocalorie** is the amount of energy needed to raise the temperature of 1 *kilogram* of water 1°C. Remember that the prefix *kilo-* means "1,000 times" the value listed. Therefore, a kilocalorie is 1,000 times more heat energy than a *calorie*. A **calorie** is the amount of heat energy

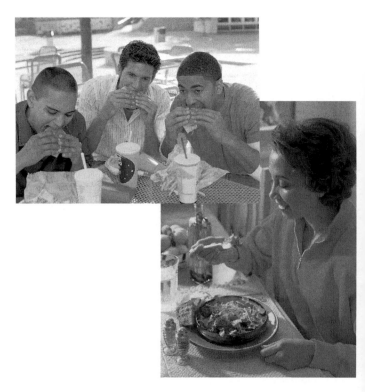

**FIGURE 25.1 Diet**
Your diet is what you eat on a daily basis.

# HOW SCIENCE WORKS 25.1

## Measuring the Caloric Value of Foods

A bomb calorimeter is an instrument used to determine the energy content of food. This is done by determining how much heat a given amount of food produces when it is burned. To operate the instrument, a small food sample is formed into a pellet and sealed inside a strong container called a bomb. The bomb is filled with oxygen under 30 atmospheres of pressure and is then placed in a surrounding jacket filled with water. The sample is electrically ignited. As it reacts with the oxygen (burns), the food sample in the bomb produces heat that is transferred to the water in the jacket that surrounds the bomb. The increase in temperature of the water is recorded. A kilocalorie (Calorie) is the amount of heat energy needed to increase the temperature of 1 kilogram of water 1°C. Therefore, if 1 gram of food results in a water temperature increase of 4°C for each kilogram of water, that food has 4 kilocalories (Calories).

Thermometer

Stirrer

Ignition wire

Calorimeter bucket

Insulated jacket

Water

$O_2$ inlet

Bomb

Sample cup

needed to raise the temperature of 1 *gram* of water 1°C. Although the energy unit for nutrition is a kilocalorie, it is usually called a Calorie with a capital C. This is unfortunate because it is easy to confuse a dietary Calorie, which is really a kilocalorie, with a calorie. Most books on nutrition and dieting use the term Calorie to refer to *food calories* (How Science Works 25.1).

## 25.1 CONCEPT REVIEW

1. What is a nutrient?
2. What is the difference between digestion and assimilation?
3. How is the energy content of food measured?

## 25.2 The Kinds of Nutrients and Their Function

Nutritionists have divided nutrients into six major classes: carbohydrates, lipids, proteins, vitamins, minerals, and water. Chapters 2 and 3 presented the chemical makeup of these types of molecules, and chapter 6 explored the nature of cellular respiration. A look at each of these classes of nutrients from a nutritionist's point of view should reveal how the human body works and how its nutritional needs can be met.

## Carbohydrates

From a nutritional point of view, there are three kinds of carbohydrates that are significant: sugars, starch, and fiber. The basic building blocks of carbohydrates are simple sugars (monosaccharides) such as glucose, fructose, and galactose. Two simple sugars can be combined to form double sugars (disaccharides) such as lactose, maltose, and sucrose. Both mono- and disaccharides are commonly called sugar. In plants, large numbers of glucose molecules can be joined to form a polysaccharide called *starch*. The function of starch in the plant is to store food. However, animals can use this energy-storage molecule for energy as well. Starch is a primary source of Calories for humans (figure 25.2).

### Functions of Carbohydrates

The primary function of sugars and starch in the diet is as a source of energy. During digestion, starch and disaccharides are broken down to simple sugars that are absorbed from the gut and used by cells during respiration. There are 4 Calories (kilocalories) in a gram of carbohydrate. In addition to serving as a source of energy, most sugars (glucose, fructose, lactose, sucrose, maltose) taste sweet and stimulate the appetite. Simple sugars are also used as building blocks in the manufacture of molecules such as nucleic acids.

**Dietary fiber** consists of cellulose and several other complex carbohydrates that are indigestible. Dietary fiber has several nutritional functions. It slows the absorption of

**FIGURE 25.2 Carbohydrates**
The primary source of carbohydrates is seeds of plants such as wheat, oats, rice, and beans and things made from the seeds. For most of the people of the world, carbohydrate in the form of starch is the primary item in their diet.

sugars, which helps to regulate the level of glucose in the blood. This is particularly important for diabetics. Dietary fiber also reduces the absorption of cholesterol from the intestine and thus can have the beneficial effect of lowering cholesterol in the blood, which reduces the incidence of heart disease. It provides bulk to the contents of the intestine and stimulates peristalsis (rhythmic contractions) in the intestinal tract. It also tends to retain water in the intestine, reducing the incidence of constipation.

### Carbohydrate Quality

Food sources that contain carbohydrates are not all the same. Flour is made from seeds such as wheat, corn, rye, rice, buckwheat, and millet that are ground up. Many kinds of foods are constructed from refined flour, which is essentially pure starch. Whole-grain flour contains many other parts of the seeds and has much more fiber and other nutrients than contained in refined flours. Foods that consist primarily of refined flours and sugars (candy bars, soft drinks, white bread, cakes, etc.) are high in Calories but low in other important nutrients. Therefore, these foods sources are often said to have "empty Calories"—they provide Calories but little other nutritional value. The latest nutritional recommendations encourage people to reduce their consumption of refined flours and sugars and increase their consumption of whole grain products.

### How the Body Manages Carbohydrates

When we consume carbohydrates, we cannot use them immediately to provide energy for our cells. Our bodies store this energy in two ways. We can store small amounts as glycogen in muscles and the liver for later use. Glycogen consists of glucose molecules hooked together but in a different way from that of starch. Glycogen is sometimes called animal starch. The body can only store small amounts of carbohydrate as glycogen. Therefore, carbohydrates should be a daily part of the diet. If we consume much more carbohydrate than we need, the excess is converted to fat and stored in fat tissue.

A diet deficient in carbohydrates results in fats being oxidized and converted to ATP. In situations in which carbohydrates are absent, most of the fats are metabolized to *keto acids*. Large numbers of keto acids may be produced in extreme cases of fasting, resulting in a potentially dangerous change in the body's pH. If a person does not have stored fat to metabolize, a carbohydrate deficiency will result in use of the body's proteins as a source of energy. This is usually only encountered in starvation, extreme cases of fasting, or eating disorders. In extreme cases, this can be fatal, because the oxidation of protein results in an increase in toxic, nitrogen-containing compounds.

## Lipids

The class of nutrients technically known as *lipids* is often called *fats*. This may lead to some confusion, because fats are only one of three subclasses of lipids. Each subclass of lipids—phospholipids, steroids, and true fats—plays an important role in human nutrition.

Phospholipids are the major molecules in membrane structures (endoplasmic reticulum, plasma membrane, Golgi, etc.) of cells. Although various kinds of phospholipids are sold as dietary supplements, they are unnecessary because all food composed of cells contains phospholipids.

Many steroids are hormones that help regulate a variety of body processes. With the exception of vitamin D, it is not necessary to include steroids as a part of the diet. Cholesterol is a steroid, manufactured in the body and commonly found in foods of animal origin. Excess consumption of cholesterol causes health problems in some people.

The *true fats* (also called *triglycerides*) are composed of a glycerol molecule attached to three fatty acids.

### Functions of Fats

Fats are the primary long-term, energy-storage molecules in animals and plants. Therefore, they are an excellent source of energy. They release 9 Calories of energy per gram compared to 4 Calories per gram for carbohydrate or protein. A teaspoon holds about 5 grams of a fat like olive oil.

In addition to serving as sources of energy in the diet and energy-storage molecules in the body, fats have several other important functions. Some vitamins, such as A, D, E, and K, do not dissolve in water but dissolve in fat and, therefore, require fat in the gut for their absorption. A layer of fat under the skin is a valuable insulator against internal heat loss. The layer of fat under the skin and that which surrounds organs is also an excellent shock absorber. Fat deposits in the back of the eyes serve as cushions when the head suffers a severe blow. During starvation, these deposits are lost, and the eyes become deep-set in the eye sockets, giving the person a ghostly appearance.

The pleasant taste and "mouth feel" of many foods is the result of fats. Their ingestion provides a full feeling after a meal because they tend to remain in the stomach so that it empties later than if fat were not present.

## Kinds of Fats Important in Nutrition

Fats consist of the molecule of glycerol with three fatty acids attached. Several kinds of fats are commonly discussed with respect to nutrition (figure 25.3). *Saturated fats* have fatty acid portions that do not have any double bonds between carbons. They are generally of animal origin and are solids at room temperature. *Unsaturated fats* have double bonds between carbons in the fatty acid portion of the molecule. They are called oils because they are liquids at room temperature. They are generally of plant origin. *Polyunsaturated fats* have several double bonds in the fatty acid portion of the molecule. *Trans fats* are created when unsaturated fats are chemically altered (hydrogenated) to make them more solid. Although they are still unsaturated, they have fewer double bonds and have a slightly different structure from the fats normally produced by organisms. Trans fats cause an increase in the amount of "bad" lipids in the blood.

Some fats contain the **essential fatty acids,** linoleic acid and linolenic acid, which cannot be synthesized by the human body and, therefore, must be a part of the diet. The body requires these essential fatty acids for normal growth, blood clotting, and healthy skin. Most diets that incorporate a variety of foods, including meats and vegetable oils, have enough of these essential fatty acids. A diet high in linoleic acid has

also been shown to help reduce the amount of cholesterol in the blood. Because of negative health effects associated with saturated fats and trans fats in the diet, people are encouraged to reduce their total consumption of fats and to substitute unsaturated fats for saturated and trans fats.

## How the Body Manages Fat

Body fat is produced when food consumption is higher than the amount needed for daily energy needs. This stored energy source can be called upon when a person does not consume enough Calories to meet daily energy demands. Early in the history of our species this was vitally important because obtaining food was often irregular. Periods of food scarcity were common and stored fat was important for survival. However, today food is abundantly available for most of us and often exceeds our daily needs. Thus, what once was an important mechanism for survival has become a problem of obesity for many people.

## Proteins

Proteins are composed of amino acids linked together; however, not all proteins contain the same amino acids.

## Functions of Proteins

Proteins are involved in a great number of structures and activities in the body. Cell membranes contain protein along with phospholipids. Structures like muscles, tendons, ligaments, skin, and connective tissues all have proteins as an important constituent. Many proteins are involved in regulating particular activities of the body. Enzymes control metabolism. Antibodies protect from disease. Hormones communicate. Many other proteins are involved in sending and receiving signals between cells. Proteins also provide a last-ditch source of energy during starvation when carbohydrate and fat reserves are used up. Thus, it is accurate to say that it is the proteins of an organism that determine its structure, metabolic abilities, and capacity to regulate and coordinate the various activities of the body.

Because proteins are so important, many people have a misconception about the amount of protein necessary in the diet. The amount is actually quite small (about 50 grams/day) and can be obtained easily. A hamburger, a half chicken breast, or a fish sandwich contains the daily amount of protein needed by most people.

## Kinds of Proteins

From a nutritional point of view, proteins can be divided into two groups: *complete proteins* and *incomplete proteins*. **Complete proteins** contain all the amino acids required by the body and necessary for good health. Proteins derived from animal sources—meat, poultry, fish, eggs, milk—are

**Saturated Fats**                    **Unsaturated Fats**

**FIGURE 25.3 Saturated and Unsaturated Fats**
Animal fats are saturated. Dairy products, meats, and foods cooked in animal fats are high in saturated fats. Plant fats are usually oils and are unsaturated fats.

complete proteins (figure 25.4). **Incomplete proteins** lack certain amino acids that the body must have to build essential proteins. Most plant proteins are deficient in one or more of the essential amino acids. For example, the amino acid lysine is absent or in very low quantities in wheat, rice, and corn and the amino acid tryptophan is limited in beans. However, eating a combination of beans and rice or corn and beans provides the equivalent of a complete protein.

The human body can manufacture some amino acids but is unable to manufacture others. Those the body cannot manufacture are called **essential amino acids** (table 25.1). Without adequate amounts of these essential amino acids in the diet, a person may develop a protein-deficiency disease.

In many parts of the world, people live on diets that provide the Calories they need from carbohydrates and fats but are low in complete protein. In part, this is because carbohydrates and fats are inexpensive to grow and process, in comparison with proteins. One protein-deficiency disease is **kwashiorkor;** its symptoms are easily seen (figure 25.5). A person with this deficiency has a distended belly, slow growth, and slow movement and is emotionally depressed. If the disease is caught in time, brain damage can be prevented and death averted. This requires a change in diet, including expensive protein, such as poultry, fish, beef, shrimp, or milk. As the world food problem increases, these expensive foods will be in even shorter supply and will become more and more costly.

| TABLE 25.1 | Sources of Essential Amino Acids |
| Essential Amino Acids | Comments |
| --- | --- |
| Threonine | In most sources of protein |
| Isoleucine | In most sources of protein |
| Methionine | In most sources of protein |
| Valine | In most sources of protein |
| Phenylalanine | In most sources of protein |
| Leucine | In most sources of protein |
| Tryptophan | **Deficient in legumes** |
| Lysine | **Deficient in grains** |
| Arginine | Essential in infants only; in most sources of protein |
| Histidine | Essential in infants only; present in human and cow's milk and infant formula |

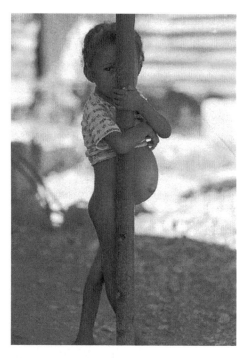

**FIGURE 25.5 Kwashiorkor**
This starving child shows the symptoms of kwashiorkor, a protein-deficiency disease. If this child were treated with adequate protein containing all the amino acids, the symptoms could be reduced.

**FIGURE 25.4 Sources of Proteins**
The muscle tissue of animals, eggs, and milk products are good sources of complete protein. Beans are also a good protein source but are an incomplete protein since they are low in the amino acid tryptophan.

## How the Body Manages Protein

Unlike carbohydrates and fats, proteins cannot be stored for later use. Because they are not stored and because they have many important functions, adequate amounts of protein must be present in the daily diet. However, a high-protein diet is not necessary. Only small amounts of protein—20 to 30 grams—are metabolized and lost from the body each day and must be replaced. A diet containing 50 grams of protein would easily cover this loss. Any protein in excess of that needed to rebuild lost molecules is metabolized to provide the body with energy.

Protein that makes up the structure of the body is protected from being metabolized to provide energy for cells. The mechanisms that protect protein are called **protein-sparing** mechanisms. During fasting or starvation, several kinds of metabolic adjustments allow the body to continue functioning without an input of food. Many of the body's cells can use fat as their primary source of energy, thus protecting the more valuable protein. The breakdown of fats results in the production of compounds called *ketones*. Some of these ketones are released in the breath and can be detected as the odor of acetone. Acetone is an odor you would associate with fingernail polish. People who are fasting, anorexic, or diabetic or have other metabolic problems often have this "ketone breath."

However, red blood cells and nervous tissue must have glucose, which can be supplied by the breakdown of glycogen stored in muscles and the liver. However, after a day or two of fasting, glycogen stores are depleted and glucose is unavailable from glycogen. Only at this point does the body begin to convert some of the amino acids from structural protein into glucose to supply these blood cells and nerve cells. During the early stages of starvation, the amount of fat in the body steadily decreases, but the amount of protein drops only slightly—20 to 30 grams per day (figure 25.6).

Although fat can supply energy for many cells during fasting or starvation, the fat cannot completely protect the proteins if there are no carbohydrates in the diet. With prolonged

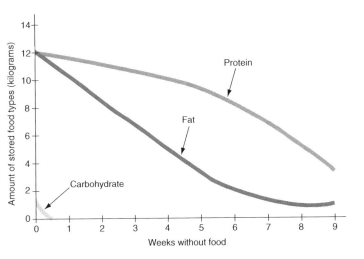

**FIGURE 25.6 Protein-Sparing Mechanisms**
The body uses various metabolic mechanisms to protect proteins during fasting or starvation. Notice that carbohydrate stores (glycogen) are depleted quickly and that fat stores fall much faster than protein. Protein-sparing mechanisms enable the body to protect essential enzymes and other proteins.

starvation, the fat stores are eventually depleted and structural proteins (as much as 125 grams per day) are used for all the body's energy needs. When starvation reaches this point, it is usually fatal. People who are chronically undernourished do not have the protective effect of fat and experience the effects of starvation much more quickly than those who have stored fat. Children are particularly at risk, because they also need nutrients as building blocks for growth.

## Vitamins

**Vitamins** are organic molecules needed in small amounts to maintain essential metabolic activities. Like essential amino acids and essential fatty acids, vitamins cannot be manufactured by the body. Table 25.2 lists vitamins for which there are recommended daily intakes.

### Functions of Vitamins
Vitamins are involved as participants in many metabolic reactions. Some vitamins are actually incorporated into the structure of enzymes. Such vitamins are called *coenzymes*. For example, the B-complex vitamin niacin helps enzymes involved in aerobic cellular respiration. Several vitamins are antioxidants that protect cells. During normal metabolic processes, compounds called *free radicals* are produced. Free radicals are extremely reactive and can combine with and alter the structure of important molecules in the cell. Some of the vitamins (in particular, vitamins A, C, and E) combine with free radicals and neutralize their effects.

### Kinds of Vitamins
From a nutritional point of view there are two kinds of vitamins: water-soluble vitamins and fat-soluble vitamins. The water-soluble vitamins are vitamin C and the various kinds of B vitamins. The fat-soluble vitamins are A, D, E, and K. Vitamin D deserves some special comment. Although vitamin D is found in certain foods, it is also formed when the ultraviolet light in sunshine strikes a cholesterol molecule in the skin, converting cholesterol to vitamin D. This means that vitamin D is not really a vitamin at all. It came to be known as a vitamin because of the mistaken idea that it was acquired only through food, rather than being formed in the skin on exposure to sunshine. It would be more correct to call vitamin D a hormone, but most people do not.

### How Vitamins Are Managed in the Body
The water-soluble vitamins are not stored in the body and thus must be obtained in the diet on a daily basis because they are lost in the urine. Excess fat-soluble vitamins are stored in the liver and can be released for use when needed. Therefore, it is not necessary to have these vitamins in the diet every day.

Because many vitamins are inexpensive and their functions are poorly understood, many advocate large doses (megadoses) of vitamins to prevent a wide range of diseases. Often,

**TABLE 25.2** Sources and Functions of Vitamins

| Name | Recommended Daily Intake for Young Adults | | Physiological Value | Readily Available Sources | Other Information |
|------|-------|------|---------------------|---------------------------|-------------------|
| | Women | Men | | | |
| **Water-Soluble Vitamins** | | | | | |
| Vitamin B$_1$ (thiamin) | 1.1 mg/d | 1.2 mg/d | Maintains nerves and heart; involved in carbohydrate metabolism | Whole grains, legumes, pork | Larger amounts needed during pregnancy and lactation |
| Vitamin B$_2$ (riboflavin) | 1.1 mg/d | 1.3 mg/d | Important in aerobic respiration reactions; maintains skin and mucous membranes | Whole grains, dairy products, green vegetables; liver | |
| Vitamin B$_3$ (niacin) | 14 mg/d | 16 mg/d | Important in aerobic respiration reactions | Whole grains, meat | |
| Vitamin B$_6$ (pyridoxine pyridoxol, pyridoxamine) | 1.3 mg/d | 1.3 mg/d | Builds red blood cells; maintains nervous system | Whole grains, milk, meat, legumes, nuts, leafy green vegetables | Large doses cause pain and numbness in the extremities |
| Vitamin B$_{12}$ (cobalamin) | 2.4 µg/d | 2.4 µg/d | Protein and fat metabolism; forms red blood cells; maintains nervous system | Animal foods only—dairy products, meat, poultry, seafood | Stored in the liver; vegetarians must consume yeast or cereals with B$_{12}$ added |
| Vitamin C | 75 mg/d | 90 mg/d | Antioxidant; maintains connective tissue | Many fruits and vegetables; leafy green vegetables, tomatoes, potatoes | |
| Folate (folic acid) | 400 µg/d | 400 µg/d | Coenzyme in metabolism; production of red blood cells | Most foods, fortified cereals, beans | Adequate amounts needed in pregnancy; low levels associated with neural tube defects |
| Choline (lecithin) | 425 mg/d | 550 mg/d | Component of cell membranes; component of acetylcholine—a neurotransmitter | All foods | Only important in people unable to consume food normally |
| **Fat-Soluble Vitamins** | | | | | |
| Vitamin A | 700 µg/d | 900 µg/d | Antioxidant; important in vision; maintains skin and intestinal lining | Orange, red, and leafy green vegetables, liver | Stored in liver; children have little stored; blindness results from lack of vitamin |
| Vitamin D | 5 µg/d | 5 µg/d | Needed to absorb calcium from gut; necessary for strong bones and teeth | Vitamin D fortified milk; exposure of skin to sunlight | Toxic in high concentrations |
| Vitamin E | 15 mg/d | 15 mg/d | Antioxidant; protects cell membranes | Whole grains, nuts, vegetables, vegetable oils | Only two cases of deficiency ever identified |
| Vitamin K | 90 µg/d | 120 µg/d | Blood clotting | Leafy green vegetables | Recommended for newborns |

the benefits advertised are based on fragmentary evidence and lack a clearly defined mechanism of action. The consumption of high doses of vitamins is unwise, because megadoses of many vitamins are toxic. For example, fat-soluble vitamins, such as vitamins A and D, are stored in body fat and the liver and can reach such high levels that ill health results. Excess vitamin A causes joint pain, hair loss, and jaundice. Excess vitamin D results in calcium deposits in the kidneys, high

## Preventing Scurvy

Scurvy is a nutritional disease caused by a lack of vitamin C in the diet. Vitamin C is essential to the formation of collagen, a fiber-like protein important in most tissues. The symptoms of scurvy include the poor healing of wounds; fragile blood vessels, resulting in bleeding; a lack of bone growth; and a loosening of the teeth.

Scurvy is not common today; however, in the past, many people on long sea voyages developed scurvy because their diets lacked fresh fruits and vegetables. This was such a common problem that the disease was often called sea scurvy. Excerpts from a letter by a Dr. Harness to the First Lord of the Admiralty of the British navy describe the practice of using lemons to prevent scurvy on British ships: "During

the blockade of Toulon in the summer of 1793, many of the ships' companies were afflicted with symptoms of scurvy; . . . I was induced to propose . . . the sending a vessel into port for the express purpose of obtaining lemons for the fleet; . . . and the good effects of its use were so evident . . . that an order was soon obtained from the commander in chief, that no ship under his lordship's command should leave port without being previously furnished with an ample supply of lemons. And to this circumstance becoming generally known may the use of lemon juice, the effectual means of subduing scurvy, while at sea, be traced."

A common term applied to British seamen during this time was *limey*.

amounts of calcium in the blood, and bone pain. High doses of some of the water-soluble vitamins also have toxic effects: Vitamin $B_6$ (pyridoxine) in high concentrations causes symptoms related to the nervous system, such as unsteady gait and numbness in the hands. However, inexpensive multivitamins that provide 100% of the recommended daily allowance can prevent or correct deficiencies caused by a poor diet without the danger of toxic consequences. Most people do not need vitamin supplements *if they eat a well-balanced diet* (How Science Works 25.2).

The lack of a particular vitamin in the diet can result in a **vitamin-deficiency disease.** Vitamin-deficiency diseases that show recognizable symptoms are extremely rare, except in countries with extreme food emergencies. Since vitamin A is necessary for vision, vitamin A deficiency is a leading cause of preventable blindness in children in developing countries. Night blindness is another manifestation of a lack of vitamin A.

## Minerals

**Minerals** are elements found in nature that cannot be synthesized by the body. Table 25.3 lists the sources and functions of several common minerals. Because minerals are elements, they cannot be broken down or destroyed by metabolism or cooking. They commonly occur in many foods and in water.

### Functions of Minerals

Minerals retain their characteristics whether they are in foods or in the body, and each plays a different role in metabolism. Minerals can function as regulators, activators, transmitters, and controllers of various enzymatic reactions. For example, sodium ($Na^+$) and potassium ions ($K^+$) are involved in

maintaining the polarity of cell membranes and are important in the transmission of nerve impulses, whereas magnesium ions ($Mg^{++}$) facilitate energy release during reactions involving ATP. Without iron, not enough hemoglobin would be formed to transport oxygen, a condition called *anemia*, and a lack of calcium may result in *osteoporosis*. **Osteoporosis** is a calcium-deficiency disease in older adults that is tied to diet. Persons with this disease lose bone mass; their bones become more brittle and subject to fracture. The body needs calcium to maintain bone, so many adults take calcium supplements. However, calcium alone does not prevent osteoporosis. Bone strength is directly related to the amount of stress placed on the bone. Therefore, exercise is extremely important to assure that calcium will be incorporated into bones and improve their strength. Folic acid and other B vitamins may also help in preventing osteoporosis. Many minerals are important in the diet. In addition to those just mentioned, we need chlorine, cobalt, copper, iodine, phosphorus, sulfur, and zinc to remain healthy. With few exceptions, adequate amounts of minerals are obtained in a normal diet. Calcium and iron supplements may be necessary, however, particularly in women.

### How the Body Manages Minerals

Many minerals such as sodium, potassium, and chloride are balanced by having excess amounts excreted in the urine. Minerals such as calcium and phosphorus are part of the structure of bone. These sources can be mobilized if the diet is low in these minerals, with the consequence of weakened bones. Pregnant and nursing mothers need to supplement their calcium intake to prevent bone loss. The body stores some iron bound to the protein ferritin in the liver, bone marrow, and spleen.

**TABLE 25.3**   Sources and Functions of Minerals

| Name | Recommended Daily Intake for Young Adults | | Physiological Value | Readily Available Sources | Other Information |
|------|------|------|------|------|------|
| | *Women* | *Men* | | | |
| Sodium | Less than 1,500 mg/d | Less than 1,500 mg/d | Maintains cell membrane ionic balance; osmotic balance | Present in most foods, table salt | Most people get much more than needed; high levels associated with high blood pressure; people should restrict their intake to less than 1,500 mg/d |
| Potassium | 4,700 mg/d | 4,700 mg/d | Maintains cell membrane ionic balance | Banana, legumes, potato skins, tomato | Low amounts lead to acute nervous system, muscular system, and cardiac problems |
| Calcium | 1,000 mg/d | 1,000 mg/d | Builds bones and teeth; blood clotting; muscle contraction | Dairy products, leafy green vegetables | Children need 1,300 mg/d to support bone growth; vitamin D needed for calcium absorption |
| Iron | 18 mg/d | 8 mg/d | Necessary to make hemoglobin | Meats, leafy green vegetables, seafood, legumes | Because of menstruation women need more than men; pregnant women need twice the normal dose |
| Phosphorus | 700 mg/d | 700 mg/d | Maintains acid/base balance; enzyme cofactor; component of bones and teeth | All foods | Most people get more than needed; children need 1,250 mg/d to support bone growth |
| Magnesium | 310 mg/d | 400 mg/d | Coenzyme; necessary for bone mineralization; muscle and nerve function | Leafy green vegetables, whole grains, legumes | Found in chlorophyll |
| Selenium | 55 μg/d | 55 μg/d | Involved in many enzymatic reactions | Meat, grains, seafood | Toxic in high doses |
| Zinc | 8 mg/d | 11 mg/d | Involved in many enzymatic reactions; wound healing; fetal development | Whole grains, beans, meat, fish, poultry | Toxic in high doses |
| Copper | 900 μg/d | 900 μg/d | Involved in many enzymatic reactions; involved in iron metabolism | Liver, poultry, shellfish, legumes, whole grains | Toxic in high doses |

## Water

Water is crucial to all life and plays many essential roles. Humans can survive weeks without food but would die in a matter of days without water. It is known as the universal solvent, because so many types of molecules are soluble in it.

The human body is about 65% water. Even dense bone tissue consists of 33% water. All the chemical reactions in living things take place in water. It is the primary component of blood, lymph, and body tissue fluids. Inorganic and organic nutrients and waste molecules are also dissolved in water.

Dissolved inorganic ions, such as sodium ($Na^+$), potassium ($K^+$), and chloride ($Cl^-$), are electrolytes because they form a solution capable of conducting electricity. The concentration of these ions in the body's water must be regulated to prevent electrolyte imbalances.

Excesses of many types of waste are eliminated from the body dissolved in water; that is, they are excreted from the kidneys as urine or in small amounts from the lungs or skin through evaporation. In a similar manner, the evaporation of water from the skin cools the body. Water molecules are also essential reactants in all the various hydrolytic reactions of metabolism. Without it, the breakdown of molecules such as starch, proteins, and lipids would be impossible. With all these important roles played by water, it's no wonder that nutritionists recommend that we drink the equivalent of at least eight glasses each day. This amount of water can be obtained from tap water, soft drinks, juices, and numerous food items, such as lettuce, cucumbers, tomatoes, and applesauce.

## 25.2   CONCEPT REVIEW

4. Why are some nutrients referred to as *essential*? Name them.
5. List the six main classes of nutrients as described by nutritionists. Describe the chemical nature of each and give one function of each class of nutrient.

## 25.3   Dietary Reference Intakes

The U.S. Department of Agriculture (USDA) regularly publishes updated guidelines for maintaining good nutritional health. The current guidelines, the **Dietary Reference Intakes**, provide information on the amounts of certain nutrients various members of the public should receive. These daily guidelines are very detailed. There are different guidelines for children, men, and women by age group. There are also specific guidelines for pregnant and nursing mothers. There are also guidelines about the maximum amount of certain nutrients that people should get.

Dietary Reference Intakes are used when preparing product labels. By law, labels must list ingredients from the greatest to the least in quantity. In addition to carbohydrates, fats, proteins, and fiber, about 25 vitamins and minerals have Dietary Reference Intakes. Table 25.4 gives examples of some of the more common nutrients and their reference amounts for young adults.

## 25.3   CONCEPT REVIEW

6. How much of each of the following nutrients should you get each day: iron, calcium, protein, and fiber?

## 25.4   The Food Guide Pyramid

Using Dietary Reference Intakes and product labels or counting Calories is a complicated way to plan a diet. Planning a diet around basic food groups is generally easier. The USDA's **Food Guide Pyramid** is a tool for planning a nutritious diet (figure 25.7). The basic philosophy of the Food Guide Pyramid is to provide simple, understandable recommendations that, when followed, will provide adequate amounts of the different kinds of nutrients. Furthermore, it is designed to limit the consumption of nutrients that can be harmful to health to acceptable levels. It also provides guidelines about exercise. The color and width of the bands refers to food groups and servings at one of many Calorie levels based on age, sex, and activity level. Go to www.pyramid.gov. Select MyPyramid Plan, type in your age, sex, height, weight, and typical physical activity to get a dietary plan that is designed for your specific needs.

### Grains

Grains include vitamin-enriched or whole-grain cereals and products such as breads, bagels, buns, crackers, dry and cooked cereals, pancakes, pasta, and tortillas. Most of the items in this group are dry and seldom need refrigeration. Whole-grain foods contain many more nutrients (particularly vitamins and dietary fiber) than do products made with refined flours. Refined flours are made from grains but have had the outer hulls removed. What remains after the hull is removed is essentially starch. Half of the foods consumed from this group should be whole-grain products. National studies show that nearly 100 percent of the United States population consumes more refined grains than recommended.

**Cereal group**

The Food Guide Pyramid recommends that women consume 6 oz a day and men consume 8 oz a day of foods made from grains. One oz is equal to about one slice of bread or half a bagel. Grains should provide most of the energy (Calories) in the diet. Furthermore, they provide energy in the form of complex carbohydrates, such as starch, which is the main ingredient in most grain products. These foods help satisfy the appetite, and many are very low in fat. They also provide fiber, which assists in the proper functioning of the digestive tract. Foods high in fiber are also a source of several vitamins and minerals.

Significant nutritional components of grains are complex carbohydrate (starch), dietary fiber, several B vitamins, vitamin E, and the minerals iron and magnesium.

### Fruits

The separation of plant foods into fruits and vegetables is sometimes confusing. Is a tomato a vegetable or a fruit? The confusion arises from the fact that the term *vegetable* is not scientifically precise but for nutritional purposes

## TABLE 25.4    Dietary Reference Intakes for Some Common Nutrients

| Nutrient | Women, 19–30 Years Old | Men, 19–30 Years Old | Maximum, Persons 19–30 Years Old | Value of Nutrient |
|---|---|---|---|---|
| Carbohydrates | 130 g/day (45–65% of Calories) | 130 g/day (45–65% of Calories) | No maximum set but refined sugars should not exceed 25% of total Calories | A source of energy |
| Proteins | 46 g/day (10–35% of Calories) | 56 g/day (10–35% of Calories) | No maximum but high-protein diets stress kidneys | Proteins are structural components of all cells; there are 10 essential amino acids that must be obtained in the diet |
| Fats | 20–35% of Calories | 20–35% of Calories | Up to 35% of total Calories | Energy source and building blocks for many molecules needed |
| Saturated and *trans* fatty acids | As low as possible | As low as possible | Less than 10% of Calories | |
| Linoleic acid | 12 g/day | 17 g/day | No maximum set | Essential fatty acid needed for enzyme function and maintenance of epithelial cells |
| Linolenic acid | 1.1 g/day | 1.6 g/day | No maximum set | Essential fatty acid needed to reduce coronary heart disease |
| Cholesterol | As low as possible | As low as possible | Less than 300 mg/day | None needed, because the liver makes cholesterol |
| Water | 2.7 liters/day | 3.7 liters/day | No maximum set | |
| Total fiber | 28 g/day | 34 g/day | No maximum set | Improve gut function |
| Calcium | 1 g/day | 1 g/day | 2.5 g/day | Needed for the structure of bones and many other functions |
| Iron | 18 g/day | 8 g/day | 45 g/day | Needed to build the hemoglobin of red blood cells |
| Sodium | 1.5 g/day | 1.5 g/day | 2.3 g/day (most people exceed this limit) | Needed for normal cell function |
| Vitamin A | 700 µg/day | 900 µg/day | 3,000 µg/day | Maintains skin and intestinal lining |
| Vitamin C | 75 mg/day | 90 mg/day | 2,000 mg/day | Maintains connective tissue and skin |
| Vitamin D | 5 µg/day | 5 µg/day | 50 µg/day | Needed to absorb calcium for bones |

generally means a plant material that is not sweet and is eaten during the main part of a meal. *Fruit,* on the other hand, is a botanical term for the structure produced from the female part of the flower that contains the seeds. Although botanically green beans, peas, and corn are all fruits, nutritionally speaking they are placed in the vegetable category, because they are generally eaten during the main

part of a meal. From a nutritional point of view, fruits include such sweet plant products as melons, berries, apples, oranges, and bananas. The Food Guide Pyramid recommends 1 to 2 cups of fruit per day, depending on age. Only about 25 percent of the U. S. population consumes the minimum recommended amount of fruit. However, because fruits tend to be high in natural sugars, the consumption of large

**FIGURE 25.7  The Food Guide Pyramid**

The Food Guide Pyramid suggests that we eat certain amounts of five food groups while decreasing our intake of fats and sugars. This guide simplifies menu planning and helps us ensure that we get all the recommended amounts of basic nutrients. In order to be healthy, exercising on a regular basis is also essential.

**Fruits group**

amounts of fruits can add a significant number of Calories to the diet. In addition to cellulose in the cell walls, fruits contain many other kinds of indigestible complex carbohydrates that are important as dietary fiber.

Significant nutritional components of fruits are carbohydrate (sugars), dietary fiber, water, minerals such a potassium, and vitamin C.

## Vegetables

Vegetables include nonsweet plant materials, such as broccoli, carrots, cabbage, corn, green beans, tomatoes, potatoes, lettuce,

**Vegetables group**

and spinach. The Food Guide Pyramid suggests 4 1/2 cups be eaten from this group each day for those who need 2,000 calories to maintain their weight and health. A cup is considered 1 cup of raw, leafy vegetables or 1/2 cup of other types. There is increasing evidence that cabbage, broccoli, and cauliflower can provide some protection from certain types of cancers. This is a good reason to include these foods in your diet. National studies indicate that most Americans do not consume at least the minimum recommended quantities of vegetables for their age and sex.

Vegetables are the primary source of many vitamins. Because different vegetables contain different kinds and amounts of vitamins, you should include many different kinds in your diet. In particular you should include some from each of the following kinds: leafy, dark green vegetables (lettuce, kale, "greens," spinach, chard, etc.); orange vegetables (carrots, squash, sweet potatoes, pumpkin, yams, etc.); dry beans or peas; starchy vegetables (potatoes, green peas, lima beans, corn, etc.); other kinds of vegetables (cucumbers, celery, tomatoes, green beans, turnips, cabbage, egg plant, etc.). Vegetables—particularly those that are eaten raw—provide dietary fiber, which assists in the proper functioning of the digestive tract.

Significant nutritional components of vegetables are carbohydrate; fiber; several B vitamins; vitamins A, C, E, and K; and the minerals potassium, iron, and magnesium.

## Milk

All of the cheeses, ice cream, yogurt, and milk are in this group. Two to 3 cups, depending on age, are recommended each day. One and one-half ounces of hard cheese is equivalent to a cup.

Product labels state the appropriate serving size of individual items. Vitamin D–fortified dairy products are the primary dietary source of vitamin D. Remember that many cheeses contain large amounts of cholesterol and fat per serving. Low-fat

**Dairy group**

dairy products are now recommended in the pyramid and are becoming increasingly common as manufacturers seek to match their products with the public's desire for less fat in the diet.

Significant nutritional components of milk are protein, carbohydrate, fat, several B vitamins, vitamin D, and the minerals calcium and potassium. Some milk has vitamin A added.

## Meat and Beans

This group contains most of the things we eat as a source of protein—for example, beef, chicken, fish, nuts, beans, peas, tofu, and eggs. Recall that daily protein intake is essential, because protein is not stored in the body, as are fats and carbohydrates, and that the body cannot manufacture the 10 essential amino acids, so they must be included in the diet. Animal proteins are complete proteins. The Food

**Meat group**

Guide Pyramid recommends 5.5–6.5 oz of protein per day for young adults. This means that one small hamburger meets about half of your daily needs. Most people eat many times what they need.

Because many sources of protein also contain significant amounts of fat, and health recommendations suggest reducing our fat intake, more attention is being paid to the quantity of the protein-rich foods in the diet. Beans (except for the oil-rich soybean) are excellent sources of protein without unwanted fat. Food selection and preparation are also important in reducing fat consumption. Selecting foods that have less fat, broiling rather than frying, and removing the fat before cooking all reduce fat in the diet. For example, most of the fat in chicken and turkey is attached to the skin, so removing the skin removes most of the fat.

Since the body cannot store protein, any protein consumed above what is needed to replace lost proteins is metabolized to provide energy. Eating excessive amounts of protein, however, can stress the kidneys by causing higher concentrations of calcium in the urine, can increase the demand for water to remove toxic keto acids produced from the breakdown of amino acids, and can lead to weight gain because of the intake of fat normally associated with many sources of protein.

Vegetarians must pay particular attention to acquiring adequate sources of protein, because they have eliminated a major source from their diet. They can get all the essential amino acids if they eat proper combinations of plant materials. Although nuts and soybeans are high in protein, they should not be consumed in large quantities because they are also high in fats.

Significant nutritional components of this food group are protein, fat, several B vitamins, vitamin E from seeds and nuts, and the minerals iron, zinc, and magnesium. Fish in the diet provides essential fatty acids.

## Oils

The oils group includes canola, corn, olive, and sunflower oils, which are used in cooking. Some oils, such as olive, sesame, and walnut, are used to flavor foods. Small amounts of oils are important in the diet, because certain essential fatty acids cannot be manufactured by the body and must be obtained in the diet. However, because oils are fats, they have a high Caloric content. Most oils are high in monounsaturated or polyunsaturated fats and low in saturated fats. Plant oils do not contain cholesterol. Mayonnaise, some salad dressings, and soft margarine are almost entirely made of oils.

Oils group

The Food Guide Pyramid recommends that for an adult, total fat intake should be between 20 and 35% of total Calories consumed daily. Most fats should be polyunsaturated and monounsaturated fatty acids, from fish, nuts, and vegetable oils. For most people this is equivalent to about 6 to 7 teaspoons of oil per day. Other recommendations are that saturated fats, trans fats, and cholesterol be as low as possible. Saturated fats come from animals and include butter, beef fat (suet), chicken fat, and pork fat (lard). Saturated fats and cholesterol are associated with the consumption of animal products, so choosing lean meats and cooking to remove fat are important for reducing total fat consumption. Unsaturated fats can be made into saturated fats by adding hydrogen (hydrogenated). When this occurs, an oil (unsaturated fat) is converted to a saturated fat. When oils are hydrogenated some of the fats are converted to trans fats. Margarine and shortening are examples of hydrogenated oils.

A few plant oils, such as coconut and palm oil, are high in saturated fats and have health effects similar to those of saturated fats from animal sources.

Significant nutritional components of oils are Calories, essential fatty acids, and vitamin E.

## Exercise

Since over 65 percent of adult Americans are overweight and over 30 percent are obese, exercise is important to improving health. Therefore, exercise is included in the Food Guide Pyramid. Although it is not directly related to nutrition, the amount of exercise people get affects the number of Calories they can consume on a daily basis without gaining weight. Exercise has other health benefits as well. The pyramid recommends at least 30 minutes of moderate exercise per day; longer periods and more vigorous exercise have additional health benefits (Outlooks 25.1). Moderate exercise is that which elevates the heart rate significantly. Activities such as doing household chores or walking while shopping do not elevate heart rate and, therefore, do not count as moderate exercise. Moderate physical activities include walking briskly (about 3½ miles per hour), hiking, doing gardening/yard work, dancing, golf (walking and carrying clubs), bicycling (less than 10 miles per hour), and weight training (general light workout).

The Food Guide Pyramid includes a discussion of discretionary Calories. A basic plan for any nutritional program should be to match the Calories consumed with the Calories expended and thus maintain a desirable weight. People with very active lifestyles expend more Calories and, therefore, need to consume more Calories. These Calories can come from any of the food groups simply by eating more. Extremely active persons need to add concentrated sources of carbohydrates and fats to their diet. However, these fats should still be unsaturated fats. Table 25.5 lists the Calories required for persons involved in various activities.

### 25.4 CONCEPT REVIEW

7. Name the six basic food groups and give two examples of each.
8. Why has exercise been included in the Food Guide Pyramid?

## 25.5 Determining Energy Needs

Significant energy expenditure is required for muscular activity. However, even when the body is at rest, energy is required to maintain breathing, heart rate, and other normal body functions. The **basal metabolic rate (BMR)** is the rate at which the body uses energy when it is at rest. The basal metabolic rate of most people requires more energy than their voluntary muscular activity. Much of this energy is used to keep the body temperature constant. A true measurement of basal metabolic rate requires a measurement of oxygen used over a specific period under controlled conditions.

# OUTLOOKS 25.1

## Exercise: More than Just Maintaining Your Weight

The Food Guide Pyramid recommends 30 minutes of moderate exercise above normal daily activities. This might be a brisk walk at 3.5 miles/hour, golfing, bicycling (10 miles/hour), and hiking. Workouts such as weight lifting—or riding a cart while golfing—do not fall into this category. In addition to planned exercise, there are other ways to be active—such as taking the stairs instead of the elevator or escalator, parking at the far end of the lot when shopping, walking to the corner store instead of driving, or cutting the grass with a push mower instead of a riding mower.

When most people talk about exercise, they often focus on weight control. However, research in many diverse areas has revealed benefits that influence many aspects of a person's health. In addition to helping control weight, exercise:

- Increases the strength of muscles and general muscle tone
- Reduces the likelihood of injuries because of improved strength and balance
- Strengthens bones and joints; bones respond to the stress placed on them by exercise by adding bone mass
- Improves flexibility
- Increases efficiency of the respiratory system
- Increases the efficiency of aerobic respiration in mitochondria
- Heightens the immune response to better protect against infection
- Increases endorphins in the brain to reduce pain threshold and increase pleasure sensation
- Improves self-esteem and feelings of well-being
- Reduces feelings of depression and anxiety
- Helps control diabetes
- Strengthens heart muscle
- Improves cardiovascular health
- Lowers serum cholesterol
- Lowers blood pressure
- Improves sex life

---

**TABLE 25.5   Typical Energy Requirements for Common Activities**

| Light Activities (120–150 Calories/hr) | Light to Moderate Activities (150–300 Calories/hr) | Moderate Activities (300–400 Calories/hr) | Heavy Activities (420–600 Calories/hr) |
|---|---|---|---|
| Dressing | Sweeping floors | Pulling weeds | Chopping wood |
| Typing | Painting | Walking behind a lawnmower | Shoveling snow |
| Slow walking | Walking 2–3 mi/hr | Walking 3.5–4 mi/hr on a level surface | Walking or jogging 5 mi/hr |
| Standing | Bowling | Golf (no cart) | Walking up hills |
| Studying | Store clerking | Doubles tennis | Cross-country skiing |
| Sitting activities | Canoeing 2.5–3 mi/hr | Canoeing 4 mi/hr | Swimming |
| | Bicycling on a level surface at 5.5 mi/hr | Volleyball | Bicycling 11–12 mi/hr or up and down hills |

---

Several factors affect an individual's basal metabolic rate, including age, gender, height, weight, and fundamental differences in metabolism. Basal metabolic rates decline throughout life. Children have high basal metabolic rates and elderly people have low basal metabolic rates. In general, men have higher metabolic rates than women. The larger a person, the higher his or her metabolic rate. With all of these factors taken into account, most young adults fall into the range of 1,200 to 2,200 Calories per day for a basal metabolic rate.

Because few of us rest 24 hours a day, we normally require more than the energy needed for basal metabolism. One of these requirements is **specific dynamic action (SDA),** the amount of energy needed to process the food we eat. It is equal to approximately 10% of the total daily Caloric intake.

In addition to basal metabolic rate and specific dynamic action, the activity level of a person determines the number of Calories needed. This is known as voluntary muscular activity. A good general indicator of the number of Calories needed above

**TABLE 25.6   Additional Calories as Determined by Occupation**

| Occupation | Calories Needed per Day Above Basal Metabolic Rate* |
|---|---|
| Sedentary (student) | 500–700 |
| Light work (businessperson) | 750–1,200 |
| Moderate work (laborer) | 1,250–1,500 |
| Heavy work (professional athlete) | 1,550–5,000 and up |

*These are general figures and will vary from person to person, depending on the specific activities performed in the job.

basal metabolic rate is the type of occupation a person has (table 25.6). Because most adults are relatively sedentary, they would receive adequate amounts of energy if women consumed 2,200 Calories and men consumed 2,900 Calories per day.

## 25.5   CONCEPT REVIEW

9. Define the terms *basal metabolic rate, specific dynamic action,* and *voluntary muscular activity.*

## 25.6   Eating Disorders

The three most common health problems related to diet and patterns of food consumption are obesity, bulimia, and anorexia nervosa. All three disorders involve behaviors that lead to ill health. The causes of these behaviors are complex and often involve a strong psychological component. Metabolic imbalances may also contribute to the development of these disorders, particularly obesity. Culture has a strong influence on our perceptions of ourselves and influences our behavior. Some studies have shown that there is a tendency for members of a family to develop the same kinds of eating disorders. Therefore, it has been suggested that genetic factors influence the risk of developing eating disorders. On the other hand, members of the same family also are likely to develop patterns of eating related to culture and other factors. Eating disorders are often associated with psychological depression.

### Obesity

**Obesity** is the condition of being overweight to the extent that a person's health, quality of life, and life span are adversely affected (figure 25.8). Obesity occurs when people consistently take in more food energy than is necessary to meet their daily requirements. About 30% of the U.S. population is considered to be obese, based on their having a body mass index above 30 kg/m². An obese person has a significantly increased risk for many diseases. In general, the higher the body mass index, the more significant the risk.

**FIGURE 25.8   Obesity**
Obesity is a serious health problem for about 30% of North Americans.

### Determining Body Mass Index (BMI)

**Body mass index (BMI)** is a measure of body weight compared with height. BMI is calculated by determining a person's weight (without clothing) in kilograms and their barefoot height in meters. The BMI is the weight in kilograms divided by height in meters squared:

$$\text{BMI} = \frac{\text{weight in kilograms}}{(\text{height in meters})^2}$$

(Appendix 1 of this book gives conversions to the metric system of measurements.) For example, a person with a height of 5 feet 6 inches (1.68 meters) who weighs 165 pounds (75 kilograms) has a body mass index of 26.6 kg/m²:

$$\text{BMI} = \frac{\text{kg}}{\text{m}^2} = \frac{75 \text{ kg}}{(1.68 \text{ m})^2} = \frac{75 \text{ kg}}{2.82 \text{ m}^2} = 26.6 \text{ kg/m}^2$$

A person with a body mass index of less than 18.5 kg/m² is considered to be underweight. A body mass index between 18.5 and 25 kg/m² is considered a healthy weight; between 25 and 30 kg/m² overweight; and over 30 kg/m² is considered obese. Figure 25.9 allows you to determine what weight category you are in.

### Contributing Causes to Obesity

While all obese people have an imbalance between their food intake and their energy expenditure, the reasons for this imbalance are complex and varied. It appears that for most people, the imbalance is related to culture and lifestyle, although for some there are underlying biological reasons as well.

1. *Cultural Influences* Our culture encourages food consumption. Social occasions and business meetings frequently involve eating. It is clear that these and other cultural factors have much to do with the incidence of

**Height without shoes**

6′ 6″
6′ 5″
6′ 4″
6′ 3″
6′ 2″
6′ 1″
6′ 0″
5′ 11″
5′ 10″
5′ 9″
5′ 8″
5′ 7″
5′ 6″
5′ 5″
5′ 4″
5′ 3″
5′ 2″
5′ 1″
5′ 0″
4′ 11″
4′ 10″

BMI = 18.5   BMI = 25   BMI = 30

UNDER WEIGHT   HEALTHY WEIGHT   OVERWEIGHT   OBESE

50   75   100   125   150   175   200   225   250
**Pounds without clothes**

**FIGURE 25.9 Body Mass Index**
This graph allows you to determine which body mass index category you fall into.

obesity. For example, obesity rates have increased over time, which strongly suggests that most cases of obesity are due to changes in lifestyle, not inherent biological factors. Furthermore, immigrants from countries with low rates of obesity show increased rates of obesity when they integrate into the American culture.

*Snack foods* are an important cultural influence. Snack foods typically have high amounts of sugars and fats. Consumption of these foods at other than meal times increases the total number of Calories consumed during the day. Furthermore, many of these foods are said to provide "empty Calories"—Calories are provided by sugar or fat but there is little or no other nutritional benefit (protein, vitamins, minerals, or fiber).

*Restaurants* play a role. Less than half the meals consumed in the United States are prepared in the home. This means that the consumer has reduced choices in the kind of food available, no control over the way foods are prepared, and little control over serving size. Meals prepared in restaurants and fast-food outlets emphasize meat and minimize the fruit, vegetable, and cereal portions, in direct contradiction to the Food Guide Pyramid. The methods of preparation also typically involve cooking with oils and serving with dressings or fat-containing condiments. In addition, portion sizes are generally much larger than recommended. Furthermore, restaurants and other food preparers have increased the size of portions significantly over the past 50 years. For example, in the 1950s, a fast-food serving of French fries was 2.4 ounces. Today, that size is still available, but it is the small size, and medium and large sizes contain two to three times the quantity of the small size.

*An inactive lifestyle* contributes to the incidence of obesity. Often, exercise is all that is needed to control a weight problem. In addition to increasing metabolism during the exercise itself, exercise tends to raise the basal metabolic rate for a period of time following exercise.

2. *Psychological Factors* Overeating is associated with a variety of psychological factors. Eating is a pleasurable activity and, as with all pleasurable activities, it is sometimes difficult to determine when to stop. Conversely, overeating also is often associated with depression.

3. *Genetic and Metabolic Differences* Recent discoveries of genes in mice suggest that there are genetic components that contribute to obesity. In one study, mice without a crucial gene gained an extraordinary amount of weight. There may be similar genes in humans. It is also clear that some people have much lower metabolic rates than most of the population and, therefore, need much less food than is typical. Still other obese individuals have a chemical imbalance of the nervous system that prevents them from feeling "full" until they have eaten an excessive amount of food. This imbalance prevents the brain from turning off the desire to eat. Research into the nature and action of this brain chemical indicates that, if obese people lacking this chemical receive it in pill form, they can feel "full" even when their food intake is decreased by 25% (Outlooks 25.2).

## Dealing with Obesity

Weight control is a matter of balancing the Calories ingested with the Calories expended by normal daily activities and exercise. The Food Guide Pyramid is clearly designed to provide information that will aid people in maintaining an appropriate weight.

*Medical advice* is important in dealing with obesity. Although it is likely that most cases of obesity do not involve underlying medical causes, it is wise to rule out that possibility before beginning a program to deal with obesity. Health practitioners are changing their view of obesity from one of blaming the obese person for lack of self-control to one of treating the condition as a chronic disease that requires a varied approach to control. For most people, dietary counseling and increased exercise are all that is needed, but some need psychological counseling, drug therapy, or surgery. Regardless, controlling obesity can be very difficult because it requires basic changes in a person's eating habits, lifestyle, and value system.

*Diet plans* provide many different approaches to managing one's diet to maintain an appropriate weight. Not all of these plans are the same, and not all are suitable to a particular situation. Some of these are based on solid nutritional and biological research while others are not. If a diet plan is to be valuable in promoting good health, it must satisfy a person's needs in several ways. It must provide Calories and the nutrients important to good health. It should also contain readily available foods from all the basic food groups, and it should provide enough variety to prevent the person from becoming bored. In the final analysis, it should change how he or she eats.

# OUTLOOKS 25.2

## The Genetic Basis of Obesity

Advances have been made in identifying the genetic and biochemical factors that regulate body weight. While not yet fully understood, a person's ability to regulate food intake and control body weight is at least partly controlled by the actions of several genes.

The molecules produced by these genes are messengers that control the flow of information between the stomach and nerve cells in a portion of the brain called the *hypothalamus*. This flow of information controls the appetite—whether one is hungry or not depends on how these cells are stimulated. Several molecules are involved in this control:

1. *Leptin* is a hormone produced by white fat tissue; it is the product of the *ob* gene (formerly called the "obesity" gene). Leptin acts on nerve cells in the brain to regulate food intake. The *absence* of leptin causes severe obesity; the presence of leptin suppresses the appetite center of the brain. As a person's weight increases, the additional fat cells increase the production of leptin. In animals, the increase in leptin signals the brain to send signals that cause the animal to eat less and the body to do more. In humans, however, this does not appear to be the case, because many obese people have high levels of leptin and no suppression of appetite.

2. *Neuropeptide Y (NPY)* is a small protein that increases appetite. Leptin's appetite-suppressing effects may be due to the fact that leptin can inhibit NPY.

3. *Alpha-melanocyte-stimulating hormone (α-MSH)*, which also increases production of the brown pigmentation of the skin, suppresses the appetite by acting on the hypothalamus. Leptin is believed to stimulate the production of α-MSH, which suppresses the appetite.

4. *Melanin-concentrating hormone (MCH)* is another neuropeptide. High levels of MCH in the brain increase food consumption and low levels decrease food consumption. Some believe that the smell of food may stimulate the production of MCH and enhance appetite. The gene for MCH is significantly more active in the brains of the obese.

5. *Ghrelin* is a growth hormone peptide secreted by the stomach. It has the opposite effect of leptin—it appears to be a powerful appetite stimulant.

---

Fad diets promise large, rapid weight loss but, in fact, may result only in temporary water loss. They may encourage eating and drinking foods that are diuretics, which increase the amount of urine produced and thus increase water loss. Or they may encourage exercise or other activities that cause people to lose water through sweating. Or they may simply encourage people to eat less for a period of time, which results in a temporary weight loss because there is less food in the gut.

*Exercise* should be a part of any program dealing with obesity. The health risks associated with being overweight or obese can be lessened by increasing one's *fitness*. **Fitness** is a measure of how efficiently a person can function both physically and mentally. A person with a BMI of 30 kg/m² may be more fit than someone with a BMI of 23 kg/m² if he or she is involved in a regular program of physical and mental exercise. As fitness increases, so does metabolism, strength, mental acuity, and coordination. The use of body mass index to assess healthy weights is based on the assumption that excess weight is the result of fat tissue. In most cases this is true. However, since muscle is more dense than fat, very muscular people may have a high BMI and fall into the overweight or obese category when, in fact, they may not be.

An exercise program can involve organized exercise in sports or fitness programs. It can also include simple lifestyle changes, such as walking up stairs rather than taking an elevator, parking at the back of the parking lot so you walk farther, riding a bike for short errands, and walking down the hall to someone's office rather than using the phone or e-mail.

Many people who initiate exercise plans as a way of reducing weight are frustrated because they initially gain weight rather than lose it. This is because a given volume of muscle weighs more than fat. Typically, they are "out of shape" and have low muscle mass. If they gain a pound of muscle at the same time they lose a pound of fat, they do not lose weight. However, if the fitness program continues, they will eventually stop increasing muscle mass and will lose weight. Even so, weight as muscle is more healthy than weight as fat.

## Bulimia

**Bulimia** ("hunger of an ox") is a disease condition in which the person engages in a cycle of eating binges followed by fasting or purging the body of the food by inducing vomiting or using laxatives (figure 25.10). The following are behaviors typically shown by bulimics:

- Excessive preoccupation with body image
- Excessive preoccupation with exercise
- Going to the bathroom after meals (to vomit)
- Hiding the fact that they are eating
- The use of laxatives or diuretics
- Irregular eating habits

Many bulimics also use diuretics, which cause the body to lose water, resulting in the loss of weight. A bulimic person may induce vomiting physically or by using nonprescription drugs. Case studies have shown that some bulimics take 40 to 60 laxatives a day to rid themselves of food. For some, the laxatives become addictive.

Bulimics are usually of normal body weight or are overweight. Although women are more likely than men to become bulimic, there has been an increasing number of men with this disorder. The cause is thought to be psychological, stemming from depression or other psychological problems.

The binge-purge cycle and the associated use of diuretics and laxatives result in a variety of symptoms that can be deadly. It is often called the silent killer because it is difficult to detect. The following is a list of the major health problems observed in many bulimics:

- Excessive water loss
- Diminished blood volume

- Extreme mineral deficiencies
- Kidney malfunction
- Increased heart rate
- Loss of rhythmic heartbeat
- Lethargy
- Diarrhea
- Severe stomach cramps
- Damage to teeth and gums
- Loss of body proteins
- Migraine headaches
- Fainting spells

## Anorexia Nervosa

**Anorexia nervosa** (figure 25.11) is a nutritional deficiency disease characterized by severe, prolonged weight loss as a result of a voluntary severe restriction in food intake. It is most common among adolescent and preadolescent women. An anorexic person's fear of becoming overweight is so intense that, even though weight loss occurs, it does not lessen the fear of obesity, and the person continues to diet, even refusing to maintain the optimum body weight for his or her age, sex, and height. Persons who have this disorder have a distorted perception of their bodies. They see themselves as fat when, in fact, they are starving to death. Society's preoccupation with body image, particularly

**FIGURE 25.11 Anorexia Nervosa**
Anorexia nervosa is a psychological eating disorder afflicting many Americans. These photographs were taken of an individual before and after treatment. Restoring a person with this disorder requires both medical and psychological efforts.

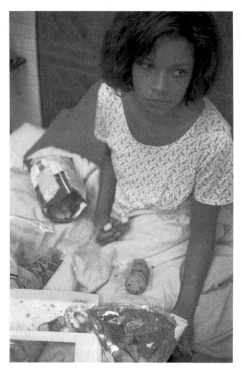

**FIGURE 25.10 Bulimia**
Persons with bulimia go on eating binges followed by fasting or activities to get rid of food such as inducing vomiting, using laxatives, or using diuretics.

## OUTLOOKS 25.3

# Muscle Dysmorphia

A cousin to anorexia, *muscle dysmorphia* is an obsession with being muscular. Commonly called "big-orexia," it has been an under-diagnosed condition because, for men, being big is acceptable. Their muscles may be sculptured and bulging, yet no amount of persuasion can convince them their body is big enough. Those with this condition feel they are the objects of hate, resentment, fear, and loathing, and therefore must

continue to "bulk up." To accomplish this, they exercise to the extreme and take anabolic steroids. Long-term use of these steroids, whether injectable or tablet form, can result in damage to the liver, heart, and muscles; raised cholesterol levels; mood swings; acne; enlarged breasts; and "'roid-rage." The common misconception about these steroids is that, when properly taken, they are safe. They are not.

---

among young people, may contribute to the incidence of this disease. Outlooks 25.3 describes an additional example of a problem with distorted body image. The following are some of the symptoms of anorexia nervosa:

Thin, dry, brittle hair
Degradation of fingernails
Constipation
Amenorrhea (lack of menstrual periods)
Decreased heart rate
Loss of body proteins
Weaker than normal heartbeat
Calcium deficiency
Osteoporosis
Hypothermia (low body temperature)
Hypotension (low blood pressure)
Increased skin pigmentation
Reduction in the size of the uterus
Inflammatory bowel disease
Slowed reflexes
Fainting
Weakened muscles

### 25.6  CONCEPT REVIEW

10.  What is BMI? How is it calculated?
11.  What are the three primary eating disorders?
12.  What is the role of leptin in controlling appetite?

### 25.7  Nutrition Through the Life Cycle

Nutritional needs vary throughout life and are related to many factors, including age, sex, reproductive status, and level of physical activity. Infants, children, adolescents, adults, and the elderly all require essentially the same types of nutrients but have special nutritional needs related to their stage of life, requiring slight adjustments in the kinds and amounts of nutrients they consume.

## Infancy

A person's total energy requirements per kilogram are highest during the first 12 months of life: 100 Calories per kilogram of body weight per day; 50% of this energy is required for an infant's basal metabolic rate. Infants triple their weight and increase their length by 50% during their first year; this is their so-called first growth spurt. Because they are growing so rapidly, they require food that contains adequate proteins, vitamins, minerals, and water. They also need food that is high in Calories. For many reasons, the food that most easily meets these needs is human breast milk (table 25.7). Even with breast milk's many nutrients, many physicians strongly recommend multivitamin supplements as part of an infant's diet.

Studies have shown that kids under the age of 2 are "self regulating" when it comes to food intake. They eat only the amount they need. However, as they enter childhood, other factors begin to affect diet and they are likely to follow the eating patterns of their family.

## Childhood

As infants reach childhood, their dietary needs change. The rate of growth generally slows between 1 year of age and puberty, and girls increase in height and weight slightly faster than boys.

**First growth spurt**

**TABLE 25.7**  Comparison of Human Breast Milk and Cow's Milk*

| Nutrient | Human Milk | Cow's Milk (whole milk) |
|---|---|---|
| Energy (Calories/1,000 grams) | 690 | 660 |
| Protein (grams per liter) | 9 | 35 |
| Fat (grams per liter) | 40 | 38 |
| Lactose (grams per liter) | 68 | 49 |
| **Vitamins** | | |
| A (international units) | 1,898 | 1,025 |
| C (micrograms) | 44 | 17 |
| D (activity units) | 40 | 14 |
| E (international units) | 3.2 | 0.4 |
| K (micrograms) | 34 | 170 |
| Thiamin ($B_1$) (micrograms) | 150 | 370 |
| Riboflavin ($B_2$) (micrograms) | 380 | 1,700 |
| Niacin ($B_3$) (milligrams) | 1.7 | 0.9 |
| Pyridoxine ($B_6$) (micrograms) | 130 | 460 |
| Cobalamin ($B_{12}$) (micrograms) | 0.5 | 4 |
| Folic acid (micrograms) | 41–84.66 | 2.9–68 |
| **Minerals (All in Milligrams)** | | |
| Calcium | 241–340 | 1,200 |
| Phosphorus | 150 | 920 |
| Sodium | 160 | 560 |
| Potassium | 530 | 1,570 |
| Iron | 0.3–0.56 | 0.5 |
| Iodine | 200 | 80 |

*All milks are not alike. Each milk is unique to the species that produces it for its young, and each infant has its own growth rate. Humans have one of the slowest infant growth rates, and human milk contains the least amount of protein. Because cow's milk is so different, many pediatricians recommend that human infants be fed either human breast milk or formulas developed to be comparable to breast milk during the first 12 months of life. The use of cow's milk is discouraged. This table lists the relative amounts of the nutrients in human breast milk and cow's milk.

During childhood, the body becomes leaner and the bones elongate; the brain reaches 100% of its adult size between the ages of 6 and 10. To meet children's growth and energy needs adequately, protein intake should be high enough to take care of the development of new tissues. Minerals, such as calcium, zinc, and iron, as well as vitamins, are necessary to support growth and prevent anemia. Many parents continue to give their children multivitamin supplements, but this should be done only after a careful evaluation of their children's diets. Three groups of children are at risk for vitamin deficiency and should receive such supplements:

1. Children from deprived families and those suffering from neglect or abuse

2. Children who have anorexia nervosa or poor eating habits or who are obese
3. Children who are strict vegetarians

During childhood, eating habits are very erratic and often cause parental concern. Children often limit their intake of milk, meat, and vegetables while increasing their intake of sweets. To get around these problems, parents can provide calcium by serving cheeses, yogurt, and soups as alternatives to milk. Meats can be made more acceptable if they are in easy-to-chew, bite-sized pieces, and vegetables might be more readily accepted if smaller portions are offered on a more frequent basis. Steering children away from high-fat foods (e.g., french fries, potato chips) and sugar (e.g., cookies, soft drinks) by offering healthy alternatives can lower their risk for potential health problems. For example, sweets in the form of fruits can help reduce dental caries (*carrion* = rotten). Parents can better meet the dietary needs of children by making food available on a more frequent basis, such as every 3 to 4 hours. Obesity is an increasing problem among children. Parents sometimes encourage this by insisting that children eat everything served to them. Before the age of 2, most children automatically regulate the food they eat to an appropriate amount. After that age, parents should be concerned about both the kinds and the amounts of food children eat.

## Adolescence

The nutrition of an adolescent is extremely important because, during this period, the body changes from nonreproductive to reproductive. Puberty is usually considered to last between 5 and 7 years. Before puberty, males and females have similar proportions of body fat and muscle. Both body fat and muscle make up between 15% and 19% of the body's weight. Lean body mass, primarily muscle, is about equal in males and females. During puberty, female body fat increases to about 23%, and in males it decreases to about 12%. Males double their muscle mass in comparison with females. The changes in body form that take place during puberty constitute the second growth spurt. Because of their more rapid rate of growth and unique growth patterns, males require more of certain nutrients than females (protein, vitamin A, magnesium, and zinc). During adolescence, youngsters gain as much as 20% of their adult height and 50% of their adult weight, and many body organs double in size. Nutritionists have taken these growth patterns and spurts into account by establishing Dietary Reference Intakes for males and females 10 to 20 years old, including requirements at the peaks of growth spurts. Dietary Reference Intakes at the peak of the growth spurt are much higher than they are for adults and children.

## Adulthood

People who have completed the changes associated with adolescence are considered to have entered adulthood. During adulthood, the body enters a plateau phase, and diet and nutrition focus on maintenance and disease prevention. Nutrients are used primarily for tissue replacement and repair, and changes such as weight loss occur slowly. Because the BMR slows, as does physical activity, the need for food energy decreases from about 2,900 Calories in average young adult males (ages 20 to 40) to about 2,300 for elderly men. For women, the corresponding numbers decrease from 2,200 to 1,900 Calories. Protein intake for most U.S. citizens is usually in excess of the recommended amount. The Dietary Reference Intakes standard for protein is about 56 grams for men and 46 grams for women each day. About 25–50% should come from animal foods to ensure intake of the essential amino acids. The rest should be from plant-protein foods, such as whole grains, legumes, nuts, and vegetables.

## Old Age

As people move into their sixties and seventies, the digestion and absorption of all nutrients through the intestinal tract slows down. The number of cells undergoing mitosis is reduced, resulting in an overall loss in the number of body cells. With age, complex organs, such as the kidneys and brain, function less efficiently, and protein synthesis becomes

inefficient. With regard to nutrition, energy requirements for the elderly decrease as the BMR slows, physical activity decreases, and eating habits change.

The change in eating habits is significant, because it can result in dietary deficiencies. For example, linoleic acid, an essential fatty acid, may fall below required levels as an older person reduces the amount of food he or she eats. The same is true for some vitamins and minerals. Therefore, it may be necessary to supplement the diet daily with 1 tablespoon of vegetable oil. Vitamin E, multiple vitamins, or a mineral supplement may also be necessary. The loss of body protein means that people must be certain to meet their daily Dietary Reference Intakes for protein and participate in regular exercise to prevent muscle loss. As with all stages of the life cycle, regular exercise is important in maintaining a healthy, efficiently functioning body.

The two minerals that demand special attention are calcium and iron, especially for women. A daily intake of 1,200 milligrams of calcium should prevent calcium loss from bones (figure 25.12), and a daily intake of 15 milligrams of iron should allow adequate amounts of hemoglobin to be manufactured to prevent anemia in women over 50 and men over 60. In order to reduce the risk for chronic

**(a) Normal bone**

**(b) Osteoporosis**

**(c) Bone breaks occur with osteoporosis**

**FIGURE 25.12 Osteoporosis**
*(a)* Healthy bone and *(b)* a section of bone from a person with osteoporosis. This calcium-deficiency disease results in a change in the density of the bones as a result of the loss of bone mass. Bones that have undergone this change look "lacy" or like Swiss cheese, with larger than normal holes. *(c)* A few risk factors associated with this disease are being female and fair-skinned; having a sedentary lifestyle; using alcohol, caffeine, and tobacco; and having reached menopause.

diseases such as heart attack and stroke, adults should eat a balanced diet, participate in regular exercise programs, control their weight, avoid tobacco and alcohol, and practice stress management.

## Pregnancy and Lactation

The period of pregnancy and milk production (lactation) requires that special attention be paid to the diet to ensure proper fetal development, a safe delivery, and a healthy milk supply. Studies have shown that an inadequate supply of essential nutrients can result in infertility, spontaneous abortion, and abnormal fetal development.

The daily amount of essential nutrients must be increased, as should Caloric intake. Calories must be increased by 300 per day to meet the needs of an increased BMR; the development of the uterus, breasts, and placenta; and the work required for fetal growth. Some of these Calories can be obtained by drinking milk, which simultaneously supplies the calcium needed for fetal bone development. Women who cannot tolerate milk should consume supplementary sources of calcium. In addition, their protein intake should be at least 71 grams per day; however, as mentioned earlier, most people in developed countries consume much more than this per day. Two essential nutrients, folic acid and iron, should be obtained through prenatal supplements, because they are essential to cell division and the development of the fetal blood supply.

The mother's nutritional status affects the developing baby in several ways (figure 25.13). If she is under 15 years of age or has had three or more pregnancies in a 2-year period, her nutritional stores are inadequate to support a successful pregnancy. The use of drugs, such as alcohol, caffeine, nicotine, and "hard" drugs (e.g., heroin), can result in decreased nutrient exchange between the mother and fetus. In particular, heavy smoking can result in low birth weight, and alcohol abuse is responsible for *fetal alcohol syndrome (FAS)*. Children with FAS may show the characteristics such as: small size for their age, facial abnormalities, poor coordination, hyperactive behavior; learning disabilities; developmental disabilities (e.g., speech and language delays); mental retardation or low IQ.

**FIGURE 25.13  Diet Is Important During Pregnancy**
During pregnancy diet is extremely important. Whatever the mother eats can influence the development of the embryo. A healthy diet assures that the embryo will get the nutrients it needs. The use of drugs and alcohol during pregnancy can have severe effects on the developing embryo.

---

| 25.7 | CONCEPT REVIEW |
|------|----------------|

13. During which phase of the life cycle is a person's demand for Calories per unit of body weight the highest?
14. What changes need to be made to the diet of the elderly?
15. What changes should be made in the diet of pregnant and nursing mothers?

---

## 25.8  Nutrition for Fitness and Sports

Many people are very interested in the value of fitness and sports to a healthy lifestyle. Along with this, an interest has developed in the role nutrition plays in providing fuel for activities, controlling weight, and building muscle. The cellular respiration process described in chapter 6 is the source of the energy needed to take a leisurely walk or run a marathon. However, the specific molecules used to get energy depend on the length of the period of exercise, whether or not one warms up before exercise, and how much effort one exerts during exercise. The molecules respired by muscle cells to produce ATP may be glucose, fatty acids, or amino acids. Glucose is stored as glycogen in the muscles, liver, and some other organs. Fatty acids are stored as triglycerides in fat cells. Amino acids are found in small amounts in the blood. Which molecules are respired depends on the duration and intensity of exercise. Glucose from glycogen and fatty acids from triglycerides are typically the primary fuels. Amino acids provide 10% or less of a person's energy needs, even in highly trained athletes.

*Conditioning* includes many interrelated body adjustments in addition to energy considerations. Training increases the strength of muscles, including the heart, and increases the efficiency of their operation. Practicing a movement allows for the development of a smooth action, which is more energy-efficient than a poorly trained motion. As the body is conditioned, the number of mitochondria per cell increases, the Krebs cycle and the ETS run more efficiently, the number of capillaries increases, fats are respired more efficiently and for longer periods, and weight control becomes easier.

## Anaerobic and Aerobic Exercise

**Anaerobic exercise** involves bouts of exercise that are so intense that the muscles cannot get oxygen as fast as they need it; therefore, they must rely on the anaerobic respiration of glucose to provide the energy needed. Activities such as weight-lifting or running short sprints are almost entirely anaerobic. During anaerobic respiration lactic acid builds up in muscles. The lactic acid is eventually transferred to the blood and delivered to the liver where it is metabolized. Following a bout of anaerobic exercise, one breathes rapidly for a period until the lactic acid is metabolized.

**Aerobic exercise** occurs when the level of exertion allows the heart and lungs to keep up with the oxygen needs of the muscles (figure 25.14).

## Metabolic Changes During Aerobic Exercise

Most exercise programs encourage participants to do warm-up activities before beginning strenuous exercise. These activities serve several purposes. A primary function is to increase heart rate, which has several benefits. Blood is pumped more rapidly, resulting in more blood reaching the muscles. In addition, the capillaries in the muscles dilate so that more blood is able to flow through muscles. Finally, the warm-up exercise actually increases the temperature of the muscles, which makes them less stiff and also reduces the viscosity ("thickness") of the blood. All of these actions are important because they increase the flow of blood to muscles and allow the blood to supply oxygen efficiently to the muscles and increase the speed and power of muscular contraction. These activities also lead to an increased speed of nerve conduction and provide a psychological benefit to the athlete. Finally, the warm-up activities begin a metabolic shift toward breaking down glycogen in muscle to provide the energy for muscular activity.

The body goes through several metabolic changes during aerobic exercise. For a short time at the beginning of exercise, anaerobic respiration provides the energy muscles need. As exercise continues, the body shifts to aerobic respiration as the circulatory system and respiratory system make adjustments to be able to supply oxygen to the muscles as fast as it is used. This metabolic shift is often experienced as a "second wind." The athlete experiences a period of "shortness of breath" at the beginning of exercise that disappears with the switch to aerobic respiration. This is particularly true if he or she did no warm-up activities.

There are shifts even after the body has switched to aerobic exercise. Initially the energy supplied to muscles comes from glycogen stored in the muscles. As the period of activity increases, there is another metabolic shift in which fats (triglycerides) begin to be metabolized. Fatty acids released into the blood from fat cells begin to be used to provide some of the energy. (A small amount of protein is also metabolized, particularly if the exercise is of long duration.) At this point both glycogen and fats are being used to supply energy. The balance between glycogen and fat metabolism shifts toward fat metabolism the longer the exercise continues. This is why moderate, longer periods of exercise are most beneficial in weight loss. Eventually, if the exercise continues for long enough, the body's store of glycogen is exhausted and the athlete experiences a debilitating fatigue known as "hitting the wall." This occurs because glucose is not available in high enough quantities.

After a period of exercise it is recommended that people engage in cool-down activities that allow the body to return slowly to a resting state. These activities generally involve 5 to 10 minutes of jogging or walking accompanied by stretching exercises. This allows lactic acid and other metabolic waste products to be removed from muscles and metabolized or eliminated. The muscles involved in exercise had been receiving large amounts of blood, so they also need to return to a resting state. This involves reducing blood flow to the muscles and actually using the muscle contractions of the cool-down activities to squeeze veins to assist in the return of blood from the muscles. There is also a metabolic shift back to one that is less demanding of glycogen.

## Diet and Exercise

Diet is an important adjunct to any exercise program. During exercise a primary concern is to take in adequate amounts of water. Water is important for two reasons: (1) Evaporation of water is a primary mechanism for preventing overheating of the body during exercise; and (2) loss of water during exercise also causes the viscosity of the blood to increase and makes the heart work harder to pump the "thicker" blood. A water loss of only 5% of body weight can decrease muscular activity by as much as 30%. Drinking tap water is the best way for most casual athletes to replace the water they lose. Sports drinks that contain salts

**Anaerobic Exercise**

**Aerobic Exercise**

**FIGURE 25.14 Anaerobic and Aerobic Exercise**
Sprinters are involved in anaerobic exercise—the runners cannot get enough oxygen to their muscles during the short race. Exercise walkers and joggers are involved in aerobic exercise—they are exercising at a rate that allows oxygen to get to muscles as fast as it is used up.

## OUTLOOKS 25.4

# Myths or Misunderstandings About Diet and Nutrition

| Myth or Misunderstanding | Scientific Basis |
|---|---|
| 1. Exercise burns calories. | 1. Calories are not molecules, so they cannot be burned in the physical sense, but we do oxidize (burn) the fuels (carbohydrates, fats, and proteins) to provide the energy (measured in Calories) needed to perform various activities. |
| 2. Active people who are increasing their fitness need more protein. | 2. The amount of protein needed is very small—about 50 grams. Most people get many times the amount of protein required from their normal diet. |
| 3. Vitamins supply energy. | 3. Most vitamins assist enzymes in bringing about chemical reactions, some of which may be energy yielding, but they are not sources of energy. |
| 4. Large amounts of protein are needed to build muscle. | 4. A person can build only a few grams of new muscle per day. Therefore, consuming large amounts of protein will not increase the rate of muscle growth. |
| 5. Large quantities (megadoses) of vitamins will fight disease, build strength, and increase the lifespan. | 5. Quantities of vitamins that greatly exceed recommendations have not been shown to be beneficial. Large doses of some vitamins (e.g., vitamins A, D, and $B_3$) are toxic. |
| 6. Protein supplements are more quickly absorbed than dietary protein and can build muscle faster. | 6. There is adequate protein in nearly all diets. The supplements may be absorbed faster, but that does not mean that they are incorporated into muscle mass faster. |
| 7. Vitamins prevent cancer, heart disease, and other health problems. | 7. Vitamins are important to health. However, it is a gross oversimplification to suggest that the consumption of excess amounts of specific vitamins will prevent certain diseases. Many factors contribute to the causes of disease. |

(electrolytes) and glucose may be helpful to those who lose a great deal of water during hot weather or prolonged exercise. The general rule is to replace the water you lose.

Individuals who are engaged in long bouts of exercise, such as long-distance running or cycling, need to take in additional Calories in the form of glucose. Because they are using up larger amounts of glycogen in their muscles, providing glucose during exercise can help them prolong their exercise. Some serious athletes practice *carbohydrate loading*. This practice involves consuming meals with large amounts of carbohydrates in the days before a competition. It has been demonstrated that when carbohydrate loading is coupled with training for endurance events, the amount of glycogen stored in the liver increases, allowing, the athlete to go longer before running out of glycogen.

The need for protein in an athlete's diet has also been investigated. An increase in dietary protein does not automatically increase strength, endurance, or speed. In fact, most Americans eat the 10% additional protein that athletes require as a part of their normal diets. The body uses the additional protein for many things, including muscle growth; however, increasing protein intake does not automatically increase muscle size. Only when there is a need is the protein used to increase muscle mass. Exercise provides that need. The body will build the muscle it needs to meet the demands placed on it. Vitamins and minerals operate in much the same way. No supplements should be required as long as the diet is balanced and complex (Outlooks 25.4 and 25.5).

Carbohydrates

### 25.8 CONCEPT REVIEW

16. How do anaerobic and aerobic exercise differ?
17. Describe what metabolic changes take place during prolonged exercise.
18. What is *carbohydrate loading*?
19. Describe the importance of water, carbohydrate, and protein in the diet of a typical healthy active person.

## OUTLOOKS 25.5

# Nutritional Health Products and Health Claims

Drug stores, supermarkets, health-food stores, and websites sell a wide variety of products that are not drugs but claim to provide benefits to health. Drugs must be proven to work as described and be safe. Nutritional health products are considered to be foods and manufacturers are not required to prove they function as described. There are three common categories of these products.

*Dietary supplements* are materials that are consumed by mouth that the manufacturer claims have beneficial health effects. These materials can be vitamins, minerals, plant materials, amino acids, enzymes, hormones, tissues, extracts of tissues, or a metabolite (any substance involved in metabolism). Manufacturers of dietary supplements are not allowed to make *specific* health claims ("Vitamin A prevents blindness.") but are allowed to make three general kinds of claims:

1. Health claims ("Improves immune system function." or "Consumption of folate may reduce birth defects.")
2. Structure/function claims ("Promotes bone and joint health." or "Calcium builds strong bones.")

    If the manufacturer makes a structure/function claim, it must provide the following disclaimer on the label. *This statement has not been evaluated by the FDA. This*

*product is not intended to diagnose. treat, cure, or prevent any disease.*
3. Nutrient content claims ("High in fiber." or "Excellent source of lycopene.")

    Manufacturers do not need permission to produce and sell their products, but must determine for themselves that the product is not harmful and that the claims they make are not false or misleading. They do not need to provide any government agency with proof of their claims.

*Probiotics* are live microorganisms thought to be beneficial to health when consumed. There are suggestions that these microorganisms may inhibit harmful microbes, and thus relieve several kinds of intestinal problems (diarrhea, colitis). Probiotics are typically consumed in fermented foods such as yogurt, sauerkraut, pickled vegetables, or in capsules as dietary supplements. A common use of certain lactic acid bacteria is to alleviate symptoms of lactose intolerance.

*Prebiotics* are nondigestible food substances that are thought to support the growth of "good" bacteria in the gut. The most commonly described prebiotic is dietary fiber. Soluble fiber is thought to be best for the growth of beneficial bacteria.

## Summary

To maintain good health, people must ingest nutrient molecules that can enter the cells and function in the metabolic processes. The proper quantity and quality of nutrients are essential to good health. Nutritionists have classified nutrients into six groups: carbohydrates, proteins, lipids, minerals, vitamins, and water. Energy for metabolic processes can be obtained from carbohydrates, lipids, and proteins and is measured in Calories. An important measure of the amount of energy required to sustain a human at rest is the basal metabolic rate. To meet this and all additional requirements, the U.S. Department of Agriculture (USDA) has established the Dietary Reference Intakes, recommended dietary allowances for each nutrient. The USDA publishes the Food Guide Pyramid, which places foods into the following categories: grains, fruits, vegetables, milk, oils, and meat and beans. It also provides recommendations about exercise. The goal of the Food Guide Pyramid is to provide easily understood guidelines that will help people develop a healthy diet and lifestyle.

Should there be metabolic or psychological problems associated with a person's normal metabolism, a variety of disorders can occur, including obesity, anorexia nervosa, and bulimia. As people move through the life cycle, their nutritional needs change, requiring a reexamination of their

eating habits to maintain good health. Exercise is an important part of a healthy lifestyle. A person's diet may need to be adjusted to support the level of exercise he or she maintains. For most people, the most important nutritional need associated with exercise is water to replace that lost through sweating. Serious athletes often require diets that contain higher numbers of Calories, particularly in the form of carbohydrates.

## Key Terms

*Use the interactive flash cards on the **Concepts in Biology**, 14/e website to help you learn the meaning of these terms.*

## Basic Review

1. _____ is the modification and incorporation of absorbed molecules into the structure of an organism.
   a. Nutrition
   b. Assimilation
   c. Dieting
   d. Absorption

2. The rate at which the body uses energy when at rest is called its
   a. basal metabolic rate.
   b. basal metabolic index.
   c. specific dynamic action.
   d. work.

3. A body mass index between 25 and 30 kg/m$^2$ indicates that a person is
   a. within a normal range.
   b. obese.
   c. overweight.
   d. extremely active.

4. Some complex carbohydrates are a source of _____, which slows the absorption of nutrients and stimulate peristalsis (rhythmic contractions) in the intestinal tract.
   a. fiber
   b. vitamins
   c. minerals
   d. lipids

5. Linoleic acid and linolenic acid are called _____ because they cannot be synthesized by the human body and, therefore, must be a part of the diet.
   a. amino acids
   b. fatty acids
   c. essential fatty acids
   d. B-complex vitamins

6. Inorganic elements, found throughout nature, that cannot be synthesized by the body are called
   a. vitamins.
   b. essential amino acids.
   c. electrolytes.
   d. minerals.

7. When proteins are conserved and carbohydrates and fats are oxidized first as a source of ATP energy, the body is involved in
   a. protein-sparing.
   b. specific dynamic action.
   c. absorption.
   d. dieting.

8. Information on the amounts of certain nutrients various members of the public should receive is contained in
   a. the Food Guide Pyramid.
   b. the Protein-Sparing Guide.
   c. kwashiorkor.
   d. the Dietary Reference Intakes.

9. A person with _____ has a cycle of eating binges followed by purging of the body of the food by inducing vomiting or using laxatives.
   a. bulimia
   b. anorexia nervosa
   c. obesity
   d. kwashiorkor

10. The use of alcohol during pregnancy can result in decreased nutrient exchange between the mother and fetus, as well as other developmental abnormalities called
    a. osteoporosis.
    b. fetal alcohol syndrome (FAS).
    c. bulimia.
    d. fetal deficiency disease.

11. Eating large amounts of protein is required to build large muscles. (T/F)

12. Which of the following categories of people would be affected the most by a shortage of protein in their diet?
    a. athletes
    b. children
    c. people in old age
    d. adult men

13. Items in the grain food group are important because they supply
    a. carbohydrates.
    b. vitamins.
    c. fiber.
    d. All of the above are correct.

14. Which food group provides protein, calcium, and vitamin D in the diet?
    a. meat and beans
    b. fruit
    c. vegetables
    d. milk

15. For most persons who exercise, the most important nutrient is
    a. carbohydrates.
    b. protein.
    c. fats.
    d. water.

**Answers**
1. b   2. a   3. c   4. a   5. c   6. d   7. a   8. d   9. a   10. b
11. F   12. b   13. d   14. d   15. d

## Thinking Critically

**Getting Ready for Exercise**
Imagine that you're a 21-year-old woman who has never been involved in any kind of sport, but suddenly you have become interested in playing rugby, a very demanding contact sport. If you are to play well with only minor injuries, you must get into condition. Describe the changes you should make in your daily diet and exercise program to prepare for this new experience.

# The Body's Control Mechanisms and Immunity

## Court Finds No Link Between Vaccination and Autism

*Measles/Mumps/Rubella vaccination important for public health.*

## CHAPTER OUTLINE

Autism is a disorder of the brain that results in a variety of abnormal behavior patterns. General symptoms include difficulty in participating in social situations, repetitive behaviors, late development of language skills, and preoccupation with certain topics. The disorder may also range from severe to mild and affects about 1 in 150 births. It is clear that genes are involved in the development of autism, but it is also strongly suspected that there are environmental factors that trigger its development.

Because parents and their physicians often recognize autism's symptoms when the children are going through their initial immunizations for childhood diseases, many people have associated the onset of autism with vaccines. This has led to a significant number of people wanting to exclude their children from immunizations, particularly the measles, mumps, and rubella (MMR) vaccine.

However, avoiding immunization also has significant risk. About 1 in 100 children infected with measles develops blindness, 5 in 100 develop ear infections, and 1 in 1000 develops encephalitis. Rubella also has serious consequences. Pregnant women who develop rubella in the first trimester of their pregnancy have about an 85% chance of having a child with a significant birth defect.

In 2008 a special federal appeals court ruled that, based on scientific evidence, there was no link between the MMR vaccine and autism. This legal decision cleared the way for stronger requirements for the vaccination of children. However, some people still will be unconvinced, and avoid having their children vaccinated.

- **What is a vaccine?**
- **How do vaccines work to prevent disease?**
- **Should vaccinations for childhood infectious diseases be mandatory?**

## Background Check

Concepts you should understand in order to get the most out of this chapter:
- The various types of chemical reactions (chapter 2)
- The structure of eukaryotic cells (chapter 4)
- How cellular processes are controlled by enzymes (chapter 5)

## 26.1 Coordination in Multicellular Animals

A large, multicellular organism, which consists of many kinds of systems, must have a way of integrating various functions so that it can survive. Its systems must be coordinated to maintain a reasonably constant internal environment. Recall from chapter 1 that **homeostasis** is the maintenance of a constant internal environment as a result of monitoring and modifying the functioning of various systems. Homeostatic mechanisms are involved in maintaining blood pressure, body temperature, body fluid levels, and blood pH. When we run up a hill, our leg and arm muscles move in a coordinated way to provide power. They burn fuel (glucose) for energy and produce carbon dioxide and lactic acid as waste products, which tend to lower the pH of the blood. The heart beats faster to provide oxygen and nutrients to the muscles, we breathe faster to supply the muscles with oxygen and get rid of carbon dioxide, and the blood vessels in the muscles dilate to allow more blood to flow to them. Running generates excess heat. As a result, more blood flows to the skin to get rid of the heat, and sweat glands begin to secrete fluid, thus cooling the skin. All these automatic internal adjustments help the body maintain a constant level of oxygen, carbon dioxide, and glucose in the blood; constant pH; and constant body temperature.

One common homeostatic mechanism is **negative-feedback inhibition**, a mechanism in which an increase in the output of a reaction causes a decrease in the stimulus, which eventually causes a decrease in the output (figure 26.1a). A common negative-feedback inhibition mechanism is a household heating system. The thermostat is set to a particular temperature. When the temperature in the room drops too low, the thermostat sends a message (stimulus) to the furnace to produce heat, and the temperature in the room rises. As the temperature rises to the set point, it eventually causes the thermostat to send a message that turns the furnace off.

Negative-feedback systems work in your body in a similar manner. Various body functions have set points, such as body temperature, blood pH, and blood osmotic pressure. When the body drifts from the set point, messenger molecules move throughout the body and provide a stimulus to cause a response that will correct the change from the set point. When a response causes a change that brings the body back to the set point, a message is sent back to a control center telling it to stop producing the stimulus. For example, your

**(a) Negative-feedback control**

**(b) Positive-feedback regulation**

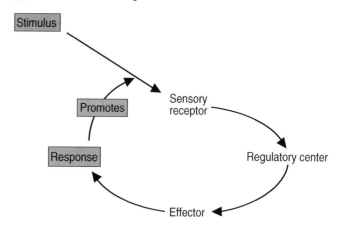

**FIGURE 26.1  Negative- and Positive-Feedback Control**
*(a)* Negative-feedback control occurs when the response to a stimulus inhibits the stimulus, thus reducing the response.
*(b)* Positive-feedback happens when a response to a stimulus causes an increase in the stimulus which further increases the response.

body seeks to maintain a constant level of glucose in the blood. After you eat a meal, the level of glucose begins to rise, which is the stimulus for the pancreas to release the hormone insulin. The insulin causes cells of the muscles and liver to remove glucose from the blood and store it as glycogen. As the glucose is removed from the blood, the pancreas is no longer stimulated to release insulin and removal of glucose from the blood stops. A companion hormone, glucagon, is released from the pancreas when blood glucose levels fall below the set point. It stimulates the liver to break down glycogen and release glucose into the blood. As the blood glucose level rises, the amount of glucagon falls. Thus these two negative-feedback mechanisms result in a fluctuation around the set point, thus maintaining a relatively constant concentration of glucose.

The alternative to negative feedback is *positive-feedback regulation*. In **positive-feedback regulation,** a stimulus causes a response that leads to an even stronger stimulus (figure 26.1b). Obviously, this does not result in homeostasis. There are a few situations in which positive feedback is useful. For example, positive feedback occurs during childbirth. The release of the hormone oxytocin causes contractions of the uterus. Each time the uterus contracts, signals are sent to the brain, where more oxytocin is produced, causing the uterine muscles to contract again. This repeated stimulation continues until the baby is born. Blood clotting is another example of positive feedback. Chemicals released at the site of injury cause platelets to collect at the site and disintegrate, releasing substances that attract additional platelets. In both of these cases there is a limit to how long the positive feedback continues. Uterine contractions stop shortly after the baby is born and clots stop forming once the hole has been plugged.

## 26.1 CONCEPT REVIEW

1. Describe how insulin, the liver, and the level of glucose in the blood demonstrate negative feedback.
2. Explain why positive feedback is not involved in maintaining homeostasis.

## 26.2 Nervous System Function

The nervous, endocrine, and immune systems are the three major systems of the body that play key roles by integrating stimuli and generating the appropriate responses necessary to maintain homeostasis.

The nervous system is well suited to managing the rapid adjustments that must take place within the body. As we discuss the structure and function of the nervous system it is useful to have a basic understanding of how it is organized. The nervous system is organized in a fashion similar to a computer. Information from various input devices (sense organs) is delivered to the central processing unit (brain) by way of wires (sensory nerves). The information is interpreted in the central processing unit. Eventually, messages can be sent by way of cables (motor nerves) to drive external machinery (muscles and glands). The following sections describe the major structural and functional characteristics of the nervous system.

## The Structure of the Nervous System

The **nervous system** consists of a network of cells, with fibrous extensions, that carry information along specific pathways from one part of the body to another. A **neuron,** or **nerve cell,** is the basic unit of the nervous system. A neuron consists of a central body, called the **soma** or *nerve cell body,* which contains the nucleus. It has several long extensions called nerve fibers. There are two kinds of nerve fibers: **axons,** which carry information away from the cell body, and **dendrites,** which carry information toward the cell body (figure 26.2). Most neurons have one axon and several dendrites.

**FIGURE 26.2  Structure of Neurons**
Neurons consist of a nerve cell body, which contains the nucleus, and several fibrous extensions. The fibers that carry impulses to the nerve cell body are dendrites. The fiber that carries the impulse away from the cell body is the axon. Sensory neurons have a long dendrite that carries information from the sense organ to the cell body. Motor neurons have a long axon that carries information from the cell body to a muscle or gland. Most neurons other than sensory neurons have many dendrites but only one axon.

Neurons are arranged into two major systems. The **central nervous system,** which consists of the brain and spinal cord, is surrounded by the skull and the vertebrae of the spinal column. The **spinal cord** is a collection of nerve cells and nerve fibers surrounded by the vertebrae that conveys information to and from the brain. The central nervous system receives input from sense organs, interprets information, and generates responses. The **peripheral nervous system** is located outside the skull and spinal column; it consists of bundles of long axons and dendrites called **nerves.** In the peripheral nervous system, cranial nerves connect to the brain, whereas spinal nerves connect to the spinal cord. There are two sets of neurons in the peripheral nervous system: the sensory neurons and the motor neurons. **Sensory neurons** have long dendrites that carry input from sense organs to the central nervous system. **Motor neurons** carry messages from the central nervous system to muscles and glands. Motor neurons have one long axon that runs from the spinal cord to a muscle or gland. Some motor nerves constituting the *somatic nervous system,* control the skeletal (voluntary) muscles. Other motor nerves, collectively called the *autonomic nervous system,* control the smooth (involuntary) muscles, the heart, and glands. Figure 26.3 summarizes the different structural and functional portions of the nervous system.

## The Nature of the Nerve Impulse

Because most neurons have long, fibrous extensions, information can be passed along the nerve cell from one end to the other. The **nerve impulse** is the message that travels along a neuron. A nerve impulse is not like an electric current; instead, it involves a specific sequence of chemical events at the cell membrane.

Because all cell membranes are differentially permeable, it is difficult for some ions to pass through the membrane, and the combination of ions inside the membrane is different from that outside it. Cell membranes also contain proteins that actively transport specific ions from one side of the membrane to the other. Active transport involves the cell's use of adenosine triphosphate (ATP) to move materials from one side of the cell membrane to the other. Because ATP is required, cells lose this ability when they die. One of the ions that is actively transported from cells is the sodium ion ($Na^+$). At the same time sodium ions are being transported out of cells, potassium ions ($K^+$) are being transported into the normal resting (not stimulated) cells. However, there are more sodium ions transported out than potassium ions transported in.

Because a normal resting cell has more positively charged $Na^+$ ions on the outside of the cell than on the inside, a small but measurable voltage exists across the membrane of the cell. (**Voltage** is a measure of the electrical charge difference that exists between two points or objects.) The voltage difference between the inside and the outside of a cell membrane is about 70 millivolts (0.07 volt). The two sides of the cell membrane are, therefore, polarized in the same sense that a battery is polarized, with a positive (+) and a negative (−) pole.

(a)

(b)

**FIGURE 26.3 Organization of the Nervous System**
*(a)* A generalized view of the central nervous system and some of the nerves of the peripheral nervous system. *(b)* The chart shows how the various functional portions of the nervous system are related to one another.

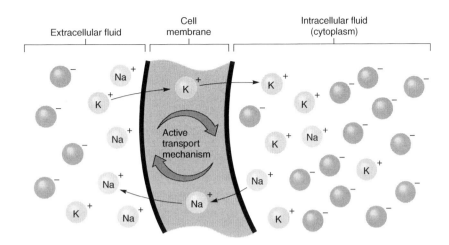

**FIGURE 26.4  The Polarization of Cell Membranes**
All cells, including neurons have an active transport mechanism that pumps $Na^+$ out of cells and simultaneously pumps $K^+$ into them. The end result is that there are more $Na^+$ ions outside the cell and more $K^+$ ions inside the cell. In addition, negative ions, such as $Cl^-$, are more numerous inside the cell. Consequently, the outside of the cell is positive ($+$) compared with the inside, which is negative ($-$).

A resting neuron has its positive pole on the outside of the cell membrane and its negative pole on the inside of the membrane (figure 26.4).

When a cell is stimulated at a specific point on the cell membrane, the cell membrane changes its permeability and lets sodium ions ($Na^+$) pass through it from the outside to the inside. The membrane is thus **depolarized**; it loses its difference in charge as sodium ions diffuse into the cell from the outside. Sodium ions diffuse into the cell because, initially, they are in greater concentration outside the cell than inside. When the membrane becomes more permeable, they are able to diffuse into the cell, toward the area of lower concentration. The depolarization of one point on the cell membrane causes the adjacent portion of the cell membrane to change its permeability as well, and it also depolarizes. Thus, a wave of depolarization passes along the length of the neuron from one end to the other (figure 26.5). The depolarization and passage of an impulse along any portion of the neuron is a momentary event. As soon as a section of the membrane has been depolarized, potassium ions diffuse out of the cell. This reestablishes the original polarized state, and the membrane is said to be *repolarized*. Subsequently, the continuous active transport of sodium ions out of the cell and potassium ions into the cell restores the original concentration of ions on both sides of the cell membrane. This is similar to a "wave" passing around a stadium. The "wave" is initiated by specific individuals as they stand up and "wave" (depolarization). People adjacent participate as they are affected by the initiators while at the same time the originators are sitting down (repolarization). As long as the next people in line participate, the "wave" continues. There is an "impulse" that moves around the stadium but the individuals remain in place.

When the nerve impulse reaches the end of the axon, it stimulates the release of a molecule that stimulates depolarization of the next neuron in the chain.

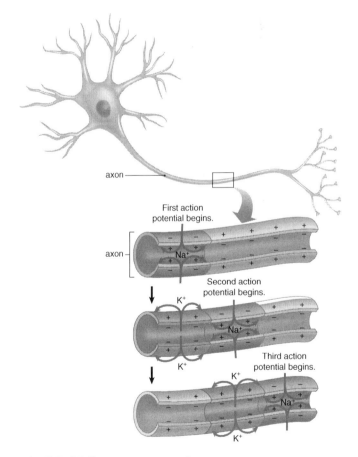

**FIGURE 26.5  A Nerve Impulse**
When a neuron is stimulated, a small portion of the cell membrane depolarizes as $Na^+$ flows into the cell through the membrane. This encourages the depolarization of an adjacent portion of the membrane, and it depolarizes a short time later. In this way, a wave of depolarization passes down the length of the neuron. Shortly after a portion of the membrane is depolarized, the ionic balance is reestablished. It is repolarized and ready to be stimulated again.

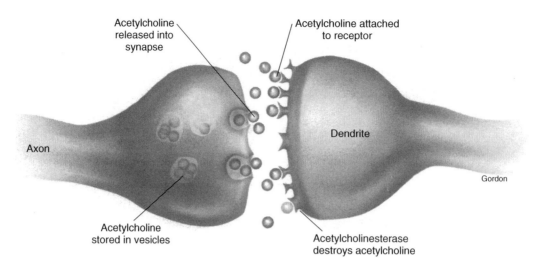

**FIGURE 26.6** **Activities at the Synapse**
When a nerve impulse reaches the end of an axon, it releases a neurotransmitter into the synapse. In this illustration, the neurotransmitter is acetylcholine. When acetylcholine is released into the synapse, acetylcholine molecules diffuse across the synapse and bind to receptors on the dendrite, initiating an impulse in the next neuron. Acetylcholinesterase is an enzyme that destroys acetylcholine, preventing continuous stimulation of the dendrite.

## Activities at the Synapse

The **synapse** is the space between the fibers of adjacent neurons in a chain. Many chemical events occur in the synapse that are important in the function of the nervous system. When a neuron is stimulated, an impulse passes along its length from one end to the other. When the impulse reaches a synapse, a molecule called a **neurotransmitter** is released into the synapse from the axon. It diffuses across the synapse and binds to specific receptor sites on the dendrite of the next neuron. When enough neurotransmitter molecules have been bound to the second neuron, an impulse is initiated in it as well. Several kinds of neurotransmitters are produced by specific neurons. These include dopamine, epinephrine, acetylcholine, and several other molecules. The first neurotransmitter to be identified was *acetylcholine*. **Acetylcholine** molecules are neurotransmitters manufactured in the soma; they migrate down the axon, where they are stored until needed.

As long as a neurotransmitter is attached to its receptor, it continues to stimulate the neuron. Thus, if acetylcholine continues to occupy receptors, the neuron continues to be stimulated again and again. **Acetylcholinesterase,** an enzyme, destroys acetylcholine and prevents this from happening. (The breakdown products of the acetylcholine can be used to remanufacture new acetylcholine molecules.) The destruction of acetylcholine allows the second neuron in the chain to return to normal (figure 26.6). Thus, it will be ready to accept another burst of acetylcholine from the first neuron a short time later. Neurons must also constantly manufacture new acetylcholine molecules, or they will exhaust their supply and be unable to conduct an impulse across a synapse.

Certain drugs, such as curare and strychnine, interfere with the activities at the synapse. Curare blocks the synapse and causes paralysis, whereas strychnine causes neurons to be

stimulated continually. Many insecticides are nerve poisons and, therefore, are quite hazardous.

Because of the way the synapse works, impulses can go in only one direction: Only axons secrete acetylcholine, and only dendrites have receptors. This explains why there are sensory and motor neurons to carry messages to and from the central nervous system.

## The Organization of the Central Nervous System

The brain consists of several regions, each with a specific function. Certain parts of the brain are involved in controlling fundamental functions, such as breathing and heart rate. Others are involved in generating emotions, others decode sensory input, and others coordinate motor activity. The human brain also has considerable capacity to store information and create new responses to stimuli.

The functions of the brain can be roughly divided into three major levels: automatic activities, basic decision making and emotions, and thinking and reasoning. If we begin with the spinal cord and work our way forward, we will proceed from the more fundamental, automatic activities of the brain to its more complex, thinking portions. The **medulla oblongata** is at the base of the brain, where the spinal cord enters the skull. It controls fundamental activities, such as blood pressure, breathing, and heart rate. Most of the fibers of the spinal cord cross from one side of the body to the other in the medulla oblongata. This is why the left side of the brain affects the right side of the body.

The **cerebellum** is the large bulge at the base of the brain that is connected to the medulla oblongata. The primary function of the cerebellum is the coordination of muscle activity. It receives information from sense organs, such as the portions of the ear involved in balance, the eyes, and pressure sensors

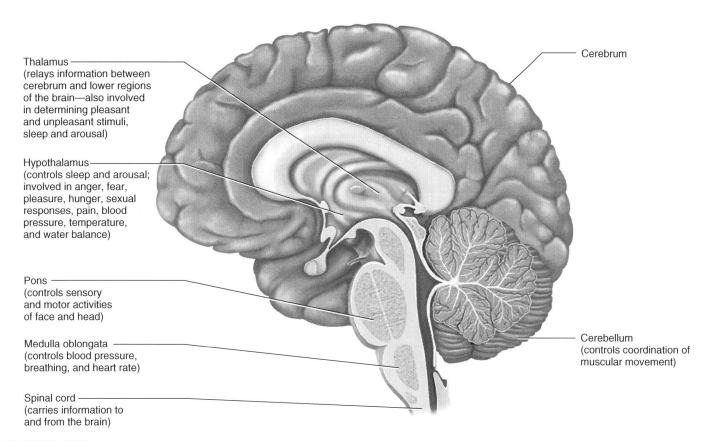

Thalamus
(relays information between
cerebrum and lower regions
of the brain—also involved
in determining pleasant
and unpleasant stimuli,
sleep and arousal)

Hypothalamus
(controls sleep and arousal;
involved in anger, fear,
pleasure, hunger, sexual
responses, pain, blood
pressure, temperature,
and water balance)

Pons
(controls sensory
and motor activities
of face and head)

Medulla oblongata
(controls blood pressure,
breathing, and heart rate)

Spinal cord
(carries information to
and from the brain)

Cerebrum

Cerebellum
(controls coordination of
muscular movement)

**FIGURE 26.7 Functions of the More Primitive Brain Regions**
The brain is organized into several levels of function. The more primitive regions of the brain connected to the spinal cord monitor and manage many essential functions automatically.

in muscles and tendons. The cerebellum uses this information to make adjustments in the strength and sequence of muscle contractions, so that the body moves in a coordinated fashion.

The **pons** is the region of the brain that is connected to the anterior end of the medulla oblongata. It also connects to the cerebellum and to higher levels of the brain. It is involved in controlling many sensory and motor functions of the sense organs of the head and face. The pons is also connected to a portion of the brain known as the *midbrain* that is connected to regions of the brain that control many automatic activities, but also are involved in some level of decision making. The primary regions are the *thalamus* and the *hypothalamus*.

The **thalamus** is the region of the brain that relays information between the cerebrum and lower portions of the brain. It also provides a level of awareness in that it determines pleasant and unpleasant stimuli and is involved in sleep and arousal. The **hypothalamus** is the region of the brain involved in regulating sleep cycles; it is important in emotions such as anger, fear, pleasure, and the sensations that accompany hunger, sexual response, and pain. Several other, more automatic functions are regulated in this region, such as body temperature, blood pressure, and water balance. The hypothalamus also is connected to the pituitary gland and influences the manufacture and release of its hormones. Figure 26.7 shows the relationship of the various, more primitive parts of the brain.

The **cerebrum** is the thinking part of the brain. It receives, interprets, and integrates information from sense organs and generates responses that involve the actions of muscles and glands. It is also the largest portion of the brain in humans. The two hemispheres of the cerebrum cover all other portions of the brain except the cerebellum. The surface of the cerebrum has been extensively mapped as to the locations of many functions. Abilities such as memory, language, the control of movement, the interpretation of sensory input, and thought are associated with specific areas of the cerebrum. Figure 26.8 illustrates the cerebrum and the locations of specific functions.

The function of the brain is not determined by structure alone. Many parts of the brain have specialized neurons, which produce specific neurotransmitter molecules used only to stimulate particular neurons that have the proper receptor sites. As scientists learn more about the functioning of the brain, they are finding more kinds of specialized neurotransmitter molecules, allowing for the treatment of many types of mental and emotional diseases. Manipulating these neurotransmitter molecules can help correct inappropriate functioning of the brain. However, the brain is still not completely understood. Scientists are at an early stage in their search to comprehend this organ, which sets us apart from other animals (How Science Works 26.1).

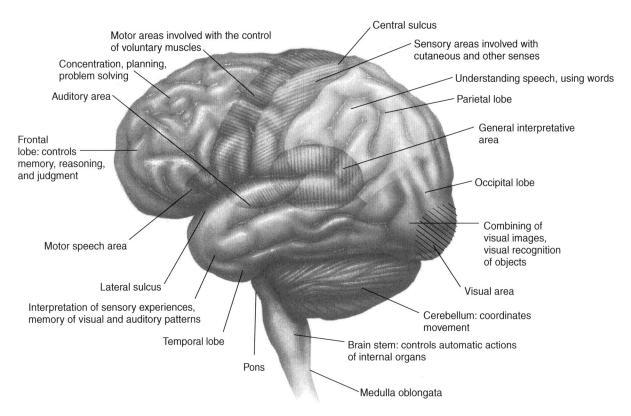

**FIGURE 26.8 Specialized Areas of the Cerebrum**
Each portion of the cerebrum has particular functions.

## HOW SCIENCE WORKS 26.1

## How Do We Know What the Brain Does?

Scientists know a great deal about the function of the brain, although there is still much more to learn. Certain functions have been identified as residing in specific portions of the brain, as a result of many kinds of studies over the past century. For example, persons who have had specific portions of their brains altered by damage from accidents or strokes have been studied. Their changes in behavior or the way they perceive things can be directly correlated with the portion of the brain that was damaged. During surgeries that require the brain to be exposed, a local anesthetic can be given and the patient can be conscious while the surgery is taking place. (The brain perceives pain from pain receptors throughout the body; however, because the brain does not have many pain receptors within it, touching or manipulating the brain does not cause pain to be perceived.) Specific portions of the brain can be stimulated and the patient can be asked to describe his or her sensations and the patient's motor functions can be observed.

Many kinds of experiments have also been done with animals, in which specific portions of the brain have been destroyed and the

animals' changes in behavior noted. Electrodes have been inserted into the brains of animals to stimulate certain portions of the brain.

Modern brain-imaging techniques are used to observe changes in the electrical activity of specific portions of the brain without electrodes or other invasive procedures. This allows researchers to present stimuli to human subjects and determine which parts of the brain alter their activity. In addition to localizing the part of the brain that responds, it is also possible to determine what parts of a complex stimulus are most important in changing brain activity. For example, these techniques have revealed that languages learned by adults are processed in different places in the brain than the languages they learned as children and that the brain has a built-in mechanism for recognizing unexpected words or musical notes.

Although much is known about the brain, there is still much to learn. Current experiments are seeking ways to regenerate neurons that have been damaged. A better understanding of the chemical events that take place in the brain would enable us to cure many kinds of debilitating mental illnesses.

## 26.3 The Endocrine System

In the 1890s, many physicians began to describe the workings of chemicals in the body, suggesting that they were "internal secretions." Ernest Starling named these chemical messengers *hormones*. A **hormone** is a specific molecule that is released by one organ and transported to another organ, where it triggers a change in the other organ's activity. The **endocrine system** consists of a number of glands that communicate with one another and with other tissues through chemicals distributed throughout the organism. **Glands** are organs that manufacture molecules that either are secreted into surrounding tissue, where they are picked up by the circulatory system, or are secreted through ducts into the cavity of an organ or to the body surface. **Endocrine glands** have no ducts; they secrete their products—hormones—into the circulatory system (figure 26.9). Other glands, such as the digestive glands and sweat glands, empty their contents through ducts. These kinds of glands are called **exocrine glands.**

## Endocrine System Function

As with the nervous system, it is helpful to have a general idea about how the endocrine system works as it is discussed.

The endocrine system functions the way a radio broadcast system does. Radio stations send their signals in all directions, but only the radio receivers that are tuned to the correct frequency can receive the signals. Messenger molecules (hormones) are distributed throughout the body by the circulatory system, but only the cells that have the proper receptor sites can receive and respond to them. The cells that are able to respond to a hormone are called *target cells;* they respond in one of three ways: (1) Some cells release products that have been previously manufactured; (2) some cells synthesize molecules or begin metabolic activities; and (3) some cells divide and grow. As a result of these different kinds of responses, some endocrine responses are relatively rapid, whereas others are very slow. For example, the release of the hormones **epinephrine** and **norepinephrine** (formerly called adrenalin and noradrenalin) from the adrenal medulla, located near the kidney, causes a rapid change in an organism's behavior. The heart rate increases, blood pressure rises, blood is

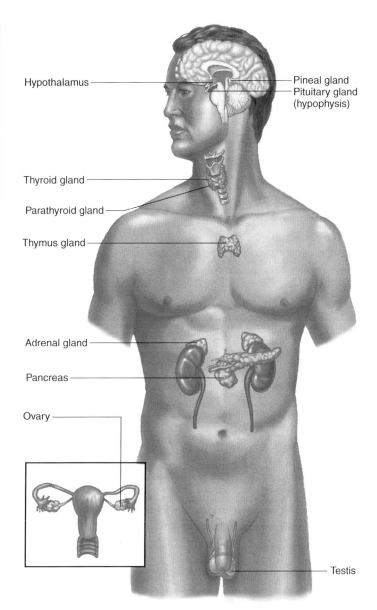

**FIGURE 26.9 Endocrine Glands**
The endocrine glands, located in various places in the body, secrete hormones.

shunted to the muscles, and the breathing rate increases. You have certainly experienced this reaction many times in your lifetime, such as when you nearly had an automobile accident or slipped and nearly fell.

**Antidiuretic hormone (ADH)** acts more slowly. It is released from the posterior pituitary gland at the base of the brain; it regulates the rate at which the body loses water through the kidneys. It does this by encouraging the reabsorption of water from the collecting ducts of the kidneys (see chapter 24). The effects of ADH can be noticed in a matter of minutes to hours.

Insulin is another hormone whose effects occur within minutes. It is produced by the pancreas, located near the stomach. Insulin stimulates cells—particularly muscle, liver, and fat cells—to take up glucose from the blood. After a high-carbohydrate meal, the glucose level in the blood begins to rise, stimulating the pancreas to release insulin. The increased insulin causes glucose levels to fall as the sugar is taken up by the cells. People with diabetes have insufficient or improperly acting insulin or lack the receptors to respond to the insulin; therefore, they have difficulty regulating glucose levels in their blood.

The responses that result from the growth of cells may take weeks or years to occur. For example, **growth-stimulating hormone (GSH)** is produced by the anterior pituitary gland over a period of years and results in typical human growth. After sexual maturity, the amount of this hormone generally drops to very low levels, and body growth stops. Sexual development is also largely the result of the growth of specific tissues and organs. The male sex hormone **testosterone**, produced by the testes, causes the growth of male sex organs and a change to the adult body form. The female counterpart, **estrogen**, results in the development of female sex organs and body form. In all of these cases, it is the release of hormones over long periods, continually stimulating the growth of sensitive tissues, that results in a normal developmental pattern. The absence or inhibition of any of these hormones early in life changes the normal growth process.

## Negative-Feedback Inhibition and Hormones

Many endocrine glands and their hormones are under negative-feedback inhibition. At the beginning of the chapter, insulin and glucagon were used as examples of molecules involved in simple negative-feedback inhibition. However, glands within the endocrine system often interact with one another so that the secretions of one gland alter the actions of others. When several glands interact in negative-feedback inhibition, an increased amount of one hormone interferes with the production of a different hormone in the chain of events. The production of *thyroxine* and *triiodothyronine* by the thyroid gland is regulated by negative-feedback inhibition involving the actions of other glands. The production of these two hormones is stimulated by the increased production of a hormone from the hypothalamus called *thyroid-releasing hormone (TRH)* which stimulates the anterior pituitary to produce a hormone called *thyroid-stimulating hormone (TSH)*. The thyroid gland's control lies in the quantity of TSH produced. When the anterior pituitary produces high levels of thyroid-stimulating hormone, the thyroid is stimulated to grow and secrete more thyroxine and triiodothyronine. But when increased amounts of thyroxine and triiodothyronine are produced, these hormones have a negative effect on the pituitary and hypothalamus, so that production of thyroid-stimulating hormone and thyroid-releasing hormone are decreased, leading to reduced production of thyroxine and triiodothyronine. If the amount of the

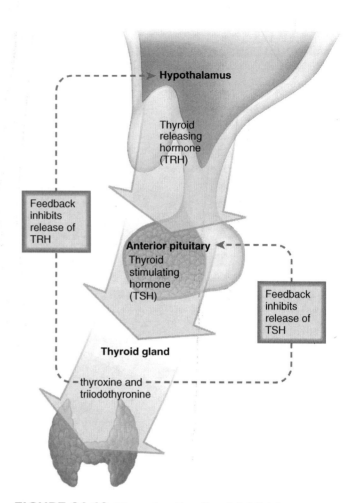

**FIGURE 26.10 Negative-Feedback Inhibition of Thyroid Secretion**
The hypothalamus sends the thyroid-releasing hormone (TRH) to the pituitary, which releases thyroid-stimulating hormone (TSH). Thyroid-stimulating hormone causes the thyroid to produce thyroxine and triiodothyronine. These two hormones inhibit the hypothalamus and pituitary.

thyroid hormones falls too low, the pituitary and hypothalamus are no longer inhibited and begin to release their hormones. As a result of the interaction of these hormones, their concentrations are maintained within certain limits (figure 26.10).

## 26.3 CONCEPT REVIEW

6. How do exocrine and endocrine glands differ?
7. Give an example of negative-feedback control in the endocrine system.
8. List three hormones and give their functions.

## 26.4 The Integration of Nervous and Endocrine Function

Although we still tend to think of the nervous and endocrine systems as separate and different, it is becoming clear that they are interconnected and cooperate to bring about appropriate responses to environmental challenges. The nervous system is particularly involved in activities that are of short duration, such as sensory input and muscle contractions. The endocrine system participates in some short-duration activities, such as the actions of epinephrine, but is more typically involved in medium- to long-term activities such as regulating glucose levels or modifying growth.

When endocrine and nervous systems interact, usually the pituitary gland is involved. The pituitary gland is located at the base of the brain and is divided into two parts. The posterior pituitary, which is directly connected to the brain, develops from nervous tissue during embryology. The other part, the anterior pituitary, develops from the lining of the roof of the mouth in early fetal development. Certain pituitary hormones are produced in the brain and transported down axons to the posterior pituitary, where they are stored before being released. The anterior pituitary also receives a continuous input of messenger molecules from the brain, but these are delivered by way of blood vessels, which pick up hormones produced by the hypothalamus and deliver them to the anterior pituitary.

The pituitary gland produces a variety of hormones that are responsible for causing other endocrine glands, such as the thyroid, ovaries and testes, and adrenals, to secrete their hormones. Pituitary hormones also influence milk production, skin pigmentation, body growth, mineral regulation, and blood glucose levels (figure 26.11).

Because the pituitary is constantly receiving information from the hypothalamus, many kinds of sensory stimuli to the body can affect the functioning of the endocrine system. One example is the way in which the nervous system and endocrine system interact to influence the menstrual cycle. At least three hormones are involved in the cycle of changes that affects the ovary and the lining of the uterus (see chapter 27 for details). It is well documented that stress caused by tension or worry can interfere with the normal cycle of hormones and delay or stop menstrual cycles. In addition, young women living in groups, such as those in college dormitories, often find that their menstrual cycles become synchronized. Although the exact mechanism involved in this phenomenon is unknown, it is suspected that input from the nervous system causes this synchronization. (Odors and sympathetic feelings have been suggested as causes.)

In many animals, the changing length of the day causes hormonal changes related to reproduction. In the spring, birds respond to lengthening days and begin to produce hormones that gear up their reproductive systems for the summer breeding season. The pineal body, a portion of the brain, serves as the receiver of light stimuli and changes the amounts of hormones secreted by the pituitary, resulting in changes in the levels of reproductive hormones. These hormonal changes modify the birds' behavior. Courtship, mating, and nest-building behaviors increase in intensity. Therefore, it appears that a change in hormone level is affecting the animals' behavior; the endocrine system is influencing the nervous system (figure 26.12). It has been known for centuries that changes in the levels of sex hormones cause changes in animals' behavior. The castration (the removal of the testes) of male domesticated animals, such as cattle, horses, and pigs, is sometimes done in part to reduce their aggressive behavior and make them easier to control. The use of anabolic steroids by humans to increase muscle mass is known to cause behavioral changes and "moodiness."

As scientists learn more about the molecules produced in the brain, it is becoming clear that the brain produces many molecules that act as hormones. Some of these molecules affect adjacent parts of the brain, others affect the pituitary, and still others may have effects on more distant organs (How Science Works 26.2).

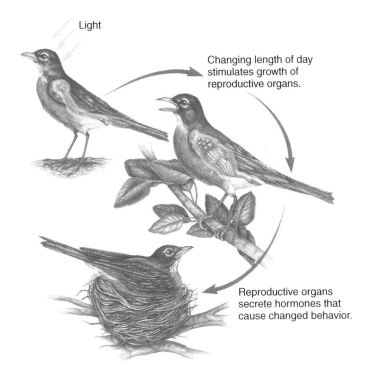

Light

Changing length of day stimulates growth of reproductive organs.

Reproductive organs secrete hormones that cause changed behavior.

**FIGURE 26.12 Interaction Between the Nervous and Endocrine Systems**
In birds and many other animals, reproduction is a seasonal activity triggered by changing length of day. The brain receives information about the changing length of day, which causes the pituitary to produce hormones that stimulate sex organs. The testes or ovaries grow and secrete their hormones in increased amounts. Increased levels of testosterone or estrogen result in changed behavior, including increased aggression, mating behavior, and nest-building activity.

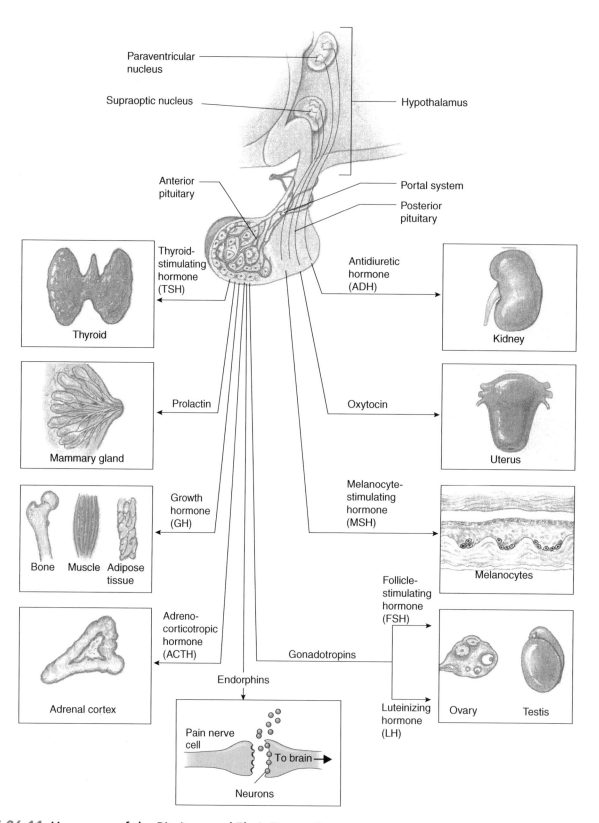

**FIGURE 26.11 Hormones of the Pituitary and Their Target Organs**
The anterior pituitary gland produces several hormones that regulate growth and the secretions of target tissues. The posterior pituitary produces hormones that change the behavior of the kidney and uterus but do not influence the growth of these organs.

# HOW SCIENCE WORKS 26.2

## Endorphins: Natural Pain Killers

The pituitary gland and the brain produce a group of small molecules that act as pain suppressors, called *endorphins*. It is thought that these molecules are released when excessive pain or stress occurs in the body. They attach to the same receptor molecules of brain cells associated with the feeling of pain. Endorphins work on the brain in the same manner as morphine and opiate drugs. Once endorphins are attached to the brain cells, the feeling of pain goes away, and a euphoric feeling takes over. Long-distance runners and other athletes talk about feeling good as a "runner's high." These responses may be due to an increase in endorphin production. It is thought that endorphins are also released by mild electric stimulation and the use of acupuncture needles.

## 26.4   CONCEPT REVIEW

9. Describe two ways in which the function of the nervous system differs from that of the endocrine system.
10. Give an example of the interaction between the endocrine system and the nervous system.

## 26.5   Sensory Input

The activities of the nervous and endocrine systems are often responses to input received from the sense organs. Sense organs of various types are located throughout the body. Many of them are located on the surface, where environmental changes can be detected easily. Hearing, sight, and touch are good examples. Other sense organs are located within the body and indicate to the organism how its various parts are changing. For example, pain and pressure are often used to monitor internal conditions. The sense organs detect changes, but the brain is responsible for **perception**—the recognition that a stimulus has been received. Sensory input is detected through many kinds of mechanisms, including chemical recognition, the detection of energy changes, and the monitoring of physical forces.

## Chemical Detection

All cells have receptors on their surfaces that can bind selectively to molecules they encounter. This binding process can cause changes in the cells in several ways. In some cells, it causes depolarization. When this happens, the binding of molecules to the cell can stimulate neurons and cause messages to be sent to the central nervous system, informing it of a change in the surroundings. Many internal sense organs respond to specific molecules. For example, the brain and aorta contain cells that respond to concentrations of hydrogen ions, carbon dioxide, and oxygen in the blood. In other cases, a molecule binding to the cell surface may cause certain genes to be expressed, and the cell responds by changing the molecules it produces. This is typical of the way the endocrine system receives and delivers messages. Taste and smell are two ways of detecting chemicals in our surroundings.

### Taste

Most cells have specific binding sites for specific molecules. Some, such as the taste buds on the tongue, soft palate, and throat appear to respond to classes of molecules. Traditionally, four kinds of tastes have been identified: sweet, sour, salt, and bitter. However, recently, a fifth kind of taste, *umami* (meaty), has been identified. Umami receptors respond to the amino acid glutamate, which is present in many kinds of foods and often is added to food as a flavor enhancer (monosodium glutamate—MSG).

The taste buds that give us the sour sensation respond to the presence of hydrogen ions ($H^+$). (Acidic foods taste sour.) The hydrogen ions stimulate the cells in two ways: They enter the cell directly or they alter the normal movement of sodium and potassium ions across the cell membrane. In either case, the cell depolarizes and stimulates a neuron. In similar fashion, sodium ions ($Na^+$) stimulate the taste buds that give us the sensation of a salty taste by directly entering the cell, which causes the cell to depolarize.

However, the sensations of sweetness, bitterness, and umami occur when molecules bind to specific surface receptors on the cell. Sweetness can be stimulated by many kinds of organic molecules, including sugars and artificial sweeteners, as well as by inorganic lead compounds. When a molecule binds to a sweetness receptor, a series of molecular changes occurs within the cell that leads to the depolarization of the cell. The sweet taste of lead salts in old paints partly explains why children sometimes eat paint chips. Because the lead interferes with normal brain development, this behavior can have disastrous results.

The cells that respond to bitter sensations have a variety of receptor molecules on their surface that bind to many kinds of compounds. When a substance binds to one of the receptors, the cell depolarizes. In the case of umami, it is the glutamate molecule that binds to receptors on the receptor cells.

Each of these tastes has a significance from an evolutionary point of view. Carbohydrates are a major food source, and many carbohydrates taste sweet; therefore, this sense is useful in identifying foods that have high food value. Similarly, proteins and salts are necessary in the diet. Therefore, being able to identify these items in potential foods is extremely valuable. This is true for salt, which must often be obtained from mineral sources. On the other hand, many bitter and sour materials are harmful. Many plants produce bitter-tasting toxic materials, and acids are often the result of the bacterial decomposition (spoiling) of foods. Being able to identify bitter and sour allows organisms to avoid potentially harmful foods.

Much of what we often refer to as *taste* involves such inputs as appearance, temperature, texture, and smell. If food does look appealing, it will probably influence how it tastes to a person. Cold coffee has a different taste than hot coffee, even though they are chemically the same. Lumpy, cooked cereal and smooth cereal have different tastes. If we are unable to smell food, it doesn't taste as it should, which is why we sometimes lose our appetite when we have a stuffy nose. There still is much to learn about how taste cells detect chemicals and the role of associated senses in modifying taste.

## Smell

The sense of smell is much more versatile than taste; it can detect thousands of different molecules at very low concentrations. The cells that make up the **olfactory epithelium,** the lining of the nasal cavity, which responds to smells, bind molecules to receptors on their surfaces. Recent research shows that each receptor cell binds to only one kind of odor molecule. The difference in cells is determined by the expression of genes. Each cell contains thousands of genes for detecting odors but only one of those is activated in each receptor cell and is expressed as a particular receptor molecule on the surface of the cell. The receptor cells are extremely sensitive. In some cases, a single molecule of a substance is sufficient to cause a receptor cell to send a message to the brain, where the sensation of odor is perceived. These sensory cells also fatigue rapidly. For instance, when we first walk into a room, we readily detect specific odors; however, after a few minutes, we are unable to detect them. Most perfumes and aftershaves are undetectable after 15 minutes of continuous exposure to them.

## Vision

The eyes primarily respond to changes in the flow of light energy. The curved surfaces of the cornea and the lens focus light on a light-sensitive layer of the back of the eye, known as the **retina** (figure 26.13). Muscles attached to the lens allow it to change shape so that we can focus on both near and far objects.

There are two kinds of receptors in the retina of the eye (figure 26.14). The cells called **rods** respond to a broad range of wavelengths of light and are responsible for black-and-white vision. Because rods are very sensitive to light, they are useful in dim light. Rods are located over most of the retinal surface, except for the area of most acute vision, known as the **fovea centralis.** The other kind of receptor cells, called **cones,** are not as sensitive to light, but they can

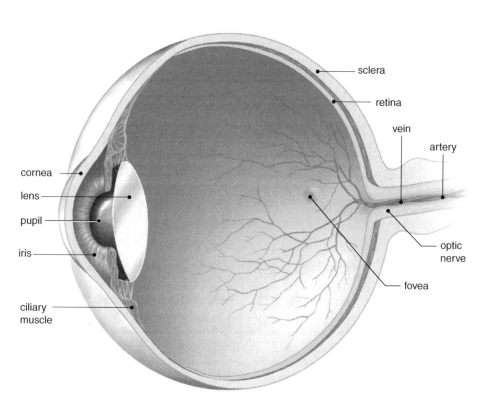

**FIGURE 26.13  Structure of the Eye**
Light enters the eye through the an opening in the iris known as the pupil. The cornea and lens focus light on the retina where the light is detected.

**FIGURE 26.14 Structure of the Retina**
The retina contains two kinds of receptor cells—rods and cones. When light strikes the rods and cones, they depolarize and stimulate nerve cells that send impulses to the brain.

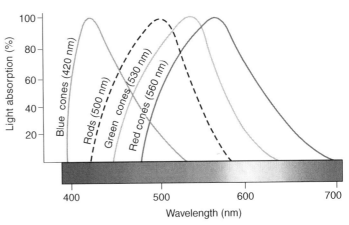

**FIGURE 26.15 Light Reception by Cones**
There are three different kinds of cones. Each responds differently to red, green, and blue wavelengths of light. Stimulation of combinations of these three kinds of cones gives us the ability to detect many different shades of color.

detect different wavelengths of light. They are found throughout the retina but are concentrated in the fovea centralis. This combination of receptors gives us the ability to detect color when light levels are high, but we rely on black-and-white vision at night. There are three varieties of cones: One type responds best to red light, one type responds best to green light, and the third type responds best to blue light. The stimulation of various combinations of these three kinds of cones allows us to detect different shades of color (figure 26.15).

Rods and the three kinds of cones each contain a pigment that decomposes when struck by light of the proper wavelength and sufficient strength. **Rhodopsin** is the pigment found in rods. This change in the structure of rhodopsin causes the rod to depolarize. Cone cells have a similar mechanism of action, and each of the three kinds of cones has a different pigment. Because rods and cones synapse with neurons, they stimulate a neuron when depolarized and cause a message to be sent to the brain. Thus, the pattern of color and light intensity recorded on the retina is detected by rods and cones and converted into a series of nerve impulses, which the brain receives and interprets.

## Hearing and Balance

Sound is produced by the vibration of molecules. The ears respond to changes in sound waves. Consequently, the ears detect changes in the quantity of energy and the quality of sound waves. Sound has several characteristics. Loudness, or volume, is a measure of the intensity of sound energy that arrives at the ear. Very loud sounds literally vibrate the body and can cause hearing loss if they are too intense. Pitch is a quality of sound that is determined by the frequency of the sound vibrations. High-pitched sounds have short wavelengths; low-pitched sounds have long wavelengths.

The sound that arrives at the ear is first funneled by the external ear to the **tympanum,** also known as the *eardrum.* The cone shape of the external ear focuses sound on the tympanum and causes it to vibrate at the same frequency as the sound waves reaching it. Attached to the tympanum are three tiny bones: the **malleus** (hammer), **incus** (anvil), and **stapes** (stirrup). The malleus is attached to the tympanum, the incus is attached to the malleus and stapes, and the stapes is attached to a small, membrane-covered opening called the **oval window,** in a snail-shaped, fluid-filled structure known as the **cochlea.** The vibration of the tympanum causes the tiny bones (malleus, incus, and stapes) to vibrate; in turn, they cause a corresponding vibration in the membrane of the oval window.

The cochlea detects sound. When the oval window vibrates, the fluid in the cochlea begins to move, causing the **basilar membrane** to vibrate. Cells on this membrane depolarize when they are stimulated by its vibrations. Because they synapse with neurons, messages can be sent to the brain (figure 26.16).

Most sounds consist of a mixture of pitches. High-pitched, short-wavelength sounds cause the basilar membrane to vibrate at the base of the cochlea near the oval window. Low-pitched, long-wavelength sounds vibrate the basilar membrane far from the oval window. Loud sounds cause the basilar membrane to vibrate more vigorously than do faint sounds. Thus, the brain can perceive the loudness of various sounds as well as their pitch.

Associated with the cochlea are two fluid-filled chambers and a set of fluid-filled tubes, called the *semicircular canals.* The **semicircular canals** are not involved in hearing but are

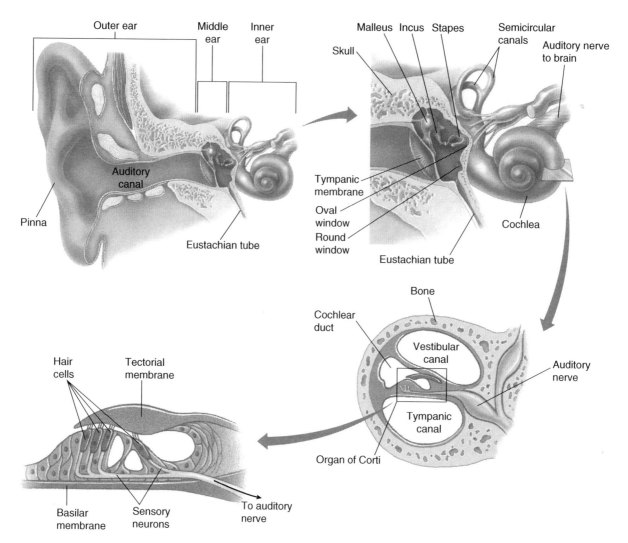

**FIGURE 26.16  The Anatomy of the Ear**
The ear consists of an external cone, which directs sound waves to the tympanum. Vibrations of the tympanum move the ear bones and vibrate the oval window of the cochlea, where the sound is detected. The semicircular canals monitor changes in the position of the head, helping us maintain balance.

involved in maintaining balance and posture. In the walls of these canals and chambers are cells similar to those found on the basilar membrane. These cells are stimulated by movements of the head and by the position of the head with respect to the force of gravity. The head's constantly changing position gives sensory input that is important in maintaining balance.

## Touch

What we normally call the sense of *touch* consists of a variety of kinds of input, which are responded to by three kinds of receptors: Some receptors respond to pressure, others to temperature, and others, which we call *pain receptors,* to cell damage (figure 26.17). When these receptors are appropriately stimulated, they send a message to the brain. Because receptors are stimulated in particular parts of the body, the brain can localize the sensation. However, not all parts of the

body are equally supplied with these receptors. The finger tips, lips, and external genitals have the highest density of these nerve endings, whereas the back, legs, and arms have far fewer receptors.

Some internal receptors, such as pain and pressure receptors, are important in allowing us to monitor our internal activities. Many pains generated by the internal organs are often perceived as if they were somewhere else. For example, the pain associated with a heart attack is often perceived to be in the left arm or jaw. Pressure receptors in joints and muscles provide information about the degree of stress being placed on a portion of the body. This is also important information to send back to the brain so that adjustments can be made in movements to maintain posture. If you have ever had your foot "go to sleep" because the nerve stopped functioning, you have experienced what it is like to lose this constant input of nerve messages from the pressure sensors that assist in guiding

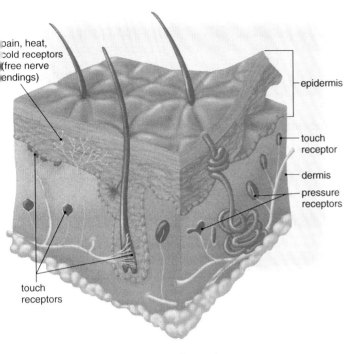

**FIGURE 26.17  The Sense of Touch**
The sense of touch is really a mixture of sensory cells located in the skin, muscles, joints, and certain internal organs. They send impulses to the brain, which interprets the input and generates responses to the stimuli.

the movements you make. Your movements become uncoordinated until the nerve function returns to normal.

## 26.6  Output Coordination

The nervous system and endocrine system cause changes in several ways. Both systems can stimulate muscles to contract and glands to secrete. The endocrine system is also able to change the metabolism of cells and regulate the growth of tissues. The nervous system acts on two kinds of organs: muscles and glands. The actions of muscles and glands are simple and direct: Muscles contract and glands secrete.

### Muscular Contraction

The ability to move is one of the fundamental characteristics of animals. Through the coordinated contraction of many muscles, the intricate, precise movements of a dancer, basketball player, or writer are accomplished. Muscles can do work

**FIGURE 26.18  Antagonistic Muscles**
Because muscles cannot actively lengthen, sets of muscles oppose one another. The contraction and shortening of one muscle causes the stretching of its relaxed antagonistic partner.

only when they pull while contracting. When muscles relax, they do not lengthen unless there is some force available to stretch a muscle after it has stopped contracting and relaxes. Therefore, the muscles that control the movements of the skeleton are present in antagonistic sets—for every muscle's action there is another muscle with the opposite action. For example, the biceps muscle causes the arm to flex (bend) as the muscle shortens. The contraction of its antagonist, the triceps muscle, causes the arm to extend (straighten) and simultaneously stretches the relaxed biceps muscle (figure 26.18).

What we recognize is that a muscle is composed of many muscle cells, which in turn are made up of threadlike fibers, myofibrils, composed of two kinds of myofilaments arranged in a regular pattern. Thin myofilaments composed of the proteins **actin, tropomyosin,** and **troponin** alternate with thick myofilaments composed primarily of the protein **myosin** (figure 26.19). The mechanism by which muscle contracts involves the movement of protein filaments past one another as adenosine triphosphate (ATP) is used.

Myosin molecules are shaped like a golf club. The head of the club-shaped molecule sticks out from the thick myofilament and can combine with the actin of the thin myofilament. However, the troponin and tropomyosin proteins associated with the actin (i.e., a troponin-tropomyosin-actin complex), cover actin in such a way that myosin cannot bind with it. When actin is uncovered, myosin can bind to it, and muscle contraction occurs when ATP is used.

(a) Nerve impulses from spinal cord travel down motor neuron to a muscle.

**Spinal cord**

Motor neuron

Neuromuscular junction

Skeletal muscle fibers

(b) Each motor neuron branch terminates at the neuromuscular junction of a muscle fiber called a motor unit.

Sarcolemma of muscle fiber

Sarcoplasmic reticulum

T tubule

One myofibril

**One sarcomere**

Z line

Z line

(c) Impulses travel down the T system of a muscle fiber to the sarcoplasmic reticulum, where calcium ($Ca^{2+}$) is stored.

Cross-bridge

Myosin

Actin

Z line

H zone

A band

I band

**Contracted sarcomere**

(d) Calcium is released, and the actin filaments slide past the myosin filaments of a sarcomere.

## FIGURE 26.19 The Microanatomy of a Muscle

*(a–c)* Muscles are made of cells that contain bundles known as myofibrils. The myofibrils are composed of two kinds of myofilaments: thick myofilaments composed of myosin, and thin myofilaments containing actin, troponin, and tropomyosin. *(d)* The actin- and myosin-containing myofilaments are arranged in a regular fashion into units called sarcomeres. Each sarcomere consists of two sets of actin-containing myofilaments inserted into either end of bundles of myosin-containing myofilaments. The actin-containing myofilaments slide past the myosin-containing myofilaments, shortening the sarcomere.

The process of muscle-cell contraction involves several steps. The arrival of a nerve impulse at a muscle cell causes the muscle cell to depolarize. When muscle cells depolarize, calcium ions ($Ca^{2+}$) contained within membranes are released among the actin and myosin myofilaments. The calcium ions ($Ca^{2+}$) combine with the troponin molecules, causing the troponin-tropomyosin complex to expose actin, so that it can bind with myosin. While the actin and myosin molecules are attached, the head of the myosin molecule can flex as ATP is used and the actin molecule is pulled past the myosin molecule. Thus, a tiny section of the muscle cell shortens (figure 26.20).

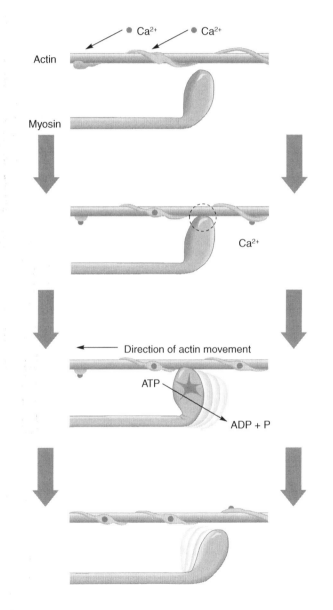

**FIGURE 26.20  Interaction Between Actin and Myosin**
When calcium ions ($Ca^{2+}$) enter the region of the muscle cell containing actin and myosin, they allow the actin and myosin to bind to each other. ATP is broken down to ADP and P with the release of energy. This energy allows the club-shaped head of the myosin to flex and move the actin along, causing the two molecules to slide past each other.

When one muscle contracts, thousands of such interactions take place within a tiny portion of a muscle cell, and many cells within a muscle contract at the same time.

## The Types of Muscle

There are three major types of muscle: skeletal, smooth, and cardiac. These differ from one another in several ways.

*Skeletal muscle* is voluntary muscle; it is under the control of the nervous system. The brain or spinal cord sends a message to skeletal muscles, and they contract to move the legs, fingers, and other parts of the body. This does not mean that we must make a conscious decision every time we want to move a muscle. Many of the movements we make are learned initially but become automatic as a result of practice. For example, walking, swimming, and riding a bicycle required a great amount of practice originally but become automatic for many people. They are, however, still considered voluntary actions.

Skeletal muscles are constantly bombarded with nerve impulses, which result in repeated contractions of differing strength. Many neurons end in each muscle, and each one stimulates a specific set of muscle cells, called a *motor unit* (figure 26.21). A **motor unit** is a single neuron and all the muscle fibers to which it connects. Because each muscle consists of many motor units, it is possible to have a wide variety of intensities of contraction within one muscle organ. This allows a single set of muscles to have a wide variety of functions. For example, the same muscles of the arms and shoulders that are used to play a piano can be used in other combinations to grip and throw a baseball.

If the nerves going to a muscle are destroyed, the muscle becomes paralyzed and begins to shrink. The regular nervous stimulation of skeletal muscle is necessary for it to maintain its size and strength. Any kind of prolonged inactivity leads to the degeneration of muscles, known as *atrophy*. Muscle maintenance is one of the primary functions of physical therapy and a benefit of regular exercise.

**FIGURE 26.21  Motor Unit**
This photo shows a motor unit—the muscle fibers stimulated by the endings of one axon.

Skeletal muscles can contract quickly, but they cannot remain contracted for long periods. Even when we contract a muscle for a minute or so, the muscle is constantly shifting the individual motor units within it that are in a state of contraction. A single skeletal muscle *cell* cannot stay in a contracted state but by shifting the individual muscle *cells* that are contracted, the muscle *organ* can remain contracted for a short time.

*Smooth muscles* make up the walls of muscular internal organs, such as the gut, blood vessels, and reproductive organs. They contract as a response to being stretched. Because much of the digestive system is being stretched constantly, the responsive contractions contribute to the normal rhythmic movements associated with the digestive system. These are involuntary muscles; they can contract on their own without receiving direct messages from the nervous system. This can be demonstrated by removing portions of the gut or uterus from experimental animals. When these muscular organs are kept moist with special solutions, they go through cycles of contraction without any possible stimulation from neurons. However, they do receive nervous stimulation, which can modify the rate and strength of their contraction. This kind of muscle also has the ability to stay contracted for long periods without becoming fatigued. Many kinds of smooth muscle, such as the muscle of the uterus, also respond to the presence of hormones. Specifically, the hormone **oxytocin,** which is released from the posterior pituitary, causes strong contractions of the uterus during labor and childbirth. Similarly, several hormones produced by the duodenum influence certain muscles of the digestive system to either contract or relax.

*Cardiac muscle* makes up the heart. It can contract rapidly, like skeletal muscle, but does not require nervous stimulation to do so. Nervous stimulation can, however, cause the heart to speed or slow its rate of contraction. Hormones, such as epinephrine and norepinephrine, also influence the heart by increasing its rate and strength of contraction. Cardiac muscle also has the characteristic of being *unable* to stay contracted; it will contract quickly but must have a short period of relaxation before it is able to contract a second time. This makes sense in light of its continuous, rhythmic, pumping function. Table 26.1 summarizes the differences among skeletal, smooth, and cardiac muscles.

## The Activities of Glands

Recall that there are two types of glands: endocrine glands, such as the pituitary, thyroid, ovary, and testis; and exocrine glands, such as the salivary glands, intestinal mucous glands, and sweat glands. Some of these glands, such as salivary glands and sweat glands, are under nervous control. When stimulated by the nervous system, they secrete their contents.

Russian physiologist Ivan Petrovich Pavlov showed that salivary glands are under the control of the nervous system, when he trained dogs to salivate in response to hearing a bell. You may recall from chapter 18 that, initially, the animals were presented with food at the same time the bell was rung. Eventually, they would salivate when the bell was rung even if food was not present. This demonstrated that saliva release is under the control of the central nervous system.

Many other exocrine glands are under hormonal control. Many of the digestive enzymes of the stomach and intestine are secreted in response to local hormones produced in the gut. These are circulated through the blood to the digestive glands, which respond by secreting the appropriate digestive enzymes and other molecules.

## Growth Responses

The hormones produced by the endocrine system can have a variety of effects. Hormones can stimulate smooth muscle to contract and can influence the contraction of cardiac muscle. In addition, the hormones released by one gland can cause another gland to secrete its own hormone. However, the endocrine system has one major effect that is not equaled by the nervous system: Hormones regulate growth. Several examples of the many kinds of long-term growth changes that are caused by the endocrine system were given earlier in the chapter. Growth-stimulating hormone (GSH) is produced over a period of years to bring about the increase in size of most of the structures of the body. A low level of this hormone results in a person with small body size. The amount of growth-stimulating hormone (GSH) present varies from time to time; it is present in fairly high amounts throughout childhood and results in steady growth. It also appears to be present at higher levels at certain times, resulting in growth spurts. Finally, as adulthood is reached, the level of this hormone falls, and growth stops.

Similarly, testosterone produced during adolescence influences the growth of bone and muscle to provide men with larger, more muscular bodies than those of women. In addition, there is growth of the penis, of the larynx, and of hair on the face and body. The primary female hormone, estrogen, causes the growth of reproductive organs and the

| **TABLE 26.1**   Characteristics of the Three Kinds of Muscle | | | |
|---|---|---|---|
| Kind of Muscle | Stimulus | Length of Contraction | Rapidity of Response |
| Skeletal | Nervous system | Short; tires quickly | Most rapid |
| Smooth | Self-stimulated; also responds to nervous and endocrine systems | Long; doesn't tire quickly | Slow |
| Cardiac | Self-stimulated; also responds to nervous and endocrine systems | Short; cannot stay contracted | Rapid |

development of breast tissue. It is also involved, along with other hormones, in the cyclic growth and sloughing of the wall of the uterus.

## 26.6  CONCEPT REVIEW

14. How do skeletal, cardiac, and smooth muscles differ in (1) speed of contraction, (2) ability to stay contracted, and (3) cause of contraction?
15. What is the role of each of the following in muscle contraction: actin, myosin, ATP, troponin, and tropomyosin?
16. Why must muscles be in antagonistic pairs?
17. What determines the timing and rate of growth of tissues?

## 26.7  The Body's Defense Mechanisms—Immunity

**Immunity** is the body's ability to maintain homeostasis by resisting or defending against potentially harmful agents, including microbes, toxins, and abnormal cells, such as cancer cells. The body's **immune system** comprises specialized cells and messenger molecules, that work together to defend against infection and disease. Immune responses can be divided into two general categories: innate immune mechanisms and adaptive immune mechanisms. *Innate immune mechanisms* (also known as *nonspecific immune mechanisms*) are generic and protect the body against many kinds of agents. They are present and function from birth. *Adaptive immune mechanisms* (also known as *specific immune mechanisms*) are able to identify specific pathogens based on their exact chemical makeup. They are not present at birth and require exposure to a harmful agent to be activated. Once activated, adaptive immune mechanisms use specific combinations of chemicals and cells to destroy a specific enemy. Adaptive immune mechanisms also involve cellular memory, which allows the body to mount a rapid response to an enemy it has encountered previously.

### Innate Immunity

The body has three kinds of innate defenses—physical barriers, protective chemicals, and certain kinds of defensive cells. All three may work together to safeguard the body.

Physical barriers are extremely important in protecting the body. For example, the skin and mucous membranes are barriers that prevent most bacteria, viruses, parasitic worms, and large toxic molecules from getting through and causing harm. The cells of the upper respiratory system are ciliated and covered with mucus. Should bacteria or dust particles be caught in the fluid, the cilia's upward beating moves them toward the mouth and nose, where they can be eliminated by sneezing, coughing, or swallowing. If the threatening agent is

swallowed, stomach acid (about pH 2) also acts as an innate defense. A mixture of materials with a low pH forms a protective barrier in the vagina.

Protective chemicals are produced by several kinds of cells and are involved in various ways in destroying pathogens. The enzyme *lysozyme*, found in sweat, tears, mucus, saliva, breast milk, and gastric secretions, destroys the cell walls of bacteria. *Complement* is a group of proteins primarily manufactured in the liver that circulate in the blood and help other systems defend against threats of cellular pathogens, such as bacteria, fungi, and protozoa. Complement proteins can help form holes in pathogens, allowing their content to leak out. *Interferons* are proteins that attach to the surface of cells and cause the cells to interfere with the ability of viruses to replicate. If a cell becomes infected with a virus, it produces interferons, which help control the virus in the cell but also act as messengers. These are sent to nearby cells, preparing them to produce their own interferons and initiate reactions that will inhibit viral replication should the virus arrive.

Many kinds of cells are involved in innate immunity. Various kinds of white blood cells recognize pathogens and communicate to other cells that there is a problem. Other white blood cells respond by producing and releasing a variety of chemicals. These chemicals can recruit other defensive cells to the site of injury or infection, kill pathogens directly, cause dilation of blood vessels, or perform other defensive functions. Certain white blood cells actively attack pathogens and kill them. Others engulf pathogens and the body cells that have been killed by infection. This pattern of interaction at the site of an infection is commonly called *inflammation*. **Inflammation** is a pattern of events that leads to increased temperature, redness, swelling, and pain in the affected area.

Because of the pain and swelling associated with inflammation, most people don't think of it as a good thing. However, it is an important part of the innate immune response.

Inflammation also occurs when tissue cells are damaged even though there may not be pathogens present. If you hit your thumb with a

**Inflamed tonsils**

hammer or are stung by a bee, inflammation occurs because damaged tissue cells release chemicals that initiate inflammation. The events that occur during inflammation are summarized in table 26.2.

Under certain circumstances, the inflammatory process can get out of hand. If inflammation continues unchecked, the process can result in tissue damage. Under such circumstances, anti-inflammatory medications, such as nonsteroidal anti-inflammatory drugs (NSAIDs), can be used to interfere with the inflammatory process. Aspirin, ibuprofen, ketoprofen, and naproxen are all over-the-counter NSAIDs.

| TABLE 26.2 | Inflammation |
|---|---|
| **What You Observe** | **What's Really Happening** |
| The event that triggers inflammation | Damage to tissue by molecules, microbes, or other materials; for example, a scratch, infecting bacteria releasing toxins, a splinter. |
| General events of inflammation | Inflammatory chemicals released by injured cells and immune system cells serve as signals calling neutrophils from nearby capillaries. White blood cells (lymphocytes, monocytes, macrophages) go through the blood vessel walls and move to the damaged area, where they attack the enemy and clean up damaged cells by phagocytosis. The pH of tissue fluid decreases, helping control pathogens. |
| Increased temperature | Inflammatory chemicals such as histamine cause dilation (an increase in the diameter) of capillaries which causes increased flow of warm blood to the area. |
| Swelling | As capillaries dilate, they also become more porous, allowing fluid and white blood cells to move from the vessel into the tissue. |
| Redness | Inflammatory chemicals cause increased blood flow in the area. |
| Pain | Inflammatory chemicals and the pressure caused by swelling affect nerve endings. |

## Adaptive Immunity

Adaptive immune mechanisms are targeted at specific pathogens. Although a person is born with an immune system with the ability to develop adaptive immunity, these defenses must be "turned on" in order to work. To be "turned on," the body must be exposed to an *antigen* associated with the pathogen. An **antigen** is a large organic molecule, usually a protein, that is recognized by cells of the immune system, which stimulate them to begin a series of events that result in the destruction of that specific antigen-bearing agent. Antigens can be individual molecules, such as botulism toxin. They can also be parts of cells, such as molecules found on the surface or inside bacteria, viruses, or eukaryotic cells. Furthermore, with adaptive immunity, the immune system cells remember the antigen and can react quickly to the pathogen if the body encounters the pathogen again. This mechanism is often called *acquired immunity* because it begins to work only after certain cells of the immune system have come into contact with a specific antigen. The cells that respond to antigens are primarily T-lymphocytes and B-lymphocytes. The way each of these cells responds is very different, so adaptive immune mechanisms are subdivided into *B-cell* or *antibody-mediated immunity* and *T-cell* or *cell-mediated immunity*. However, a great deal of interaction between these two cell types must occur to defend a person against a specific enemy.

### B-Cells and Antibody-Mediated Immunity

B-lymphocytes (B-cells) are produced and mature in the bone marrow. They are hard to find in the blood but are found in large numbers in the lymph nodes and spleen. When a B-cell contacts an antigen, chemical messengers are sent from the cell surface to its nucleus and genes are activated. In these B-cells, certain portions of the DNA are cut and spliced to produce a new nucleotide sequence. This new gene causes the synthesis of a specific protein able to combine with that antigen. These protein molecules are called immunoglobulins or

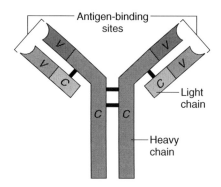

**FIGURE 26.22 Structure of an Immunoglobulin Gamma (IgG) Antibody**
An IgG antibody contains two heavy (long) polypeptide chains and two light (short) chains arranged so that there are two "variable regions" at the top of the Y-shaped molecule. This is where the antigen combines with the antibody (V = variable region, C = constant region).

*antibodies*. An **antibody** is a protein made by the B-cells in response to an antigen (figure 26.22). There are five classes of antibodies, differing in their structures and functions (table 26.3).

When B-cells become specialized for the production of a specific antibody, they remain specialized for the rest of their lives. These specialized B-cells undergo mitosis, and their descendents become either plasma cells, which produce antibodies, or memory B-cells. Plasma cells produce large quantities of antibodies, which enter the circulatory system. When an antibody molecule contacts the antigen, they combine. Figure 26.23 summarizes these events. If the antigen is an isolated toxin molecule or a virus, it is prevented from causing harm or *neutralized*. If the antigen is part of a pathogen, the antigen-antibody combination along with other molecules such as complement, causes holes to be formed in the cell, killing the pathogen. The antigen-antibody combination can also act as an attractant for phagocytes, such as macrophages

**TABLE 26.3**   Classes of Antibodies

| Class | Location | Function |
|---|---|---|
| Immunoglobulin gamma (IgG) (also called gamma globulin) | Blood and tissue fluids | 1. Most abundant immunoglobulin in the blood<br>2. Binds with free antigens or those on cell surfaces<br>3. Activates complement proteins to destroy pathogens<br>4. Encourages phagocytosis of pathogens<br>5. The only class that passes to the fetus through the placenta, which gives passive immunity to fetus |
| Immunoglobulin mu (IgM) | Blood | 1. The first immunoglobulin produced after B-cell encounters antigen<br>2. Activates complement<br>3. Causes pathogen cells to clump, encouraging phagocytosis |
| Immunoglobulin alpha (IgA) | Blood, mucus, saliva, tears, breast milk | 1. Produced in huge quantities on mucous membranes of the digestive, urogenital, and respiratory systems<br>2. Prevents pathogens from attaching to the surface of cells |
| Immunoglobulin delta (IgD) | Blood | 1. Found on surface of B-cells<br>2. Probably involved in development and activation of B-cells |
| Immunoglobulin epsilon (IgE) | Blood—attached to basophils | 1. Protects against parasitic worm infections<br>2. Binds to allergens and causes release of histamine from basophils; therefore, responsible for many allergic reactions, such as asthma and hay fever |

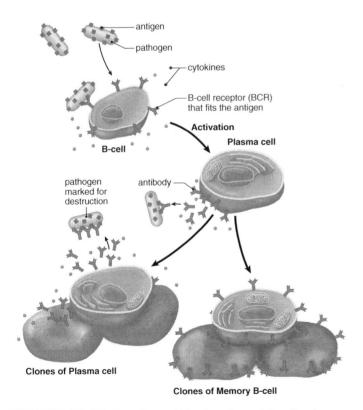

**FIGURE 26.23 B-cells and Production of Antibodies**
When a B-cell first encounters an antigen, it is triggered to express genes that produce antibodies against the antigen. The activated B-cell divides and produces large numbers of plasma cells that produce the antibodies and memory cells that can be activated later when the person is again exposed to the same pathogen.

and neutrophils, causing them to engulf and destroy the pathogen.

Once the trouble is brought under control, the number of plasma cells slowly drops and so does the antibody level. This leaves the memory B-cells to serve as a backup team, should that antigen appear in the future. Memory B-cells know how to make the correct antibody to defend against that specific antigen, but they don't make much of it. The antibodies they produce are on their surface. If the same antigens appear again, they attach to the antibodies causing the memory B-cells to undergo mitosis, changing into a large population of antibody-secreting plasma cells. A second exposure to an antigen results in a more rapid increase in the level of antibodies because the memory cells already have the ability to produce the antibody needed. The amount of antibody increases rapidly and again protects the body from harm.

**Immunization** is the technique used to induce the immune system to develop an acquired immunity to a specific disease by the use of a *vaccine*. **Vaccines** are antigens made so they can start an active immunity without causing disease. A vaccine can be a solution that contains whole, live pathogens in a form so changed that they are not harmful. It can also contain dead organisms or just the antigenic portion of the pathogen; some vaccines are synthetic. When the vaccine is first given, B-cells become activated, just as they do when they encounter an actual disease organism. This is called the primary immune response (figure 26.24). The next time the person is exposed to the vaccine, there is a sharp increase in the amount of antibody produced. This is called the secondary immune response. As time passes, the amount of antibody

(a)

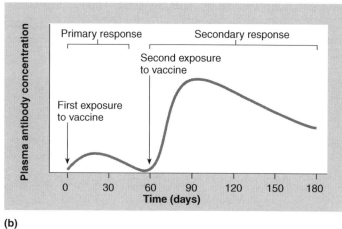

(b)

**FIGURE 26.24 Active Immunity Due to Immunization**
*(a)* Vaccines immunize children against various childhood diseases. *(b)* The primary immune response, after the first exposure to a vaccine, is minimal, but the secondary immune response, which may occur after the second exposure, shows a dramatic rise in the amount of antibody present in the plasma.

will begin to fall. It will remain high only if the person is repeatedly exposed to the same antigen, either by accident or as the result of a booster shot. For example, if a person lives or works in an area where tetanus toxin can regularly stimulate a secondary immune response (e.g., through a puncture wound), a constant high level of immunity to tetanus toxin is naturally maintained. Each time the memory B-cells come in contact with tetanus toxin, the amount of antibody is "boosted" to its maximum protective level. If natural exposure does not occur, the amount of antibody falls slowly, sometimes reaching a low, unprotective level. There are no quick ways to determine how "naturally" protected someone is. If a physician suspects that a patient might develop a case of tetanus, a booster injection of tetanus vaccine is given to stimulate antibody production artificially to ensure a high level of protection.

As a disease travels through a population, surviving individuals have developed an immunity that makes them resistant to reinfection. It also keeps them from becoming the source of infection to others. Thus, the population as a whole develops what is known as *herd immunity*. This concept is based on the relative proportions of immune and susceptible individuals in the population (herd). In other words, if enough people become immune as the result of contracting the illness or immunization, there is less chance that the susceptible people will get the illness. You see herd immunity develop during the "flu season." At first, there is an increase in the number of cases, they reach a peak, and finally the number of cases decreases as more people become immune. If enough people in the population (herd) were to be vaccinated before the virus arrived, the immunized people would protect those who, for whatever reason, did not or could not get the vaccine. Public health officials try to immunize large portions of the susceptible population in an attempt to maintain a high level of herd immunity. The proportion of immune to susceptible persons must be constantly monitored

because new susceptible individuals continuously enter a population through migration and birth and because pathogens change so that they do not necessarily display the same antigens.

## T-Cells and Cell-Mediated Immunity
Cells that will become T-lymphocytes (T-cells) are initially produced in the bone marrow but travel to the thymus gland where they differentiate into T-cells. After they are differentiated they leave the thymus and are found in the blood, lymph, and lymph tissue. Like B-cells, T-cells must be brought into battle through an activation process. To activate T-cells, the antigen must be "presented" to them by other cells, called antigen-presenting cells (APCs) which are often macrophages that have phagocytosed the pathogen. Phagocytosis was covered in chapter 4. Inside an APC, the pathogen is broken down, and each antigenic molecule is attached to a molecule already present in the APC. This new combination is inserted into the APC's cell membrane so that each molecule sticks out on the APC's surface like a microscopic hair. The APC activates the T-cells by presenting the antigen to T-cells when they attach to one another at receptor sites on the surface of the T-cells (figure 26.25). Several kind of T-cells with specific functions have been identified.

*T-helper cells* produce chemicals called *cytokines*. When disease organisms invade the body or other cellular abnormalities occur, cytokines stimulate the actions of B-cells to produce antibodies; stimulate cytotoxic T-cells to kill infected body cells; and recruit macrophages and phagocytes to consume damaged cells.

*T-regulator cells* produce cytokines that are responsible for shutting down the immune response of both B- and T-cells following a period when they were activated to fight an infection. They are also important in preventing immune system cells from attacking normal body cells.

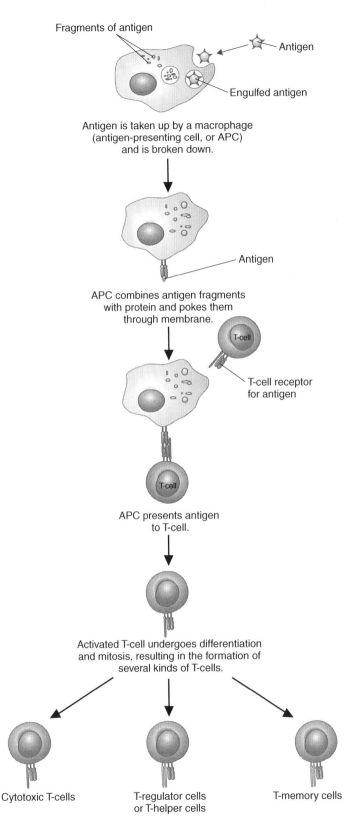

Fragments of antigen

Antigen

Engulfed antigen

Antigen is taken up by a macrophage
(antigen-presenting cell, or APC)
and is broken down.

Antigen

APC combines antigen fragments
with protein and pokes them
through membrane.

T-cell

T-cell receptor
for antigen

T-cell

APC presents antigen
to T-cell.

Activated T-cell undergoes differentiation
and mitosis, resulting in the formation of
several kinds of T-cells.

Cytotoxic T-cells

T-regulator cells
or T-helper cells

T-memory cells

**FIGURE 26.25 Specialized T-Cells**
T-cells become specialized as T regulator cells, T-helper cells, cytotoxic T-cells, or T-memory cells by interaction with an antigen-presenting cell (APC). APCs are macrophages that have engulfed an antigen and present it to undifferentiated T-cells. Once differentiated, each kind of T-cell has a special job to perform in defending the body against harm.

*Cytotoxic T-cells* are specialized for killing body cells that cause disease. After identifying the enemy cells, cytotoxic T-cells move toward their target cells, press up against their surface, and make holes in them. Cytotoxic T-cells target cancer cells, cells infected with viruses or intracellular bacteria or protozoa, and foreign cells, such as cells from an organ transplant.

*T-memory* cells are generated in much the same fashion as B-memory cells, and they play a similar role. They remember the specific antigen of their enemy and can multiply when exposed to the same antigen at a later time (Outlooks 26.1).

## Immune System Diseases

As with other body systems, the immune system can malfunction, resulting in diseases. The most common are allergic reactions, autoimmune diseases, and immunodeficiency diseases. An **allergy** is an abnormal immune reaction to an antigen. Possibly the most familiar are allergies to foods, pollens, and drugs. Such allergies are also known as *type I hypersensitivities*. All allergies involve the interaction of an antigen with a B-cell antibody. An antigen that causes an allergy and comes from outside the body, such as dust, pollen, tobacco, fungi, eggs, and penicillin, is called an *allergen*.

Type I hypersensitivities are associated with immunoglobulin E (IgE). B-cells capable of producing IgE are first exposed to the allergen through the skin, respiratory tract, or intestinal tract and become activated. Unlike most other immunoglobulins, IgE can bind to the surface of mast cells and basophils (figure 26.26). When a person comes in contact with the allergen a second time, the allergen (antigen) attaches to the antibody, which is already attached to mast cells and basophils. This causes the release of large amounts of histamine, leukotrienes, and prostaglandins that cause a variety of symptoms. Symptoms vary greatly in people and include skin rashes, hives, itching throat, asthma, eczema, migraine headaches, and bedwetting.

The most severe allergic reaction is anaphylactic shock. Within minutes after exposure to the allergen, this shock reaction progresses from (1) extensive skin reddening and itching to (2) smooth muscle spasms to (3) capillary breakage in the skin, eyes, and internal organs to (4) a burning sensation in the rectum, the mouth, and possibly the vagina to (5) severe headache to (6) hot flashes to (7) a quick drop in blood pressure to (8) a constriction of bronchial smooth muscle, resulting in respiratory failure, to (9) death. To counteract anaphylactic shock, people with severe allergic reactions are advised to carry and use an EpiPen as soon as they are exposed to the allergen. The medication in this single-use hypodermic syringe is epinephrine (adrenalin), which quickly counteracts the symptoms. However, after using the pen, the person should seek medical attention immediately, because the EpiPen may not totally control the reaction.

**First Exposure**

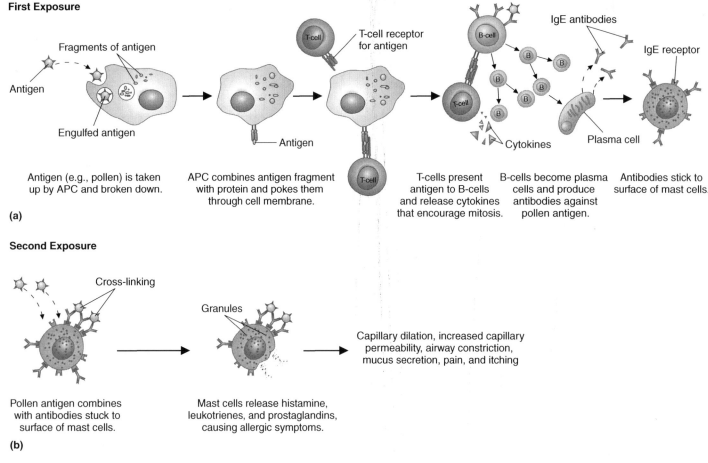

Antigen (e.g., pollen) is taken up by APC and broken down.

APC combines antigen fragment with protein and pokes them through cell membrane.

T-cells present antigen to B-cells and release cytokines that encourage mitosis.

B-cells become plasma cells and produce antibodies against pollen antigen.

Antibodies stick to surface of mast cells.

**(a)**

**Second Exposure**

Pollen antigen combines with antibodies stuck to surface of mast cells.

Mast cells release histamine, leukotrienes, and prostaglandins, causing allergic symptoms.

Capillary dilation, increased capillary permeability, airway constriction, mucus secretion, pain, and itching

**(b)**

**FIGURE 26.26 How an IgE Allergy Works**
*(a)* When a person is first exposed to an allergen, such as pollen, the allergen is taken up by an antigen-presenting cell (APC), which initiates a complex series of events that lead to the release of IgE antibodies, which stick to the surface of mast cells and basophils. A few days later, when pollen is encountered again, *(b)* the increased population of antibody-coated mast cells combines with the allergen, causing them to release the chemicals responsible for the symptoms.

**Autoimmune diseases** are disorders that result from the immune system's turning against the normal chemicals and cells of the body. In other words, the immune response makes a mistake, sees healthy cells as harmful, and attacks them. Some examples of autoimmune diseases are rheumatoid arthritis, type 1 (insulin-dependent) diabetes, systemic lupus, Crohn's disease, and psoriasis. In rheumatoid arthritis, B-cells produce antibodies that mistakenly identify proteins in the cartilage and bone as dangerous and destroy them. In type 1 diabetes, the insulin-producing cells of the pancreas are destroyed by T-cells.

**Immunodeficiency diseases** are disorders that result from the immune system's not producing one or more component cells or chemicals. In this situation, the system cannot provide the protection needed to maintain health. People with such disorders are more susceptible to infections and cancers. People born with the genetic disorder severe combined immunodeficiency disease (SCIDS), or "boy-in-the-bubble" disease, lack the ability to synthesize the enzyme adenosine deaminase (ADA), which is crucial to the formation of T-cells.

Acquired immunodeficiency syndrome (AIDS) is also an immunodeficiency disease but is not genetic. AIDS is the result of a virus infection caused by the human immunodeficiency virus (HIV). HIV infects T- and B-cells and eventually destroys them. When the immune system's population of T-cells has been reduced significantly, it can no longer defend the body against microbial infections. It also loses its ability to recognize and destroy tumor cells.

## 26.7 CONCEPT REVIEW

18. What are the differences between innate and adaptive immunity?
19. How do B-cell and T-cell systems work to defend against disease?

## OUTLOOKS 26.1

# The Immune System and Transplants

People who have damaged tissues or organs often die even though the other parts of their body are functioning normally. Therefore, transplantation of healthy tissues or organs from one person to another could save lives. Because our immune system is designed to attack organisms or cells that display foreign antigens on their surface, successful transplants must avoid being attacked by the recipient's immune system.

There are genes on chromosome 6 in humans that produce proteins that are displayed on the surface of all cells. The proteins are called human leukocyte antigen (HLA) proteins. (The genes are also called major histocompatibility complex [MHC] genes and are found in nearly all vertebrates.) There are on the order of 200 different alleles for these genes. Each person has a specific set of these genes and the proteins they produce and, since there are so many possible combinations of these alleles, each person displays a unique combination of these antigens on their cell surfaces. For the transplant of most tissues or organs to be successful, the antigens of the donor tissue must resemble those of the recipient as closely as possible.

Determining whether the tissues of a donor and recipient are closely matched is a three-step process. First, the blood types (A, B, AB, O) of the donor and the recipient must be compatible (see chapter 10 for a discussion of blood type). Second, a set of HLA proteins are matched. Six of these proteins are considered when making a match. The greatest success is achieved when all six antigens are the same for both the donor and the recipient. Finally, a cross-match is made to make sure that the recipient has not been exposed previously to an antigenic substance in the donor tissue that would trigger a reaction against the donor tissue. The most common causes of exposure to other human antigens are pregnancy (exposure to some of a fetus's antigens), blood transfusions, and previous transplants.

A few kinds of tissues do not have blood vessels (cornea of the eye, tendons, cartilage). Because the recipient's blood and the B- and T-lymphocytes in the blood do not flow through these tissues, the recipient does not become sensitized to the foreign

material. Therefore, transplanting these structures usually does not cause the recipient's immune system to reject the transplant.

Blood transfusions are also a special case of tissue transplantation that does not require matching of the HLA antigens. This is because the red blood cells do not express the HLA genes and platelets express these genes very weakly. Although lymphocytes do express the HLA genes, the rejection reaction is usually not a problem because blood transfusions are a temporary replacement. Instead of the three-step process, the blood type (A, B, AB, and O) and a second blood type called the Rh factor, of the donor and recipient are matched and a sample of the donor's red blood cells is mixed with a sample of the recipient's plasma to determine if there are any antigens on the donor's red blood cells that will cause a problem.

All other organ and tissue transplants require all three steps to assure that there is a reasonable chance that the donated tissue will be accepted by the recipient's immune system. Even when the match is as close as possible, most transplant recipients must use drugs that suppress the immune system for their lifetime.

## Summary

A nerve impulse is caused by sodium ions entering the cell as a result of a change in the permeability of the cell membrane. Thus, a wave of depolarization passes down the length of a neuron to the synapse. The axon of a neuron secretes a neurotransmitter, such as acetylcholine, into the synapse, where these molecules bind to the dendrite of the next cell in the chain, resulting in an impulse in it as well. The acetylcholinesterase present in the synapse destroys acetylcholine, so that it does not repeatedly stimulate the dendrite. The brain is composed of several functional units. The lower portions of the brain control automatic activities, the middle portion of the brain controls the basic categorizing of sensory input, and the higher levels of the brain are involved in thinking and self-awareness.

Several kinds of sensory inputs are possible. Many kinds of chemicals can bind to cell surfaces and be recognized. This is how the senses of taste and smell function. Light energy can be detected because light causes certain molecules in the retina of the eye to decompose and stimulate neurons. Sound can be detected because fluid in the cochlea of the ear is caused to vibrate, and special cells detect this movement and stimulate neurons. The sense of touch consists of a variety of receptors that respond to pressure, cell damage, and temperature.

Muscles shorten because of the ability of actin and myosin to bind to one another. A portion of the myosin molecule is caused to bend when ATP is used, resulting in the sliding of actin and myosin molecules past each other. Skeletal muscle responds to nervous stimulation to cause movements of the skeleton. Smooth muscle and cardiac muscle have internally generated contractions, which can be modified by nervous stimulation or hormones.

There are two types of glands: exocrine glands, which secrete through ducts into the cavity of an organ or to the surface of the skin; and endocrine glands, which release their secretions into the circulatory system. Digestive glands and sweat glands are examples of exocrine glands. Endocrine glands, such as the ovaries, testes, and pituitary gland, change the activities of cells and often cause responses resulting in growth over a period of time. The endocrine system and the nervous system are interrelated. Actions of the endocrine system can change how the nervous system functions, and the reverse is also true.

The immune system defends the body against potentially harmful agents, including microbes, toxins, and abnormal cells. Innate immune mechanisms protect the body against many kinds of harmful agents. Adaptive immune mechanisms can tell the difference between one kind of threat and another based on their exact chemical makeup. After recognizing the enemy, the body selects a specific combination of chemicals and cells to send into the battle to destroy only that enemy. Cells important to the system include B-lymphocytes, T-lymphocytes, and macrophages. Abnormally functioning immune systems can result in allergies, immunodeficiency, and autoimmune diseases.

incus 597
inflammation 603
malleus 597
medulla oblongata 588
motor neurons 586
motor unit 601
myosin 599
negative-feedback inhibition 584
nerve cell 585
nerve impulse 556
nerves 586
nervous system 585
neuron (nerve cell) 585
neurotransmitter 588
norepinephrine 591
olfactory epithelium 596
oval window 597
oxytocin 602
perception 595

peripheral nervous system 586
pons 589
positive-feedback regulation 585
retina 596
rhodopsin 597
rods 596
semicircular canals 597
sensory neurons 586
soma 585
spinal cord 586
stapes 597
synapse 588
testosterone 592
thalamus 589
tropomyosin 599
troponin 599
tympanum 597
vaccines 605
voltage 586

## Key Terms

*Use the interactive flash cards on the **Concepts in Biology**, 14/e website to help you learn the meaning of these terms.*

acetylcholine 588
acetylcholinesterase 588
actin 599
allergy 607
antibody 604
antidiuretic hormone (ADH) 591
antigen 604
autoimmune diseases 608
axons 585
basilar membrane 597
central nervous system 586
cerebellum 588
cerebrum 589
cochlea 597
cones 596
dendrites 585

depolarized 587
endocrine glands 591
endocrine system 591
epinephrine 591
estrogen 592
exocrine glands 591
fovea centralis 596
glands 591
growth-stimulating hormone (GSH) 592
homeostasis 584
hormone 591
hypothalamus 589
immune system 603
immunity 603
immunization 605
immunodeficiency diseases 608

## Basic Review

1. The _____ is the space between the fibers of adjacent neurons in a chain.

2. In the _____, the somatic nervous system controls the skeletal (voluntary) muscles and the autonomic nervous system controls smooth (involuntary) muscles, the heart, and glands.
   a. peripheral nervous system
   b. central nervous system
   c. immune system
   d. medulla oblongata

3. The cells that a specific hormone affects are called
   a. target cells.
   b. neurons.
   c. motor units.
   d. T-lymphocytes.

4. _____ glands have no ducts and secrete their products into the circulatory system.
   a. Exocrine
   b. Endocrine
   c. Salivary
   d. Sweat

5. The mechanism by which an increase in a stimulus causes a reduction in a response is called

   a. positive-feedback regulation.

   b. immune.

   c. negative-feedback control.

   d. absolute.

6. Molecules that are neurotransmitters manufactured in the soma and migrate down the axon, where they are stored until needed, are called

   a. somas.

   b. acetylcholine.

   c. cytokines.

   d. estrogen.

7. Which of the following is a resulting symptom of inflammatory chemicals that cause increased blood flow and dilation of capillaries?

   a. swelling

   b. estrogens

   c. atherosclerosis

   d. nausea

8. Which cells of the immune system produce memory cells?

   a. both B- and T-lymphocytes

   b. B-lymphocytes only

   c. T-lymphocytes only

   d. macrophages

9. Histamine, leukotrienes, and prostaglandins are compounds produced and released by which cells during an allergic reaction?

   a. WBCs

   b. RBCs

   c. basophils

   d. macrophages

10. In muscle, thin myofilaments composed of the proteins actin, tropomyosin, and troponin alternate with thick myofilaments composed primarily of the protein _____.

11. A nerve impulse involves

    a. a change in the permeability of the cell membrane.

    b. the flow of sodium ions into the nerve cell.

    c. depolarization of the nerve cell membrane.

    d. All of the above are correct.

12. The chemicals produced by endocrine glands that cause changes in other tissues are called _____.

13. The cells in the retina of the eye that are able to detect different colors are called _____.

14. The chemical sense of taste

    a. has only about five kinds of chemical receptors.

    b. is only found on the tip of the tongue.

    c. fatigues very rapidly.

    d. is learned.

15. Hearing involves

    a. the movement of tiny hairs in the cochlea.

    b. the movement of fluid in the cochlea.

    c. nerve impulses from the cochlea to the brain.

    d. All of the above are correct.

### Answers

1. synapse   2. a   3. a   4. b   5. c   6. b   7. a   8. a
9. c   10. myosin   11. d   12. hormones   13. cones
14. a   15. d

## Thinking Critically

**Can We Improve Our Sense of Smell?**
Humans are considered to have a poor sense of smell. However, when parents are presented with baby clothing, they are able to identify the clothing with which their own infant had been in contact with a high degree of accuracy. Specially trained individuals, such as wine and perfume testers, are able to identify large numbers of different kinds of molecules that the average person cannot identify. Birds rely primarily on sound and sight for information about their environment; they have a poor sense of smell. Most mammals are known to have a very well-developed sense of smell. Is it possible that we have evolved into sound-and-sight-dependent organisms, like birds, and have lost the keen sense of smell of our ancestors? Or is it that we just don't use our sense of smell to its full potential? Devise an experiment that would help shed light on this question.

CHAPTER

# 27

# Human Reproduction, Sex, and Sexuality

## Are Sperm Counts Falling?

*Environmental factors could be involved.*

In recent years there have been several studies that suggest that sperm counts have been falling. One British study suggests that sperm counts have fallen by 29% in 12 years. Another study found that men with higher levels of certain pesticides in their blood had lower sperm counts. There are many critics of the various studies, who question the way the data were collected or the conclusions reached. For example, some data were collected at fertility clinics where men might be expected to have low sperm counts. Other studies had very small sample sizes or had other problems with the way the study was designed and carried out.

Regardless of the quality of the data, people with particular views have used these studies to support their concerns about environmental chemicals—pesticides, chemicals in plastics—the use of birth control pills, consumption of high amounts of beef, and a variety of other environmental factors. Some have even suggested that tight pants or the heat from laptop computers could raise the temperature of the testes and reduce sperm counts.

- Could environmental factors affect sperm production?
- Is fertility falling?
- Should a well-designed, worldwide study of sperm counts be done?

## Background Check

**Concepts you should already know to get the most out of this chapter:**
- The nature of meiosis and gamete production (chapter 9)
- The fundamentals of genetics (chapter 10)
- The basic structure and function of the endocrine system (chapter 26)

## 27.1 Sexuality from Various Points of View

Probably nothing interests people more than sex and sexuality. **Sex** is the nature of the biological differences between males and females. By **sexuality,** we mean all the factors that contribute to one's female or male nature. A person's sexuality includes the structure and function of the sex organs, sexual behavior, and the ways in which culture influences sexual behavior. Males and females have different behavior patterns for a variety of reasons. Some behavioral differences are learned (e.g., patterns of dress, the use of facial makeup), whereas others appear to be less dependent on culture (e.g., degree of aggressiveness, the frequency of sexual thoughts).

There are several ways of looking at human sexuality. The behavioral sciences tend to focus on the behaviors associated with being male and female and what is considered appropriate or inappropriate sexual behavior. Psychologists consider sexual behavior to be a strong drive, appetite, or urge. They describe the sex drive as a basic impulse to satisfy a biological, social, or psychological need. Other social scientists, such as sociologists and cultural anthropologists, are interested in sexual behavior as it occurs in various cultures. When a variety of cultures are examined, it becomes very difficult to classify various kinds of sexual behavior as normal or abnormal. What is considered abnormal in one culture may be normal in another. For example, public nudity is considered abnormal in many cultures, but not in others (figure 27.1).

Biologists have studied the sexual behavior of nonhuman animals for centuries. They have long considered the function of sexuality in light of its value to the population or species. Sexual reproduction results in new combinations of genes, which are important in the process of natural selection. Many biologists are attempting to look at human sexual behavior from an evolutionary perspective and speculate on why certain sexual behaviors are common. The behaviors of courtship, mating, the raising of the young, and the division of labor between the sexes are complex in all social animals, including humans, as demonstrated in the elaborate social behaviors surrounding picking a mate and forming a family. It is difficult to draw the line between the biological development of sexuality and the social customs related to the sexual aspects of human life. However, the biological mechanism that determines whether an individual will develop into a female or a male has been well documented.

**FIGURE 27.1  Culture and Sexuality**
In the culture of Papua New Guinea, tradition patterns of dress typically involve partial nudity. This would be unacceptable in many Muslim cultures, which regards exposure of skin as immodest. In both cultures there are differences in the dress of men and women.

### 27.1  CONCEPT REVIEW

1. Define the term *sexuality.*
2. How do psychologists, biologists, and anthropologists differ in how they view sexuality?

## 27.2 The Sexuality Spectrum

Although we tend to think of our species as being clearly divided into two genders, male and female, sexuality really is a spectrum that includes anatomical and behavioral components. Both anatomy and behavior are the result of a complex interplay between genetic and developmental processes that are influenced by environmental factors.

### Anatomy

Hermaphrodites are organisms that have both ovaries and testes in the same body. This condition is extremely rare in humans. However, incidences of partial development of the genitalia (sex organs) of both sexes in one individual may be more frequent than most people realize. About 1% of births show some level of ambiguity related to sexual anatomy. These people are referred to as *intersexual* because their sexual anatomy is not clearly male or female. Sometimes, this abnormal development occurs because the hormone levels are out of balance at critical times in the development of the embryo. This hormonal imbalance also may be related to an abnormal number of sex-determining chromosomes, or it may be the result of abnormal functioning of the endocrine glands.

When children with abnormal combinations of sex organs are born, they are usually assessed by a physician in consultation with the parents to determine which sexual structures should be retained or surgically reconstructed. The physician might also decide that hormone therapy might be a more successful treatment. These decisions are not made easily because they involve children who have not fully developed their sexual nature. An increasingly vocal group advocates that children who are diagnosed with this condition not be surgically "corrected" as infants, recommending that, if the parents can cope with the unusual genitalia, they allow the child to grow older without having the surgery. They believe that people should choose for themselves once they are more mature. However, few long-term studies have examined whether delaying reconstructive surgery presents fewer social and psychological adjustment issues than performing reconstructive surgery in children.

### Behavior

A person's gender is his or her sexual identity based on anatomy. However, a person also has a psychological gender. More and more frequently, we are becoming aware of individuals whose physical gender does not match their psychological gender. These individuals are often referred to as *transgender* persons. A male with normal male sex organs may "feel" like a female. The same situation may occur with structurally female individuals. Because some of these individuals might dress as a member of the opposite sex, they are sometimes called *cross-dressers* or *transvestites*. Some of these individuals may dress as the other sex in private but dress and behave in public appropriate to their anatomical sex. Others completely change their public and private behaviors to reflect their inner desire to function as the other sex. A male

may dress as a female, work in a traditionally female occupation, and make social contacts as a female. Tremendous psychological and emotional pressures develop from this condition. Frequently, many of these individuals choose to undergo gender reassignment surgery—a sex-change operation. Their goal is to interact with society without being detected as having been a different gender at one time. This surgery and the follow-up hormonal treatment can cost tens of thousands of dollars and take several years.

Homosexuality is a condition in which a person desires romantic and sexual relationships with members of their own sex. However, it is a complex behavioral pattern with many degrees of expression. Some individuals are exclusively homosexual, while others can be considered bisexual because they form sexual relationships with either males or females. Some are transgender individuals while others clearly accept their biological sex but prefer relationships with others of the same sex. However, it is becoming clear that sexual orientation in most cases is not a simple choice or a learned behavior. There appear to be differences in brain function and genetic makeup that are important. For example, certain studies suggest that genetic regions on chromosomes 7, 8, and 10 may influence homosexuality. Some regions on chromosome 7 and 8 have been linked with male sexual orientation, regardless of whether the male receives the chromosomes from his mother or father. The regions on chromosome 10 appear to be linked with male sexual orientation only if they were inherited from the mother.

Sexuality ranges from strongly heterosexual to strongly homosexual. Human sexual orientation is a complex trait, and evidence suggests that there is no one gene that determines where a person falls on the sexuality spectrum. It is most likely a combination of various genes acting together and interacting with environmental factors (figure 27.2).

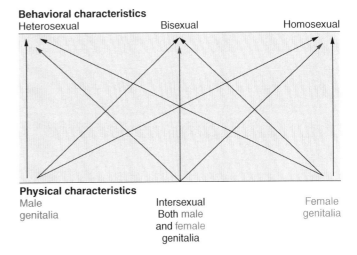

**Behavioral characteristics**
Heterosexual        Bisexual        Homosexual

**Physical characteristics**
Male genitalia        Intersexual Both male and female genitalia        Female genitalia

**FIGURE 27.2  The Sexuality Spectrum**
A person's sexuality involves both anatomical and psychological components. This figure shows how behavioral and physical sexual characteristics interrelate. At the ends of the behavioral spectrum, individuals can be strongly heterosexual or strongly homosexual, or (in the center) they might be bisexual, attracted to both sexes. On the anatomical spectrum they may be clearly anatomically male or female or be intersexual.

## 27.3 Components of Human Sexual Behavior

The primary *biological* goal of sexual intercourse (coitus, mating) is the union of sperm and egg to form offspring. However, in humans and some other animals, sexual intercourse between willing partners usually is enjoyable and is an important part of the social and psychological aspects of life. Sexuality is a complex interaction that involves distinct components.

*Sexual attraction* involves many factors, but sight and smell are probably the most important. How one person appears to another is usually what catches the other's attention. If we find a person pleasing in appearance, we say he or she is "attractive"; that is, we want to be closer. Like many other organisms, humans release chemicals that act as attractants. These chemicals are called *pheromones*. The existence of pheromones in humans has been well-documented even though we usually are not aware of their actions. The cosmetic and fashion industries are founded on these fundamentals of sexual attraction (figure 27.3). After the initial attraction, the couple will usually talk. The conversation will better acquaint the two, present the idea that there is an attraction, and may suggest that they are interested in sexual intercourse. This period is often called courtship and may be brief or develop into a long-term relationship depending on how the two respond to one another. However, ultimately, sexual intercourse occurs or the relationship ends.

*Foreplay* is the term used to describe sexual stimulation that precedes sexual intercourse. Hugging, kissing, and fondling (petting) arouse sexual excitement and desire. This leads to changes in the levels of certain hormone production and an increase blood flow in both male and female genitals. In males, tissues in the penis become engorged with blood, causing the penis to stiffen or become erect. In females, the clitoris becomes erect and the labia become swollen. In addition, lubricating fluids are released from male and female reproductive tracts. Throughout arousal, the heart rate increases, breathing quickens, and blood pressure increases.

*Sexual intercourse* involves inserting the erect penis into the vagina. Once the penis is inside the vagina, pelvic movements result in stimulation of both the male and female and usually results in ejaculation by the male. **Ejaculation** is the release of semen, which contains sperm and other fluids, from the penis. It occurs with a pulsating of smooth muscle in the tubes that lead from the testes to the penis. This release is generally accompanied by a sensation called orgasm. **Orgasm** is the pleasurable climax of sexual activity. In addition to the muscles of sex organs (vagina, uterus, and male sex organs), muscles throughout the body begin to spasm. Following orgasm, blood, which had accumulated and caused erection of the penis or clitoris and swelling of labia, leaves and these organs return to normal. This period is typically associated with a period of complete relaxation.

Two other forms of sexual intercourse practiced are anal (penis in anus) and oral (penis in mouth or oral stimulation of vagina or clitoris). These two variations may also be part of the arousal phase of a sexual encounter.

Long-term relationships usually involve a conscious decision by the two partners to live together and make joint decisions about many aspects of their lives. However, an important part of maintaining such relationships is paying attention to the sexual aspects of the relationship. Maintaining an active, enjoyable sex life in a long-term relationship requires the same amount of effort that was extended at the beginning of the relationship. Things that can interfere include work (time away, lack of free time, tiredness), family problems (kids, relatives), physical exhaustion (work, sports), affairs, emotions (depression, anger, jealousy), and a person's overall health (overweight, strength, pain, long-term illness). The use of alcohol, street drugs, or certain prescription medications can lead to a reduction of sex drive and may include erectile dysfunction (ED). Since sight plays an initial and important role in sexual attraction and self-image, changes in a person's anatomy can also dampen sexual activity; for example, changes such as a mastectomy due to cancer or disfigurement due to an accident. In addition, acquiring a sexually transmitted disease can place limits on sexual activity in socially responsible individuals.

**FIGURE 27.3 Sexual Attraction**
Both males and females find appearance to be of primary importance in mate selection.

## 27.4  Sex Determination and Embryonic Sexual Development

In humans and some other organisms, the sex of an offspring is determined by the chromosomes they inherit from their parents.

### Chromosomal Determination of Sex

Recall from chapter 10 that two of the 46 chromosomes are involved in determining sex and are called **sex-determining chromosomes**. The other 44 chromosomes are known as *autosomes*. There are two kinds of sex-determining chromosomes: the **X chromosome** and the **Y chromosome** that do not carry equivalent amounts of information, nor do they have equal functions (figure 27.4).

X chromosomes carry genetic information about the production of a variety of proteins, in addition to their function in determining sex. For example, the X chromosome carries information on blood clotting, color vision, and other characteristics. The Y chromosome, with about 80 genes, however, appears to be primarily concerned with determining male sexual differentiation.

When a human **sperm**, a haploid sex cell produced by sexually mature males, is produced, it carries 22 autosomes and a sex-determining chromosome. Unlike eggs, which always carry an X chromosome, half the sperm cells carry an X chromosome and the other half carry a Y chromosome. If an X-carrying sperm cell fertilizes an X-containing egg cell, the resultant embryo will develop into a female. If a Y-carrying sperm cell fertilizes the egg, a male embryo will develop. It is the presence or absence of the sex-determining region Y (SRY) gene located on the short arm of the Y chromosome that determines the sex of the developing individual. The SRY gene produces a chemical, called testes determining factor (TDF), which acts as a master switch that triggers the events that converts the embryo into a male. Without this gene, the embryo would become female.

The early embryo resulting from fertilization and cell division is not recognizable as either male or female. Sexual

(a)

(b)

**FIGURE 27.4  Human Male and Female Chromosomes**
The chromosomes have been arranged into homologous pairs: *(a)* a male karyotype, with an X and a Y chromosome, and *(b)* a female karyotype, with two X chromosomes.

development begins when certain cells become specialized, forming the embryonic *gonads* known as the female ovaries and the male testes. This specialization of embryonic cells is called differentiation. If the SRY gene is present and functioning, the embryonic gonads begin to differentiate into testes 5 to 7 weeks after conception (fertilization).

## Chromosomal Abnormalities and Sexual Development

Evidence that the Y chromosome and its SRY gene control male development comes from many kinds of studies, including research on individuals who have an abnormal number of chromosomes. An abnormal meiotic division that results in sex cells with too many or too few chromosomes is a form of *nondisjunction* (see chapter 9). If nondisjunction affects the X and Y chromosomes, a gamete might be produced that has only 22 chromosomes and lacks a sex-determining chromosome. On the other hand, it might have 24, with 2 sex-determining chromosomes. If a cell with too few or too many sex chromosomes is fertilized, sexual development is usually affected. If a normal egg cell is fertilized by a sperm cell with no sex chromosome, the offspring will have only 1 X chromosome. These people, always women, are designated as XO. They develop a collection of characteristics known as *Turner's syndrome* (figure 27.5).

About 1 in 2,000 girls born has Turner's syndrome. A female with this condition is short for her age and fails to mature sexually, resulting in sterility. In addition, she may have a thickened neck (termed *webbing*), hearing impairment, and some abnormalities in her cardiovascular system. When the condition is diagnosed, some of the physical conditions can be modified with treatment. Treatment involves the use of growth-stimulating hormone to increase her growth rate and female sex hormones to stimulate sexual development, although sterility is not corrected.

An individual who has XXY chromosomes is basically male (figure 27.6). This genetic condition is termed *Klinefelter's syndrome*. It is one of the most common examples of abnormal chromosome number in humans. This condition is present in about 1 in 500 to 1,000 men. Most of these men lead healthy, normal lives and it is impossible to tell them apart from normal males. However, those with Klinefelter's syndrome may be sterile and show breast enlargement, incomplete masculine body form, lack of facial hair, and some minor learning problems. These traits vary greatly in degree, and many men are diagnosed only after they undergo testing to determine why they are infertile. Treatments include breast-reduction surgery and testosterone therapy.

## Fetal Sexual Development

The development of embryonic gonads begins very early during fetal growth. First, a group of cells begins to differentiate into primitive gonads at about week 5 (figure 27.7). By week 5 to 7, if a Y chromosome is present, the gene product (testes determining factor) from the chromosome begins the differentiation

**FIGURE 27.5  Turner's Syndrome**
Individuals with Turner's syndrome have 45 chromosomes. They have only 1 of the sex chromosomes, and it is an X chromosome. Individuals with this condition are female, have delayed growth, and fail to develop sexually. This woman is less than 150 cm (5 ft) tall and lacks typical secondary sexual development for her age. She also has the "webbed neck" that is common among individuals with Turner's syndrome.

**(a) Before hormone therapy**          **(b) After hormone therapy**

**FIGURE 27.6  Klinefelter's Syndrome**
Individuals with two X chromosomes and a Y chromosome are male, are sterile, and often show some degree of breast development and female body form. They are typically tall. The two photos show an individual with Klinefelter's syndrome before and after receiving testosterone hormone therapy.

of these embryonic gonads into testes. They will develop into ovaries beginning about week 12 if 2 X chromosomes are present (and the Y chromosome is absent).

As soon as the gonad has differentiated into an embryonic testis at about week 8, it begins to produce testosterone. The presence of testosterone results in the differentiation of male sexual anatomy, and the absence of testosterone results in the differentiation into female sexual anatomy in the developing embryo (Outlooks 27.1).

**(a) Development of internal sexual anatomy**

Gonad

**Undifferentiated**

Seminal vesicle

Prostate
Vas deferens
Epididymis
Testis

**Male**

Fallopian tubes
Ovary

Uterus
Vagina

**Female**

**(b) Development of external sexual anatomy**

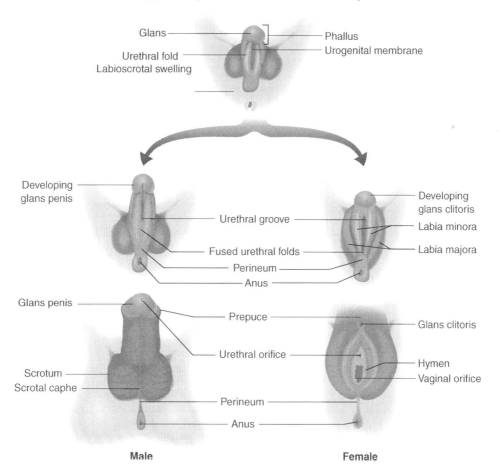

Glans
Urethral fold
Labioscrotal swelling

Phallus
Urogenital membrane

Developing
glans penis

Urethral groove

Fused urethral folds

Perineum

Anus

Developing
glans clitoris

Labia minora

Labia majora

Glans penis

Prepuce

Urethral orifice

Scrotum
Scrotal caphe

Perineum

Anus

Glans clitoris

Hymen

Vaginal orifice

**Male**

**Female**

**FIGURE 27.7  Differentiation of Sexual Characteristics**
The early embryo grows without showing any sexual characteristics. The male and female sexual organs eventually develop from a common basic structure. *(a)* Shows the development of the internal anatomy. *(b)* Shows the development of the external anatomy.

## OUTLOOKS 27.1

# Cryptorchidism—Hidden Testes

At about the seventh month of pregnancy (gestation), in normal males each testis moves from a position in the abdominal cavity to an external sac, called the scrotum. The testes pass through an opening called the **inguinal canal.** This canal closes off but continues to be a weak area in the abdominal wall, and it may rupture later in life. This can happen when strain (for example, from improperly lifting heavy objects) causes a portion of the intestine to push through the inguinal canal into the scrotum, a condition known as an inguinal hernia.

Occasionally, the testes do not descend, resulting in a condition known as **cryptorchidism** (*crypt* = hidden; *orchidos* = testes). Sometimes, the descent occurs normally during puberty; if not, there is a 25 to 50 times increased risk for testicular cancer. Because of this increased risk, surgery can be done to allow the undescended testes to be moved into the scrotum. Sterility will result if the testes remain in the abdomen. This happens because normal sperm cell development cannot occur in a very warm environment. The temperature in the abdomen is higher than the temperature in the scrotum. Normally, the temperature of the testes is very carefully regulated by muscles that control their distance from the body. Physicians have even diagnosed cases of male infertility as being caused by tight-fitting pants that hold the testes so close to the body that the temperature increase interferes with normal sperm development. Recent evidence has also suggested that teenage boys and young men working with computers in the laptop position for extended periods may also be at risk for lowered sperm counts.

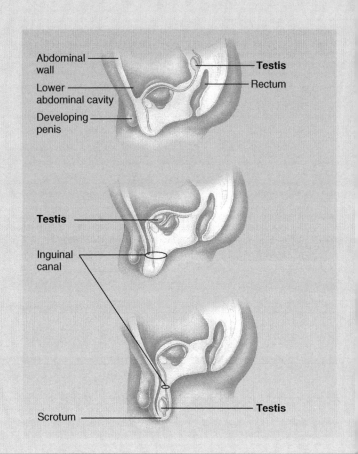

## 27.4 CONCEPT REVIEW

7. Describe the processes that cause about 50% of babies to be born male and 50% to be born female.
8. Name two developmental abnormalities associated with nondisjunction of chromosomes.
9. When in embryological development does sexual differentiation begin?
10. What triggers sexual differentiation in embryos?

## 27.5 The Sexual Maturation of Young Adults

Following birth, sexuality plays only a small part in physical development for several years. However culture and environment shape the responses that the individual will come to recognize as normal behavior for his or her age. **Puberty** is the developmental period when the body changes to the adult form and becomes able to reproduce. During puberty, which begins at about 10 years of age in females and about 12 years of age in males, an increased production of sex hormones causes major changes as the individual reaches sexual maturity. These changes are generally completed by 15–18 years of age.

### The Maturation of Females

Girls typically begin to produce sex hormones from several glands, marking the onset of puberty. The hypothalamus, pituitary gland, ovaries, and adrenal glands begin to produce sex hormones at 9 to 12 years of age (figure 27.8). Table 27.1 lists the principal hormones involved in human reproduction.

The hypothalamus is a portion of the brain that controls the functioning of many glands throughout the body, including the **pituitary gland.** At puberty, the hypothalamus begins to release **gonadotropin-releasing hormone (GnRH),** which stimulates the pituitary to release **luteinizing hormone (LH)** and **follicle-stimulating hormone (FSH).** Increased levels of FSH stimulate the development of **follicles,** saclike structures that produce eggs in the ovaries. The increased luteinizing

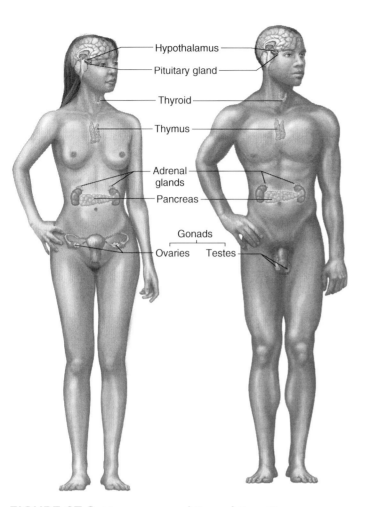

**FIGURE 27.8  Hormones and Sexual Function**
The hypothalamus, pituitary gland, adrenal gland, and ovaries and testes are the primary hormone-producing glands that affect sexual development and behavior.

hormone stimulates the ovary to produce larger quantities of estrogens. The increasing supply of estrogens is responsible for the many changes in sexual development. These changes include breast growth, changes in the walls of the uterus and vagina, changes in the pelvic bone structure, and increased blood supply to the **clitoris,** a small, elongated erectile structure located at the head of the labia; it develops from the same embryonic tissue as the male penis. Estrogens also stimulate the female adrenal gland to produce **androgens,** male sex hormones. The androgens are responsible for the production of pubic hair, and they seem to have an influence on the female sex drive.

The features that are not primarily involved in sexual reproduction but are characteristic of a sex are called **secondary sexual characteristics.** In women, breast development, the distribution of body hair, the patterns of fat deposits, wider hips, and a higher voice are secondary sexual characteristics.

Major developments during this time are **ovulation,** the release of eggs from the ovary, and the establishment of the **menstrual cycle,** the periodic growth and shedding of the lining

of the uterus. These changes are under the control of a number of hormones produced by the pituitary gland and ovaries.

Initially, as girls go through puberty, menstruation and ovulation may be irregular; however, in most women hormone production eventually becomes regulated, so that ovulation and menstruation take place on a monthly basis, although normal cycles vary from 21 to 45 days.

As girls progress through puberty, curiosity about their changing body form and new feelings lead to self-investigation. Studies have shown that sexual activity, such as stimulation of the clitoris, vagina, or anus, which causes a pleasurable sensation, orgasm, is performed by a large percentage of young women. This stimulation is termed **masturbation,** and it is a normal part of sexual development.

## The Maturation of Males

Males typically reach puberty about 2 years later than females, but puberty in males also begins with a change in hormone levels. At puberty, the hypothalamus releases increased amounts of gonadotropin-releasing hormone (GnRH), resulting in increased levels of follicle-stimulating hormone (FSH) and luteinizing hormone (LH). These are the same changes that occur in female development. Luteinizing hormone is often called interstitial cell-stimulating hormone (ICSH) in males. LH stimulates the testes to produce testosterone, the primary sex hormone in males. The testosterone produced by the embryonic testes causes the differentiation of internal and external genital anatomy in the male embryo. At puberty, the increase in testosterone is responsible for the development of male secondary sexual characteristics and is important in the maturation and production of sperm.

The major changes during puberty include growth of the testes and scrotum, pubic hair development, and increased penis size. Secondary sex characteristics also begin to become apparent; facial hair, underarm hair, and chest hair are some of the most obvious. The male voice changes as the larynx (voice box) begins to change shape. Body contours also change, and a growth spurt increases height. In addition, the proportion of the body that is muscle increases and the proportion of body fat decreases. At this time, a boy's body begins to take on the characteristic adult male shape, with broader shoulders and heavier muscles.

In addition to these external changes, increased testosterone causes the production of **semen,** also known as *seminal fluid,* a mixture of sperm and secretions from three *accessory glands*—the *seminal vesicles, prostate,* and *bulbourethral glands.* They produce secretions that nourish and activate the sperm. Semen also lubricates the reproductive tract and acts as the vehicle to help carry the sperm.

Seminal vesicles secrete an alkaline fluid, containing fructose, and hormones. Its alkaline nature helps neutralize the acidic environment in the female reproductive tract, improving the sperm's chances of reaching the egg. The fructose provides energy for the sperm. Seminal vesicle secretions make up about 60% of the seminal fluid. The prostate gland

## TABLE 27.1  Human Reproductive Hormones

| Hormone | Production Site | Target Organ | Function |
|---|---|---|---|
| Prolactin, lactogenic, or luteotropic hormone | Anterior pituitary | Breast, ovaries | Stimulates milk production; also helps maintain normal ovarian cycle |
| Follicle-stimulating hormone (FSH) | Anterior pituitary | Ovaries, testes | Stimulates ovary and testis development; stimulates egg production in females and sperm production in males |
| Luteinizing hormone (LH) or interstitial cell-stimulating hormone (ICSH) | Anterior pituitary | Ovaries, testes | Stimulates ovulation in females and sex-hormone (estrogen and testosterone) production in both males and females |
| Estrogen | Ovaries | Entire body | Stimulates the development of the female reproductive tract and secondary sexual characteristics |
| Testosterone | Testes | Entire body | Stimulates the development of the male reproductive tract and secondary sexual characteristics |
| Progesterone | Corpus luteum of ovaries | Uterus, breasts | Causes uterine wall thickening and maturation; maintains pregnancy; contributes to milk production |
| Oxytocin | Posterior pituitary | Uterus, breasts | Causes the uterus to contract and breasts to release milk |
| Androgens | Testes, adrenal glands | Entire body | Stimulates the development of the male reproductive tract and secondary sexual characteristics in males and females |
| Gonadotropin-releasing hormone (GnRH) | Hypothalamus | Anterior pituitary | Stimulates the release of FSH and LH from the anterior pituitary |
| Human chorionic gonadotropin | Placenta | Corpus luteum | Maintains the corpus luteum, so that it continues to secrete progesterone and maintains pregnancy |

produces a thin, milky fluid, which makes up about 25% of semen. It contains sperm-activating enzymes. Bulbourethral gland secretions make up the remaining 15%; they, too, are alkaline.

FSH stimulates the production of sperm cells. The release of sperm cells and seminal fluid, ejaculation, begins during puberty. This release is generally accompanied by a pleasurable sensation, orgasm. During sleep, males frequently have erections, sometimes resulting in ejaculation of seminal fluid. This is termed a *wet dream*. It is normal and related to the amount of seminal fluid produced. Wet dreams occur less often in men who engage in frequent sexual intercourse or masturbation. Masturbation is a common and normal activity as a boy goes through puberty. Studies of adult sexual behavior have shown that nearly all men masturbate at some time during their lives.

### 27.5  CONCEPT REVIEW

11. What are the effects of the secretions of the pituitary, the gonads, and the adrenal glands at puberty in females?
12. What role does testosterone play in male sexual maturation?

## 27.6  Spermatogenesis

The process of producing gametes is called **gametogenesis.** It includes meiosis and other processes involved in producing mature sex cells. **Spermatogenesis** is gametogenesis that takes place in the testes of males, producing sperm (figure 27.9). The two, olive-shaped testes are composed of many small, sperm-producing tubes, called **seminiferous tubules.** The seminiferous tubules empty into collecting ducts that eventually empty into the epididymis—a long, narrow, twisted tube in which sperm cells are stored and mature before ejaculation. The testes and their associated ducts are held together by a thin covering membrane (figure 27.10). Leading from the epididymis is the vas deferens, or sperm duct; this empties into the urethra, which conducts the sperm out of the body through the penis (figure 27.11).

Before puberty, the seminiferous tubules are packed solid with diploid cells. These cells, which are found just inside the tubule wall, undergo *mitosis,* thus providing a continuous supply of cells. Beginning at puberty, some of these cells specialize and begin the process of *meiosis,* whereas others continue to divide by mitosis. Spermatogenesis needs to occur below body temperature, which is why the testicles are in a sac, the scrotum, outside the body cavity. Once spermatogenesis begins, the seminiferous tubules become hollow and can transport the mature sperm.

**Spermatogenesis**

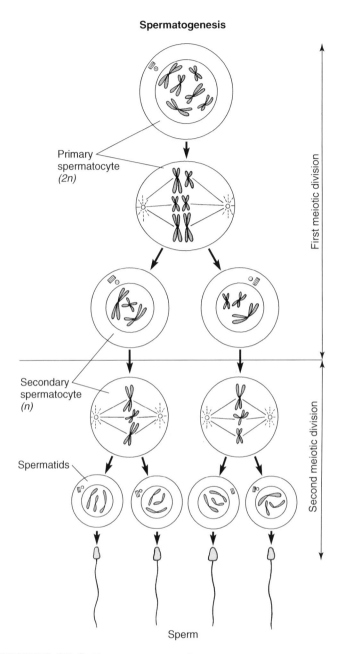

Primary
spermatocyte
*(2n)*

First meiotic division

Secondary
spermatocyte
*(n)*

Spermatids

Second meiotic division

Sperm

**FIGURE 27.9  Spermatogenesis**
This diagram illustrates the process of spermatogenesis in human males. Not all of the 46 chromosomes are shown. Carefully follow the chromosomes as they segregate, recalling the details of the process of meiosis.

Spermatogenesis consists of several steps. It begins when some of the cells in the walls of the seminiferous tubules differentiate and enlarge. These diploid cells undergo the first meiotic division, which produces two haploid cells. These cells go through the second meiotic division, resulting in four haploid cells called spermatids. Spermatids then lose much of their cytoplasm, develop long tails, and mature into sperm. Sperm have only a small amount of food reserves. Therefore, once they are released and become active swimmers, they live

no more than 72 hours. However, if the sperm are placed in a protective solution, the temperature can be lowered drastically to −196°C. Under these conditions, the sperm become deactivated, freeze, and can survive for years outside the testes. This has led to the development of sperm banks. The artificial insemination (placing stored sperm into the reproductive tract of a female) of cattle, horses, and other domesticated animals with sperm from sperm banks is a common breeding practice. This technique is also used in humans who experience infertility.

Spermatogenesis takes place continuously throughout a male's reproductive life, although the number of sperm produced decreases as a man ages. A healthy male releases about 150 million sperm per milliliter with each ejaculation. A man must be able to release at least 100 million sperm per milliliter to be fertile. Sperm counts can be taken and used to determine the probability of successful fertilization. Many men with sperm counts under 50 million per milliliter are infertile; those with sperm counts below 20 million per milliliter are clinically infertile. These vast numbers of sperm are necessary because so many die during their journey. Large numbers are needed in order for the few survivors to reach the egg. In addition, each sperm contains enzymes in its cap that are able to digest through the mucus and protein found in the female reproductive tract. Millions of sperm contribute in this way to the process of fertilization, but only one fertilizes the egg.

**27.6  CONCEPT REVIEW**

13. What structures are associated with the human male reproductive system? What are their functions?
14. How is meiosis involved in spermatogenesis?

## 27.7  Oogenesis, Ovulation, and Menstruation

**Oogenesis** is the production of egg cells. This process starts before a girl is born, during prenatal development of the ovaries. This occurs when diploid cells in each ovary cease dividing by mitosis and enlarge in preparation to divide by meiosis. These are the potential egg cells. All of these cells form in the embryonic ovaries before a female is born. At birth, they number approximately 2 million, but that number has been reduced by cell death to between 300,000 and 400,000 cells by puberty. These cells stop their development in an early stage of meiosis and remain in the ovary inside a follicle.

At puberty and on a regular monthly basis thereafter, the sex hormones stimulate one of these cells to continue meiosis. However, in telophase I, the two cells that form receive unequal portions of cytoplasm, a kind of lopsided division

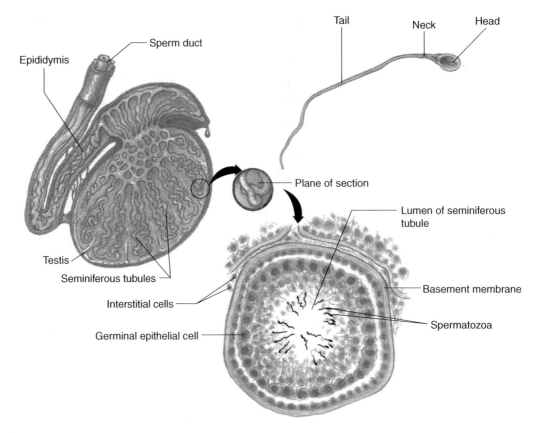

## FIGURE 27.10 Sperm Production

The testis consists of many tiny tubes called seminiferous tubules. The walls of the tubes consist of cells that continually divide, producing large numbers of sperm. The sperm leave the seminiferous tubules and enter the epididymis, where they are stored prior to ejaculation through the sperm duct. Sperm cells have a head region, with an enzyme-containing cap and the DNA. They also have a neck region, with ATP-generating mitochondria, and a tail flagellum, which propels the sperm.

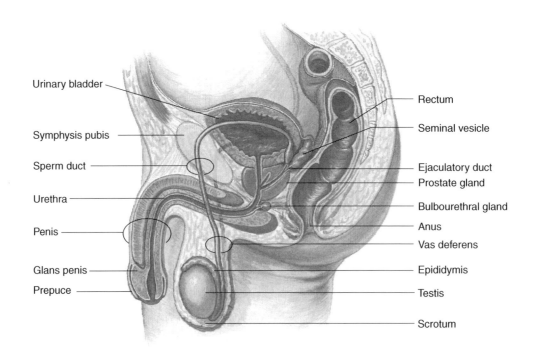

## FIGURE 27.11 The Human Male Reproductive System

The male reproductive system consists of two testes, which produce sperm; ducts, which carry the sperm; and various glands. Muscular contractions propel the sperm through the vas deferens past the seminal vesicles, prostate gland, and bulbourethral gland, where most of the liquid of the semen is added. The semen passes through the urethra of the penis to the outside of the body.

**Oogenesis**

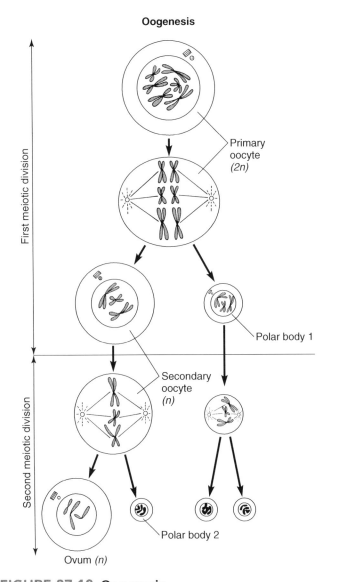

First meiotic division

Second meiotic division

Primary
oocyte
*(2n)*

Polar body 1

Secondary
oocyte
*(n)*

Polar body 2

Ovum *(n)*

**FIGURE 27.12 Oogenesis**
This diagram illustrates the process of oogenesis in human females.
Not all of the 46 chromosomes are shown. Carefully follow the
chromosomes as they segregate, recalling the details of the process
of meiosis.

(figure 27.12). The smaller of the two cells is called a **polar
body,** and the larger haploid cell is commonly referred to as
an *egg* or *ovum,* although technically it is not. Just prior to
ovulation, the follicle of the soon-to-be-released egg grows
and moves near the surface of the ovary. When this maturation is complete, ovulation occurs when the follicle ruptures
and the egg is released. It is swept into the **oviduct** (fallopian tube) by ciliated cells and travels toward the uterus
(figure 27.13). Because of the action of luteinizing hormone,
the follicle from which the egg was ovulated develops into a
glandlike structure, the corpus luteum. This gland produces
hormones (progesterone and estrogen), which prevent the
release of other eggs. If the egg is fertilized, it completes meiosis with the sperm DNA inside and the haploid egg and sperm

nuclei unite to form the zygote. If the egg is not fertilized, it
passes through the vagina to the outside of the body during
menstruation (figure 27.14).

One distinguishing characteristic between eggs and sperm
is their relative age. In males, sperm production continues
throughout the life span. Sperm do not remain in the tubes of
the male reproductive system for very long; they are either
released shortly after they form or they die and are harmlessly
absorbed. In females, meiosis begins before birth, but the
oogenesis process is not completed, and an egg cell is not
released for many years. An egg released when a woman is
37 years old began meiosis 37 years earlier. During that time,
the cell was exposed to many influences, a number of which
may have damaged the DNA or interfered with the meiotic
process. The increased risk for abnormal births in older mothers may be related to the age of their eggs. Damaged DNA in
sperm is less likely to be a problem because new sperm are
being produced daily.

Hormones control the cycle of changes in breast tissue,
the ovaries, and the uterus. In particular, estrogen and progesterone stimulate milk production by the breasts and cause the
uterine lining to become thicker and filled with blood vessels
prior to ovulation. This ensures that, if fertilization occurs,
the resultant embryo will be able to attach itself to the uterine
wall and receive nourishment. If the cell is not fertilized, the
lining of the uterus, known as the endometrium, is shed. This
is known as *menstruation, menstrual flow,* the *menses,* or a
*period.* Once the endometruim has been shed, it begins to
build up again (figure 27.15).

The activities of the ovulatory cycle and the menstrual
cycle are coordinated. During the first part of the menstrual
cycle, increased amounts of FSH cause the follicle to increase
in size. Simultaneously, the follicle secretes increased amounts
of estrogen, which cause the uterine lining to thicken. When
ovulation occurs, the remains of the follicle are converted into
a corpus luteum by LH. The corpus luteum begins to secrete
progesterone and the nature of the uterine lining changes as a
result of the development of many additional blood vessels.
This is organized so that, if an embryo arrives in the uterus
shortly after ovulation, the uterine lining is prepared to accept
it. If pregnancy does not occur, the corpus luteum degenerates,
resulting in a reduction in the amount of progesterone needed
to maintain the uterine lining, and it is shed. At the same time
that hormones are regulating ovulation and the menstrual
cycle, changes are taking place in the breasts. The same hormones that prepare the uterus to receive the embryo also
prepare the breasts to produce milk. These changes in the
breasts, however, are relatively minor unless pregnancy occurs.

## 27.7 CONCEPT REVIEW

15. What structures are associated with the human female
    reproductive system? What are their functions?
16. What are the differences between oogenesis and
    spermatogenesis in humans?

**FIGURE 27.13 Ovarian Cycle and Ovulation**
After puberty the ovary goes through a regular monthly cycle that involves growth of follicles, ovulation, and the development of a corpus luteum.

## 27.8 The Hormonal Control of Fertility

An understanding of how various hormones influence the menstrual cycle, ovulation, milk production, and sexual behavior has led to the medical use of certain hormones. Some women are unable to have children because they do not release eggs from their ovaries, or they release them at the wrong time (Outlooks 27.2). Physicians can regulate the release of eggs using certain hormones, commonly called *fertility drugs*. These hormones can be used to stimulate the release of eggs for capture and use in what is called *in vitro* fertilization (IVF), also called *test-tube* fertilization. The hormones can also be used to stimulate the release of eggs in women with irregular cycles to increase the probability of natural conception; that is, *in vivo* fertilization (*in-life* fertilization) (How Science Works 27.1).

The use of these techniques often results in multiple embryos being implanted in the uterus. This is likely to occur because the drugs may cause too many eggs to be released at one time. In the case of in vitro fertilization, because there is a high rate of failure and the process is expensive, typically several early-stage embryos are inserted into the uterus to increase the likelihood that one will implant. If several are successful, multiple embryos implant. The implantation of multiple embryos makes it difficult for one embryo to develop properly and be carried through the entire nine-month pregnancy. When scientists understand the action of hormones better, they may be able to control the effects of fertility drugs and eliminate the problem of multiple implantations.

Another medical use of hormones is the control of conception with birth-control pills—oral contraceptives. Birth-control pills have the opposite effect of fertility drugs. They raise the levels of estrogen and progesterone, which slows the production of FSH and LH, preventing the release of eggs from the ovaries. They can also help relieve premenstrual syndrome (PMS), which causes irritability, emotional instability, depression, headache, and other aches and pains.

The hormonal control of fertility is not as easy to achieve in men, because there is no comparable cycle of gamete release. However a new, reversible male conception control method for males has been developed. It relies on using a combination of progestin, a hormone used in female contraceptive pills, and testosterone. The combination of the two hormones temporarily turns off the normal brain signals that stimulate sperm production.

### 27.8  CONCEPT REVIEW

17. How do birth control pills prevent ovulation?

**(a)**

**(b)**

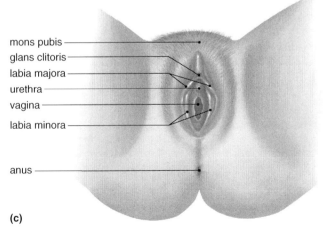

**(c)**

## FIGURE 27.14  The Human Female Reproductive System

*(a)* After ovulation, the cell travels down the oviduct to the uterus. If it is not fertilized, it is shed when the uterine lining is lost during menstruation. *(b)* The human female reproductive system, side view. *(c)* External view of female reproductive structures.

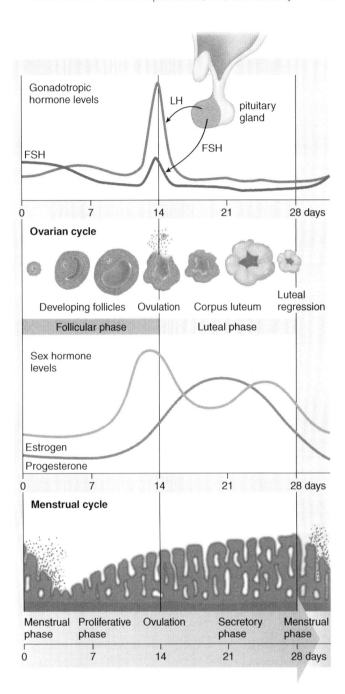

## FIGURE 27.15  The Ovarian and Uterine Cycles in Human Females

The release of an egg (ovulation) is timed to coincide with the thickening of the lining of the uterus. The uterine cycle in humans involves the preparation of the uterine wall to receive the embryo if fertilization occurs. Knowing how these two cycles compare, it is possible to determine when pregnancy is most likely to occur by noting when menstruation begins.

## OUTLOOKS 27.2

## Causes of Infertility

Infertility is a problem that has generated a major branch of medicine to diagnose and treat the causes. Either or both partners can be the cause of the infertility in a relationship, so both need to be assessed in the process of diagnosis and treatment. In about 35% of cases, the fertility problem involves the female; in about 35%, of cases, the fertility problem involves the male. In about 20% of cases, both partners have a problem, and no cause has been identified in about 10% of cases.

### Common Causes of Infertility

#### Lifestyle Causes
Heavy use of alcohol and drugs
Low body fat or anorexia in women
Tight clothing in men may raise the temperature in the scrotum and affect sperm development.
Stress may cause irregular ovulation in women or reduce sperm count in men.

#### Infections
Sexually transmitted diseases often result in scarring of blockage of reproductive tubes.
Pelvic inflammatory disease (PID) is the most common cause of infertility in women.

#### Physical Causes
Fibroids and endometriosis may cause blockage.
Retrograde ejaculation—the semen is forced into the bladder rather than being ejaculated.

#### Developmental Causes
Undescended testes
Swollen veins (varicocoele) in scrotum
Undeveloped ovaries or testes (developmental defect, infection, etc.)

#### Hormonal Causes
Any imbalance in the timing and quantity of the several sex hormones can result in lack of ovulation.
The uterus may not be prepared to accept the embryo.
Low progesterone levels may cause premature shedding of the uterine lining.
Low testosterone levels results in low sperm counts.

#### Immune System Causes
Females may develop antibodies against her partner's sperm.
Males may develop an autoimmune response to their own sperm.

#### Illness and Medication Causes
Diseases such as diabetes, kidney disease, and high blood pressure contribute to infertility.
Tranquilizers and blood pressure drugs may interfere with erection.

## 27.9 Fertilization, Pregnancy, and Birth

In most women, an egg (actually a secondary oocyte) is released from the ovary about 14 days before the next menstrual period. The menstrual cycle is usually said to begin on the first day of menstruation. Therefore, if a woman has a regular 28-day cycle, the egg is released approximately on day 14 (review figure 27.15). If a woman normally has a regular 21-day menstrual cycle, ovulation occurs about day 7 in the cycle. If a woman has a regular 40-day cycle, ovulation occurs about day 26. Some women, however, have very irregular menstrual cycles, and it is difficult to determine just when the egg will be released to become available for fertilization. Once the egg is released, it is swept into the oviduct and moved toward the uterus. If sperm are present, they swarm around the egg as it passes down the oviduct, but only one sperm penetrates the outer layer to fertilize it and cause it to complete meiosis. The other sperm contribute enzymes, which digest away the protein and mucous barrier between the egg and the successful sperm.

During the second meiotic division, the second polar body is pinched off and the larger of the two cells, the true ovum, is formed. Because chromosomes from the sperm are already inside, they simply intermingle with those of the ovum, forming a diploid zygote. As the zygote continues to travel down the oviduct, it begins to divide by mitosis into smaller and smaller cells, without an increase in the mass of cells (figure 27.16). This division process is called *cleavage*.

Eventually, a solid ball of cells is produced, known as the morula stage of embryological development. The morula continues down the oviduct and continues to divide by mitosis. The result is called a *blastocyst*. The blastocyst becomes embedded or implanted in the uterine lining when it reaches the uterus (How Science Works 27.2).

The blastocyst stage of the embryo eventually develops a tube, which becomes the gut. The formation of the primitive digestive tract is just one of a series of changes that result in an embryo that is recognizable as a miniature human being.

**3 Cleavage**

2-cell stage    4-cell stage

8-cell stage

**2 Fertilization**

sperm
nucleus

egg
nucleus

**4 Morula**

**1 Ovulation**

oviduct

fimbriae
ovary

**5 Early blastocyst**

inner cell
mass

prechorion

egg

**6 Implantation**

**FIGURE 27.16  Human Embryonic Development**
Between fertilization and birth, many changes take place in the embryo. Fertilization
of the egg takes place in the oviduct and early stages of development take place as
the embryo travels to the uterus. By about day 7 following fertilization, the
blastocyst has embedded in the lining of the uterus.

Most of the time during its development, the embryo is
enclosed in a water-filled membrane, the amnion, which protects it from blows and keeps it moist. Two other membranes,
the chorion and allantois, fuse with the lining of the uterus to
form the **placenta** (figure 27.17). A fourth sac, the yolk sac, is
well developed in reptiles, fish, amphibians, and birds. The
yolk sac in these animals contains a large amount of food
used by the developing embryo. Although a yolk sac is present in mammals, it is small and does not contain yolk. The
embryo's nutritional needs are met through the placenta. The
placenta also produces the hormone chorionic gonadotropin,
which stimulates the corpus luteum to continue producing
progesterone and thus prevents menstruation and ovulation
during pregnancy.

As the embryo's cells divide and grow, some of them
become differentiated into nerve cells, bone cells, blood cells,
or other specialized cells. In order to divide, grow, and differentiate, cells must receive nourishment. This is provided
by the mother through the placenta, in which both fetal
and maternal blood vessels are abundant, allowing for the
exchange of substances between the mother and embryo. The

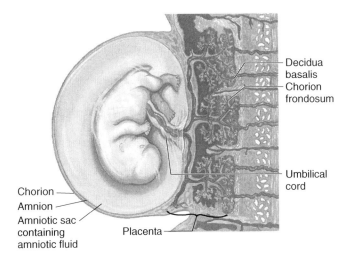

Decidua
basalis
Chorion
frondosum

Umbilical
cord

Chorion
Amnion
Amniotic sac
containing
amniotic fluid

Placenta

**FIGURE 27.17  Placental Structure**
The embryonic blood vessels that supply the developing embryo
with nutrients and remove the metabolic wastes are separate from
the blood vessels of the mother. Because of this separation, the
placenta can selectively filter many types of incoming materials
and microorganisms.

# HOW SCIENCE WORKS 27.1

## Assisted Reproductive Technology

The Centers for Disease Control and Prevention defines assisted reproductive technology (ART) as "all fertility treatments in which both eggs and sperm are manipulated. In general, ART involves surgically removing eggs from a woman's ovaries, combining them with sperm in the laboratory, and returning them to the woman's body or donating them to another woman. It does NOT include procedures in which only sperm are manipulated (i.e., artificial insemination or intrauterine insemination) or procedures in which a woman takes drugs only to stimulate egg production, without the intention of having eggs retrieved." There are three types of ART: in vitro fertilization (IVF), gamete intra-fallopian transfer (GIFT), and zygote intra-fallopian transfer (ZIFT).

In vitro fertilization is a method that uses hormones to stimulate egg production, removing the egg or eggs from the ovary, and fertilizing it with donated sperm. The fertilized egg is incubated to stimulate cell division in a laboratory dish and then placed in the uterus. (See figure.)

GIFT relies on the same hormonal treatment as IVF to stimulate ovulation. The physician observes the transfer of unfertilized eggs and sperm into the woman's fallopian tube through an instrument inserted through a small incision in her abdomen. Once fertilized, the zygote moves down through the fallopian tube into the uterus and implants. GIFT is only an option for women with open fallopian tubes.

In the ZIFT procedure, a woman's mature eggs are collected and fertilized in the laboratory. Then, the zygote is inserted into

the fallopian tube through a small abdominal incision. The embryo will then travel down the fallopian tube and implant in the uterus in a normal manner.

---

materials diffusing across the placenta include oxygen, carbon dioxide, nutrients, and a variety of waste products. The materials entering the embryo travel through blood vessels in the umbilical cord. The diet and behavior of the mother are extremely important. Any molecules consumed by the mother can affect the embryo. Cocaine; alcohol; heroin; the chemicals in cigarette smoke; and medications, such as Phenytoin (or Dilantin) and Accutane (acne treatment), can all cross the placenta and affect the development of the embryo. Infections by such microbes as rubella virus (German measles), Varicella (chicken pox), and the protozoan *Toxoplasma* can also result in fetal abnormalities or even death.

The growth of the embryo results in the development of major parts of the body by the tenth week of pregnancy. After this time, the embryo continues to increase in size, and the structure of the body is refined.

## Twins

In the United States, women giving birth have a 1 in 40 chance of delivering twins and a 1 in 650 chance of triplets or other multiple births. Twins happen in two ways. In the case of identical

**Identical twins**

**Fraternal twins**

twins (approximately one-third of all twins), the embryo splits during cleavage into two separate groups of cells. Each group develops into an independent embryo. Because they come from the same single fertilized ovum, they have the same genes and are the same sex.

Should separation be incomplete, the twins would be born attached to one another, a condition referred to as conjoined twins. Conjoined twins occur once in every 70,000 to 100,000 live births.

Fraternal twins result from the fertilization of two separate eggs by two different sperm. Therefore, they resemble each other no more than do regular brothers and sisters. They do not contain the same genes and are not necessarily the same sex.

# HOW SCIENCE WORKS 27.2

## History of Pregnancy Testing

The answer to the question "Am I pregnant?" once demanded a combination of guesswork, "old wives' tales" and time. An ancient Egyptian papyrus described a test in which a woman who might be pregnant urinated on wheat and barley seeds over the course of several days: "If the barley grows, it means a male child. If the wheat grows, it means a female child. If both do not grow, she will not bear at all."

In the Middle Ages, so-called "piss prophets" said they could tell if a woman was pregnant by the color of her urine. Urine was described as a "clear, pale lemon color leaning toward off-white, having a cloud on its surface" if she was pregnant. Some mixed wine with urine and watched for changes. In fact, alcohol reacts with certain proteins in urine, so they may have had a little help in guessing.

In 1927, a test was developed that required the injection of a women's urine into an immature female rat or mouse. If the woman was not pregnant, the animal showed no reaction. If she was pregnant, the animal went into heat (displayed behaviors associated with a desire to mate) despite its immaturity. This test implied that, during pregnancy, there was an increased production of certain hormones, and that they were excreted in the urine. In the 1930s, a similar test involved injecting urine into rabbits, frogs, toads, and rats. If pregnancy hormones were in the urine, they induced ovulation in the animals.

However, in 1976, advertisements proclaimed "a private little revolution," the first home pregnancy tests. The FDA granted approval to four tests: Early Pregnancy Test, Predictor,

ACU-TEST, and Answer. All the tests identified changes in hormone levels in the urine of pregnant women.

The next generation of home pregnancy tests arrived in 2003, when the FDA approved Clearblue Easy's digital pregnancy test. Instead of showing a thin blue line, the indicator screen now displayed the words "pregnant" or "not pregnant."

# Birth

The process of giving birth is also known as parturition, or birthing. At the end of about 9 months, hormonal changes in the mother's body stimulate contractions of the uterine muscles during a period prior to birth called *labor*. These contractions are stimulated by the hormone oxytocin, which is released from the posterior pituitary. The contractions normally move the baby headfirst and face down through the vagina, or birth canal. One of the first effects of these contractions may be the bursting of the amnion ("bag of water") surrounding the baby. Following this, the uterine contractions become stronger, and shortly thereafter the baby is born (figure 27.18). In some cases, the baby becomes turned in the uterus before labor. If this occurs, the feet or buttocks appear first. Such a birth is called a *breech birth*. This can be a dangerous situation, because the baby's source of oxygen may be cut off as the placenta begins to separate from the mother's body before the baby's head emerges. If for any reason the baby does not begin to

**FIGURE 27.18 Childbirth**
What many people refer to as "natural" childbirth is really called a vaginal delivery.

breathe on its own, it will not receive enough oxygen to prevent the death of nerve cells; thus, brain damage or death can result.

Occasionally, a baby cannot be born vaginally because of its position in the uterus. Other factors include the location of the placenta on the uterine wall and the size of the birth canal. A procedure to resolve this problem is the surgical removal of the baby through the mother's abdomen. This procedure is known as a cesarean, or C-section. The procedure was apparently named after Roman Emperor Julius Caesar, who was said to have been the first child to be delivered by this method. While C-sections are known to have been performed before Caesar, the name stuck.

Following the birth of the baby, the placenta, also called the *afterbirth*, is expelled. Once born, the baby begins to function on its own. The umbilical cord collapses and the baby's lungs, kidneys, and digestive system must now support all bodily needs. Birth is quite a shock, but the baby's loud protests fill the lungs with air and stimulate breathing.

Over the next few weeks, the mother's body returns to normal, with one major exception. The breasts, which underwent changes during pregnancy, are ready to produce milk to feed the baby. Following birth, prolactin, a hormone from the pituitary gland, stimulates the production of milk, and oxytocin stimulates its release. If the baby is breast-fed, the stimulus of the baby's sucking prolongs the time during which milk is produced. This response involves both the nervous and endocrine systems. The sucking stimulates nerves in the nipples and breasts, resulting in the release of prolactin and oxytocin from the pituitary.

Recent studies have found that breast-fed babies are 20% less likely to die between the ages of 1 and 12 months than are those who are not breast-fed. In addition, the longer babies are breast-fed, the lower their risk for early death. The American Academy of Pediatrics has recommended exclusive breast-feeding (that is, only human breast milk—no formula, water, or solids) for the first 6 months of life. Breast-feeding should continue throughout the second half of the baby's first year with the introduction of solid foods.

In some cultures, breast-feeding continues for 2 to 3 years, and the continued production of milk often delays the reestablishment of the normal cycles of ovulation and menstruation. Many people believe that a woman cannot become pregnant while she is nursing a baby, a method of birth control called Lactation Amenorrhea Method (LAM). For a woman breast-feeding, the probability of becoming pregnant during the first three months is practically zero. However, because there is so much variation among women, relying on this as a natural conception-control method after the first three months is not a good choice. Many women have been surprised to find themselves pregnant again a few months after delivery.

## 27.9   CONCEPT REVIEW

18. What changes occur in ovulation and menstruation during pregnancy?
19. What are the functions of the placenta?
20. What causes the genetic differences between fraternal twins?

## 27.10   Contraception

Throughout history, people have tried various methods of conception control. In ancient times, conception control was encouraged during times of food shortage or when tribes were on the move from one area to another in search of a new home. Writings from as early as 1500 B.C. indicate that the Egyptians used a form of tampon medicated with the ground powder of a shrub to prevent fertilization. This may sound primitive, but we use the same basic principle today to destroy sperm in the vagina. As you read about the various methods of contraception, remember that no method except abstinence is 100% effective for avoiding pregnancy. Another important consideration is that only condoms are effective in preventing the spread of sexually transmitted diseases (STDs).

### Barrier Methods

One way to prevent conception is to physically prevent the sperm from reaching the egg.

The male condom is probably the most popular contraceptive device. It is a thin sheath placed over the erect penis before intercourse. In addition to preventing sperm from reaching the egg, this physical barrier also helps prevent the transmission of the microbes that cause sexually transmitted diseases (STDs), such as syphilis, gonorrhea, and AIDS, from being passed from one person to another during sexual intercourse  (Outlooks 27.3). The most desirable condoms are made of a thin layer of latex that does not reduce the sensitivity of the penis. Latex condoms have also been determined to be the most effective in preventing transmission of HIV. The condom is most effective if it is prelubricated with a spermicidal material, such as nonoxynol-9. This lubricant also has the advantage of providing some protection against the spread of HIV.

Condoms for women are also available. One, called the Femidom, is a polyurethane sheath, which, once inserted, lines the contours of the woman's vagina. It has an inner ring, which sits over the cervix, and an outer ring, which lies flat against the labia. Research shows that this device protects against STDs and is as effective a contraceptive as the condom used by men.

# OUTLOOKS 27.3

## Sexually Transmitted Diseases

*Sexually transmitted diseases (STDs)* were formerly called *venereal diseases (VDs)*. Although these kinds of illnesses are most frequently transmitted by sexual activity, many can also be spread by other methods of direct contact, such as hypodermic needles, blood transfusions, and blood-contaminated materials. Currently, the Centers for Disease Control and Prevention (CDC) in Atlanta, Georgia, recognizes over 25 diseases as being sexually transmitted (table 27.A).

The United States has the highest rate of sexually transmitted disease among the industrially developed countries. There are about 19 million new infections each year. About half of the infections occur in young adults aged 15–24 years of age. Table 27.B lists the most common STDs and estimates of the number of new cases each year. Some of the most important STDs are described here because of their high incidence in the population and the inability to bring some of them under control. For example, there is no known cure for HIV, responsible for AIDS.

Despite efforts to educate the public and the availability of effective methods for treatment, several STDs are actually increasing in frequency. In particular, *Chlamydia* infections have increased to over a million new infections per year. There has also

### TABLE 27.A  Sexually Transmitted Diseases

| Disease | Agent |
|---|---|
| Genital herpes | Virus |
| Gonorrhea | Bacterium |
| Syphilis | Bacterium |
| Acquired immunodeficiency syndrome (AIDS) | Virus |
| Candidiasis | Yeast |
| Chancroid | Bacterium |
| Genital warts | Virus |
| *Gardnerella vaginalis* | Bacterium |
| Genital *Chlamydia* infection | Bacterium |
| Genital cytomegalovirus infection | Virus |
| Genital *Mycoplasma* infection | Bacterium |
| Group B *Streptococcus* infection | Bacterium |
| Nongonococcal urethritis | Bacterium |
| Pelvic inflammatory disease (PID) | Bacterium |
| Molluscum contagiosum | Virus |
| Crabs | Body lice |
| Scabies | Mite |
| Trichomoniasis | Protozoan |
| Hepatitis B | Virus |
| Gay bowel syndrome | Variety of agents |

### TABLE 27.B  Cases of Sexually Transmitted Diseases in the United States Reported in 2008

| Disease | Cases Reported in 2008 | Comments |
|---|---|---|
| Chancroid | 25 | |
| Hepatitis B | 4,519 | Up to 1.4 million people may have undiagnosed disease |
| HIV/AIDS | 37,041 | About 1.1 million people infected |
| Syphilis | 46,277 | Incidence is increasing |
| Vaginal trichomoniasis | 204,000 | Probably over 7 million cases/year |
| Genital herpes | 292,000 | About 16% of population infected (about 50 million) |
| Gonorrhea | 336,742 | 700,000 cases/year estimated |
| Genital warts | 385,000 | About 1% of sexually active persons have genital warts |
| Chlamydia | 1,213,523 | Estimated 2.3 million infected |
| Other vaginal infections | 3,571,000 | Most common sexually transmitted disease |

been an increase in the number of cases of syphilis, especially among gay and bisexual men. In addition, a penicillin-resistant strain of *Neisseria gonorrhoeae* has led to an increase in the number of cases of gonorrhea.

The spread of STDs during sexual intercourse is significantly diminished by the use of condoms. Other types of sexual contact (e.g., hand, oral, anal) and transmission from a mother to the fetus during pregnancy help maintain some of these diseases in the population. Therefore, public health organizations, such as the U.S. Public Health Service, the CDC, and state and local public health agencies, regularly keep an eye on the number of cases of STDs. All of these agencies are involved in attempts to raise the general public health to a higher level. Their investigations have resulted in the successful control of many diseases and the identification of special problems, such as those associated with the STDs. Because the United States has an incidence rate of STDs that is 50 to 100 times higher than that of other industrially developed countries, there is still much that needs to be done.

The high-risk behaviors associated with contracting STDs include sex with multiple partners and the failure to use condoms. Whereas some STDs are simply inconvenient or annoying, others severely affect health and can result in death. As one health official stated, "We should be knowledgeable enough about our own sexuality and the STDs to answer the question, 'Is what I'm about to do worth dying for?'"

Other methods of conception control that prevent sperm from reaching the egg include the diaphragm, cervical cap, and sponge. A diaphragm is a specially fitted membranous shield that is inserted into the vagina before intercourse and positioned so that it covers the cervix, which has the opening of the uterus. Because of anatomical differences among females, diaphragms must be fitted by a physician. The diaphragm's effectiveness is increased if spermicidal foam or jelly is also used. A cervical cap functions in a similar way. A contraceptive sponge, as the name indicates, is a small amount of absorbent material soaked in a spermicide. The sponge is placed within the vagina, where it chemically and physically prevents sperm cells from reaching the egg.

## Chemical Methods

Contraceptive jellies and foams make the vaginal environment more acidic, which diminishes the sperm's chances of survival. Spermicidal (sperm-killing) foam or jelly is placed in the

vagina before intercourse. When the sperm make contact with the acidic environment, they stop swimming and soon die. These methods of contraception are often used in combination with other methods of contraception (condoms, diaphragm etc.) as additional protection in the event that the other methods fail.

## Hormonal Control Methods

The first successful method of hormonal control was "the pill," or "birth-control pill," which contained a combination of the hormones estrogen and progesterone. Today there are two kinds of birth-control pills: those that contain estrogen and progesterone and those that contain progesterone only. The combination birth-control pill works

primarily by preventing ovulation, and secondarily by interfering with implantation. The quantity and balance of hormones (estrogen and progesterone) in the pill fools the ovaries into functioning as if the woman were already pregnant. Therefore, ovulation does not occur, so conception is highly unlikely. The combination pills are taken daily for 21 days and then stopped (some brands have 21 pills with hormones and the last 7 do not contain hormones). This allows for menstruation to occur.

The progesterone-only pill (POP, or mini pill) is taken continuously without a break. The progesterone in these pills has several effects that helps to prevent conception. Progesterone thickens the mucus at the cervix, alters the uterine lining to make implantation unlikely, and appears to interfere with the movement of sperm and egg.

Other hormone methods involve delivering the hormones by way of implants, adhesive patches, or vaginal rings that slowly release hormones and prevent the maturation and release of eggs from the follicle. The major advantage of an implant is its convenience. Once the implant has been inserted, the woman can forget about contraceptive protection for several years. If she wants to become pregnant, the implants are removed and her normal menstrual and ovulation cycles return over a period of weeks. Similarly, discontinuing the use of the patch allow normal ovulation to resume.

The vaginal ring releases a continuous low dose of estrogen and progestin for 21 days. At the end of the 21 days, the ring is removed for 7 days to allow the menstrual period to occur. A new ring is then inserted monthly.

Contraceptive hormones can also be used to stop menstrual periods, preventing the symptoms of premenstrual syndrome and improving a woman's sex life.

The emergency contraceptive pill (ECP), or "morning-after pill," uses a high dose of the same hormones found in oral contraceptives, which prevents the woman from becoming pregnant in the first place. In fact, "the pill" in higher dosages can be used as an ECP. The common medication available in the United States is known as Plan B®. These pills work by inhibiting ovulation and thickening mucus, which makes it difficult for the sperm to get to the egg.

## The Timing Method

Not all methods of birth control require the use of physical barriers, spermicides, or hormones. Any method that prevents sperm from reaching the egg prevents conception. One method is to avoid intercourse during the times of the month when an egg may be present. This is known as the *rhythm method* of conception control. Although at first glance it appears to be the simplest and least expensive, determining when an egg is likely to be present can be very difficult. A woman with a regular 28-day menstrual cycle typically ovulates about 14 days before the onset of the next menstrual flow. To avoid pregnancy, couples need to abstain from intercourse a few days before and after this date. However, if a woman has an irregular menstrual cycle, there may be only a few days each month for intercourse without the possibility of pregnancy. In addition to calculating safe days based on the length of the menstrual cycle, a woman can better estimate the time of ovulation by keeping a record of changes in her body temperature and vaginal pH. Both changes are tied to the menstrual cycle and can therefore help a woman predict ovulation. In particular, at about the time of ovulation, a woman has a slight rise in body temperature—less than 1°C. Thus, she should use an extremely sensitive thermometer. A digital-readout thermometer on the market spells out the word *yes* or *no*.

However, all variations of the rhythm method have high failure rates—up to 25 percent per year.

## Intrauterine Devices (IUD)

The intrauterine device (IUD) is an object that must be fitted and inserted into the uterus by a physician. IUDs are very effec-

tive. This method of contraception has a failure rate of about 1%. How this device works is not completely known. There are two major kinds of IUDs: those that contain copper and those that contain the hormone progesterone. It appears that the copper interferes with the sperm's swimming ability and also alters the lining of the uterus, which makes implantation unlikely. IUDs with progesterone appear to thicken the layer of mucus around the cervix and also alter the nature of the

uterine lining, making implantation less likely. A major advantage of an IUD is that it can be left in place and be effective for years, but it can be removed if pregnancy is desired.

The IUD can also be used for "emergency contraception"—in cases of unprotected sex, forced sex, or the failure of a conception-control method (e.g., a broken condom). To be used for this purpose, the IUD must be inserted within 7 days of unprotected sex.

## Surgical Methods

Two contraceptive methods that require surgery are tubal ligation and vasectomy (figure 27.19). Tubal ligation is the cutting and tying off of the oviducts; it can be done on an outpatient basis, in most cases. An alternative to sterilization by tubal ligation involves the insertion of small, flexible devices, called Micro-inserts, into each oviduct (fallopian tube). Once inserted, tissue grows into the inserts, blocking the tubes. Ovulation continues as usual, but the sperm and egg cannot unite.

A vasectomy can be performed in a physician's office. A small opening is made above the scrotum, and the spermatic cord (vas deferens) is cut and tied. This prevents sperm from moving through the ducts to the outside. Because most of the semen is produced by the seminal vesicles, prostate gland, and bulbourethral glands, a vasectomy does not interfere with normal ejaculation. The sperm that are still being produced die and are reabsorbed in the testes. Vasectomy is not the same as castration. Castration is the surgical removal of testes.

(a)

(b)

**FIGURE 27.19  Tubal Ligation and Vasectomy**
Two very effective contraceptive methods require surgery. *(a)* Tubal ligation involves severing the oviducts and suturing or sealing the cut ends. This prevents the sperm cell and the egg from meeting. This procedure is generally considered ambulatory surgery; at most, it requires a short hospitalization period. *(b)* Vasectomy requires minor surgery, usually in a clinic under local anesthesia. Following the procedure, minor discomfort may be experienced for several days. The severing and sealing of the vas deferens prevents the release of sperm cells from the body during ejaculation.

Neither tubal ligation nor vasectomy interferes with normal sex drives. However, these medical procedures are difficult to reverse and should not be considered by those who may want to have children at a future date. These procedures are not 100% effective since, in rare instances, the tubes might reattach, allowing gametes to pass from one severed side of the duct to the other.

## 27.10  CONCEPT REVIEW

21. Describe hormonal methods of conception control.
22. Describe barrier methods of conception control.

## 27.11 Termination of Pregnancy— Abortion

Another medical procedure often associated with birth control is abortion, which has been used throughout history. Abortion is the death and removal of a developing embryo through various medical procedures. Abortion is not a method of conception control; rather, it prevents the normal development of the embryo. Abortion is a highly charged subject: Some people believe that abortion should be prohibited by law in all cases; others think that abortion should be allowed in certain situations, such as in pregnancies that endanger the mother's life or in pregnancies that are the result of rape or incest. Still others think that abortion should be available to any woman under any circumstances. Regardless of the moral and ethical issues that surround abortion, it is still a common method of terminating unwanted pregnancies.

The three most common techniques performed early in pregnancy are scraping the inside of the uterus with instruments (called *dilation and curettage, or D and C)*, injecting a saline solution into the uterine cavity, and using a suction device to remove the embryo from the uterus. RU-486 is a drug that causes abortion and must be used under a doctor's supervision. The medication is administered orally and several days later, a hormone is administered. This usually results in the onset of contractions, which expel the fetus. A follow-up examination of the woman is made after several weeks to ensure that there are no serious side effects.

Late-term abortions are done after the *20th week* of gestation. Late-term abortion is not a medical term, and the exact point when a pregnancy becomes late term has not been defined. Nor is there exact data for the number performed. Late-term abortions performed for fetal abnormality are involved procedures called *intact dilation and extraction* (IDX or D&X), also known as partial-birth abortion.

### 27.11 CONCEPT REVIEW

23. What is dilation and curettage?
24. How does RU-486 work?

## 27.12 Changes in Sexual Function with Age

Although there is a great deal of variation, at about age 50, a woman's hormonal balance begins to change because of changes in the ovaries' production of hormones. At this time, the menstrual cycle becomes less regular and ovulation is often unpredictable. Over several years, the changes in hormone levels cause many women to experience mood swings and physical symptoms, including cramps and hot flashes. **Menopause** is the period when a woman's body becomes

nonreproductive, because reproductive hormones stop being produced. This causes the ovaries to stop producing eggs, and menstruation ends. Occasionally, the symptoms associated with menopause become so severe that they interfere with normal life and the enjoyment of sexual activity. A physician might recommend *hormone replacement therapy (HRT)* which involves administering either estrogen alone or estrogen and progestin together, to augment the natural production of estrogen and progesterone. Normally, the sexual enjoyment of a healthy woman continues during menopause and for many years thereafter.

Although human males do not experience a relatively abrupt change in their reproductive or sexual lives, recent evidence indicates that men also experience hormonal and emotional changes similar to those seen as women go through menopause. As men age, their production of sperm declines and they may experience a variety of problems related to their sexuality. The word *impotence* is used to describe problems that interfere with sexual intercourse and reproduction. These may include a lack of sexual desire, problems with ejaculation or orgasm, and erectile dysfunction (ED). Erectile dysfunction is the recurring inability to get or keep an erection firm enough for sexual intercourse. Most incidences of ED at any age are physical not psychological. In older men, this is usually the result of injury, disease, or the side effects of medication. Damage to nerves, arteries, smooth muscles, and other tissues associated with the penis is the most common cause of ED. Diseases linked with ED include diabetes, kidney disease, chronic alcoholism, multiple sclerosis, atherosclerosis, vascular disease, and neurologic disease. Blood pressure drugs, antihistamines, antidepressants, tranquilizers, appetite suppressants, and certain ulcer drugs have been associated with ED. Other possible causes are smoking, which reduces blood flow in veins and arteries, and lowered amounts of testosterone. ED is frequently treated with psychotherapy, behavior modification, oral or locally injected drugs, vacuum devices, and surgically implanted devices. ED is not an inevitable part of aging. Rather, sexual desires tend to wane slowly as men age. They produce fewer sperm cells and less seminal fluid. Nevertheless, healthy individuals can experience a satisfying sex life during aging.

Human sexual behavior is quite variable. The same is true of older persons. The range of responses to sexual partners continues, but generally in a diminished form. People who were very active sexually when young continue to be active, but less so as they reach middle age. Those who were less active tend to decrease their sexual activity also. It is reasonable to state that one's sexuality continues from before birth until death.

## 27.12  CONCEPT REVIEW

25. What is menopause?
26. How does sexual function change with age?

## Summary

The human sex drive is a powerful motivator for many activities in our lives. Although from a biological perspective it provides for reproduction and generates new gene combinations, it also has a nonbiological, sociocultural dimension. Sexuality begins before birth, as sexual anatomy is determined by the sex-determining chromosome complement received at fertilization. Females receive 2 X chromosomes. A male receives 1 X and 1 Y sex-determining chromosome. It is the presence of the Y chromosome that causes male development and the absence of a Y chromosome that allows female development.

At puberty, hormones stimulate the maturation of the ovaries and testes and the development of secondary sex characteristics. As the ovaries and testes begin to produce gametes, fertilization becomes possible. Sexual reproduction involves the production of gametes by meiosis in the ovaries and testes. The production and release of these gametes is controlled by the interaction of hormones. In males, each cell that undergoes spermatogenesis results in four sperm; in females, each cell that undergoes oogenesis results in one egg and two polar bodies. Humans have specialized structures for the support of the developing embryo, and many factors influence its development in the uterus. Sexual reproduction depends on proper hormone balance, proper meiotic division, fertilization, placenta formation, proper diet of the mother, and birth. Hormones regulate ovulation and menstruation and can be used to encourage or discourage ovulation. Fertility drugs and birth-control pills, for example, involve hormonal control. In addition to the pill, a number of contraceptive methods have been developed, including the diaphragm, condom, IUD, spermicidal jellies and foams, contraceptive implants, the sponge, tubal ligation, and vasectomy.

Hormones continue to direct our sexuality throughout our lives. Even after menopause, when fertilization and pregnancy are no longer possible for a female, normal sexual activity can continue in both men and women.

## Key Terms

*Use the interactive flash cards on the **Concepts in Biology, 14/e** website to help you learn the meaning of these terms.*

androgens 621
clitoris 621
cryptorchidism 620
ejaculation 616
follicles 620
follicle-stimulating hormone (FSH) 620
gametogenesis 622
gonadotropin-releasing hormone (GnRH) 620
inguinal canal 620
luteinizing hormone (LH) 620
masturbation 621
menopause 636
menstrual cycle 621
oogenesis 623
orgasm 616
oviduct 625
ovulation 621
pituitary gland 620
placenta 629
polar body 625
puberty 620
secondary sexual characteristics 621
semen 621
seminiferous tubules 622
sex 614
sex-determining chromosomes 617
sexuality 614
sperm 617
spermatogenesis 622
X chromosome 617
Y chromosome 617

## Basic Review

1. All the factors that contribute to one's female or male nature are referred to as _____.
2. Humans have a total of _____ chromosomes, _____ of which are considered sex-determining.
   a. 44, 2
   b. 23, 2
   c. 48, 4
   d. 46, 2
3. In humans, the _____ acts as a master switch, triggering the events that convert an embryo into a male.
   a. SRY gene
   b. TDF gene
   c. Y-gene
   d. Turner's gene

4. Men with Klinefelter's syndrome may be sterile and show breast enlargement, an incomplete masculine body form, a lack of facial hair, and some minor learning problems. (T/F)

5. Semen is produced by the testes. (T/F)

6. Gonadotropin-releasing hormone (GnRH) is produced by the
   a. hypothalamus.
   b. pituitary.
   c. testes.
   d. corpus leuteum.

7. Birth control pills contain hormones. (T/F)

8. The unequal division that occurs during oogenesis results in the formation of smaller cells that do not develop into true eggs, called _____.

9. If a woman normally has a regular 21-day menstrual cycle, ovulation occurs about day _____ in the cycle.

10. If an embryo splits during cleavage into two separate groups of cells, _____ twins may develop.

11. Transgender individuals have a psychological view of themselves that is different from their physical bodies. (T/F)

12. Homosexuality appears to have a genetic basis. (T/F)

13. The cells released during ovulation
    a. are diploid.
    b. were present in the ovaries for several years.
    c. contain Y chromosomes.
    d. None of the above is correct.

14. The hormone progesterone is produced by the
    a. corpus luteum.
    b. pituitary.
    c. hypothalamus.
    d. uterus.

15. Fertilization of an egg usually takes place in the _____.

**Answers**
1. sexuality  2. d  3. a  4. T  5. F  6. a  7. T  8. polar bodies  9. 7  10. identical  11. T  12. T  13. b  14. a  15. oviduct (fallopian tube)

## Thinking Critically

**Hormones in the Environment**
The practice of medicine has increasingly moved in the direction of using medications containing steroids to control disease or regulate function, as in birth-control pills. To meet these demands, the pharmaceutical industry produces enormous amounts of these drugs. However, what happens to these drugs once they enter the body? Although some of the drug is destroyed in controlling disease or regulating a function, such as ovulation, a certain amount is not and is excreted. There is some concern about the amount of medical steroids entering the environment in this way. What effects might they have on the public, who unintentionally ingest these as environmental contaminants? Consider the topics of sexual reproduction, the regulation of hormonal cycles, and fetal development, and explain (1) how you would determine "acceptable levels" of such contaminants, (2) what might happen if these levels were exceeded, and (3) what steps might be taken to control such environmental contamination.

# Appendix 1

## The Metric System

**Standard Metric Units**

| | | Abbreviation |
|---|---|---|
| Standard unit of mass | gram | g |
| Standard unit of length | meter | m |
| Standard unit of volume | liter | L |

**Common Prefixes** / **Examples**

| | | |
|---|---|---|
| kilo | 1,000 | A kilogram is 1,000 grams. |
| centi | 0.01 | A centimeter is 0.01 meter. |
| milli | 0.001 | A milliliter is 0.001 liter. |
| micro ($\mu$) | one-millionth | A micrometer is 0.000001 (one-millionth) of a meter. |
| nano (n) | one-billionth | A nanogram is $10^{-9}$ (one-billionth) of a gram. |
| pico (p) | one-trillionth | A picogram is $10^{-12}$ (one-trillionth) of a gram. |

## Units of Length

| Unit | Abbreviation | Equivalent |
|---|---|---|
| meter | m | approximately 39 in. |
| centimeter | cm | $10^{-2}$ m |
| millimeter | mm | $10^{-3}$ m |
| micrometer | $\mu$m | $10^{-6}$ m |
| nanometer | nm | $10^{-9}$ m |
| angstrom | Å | $10^{-10}$ m |

**Length Conversions**

| | |
|---|---|
| 1 in. = 2.5 cm | 1 mm = 0.039 in |
| 1 ft = 30 cm | 1 cm = 0.39 in |
| 1 yd = 0.9 m | 1 m = 39 in |
| 1 mi = 1.6 km | 1 m = 1.094 yd |
| | 1 km = 0.6 mi |

| To Convert | Multiply By | To Obtain |
|---|---|---|
| inches | 2.54 | centimeters |
| feet | 30 | centimeters |
| centimeters | 0.39 | inches |
| millimeters | 0.039 | inches |

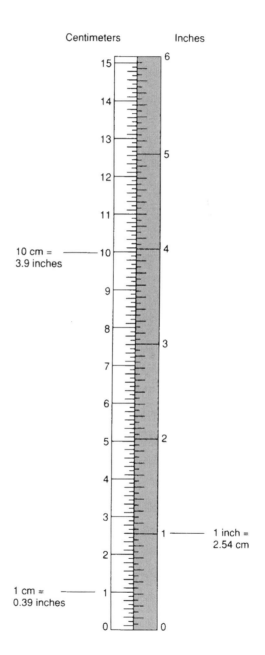

Centimeters    Inches

10 cm = 3.9 inches

1 inch = 2.54 cm

1 cm = 0.39 inches

# Units of Volume

| Unit | Abbreviation | Equivalent |
|---|---|---|
| liter | L | approximately 1.06 qt |
| milliliter | mL | $10^{-3}$ L (1 mL = 1 cm$^3$ = 1 cc) |
| microliter | μL | $10^{-6}$ L |

### Volume Conversions

| | | | | | |
|---|---|---|---|---|---|
| 1 tsp | = | 5 mL | 1 mL | = | 0.03 fl oz |
| 1 tbsp | = | 15 mL | 1 L | = | 2.1 pt |
| 1 fl oz | = | 30 mL | 1 L | = | 1.06 qt |
| 1 cup | = | 0.24 L | 1 L | = | 0.26 gal |
| 1 pt | = | 0.47 L | | | |
| 1 qt | = | 0.95 L | | | |
| 1 gal | = | 3.8 L | | | |

| To Convert | Multiply By | To Obtain |
|---|---|---|
| fluid ounces | 30 | milliliters |
| quarts | 0.95 | liters |
| milliliters | 0.03 | fluid ounces |
| liters | 1.06 | quarts |

# Units of Weight

| Unit | Abbreviation | Equivalent |
|---|---|---|
| kilogram | kg | $10^3$ g (approximately 2.2 lb) |
| gram | g | approximately 0.035 oz |
| milligram | mg | $10^{-3}$ g |
| microgram | μg | $10^{-6}$ g |
| nanogram | ng | $10^{-9}$ g |
| pictogram | pg | $10^{-12}$ g |

### Weight Conversions

| | |
|---|---|
| 1 oz = 28.3 g | 1 g = 0.035 oz |
| 1 lb = 453.6 g | 1 kg = 2.2 lb |
| 1 lb = 0.45 kg | |

| To Convert | Multiply By | To Obtain |
|---|---|---|
| ounces | 28.3 | grams |
| pounds | 453.6 | grams |
| pounds | 0.45 | kilograms |
| grams | 0.035 | ounces |
| kilograms | 2.2 | pounds |

# Apothecary System of Weight and Volume*

| Metric Weight | | Apothecary Weight | Metric Volume | | Apothecary Volume |
|---|---|---|---|---|---|
| 30 g | = | 1 ounce | 1,000 mL | = | 1 quart |
| 15 g | = | 4 drams | 500 mL | = | 1 pint |
| 10 g | = | 2.5 drams | 250 mL | = | 8 fl ounces |
| 4 g | = | 60 grains | 90 mL | = | 3 fl ounces |
| | | (= 1 dram) | 30 mL | = | 1 fl ounce |
| 2 g | = | 30 grains | | | |
| 1 g | = | 15 grains | | | |

*Used by pharmacists in preparing medications.

# Temperature

Boiling point of water
100°C (212°F)

Human body temperature
37°C (98.6°F)

Freezing point of water
0°C (32°F)

### Temperature Conversions

$$°C = \frac{(°F - 32) \times 5}{9}$$

$$°F = \frac{(°C \times 9)}{5} + 32$$

### Some Equivalents

0°C = 32°F
37°C = 98.6°F
100°C = 212°F

# Appendix 2

## Acronyms

| | |
|---|---|
| ADH | antidiuretic hormone |
| AIDS | acquired immunodeficiency syndrome |
| AMU | atomic mass unit |
| ATP | adenosine triphosphate |
| BMI | body mass index |
| BMR | basal metabolic rate |
| CAM | crassulacean acid metabolism |
| DDT | dichlorodiphenyltrichloroethane |
| DNA | deoxyribonucleic acid |
| DRI | dietary reference intakes |
| EGF | epidermal growth factor |
| ER | endoplasmic reticulum |
| ETS | electron-transport system |
| FAD | flavin adenine dinucleotide |
| FAS | fetal alcohol system |
| FSH | follicle-stimulating hormone |
| GnRH | gonadotropin-releasing hormone |
| GSH | growth stimulating hormone |
| HDL | high-density lipoprotein |
| HIV | human immunodeficiency virus |
| HLA | human leukocyte antigens |
| ICSH | interstitial cell-stimulating hormone |
| IPCC | Intergovernmental Panel on Climate Change |
| LDL | low-density lipoprotein |
| LH | luteinizing hormone |
| Lp(a) | lipoprotein a |
| NAD | nicotinamide adenine dinucleotide |
| NADP | nicotinamide adenine dinucleotide phosphate |
| PCB | polychlorinated biphenyl |
| pH | hydrogen ion concentration |
| PKU | phenylketone urea |
| RBC | red blood cell |
| RNA | ribonucleic acid |
| RuBisCo | ribulose bisphosphate carboxylase |
| SARS | severe acute respiratory syndrome |
| SDA | specific dynamic action |
| STD | sexually transmitted disease |
| TCA | tricarboxylic acid cycle |
| TSH | thyroid-stimulating hormone |
| UNAIDS | United Nations Joint HIV/AIDS Program |
| USAMRIID | U.S. Army Medical Research Institute of Infectious Diseases |
| VLDL | very-low-density lipoprotein |
| WBC | white blood cell |

# Glossary

## A

**abiotic factors** (ā-bī-'ä-tik fak-tərz) Nonliving parts of an organism's environment.

**absorption** (əb-'sorp-shən) The movement of simple molecules from the digestive system to the circulatory system for dispersal throughout the body.

**abyssal ecosystem** (ə-bi-səl eco-sis-təm) A benthic ecosystem that occurs at great depths in the ocean.

**accessory pigments** (ak-ses-uh-ree pig-mənt) Photosynthetic pigments other than the chlorophylls that enable an organism to use more colors of the visible light spectrum for photosynthesis (e.g., carotinoids [yellow, red, and orange]; phycoerythrins [red]; and phycocyanin [blue]).

**acetyl** (ə-'sē-tə) The 2-carbon remainder of the carbon skeleton of pyruvic acid (CH3CO–) that is able to enter the mitochondrion for oxidation in the Krebs cycle.

**acetyl-CoA** (ə-'sē-tə kō-'ā) The 2-carbon remainder of the carbon skeleton of pyruvic attached to a coenzyme A molecule.

**acetylcholine** (ə-se-təl-kō-lēn) A neurotransmitter secreted into the synapse by many axons and received by dendrites.

**acetylcholinesterase** (uh-seet-kō-lə-'nes-tə-'rās) An enzyme present in the synapse that destroys acetylcholine.

**acid-base reactions** (a-səd bās rē-'ak-shən) When the ions of one compound (acid) interact with the ions of another compound (base), forming a salt and water.

**acids** (a-səds) Compounds that release a hydrogen ion in a solution.

**acoelomate** (ā-'sē-lə-māt) Without a coelom; the internal organs have no spaces between them.

**acquired characteristics** (ə-'kwī(-ə)r ker-ik-tə-'ris-tik) Characteristics of an organism gained during its lifetime, not determined genetically and therefore not transmitted to the offspring.

**actin** (ak-tən) A protein found in the thin myofilaments of muscle fibers that binds to myosin.

**actin filaments** (ak-tən fi-lə-mənts) Filaments composed of the protein actin that are part of a cell's cytoskeleton.

**activation energy** (ak-tĭ-va'shun e-nər-jē) Energy required to start a reaction.

**active site** (ak-tiv sīt) The place on the enzyme that causes the substrate to change.

**active transport** (ak-tiv trans-'port) The use of a carrier molecule to move molecules across a plasma membrane in a direction opposite that of the concentration gradient. The carrier requires an input of energy other than the kinetic energy of the molecules.

**adaptive radiation** (ə-'dap-tiv rā-dē-'ā-shən) A specific evolutionary pattern in which there is a rapid increase in the number of kinds of closely related species.

**adenine** (a-də-nēn) A double-ring nitrogenous-base molecule in DNA and RNA; the complementary base of thymine or uracil.

**adenosine triphosphate** (ATP) (ə-'de-nə-sēn trī-'fäs-fāt) A molecule formed from the building blocks of adenine, ribose, and phosphates; it functions as the primary energy carrier in the cell.

**aerobic cellular respiration** (er-'ō-bik 'sel-yə-lər res-pə-'rā-shən) The biochemical pathway that requires oxygen and converts food, such as carbohydrates, to carbon dioxide and water. During this conversion, it releases the chemical-bond energy as ATP molecules.

**aerobic exercise** (er-'ō-bik ek-sər-sīz) The level of exercise at which the level of exertion allows the heart and lungs to keep up with the oxygen needs of the muscles.

**age distribution** (āj dis-trə-'byü-shən) The number of organisms of each age in the population.

**alcoholic fermentation** (al-kə-'ho-lik fər-mən-'tā-shən) The anaerobic respiration pathway in yeast cells; during this process, pyruvic acid from glycolysis is converted to ethanol and carbon dioxide.

**algae** ('al-gə) Protists that have cell walls and chlorophyll and can therefore carry on photosynthesis.

**allele** (ə-'lēl) An alternative form of a gene for a particular characteristic (e.g., attached earlobe and free earlobe are alternative alleles for ear shape).

**allele frequency** (ə-'lēl frē-kwən(t)-sē) A measure of how common a specific allele is, compared with other alleles for the same characteristic.

**allergy** ('a-lər-jē) An abnormal immune reaction to an antigen. Possibly the most familiar are allergies to foods, pollens, and drugs.

**alternation of generations** (ol-tər-'nā-shən əv je-nə-'rā-shənz) The aspect of the life cycle in which there are two distinctly different forms of an organism; each form is involved in the production of the other and only one form is involved in producing gametes; the cycling of a diploid sporophyte generation and a haploid gametophyte generation in plants.

**alternative splicing** (ol-'tər-nə-tiv splī-siŋ) A process that selects which exons will be retained as part of the mature mRNA that will be used during translation. Alternative splicing allows for the possibility that a single gene can produce more than one type of protein.

**altruism** ('al-trü-i-zəm) Behavior in which an individual animal gives up an advantage or puts itself in danger to aid others.

**alveoli** (al-'vē-əlē) Tiny sacs found in the lungs; where gas exchange takes place.

**amino acid** (ə-'mē-nō 'a-səd) A basic subunit of protein consisting of a short carbon skeleton that contains an amino group, a carboxylic acid group, and one of various side groups.

**anabolism** (ə-'na-bə-li-zəm) Metabolic pathways that result in the synthesis of new, larger compounds (e.g., protein synthesis).

**anaerobic cellular respiration** (a-nə-'rō-bik 'sel-yə-lər res-pə-'rā-shən) A biochemical pathway that does not require oxygen for the production of ATP and does not use $O_2$ as its ultimate hydrogen ion acceptor.

**anaerobic exercise** (a-nə-'rō-bik 'ek-sər-sīz) Bouts of exercise that are so intense that the muscles cannot get oxygen as fast as they need it.

**analogous structures** (ə-'na-lə-gəs 'strək-chər) Structures that have the same function (ex., the wing of a butterfly and the wing of a bird) but different evolutionary backgrounds.

**anaphase** ('a-nə-fāz) The third stage of mitosis, characterized by division of the centromeres and movement of the chromosomes to the poles.

**androgens** ('an-drə-jən) Male sex hormones, produced by the testes, that cause the differentiation of typical internal and external genital male anatomy.

**angiosperms** ('an-jē-ə-spərmz) Plants that produce flowers, seeds, and fruits.

**anorexia nervosa** (a-nə-'rek-sē-ə nər-'vō-sə) A nutritional deficiency disease characterized by severe, prolonged weight loss for fear of becoming obese; this eating disorder is thought to stem from sociocultural factors.

**anther** ('an-thər) The sex organ in plants that produces the pollen that contains the sperm.

**antheridium** (an-thə-'ri-dē-əm) The structure in lower plants that bears sperm.

**anthropomorphism** ('an-thrə-pə-mor- fi-zəm) The ascribing of human feelings, emotions, or meanings to the behavior of animals.

**antibiotics** (an-tē-bī-'ä-tiks) Drugs that selectively kill or inhibit the growth of a particular cell type.

**antibody** ('an-ti-bä-dē) A protein made by B-cells in response to a molecule known as the antigen.

**anticodon** (an-ti-'kō-dän) The trio of bases in the tRNA that is involved in base-pairing.

**antidiuretic hormone (ADH)** (an-ti-dī-yu-'re-tik 'hor-mōn) The hormone produced by the pituitary gland that stimulates the kidney to reabsorb water.

**antigen** ('an-ti-jən) A large organic molecule, usually a protein, which is able to stimulate the production of a specific defense response and becomes neutralized or destroyed by that response.

**aorta** (ā-'or-tə) The large blood vessel that carries blood from the left ventricle to the majority of the body.

**apoptosis** (a-pəp-'tō-səs) Death that has a genetic basis and not the result of injury.

**Archaea** (är-'kē-ə) one of two domains of prokaryotic organisms: Archaea and Bacteria. Distinguished from the domain Bacteria by differences in the nature of the DNA, cell wall, and cell membrane.

**archegonium** (är-ki-'gō-nē-əm) The structure in lower plants that bears eggs.

**arteries** ('är-tə-rēz) The blood vessels that carry blood away from the heart.

**arterioles** (är-'tir-ē-ōlz) Small arteries, located just before capillaries, that can expand and contract to regulate the flow of blood to parts of the body.

**asexual reproduction** (ā-'sek-shwəl rē-prə-'dək-shən) A form of duplication that requires only one parent and results in two organisms that are genetically identical to the parent.

**assimilation** (ə-si-mə-'lā-shən) The physiological process that takes place in a living cell as it converts nutrients in food into specific molecules required by the organism.

**association** (ə-sō-sē-'ā-shən) An animal learns that a particular outcome is associated with a particular stimulus.

**aster** ('as-tər) Microtubules that extend from the centrioles to the plasma membrane of an animal cell.

**asymmetry** (ā-'si-mə-trē) The characteristic of animals with no particular body shape.

**atomic mass unit** (ə-'tä-mik 'mas 'yü-nət) A unit of measure used to describe the mass of atoms and is equal to $1.67 \times 10^{-24}$ grams, approximately the mass of 1 proton.

**atomic nucleus** (ə-'tä-mik 'nü-klē-əs) The central region of an atom.

**atomic number** (ə-'tä-mik 'nəm-bər) The number of protons in an atom.

**atomic weight** (ə-'tä-mik 'wāt) The weight of an atomic nucleus, expressed in atomic mass units (the sum of the protons and neutrons).

**atoms** ('a-təmz) The fundamental units of matter; the smallest parts of an element that still act like that element.

**atria** ('ā-trē-ə) Thin-walled sacs of the heart that receive blood from the veins of the body and empty into the ventricles.

**atrioventricular valves** (ā-trē-ō-ven-'tri-kyə-lər 'valvz) Valves, located between the atria and ventricles of the heart, that prevent the blood from flowing backwards from the ventricles into the atria.

**attachment site** (ə-'tach-mənt 'sīt) A specific point on the surface of the enzyme where it can physically attach itself to the substrate; also called binding site.

**autoimmune diseases** ('o-tō-i-'myün di-'zēz) Disorders that result from the immune system turning against normal chemicals and cells of the body.

**autosomes** ('o-tə-sōmz) Chromosomes that typically carry genetic information used by an organism for characteristics other than the primary determination of sex.

**autotrophs** ('o-tə-trofs) Organisms that are able to make their food molecules from inorganic raw materials by using basic energy sources, such as sunlight.

**axon** ('ak-sän) A neuronal fiber that carries information away from the nerve cell body.

# B

**bacteria** (bak-'tir-ē-ə) Noneukaryotic, unicellular organisms of the Domain Bacteria; formerly used to refer to members of both the Domain Bacteria and the Domain Archaea.

**basal metabolic rate (BMR)** ('bā-səl me-tə-'bä-lik 'rāt) The amount of energy required to maintain normal body activity while at rest.

**bases** ('bā-sez) Compounds that release hydroxide ions or accept hydrogen ions in a solution.

**basilar membrane** ('ba-zə-lər 'mem-brān) A membrane in the cochlea containing sensory cells that are stimulated by the vibrations caused by sound waves.

**behavior** (bi-'hā-vyər) How an organism acts, what it does, and how it does it.

**behavioral isolating mechanisms** (bi-'hā-vyər-rəl 'ī-sə-lāt-ing 'me-kə-ni-zəmz) Reproductive isolating mechanisms that prevent interbreeding between species because of differences in behavior.

**benign tumor** (bi-'nīn 'tü-mər) A cell mass that does not fragment and spread beyond its original area of growth.

**benthic** ('ben-thik) A term used to describe organisms that live in bodies of water, attached to the bottom or to objects in the water.

**benthic ecosystem** ('ben-thik 'ē-kō-sis-təm) An aquatic ecosystem that exists on the bottom of a body of water.

**bilateral symmetry** (bī-'la-tə-rəl 'si-mə-trē) The characteristic of animals that are constructed along a plane running from a head to a tail region, so that only a cut along one plane of this axis results in two mirror halves.

**bile** ('bīl) The product of the liver, stored in the gallbladder, that is responsible for the emulsification of fats.

**binary fission** ('bī-nə-rē 'fi-shən) A method of asexual cell division used by non-eukaryotic cells.

**binding site (attachment site)** ('bīn-diŋ 'sīt) A specific point on the surface of the enzyme where it can physically attach itself to the substrate.

**binomial system of nomenclature** (bī-'nō-mē-əl 'sis-təm 'əv 'nō-mən-klā-chər) A naming system that uses two Latin names, genus and specific epithet, for each species of organism.

**biochemical isolating mechanisms** (bī-ō-'ke-mi-kəl 'ī-sə-lāt-ing 'me-kə-ni-zəmz) Differences in biochemical activities that prevent mating between individuals of different species.

**biochemical pathway (metabolic pathway)** (bī-ō-'ke-mi-kəl 'path-wā) A major series of enzyme-controlled reactions linked together.

**biochemistry** (bī-ō-'ke-mə-strē) The chemistry of living things, often called biological chemistry.

**biogenesis** (bī-ō-'je-nə-səs) The concept that life originates only from preexisting life.

**biological species concept** (bī-ō-'lä-ji-kəl 'spē-shēz 'kän-sept) The concept that species are distinguished from one another by their inability to interbreed.

**biology** (bī-'ä-lə-jē) The science that deals with the study of living things and how living entities interact with things around them.

**biomagnification** (bī-ō-mag-nə-fə-'kā-shən) The accumulation of a compound in increasing concentrations in organisms at successively higher trophic levels.

**biomass** ('bī-ō-mas) The dry weight of a collection of designated organisms.

**biomes** ('bī-ōmz) Large, regional communities primarily determined by climate.

**bioremediation** ('bī-ō-ri-mē-dē-'ā-shən) The use of living organisms to remove toxic agents from the environment.

**biosphere** ('bī-ə-sfir) The worldwide ecosystem.

**biotechnology** (bī-ō-tek-'nä-lə-jē) The science of gene manipulation.

**biotic factors** (bī-'ä-tik 'fak-tərz) Living parts of an organism's environment.

**blood** ('bləd) The fluid medium, consisting of cells and plasma, that assists in the transport of materials and heat.

**bloom** ('blüm) A rapid increase in the number of microorganisms in a body of water.

**body mass index (BMI)** ('bä-dē 'mas 'in-deks) The weight of a person in kilograms divided by the person's height in meters squared.

**Bowman's capsule** ('bō-mənz- 'kap-səl) The saclike structure at the end of a nephron that surrounds the glomerulus.

**breathing** ('brē-thiŋ) The process of pumping air into and out of the lungs.

**bronchi** ('bräŋ-kī) Major branches of the trachea that ultimately deliver air to bronchioles in the lungs.

**bronchioles** ('bräŋ-kē-ōlz) Small tubes that deliver air to the alveoli in the lungs.

**budding** ('bə-diŋ) A type of asexual reproduction in which the new organism is an outgrowth of the parent.

**bulimia** (bü-'lē-mē-ə) A nutritional deficiency disease characterized by a binge-and-purge cycle of eating; it is thought to stem from psychological disorders.

## C

**calorie** ('ka-lə-rē) The amount of heat energy necessary to raise the temperature of 1 gram of water 1°C.

**Calvin cycle** ('kal-vən- 'sī-kəl) A cyclic sequence of reactions that make up the light-independent reactions stage of photosynthesis.

**capillary** ('ka-pə-ler-ē) The thinnest blood vessel that exchanges materials between the blood and tissues that surround these vessels.

**carbohydrates** (kär-bō-'hī-drāts) One class of organic molecules composed of carbon, hydrogen, and oxygen in a ratio of 1:2:1; the basic building block of carbohydrates is a simple sugar (monosaccharide).

**carbon cycle** ('kär-bən 'sī-kəl) The processes and pathways involved in capturing inorganic carbon-containing molecules, converting them into organic molecules that are used by organisms, and the ultimate release of inorganic carbon molecules back to the abiotic environment.

**carbon skeleton** ('kär-bən 'ske-lə-tən) The central portion of an organic molecule composed of rings or chains of carbon atoms.

**carcinogens** (kär-'si-nə-jənz) Agents that cause cancer.

**cardiovascular system** ('kär-dē-ō-'vas-kyə-lər 'sis-təm) The organ system of all vertebrates including humans that pumps blood around the body and consists of blood, the heart, and vessels.

**carnivores** ('kär-nə-vórz) Animals that eat other animals.

**carrier proteins** ('ker-ē-ər 'prō-tēnz) A category of proteins that pick up molecules at one place and transport them to another.

**carrying capacity** ('ka-rē-ing kə-'pa-sə-tē) The maximum sustainable population for an area.

**catabolism** (kə-'ta-bə-li-zəm) Metabolic pathways that result in the breakdown of compounds (e.g., glycolysis).

**catalyst** ('ka-tə-ləst) A chemical that speeds up a reaction but is not used up in the reaction.

**cell cycle** ('sel 'sī-kəl) All the stages of growth and division for a eukaryotic cell.

**cell division** ('sel də-'vi-zhən) The process in which a cell becomes two new cells.

**cell plate** ('sel 'plāt) A plant-cell structure that begins to form in the center of the cell and proceeds to the cell membrane, resulting in cytokinesis.

**cells** ('selz) The basic structural units of all living things; the smallest units that display the characteristics of life.

**cell theory** ('sel 'thē-ə-rē) The concept that all living things are made of cells.

**cellular membranes** ('sel-yə-lər 'mem-brānz) Thin sheets of material composed of phospholipids and proteins; some of the proteins have attached carbohydrates or fats.

**cellular respiration** ('sel-yə-lər res-pə-'rā-shən) A major biochemical pathway by which cells release the chemical-bond energy from food and convert it into a usable form (ATP).

**cell wall** ('sel 'wȯl) An outer covering on some cells; may be composed of cellulose, chitin, or peptidoglycan, depending on the kind of organism.

**central nervous system** ('sen-trəl 'nər-vəs 'sis-təm) The portion of the nervous system consisting of the brain and spinal cord.

**centriole** ('sen-trē-ōl) Two sets of nine short microtubules; each set of tubules is arranged in a cylinder.

**centromere** ('sen-trə-mir) The sequence of bases at the site where the sister chromatids are attached.

**cerebellum** (ser-ə-'be-ləm) The region of the brain, connected to the medulla oblongata, that receives many kinds of sensory stimuli and coordinates muscle movement.

**cerebrum** (sə-'rē-brəm) The region of the brain that surrounds most of the other parts of the brain and is involved in consciousness and thought.

**chemical bonds** ('ke-mi-kəl 'bändz) Forces that combine atoms or ions and hold them together.

**chemical equation** ('ke-mi-kəl i-'kwā-zhən) A way of describing what happens in a chemical reaction.

**chemical reaction** ('ke-mi-kəl rē-'ak-shən) The formation or rearrangement of chemical bonds, usually indicated in an equation by an arrow from the reactants to the products.

**chemicals** ('ke-mi-kəlz) Substances used or produced in processes that involve changes in matter.

**chemistry** ('ke-mə-strē) The science concerned with the study of the composition, structure, and properties of matter and the changes it undergoes.

**chemosynthesis** ('kē-mō-'sin-thə-səs) The use of inorganic chemical reactions as a source of energy to make larger, organic molecules.

**chlorophyll** ('klȯr-ə-fil) The green pigment located in the chloroplasts of plant cells associated with trapping light energy.

**chloroplasts** ('klȯr-ə-plasts) Energy-converting, membranous, saclike organelles in plant cells containing the green pigment chlorophyll.

**chromatid** ('krō-mə-təd) One of two component parts of a chromosome formed by replication and attached at the centromere.

**chromatin** ('krō-mə-tən) An area or a structure within the nucleus of a cell composed of long molecules of deoxyribonucleic acid (DNA) in association with proteins.

**chromosomal aberration** ('krō-mə-sōm-al a-bə-'rā-shən) A change in the structure of chromosomes that can affect the expression of genes (e.g., translocation, duplication mutations).

**chromosomes** (krō-mə-'sōmz) Double-stranded DNA molecules with attached protein (nucleoprotein) coiled into a short, compact unit.

**cilia** ('si-lē-ə) Numerous short, hairlike structures projecting from the cell surface that enable locomotion.

**class** ('klas) A group of closely related families within a phylum.

**classical conditioning** ('kla-si-kəl kən-'di-sh-niŋ) Learning that occurs when an involuntary, natural, reflexive response to a natural stimulus is transferred from the natural stimulus to a new stimulus.

**cleavage furrow** ('klē-vij 'fər-ō) An indentation of the cell membrane of an animal cell that pinches the cytoplasm into two parts during cell division.

**climax community** ('klī-maks kə-'myü-nə-tē) A relatively stable, long-lasting community.

**clitoris** ('kli-tə-rəs) A small, elongated erectile structure located between and at the head of the labia; it is equivalent to the penis.

**clone** ('klōn) Exact copies of biological entities such as genes, organisms, or cells.

**cochlea** ('kō-klē-ə) The part of the ear that converts sound into nerve impulses.

**coding strand** ('kō-ding 'strand) One of the two DNA strands that serves as a template, or pattern, for the synthesis of RNA.

**codominance** (kō-'dä-mə-nəns) A situation in which both alleles in a heterozygous organism express themselves.

**codon** ('kō-dän) A sequence of three nucleotides of an mRNA molecule that directs the placement of a particular amino acid during translation.

**coelom** ('sē-ləm) A body cavity in which internal organs are suspended.

**coenzyme** (kō-'en-zīm) A molecule that works with an enzyme to enable the enzyme to function as a catalyst.

**cofactor** ('kō-fak-tər) Inorganic ions or organic molecules that serve as enzyme helpers.

**commensalism** (kə-'men-sə-li-zəm) A relationship between two organisms in which one organism is helped and the other is not affected.

**communication** (kə-myü-nə-'kā-shən) The use of signals to convey information from one animal to another.

**community** (kə-'myü-nə-tē) Populations of different kinds of organisms that interact with one another in a particular place.

**competition** (käm-pə-'ti-shən) A relationship between two organisms in which both organisms are harmed.

**competitive exclusion principle** (kəm-'pe-tə-tiv iks-'klü-zhən 'prin-sə-pəl) No two species can occupy the same niche at the same time.

**competitive inhibition** (kəm-'pe-tə-tiv in-hə-'bi-shən) The formation of a temporary enzyme-inhibitor complex that interferes with the normal formation of enzyme-substrate complexes, resulting in a decreased turnover.

**complete proteins** (kəm-'plēt 'prō-tēnz) Protein molecules that provide all the essential amino acids.

**complex carbohydrates** ('käm-pleks kär-bō-'hī-drāts) Macromolecules composed of simple sugars combined by dehydration synthesis to form a polymer.

**compound** (käm-'paund) A kind of matter that consists of a specific number of atoms (or ions) joined to each other in a particular way and held together by chemical bonds.

**concentration gradient (diffusion gradient)** (kän-sən-'trā-shən 'grā-dē-ənt) (di-'fyü-zhən 'grā-dē-ənt) The gradual change in the number of molecules per unit of volume over distance.

**conditioned response** (kən-'di-shənd ri-'späns) The modified behavior displayed in which a new response is associated with a natural stimulus.

**cones** ('kōnz) Reproductive structures of gymnosperms that produce pollen in males or eggs in females.

**consumers** (kən-'sü-mərs) Organisms that must obtain energy in the form of organic matter.

**control group** (kən-'trōl 'grüp) The situation used as the basis for comparison in a controlled experiment. The group in which there are no manipulated variables.

**controlled experiment** (kən-'trōld ik-'sper-ə-mənt) An experiment that includes two groups, one in which the variable is manipulated in a particular way and one in which there is no manipulation.

**control processes** (kən-'trl 'prä-se-səz) Mechanisms that ensure an organism will carry out all life activities in the proper sequence (coordination) and at the proper rate (regulation).

**convergent evolution** (kən-'vər-jənt e-və-'lü-shən) An evolutionary pattern in which widely different organisms show similar characteristics.

**coral reef ecosystem** ('kȯr-əl 'rēf 'ē-kō-sis-təm) A benthic ecosystem in shallow water produced by coral animals that build cup-shaped external skeletons around themselves. A symbiotic relationship between corals and algae provides the organic matter that supports other kinds of organisms.

**cotyledons** (kä-tə-'lē-dən) Embryonic leaves that have food stored in them; also known as seed leaves.

**covalent bond** (kō-'vā-lənt 'bänd) The attractive force formed between two atoms that share a pair of electrons.

**cristae** ('kris-tə) Folded surfaces of the inner membranes of mitochondria.

**critical period** ('kri-ti-kəl 'pir-ē-əd) The period of time during the life of an animal when imprinting can take place.

**crossing-over** ('krȯ-siŋ 'ō-vər) The exchange of a part of a chromatid from 1 chromosome with an equivalent part of a chromatid from a homologous chromosome.

**cryptorchidism** (krip-'tȯr-kə-di-zəm) A developmental condition in which the testes do not migrate from the abdomen through the inguinal canal to the scrotum.

**cytokinesis** (sī-tō-kə-'nē-səs) The division of the cytoplasm of one cell into two new cells.

**cytoplasm** ('sī-tə-pla-zəm) The portion of the protoplasm that surrounds the nucleus.

**cytosine** ('sī-tə-sēn) A single-ring nitrogenous-base molecule in DNA and RNA; it is complementary to guanine.

**cytoskeleton** (sī-tə-'ske-lə-tən) The internal framework of eukaryotic cells composed of intermediate filaments, microtubules, and microfilaments; provides the cell with a flexible shape, and the ability to move through the environment, to move molecules internally, and to respond to environmental changes.

# D

**death phase** ('deth 'fāz) The portion of some population growth curves in which the size of the population declines.

**deceleration phase** (dē-se-lə-'rā-shen 'fāz) A phase in the population growth curve during which the population growth rate begins to slow.

**deciduous** (di-'si-jə-wəs) A type of tree that loses its leaves at the end of the growing season.

**decomposers** (dē-kəm-'pō-zərs) Organisms that use dead organic matter as a source of energy.

**deductive reasoning (deduction)** (di-'dək-tiv 'rēz-niŋ) (di-'dək-shən) The mental process of using accepted generalizations to predict the outcome of specific events; from the general to the specific.

**dehydration synthesis reaction** (dē-hī-'drā-shən 'sin-thə-səs rē-'ak-shən) A reaction that results in the formation of a macromolecule when water is removed from between the two smaller component parts.

**deletion aberration** (di-'lē-shən a-bə-'rā-shən) A major change in DNA that can be observed at the level of the chromosome.

**deletion mutation** (di-'lē-shən myü-'tā-shən) A change in the DNA that has resulted from the removal of one or more nucleotides.

**denatured** (dē-'nā-chərd) Altered so that some of the protein's original properties are diminished or eliminated.

**dendrites** ('den-drīts) Neuronal fibers that receive information from axons and carry it toward the nerve-cell body.

**denitrifying bacteria** (dē-'nī-trə-fī-ing bak-'tir-ē-ə) Several kinds of bacteria capable of converting nitrite to nitrogen gas.

**density-dependent limiting factors** ('den-sə-tē di-'pen-dənt 'li-mə-tiŋ 'fak-tərz) Population-limiting factors that become more effective as the size of the population increases.

**density-independent limiting factors** ('den-sə-tē in-də-'pen-dənt 'li-mə-tiŋ 'fak-tərz) Population-controlling factors that are not related to the size of the population.

**deoxyribonucleic acid (DNA)** (dē-'äk-si-rī-bō-nü-klē-ik 'a-səd) A polymer of nucleotides that serves as genetic information. In noneukaryotic cells, it is a double-stranded loop and contains attached HU proteins. In eukaryotic cells, it is found in strands with attached histone proteins. When tightly coiled, the DNA and histone structure is known as a chromosome.

**dependent variable** (di-'pen-dənt 'ver-ē-ə-bəl) A variable that changes in direct response to (depends on) how another variable (independent variable) is manipulated.

**depolarized** (dē-'pō-lə-rīzd) Having lost the electrical difference existing between two points or objects.

**determination** (di-tər-mə-'nā-shən) The process a cell goes through to select which genes it will eventually express on a more or less permanent basis.

**diaphragm** ('dī-ə-fram) The muscle separating the lung cavity from the abdominal cavity; it is involved in exchanging the air in the lungs.

**diastolic blood pressure** (dī-ə-'stä-lik 'bləd 'pre-shər) The pressure present in a large artery when the heart is not contracting.

**dicot** ('dī-kät) An angiosperm whose embryo has two seed leaves.

**diet** ('dī-ət) The food and drink consumed by a person from day to day.

**dietary fiber** ('dī-ə-ter-ē 'fī-bər) Natural (plant) or industrially produced polysaccharides that are resistant to hydrolysis by human digestive enzymes.

**Dietary Reference Intakes** ('dī-ə-ter-ē 're-fərns 'in-tāks) Published by the USDA, these guidelines provide information on the amounts of certain nutrients various members of the public should receive.

**differentiation** (dif-ə-'ren-shē-'ā-shən) The process of forming specialized cells within a multicellular organism.

**diffusion** (di-'fyü-zhən) The net movement of a kind of molecule from an area of higher concentration to an area of lesser concentration.

**digestion** (dī-'jes-chən) The breakdown of complex food molecules to simpler molecules; the chemical reaction of hydrolysis.

**digestive system** (dī-'jes-tiv 'sis-təm) The organ system responsible for the processing and distribution of nutrients and consists of a muscular tube and glands that secrete digestive juices into the tube.

**diploblastic** (dip-lō-'blas-tik) A condition in which some simple animals consist of only two layers of cells.

**diploid** ('di-plȯid) Having two sets of chromosomes: one set from the maternal parent and one set from the paternal parent.

**directional selection** (də-'rek-shnəl sə-'lek-shən) Selection that occurs when individuals at one extreme of the range of a characteristic are consistently selected for.

**disruptive selection** (dis-'rəp-tiv sə-'lek-shən) Selection that occurs when both extremes of a range for a charcteristic are selected for and the intermediate condition is selected against.

**distal convoluted tubule** ('dis-təl 'kän-və-lü-təd 'tü-byül) The downstream end of the nephron of the kidney, primarily responsible for regulating the amount of hydrogen and potassium ions in the blood.

**divergent evolution** (də-'vər-jənt e-və-'lü-shən) A basic evolutionary pattern in which individual speciation events cause many branches in the evolution of a group of organisms.

**DNA fingerprinting** (DNA 'fiŋ-gər-print-ing) A laboratory technique that detects differences in DNA to identify a unique individual; the differences in DNA are detected by using variable number tandem repeats, restriction enzymes, and electrophoresis.

**DNA library** (DNA 'lī-brer-ē) A collection of cloned DNA fragments that represent all the genetic information of an organism.

**DNA replication** (re-plə-'kā-shən) The process by which the genetic material (DNA) of the cell reproduces itself prior to its distribution to the next generation of cells.

**domain** (dō-'mān) The first (broadest) classification unit of organisms; there are three domains: Bacteria, Archaea, and Eucarya.

**dominance hierarchy** ('dä-mə-nəns 'hī-rär-kē) A relatively stable, mutually understood order of priority within a group.

**dominant allele** ('dä-mə-nənt ə-'lēl) An allele that expresses itself and masks the effects of other alleles for the trait.

**double bond** ('də-bəl 'bänd) A pair of covalent bonds formed between two atoms when they share two pairs of electrons.

**double-factor cross** ('də-bəl 'fak-tər 'krȯs) A genetic study in which two pairs of alleles are followed from the parental generation to the offspring.

**Down syndrome** ('daȯn 'sin-drōm) A genetic disorder resulting from the presence of an extra chromosome 21. Symptoms include slightly slanted eyes, flattened facial features, a large tongue, and a tendency toward short stature and fingers. Individuals usually display mental retardation.

**duodenum** (dü-ə-'dē-nəm) The first part of the small intestine, which receives food from the stomach and secretions from the liver and pancreas.

**duplications** (dü-pli-'kā-shənz) A form of chromosomal aberration in which a portion of a chromosome is replicated and attached to the original section in sequence.

**dynamic equilibrium** (dī-'na-mik ē-kwə-'li-brē-əm) The condition in which molecules are equally dispersed; therefore, movement is equal in all directions.

# E

**ecology** (i-'kä-lə-jē) The branch of biology that studies the relationships between organisms and their environment.

**ecosystem** ('ē-kō-sis-təm) A unit consisting of a community of organisms (populations) and its interactions with the physical surroundings.

**ectoderm** ('ek-tə-dərm) The outer embryonic layer.

**ectotherms** ('ek-tə-thərmz) Animals that are unable to regulate their body temperature by automatic physiological processes but can regulate their temperature by moving to places where they can be most comfortable.

**ejaculation** (i-ja-kyə-'lā-shən) The release of sperm cells and seminal fluid through the penis of a male.

**electron** (i-'lek-trän) A negatively charged particle moving at a distance from the nucleus of an atom; it balances the positive charges of the protons.

**electron-transport system (ETS)** (i-'lek-trän trans-'pȯrt 'sis-təm) The series of oxidation-reduction reactions in aerobic cellular respiration in which the energy is removed from hydrogens and transferred to ATP.

**electrophoresis** (i-lek-trə-fə-'rē-səs) A technique that separates DNA fragments, proteins, or other molecules on the basis of size.

**elements** ('e-lə-mənts) Fundamental chemical substances that are made up of collections of only one kind of atom.

**emergent properties** (i-'mər-jənt 'prä-pər-tēz) Never-before-seen features that result from the interaction of simple components when they form much more complex substances.

**endocrine glands** ('en-də-krən 'glandz) Glands that secrete into the circulatory system.

**endocrine system** ('en-də-krən 'sis-təm) A number of glands that communicate with one another and other tissues through chemical messengers transported throughout the body by the circulatory system.

**endocytosis** (en-dō-sī-'tō-səs) The process cells use to wrap membrane around a particle (usually food) and engulf it.

**endoderm** ('en-də-dərm) The inner embryonic layer.

**endoplasmic reticulum (ER)** (en-də-plaz-mik ri-'ti-kyə-ləm) Folded membranes and tubes throughout the eukaryotic cell that provide a large surface on which chemical activities take place.

**endoskeletons** (en-dō-'ske-lə-tənz) Skeletons typical of vertebrates in which the skeleton is surrounded by muscles and other organs.

endospore ('en-dō-spór) A unique bacterial structure with a low metabolic rate that germinates under favorable conditions to grow into a new cell.

endosymbiotic theory (en-dō-sim-bī-'ä-tik 'thē-ə-rē) A theory suggesting that some organelles found in eukaryotic cells may have originated as free-living cells.

endotherms ('en-dō-thərmz) Animals that have internal temperature-regulating mechanisms and can maintain a relatively constant body temperature in spite of wide variations in the temperature of their environment.

energy ('e-nər-jē) The ability to do work or cause things to move.

energy level ('e-nər-jē 'le-vəl) A region surrounding an atomic nucleus that contains electrons moving at approximately the same speed and having approximately the same amount of kinetic energy.

enhancer sequence (in-'han-sər 'sē-kwəns) A DNA sequence that regulates gene expression by acting as a binding site for proteins that increase the ability of RNA polymerase to transcribe a specific protein.

environment (in-'vī-rə-mənt) Anything that affects an organism during its lifetime.

environmental resistance (in-'vī-rə-mən-təl ri-'zis-təns) The collective factors that limit population growth.

enzymatic competition (en-zə-'ma-tik käm-pə-'ti-shən) Competition among several different available enzymes to combine with a given substrate material.

enzymes ('en-zīmz) Molecules, produced by organisms, that are able to control the rate at which chemical reactions occur.

enzyme-substrate complex ('en-zīm 'səb-strāt 'käm-pleks) A temporary molecule formed when an enzyme attaches itself to a substrate molecule.

epigenetics (e-pi-jə-'ne-tiks) The study of changes in gene expression caused by factors other than alterations in a cell's DNA.

epinephrine (e pə-'ne-frən) A hormone produced by the adrenal medulla and certain nerve cells that increases heart rate, blood pressure, and breathing rate.

epiphytes ('e-pə-fīts) Plants that live on the surface of other plants without doing harm.

essential amino acids (i-'sen-shəl ə-'mē-nō 'a-sədz) Amino acids that cannot be synthesized by the human body and must be part of the diet (e.g., lysine, tryptophan, and valine).

essential fatty acids (i-'sen-shəl 'fa-tē 'a-sədz) The fatty acids linoleic and linolenic, which cannot be synthesized by the human body and must be part of the diet.

estrogen ('es-trə-jən) One of the female sex hormones responsible for the growth and development of female sexual anatomy.

estuary ('es-chə-wer-ē) A special category of aquatic ecosystem that consists of shallow, partially enclosed areas where freshwater enters the ocean; intermediate in saltiness between freshwater and the ocean.

Eucarya (yu'ka-re-ah) The domain of life that includes all organisms that have eukaryotic cells (plants, animals, fungi, protozoa, and algae).

eukaryotic cells (yü-ker-rē-'ä-tik 'sels) One of the two major types of cells; cells that have a true nucleus, as in plants, fungi, protists, and animals.

euphotic zone (yü-'fō-tik 'zōn) The upper layer of the ocean, where the sun's rays penetrate.

evolution (e-və-'lü-shən) A change in the frequency of genetically determined characteristics within a population over time.

excretory system ('ek-skrə-tór-ē 'sis-təm) The organ system responsible for the processing and elimination of metabolic waste products and consists of the kidneys, ureters, urinary bladder, and urethra.

exocrine glands ('ek-sə-krən 'glandz) Glands that secrete through ducts to the surface of the body or into hollow organs of the body.

exocytosis (ek-sō-sī-'tō-səs) The process cells use to wrap membrane around a particle (usually cell products or wastes) and eliminate it from a cell.

exon ('ek-sän) Sequences of mRNA that are used to code for proteins.

exoskeletons (ek-sō-'ske-lə-tənz) Skeletons typical of many invertebrates, in which the skeleton is on the outside of the animal.

experiment (ik-'sper-ə-mənt) A re-creation of an event that enables a scientist to gain valid and reliable empirical evidence.

experimental group (ik-sper-ə-'men-təl 'grüp) The group in a controlled experiment that has a variable manipulated.

exponential growth phase (ek-spə-'nen-chəl 'grōth 'fāz) The period of time during population growth when the population increases at an accelerating rate.

expressivity (ek-spre-'si-və-tē) A term used to describe situations in which the gene expresses itself but not equally in all individuals that have it.

external parasites (ek-'stər-nəl 'per-ə-sīts) Parasites that live on the outside of their hosts.

extinction (ik-'stiŋ-shən) The loss of a species.

extrinsic limiting factors (ik-'stiŋ-shən 'li-mə-tiŋ 'fak-tərz) Population-controlling factors that arise outside the population.

# F

facilitated diffusion (fə-'si-lə-tāt-ed di-'fyü-zhən) Diffusion assisted by carrier molecules.

family ('fam-lē) A group of closely related genera within an order.

fats ('fats) A class of water-insoluble macromolecules composed of a glycerol and fatty acids.

fatty acid ('fa-tē 'a-səd) One of the building blocks of a fat, composed of a long-chain carbon skeleton with a carboxylic acid functional group.

fermentation (fər-mən-'tā-shən) Pathways that oxidize glucose to generate ATP energy using something other than $O_2$ as the ultimate hydrogen acceptor.

fertilization (fər-tə-lə-'zā-shən) The joining of haploid nuclei, usually from an egg and a sperm cell, resulting in a diploid cell called a zygote.

filter feeders ('fil-tər 'fē-dərz) Animals that use cilia or other appendages to create water currents and filter food out of the water.

fitness ('fit-nəs) The concept that those who are best adapted to their environment produce the most offspring. Nutritionally, a measure of how efficiently a person can function both physically and mentally.

G-8

**flagella** (flə-'je-lə) Long, hairlike structures, projecting from the cell surface, that enable locomotion.

**flavin adenine dinucleotide (FAD)** ('flā-vən 'a-də-nēn dī-'nü-klē-ə-tīd) A hydrogen carrier used in respiration.

**flower** ('flaur) A complex plant reproductive structure made from modified stems and leaves that produces pollen and eggs.

**fluid-mosaic model** ('flü-əd mō-'zā-ik 'mä-dəl) The concept that the cellular membrane is composed primarily of protein and phospholipid molecules that are able to shift and flow past one another.

**follicles** ('fä-li-kəlz) Saclike structures near the surface of the ovary, which encases the soon-to-be-released secondary oocyte.

**follicle-stimulating hormone (FSH)** ('fä-li-kəl 'stim-yə-lā-tiŋ 'hȯr-mōn) The pituitary secretion that causes the ovaries to begin to produce larger quantities of estrogen and to develop the follicle and prepare the egg for ovulation.

**food chain** ('füd 'chān) A sequence of organisms that feed on one another, resulting in a flow of energy from a producer through a series of consumers.

**Food Guide Pyramid** ('füd 'gīd 'pir-ə-mid) A tool developed by the U.S. Department of Agriculture to help the general public plan for good nutrition; it contains guidelines for required daily intake from each of the six food groups.

**food web** ('füd 'web) A system of interlocking food chains.

**formed elements** ('fȯrmd 'e-lə-mənts) Red, white blood cells and platelets suspended in a watery matrix called plasma.

**formula** ('fȯr-myə-lə) Pertains to a chemical compound; describes what elements it contains (as indicated by a chemical symbol) and in what proportions they occur (as indicated by the subscript number).

**fossil** ('fä-səl) Physical evidence of former life.

**founder effect** ('faùn-dər i-'fekt) The concept that small, newly established populations are likely to have reduced genetic diversity because of the small number of individuals in the founding population.

**fovea centralis** ('fō-vē-ə sen-'tra-ləs) The area of sharpest vision on the retina, containing only cones, where light is sharply focused.

**frameshift mutation** ('frām-shift myü-'tā-shən) A form of mutation that occurs when insertions or deletions cause the ribosome to read the wrong sets of three nucleotides.

**free-living nitrogen-fixing bacteria** ('nī-trə-jən 'fiks-siŋ bak-'tir-ē-ə) Soil bacteria that convert nitrogen gas molecules into nitrogen compounds plants can use.

**fruit** ('früt) The structure (mature ovary) in angiosperms that contains seeds.

**functional groups** ('fəŋ-shnəl 'grüps) Specific combinations of atoms attached to the carbon skeleton that determine specific chemical properties.

**fungus** ('fəŋ-gəs) The common name for members of the kingdom Fungi.

# G

**gallbladder** ('gȯl-bla-dər) The organ, attached to the liver, that stores bile.

**gametes** ('ga-mēts) Haploid sex cells.

**gametogenesis** (gə-mē-tə-'je-nə-səs) The generating of gametes; the meiotic cell-division process that produces sex cells; oogenesis and spermatogenesis.

**gametophyte** (gə-'mē-tə-fīt) A haploid plant that produces gametes; it alternates with the sporophyte through the life cycle.

**gametophyte generation** (gə-'mē-tə-fīt je-nə-'rā-shən) A life cycle stage in plants in which a haploid sex cell is produced by mitosis.

**gas** ('gas) The phase of matter in which the molecules are more energetic than the molecules of a liquid, resulting in only a slight attraction for each other.

**gastric juice** ('gas-trik 'jüs) The secretions of the stomach; they contain enzymes and hydrochloric acid.

**gene** ('jēn) Any molecule usually segments of DNA, able to (1) replicate by directing the manufacture of copies of themselves; (2) mutate, or chemically change, and transmit these changes to future generations; (3) store information that determines the characteristics of cells and organisms; and (4) use this information to direct the synthesis of structural and regulatory proteins.

**gene expression** ('jēn ik-'spre-shən) The cellular process of transcribing and translating genetic information.

**gene flow** ('jēn 'flō) The movement of genes within a population because of migration or the movement of genes from one generation to the next by gene replication and reproduction.

**gene frequency** ('jēn 'frē-kwən-sē) A measure of how often a specific gene shows up in the gametes of a population.

**gene pool** ('jēn 'pül) All the genes of all the individuals of a species.

**generative processes** ('jen-rə-tiv 'prä-ses-es) Actions that increase the size of an individual organism (growth) or increase the number of individuals in a population (reproduction).

**gene-regulator proteins** ('jēn 're-gyə-lā-tər 'prō-tēns) Chemical messengers within a cell that inform the genes as to whether protein-producing genes should be turned on or off or whether they should have their protein-producing activities increased or decreased (e.g., gene-repressor proteins and gene-activator proteins).

**gene therapy** ('jēn 'ther-ə-pē) A technique that introduces new genetic material into an organism to correct a genetic deficiency.

**genetically modified (GM)** (jə-'ne-tik-lē 'mä-də-fīd) Engineered to contain genes from at least one other species.

**genetic bottleneck** (jə-'ne-tik 'bä-təl-nek) The concept that, when populations are severely reduced in size, they may lose some of their genetic diversity.

**genetic cross** (jə-'ne-tik 'krȯs) A planned breeding or mating between two organisms.

**genetic diversity** (jə-'ne-tik də-'vər-sə-tē) The degree to which individuals in a population possess alternative alleles for characteristics.

**genetic drift** (jə-'ne-tik 'drift) A change in gene frequency that is not the result of natural selection; this typically occurs in a small population.

**genetic recombination** (jə-'ne-tik rē-käm-bə-'nā-shən) The gene mixing that occurs during sexual reproduction.

**genetics** (jə-'ne-tiks) The study of genes, how genes produce characteristics, and how the characteristics are inherited.

**genome** ('jē-nōm) A set of all the genes necessary to specify an organism's complete list of characteristics.

**genomics** (jē-'nō-miks) A new field of science that has developed since the sequencing of the human genome; the field looks at how genomes are organized and compares them with genomes of other organims.

**genotype** ('jē-nə-tūp) The catalog of genes of an organism, whether or not these genes are expressed.

**genus** ('jē-nəs) A group of closely related species within a family.

**geographic isolation** (jē-ə-'gra-fik ī-sə-'lā-shən) A condition in which part of the gene pool is separated by geographic barriers from the rest of the population.

**glands** ('glandz) Organs that manufacture and secrete a material either through ducts or directly into the circulatory system.

**glomerulus** (glə-'mer-ə-ləs) A cluster of blood vessels, surrounded by Bowman's capsule in the kidney.

**glyceraldehyde-3-phosphate** (gli-sə-'ral-də-hīd 3 'fäs-fāt) A 3-carbon compound, produced during glycolysis and photosynthesis, that can be converted to other organic molecules.

**glycerol** ('gli-sə-ról) One of the building blocks of a fat, composed of a carbon skeleton that has three alcohol groups (OH) attached to it.

**glycolysis** (glī-'kä-lə-səs) The anaerobic first stage of cellular respiration, consisting of the enzymatic break-down of a sugar into two mole-cules of pyruvic acid.

**Golgi apparatus** ('gól-jē a-pə-'ra-təs) A stack of flattened, smooth, membranous sacs; the site of synthesis and packaging of certain molecules in eukaryotic cells.

**gonads** ('gō-nads) Organs in which meiosis occurs to produce gametes; ovaries or testes.

**gonadotropin-releasing hormone (GnRH)** ('gō-na-də-'trō-pən ri-'lē-siŋ 'hór-mōn) A hormone released from the hypothalamus that stimulates the release of follicle-stimulating hormone (FSH) and luteinizing hormone (LH).

**gradualism** ('gra-jə-wə-li-zəm) A model for evolutionary change that assumes that evolution occurred slowly by accumulating small changes over a long period of time.

**grana** ('grā-nə) Stacks of sacs of the chloroplast membrane (thylakoids) where chlorophyll molecules are concentrated.

**granules** ('gran-yül) Materials whose structure is not as well defined as that of other organelles.

**growth-stimulating hormone (GSH)** ('grōth stim-yə-lā-tiŋ 'hór-mōn) The hormone produced by the anterior pituitary gland that stimulates tissues to grow.

**guanine** ('gwä-nēn) A double-ring nitrogenous-base molecule in DNA and RNA; it is the complementary base of cytosine.

**gymnosperms** ('jim-nə-spərmz) Plants that produce their seeds in cones.

## H

**habitat** ('ha-bə-tat) The place or part of a community occupied by an organism.

**habitat preference (ecological isolating mechanisms)** ('ha-bə-tat 'pre-fərns) Reproductive isolating mechanisms that prevent interbreeding between species because they live in different areas.

**habituation** (hə-bi-chə-'wā-shən) A change in behavior in which an animal ignores a stimulus after repeated exposure to it.

**haploid** ('ha-plóid) Having a single set of chromosomes, resulting from the reduction division of meiosis.

**Hardy-Weinberg concept** ('här-dē 'wīn-bərg 'kän-sept) Populations of organisms will maintain constant gene frequen-cies from generation to generation as long as mating is random, the population is large, mutation does not occur, migration does not occur, and no genes provide more advantageous characteristics than others.

**heart** ('härt) The muscular pump that forces blood through the blood vessels of the body.

**heat** (hēt) The total internal kinetic energy of molecules.

**hemoglobin** ('hē-mə-glō-bən) An iron-containing molecule found in red blood cells, to which oxygen molecules bind.

**hepatic portal vein** (hi-'pa-tik 'pór-təl 'vā n) A blood vessel that collects blood from capillaries in the intestine and delivers it to a second set of capillaries in the liver.

**herbivores** ('ər-bə-vórz) Animals that feed directly on plants.

**heterotrophs** ('he-tə-rə-trōfs) Organisms that require a source of organic material from their environment; they cannot produce food on their own.

**heterozygous** ('he-tə-rə-ō-zī-gus) Describes a diploid organism that has 2 different alleles for a particular characteristic.

**high-energy phosphate bond** ('hī 'e-nər-jē 'fäs-fāt 'bänd) The bond between two phosphates in an ADP or ATP molecule that readily releases its energy for cellular processes.

**homeostasis** (hō-mē-ō-'stā-səs) The maintenance of a constant internal environment.

**homeotherms** (hō-mē-ō-'thərmz) Animals that maintain a constant body temperature.

**homologous chromosomes** (hō-'mä-lə-gəs 'krō-mə-sōmz) A pair of chromosomes in a diploid cell that contain similar genes at corresponding loci throughout their length.

**homologous structures** (hō-'mä-lə-gəs 'strək-chərz) Structures in different species that have been derived from a common ancestral structure.

**homozygous** (hō-mə-'zī-gəs) Describes a diploid organism that has 2 identical alleles for a particular characteristic.

**hormone** ('hór-mōn) A chemical messenger secreted by an endocrine gland to regulate other parts of the body.

**host** ('hōst) An organism that a parasite lives in or on and uses as a source of food.

**hybrid inviability** ('hī-brəd in-vī-ə-'bi-lə-tē) Mechanisms that prevent the off-spring of two different species from continuing to reproduce.

**hydrogen bonds** ('hī-drə-jən 'bändz) Weak attractive forces between molecules; important in determining how groups of molecules are arranged.

**hydrolysis reactions** (hī-'drä-lə-səs rē-'ak-shəns) Processes that occur when large molecules are broken down into smaller parts by the addition of water.

**hydrophilic** (hī-drə-'fi-lik) Readily absor-bing or dissolving in water.

**hydrophobic** (hī-drə-'fō-bik) Tending not to combine with, or incapable of dissolving in, water.

**hydroxide ions** (hī-'dräk-sīd 'ī-ənz) Negatively charged particles (OH⁻) composed of oxygen and hydrogen atoms released from a base when dissolved in water.

**hypertonic** (hī-pər-'tä-nik) A comparative term describing one of two solutions; a hypertonic solution is one with higher amount of dissolved material.

**hypothalamus** (hī-pō-'tha-lə-məs) The region of the brain located in the floor of the thalamus and connected to the pituitary gland; it is involved in sleep and arousal; emotions, such as anger, fear, pleasure, hunger, sexual response, and pain; and automatic functions, such as temperature, blood pressure, and water balance.

**hypothesis** (hī-'pä-thə-səs) A possible answer to or explanation for a question that accounts for all the observed facts and that is testable.

**hypotonic** (hī-pə-'tä-nik) A comparative term describing one of two solutions; a hypotonic solution is one with a lower amount of dissolved material.

## I

**immune system** (i-'myün 'sis-təm) The system of white blood cells specialized to provide the body with resistance to disease.

**immunity** (i-'myü-nə-tē) The ability to maintain homeostasis by resisting or defending against potentially harmful agents including microbes, toxins, and abnormal cells such as tumor cells.

**immunization** ('i-myə-nə-zā-shən) The technique used to induce the immune system to develop an acquired immunity to a specific disease by the use of a vaccine.

**immunodeficiency diseases** (i-myə-nō-di-'fi-shən-sē di-'zēz) Disorders that result from the immune system not having one or more component cells or chemicals.

**imperfect flower** (im-'pər-fikt 'flaür) A flower that contains either male (stamens) or female (pistil) reproductive structures, but not both.

**imprinting** ('im-prin-tiŋ) A form of learning that occurs in a very young animal that is genetically primed to learn a specific behavior in a very short period.

**inclusions** (in-'klü-zhəns) Materials inside a cell that are usually not readily identifiable; stored materials.

**incomplete dominance** (in-kəm-'plēt 'dä-mə-nəns) Occurs when the phenotype of a hetrozygote is intermediate between the two homozygotes on a phenotypic gradient; that is, the phenotypes appear to be "blended" in heterozygotes.

**incomplete proteins** (in-kəm-'plēt 'prō-tēnz) Protein molecules that do not provide all the essential amino acids.

**incus** ('iŋ-kəs) The ear bone that is located between the malleus and the stapes.

**independent assortment** (in-də-'pen-dənt ə-sórt-mənt) The segregation, or assortment, of one pair of homologous chromosomes independently of the segregation, or assortment, of any other pair of chromosomes.

**independent variable** (in-də-'pen-dənt 'ver-ē-ə-bəl) A variable that is purposely manipulated to determine how it will affect the outcome of an event.

**inductive reasoning (induction)** (in-'dək-tiv 'rē-zə-niŋ) (in-'dək-shən) The mental process of examining many sets of facts and developing generalizations; from the specific to the general.

**inflammation** (in-flə-'mā-shən) A non-specific defense method that is a series of events that clear an area of harmful agents and damaged tissue.

**ingestion** (in-'jes-chən) The process of taking food into the body through eating.

**inguinal canal** ('iŋ-gwə-nəl kə-'nal) The opening in the floor of the abdominal cavity through which the testes in a human male fetus descend into the scrotum.

**inhibitor** (in-'hi-bə-tər) A molecule that temporarily attaches itself to an enzyme, thereby interfering with the enzyme's ability to form an enzyme-substrate complex.

**inorganic molecules** (in-or-'ga-nik 'mä-li-kyülz) Molecules that do not contain carbon atoms in rings or chains.

**insertion mutation** (in-'sər-shən myü-'tā-shən) A change in DNA resulting from the addition of one or more nucleotides to the normal DNA sequence.

**insight** ('in-sīt) Learning in which past experiences are reorganized to solve new problems.

**instinctive behavior** (in-'stiŋ-tiv bi-'hā-vyər) Automatic, preprogrammed, genetically determined behavior.

**intermediate filaments** (in-tər-'mē-dē-ət 'fi-lə-mənts) Protein fibers that connect microtubules and micro-filaments as part of the cytoskeleton.

**internal parasites** (in-'tər-nəl 'per-ə-sīt) Parasites that live inside their hosts.

**interphase** ('in-tər-fāz) The stage between cell divisions in which the cell is engaged in metabolic activities.

**interspecific competition** (in-tər-spi-'si-fik käm-pə-'ti-shən) Interaction between two members of *different* species that is harmful to both organisms.

**interspecific hybrids** (in-tər-spi-'si-fik 'hī-brədz) Hybrids between two different species.

**intraspecific competition** (in-trə-spi-'si-fik käm-pə-'ti-shən) Interaction between two members of the *same* species that is harmful to both organisms.

**intraspecific hybrids** (in-trə-spi-'si-fik 'hī-brədz) Organisms that are produced by the controlled breeding of separate varieties of the same species.

**intrinsic limiting factors** (in-'trin-zik 'li-mə-tiŋ 'fak-tərz) Population-controlling factors that arise from within the population.

**intron** ('in-trän) Sequences of mRNA that do not code for protein.

**inversion** (in-'vər-zhən) A chromosomal aberration in which a chromosome is broken and a piece becomes reattached to its original chromosome, but in a flipped orientation.

**invertebrates** (in-'vər-tə-brəts) Animals without backbones.

**ion** ('ī-ən) Electrically unbalanced or charged atoms.

**ionic bonds** (ī-'ä-nik 'bändz) The attractive forces between ions of opposite charge.

**isotonic** (ī-sə-'tä-nik) A term used to describe two solutions that have the same concentration of dissolved material.

**isotope** ('ī-sə-tōp) An atom of the same element that differs only in the number of neutrons.

## K

**kidneys** ('kid-nēz) The primary organs involved in regulating blood levels of water, hydrogen ions, salts, and urea.

**kilocalorie (kcal)** ('kē-lō-ka-lə-rē) A measure of heat energy 1,000 times larger than a calorie; food Calories are kilocalories.

**kinetic energy** (kə-'ne-tik 'e-nər-jē) Energy of motion.

**kinetic molecular theory** (kə-'ne-tik mə-'le-kyə-lər 'thē-ə-rē) All matter is made up of tiny particles that are in constant motion.

**kinetochore** (kə-'ne-tə-kór) A multi-protein complex attached to each chromatid at the centromere.

**kingdom** ('kiŋ-dəm) A classification category larger than a phylum and smaller than a domain.

**Krebs cycle** ('krebz 'sī-kəl) The series of reactions in aerobic cellular respiration that results in the production of two carbon dioxides, the release of four pairs of hydrogens, and the formation of an ATP molecule.

**kwashiorkor** (kwä-shē-'ór-kər) A protein-deficiency disease, common in malnourished children, caused by prolonged protein starvation leading to reduced body size, lethargy, and low mental ability.

# L

**lacteal** ('lak-tē-əl) A tiny lymphatic vessel located in a villus.

**lactic acid fermentation** ('lak-tik 'a-səd fər-mən-'tā-shən) A process during which the pyruvic acid (CH₃COCOOH) that results from glycolysis is converted to lactic acid (CH₃CHOHCOOH) by the transfer of electrons that had been removed from the original glucose.

**lag phase** ('lag 'fāz) The period of time following colonization when a population remains small or increases slowly.

**large intestine (also colon)** ('lärj in-'tes-tən) The last portion of the food tube; it is primarily involved in reabsorbing water.

**law of conservation of energy** ('ló əv kän-sər-'vā-shən əv 'e-nər-jē) The law that states that energy is never created or destroyed.

**Law of Dominance** ('ló əv 'dä-mə-nəns) When an organism has 2 different alleles for a trait, the allele that is expressed and overshadows the expression of the other allele is said to be dominant; the allele whose expression is overshadowed is said to be recessive.

**Law of Independent Assortment** ('ló əv in-də-'pen-dənt ə-'sórt-mənt) Members of one allelic pair will separate from each other independently of the members of other allele pairs.

**Law of Segregation** ('ló əv se-gri-'gā-shən) When haploid gametes are formed by a diploid organism, the 2 alleles that control a trait separate from one another into different gametes, retaining their individuality.

**leaf** ('lēf) Plant structure specialized for carrying out the process of photosynthesis.

**learned behavior** ('lərnd bi-'hā-vyər) A change in behavior as a result of experience.

**learning** ('lərn-iŋ) A change in behavior as a result of experience.

**lichen** ('li-chən) An organism comprised of a fungus and an alga protist or cyanobacterium existing in a mutualistic relationship.

**light-capturing events** ('līt 'kap-chər-iŋ i-'vent) The first stage in photosynthesis; involves photosynthetic pigments capturing light energy in the form of excited electrons.

**light-dependent reactions** ('līt di-'pen-dənt rē-'ak-shəns) The second stage in photosynthesis, during which excited electrons from the light-capturing events are used to make ATP, and water is broken down to hydrogen and oxygen. The hydrogens are transferred to electron carrier coenzymes, NADP⁺.

**light-independent reactions** ('līt in-di-'pen-dənt rē-'ak-shəns) The third stage of photosynthesis; involves cells using ATP and NADPH from the light-dependent reactions to attach CO₂ to 5-carbon starter molecules to manufacture organic molecules (e.g., glucose [C₆H₁₂O₆]).

**limiting factors** ('li-mə-tiŋ 'fak-tərz) Environmental influences that limit population growth.

**limnetic zone** (lim-'ne-tik 'zōn) In freshwater ecosystems, the portion of a lake that does not have rooted vegetation.

**linkage** ('liŋ-kij) A situation in which the genes for different characteristics are inherited together more frequently than would be predicted by probability.

**linkage group** ('liŋ-kij 'grüp) A group of genes located on the same chromosome that tend to be inherited together.

**lipids** ('li-pədz) Large organic molecules that do not easily dissolve in water; classes include true (neutral) fats, phospholipids, and steroids.

**liquid** ('li-kwəd) The phase of matter in which the molecules are strongly attracted to each other, but, because they have more energy and are farther apart than in a solid, they move past each other more freely.

**littoral zone** ('li-tə-rəl 'zōn) In freshwater ecosystems, the region with rooted vegetation.

**locus** ('lō-kəs) The spot on a chromosome where an allele is located.

**loop of Henle** ('lüp 'əv 'hen-lē) The middle portion of the nephron; primarily involved in regulating the amount of water lost from the kidney.

**lung** ('ləŋ) Organs of the body that allow gas exchange to take place between the air and blood.

**luteinizing hormone (LH)** (lü-tē-ən-ī-ziŋ 'hór-mōn) A hormone produced by the anterior pituitary gland, which stimulates ovulation.

**lymph** ('limf) Liquid material that leaves the circulatory system to surround cells.

**lymphatic system** (lim-'fa-tik 'sis-təm) A collection of thin-walled tubes that collect, filter, and return lymph from the body to the circulatory system.

**lymph nodes** ('limf 'nōdz) Small encapsulated bodies found along the lymph vessels that contain large numbers of white blood cells (WBCs), macrophages, and lymphocytes that remove microorganisms and foreign particles from the lymph.

**lysosomes** ('lī-sə-sōmz) Specialized, submicroscopic organelles that hold a mixture of hydrolytic enzymes.

# M

**macromolecules** (ma-krō-'mä-li-kyülz) Very large molecules, many of which are composed of many smaller, similar monomers that are chemically bonded together.

**malignant tumors** (mə-'lig-nənt 'tü-mərz) Nonencapsulated growths of tumor cells that are harmful; they may spread to or invade other parts of the body.

**malleus** ('ma-lē-əs) The ear bone that is attached to the tympanum.

**mass number** ('mas 'nəm-bər) The weight of an atomic nucleus expressed in atomic mass units (the sum of the protons and neutrons).

**masturbation** (mas-tər-'bā-shən) Stimulation of one's own sex organs.

**matter** ('ma-tər) Anything that has weight (mass) and takes up space (volume).

**mechanical (morphological) isolating mechanisms** (mi-'ka-ni-kəl [mȯr-'fǎ-lä-ji-kəl] 'ī-sə-lā-tiŋ 'me-kə-ni-zəm) Structural differences that prevent mating between members of different species.

**medulla oblongata** (mə-'də-lə ä-blȯŋ-'gä-tə) The region of the more primitive portion of the brain, connected to the spinal cord, that controls such automatic functions as blood pressure, breathing, and heart rate.

**medusa** (mi-'dü-sə) A free-swimming adult stage in the phylum Cnidaria that reproduces sexually.

**meiosis** (mī-'ō-səs) The specialized pair of cell divisions that reduces the chromosome number from diploid (2*n*) to haploid (*n*).

**meiosis I** (mī-'ō-səs 'wən) The first stage in a form of cell division involved in the production of gametes; results in the reduction of the number of chromosomes from 2*n* (diploid) to *n* (haploid).

**meiosis II** (mī-'ō-səs 'tü) The second stage in a form of cell division involved in the production of gametes; results in the doubling of the number of newly produced haploid cells from meiosis I.

**Mendelian genetics** (men-'dē-lē-ən jə-'ne-tiks) The pattern of inheriting characteristics that follows the laws formulated by Gregor Mendel.

**menopause** ('me-nə-pȯz) The period beginning at about age 50 when the ovaries stop producing viable secondary oocytes and ovarian hormones.

**menstrual cycle** ('men-strü-əl 'sī-kəl) The repeated building up and shedding of the lining of the uterus.

**mesenteries** ('me-zən-ter-ēz) Connective tissues that hold the organs in place and serve as support for blood vessels connecting the various organs.

**mesoderm** ('me-zə-dərm) The middle embryonic layer.

**messenger RNA (mRNA)** ('me-sən-jər) A molecule composed of ribonucleotides that functions as a copy of the gene and is used in the cytoplasm of the cell during protein synthesis.

**metabolism** (mə-'ta-bə-li-zəm) The total of all the chemical reactions and energy changes that take place in an organism.

**metaphase** ('me-tə-fāz) The second stage in mitosis, characterized by alignment of the chromosomes at the equatorial plane.

**metastasize** (mə-'tas-tə-sīz) The process by which cells of tumors move from the original site and establish new colonies in other regions of the body.

**microfilaments** (mī-krō-'fi-lə-mənts) Long, fiberlike, submicroscopic structures made of protein and found in cells, often in close association with the microtubules; provide structural support and enable movement.

**microorganism (microbe)** (mī-krō-'ȯr-gə-ni-zəm) A small organism that cannot be seen without magnification.

**microtubules** (mī-krō-'tü-byüls) Submicroscopic, hollow tubes of protein that function throughout the cytoplasm to provide structural support and enable movement.

**minerals** ('min-rəlz) Inorganic elements that cannot be manufactured by the body but are required in low concentrations; essential to metabolism.

**missense mutation** ('mis-sens myü-'tā-shən) A change in the DNA at a single point that causes the wrong amino acid to be used in making a protein.

**mitochondria** (mī-tə-'kän-drē-ə) Membranous organelles resembling small bags with a larger bag inside that is folded back on itself; serve as the site of aerobic cellular respiration.

**mitosis** (mī-'tō-səs) A process that results in equal and identical distribution of replicated chromosomes into two newly formed nuclei.

**mixture** ('miks-chər) Matter that contains two or more substances *not* in set proportions.

**molecules** ('mä-li-kyül) The smallest particles of a chemical compound; the smallest naturally occurring parts of an element or a compound.

**monocot** ('mä-nə-kät) An angiosperm whose embryo has one seed leaf (cotyledon).

**monoculture** ('mä-nə-kəl-chər) The agricultural practice of planting the same varieties of a species over large expanses of land.

**monohybrid cross** (mä-nō-'hī-brəd 'krȯs) A mating between two organisms that are both heterozygous for the one observed gene.

**monosomy** (mä-nə-'sō-mē) A cell with only 1 of the 2 chromosomes of a homologous pair.

**mortality** (mȯr-'ta-lə-tē) The number of individuals leaving the population by death per thousand individuals in the population.

**motor neurons** ('mō-tər 'nü-ränz) Neurons that carry information from the central nervous system to muscles or glands.

**motor unit** ('mō-tər 'yü-nət) All the muscle cells stimulated by a single neuron.

**multigene families** ('məl-tə-jēn 'fam-lēz) A type of variation in an organism's DNA sequence; this variation consists of several different genes that produce different proteins that are related in function.

**multiple alleles** ('məl-tə-pəl ə-'lēlz) Several different alleles for a particular characteristic within a population, not just 2.

**multiregional hypothesis** ('məl-tə-rēj-nəl hī-'pä-thə-səs) The concept that *Homo erectus* migrated to Europe and Asia from Africa and evolved into *Homo sapiens*.

**mutagens** ('myü-tə-jən) Agents that mutate, or chemically damage, DNA.

**mutation** (myü-'tā-shən) Any change in the genetic information of a cell.

**mutualism** ('myü-chə-wə-li-zəm) A relationship between two organisms in which both organisms benefit.

**mycorrhizae** (mī-kə-'rī-zē) Symbiotic relationships between fungi and plant roots.

**mycotoxins** (mī-kə-'täk-sənz) Deadly poisons produced by fungi.

**myosin** ('mī-ə-sən) The protein molecule, found in the thick filaments of muscle fibers, that attaches to actin, bends, and moves actin molecules along its length, causing the muscle fiber to shorten.

# N

**natality** (nā-'ta-lə-tē) The number of individuals entering the population by reproduction per thousand individuals in the population.

**negative-feedback inhibition** ('ne-gə-tiv 'fēd-bak in-hə-'bi-shən) A regulatory mechanism in which an increase in the stimulus causes a decrease of the response and results in homeostasis.

**nekton** ('nek-tən) Many kinds of aquatic animals that are large enough and strong enough to be able to swim against currents and tides and go where they want to.

**nephrons** ('ne-fränz) Tiny tubules that are the functional units of kidneys.

**nerve cell** ('nərv 'sel) The basic unit of the nervous system that consists of a central body and several long fibrous extensions.

**nerve impulse** ('nərv 'im-pəls) A series of changes that take place in the neuron, resulting in a wave of depolarization, which passes from one end of the neuron to the other.

**nerves** ('nərvz) Bundles of neuronal fibers.

**nervous system** ('nər-vəs 'sis-təm) A network of neurons that carry information from sense organs to the central nervous system and from the central nervous system to muscles and glands.

**net movement** ('net 'müv-mənt) Movement in one direction minus the movement in the other.

**neuron (nerve cell)** ('nü-rän) The cellular unit consisting of a cell body and fibers that makes up the nervous system.

**neurotransmitter** (nür-ō-trans-'mi-tər) A molecule released by the axons of neurons that stimulates other cells.

**neutron** ('nü-trän) A particle in the nucleus of an atom that has no electrical charge; named *neutron* to reflect this lack of electrical charge.

**niche** ('nich) An organisms specific functional role in its community.

**nicotinamide adenine dinucleotide** (NAD$^+$) (ni-kə-'tē-nə-mīd 'a-də-nēn dī-'nü-klē-ə-tīd) An electron acceptor and hydrogen carrier used in respiration.

**nitrifying bacteria** ('nī-trə-fī-iŋ bak-'tir-ē-ə) Several kinds of bacteria capable of converting ammonia to nitrite, or nitrite to nitrate.

**nitrogen cycle** ('nī-trə-jən 'sī-kəl) The cycling of nitrogen atoms between the abiotic and biotic components and among the organisms in an ecosystem.

**nitrogen-fixing bacteria** ('nī-trə-jən 'fik-siŋ bak-'tir-ē-ə) Bacteria that are able to convert the nitrogen gas ($N_2$) that enters the soil into ammonia that plants can use.

**non-coding strand** (nän-'kō-diŋ 'strand) The strand of DNA that is not read directly by the enzymes.

**nondeciduous** (nän-di-'si-jə-wəs) A type of tree that does not lose its leaves all at once.

**nondisjunction** (nän-dis-'jəŋ-shən) An abnormal meiotic division that results in sex cells with too many or too few chromosomes.

**noneukaryotic** (nän-ker-ē-'ä-tik) One of two general types of living cells: eukaryotic and noneukaryotic. Two forms of noneukaryotic organisms are recognized: Bacteria and Archaea.

**non-homologous chromosomes** (nän-hō-'mä-lə-gəs 'krō-mə-sōmz) Chromosomes that have different genes on their DNA.

**nonsense mutation** ('nän-sens myü-'tā-shən) A type of point mutation that causes a ribosome to stop protein synthesis by introducing a stop codon too early.

**norepinephrine** (nȯr-e-pə-'ne-frən) The hormone produced by the adrenal medulla and certain nerve cells that increases heart rate, blood pressure, and breathing rate.

**nuclear membrane** ('nü-klē-ər 'mem-brān) The structure surrounding the nucleus that separates the nucleoplasm from the cytoplasm.

**nucleic acids** (nü-'klē-ik 'a-sədz) Complex molecules that store and transfer information within a cell. They are constructed of fundamental monomers known as nucleotides.

**nucleolus** (nü-'klē-ə-ləs) A nuclear structure composed of completed or partially completed ribosomes and the specific parts of chromosomes that contain the information for their construction.

**nucleoplasm** ('nü-klē-ə-pla-zəm) The liquid matrix of the nucleus, composed of a mixture of water and the molecules used in the construction of the rest of the nuclear structures.

**nucleoprotein** (nü-klē-ō-'prō-tēn) DNA strands with attached proteins that become visible during cell division.

**nucleosome** (nü-klē-ō-sōm) Histone protein with their encircling DNA.

**nucleotides** ('nü-klē-ə-tīdz) Fundamental subunits of nucleic acid constructed of a phosphate group, a sugar, and an organic nitrogenous base.

**nucleus** ('nü-klē-əs) The central body that contains the information system for the cell; also the central part of an atom, containing protons and neutrons.

**nutrients** ('nü-trē-ənts) Molecules required by organisms for growth, reproduction, or repair.

**nutrition** (nü-'tri-shən) Collectively, the processes involved in taking in, assimilating, and utilizing nutrients.

# O

**obesity** (ō-'bē-sə-tē) The condition of being overweight to the extent that a person's health, quality of life, and life span are adversely affected.

**observation** (äb-sər-'vā-shən) The process of using the senses or extensions of the senses to record events.

**observational learning (imitation)** (äb-sər-'vā-shən-əl 'lərn-iŋ) A form of association that involves a complex set of associations used in watching another animal being rewarded for performing a particular behavior and then performing the same behavior oneself.

**offspring** ('ȯf-spriŋ) Descendants of a set of parents.

**olfactory epithelium** (äl-'fak-trē e-pə-'thē-lē-əm) The cells of the nasal cavity that respond to chemicals.

**omnivores** ('äm-ni-vȯrz) Animals that are carnivores at some times and herbivores at others.

**oogenesis** (ō-ə-'je-nə-səs) The gametogenesis process that leads to the formation of eggs.

**operant (instrumental) conditioning** ('ä-pə-rənt kən-'di-shniŋ) A change in behavior that results from associating a stimulus with a response by either rewarding or punishing the behavior after it has occurred.

**order** ('ȯr-dər) A group of closely related classes within a phylum.

**organ** ('ȯr-gən) A structure composed of groups of tissues that perform particular functions.

**organelles** (ȯr-gə-'nelz) Cellular structures that perform specific functions in the cell; the function of organelles is directly related to their structure.

organic molecules (or-'ga-nik 'mä-li-kyülz) Complex molecules whose basic building blocks are carbon atoms in chains or rings.

organism ('or-gə-ni-zəm) An independent living unit.

organ system ('or-gən 'sis-təm) A structure composed of groups of organs that perform particular functions.

orgasm ('or-ga-zəm) The complex series of responses to sexual stimulation that results in an intense frenzy of sexual excitement.

osmosis (äz-'mō-səs) The net movement of water molecules through a selectively permeable membrane.

osteoporosis (äs-tē-ō-pə-'rō-səs) A disease condition resulting from the demineralization of the bone, resulting in pain, deformities, and fractures; related to a loss of calcium.

out-of-Africa hypothesis ('aut əv 'a-fri-kə hī-'pä-thə-səs) The concept that modern humans (*Homo sapiens*) originated in Africa and migrated from Africa to Europe and Asia and displaced existing hominins.

oval window ('ō-vəl 'win-dō) The membrane-covered opening of the cochlea, to which the stapes is attached.

ovaries ('ō-və-rēz) Female sex organs, which produce haploid sex cells, called eggs.

oviduct ('ō-və-dəkt) The tube (*fallopian tube*) that carries the egg to the uterus.

ovulation (äv-yə-'lā-shən) The release of a secondary oocyte from the surface of the ovary.

oxidation-reduction reaction (äk-sə-'dā-shən ri-'dək-shən rē-'ak-shən) An electron-transport reaction in which the molecules losing electrons become oxidized and those gaining electrons become reduced.

oxidizing atmosphere ('äk-sə-dīz-iŋ 'at-mə-sfir) An atmosphere that contains molecular oxygen.

oxytocin (äk-sē-'tō-sən) The hormone, released from the posterior pituitary, that causes contraction of the uterus.

## P

pancreas ('paŋ-krē-əs) The organ of the body that secretes many kinds of digestive enzymes into the duodenum.

panspermia ('pan-spər-mē-ə) A hypothesis by Svante Arrhenius in the early 1900s that life arose outside the Earth and that living things were transported to Earth to seed the planet with life.

parasite ('per-ə-sīt) An organism that lives in or on another organism and derives nourishment from it.

parasitism ('per-ə-sə-ti-zəm) A relationship between two organisms that involves one organism living in or on another organism and deriving nourishment from it.

pathogens ('pa-thə-jənz) Agents that cause specific diseases.

pelagic (pə-'la-jik) Aquatic organisms that are not attached to the bottom.

pelagic ecosystem (pə-'la-jik 'ē-kō-sis-təm) An aquatic ecosystem which exists in open water in which the organisms are not attached to the bottom.

penetrance ('pe-nə-trəns) A term used to describe how often an allele expresses itself when present.

pepsin ('pep-sən) The enzyme, produced by the stomach, that is responsible for beginning the digestion of proteins.

perception (pər-'sep-shən) Recognition by the brain that a stimulus has been received.

perfect flower ('pər-fikt 'flaur) A flower that contains both male (stamen) and female (pistil) reproductive structures.

peripheral nervous system (pə-'ri-frəl 'nər-vəs 'sis-təm) The fibers that communicate between the central nervous system and other parts of the body.

peroxisomes (pə-'räk-sə-sōmz) Membrane-bound, submicroscopic organelles that hold enzymes capable of producing hydrogen peroxide that aids in the control of infections and other dangerous compounds.

petals ('pe-təls) Modified leaves of angiosperms; accessory structures of a flower.

pH A scale used to indicate the concentration of an acid or a base.

phagocytosis (fa-gə-sə-'tō-səs) The process by which the cell wraps around a particle and engulfs it.

pharynx ('fa-riŋs) The region at the back of the mouth cavity; the throat.

phases of matter ('fāzez əv 'ma-tər) Physical conditions of matter (solid, liquid, and gas) determined by the relative amounts of energy of the molecules.

phenotype ('fē-nə-tīp) The physical, chemical, and behavioral expression of the genes possessed by an organism.

pheromones ('fer-ə-mōnz) Chemicals produced by an animal and released into the environment to trigger behavioral or developmental processes in another animal of the same species.

phloem ('flō-em) One kind of vascular tissue found in higher plants; it transports food materials from the leaves to other parts of the plant.

phospholipids (fäs-fō-'li-pədz) A class of water-insoluble molecules that resembles fats but contains a phosphate group ($PO_4$) in its structure.

phosphorylation reaction (fäs-for-ə-'lā-shən rē-'ak-shən) The reaction that takes place when a cluster of atoms, known as a phosphate group, is added to another molecule.

photoperiod (fō-tō-'pir-ē-əd) The length of the light part of the day.

photosynthesis (fō-tō-'sin-thə-səs) A series of reactions that take place in chloroplasts and results in the storage of sunlight energy in the form of chemical-bond energy.

photosystems (fō-tō-'sis-təmz) Clusters of photosynthetic pigments (e.g., chlorophyll) that serve as energy-gathering or energy-concentrating mechanisms; used during the light-capturing events of photosynthesis.

phylogeny (fī-'lä-jə-nē) The science that explores the evolutionary relationships among organisms and seeks to reconstruct evolutionary history.

phylum ('fī-ləm) A subdivision of a kingdom.

phytoplankton (fī-tō-'plaŋ-tən) Microscopic, photosynthetic species that form the basis for most aquatic food chains.

pinocytosis (pi-nə-sə-'tō-səs) The process by which a cell engulfs some molecules dissolved in water.

pioneer community (pī-ə-'nir kə-'myü-nə-tē) The first community of organisms in the successional process established in a previously uninhabited area.

pioneer organisms (pī-ə-'nir 'or-gə-ni-zəms) The first organisms in the successional process.

pistil ('pis-təl) The female reproductive structure in flowers; contains the ovary, which produces eggs.

**pituitary gland** (pə-'tü-ə-ter-ē 'gland) The gland at the base of the brain that controls the functioning of other glands throughout the organism.

**placenta** (plə-'sen-tə) An organ made up of tissues from the embryo and the uterus of the mother; allows for the exchange of materials between the mother's bloodstream and the embryo's bloodstream; also produces hormones.

**plankton** ('plaŋ-tən) Small, floating or weakly swimming organisms.

**plasma** ('plaz-mə) The watery matrix that contains the molecules and cells of the blood.

**plasma membrane (cell membrane)** ('plaz-mə 'mem-brān) The outer boundary membrane of the cell.

**plasmid** ('plaz-məd) A plasmid is a circular piece of DNA that is found free in the cytoplasm of some bacteria.

**platelets** ('plāt-ləts) Fragments of specific kinds of white blood cells; important in blood clotting.

**pleiotropy** ('plī-ä-trə-pē) The multiple effects that a gene may have on the phenotype of an organism.

**poikilotherms** (pói-'kē-lə-thərmz) Animals with a variable body temperature that changes with the external environment.

**point mutation** ('póint myü-'tā-shən) A change in the DNA of a cell as a result of a loss or change in a nitrogenous-base sequence.

**polar body** ('pō-lər 'bä-dē) The smaller of two cells formed by unequal meiotic division during oogenesis.

**pollen** ('pä-lən) The male gametophyte in gymnosperms and angiosperms.

**pollination** (pä-lə-'nā-shən) The transfer of pollen in gymnosperms and angiosperms.

**polygenic inheritance** ('pä-lē-jēn in-'her-ə-təns) The concept that a number of different pairs of alleles may combine their efforts to determine a characteristic.

**polymerase chain reaction (PCR)** (pə-'lim-ə-rās 'chān rē-'ak-shən) A laboratory technique that is able to generate useful quantities of DNA from very small amounts of DNA.

**polymers** ('pä-lə-mərs) Combinations of many smaller, similar building blocks called monomers (mono = single) bonded together.

**polyp** ('pä-ləp) A sessile larval stage in the phylum Cnidaria that reproduces asexually.

**polypeptide** (pä-lē-'pep-tīd) A macromolecule composed of a specific sequence of amino acids.

**polyploidy** ('pä-lē-plóid) A condition in which cells contain multiple sets of chromosomes.

**pons** ('pänz) The region of the brain, immediately anterior to the medulla oblongata, that connects to the cerebellum and higher regions of the brain and controls several sensory and motor functions of the head and face.

**population** (pä-pyə-'lā-shən) A group of organisms of the same species located in the same place at the same time.

**population density** (pä-pyə-'lā-shən 'den-sə-tē) The number of organisms of a species per unit area.

**population distribution** (pä-pyə-'lā-shən dis-trə-'byü-shən) The way individuals within a population are arranged with respect to one another.

**population genetics** (pä-pyə-'lā-shən jə-'ne-tiks) The study of the kinds of genes within a population, their relative numbers, and how these numbers change over time.

**population growth curve** (pä-pyə-'lā-shən 'grōth 'kərv) A graph of the change in population size over time.

**population pressure** (pä-pyə-'lā-shən 'pre-shər) Intense competition as a result of high population density that leads to changes in the environment and the dispersal of organisms.

**positive feedback** ('pä-zə-tiv 'fēd-bak) A regulatory mechanism in which an increase in the stimulus causes an increase of the response and does not result in homeostasis.

**potential energy** (pə-'ten-shəl 'e-nər-jē) The energy an object has because of its position.

**predation** (pri-'dā-shən) A relationship between two organisms that involves the capturing, killing, and eating of one by the other.

**predator** ('pre-də-tər) An organism that captures, kills, and eats another animal.

**prey** ('prā) An organism captured, killed, and eaten by a predator.

**primary carnivores** ('prī-mer-ē 'kär-nə-vórz) Carnivores that eat herbivores and are therefore on the third trophic level.

**primary consumers** ('prī-mer-ē kən-'sü-mərz) Organisms that feed directly on plants—herbivores.

**primary succession** ('prī-mer-ē sək-'se-shən) The orderly series of changes that begins in a previously uninhabited area and leads to a climax community.

**prions** ('prī-änz) Infectious protein particles responsible for diseases such as Creutzfeldt-Jakob disease and bovine spongiform encephalitis.

**probability** (prä-bə-'bi-lə-tē) The chance that an event will happen, expressed as a percentage or fraction.

**producers** (prə-'dü-sərz) Organisms that produce new organic material from inorganic material with the aid of sunlight.

**productivity** (prō-dək-'ti-və-tē) The rate at which an ecosystem can accumulate new organic matter.

**products** ('prä-dəkts) New molecules resulting from a chemical reaction.

**prokaryotes** (prō-'ka-rē-ōts) Organisms that do not have a nucleus in their cells; Bacteria and Archaea.

**prokaryotic cells** (prō-ka-rē-'ä-tik 'sels) One of the two major types of cells; now referred to as noneukaryotic cells. They do not have a typical nucleus bound by a nuclear membrane and lack many of the other membranous cellular organelles—for example, members of Bacteria and Archaea.

**promoter sequences** (prə-'mō-tər 'sē-kwəns) Specific sequences of DNA nucleotides that RNA polymerase uses to find a protein-coding region of DNA and to identify which of the two DNA strands is the coding strand.

**prophase** ('prō-fāz) The first phase of mitosis, during which individual chromosomes become visible.

**proteins** ('prō-tēnz) Macromolecules made up of one or more polypepides attached to each other by bonds.

**protein-sparing** ('prō-tēn 'spe-riŋ) The conservation of proteins by first oxidizing carbohydrates and fats as a source of ATP energy.

**proteomics** (prō-tē-'ō-miks) A new field of science that has developed since the sequencing of the human genome; it groups proteins by similarities to help explain their function and how they may have evolved.

**proton** ('prō-tän) The particle in the nucleus of an atom that has a positive electrical charge.

**proto-oncogene** (prō-tō-'äŋ-kō-jēn) Genes that code for proteins that provide signals to the cell that encourage cell division.

**protoplasm** ('prō-tə-pla-zəm) The living portion of a cell, as distinguished from the nonliving cell wall.

**protozoa** (prō-tə-'zō-ä) Heterotrophic, eukaryotic, unicellular organisms.

**proximal convoluted tubule** ('präk-sə-məl 'kän-və-lü-təd 'tü-byül) The upstream end of the nephron of the kidney; is responsible for reabsorbing most of the valuable molecules filtered from the glomerulus into Bowman's capsule.

**pseudocoelom** (sü-dō-'sē-ləm) A body cavity located between the lining of the gut and the outer body wall and does not have muscles around the digestive system; the word means false body cavity.

**pseudoscience** (sü-dō-'sī-əns) An activity that uses the appearance or language of science to convince or mislead people into thinking that something has scientific validity.

**puberty** ('pyü-bər-tē) A time in the life of a developing individual characterized by the increasing production of sex hormones, which cause it to reach sexual maturity.

**pulmonary artery** ('pùl-mə-ner-ē 'är-tə-rē) The major blood vessel that carries blood from the right ventricle to the lungs.

**pulmonary circulation** ('pùl-mə-ner-ē sər-kyə-'lā-shən) The flow of blood through certain chambers of the heart and blood vessels to the lungs and back to the heart.

**punctuated equilibrium** ('pəŋk-chə-wā-təd ē-kwə-'li-brē-əm) The theory stating that evolution occurs in spurts, between which there are long periods with little evolutionary change.

**Punnett square** ('pə-nət 'skwer) A method used to determine the probabilities of allele combinations in a zygote.

**pyloric sphincter** (pī-'lòr-ik 'sfiŋ-tər) The valve located at the end of the stomach that regulates the flow of food from the stomach to the duodenum.

# R

**radial symmetry** ('rā-dē-əl 'si-mə-trē) The characteristic of an animal with a body constructed around a central axis; any division of the body along this axis results in two similar halves.

**reactants** (rē-'aktənts) Materials that will be changed in a chemical reaction.

**receptor mediated endocytosis** (ri-'sep-tər 'mē-dē-ā-təd en-dō-sī-'tō-səs) The process in which molecules from the cell's surroundings bind to receptor molecules on the plasma membrane, followed by the membrane folding into the cell so that the cell engulfs these molecules.

**recessive allele** (ri-'se-siv ə-'lēl) An allele that, when present with its homolog, does not express itself and is masked by the effect of the other allele.

**recombinant DNA** (rē-'käm-bə-nənt) DNA that has been constructed by inserting new pieces of DNA into the DNA of an organism.

**red blood cells (rbcs)** ('red 'bləd 'sels) Small, disk-shaped cells that lack a nucleus and contain the iron-containing pigment hemoglobin.

**reducing atmosphere** (ri-'düs-iŋ 'at-mə-sfir) An atmosphere that does not contain molecular oxygen ($O_2$).

**reduction division** (ri-'dək-shən də-'vi-zhən) A type of cell division in which daughter cells get only half the chromosomes from the parent cell.

**regulator proteins** ('re-gyə-lā-tər 'prō-tēnz) Proteins that influence the activities that occur in an organism—for example, enzymes and some hormones.

**reproductive capacity (biotic potential)** (rē-prə-'dək-tiv kə-'pa-sə-tē) The theoretical maximum rate of reproduction.

**reproductive (genetic) isolating mechanisms** (rē-prə-'dək-tiv 'ī-sə-lā-tiŋ 'me-kə-ni-zəmz) Mechanisms that prevent interbreeding between species.

**respiratory system** ('res-prə-tòr-ē 'sis-təm) The organ system that moves air into and out of the body and consists of lungs, trachea, the air-transport pathway, and diaphragm.

**response** (ri-'späns) The reaction of an organism to a stimulus.

**responsive processes** (ri-'spän-siv 'prä-se-səz) Abilities to react to external and internal changes in the environment—for example, irritability, individual adaptation, and evolution.

**restriction enzymes** (ri-'strik-shən 'en-zīmz) Proteins that catalyze the cutting of the DNA helix; these proteins cut the DNA helix into two pieces at specific DNA sequences.

**restriction fragments** (ri-'strik-shən 'frag-mənts) Pieces of DNA that are created by cutting DNA with restriction enzymes; restriction fragments are used in cloning and characterizing DNA.

**restriction sites** (ri-'strik-shən 'sīts) The DNA sequence that is recognized by a restriction enzyme; the restriction enzyme cuts at this sequence, generating two DNA fragments.

**retina** ('re-tə-nə) The light-sensitive region of the eye.

**rhodopsin** (rō-'däp-sən) A light-sensitive pigment found in the rods of the retina.

**ribonucleic acid (RNA)** (rī-bō-nü-'klē-ik 'a-səd) A polymer of nucleotides formed on the template surface of DNA by transcription; three forms are mRNA, rRNA, and tRNA.

**ribosomal RNA (rRNA)** (rī-bə-'sō-məl) A globular form of RNA; a part of ribosomes.

**ribosomes** ('rī-bə-sōmz) Small structures composed of two protein and ribonucleic acid subunits, involved in the assembly of proteins from amino acids.

**ribulose** ('rī-byə-lōs) A 5-carbon sugar molecule used in photosynthesis.

**ribulose-1,5-bisphosphate carboxylase/oxygenase (RuBisCO)** ('rī-byə-lōs bī-'fäs-fāt kär-'bäk-sə-lās 'äk-si-jə-nās) An enzyme found in the stroma of chloroplast that speeds the combining of the $CO_2$ with an already present 5-carbon carbohydrate, ribulose.

**RNA polymerase** (pə-'lim-ə-rās) An enzyme that bonds RNA nucleotides together during transcription after they have aligned on the DNA.

**rods** ('rädz) Light-sensitive cells in the retina of the eye that respond to low-intensity light but do not respond to different colors of light.

**root** ('rüt) Underground structures that anchor the plant and absorb water and minerals.

**root hairs** ('rüt 'hers) Tiny cellular outgrowths of roots that improve the ability of plants to absorb water and minerals.

# S

**salivary glands** ('sa-lə-ver-ē 'glandz) Glands that produce saliva.

**salts** ('sòlts) Ionic compounds formed from a reaction between an acid and a base.

**saprophytes** ('sa-prə-fīts) Organisms that obtain energy by the decomposition of dead organic material.

**saturated** ('sa-chə-rā-təd) A term used to describe the carbon skeleton of a fatty acid that contains no double bonds between carbons.

**science** ('sī-əns) A process used to solve problems or develop an understanding of natural events.

**scientific law** (sī-ən-'ti-fik 'lȯ) A uniform or constant fact that describes what happens in nature.

**scientific method** (sī-ən-'ti-fik 'me-thəd) A way of gaining information (facts) about the world around you that involves observation, hypothesis formation, testing of hypotheses, theory formation, and law formation.

**seasonal isolating mechanisms** ('sēz-nəl 'ī-sə-lā-tiŋ 'me-kə-ni-zəmz) Reproductive isolating mechanisms that prevent interbreeding between species because they reproduce at different times of the year.

**secondary carnivores** ('se-kən-der-ē 'kär-nə-vȯrz) Carnivores that feed on primary carnivores and are therefore at the fourth trophic level.

**secondary consumers** ('se-kən-der-ē kən-'sü-mərz) Animals that eat other animals—carnivores.

**secondary sexual characteristics** ('se-kən-der-ē 'sek-shwəl ker-ik-tə-'ris-tiks) Characteristics of the adult male or female, including the typical shape that develops at puberty: broader shoulders; heavier long-bone muscles; development of facial hair, axillary hair, and chest hair; and changes in the shape of the larynx in the male; rounding of the pelvis and breasts and changes in deposition of fat in the female.

**secondary succession** ('se-kən-der-ē sək-'se-shən) The orderly series of changes that begins with the disturbance of an existing community and leads to a climax community.

**seed** ('sēd) A specialized structure that contains an embryo along with stored food enclosed in a protective covering called the seed coat.

**seed leaves** ('sēd 'lēvz) Cotyledons; embryonic leaves in seeds.

**segmental duplications** (seg-'men-təl dü-pli-'kā-shənz) A type of variation in an organism's DNA sequence; this variation occurs when a segment of DNA, which may contain several genes, occurs twice in the genome.

**segmentation** (seg-mən-'tā-shən) The separation of the body of an animal into a number of recognizable units from the anterior to the posterior end of the animal.

**segregation** (se-gri-'gā-shən) The separation and movement of homologous chromosomes to the opposite poles of the cell.

**selecting agents** (sə-'lek-tiŋ 'ā-jənts) Factors that affect the probability that a gene will be passed on to the next generation.

**selectively permeable** (sə-'lek-tiv-lē 'pər-mē-ə-bəl) The property of a membrane that allows certain molecules to pass through it but interferes with the passage of others.

**semen** ('sē-mən) The sperm-carrying fluid produced by the seminal vesicles, prostate gland, and bulbourethral glands of males.

**semicircular canals** (se-mē-'sər-kyə-lər kə-'nalz) A set of tubular organs, associated with the cochlea, that sense changes in the movement or position of the head.

**semilunar valves** (se-mē-'lü-nər 'valvz) Valves, located in the pulmonary artery and aorta, that prevent the flow of blood backwards, into the ventricles.

**seminiferous tubules** (se-mə-'ni-frəs 'tü-byülz) Sperm-producing tubes in the testes.

**sensory neurons** ('sens-rē 'nü-ränz) Neurons that send information from sense organs to the central nervous system.

**sepals** ('sē-pəls) Accessory structures of flowers.

**sessile** ('se-sīl) Firmly attached.

**sex** ('seks) The nature of the biological differences between males and females.

**sex chromosomes** ('seks 'krō-mə-sōmz) Chromosomes that carry genes that determine the sex of an individual (X and Y in humans).

**sex-determining chromosomes** ('seks di-'tər-mə-niŋ 'krō-mə-sōmz) The chromosomes X and Y, which are primarily responsible for determining if an individual will develop as a male or a female.

**sex linkage** ('seks 'liŋ-kij) Refers to genes that are located on the chromosomes that determine the sex of an individual.

**sex ratio** ('seks 'rā-shō) The number of males in a population compared with the number of females.

**sexual reproduction** ('sek-shwəl rē-prə-'dək-shən) The propagation of organisms involving the union of gametes from two parents.

**sexual selection** ('sek-shwəl sə-'lek-shən) Selection that is the result of specific individuals being chosen by members of the opposite sex for mating purposes.

**sexuality** (sek-shə-'wa-lə-tē) All the factors that contribute to one's female or male nature.

**signal transduction** ('sig-nəl trans-'dək-shən) The process by which cells detect specific signals and transmit those signals to the cell's interior.

**silencer sequence** ('sī-lən-sər 'sē-kwəns) A DNA sequence that regulates gene expression by acting as a binding site for proteins that decrease the ability of RNA polymerase to transcribe a specific protein.

**silent mutation** ('sī-lənt myü-'tā-shən) A change of a single nucleotide that does not cause a change in the amino acids used to build a protein.

**single-factor cross** ('siŋ-gəl 'fak-tər 'krȯs) A genetic study in which a single characteristic is followed from the parental generation to the offspring.

**sister chromatids** ('sis-tər 'krō-mə-tədz) The 2 chromatids of a chromosome that were produced by replication and that contain the identical DNA.

**skeleton** ('ske-lə-tən) The part of an organism that provides structural support.

**small intestine** ('smȯl in-'tes-tən) The portion of the digestive system immediately following the stomach; it is responsible for digestion and absorption.

**society** (sə-'sī-ə-tē) Interacting groups of animals of the same species that show division of labor.

**sociobiology** (sō-sē-ō-bī-'ä-lə-jē) The systematic study of all forms of social behavior, both human and nonhuman.

**solid** ('sä-ləd) The phase of matter in which the molecules are packed tightly together; they vibrate in place.

**solute** ('säl-yüt) The component that dissolves in a solvent.

**solution** (sə-'lü-shən) A homogeneous mixture of ions or molecules of two or more substances.

**solvent** ('säl-vənt) The component present in the larger amount.

**soma** ('sō-mə) The cell body of a neuron, which contains the nucleus.

**somatic cell nuclear transfer** (sō-'ma-tik 'sel 'nü-klē-ər trans-'fər) A laboratory technique in which the nucleus of a cell is placed into an unfertilized egg cell; the cell may then be stimulated to grow; cells that are generated from this growth will have the same genetic information as the cell that donated the nucleus.

**speciation** (spē-shē-'ā-shən) The process of generating new species.

**species** ('spē-shēz) A population of organisms potentially capable of breeding naturally among themselves and having offspring that also interbreed. Also, the smallest irreversible unit of evolution; a group of organisms that shares a common ancestor with other species, but is set off from those others by having newer, genetically unique traits.

**specific dynamic action (SDA)** (spi-'si-fik dī-'na-mik 'ak-shən) The amount of energy required to digest and assimilate food. SDA is equal to approximately 10% of total daily kilocalorie intake.

**specific epithet** (spi-'si-fik 'e-pə-thet) A word added to the genus name to identify which one of several species within the genus is being identified (i.e., *Homo sapiens: Homo* is the genus name and *sapiens* is the specific epithet).

**sperm** ('spərm) The haploid sex cells produced by sexually mature males.

**spermatogenesis** (spər-ma-tə-'je-nə-səs) The gametogenesis process that leads to the formation of sperm.

**spinal cord** ('spī-nəl 'kord) A collection of nerve fibers surrounded by the vertebrae that conveys information to and from the brain.

**spindle** ('spin-dəl) An array of microtubules extending from pole to pole; used in the movement of chromosomes.

**spindle fiber** ('spin-dəl 'fī-bərs) Microtubules that are individual strands of the spindle.

**spontaneous generation** (spän-'tā-nē-əs je-nə-'rā-shən) The idea that living organisms arose from nonliving material.

**spontaneous mutations** (spän-'tā-nē-əs myü-'tā-shənz) Natural changes in the DNA caused by unidentified environmental factors.

**spore** ('spór) In the kingdom Fungi, a cell with a tough protective cell wall that can resist extreme conditions.

**sporophyte generation (or stage)** ('spór-ə-fīt je-nə-'rā-shən) A stage in the life cycle of plants in which this diploid (2*n*) plant, which has special plant parts where meiosis takes place, produces haploid (*n*) spores.

**sporophyte stage** ('spór-ə-fīt 'stāj) A life cycle stage in plants in which a haploid spore is produced by meiosis.

**stabilizing selection** ('stā-bə-lī-ziŋ sə-'lek-shən) Selection that occurs when individuals at the extremes of the range of a characteristic are consistently selected against.

**stable equilibrium phase** ('stā-bəl ē-kwə-'li-brē-əm 'fāz) The period of time during population growth when the number of individuals entering a population and the number leaving the population are equal, resulting in a stable population size.

**stamens** ('stā-mənz) Male reproductive structures of a flower.

**stapes** ('stā-pēz) The ear bone that is attached to the oval window.

**stem** ('stem) Plant structures that connect the roots with the leaves and position the leaves so that they receive sunlight.

**stem cells** ('stem 'selz) Cells that can differentiate into any type of cell, including liver cells, skin cells, and brain cells; embryonic and hematopoietic cells.

**steroids** ('stir-óidz) One of the three kinds of lipid molecules characterized by their arrangement of interlocking rings of carbon.

**stimulus** ('stim-yə-ləs) Any change in the internal or external environment of an organism that it can detect.

**stroma** ('strō-mə) The region within a chloroplast that has no chlorphyll.

**structural proteins** ('strək-chə-rəl 'prō-tēnz) Proteins that are important for holding cells and organisms together, such as the proteins that make up the cell membrane, muscles, tendons, and blood.

**subspecies (breeds, varieties, strains, races)** ('səb-spē-shēz) Regional groups within a species that are significantly different structurally, physiologically, or behaviorally yet are capable of exchanging genes by interbreeding.

**substrate** ('səb-strāt) A reactant molecule with which the enzyme combines.

**succession** (sək-'se-shən) The process of changing one type of community to another.

**successional (stage) (successional community)** (sək-'se-shə-nəl 'stāj) An intermediate stage in succession.

**symbiosis** (sim-bē-'ō-səs) A close physical relationship between two kinds of organisms; parasitism, commensalism, and mutualism are examples of symbiosis.

**symbiotic nitrogen-fixing bacteria** (sim-bē-'ō-tik 'nī-trə-jən 'fik-siŋ bak-'tir-ē-ə) Bacteria that live in the roots of certain kinds of plants, where they convert nitrogen gas molecules into compounds that plants can use.

**synapse** ('si-naps) The space between the axon of one neuron and the dendrite of the next, where chemicals are secreted to cause an impulse to be initiated in the second neuron.

**synapsis** (sə-'nap-səs) The condition in which the two members of a pair of homologous chromosomes come to lie close to one another.

**systemic circulation** (sis-'te-mik sər-kyə-'lā-shən) The flow of blood through certain chambers of the heart and blood vessels to the general body and back to the heart.

**systolic blood pressure** ('sis-tə-lik 'bləd 'pre-shər) The pressure generated in a large artery when the ventricles of the heart are contracting.

# T

**tandem clusters** ('tan-dəm 'kləs-tərs) A type of variation in an organism's DNA sequence; this variation occurs when a gene is duplicated several times in the same region of DNA.

**taxonomy** (tak-'sä-nə-mē) The science of classifying and naming organisms.

**telomere** ('te-lə-mir) A chromosome cap composed of repeated, specific sequences of nucleotide pairs; its activity or inactivity is associated with cell aging and cancer.

**telophase** ('te-lə-fāz) The last phase in mitosis, characterized by the formation of daughter nuclei.

**temperature** ('tem-pə-chúr) A measure of molecular energy of motion.

**termination sequences** (tər-mə-'nā-shən 'sē-kwəns) DNA nucleotide sequences that indicate when RNA polymerase should finish making an RNA molecule.

**territorial behavior** (ter-ə-'tȯr-ē-əl bi-'hā-vyər) Behavior involved in establishing, defending, and maintaining a territory for food, mating, or other purposes.

**territory** ('ter-ə-tȯr-ē) A space that an animal defends against others of the same species.

**testes** ('tes-təz) The male sex organs, which produce haploid cells—sperm.

**testosterone** (tes-'täs-tə-rōn) The male sex hormone, produced in the testes, that controls male sexual development.

**thalamus** ('tha-lə-məs) The region of the brain that relays information between the cerebrum and lower portions of the brain; it also provides some level of awareness in that it determines pleasant and unpleasant stimuli and is involved in sleep and arousal.

**theory** ('thē-ə-rē) A widely accepted, plausible generalization about fundamental concepts in science that is supported by many experiments and explains why things happen in nature.

**theory of natural selection** ('thē-ə-rē əv 'na-chə-rəl sə-'lek-shən) In a species of genetically differing organisms, the organisms with the genes that enable them to survive better in the environment and thus reproduce more offspring than others will transmit more of their genes to the next generation.

**thinking** ('thiŋ-kiŋ) A mental process that involves memory, a concept of self, and an ability to reorganize information.

**thylakoid** ('thī-lə-kȯid) A membranous sac found within chloroplasts of plant cells that contains chlorophyll and is the site of the light-capturing events and the light-dependent reactions of photosynthesis; a stack of thylakoids is known as a granum.

**thymine** ('thī-mēn) A single-ring, nitrogenous-base molecule in DNA but not in RNA; it is complementary to adenine.

**tissue** ('ti-shü) A group of specialized cells that work together to perform a specific function.

**tissue fluid** ('ti-shü 'flü-əd) The liquid that baths the body's cells and contains the same chemicals as plasma but smaller amounts of the blood protein albumin.

**trachea** ('trā-kē-ə) The major tube, supported by cartilage rings, that carries air to the bronchi; also known as the windpipe.

**transcription** (tran-'skrip-shən) The process of manufacturing RNA from the template surface of DNA; three forms of RNA that can be produced are mRNA, rRNA, and tRNA.

**transcription factors** (tran-'skrip-shən 'fak-tərz) Proteins that help control the transcription process by binding DNA or other transcription factors and regulating when RNA polymerase begins transcription.

**transcriptomics** (tran-skript-'tä-miks) A new field of science developed since the sequencing of the human genome; it looks at when and how much of a particular transcript is made by an organism.

**transfer RNA (tRNA)** (trans-'fər) A molecule composed of ribonucleic acid. It is responsible for transporting a specific amino acid into a ribosome for assembly into a protein.

**transformation** (trans-fər-'mā-shən) A technique or process in which an organism gains new genetic information from its environment; this is known to happen to bacteria and is used to introduce DNA fragments to bacteria during the DNA cloning process.

**translation** (trans-'lā-shən) A chromosomal aberration in which one broken segment of DNA becomes integrated into a different chromosome.

**translocation** (trans-lō-'kā-shən) The process whereby tRNA uses mRNA as a guide to arrange the amino acids in their proper sequence according to the genetic information in the chemical code of DNA.

**transpiration** (trans-pə-'rā-shən) In plants, the transportation of water from the soil by way of the roots to the leaves, where it evaporates.

**triploblastic** (tri-plō-'blas-tik) A condition typical of most animals in which their bodies consist of three layers of cells.

**trisomy** ('trī-sō-mē) The presence of 3 chromosomes instead of the normal 2, resulting from the nondisjunction of homologous chromosomes during meiosis—as in Down syndrome.

**trophic level** ('trō-fik 'le-vəl) A step in the flow of energy through an ecosystem.

**tropism** ('trō-pi-zəm) Any reaction to a particular stimulus in which the organism orients toward or away from the stimulus.

**tropomyosin** (trä-pə-'mī-ə-sən) A molecule, found in thin myofilaments of muscle, that helps regulate when muscle cells contract.

**troponin** ('trō-pə-nən) A molecule, found in thin myofilaments of muscle, that helps regulate when muscle cells contract.

**true (neutral) fats** ('trü 'fats) Important organic molecules composed of glycerol and fatty acids that are used to provide energy.

**tumor** ('tü-mər) A mass of undifferentiated cells not normally found in a certain portion of the body.

**tumor-suppressor gene** ('tü-mər sə-'pre-sər 'jēn) Code for proteins that provide signals that discourage cell division.

**turnover number** ('tərn-ō-vər 'nəm-bər) The number of molecules of substrate with which a single molecule of enzyme can react in a given time.

**tympanum** ('tim-pə-nəm) The eardrum.

## U

**unique structural organization** (yù-'nēk 'strək-chə-rəl ȯr-gə-nə-'zā-shən) One of five traits displayed by living things and not shown by nonliving things; can be seen at the molecular, cellular, and organism levels.

**unsaturated** (ən-'sa-chə-rā-təd) A term used to describe the carbon skeleton of a fatty acid containing carbons that are double-bonded to each other at one or more points.

**uracil** ('yùr-ə-sil) A single-ring nitrogenous-base molecule in RNA but not in DNA; it is complementary to adenine.

## V

**vaccines** (vak-'sēns) Antigens made so they can start an active immunity without causing disease.

**vacuoles** ('va-kyə-wōlz) Large sacs within the cytoplasm of a cell, composed of a single membrane.

**variable number tandem repeats (VNTRs)** ('ver-ē-ə-bəl 'nəm-bər 'tan-dəm ri-'pētz) A type of variation in an organism's DNA sequence that is a repeated sequence; different individuals may have the sequence repeated a different number of times; this variation can occur in regions of the DNA that do not code for genes.

**variables** ('ver-ē-ə-bəlz) Factors in an experimental situation or other circumstance that are changeable.

**vascular cambium** ('vas-kyə-lər 'kam-bē-əm) A layer of cells between the xylem and phloem in trees that is responsible for the increase in diameter of a stem.

**vascular tissue** ('vas-kyə-lər 'ti-shü) Consists of tube-like cells that allow plants to efficiently transport water and nutrients about the plant.

**vector** ('vek-tər) An organism that carries a disease or parasite from one host to the next.

**veins** ('vānz) The blood vessels that return blood to the heart.

**ventricles** ('ven-tri-kəlz) The powerful muscular chambers of the heart whose contractions force blood to flow through the arteries to all parts of the body.

**vertebrates** ('vər-tə-brəts) Animals with backbones.

**vesicles** ('ve-si-kəls) Small, intracellular, membrane-bound sacs in which various substances are stored.

**villi** ('vi-lī) Tiny, fingerlike projections in the lining of the small intestine that increase the surface area for absorption.

**viroid** ('vī-ròid) An infectious particle composed solely of single-stranded RNA.

**virus** ('vī-rəs) A nucleic acid particle coated with protein that functions as an obligate intracellular parasite.

**vitamin-deficiency disease** ('vī-tə-mən di-'fi-shən-sē di-'zēz) Poor health caused by the lack of a certain vitamin in the diet—for example, scurvy from lack of vitamin C.

**vitamins** ('vī-tə-mənz) Organic molecules that cannot be manufactured by the body but are required in very low concentrations for good health.

**voltage** ('vōl-tij) A measure of the electrical difference between two points or objects.

# W

**white blood cells (wbcs)** ('hwīt 'bləd 'selz) Formed elements in the blood that lack hemoglobin, are larger than RBCs, and have a nucleus; also called leukocytes.

**wood** ('wüd) The accumulation of the xylem in the trunk of gymnosperms.

# X

**X chromosome** ('eks 'krō-mə-sōm) The chromosome in a human female egg (and in one-half of sperm cells) that is associated with the determination of sexual characteristics.

**X-linked genes** ('eks-'liŋt 'jēnz) Genes located on the sex-determining X chromosome.

**xylem** ('zī-ləm) A kind of vascular tissue that transports water from the roots to other parts of the plant.

# Y

**Y chromosome** ('wī 'krō-mə-sōm) The sex-determining chromosome in one-half the sperm cells of human males responsible for determining maleness.

**Y-linked genes** ('wī-'liŋt 'jēnz) Genes found only on the Y chromosome.

# Z

**zooplankton** (zō-ə-'plaŋ-tən) Nonphotosynthetic aquatic protozoa and tiny animals.

**zygote** ('zī-gōt) A diploid cell that results from the union of an egg and a sperm.

# Credits

## Line Art and Text

**Chapter 1**
How Science Works 1.1 Table, p. 18, Centers for Disease Control and Prevention.

**Chapter 2**
How Science Works 2.2 Table, p. 32, Data from Intergovernmental Panel on Climate Change, with updates from Oak Ridge National Laboratory.

**Chapter 3**
Figure 3.8, p. 52, © Photodisc.

**Chapter 13**
Figure 13.8, p. 279, Data from Ian Heap, "The International Survey of Herbicide Resistant Weeds." Available at www.weedscience.com.

**Chapter 15**
How Science Works 15.1 text art Global Air Temperature Anomaly, p. 322, Data from Climatic Research Unit, University of East Anglia and Hadley Centre.

**Chapter 17**
Figure 17.11, p. 383, Gilg O., Hanski, I. and Sittler, B. 2003. Cyclic dynamics in a simple vertebrate predator-prey community. Science 302, pp. 866–868. Reprinted with permission.

Figure 17.14, p. 386, Data from Jean Van Der Tak, et al., "Our Population Predicament: A New Look," in Population Reference Bureau, Washington D.C. and updates from recent Population Data Sheets. Reprinted with permission.

**Chapter 18**
Figure 18.13, p. 404, Courtesy of James E. Lloyd.

**Chapter 23**
Outlooks 23.1 text art, p. 506, Data from Natureserve, Prescious Heritage.

**Chapter 25**
Figure 25.7, p. 567, Source: U.S. Department of Agriculture.

Figure 25.9, p. 572, Source: Report of the Dietary Guidelines Advisory Committee on the Dietary Guidelines for Americans, 2000.

**Chapter 27**
Outlooks 27.3 Table 27.A-B, p. 633, Data from the Center for Disease Control and Prevention.

## Photo

**Chapter 1**
Opener: © The McGraw-Hill Companies Inc./Barry Barker, photographer; 1.1: © Getty RF; 1.3a: © Vol. 43/PhotoDisc/Getty RF; 1.3b: © Getty RF; 1.4(top): © Vol. 86/Corbis RF; 1.4(bottom): © Corbis RF; p. 6: © Brand X/PunchStock RF; 1.5: © Getty RF; 1.6: © The McGraw-Hill Companies, Inc., John Thoeming, photographer; 1.7a: CDC; 1.7b: © Hank Morgan/Photo Researchers; 1.8(left): © Pixtal/age Fotostock; 1.8(right): © Fred Ross; 1.9a: Library of Congress; 1.9b: © Getty RF; 1.10: © The McGraw-Hill Companies, Inc./Jim Shaffer, photographer; 1.12(yeast): © Science VU/Visuals Unlimited; 1.12(orchid): © Steven P. Lynch; 1.12(kids): © Corbis RF; 1.12(helix): © Getty RF; 1.13: © Vol. 86/Corbis RF; 1.15(left): © Vol. 6/PhotoDisc/Getty RF; 1.15(right): © Vol. 50/PhotoDisc/Getty RF; 1.17: © Photodisc/Getty RF; 1.19a: © Corbis RF; 1.19b: © Getty RF; p. 18: © Bettmann/Corbis; 1.20(top): © Stockbyte RF; 1.20(bottom): © Eldon Enger.

**Chapter 2**
Opener: © Fred Ross; 2.1: © Vol. 27/Getty RF; 2.2: © Digital Vision/Getty RF; p. 30: © Vol. OS43/PhotoDisc/Getty RF; 2.7a: © Digital Vision/Getty RF; 2.7b: © Vol. 24/PhotoLink/Getty RF; 2.7c: © Fred Ross; p. 32: © Vol. 44/Getty RF; p. 34: © Erica S. Leesds; 2.11: © S04/PhotoDisc/Getty RF; 2.12: © Photolink/Getty RF; p. 37: © Vol. 46/Corbis RF; 2.14: © Vol. 172/Corbis RF; p. 41, 2.16a-b: © Fred Ross.

**Chapter 3**
Opener: © Fred Ross; 3.1(all): © Eldon Enger & Fred Ross/Jim Shaffer, photographer; 3.2a: © Vol. 275/Corbis RF; 3.2b: © Vol. 77/Getty RF; 3.2c: © Fred Ross; p. 48: © Comstock/Alamy RF; p. 50: © Vol. 187/Getty RF; p. 52(top): © Vol. 30/Getty RF; p. 52(bottom): © Vol. 19/PhotoLink/Getty RF; 3.10(man, potatoes): © Corbis RF; 3.10(bicep): © Vol. 10/PhotoLink/Getty RF; p. 54: © Getty RF; p. 56: © Vol. 8/PhotoLink/Getty RF; p. 63: © Getty RF.

**Chapter 4**
Opener: © Vol. 40/Corbis RF; 4.1a: © Stock Montage; 4.1b: National Library of Medicine; p. 75: © Vol. 13/Corbis RF; p. 77: © Vol. 18/© Getty RF; 4.17b: M. Sameni and B. F. Sloane, Wayne State University School of Medicine, Detroit, MI; 4.19(both): © William Dentler; 4.20: From William Jensen and R. B. Park, *Cell Ultrastructure*, 1967, p. 57: © Brooks/Cole Publishing, a division of International Thompson Publishing, Inc.; 4.22: Courtesy Tampa Hyperbaric Enterprise, Inc., www.oxytank.com.

**Chapter 5**
Opener: © The McGraw-Hill Companies, Inc./Rick Brady, photographer; p. 102(top): © Fred Ross; 5.3a-b: © The McGraw-Hill Companies, Inc./Jim Shaffer, photographer; p. 108: © Artville RF; 5.8b: © Digital Vision/Punchstock RF.

**Chapter 6**
Opener: © Comstock/Jupiter/Alamy RF; p. 123: © Digital Vision RF; p. 127: © Vol. 76/Getty RF; p. 128(bottom): © Vol. 30/Getty RF; p. 128(top): © Vol. RF; p. 130: © Brand X/Picture Quest RF; p. 131(top): © Vol. 19/Getty RF; p. 131 (bottom): © Fred Ross.

**Chapter 7**
Opener: © Banana Stock/PunchStock RF; p. 136: © Fred Ross; 7.1a: © Stocktrek/age footstock RF; 7.1b: © Comstock/Jupiter/Alamy RF; 7.1c: © The McGraw-Hill Companies, Inc./Andrew Resek, photographer; 7.2: © Bob Stefko/The Image Bank/Getty Images; p. 137(bottom): © Stringer/Getty Images; p. 144: Lawrence Berkeley Lab; p. 145(top): © Digital Vision/PunchStock RF; p. 145(middle): © Vol. 16/PhotoLink/Getty RF; p. 145(bottom): © Eldon Enger; 7.10a: © Vol. 18/PhotoLink/Getty RF; 7.10b: © Getty RF; 7.10c: © Vol. 19/Getty RF.

**Chapter 8**
Opener: © PhotoDisc/Getty RF; p. 152: © Vol. 18/PhotoDisc/Getty RF; p. 164: CDC; 8.13a-b: © Stanley Flegler/Visuals Unlimited; 8.16: © George Musil/Visuals Unlimited.

**Chapter 9**
Opener: © StockByte/PunchStock RF; p. 180(all): © The McGraw-Hill Companies, Inc./Kingsley Stern, photographer; p. 180(animal/daughter cell): © Ed Reschke; 9.13(tanning): © Fred Ross; 9.13b(smoker): © Brand X/Punchstock RF; 9.13(martini): © Imagestate RF; 9.13(bacon): © PhotoDisc/Punchstock RF; 9.13(asbestos): © Vol. 44/Getty RF; 9.14: Courtesy of Fred Williams, U.S. Environmental Protection Agency; 9.15: © The McGraw-Hill Companies, Inc./*Kemp Pathology: The Big Picture*; 9.17a: © Digital Vision/Getty RF; 9.17b: © Getty RF; 9.39: © Stockbyte/Veer RF.

**Chapter 10**
Opener: © Getty RF; 10.1a-b: © The McGraw-Hill Companies, Inc./Bob Coyle, photographer; p. 205: © Vol. OS23/Getty RF; p. 206: © PunchStock/Digital Vision RF; 10.3a-b: Courtesy V. Orel, Mendelianum Mussei Moraviae, Brno; p. 209: © Steven P. Lynch; 10.5(both): © Fred Ross; 10.6(left): © Getty RF; 10.6(middle): © Stockdisc/PunchStock RF; 10.6(right): © Fred Ross; 10.8a: Courtesy of Jeanette Navia; 10.8b: © Corbis RF; 10.8c-d: Courtesy of Jeanette Navia; p. 220: © Vol. 19/PhotoDisc/Getty RF; 10.11: © Vol. 91/Corbis RF; 10.12a(top): © Stockbyte/

Getty RF; 10.12b(bottom, both): Courtesy of Mary Drapeau.

**Chapter 11**
Opener: © Fred Ross; p. 237: © Brand X/PunchStock RF; 11.7a: Ken Hammond/USDA; 11.7b: © Vol. 19/PhotoDisc/Getty RF; 11.7c: © Peter Beyer, University of Freiburg, Germany; 11.10(both): Photo Courtesy: College of Veterinary Medicine, Texas A&M University.

**Chapter 12**
Opener(micrograph): CDC; (tree): © Vol. 146/Corbis RF; (cheetah): © Purestock/Punchstock RF; 12.1: © Vol. 69/PhotoDisc/Getty RF; 12.3(all): © Corbis RF; p. 251(top): © Getty RF; 12.4a: © Alamy RF; 12.4b: © Kurt Radamaker; p. 252(top): © The McGraw-Hill Companies, Inc./David Planchet, photographer; p. 253(right): © Vol. 19/PhotoLink/Getty RF; p. 252(bottom): © Fred Ross; 12.5: © Corbis RF; 12.7: Courtesy Joe N. Fries, USFWS; 12.8: Courtesy USFWS; p. 257: © Smallhorn Land & Cattle, Huson, MT; 12.10(left): © Vol. 7/PhotoLink/Getty RF; 12.10(right): © Vol. 74/Getty RF; 12.11: © 1998 Copyright IMS Communications Ltd./Capstone Design. All Rights Reserved; 12.12: Courtesy National Center for Genetic Resources Preservation (NCGRP), USDA; 12.13: © Fred Ross; 12.14a: © Getty RF; 12.14b: © Fred Ross; 12.14c: © Comstock/Alamy RF; 12.14d: © Corbis RF; p. 261(right): Courtesy Virginia Living Museum, Newport News, Virginia; p. 261(left): © Creatas/Punchstock RF; p. 261(bottom): © Ingram Publishing/age Fotostcok RF; 12.16: p. 262 © Corbis RF; p. 263: © Getty RF; p. 264: © Corbis RF.

**Chapter 13**
Opener: © Corbis RF; p. 269: USGS; p. 270(Darwin, Wallace): *National Library of Medicine, Historical Images Collection*; p. 270(bottom): © Getty RF; p. 271: © Fred Ross; p. 272: © Ingram Publishing/Superstock RF; p. 273(left): © Vol. 21/Corbis RF; p. 273(right): © Getty RF; 13.3: ImageState RF; figure 13.4: © Corbis RF; p. 275(right): © Vol. 9/PhotoLink/Getty RF; p. 275(left): © Vol. 40/Getty RF; p. 276: © Siebert/Custom Medical Stock Photo; 13.5: © Joe McDonald/Visuals Unlimited; 13.6(currents): © Eldon Enger; 13.6(ducks): © Vol. 6/PhotoLink/Getty RF; 13.6(fish): © Vol. 44/Getty RF; p. 280(top): © Vol. 6/Getty RF; 13.9: © Punchstock RF/Comstock RF; 13.11: © Alamy RF; p. 283: © Getty RF; p. 284(left): © Corbis RF; p. 284(right): © Dr. Fred Murphy, 1975, *CDC and Prevention*; p. 285(left): © Getty RF; 13.12a: © Creatas/Punchstock RF; 13.12b: © ItStock/Punchstock RF.

**Chapter 14**
Opener: Courtesy Natural History Museum, Oslo, Norway; p. 290(left): Courtesy John and Karen Hollingsworth,

# Index